Principles
of
Neural Science

Columns II (left) and IV (right) of the Edwin Smith Surgical Papyrus

This papyrus, written in the Seventeenth Century B.C., contains the earliest reference to the brain anywhere in human records. According to James Breasted, who translated and published the document in 1930, the word brain ('yś) occurs only 8 times in ancient Egyptian, 6 of them on these pages of the Smith Papyrus describing the symptoms, diagnosis and prognosis of two patients, wounded in the head, who had compound fractures of the skull. The entire treatise is now in the Rare Book Room of the New York Academy of Medicine.

Reference: Breasted, James Henry. The Edwin Smith Surgical Papyrus, 2 volumes. The University of Chicago Press, Chicago. 1930.

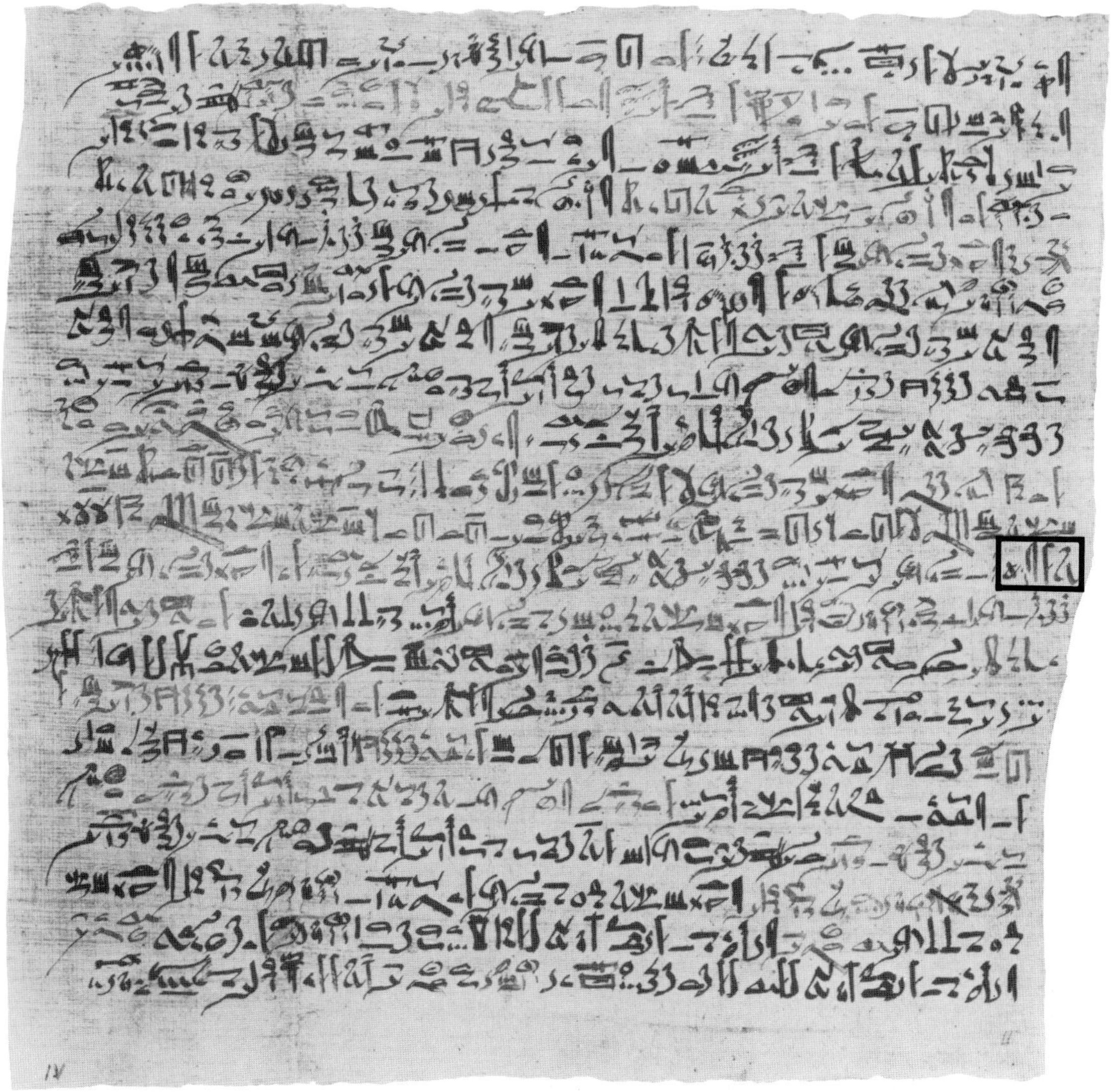

Men ought to know that from the brain, and from the brain only, arise our pleasures, joys, laughter and jests, as well as our sorrows, pains, griefs and tears. Through it, in particular, we think, see, hear, and distinguish the ugly from the beautiful, the bad from the good, the pleasant from the unpleasant . . . . It is the same thing which makes us mad or delirious, inspires us with dread and fear, whether by night or by day, brings sleeplessness, inopportune mistakes, aimless anxieties, absent-mindedness, and acts that are contrary to habit. These things that we suffer all come from the brain, when it is not healthy, but becomes abnormally hot, cold, moist, or dry, or suffers any other unnatural affection to which it was not accustomed. Madness comes from its moistness. When the brain is abnormally moist, of necessity it moves, and when it moves neither sight nor hearing are still, but we see or hear now one thing and now another, and the tongue speaks in accordance with the things seen and heard on any occasion.

But all the time the brain is still a man is intelligent.

attributed to Hippocrates,
Fifth Century, B.C.

Principles
of
Neural Science

Edited by

Eric R. Kandel, M.D.

Professor, Departments of Physiology and Psychiatry
Director, Center for Neurobiology and Behavior
College of Physicians & Surgeons of Columbia University

and

James H. Schwartz, M.D., Ph.D.

Professor, Departments of Physiology and Neurology
Center for Neurobiology and Behavior
College of Physicians & Surgeons of Columbia University

Art rendered by B. Andrew Mudryk

Elsevier/North-Holland
New York • Amsterdam • Oxford

Elsevier North Holland, Inc.
52 Vanderbilt Avenue, New York, New York 10017

Sole distributors outside the United States and Canada:

Edward Arnold (Publishers), Ltd.
41 Bedford Square, London WC1B 3DQ

Library of Congress Cataloging in Publication Data

Main entry under title:

Principles of neural science.

    Bibliography: p.
    Includes index.
    1. Neurology. 2. Neurons. I. Kandel, Eric R. II. Schwartz, James H.
    [DNLM: 1. Behavior. 2. Electrophysiology. 3. Neurophysiology. 4. Neurons.
    5. Neurochemistry. WL 102 P9547]
QP355.2.P76   599.01'88   81-5388
ISBN 0-444-00552-8 (casebound)   AACR2
ISBN 0-444-00651-6 (paperbound)

Frontispiece quotation from *Hippocrates*, Vol. 2., translated and edited by W. H. S. Jones, London and New York: William Heinemann and G. T. Putnam & Sons, 1923, Chapter XVII: "The Sacred Disease," p. 175.

Director of Editing   Barbara A. Conover
Copy Editor   Ruth Melnick
Design   Edmée Froment
Design Editors   Aimee Kudlak and Virginia Kudlak
Art rendered by B. Andrew Mudryk
Cover design   Paul Agule Design
Production Manager   Joanne Jay
Compositor   The Clarinda Company
Printer   Halliday Lithograph

To Stephen W. Kuffler
whose character, perspective, and scientific standards profoundly influenced
the development of Neural Science in the United States.

Contents

Preface

I

Principles of Neural Science is designed as an introductory text for students of biology, behavior, and medicine. Our overall goal is to convey the interest and excitement surrounding the recent attempts to apply cell-biological techniques to the study of the nervous system, its development, and its control of behavior. The text also places emphasis on those neurological and behavioral disorders that are at once instructive scientifically and important clinically.

A modern discussion of the nervous system can no longer be competently achieved by a single author. We have therefore chosen to write a multiauthored book along the lines of those currently useful in cell biology, pharmacology, and medicine. Each chapter is written by an effective classroom teacher who is also a research person with a sense of direction and taste about his particular discipline that comes only from working within it. To ensure a consistent perspective and to counterbalance the tendency in multi-authored texts for each author to speak a different dialect, we have decided, in this first edition, to limit the authors to a single teaching faculty. For five consecutive years this faculty, which includes neurophysiologists, morphologists, psychologists, biochemists, psychiatrists, and neurologists, has taught a course in the neural sciences based upon earlier versions of this text. The course has been given to graduate students, medical students, dental students, and house officers in neurology, psychiatry, and neurosurgery. A

shortened version has also been offered as continuing education for practicing physicians. Numerous discussions among the faculty and comments from students and from other colleagues around the country have helped us to develop a cohesive presentation, to stress the essential concepts, and to explain them clearly.

We have attempted to be selective and to emphasize the major principles that emerge from the study of the nervous system without becoming lost in detail. Toward this end we have divided the book into eight parts:

   I. An overall view of the brain

  II. The cell biology of nerve cells and the rules that determine their interconnections

 III. The cellular basis of perception

 IV. The control of movement

  V. The brain stem and reticular core

 VI. Motivation and homeostasis

VII. The mechanisms of development

VIII. Behavior and its disorders

Within each part we also briefly survey the relevant regional neuroanatomy. At Columbia, and at many other institutions, regional neuroanatomy is taught as a laboratory course, not a lecture course, with a separate laboratory syllabus. If neuroanatomy were to be included here in the descriptive detail it deserves, it could obscure the functional emphasis that we have striven to achieve. Nonetheless, it is impossible to consider the functions of the brain without describing its structures. Therefore, those aspects of neuroanatomy essential for understanding neuronal function are described. Detailed treatment of this subject has been left to standard textbooks of neuroanatomy.

Our ultimate aim is to integrate information from experimental studies with practical areas of interest. For the general student, it will be important to see how basic information about the nervous system can be applied to psychology. For the student of medicine, integration with clinical fields of neurology and psychiatry is of prime importance. Integration with neurology is relatively easy; neurology and neural science have long been interdependent. The bridge to psychiatry is more difficult. We have therefore made a concerted effort to provide the beginnings of a systematic introduction to the biological basis of behavior. Behavior is one of the last frontiers in biology at which we still stand in relative ignorance. We hope that this text can provide insights and enthusiasm that will encourage the student to view behavior with the same combined social and biological perspective that serves so well in other areas of biology and medicine.

II

There is a sense of excitement and optimism in the brain sciences today, a sense that we may soon have some new insights into several previously intractable problems—into the development of the brain and the mechanisms of perception, motor coordination, and learning. This optimism is not completely new to neural science, but it is probably fair to say that it is more realistic now than ever before.

The modern era in neural science began about 30 years ago. In 1953, Sir John Eccles (who later won the Nobel Prize in Physiology and Medicine with Alan Hodgkin and Andrew Huxley) reviewed results based on the first intracellular recordings from single nerve and muscle cells in a book he modestly entitled *The Neurophysiological Basis of Mind*. At the time this title seemed overly bold because so little was then known about the mechanisms of behavior. What could be learned by sticking cells with microelectrodes which could possibly help understand the mind? As time went on, many of us have returned to this marvelous book, and each time we become more impressed with its author's pro-

phetic insight. Eccles' book pointed the field in the right direction. His major message was that it is essential to study the brain in terms of its elementary units—individual nerve cells. Only by applying analytical techniques that can resolve neural processes at a cellular level can we develop a realistic and synthetic understanding of how the brain works. However, studying nerve cells with analytical techniques is necessary but not sufficient for understanding how the brain works (how people think, behave, feel, act, and relate to one another as human beings). It is also essential to relate cellular function to behavior.

We do not maintain that in the years since *The Neurophysiological Basis of Mind* was published neural science has fulfilled Eccles' prophesy. We hope, however, to show that neural science is beginning to provide insight into some of the most difficult problems of cellular differentiation on the one hand, and some of the most fascinating problems of behavior on the other. For example, considering that the brain is made up of a million million (10^{12}) cells, it is remarkable how much has been learned about the functioning of the nervous system as a whole by looking at nerve cells one at a time. It has become apparent from cellular studies that the building blocks of different regions of the vertebrate nervous system, and indeed of all nervous systems, are everywhere about the same. What distinguishes one brain region from another and one brain from the next are the number of building blocks and the way they are interconnected. Moreover, by applying a cellular approach to different sensory systems of the brain, it is possible to gain insight into how visual and other sensory stimuli are sorted out and transformed at various brain levels and how these regions contribute to perception. These studies show that the brain does not simply replicate the reality of the external world or project it onto a tabula rasa, but begins at the lowest levels of the sensory system to abstract and restructure reality according to its own rules and encode it into informational signals. These developments in neural science press upon the borders of experimental psychology.

The merger of the concepts and techniques of neural science with those of experimental psychology promises further advances in understanding perception and learning. In addition, neural science has recently benefited from vigorous interactions with other disciplines, particularly biochemistry and molecular biology, and these have resulted in fresh approaches to the investigation of brain function. Indeed, the merger of these disciplines has resulted in an integrated view of the nervous system.

It is our intention that this textbook present the important facts and the fundamental concepts of modern neural science. These not only are interesting and coherent in their own right, but also are necessary for effective work in neurology and psychiatry. The past 30 years have seen splendid progress in the techniques and practice of neurology and psychiatry, but we believe that this book would be inadequate if it merely summarized the information now accumulated that is directly pertinent to clinical practice. We also consider it our responsibility to provide a sense of direction for future developments by introducing students to the most important advances of our times, so that they will be able to evaluate the progress of this field in years to come. For this reason we are not content to consider only those aspects of neural science immediately relevant to neurology and psychiatry, but shall also discuss important scientific developments from current studies of animals that promise to provide a foundation for more effec-

tive understanding of normal and abnormal human behavior.

Engraved at the entrance to the Temple of Apollo at Delphi was the famous maxim "Know thyself." Central to enlightened Western culture from ancient times has been the idea that it is wise to understand oneself and one's behavior. Not needed only for clinical application, neural science is required for understanding human behavior, because all behavior is an expression of neural activity. Beyond medicine, in society at large, the problems of crowding, addiction, violence, and war revolve around the nature of human beings. Any intelligent solutions to the enormous problems of human behavior, individual and collective, must benefit from greater knowledge of neural function. Many of these problems are not now in the immediate domain of neural science, but progress is rapid and we can hope that neural scientists will soon be able to contribute directly to understanding them.

Eric R. Kandel
James H. Schwartz

Acknowledgments

Many colleagues read portions of the manuscript critically. We thank Michael Bennett, Floyd Bloom, Richard J. Bodnar, Nigel Daw, Marc Dichter, Howard L. Fields, Gerald Fischbach, Robert A. Fishman, Albert Fuchs, Raymond Guillery, Jeffrey M. Halperin, John Hildebrand, Olivia McKenna, Mary Parlee, Keir Pearson, Dominick Purpura, Arnold Scheibel, Ann-Judith Silverman, Charles Stevens, Edward Stricker, C. Dominique Toran-Allerand, Charles Vierck, Josh Wallman, Michael Zigmond, and Richard Zigmond for their constructive comments, many of which we have incorporated into the present text. We are once again indebted to Kathrin Hilten, who has been with the Center for Neurobiology and Behavior since its inception, for the initial preparation and final editing of the artwork. As always she took on this difficult and time consuming task by combining expertise with judgment and good humor. We thank our colleague and friend Sally Muir for editing the earlier versions of the text and the galleys. We are grateful to Fredrica Fried for editing the galleys and for coordinating the production of the book at Columbia. We thank Harriet Ayers and Inge Mayer for typing, Ruth Melnick for copyediting the manuscript, and Mildred Bobrovich for checking the bibliography.

A book by a single faculty reflects its university. It is therefore a particular pleasure to express our indebtedness to Dean Donald F. Tapley, and to the College of Physicians & Surgeons of Columbia University. Columbia has provided an intellectual environment that encourages interaction between basic science and clinical departments, an essential condition for writing an interdisciplinary book.

Contributors

College of Physicians & Surgeons of Columbia University

Craig H. Bailey, Ph.D.
Assistant Professor, Departments of Anatomy and
Psychiatry, Center for Neurobiology and Behavior

John C. M. Brust, M.D.
Professor of Clinical Neurology

Thomas J. Carew, Ph.D.
Associate Professor, Department of Psychiatry, Center
for Neurobiology and Behavior

Shu Chien, M.D., Ph.D.
Professor, Department of Physiology, Director,
Division of Circulatory Physiology and Biophysics

Lucien Côté, M.D.
Associate Professor, Departments of Neurology and
Rehabilitation Medicine

Stanley Fahn, M.D.
H. Houston Merritt Professor of Neurology

Michael D. Gershon, M.D.
Professor and Chairman, Department of Anatomy

Claude Ghez, M.D.
Associate Professor, Departments of Neurology and
Physiology, Center for Neurobiology and Behavior

Peter Gouras, M.D.
Professor, Department of Ophthalmology

Eric R. Kandel, M.D.
Professor, Departments of Physiology and Psychiatry,
Director, Center for Neurobiology and Behavior

Dennis D. Kelly, Ph.D.
Assistant Professor of Clinical Psychology,
Department of Psychiatry; Research Scientist, New
York State Psychiatric Institute

James P. Kelly, Ph.D.
Assistant Professor, Department of Anatomy

John Koester, Ph.D.
Assistant Professor, Department of Physiology, Center
for Neurobiology and Behavior

Irving Kupfermann, Ph.D.
Professor, Departments of Psychiatry and Physiology,
Center for Neurobiology and Behavior

John H. Martin, Ph.D.
Staff Associate, Department of Neurology, Center for
Neurobiology and Behavior

Richard Mayeux, M.D.
Assistant Professor of Clinical Neurology

Lewis P. Rowland, M.D.
Henry & Lucy Moses Professor and Chairman,
Department of Neurology; Director of Neurological
Service at Presbyterian Hospital

Edward J. Sachar, M.D.
Lawrence C. Kolb Professor and Chairman,
Department of Psychiatry; Director, New York State
Psychiatric Institute and the Psychiatric Services at
Presbyterian Hospital

Samuel Schacher, Ph.D.
Assistant Professor, Departments of Anatomy and
Psychiatry, Center for Neurobiology
and Behavior

James H. Schwartz, M.D., Ph.D.
Professor, Departments of Physiology and Neurology,
Center for Neurobiology and Behavior

An Overall View

I

Eric R. Kandel

Brain and Behavior

1

The key philosophical theme of modern neural science is that all behavior is a reflection of brain function. According to this view—a view that is held by most neurobiologists and that we shall try to document in this text—the mind represents a range of functions produced by the brain. The action of the brain underlies not only relatively simple behavior such as walking and smiling, but also elaborate affective and cognitive functions such as feeling, thinking, and writing a poem. As a corollary, the disorders of affective and cognitive functions that characterize neurotic and psychotic illness must result from disturbances of the brain.

The brain is made up of individual units—the nerve cells and the glial cells. The task of the neural sciences is to explain how the brain marshalls these units to control behavior and how, in turn, an individual's brain is influenced by the behavior of others in terms of the functioning of the constituent cells. In this and the next chapter we provide an introductory overall view of this task. In this chapter we shall consider the strategies used by the human brain in representing language, the most elaborate cognitive behavior. We shall examine on the *regional level* the relationship of brain function to complex behavior by considering the spatial arrangement of large groups of neurons within the nervous system. In the next chapter we shall consider on the *cellular level* the relationship between nerve cells and a simple reflex behavior by examining how sensory signals are transformed into motor acts.

Two Alternative Views Have Been Advanced on the Relationship Between Brain and Behavior

Current views of nerve cells, the brain, and behavior have emerged relatively recently from a fusion, at the end of the nineteenth century, of four experimental traditions: neuroanatomy, physiology, biochemical pharmacology, and behavior.

The anatomical complexity of nervous tissue was not appreciated before the invention of the compound microscope. Until the eighteenth century anatomists thought nervous tissue to be glandular in function. They considered nerves to be ducts conveying the fluid secreted by the brain and spinal marrow to the periphery. Histology of the nervous system became a modern science during the nineteenth century, culminating in the investigations of Camillo Golgi and Santiago Ramón y Cajal, who shared the sixth Nobel Prize for Medicine in 1906. Golgi developed the histological silver impregnation methods that allowed visualization of the whole neuron with all its processes: the cell body, the dendrites, and the axon. Cajal developed some of the key conceptual insights and much of the empirical support for the neuron doctrine—the principle that the nervous system is made up of discrete signaling elements, the neurons.

Neurophysiology, the second scientific discipline fundamental to the modern view of nervous function, also began in the eighteenth century with the discovery by Luigi Galvani of the importance of electricity to animal physiology. Again, it was during the nineteenth century that the foundations of electrophysiology were laid by Emil DuBois-Reymond and Hermann von Helmholtz. Biochemical pharmacology started with Claude Bernard, Paul Ehrlich, and J. N. Langley, each of whom realized that drugs interact with specific receptor molecules on the surface of cells, an insight that became the basis of the modern study of chemical synaptic transmission.

The fourth discipline important for determining the relationship between brain and behavior has the longest history. It is difficult to trace the history of psychology briefly. In the West, ideas about mind and soul are derived from antiquity;

behavior, the manifestation of mind in the physical world, was not approached systematically until the nineteenth century, when the work of Charles Darwin on the evolution of behavior allowed psychology to develop as a discipline independent of philosophy and to become experimental.

Aspects of the merger of anatomy, physiology, and behavior can be traced to a series of experiments by Pierre Flourens, a French neurologist working in the nineteenth century who produced lesions of various parts of the nervous system of animals in order to examine how their behavioral capability was altered by the removal of that portion of the brain. This approach led Flourens to conclude that the various sensory and motor functions are not localized to specific regions in the cerebral cortex. Thus, by the middle of the nineteenth century, it was generally believed that the cortex acted as a whole for each of its mental functions, and that any of its parts was able to perform all of its functions. Injury to a specific area of the cortex would therefore affect all higher functions equally. The acceptance of this belief (subsequently called the *aggregate field* view of the brain) was based only partially on Flourens' experimental work. It also represented a philosophical reaction against phrenologists who had argued that highly elaborate and abstract mental functions—including generosity, mother love, and secretiveness—were localized discretely in mosaic fashion to specific domains of the brain, domains that gave rise to identifiable bumps on the overlying skull (Figure 1–1).

At the end of the nineteenth century J. Hughlings Jackson, a British neurologist, broke with this aggregate field view. Jackson's clinical studies of focal epilepsy (convulsions beginning on one side of the body) showed that different motor and sensory activities are localized to different parts of the brain. These studies were later elaborated systematically by the German neurologist Karl Wernicke and by Ramón y Cajal into an alternative view of brain function called *cellular connectionism.* Cajal provided the histological basis for considering the neuron to be the signaling unit of the brain. He also showed that neurons connect to one another in a highly precise fashion. Wernicke showed that behavior is mediated by specific regions and through localizable pathways connecting sensory and motor structures.

The history of the dispute between the aggregate field and the cellular connection views of

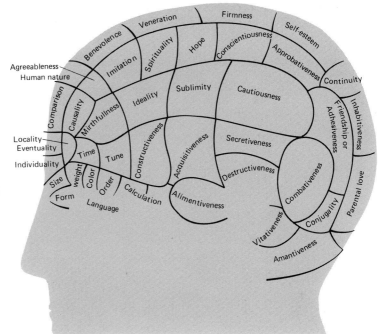

1–1 Phrenological map of the brain based upon bumps on the skull. In this drawing of the surface of the skull thirty-five distinct intellectual and emotional faculties are distinguished. (Adapted from Spurzheim, 1825.)

cortical function can best be illustrated in the analysis of language, the highest and most characteristic human function. Before we consider the relevant clinical and anatomical studies concerned with the localization of language, it is useful to survey the structure of the brain.

Introduction to the Anatomy of the Central Nervous System

The central nervous system (Figure 1–2) is a bilateral and essentially symmetrical group of structures, consisting of six main parts: (1) The *spinal cord* receives information from the skin and muscle and sends out motor commands for movement. (2) The *brain stem*, the rostral extension of the spinal cord, is subdivided into three regions: the *midbrain*, the *pons*, and the *medulla*. The brain stem receives information from the skin and muscles of the head and neck and in turn controls those muscles. The brain stem also contains collections of the cell bodies of most of the cranial nerves such as the auditory and vestibular nerves and is essential for processing the special senses. (3) The *cerebellum* is important for modulating motor movement together with (4) the *basal ganglia* (the caudate nucleus, the putamen, and the globus pallidus). (5) The

diencephalon (the thalamus, hypothalamus, subthalamus, and epithalamus) is a key relay zone for transmitting information about sensation and movement and also contains (in the hypothalamus) important control regions for homeostatic (autonomic) integration. (6) The *cerebral hemispheres*, capped by the cerebral cortex, are concerned with higher perceptual, cognitive, and motor functions. The interrelationships of several of these key structures are shown in Figure 1–3.

To understand the localization of language, we are concerned primarily with the cerebral cortex. The cortex of each hemisphere is divided into four anatomically distinct regions called lobes: the *frontal, parietal, occipital,* and *temporal.* Each lobe has a number of characteristic convolutions or infoldings (an old biological trick for increasing surface area). The crests of the convolutions are called *gyri.* The intervening grooves are called *sulci* or (when deep and prominent) *fissures.* The more prominent gyri and the sulci are similar from one individual to another and have specific names with respect to each other (for example, precentral gyrus, central sulcus, and postcentral gyrus).

The organization of the cerebral cortex is characterized by two important features. First,

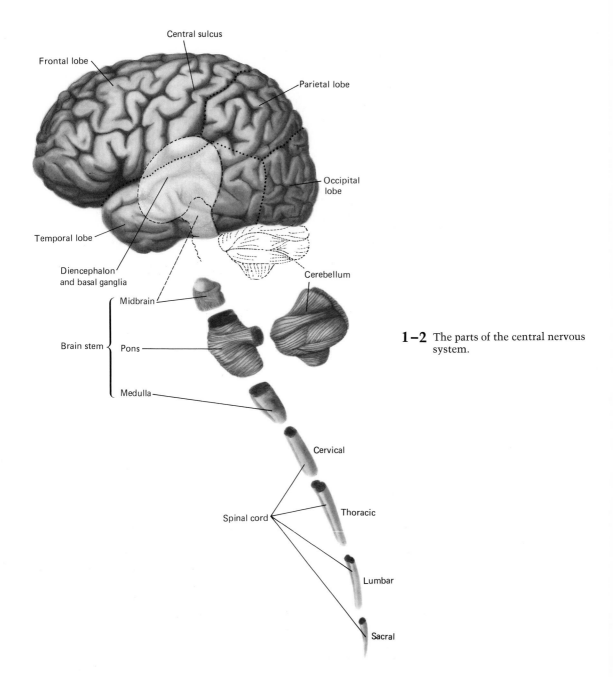

Central sulcus

Frontal lobe

Parietal lobe

Occipital lobe

Temporal lobe

Diencephalon and basal ganglia

Cerebellum

Midbrain

Brain stem

Pons

Medulla

Cervical

Thoracic

Spinal cord

Lumbar

Sacral

1-2 The parts of the central nervous system.

each hemisphere is concerned primarily with sensory and motor processes of the contralateral side of the body. Sensory information that enters the spinal cord from the left side of the body crosses over to the right side of the nervous system (either at the level of the spinal cord or subsequently at the level of the brain stem) before being conveyed to the cerebral cortex. In a similar fashion, the motor areas in one hemisphere exert control over the movements of the opposite half of the body. Second, although largely symmetrical in structure, the hemispheres are not completely symmetrical, and the two hemispheres are not equivalent in function.

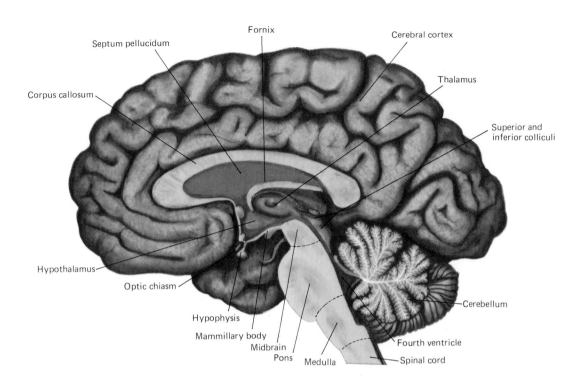

Fornix
Septum pellucidum
Cerebral cortex
Thalamus
Corpus callosum
Superior and inferior colliculi
Hypothalamus
Optic chiasm
Cerebellum
Hypophysis
Mammillary body
Midbrain
Pons
Medulla
Fourth ventricle
Spinal cord

Cognitive Function Can Be Localized Within the Cerebral Cortex

Much of what we know about the localization of normal language has come from the study of *aphasia,* a disorder of language that most commonly is found in patients who have suffered from *stroke,* an occlusion of a blood vessel supplying a portion of the cerebral cortex. Many of the really important discoveries in the study of aphasia occurred in rapid succession during the last half of the nineteenth century and formed one of the most exciting chapters in the intellectual history of human psychology. The initial advance occurred in 1861 with the publication of a paper by the French neurologist Pierre Paul Broca. Broca described the case of a patient who could understand language but who had lost the ability to speak. Postmortem examination of the brain showed a lesion in the posterior portion of the frontal lobe (an area now called *Broca's area;* Figure 1–4). Broca next collected eight cases, all of which showed a lesion at this site. In seven of the eight cases, the lesion existed in the left half of the brain. This discovery led Broca to announce, in 1864, one of the most famous principles of brain function: *"Nous parlons avec l'hémi*

1–3 Midsagittal section of the brain showing the relationship of the spinal cord and brain stem to the cerebellum, thalamus, and cerebral cortex.

sphère gauche!" ("We speak with the left hemisphere!")

Broca also noted that rare exceptions to left hemispheric localization of speech occurred, and all were in left-handed patients. This observation in turn led to the generalization that there is a crossed relationship between hemispheric dominance and hand preference.

Broca's work stimulated a wider search for the cortical loci of behavioral function—a search that was soon rewarded. In 1870, nine years after Broca's initial discovery, Gustav Theodor Fritsch and Eduard Hitzig galvanized the scientific community with their discovery that characteristic movements of the limbs can be produced in dogs by electrically stimulating the precentral gyrus in front of the central sulcus. Moreover, Fritsch and Hitzig found that there was a cortical representation for the individual muscle groups and that the region of the cortex devoted to each group was small and discrete.

A further step was taken in 1876 by Karl Wer-

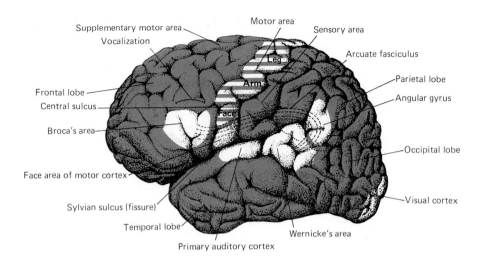

Supplementary motor area
Vocalization
Motor area
Sensory area
Arcuate fasciculus
Leg
Arm
Parietal lobe
Angular gyrus
Frontal lobe
Central sulcus
Broca's area
Face
Face area of motor cortex
Occipital lobe
Sylvian sulcus (fissure)
Visual cortex
Temporal lobe
Wernicke's area
Primary auditory cortex

1–4 Lateral view of the cerebral cortex of the left hemisphere showing the areas involved in language. (Adapted from Geschwind, 1979.)

nicke. At the age of 26 (having been out of medical school for only 4 years) Wernicke published a now classic paper entitled "The Symptom Complex of Aphasia: A Psychological Study on an Anatomical Basis." In this paper, Wernicke described a new type of aphasia—an impairment of comprehension, a sensory as opposed to a motor malfunction. Whereas Broca's patient could understand but could not speak, Wernicke's patient could speak but could not fully comprehend. Wernicke's new type of aphasia also had a different locus from that described by Broca: it was located in the posterior part of the temporal lobe, as shown in Figure 1–4.

In addition to this discovery, Wernicke formulated a theory of aphasia that attempted to reconcile and extend the two existing theories of brain function. The phrenologists had argued that the cortex was a mosaic of specific functions; even abstract mental attributes were localized to single, highly specific cortical areas. The opposing aggregate field school argued that mental functions are not at all represented topographically. Wernicke used his findings and those of Broca, Fritsch, and Hitzig to argue that fundamental mental functions are discretely localized. These functions are concerned with simple perceptual and motor activities. The elementary areas for these simple functions are interconnected in various ways. More complex intellectual functions

(with which the phrenologists concerned themselves) arise out of the neural interactions among the simple perceptual and motor areas and are mediated by the pathways that interconnect them.

By extending the mosaic view of the brain into a connectionist framework, Wernicke emphasized that the same function is processed in parallel in different regions of the brain (specific aspects of the function being processed at particular loci). Wernicke thereby initiated the notions of parallel and distributed processing that are so prominent in current thinking.

Wernicke applied this theory to his own work and that of Broca by analyzing the motor and sensory components of speech and their interactions. Fritsch and Hitzig had found that stimulating the lower end of the precentral gyrus led to bilateral movements of the mouth, tongue, and palate. Wernicke therefore argued that Broca's area—which lies immediately in front of this motor area—coordinates the muscles of the mouth, tongue, palate, and vocal cords into coherent speech (Figure 1–4). Next Wernicke considered the sensory component. The Viennese psychiatrist Theodor Meynert (the teacher of both Wernicke and Sigmund Freud) had found that the auditory pathway projected to Heschl's gyrus in the temporal lobes (Figure 1–4). Wernicke now argued that, as his patient's brain showed, the capacity for word selection is found near this zone; lesions in this area next to Heschl's gyrus cause aphasia with loss of comprehension.

Finally, Wernicke predicted a third type of aphasia (later discovered clinically) produced by a very different type of lesion from that in Broca's and Wernicke's aphasias. This additional type of aphasia spared the receptive and motor speech zones, but destroyed the pathways connecting them by interrupting the arcuate fasciculus of the lower parietal region (Figure 1–4). This syndrome, later called *conduction aphasia*, is characterized by incorrect word usage (paraphasia). Patients with paraphasia omit parts of words, substitute incorrect sounds in the word, or use words incorrectly. They cannot repeat simple phrases although they understand words that are heard and seen and they can speak fluently.

Thus, at the beginning of the twentieth century, there was compelling evidence that discrete areas of the cortex are involved in specific behaviors. However, surprisingly, the dominant view of the brain was not the cellular connection, but the aggregate field view. During the first half of this century a number of major neural scientists, including the British neurologist Henry Head, the German neuropsychologist Karl Goldstein, and the American psychologist Karl Lashley, continued to argue strongly for an aggregate field view. The most influential of these proponents was Karl Lashley, Professor of Psychology at Harvard. Lashley attempted to find the locus of learning in the rat by studying the effects of various brain lesions on the complex task of learning to master a maze. Lashley could not find any specific learning center; rather, the severity of the learning defect produced by damage to the brain depended upon the extent of the damage and not on its precise location. This discovery led Lashley—and, after him, many other psychologists—to conclude that learning did not have a special locus and therefore could not be related to specific neurons. On the basis of these conclusions, Lashley formulated a theory of brain function called *mass action*, which minimized the importance of individual neurons and of specific neuronal connections. What was important according to this *mass action* or *aggregate field* view was brain mass, not neuronal architecture.

Applying this logic to aphasia, Head and Goldstein argued that disorders of language cannot be attributed to specific lesions, but result from alterations in almost any cortical area. As a result of cortical damage, regardless of site, the patient regresses from a higher symbolic language to a simple, automatic verbal knowledge—from

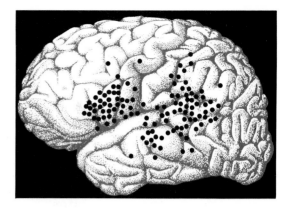

1–5 Points on the cerebral cortex where electrical stimulation arrests speech. The anterior cluster of points overlies Wernicke's area; the posterior cluster overlies Broca's area. (Adapted from Penfield and Roberts, 1959.)

an abstract to a concrete language characteristic of aphasia.

Recently the work of Lashley and of Head has been reinterpreted. A variety of studies have demonstrated that maze learning, the task used by Lashley, is unsuitable for studying localization of function because it involves complex motor and sensory capabilities. Deprived of one capability, an animal can still learn with another. In addition, a series of important clinical and experimental advances greatly strengthened the evidence for localization. In the late 1950s Wilder Penfield stimulated the cortex of conscious patients during brain surgery for epilepsy carried out with local anesthesia. As a necessary part of the surgical procedure, Penfield searched the cortex for areas that produced disorders of language upon stimulation. His findings, based upon the verbal report of conscious subjects, dramatically confirmed the localization indicated by Wernicke's studies (Figure 1–5). Moreover, Penfield extended the studies of Fritsch and Hitzig to humans; he showed that the muscles of the body were represented in great topographical detail and the resulting map formed a motor *homunculus* (Figure 1–6). Recently, these clinical studies have been synthesized and extended by Norman Geschwind at Harvard, who has pioneered in the modern study of asymmetrical representation of function in the human cerebral cortex. Experimental results from applying cellular techniques to the central nervous system, which we shall consider later, have led to similar conclusions.

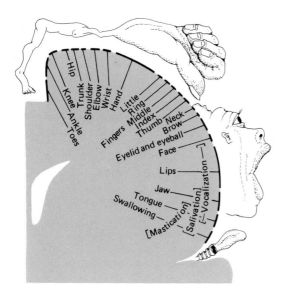

1–6   The "motor homunculus" of the right cerebral
cortex based on direct stimulation of the motor
(Rolandic) cortex of the human brain. The cartoon of
the body surface illustrates the sequence of
representation as well as the disproportionate
representation given over to the muscles involved in
skilled movement. (Adapted from Penfield and
Rasmussen. 1950.)

For example, developmental and physiological
studies have indicated that individual nerve cells
connect to one another in a precise way. As a result, individual cells respond only to specific sensory stimuli and not to others.

Affective and Character Traits Also Are Anatomically Localizable

Even in light of the compelling evidence for localization of cognitive functions related to language,
the idea still persisted that affective or emotional
functions were not localizable. Emotion, it was
held, must be an expression of the function of the
whole brain, a so-called emergent property. Only
recently has this view been modified. Quite
specific emotions can be elicited by stimulating
specific parts of the brain in experimental animals. The two most dramatic demonstrations
have come from the study of patients with certain
types of aphasias and from those who have a particular form of epilepsy originating in the temporal lobe.

In addition to the propositional aspects of language, represented in Wernicke's area and Broca's

area in the *left* hemisphere, there is an affective
component to language, consisting of the musical
intonation of speech (called *prosody*), emotional
gesturing, prosodic comprehension, and comprehension of emotional gesturing. Elliott Ross at
the University of Texas and Kenneth Heilman at
the University of Florida have recently found that
these affective aspects of language are represented
in the right hemisphere and that their anatomical
organization mirrors that for propositional language in the left hemisphere. Damage to the right
temporal area homologous to Wernicke's in the
left hemisphere leads to disturbances in the *comprehension* of the emotional aspect of language,
whereas damage to the right frontal area homologous to Broca's area leads to difficulty in *express-
ing* the emotional aspect of language. Thus, specific affective disorders of language can be localized to particular regions of the brain and these
disorders—called *aprosodia*—can be classified
as sensory, motor, and conduction, in the same
way that the aphasias are classified.

A second clue to the localizability of affect
comes from the finding that patients with
chronic temporal lobe epilepsy manifest characteristic emotional changes. Some of these
changes are present during the seizure itself;
these are called *ictal phenomena* (Latin *ictus*, a
blow or a strike). Other changes are present even
in the absence of seizure; these are called *interictal phenomena*. Among the common ictal
phenomena experienced by patients during temporal lobe seizures are feelings of unreality and
déjà vu (the sensation of having been in a place
before, or having seen a particular set of images
before), transient visual or auditory hallucinations, feelings of depersonalization, fear, anger,
delusions, sexual feelings, and paranoia. However, in some ways the more important changes
are those present in patients when they are not
having convulsions. These interictal changes are
interesting because they represent a chronic
change in personality—a true psychiatric syndrome.

A detailed personality inventory of patients
with temporal lobe epilepsy has recently been
compiled by David Bear at the National Institutes
of Health. He found that many patients with temporal lobe epilepsy lose all interest in sex. This
decrease in libidinal interest often is paralleled by
an increase in social aggressiveness. Most patients also show one or more characteristic personality traits:

1. Labile and intense emotional reactions (for example, inappropriate anger and sadness, or moralistic fervor). These patients experience run-of-the-mill events as emotionally charged.
2. An increase in religious interest, occasionally manifested as an ardent religious conversion.
3. A tendency to keep extensive diaries and autobiographical notes, often filling volumes.
4. A deep, pervasive, moralistic feeling sometimes coupled with paranoia.
5. A notable lack of humor.

Bear also found that these traits are correlated with lateralization. Patients who had right temporal lobe epilepsy displayed excessive emotional tendencies (hyperemotionality). In contrast, patients who had left temporal lobe epilepsy manifested ideational traits such as a sense of personal destiny, moral self-scrutinizing, and a tendency toward philosophical explanation. Thus, affective functions can be localized within the temporal lobe, and hemispheric asymmetry exists for emotion as well as for cognition.

Unlike patients with temporal lobe epilepsy, patients with epileptic foci outside the temporal lobe do not generally present abnormalities in emotion and behavior. Bear has argued that the irritative lesions of epilepsy have consequences opposite to those of the destructive lesions of aphasia that Wernicke analyzed. Whereas destructive lesions bring about loss of function, often through the disconnection of specialized areas, epileptic processes may bring about a functional hyperconnection leading to excessive emotional coloration.

Some of the symptoms seen in temporal lobe epilepsy are also seen in schizophrenia. Epileptic patients differ from those with schizophrenia in that patients with temporal lobe epilepsy establish meaningful interpersonal relationships with others, show a warm (rather than cold or shallow) affect, and have coherent (rather than loose) thought processes. The temporal lobe syndrome is therefore sometimes called, colloquially, "warm schizophrenia."

These clinical studies and their counterparts in experimental animals suggest that all behavior, including higher (cognitive as well as affective) mental functions, is localizable to specific regions or constellations of regions within the brain. The role of descriptive neuroanatomy is therefore to provide us with a functional guide to localization within the three-dimensional neural space—a map for behavior.

On the basis of this map we can use the patient's behavioral performance, as elicited in a clinical examination, to infer where the difficulties are located.

This discussion brings up one final point. Why has the evidence for localization, which seems so obvious and compelling in retrospect, been repeatedly rejected in the past? One reason is that the doctrine of localization of function suffered from the lack of a mature science of behavior, a lack that, to a large degree, still persists. The various aspects of behavior could not be described and measured objectively. In order to study localizable brain–behavior relationships we must be able to identify in a scientifically recognizable manner the properties of the behavior we are attempting to explain.

Second, many functions—particularly higher mental functions—are divided into subfunctions that are redundantly represented, so that neural processing for a given function is distributed within the brain and handled in parallel at several sites. Each of these stages of parallel processing presumably represents some distinctive elaboration of a particular subfunction. For example, we have already seen several distinct areas for speech, each concerned with elaborating a particular component, and there are quite likely other areas still undiscovered. As a result of redundant processing, damage to a single area need not lead to the disappearance of the function; or, if the function does disappear, it may partially return because the remaining parts can either assume the function or rearrange themselves to accomplish the primary task. Thus, localization of several related functions should not be viewed (as it sometimes has been viewed by extreme localizationists in the past) as a discrete series of functional links in a chain, whereby all related functions cease when the chain breaks (Figure 1–7A). Rather, these functions should be viewed as a number of chains distributed in parallel (Figure 1–7B). Failure of a single link will disrupt one chain, but this need not lead to permanent failure of performance of the whole system.

A third and, perhaps in the long run, most important factor is the paucity of our knowledge of brain anatomy and behavior. The brain is immensely complex and the structure and the function of many of its parts are still poorly understood. The excitement in neural science today resides in the conviction that the tools are at last in hand to explore the organ of the mind, and with

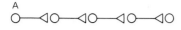

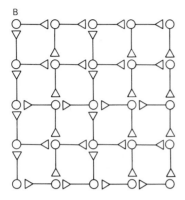

1–7 Two cellular connection models of behavioral function. (Adapted from Uttal, 1978.) **A.** Unrealistic modes consisting of neurons in series. The representation of brain organization in this model is inadequate because it presupposes that all brain function ceases when an individual neural "link" is broken. **B.** A somewhat more realistic model consisting of chains of neurons in series as well as in parallel. When a given neural "link" is broken, the system typically does not fail completely because there is parallel representation of function. As a result, the system usually rearranges itself to accomplish many of the same functions of which the original network was capable.

that excitement comes the optimism that the biological basis of mental function will prove to be fully understandable.

Selected Readings and References

Bear, D. M. 1979. The temporal lobes: An approach to the study of organic behavioral changes. In M. S. Gazzaniga (ed.), Handbook of Behavioral Neurobiology, Vol. 2. New York: Plenum, pp. 75–95.

Geschwind, N. 1974. Selected Papers on Language and the Brain. Dordrecht, Holland: Reidel.

Geschwind, N. 1979. Specializations of the human brain. Sci. Am. 241(3):180–199.

Jackson, J. H. 1884. The Croonian Lectures on Evolution and dissolution of the nervous system. Br. Med. J. 1:591–593; 660–663; 703–707.

Penfield, W., and Rasmussen, T. 1950. The Cerebral Cortex of Man. A Clinical Study of Localization of Function. New York: Macmillan.

Ross, E. D. 1981. The aprosodias: Functional-anatomical organization of the affective components of language in the right hemisphere. Arch. Neurol. (in press).

Other References

Bernard, C. 1878. Leçons sur les phénomènes de la vie communs aux animaux et aux végétaux. Paris: Baillière.

Broca, P. 1865. Sur le siége de la faculté du langage articulé. Bull. Soc. Anthropologie 6:377–393.

Cajal, S. R. 1892. A new concept of the histology of the central nervous system. D. A. Rottenberg (trans.). See also historical essay by S. L. Palay, preceding Cajal's paper. In D. A. Rottenberg and F. H. Hochberg (eds.), Neurological Classics in Modern Translation. New York: Hafner, 1977, pp. 7–29.

Cajal, S. R. 1906. The structure and connexions of neurons. In Nobel Lectures: Physiology or Medicine, 1901–1921. Amsterdam: Elsevier, 1967, pp. 220–253.

Cajal, S. R. 1908. Neuron Theory or Reticular Theory? Objective Evidence of the Anatomical Unity of Nerve Cells. M. U. Purkiss and C. A. Fox (trans.). Madrid: Consejo Superior de Investigaciones Cientificas Instituto Ramon y Cajal, 1954.

Cajal, S. R. 1937. Recollections of My Life. E. Horne Craigie (trans.). Edited in 2 vols. as Memoirs of the American Philosophical Society, Philadelphia.

Darwin, C. 1860. On the Origin of Species by Means of Natural Selection. New York: Appleton.

DuBois-Reymond, E. 1848–1849. Untersuchungen über Thierische Elektricität. Vols. I–II. Berlin: Reimer.

Ehrlich, P. 1913. Address in pathology on chemotherapeutics: Scientific principles, methods, and results. Lancet 2:445–451.

Ferrier, D. 1890. The Croonian Lectures on Cerebral Localisation. London: Smith, Elder.

Flourens, P. 1824. Recherches expérimentales sur les propriétés et les fonctions du systéme nerveux, dans les animaux vertébrés. Paris: Chez Crevot.

Fritsch, G., and Hitzig, E. 1870. Ueber die elektrische Erregbarkeit des Grosshirns. Arch. Anat. Physiol. Wiss. Med., pp. 300–332. G. von Bonin (trans.). In Some Papers on the Cerebral Cortex. Springfield, Ill.: Thomas, 1960. pp. 73–96.

Galvani, L. 1791. Commentary on the Effect of Electricity on Muscular Motion. R. M. Green (trans.). Cambridge, Mass.: Licht, 1953.

Goldstein, K. 1948. Language and Language Disturbances. New York: Grune & Stratton.

Golgi, C. 1906. The neuron doctrine—theory and facts. In Nobel Lectures: Physiology or Medicine, 1901–1921. Amsterdam: Elsevier, 1967, pp. 189–217.

Grundfest, H. 1957. Excitation at synapses. J. Neurophysiol. 20:316–327.

Head, H. 1921. Release of function in the nervous system. Proc. R. Soc. Lond. B. Biol. Sci. 92:184–209.

Head, H. 1926. Aphasia and Kindred Disorders of Speech. 2v. Cambridge: Cambridge University Press. Reprint. New York: Hafner, 1963.

Heilman, K. M., Scholes, R., and Watson, R. T. 1975. Auditory affective agnosia. Disturbed comprehension of affective speech. J. Neurol. Neurosurg. Psych. 38:69–72.

Helmholtz, H. von. 1850. Monatsber. Preuss. Akad. Wiss. Berl., pp. 14–15. Trans. in W. Dennis (comp. and ed.), Readings in the History of Psychology. New York: Appleton-Century-Crofts, 1948, pp. 197–198.

Kandel, E. R. 1976. Cellular Basis of Behavior: An Introduction to Behavioral Neurobiology. San Francisco: Freeman, chap. 1.

Langley, J. N. 1906. On nerve endings and on special excitable substances in cells. Proc. R. Soc. Lond. B. Biol. Sci. 78:170–194.

Lashley, K. S. 1929. Brain Mechanisms and Intelligence: A Quantitative Study of Injuries to the Brain. Chicago: University of Chicago Press.

Meynert, T. 1885. Psychiatry. A Clinical Treatise on Diseases of the Forebrain Based upon a Study of Its Structure, Functions, and Nutrition. Part I. B. Sachs (trans.). New York: Hafner, 1968.

Penfield, W. 1954. Mechanisms of voluntary movement. Brain 77:1–17.

Penfield, W., and Roberts, L. 1959. Speech and Brain-Mechanisms. Princeton: Princeton University Press.

Sherrington, C. S. 1897. The Central Nervous System. Part III of M. Foster, A Text Book of Physiology. 7th ed. London: Macmillan.

Spurzheim, J. G. 1825. Phrenology, or the Doctrine of the Mind. 3rd ed. London: Knight.

Uttal, W. R. 1978. The Psychobiology of Mind. Hillsdale, N.J.: Lawrence Erlbaum Associates.

Wernicke, K. 1908. The symptom-complex of aphasia. In A. Church (ed.), Diseases of the Nervous System. New York: Appleton, pp. 265–324.

Eric R. Kandel

Nerve Cells and Behavior

2

Information coming from peripheral receptors is analyzed by the brain into components that give rise to perception and are stored as memory. The brain also issues motor commands. The brain does all this by means of neurons and the interconnections between neurons. This fundamental simplicity at the cellular level is counterbalanced by an enormous numerical complexity. The best estimate is that the human brain is composed of about 10^{12} nerve cells that can be classified into perhaps 1000 different types. Within each type there are many subtypes whose properties are defined primarily by their connections—their input and output relationships. The remarkably complex abilities of the brain do not, however, stem from individual differences among nerve cells; they stem rather from similar cells taking on different functions by virtue of being connected to each other and to the periphery in different ways. Because relatively few principles of organization give rise to considerable complexity, it is possible to learn a great deal about how the nervous system works simply by paying attention to four general features:

1. The mechanisms by which neurons produce their relatively stereotypic signals
2. The ways in which neurons are connected
3. The relationship of the various patterns

of interconnections to different types of behavior

4. The means by which neurons and their connections are modified by experience.

In this chapter we shall introduce neuronal signaling by considering some structural and functional properties of nerve cells and their surrounding glial support cells. We shall then examine how nerve cells are interconnected to produce simple behavior

The Nervous System Contains Two Classes of Cells

There are two classes of cells in the nervous system: the nerve cells (or neurons) and the neuroglial cells (or glia). Nerve cells vary greatly in shape and in the extent of their processes (Figure 2–1). The typical nerve cell has four morphological regions (Figure 2–2): cell body, dendrites, axon, and presynaptic terminals of the axon. Each region has a distinctive function. The cell body or soma (or perikaryon) contains the apparatus needed for the synthesis of macromolecules. Characteristic of the cell body are the nucleus (which in neurons is often very large), ribosomes, rough endoplasmic reticulum, and Golgi apparatus. Newly synthesized macromolecules are assembled into organelles within the cell body, and these are exported into the other regions of the neuron. The cell body gives rise to the *axon*, a tubular process that sometimes extends over a considerable distance (1 m or more). Large axons are surrounded by a fatty insulating sheath called *myelin*, which is essential for achieving high-speed conduction.

Near its end the axon divides into many fine branches, each of which has a specialized ending called the *presynaptic terminal*. The terminal contacts the receptive surface of other cells and transmits, by chemical or electrical means, information about the activity of the neuron to other neurons or to effector cells. The point of contact is known as the *synapse*. It is formed by the presynaptic terminal of one cell (the *presynaptic cell*) and the receptive surface of the

2–1 Examples of various types of neurons. (Adapted from Cajal, 1933.) Neurons can be classified into multipolar, bipolar, and unipolar according to the number of processes that originate from the cell body. **A.** A multipolar cell (this one is a motor neuron in the spinal cord) has dendrites emerging from all parts of the cell body. Multipolar cells are common in the nervous system. **B.** A pyramidal cell is a variant of the multipolar cell. The cell body is pyramidal in shape and dendrites emerge from both its rostral pole (the apical dendrites) and from the caudal poles (the basilar dendrites). Pyramidal cells are found in the cerebral cortex and in the hippocampus. **C.** A Purkinje cell of the cerebellum, another variant of a multipolar cell, is characterized by its rich and extensive dendritic tree. **D.** Bipolar cells are found in the retina and have two processes: one, called the dendrite, carries information toward the cell; the other, called the axon, transmits information away from the cell. **E.** In unipolar cells the processes of the embryonic cells have apparently become fused over a short distance and a single process emerges from the cell body that splits in a T-shaped fashion into two axons, one going centrally to the spinal cord, the other going peripherally to skin or muscle. These cells are found in dorsal root ganglia and carry mechanoreceptor information from skin and muscle to the central nervous system.

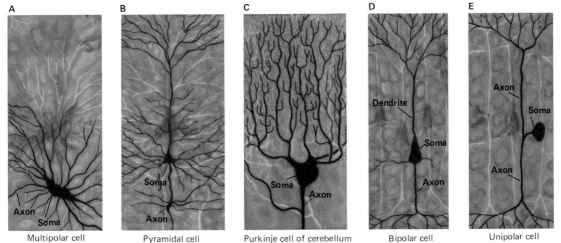

| Multipolar cell | Pyramidal cell | Purkinje cell of cerebellum | Bipolar cell | Unipolar cell |

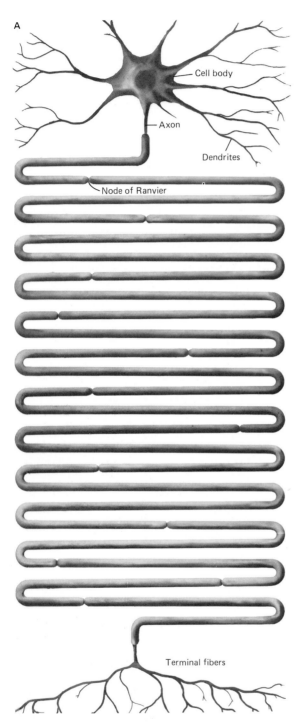

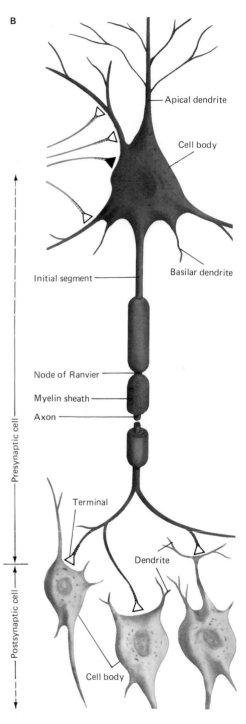

2-2 A neuron has various regions. **A.** A typical multipolar neuron drawn so as to illustrate the relative extent of each region. Nerve impulses sometimes travel along the axon over long distances. (The axon is folded for diagrammatic purposes.) Some axons are more than 1 meter long. The axon's terminal branches form synapses with as many as 1000 other neurons. Most synapses join the axon terminals of one neuron with the dendrites of another neuron. Thus the dendrites emerging from the neuron in the diagram might receive incoming signals from hundreds or even thousands of other neurons. Many axons are insulated by a myelin sheath. The sheath is interrupted at intervals by the regions known as the nodes of Ranvier. (Adapted from Stevens, 1979.) **B.** Various regions of neurons.

other cell (the *postsynaptic cell*). The receptive surfaces consist of the membrane of the cell body and the *dendrites,* a set of fine arborizing processes that extend from the cell body at its rostral pole *(apical dendrites)* or at its base near the initial segment of the axon *(basilar dendrites).*

In the central nervous system there are about nine times more glial cells than nerve cells. Glial cells (Figure 2–3) serve, in part, as supporting elements, a role played by connective tissue cells in other parts of the body. Glial cells also segregate groups of neurons from each other and may have additional, perhaps nutritive, functions. Finally, certain glial cells also make myelin. Glial cells, which lack axons, are generally divided into five major classes: astrocytes, oligodendrocytes, microglia, ependymal cells, and Schwann cells.

Astrocytes are commonly subdivided into two subclasses: protoplasmic and fibrous (Figure 2–3A). Each class is characteristically associated with a different part of the neuron. *Fibrous astrocytes* contain many filaments and are found extensively in areas of the central nervous system containing myelinated axons (these regions are called *white matter* because of the whitish appearance of myelinated axons in unstained, freshly cut brain sections). The *protoplasmic astrocytes* contain few filaments and are associated with the cell bodies, dendrites, and synapses of neurons. These components of neurons are clustered together in regions called *gray matter* because large collections of nerve cell bodies and dendrites are gray in appearance in brain sections. Fibrous and protoplasmic astrocytes contact blood capillaries on the one hand and neurons on the other and therefore are thought to have a nutritive function (Figure 2–3B). The *oligoden-*

2–3 Glial cells. **A.** Oligodendrocytes and astrocytes. These are the principal glial cell groups in the central nervous system. They are closely associated with neurons and form end-feet on blood vessels. (Adapted from Penfield, 1932.) **B.** Relationship of glial cell to capillary and neuron. (Adapted from Kuffler and Nicholls, 1976.)

A

Oligodendrocyte in white matter

Fibrous astrocyte

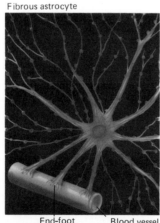

End-foot   Blood vessel

Perineuronal oligodendrocyte

Protoplasmic astrocyte

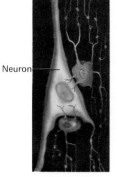

Neuron

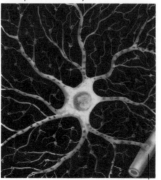

Blood vessel

B

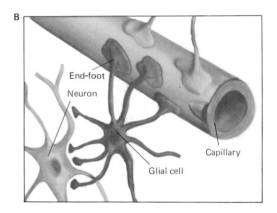

End-foot

Neuron

Capillary

Glial cell

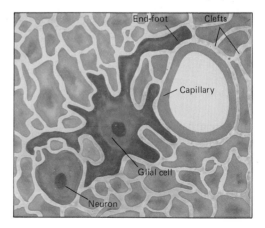

End-foot   Clefts

Capillary

Glial cell

Neuron

drocytes are found largely among myelinated central axons, where they form the myelin sheath by wrapping their processes, squeezed free of cytoplasm, around the axon in a tight spiral. A type of glial cell, the *Schwann cell*, forms the myelin sheath around the axons of peripheral nerves. The *microglia* are small and ovoid and are capable of acting as phagocytes. The *ependymal* cells line the inner surface of the brain. Although the membrane potential of glial cells can be altered by changes in external K$^+$ concentration produced by impulses in nerve cells, glia are not directly involved in signaling information. Signaling is the function of nerve cells.

Nerve Cells Are the Signaling Units of Behavioral Responses

To place electrical signaling by nerve cells in a behavioral context, we shall examine the neuronal activity underlying a simple involuntary behavioral response—a stretch reflex, the knee jerk (Figure 2–4). The stretch reflex is the basic neural mechanism for maintaining tonus in muscle. In addition to keeping otherwise relaxed muscles slightly contracted, the stretch reflex increases the tension of selected groups of muscles in order to provide a background of postural tone on which voluntary movements can be superimposed. For example, if the patellar tendon is tapped, the quadriceps femoris, an extensor muscle, is stretched and a reflex response is initiated that leads in turn to a contraction of the quadriceps femoris muscle and the concomitant relaxation of the antagonist flexor muscle, the biceps. This behavior is mediated in a large part by simple monosynaptic connections in the spinal cord. The reflex is called *monosynaptic* because the contraction is mediated by only two types of nerve cells—in this case a sensory and a motor cell—connected to each other by only one set of synapses. The sensory neurons involved are connected to receptors in the muscle which are sensitive to stretch (these receptors are called muscle spindles). The axons of these sensory neurons (called the Ia afferent fibers) run from the spindles in the muscle to the central nervous system. There the sensory axons form excitatory connections with the flexor motor neurons. The flexor motor neurons in turn send axons to innervate the gastrocnemius muscle and control its contraction. Although only two *types* of nerve cells are involved, several hundred sensory neurons are actually activated by the stretching of a single

muscle and these excite more than 100 motor cells. (For example, in humans there are roughly 150,000 motor neurons innervating skeletal muscle on each side of the spinal cord, or about 5,500 motor cells per segment. There are usually five to ten times more sensory than motor neurons.)

The reflex mediated by these two types of neurons works as follows: When a muscle is stretched, the sensory neuron is excited. The sensory neuron excites the motor neuron, which in turn causes the flexor muscle to contract and produce the behavior. The sensory neuron also excites many inhibitory interneurons, which inhibit the extensor motor neurons that go to the biceps, the antagonist muscle. Thus, in the largest sense, the electrical signals that produce this behavior perform four functions: they convey (1) sensory information from different parts of the body to the central nervous system, (2) reciprocal innervation to motor neurons (excitation of synergistic motor cells and inhibition of antagonistic ones), (3) motor commands from the central nervous system to muscles, the end-organs of effector behavior, and (4) information about this behavior to other parts of the central nervous system. In this instance, we are looking at a muscular reflex, a behavior that aids in maintaining posture in the presence of gravitational forces. A momentary imbalance of the body may stretch certain muscles. This sensory information is conveyed to the motor cells, and the motor command is sent out to these muscles to restore balance by contracting.

In producing the behavior described above, each nerve cell generates a resting potential and four types of electrical signals: an input potential, either a receptor potential in the sensory neuron, or a synaptic potential in the interneuron or motor neuron; an integrated signal; an action potential; and an output or secretory potential. The resting potential and each of these four signals are briefly described below; the underlying mechanisms are treated in more detail in Part II.

Resting Membrane Potential

The neuron, like the other cells of the body, has a separation of charge across its external membrane. It is positively charged on the outside and negatively charged on the inside. The separation of charge is responsible for the resting potential. When the neuron is completely unperturbed (the quiescent state), the

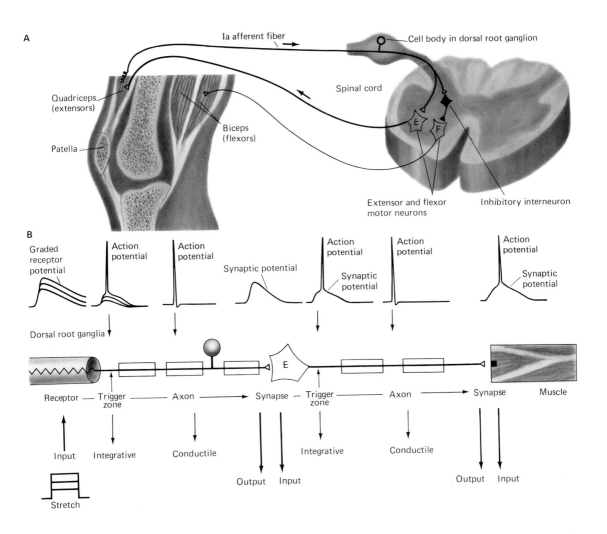

2–4 Monosynaptic stretch reflex—an example of a monosynaptic reflex system. **A.** The anatomical arrangement of this reflex. Each cell represents a population of many neurons. **B.** The sequences of signaling changes that produce the reflex action. Graded stretch of muscle produces a graded receptor potential that propagages passively to the trigger zone at the first node of Ranvier. If the potential is sufficiently large, it will trigger an action potential that will propagate actively and without fail along the axon, the conductile component of the neuron, to the terminal region. At the terminal the depolarization produced by the action potential gives rise to a secretory potential that leads to release of transmitter substance. The transmitter diffuses across the synaptic cleft and interacts with receptor molecules on the external membrane of the postsynaptic cell to initiate a synaptic potential. The synaptic potential then propagates passively to the initial segment and in turn initiates an action potential that propagates to the terminals of the motor neuron and leads ultimately to a synaptic potential in the muscle that initiates an action potential producing a contraction.

potential due to the separation of charge across the membrane is often about 60 mV. Because the inside is negative in relation to the outside, and we arbitrarily define the outside as zero, we say that the resting potential is −60 mV. In different cells the resting potential may range from −40 to −75 mV. The charge across excitable membranes is of particular interest because *most signaling involves, in one way or another, changes in the resting potential* across the membrane. The resting potential provides the background upon which signals are expressed. Signals such as the generator potentials, synaptic potentials, and action potentials are a result of electrical perturbations of the membrane which cause the membrane potential to be changed in one direction or the other.

Because the membrane is polarized, an increase in the membrane potential (e.g., from −60 to −70 mV) is called *hyperpolarization*. In contrast, a reduction in membrane potential (e.g., from −60 to −50 mV) is called *depolarization*. As we shall see later, hyperpolarization will decrease a cell's ability to generate an action potential and is therefore *inhibitory*; depolarization will increase a cell's ability to generate an action potential and is therefore *excitatory*.

Input Potentials: Receptor Potentials and Synaptic Potentials

The *receptor* (or *generator*) *potential* at the receptor surface of sensory neurons serves to transform the sensory energy (stretch, vibration, light) into electrical energy, the form of energy used by the neurons for signaling. For example, at the receptor organ of the sensory neuron in a stretch reflex the mechanical energy of stretching the muscle is converted into electricity. The change in muscle length releases the electrical energy previously stored in the resting potential of the sensory nerve endings with the result that a receptor potential is produced.

The receptor potential, like the other types of signals, is a change in the membrane potential of the cell membrane. However, it has the special property of reflecting the mechanical change in the muscle in a graded, quantitative way. Thus, the faster the stretch of the muscle, and the larger and longer lasting it is, the faster rising, the larger and longer are the resulting sensory generator potentials. The receptor potential in the sensory neurons is the first representation of stretch in the nervous system, but by itself it would not lead to any signals appearing in the rest of the nervous system. The receptor potential is a purely *local* signal that is restricted to the terminals of the sensory axon. The membrane that generates this potential lacks voltage-dependent Na^+ channels (discussed in Chapter 6) and therefore cannot support an active signal, such as an action potential. Receptor potentials therefore propagate only passively along the neuron. Passively propa-

gated signals (considered in greater detail in Chapters 4 and 5) decrease progressively in amplitude with distance and cannot be conveyed for a distance much greater than 1 or 2 mm. Typically, 1 mm down the axon, the amplitude of signal will be only about one-third what it is at the site of generation.

Receptor potentials generally last 1 to a few milliseconds. They can be either depolarizing and excitatory (these reduce the membrane potential and bring it closer to firing an action potential) or hyperpolarizing and inhibitory (these increase the membrane potential and move it away from the firing threshold for an action potential, thereby decreasing spontaneous action potential generation, or transmitter release).

The synaptic potentials of central neurons (such as motor neurons) have a function comparable to that of receptor potentials. *Synaptic potentials* are the means whereby one neuron can perturb the membrane potential of another cell to which it is connected and thereby influence its activity. The presynaptic neuron releases a chemical transmitter that interacts with receptor molecules on the surface of the postsynaptic cell. The synaptic potential is a reflection of transformation of chemical energy into an electrical potential change. Synaptic potentials are also graded and can be either depolarizing and excitatory or hyperpolarizing and inhibitory. Synaptic potentials, like sensory receptor potentials, propagate from one region of the neuron to another passively by electrotonic mechanisms (described in Chapter 4). Synaptic potentials vary greatly in duration: they usually last several milliseconds, but some synaptic potentials last seconds or even minutes. The features of receptor and synaptic potentials are summarized in Table 2−1.

Signal Integration

Because the generator potential and the synaptic potential are purely local signals that propagate passively, they cannot be faithfully transmitted

Table 2−1. Summary of Features of Action, Synaptic, and Receptor Potentials

Feature	Action potential	Synaptic potential	Receptor potential
Amplitude	Large (70−110 mV)	Small (100 μV−10 mV)	Small (100 μv−10 mV)
Duration	Brief (1−10 msec)	Brief to long (5 msec−20 min)	Brief to moderately long (5−100 msec)
Summation	All or none	Graded	Graded
Signal	Depolarizing	Hyperpolarizing or depolarizing	Hyperpolarizing or depolarizing
Propagation	Active	Passive	Passive

because they are distorted by the passive properties of neurons (considered in Chapter 4). In most neurons, the functional properties of the membrane change within 1 mm of the input component. The abutting membrane, usually a part of the axon, is capable of initiating an action potential and indeed has the lowest threshold to initiate an action potential; it is thus called the *trigger zone.* The trigger zone adds up the excitation and inhibition produced by the receptor potentials or synaptic potentials and decides whether or not an all-or-none action potential is discharged. Because this zone of membrane is the decision-making point, it is called the *integrative component.* Thus, if after propagation to the trigger zone the receptor potentials are sufficiently excitatory, their integrated sum can trigger an action potential (Figure 2–4B).

Action Potential

The action potential is a large depolarizing signal up to 110 mV in amplitude. It is often only 1 msec in duration. It differs from the graded generator and synaptic potentials in being an all-or-none signal. Moreover, whereas input potentials propagate passively and decrease in amplitude with distance, the action potential propagates actively along the neuron without decreasing in amplitude and is therefore highly effective in signaling over a distance (Table 2–1).

Output or Secretory Potential

At the terminal region of the neuron the action potential serves as a stimulus to secretion at chemical synapses. The depolarization of the action potential leads to the release of a chemical transmitter substance at chemical synapses. As we shall see later (Chapter 8), this release is also graded because it involves a local potential (the secretory potential), mediated by Ca^{++}, which is triggered by the action potential. The transmitter diffuses to the next cell, where it interacts with the input component of that cell to initiate the next electrical representation of stretch, the synaptic potential in the motor cell.

Location of Signaling Functions Within Neurons

Each type of signal not only has a specific function; some signals are also restricted to certain sites within the neuron because the external membrane of the neuron which produces these signals is quite heterogeneous.

The resting potential is generated by the surface membrane throughout the neuron. Different parts of the neuron usually have the same resting potential, and in the absence of activity there is generally no current flow from one part of the neuron to another. In contrast, the receptor or synaptic potentials are generated only at specific input sites within the neuron. The input sites for receptor potentials are called the *transducing receptors;* those for synaptic potentials are called *postsynaptic receptors.* The postsynaptic receptor molecules are most commonly located on the external membrane of the dendrites and cell bodies of the neurons. Often the receptor molecules for inhibitory and excitatory synapses are segregated from one another. For example, the inhibitory synapses are often located on the cell body of the neuron, whereas excitatory synapses are often located on dendrites. There are typically no synapses along the main portion of the axon but, as we shall see in Chapter 8, some neurons have synapses on their axon terminals.

Integration, the algebraic summation of inhibitory and excitatory receptor or synaptic potentials, occurs in that portion of the excitable membrane which has the lowest threshold for initiating an action potential, typically the *initial segment of the axon,* or at certain specialized points in the dendrites.

The action potential is produced by the membrane of the axon. In most cells the major extent of the dendritic membrane cannot generate action potentials except at specialized sites (dendritic trigger zones). Some cell bodies can generate action potentials, but even those that can usually have a high threshold for action potential generation compared to the trigger zone, in the initial segment of the axon, or in the dendrites.

The Same Signaling Mechanisms Occur in All Nerve Cells

Independent of size, shape, and function (Figure 2–1), most neurons can be depicted in terms of a generalized model neuron (Figure 2–5) that has four components: an input or receptive component; an integrative component; a long-range signaling or conductile component; and a secretory or output component.

The model presented in Figure 2–5 is not accurate for all neurons, however. Despite similar-

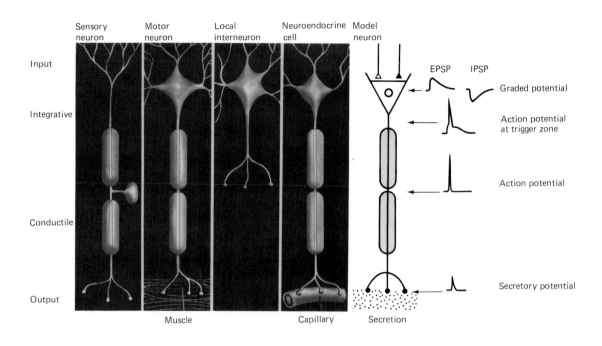

Sensory neuron | Motor neuron | Local interneuron | Neuroendocrine cell | Model neuron

Input

Integrative

Conductile

Output

EPSP IPSP

Graded potential

Action potential at trigger zone

Action potential

Secretory potential

Muscle   Capillary   Secretion

2–5 Model neuron showing functional components common to all neurons.

ity in principle, some neurons deviate from this generalization. Some cells do not generate action potentials (typically these are neurons with no axon or only a very short one, such as the receptor cells in the retina or certain interneurons in the brain). In these cells lacking the integrative and conductile components, the input signal propagates passively to the terminal region, where it directly triggers the secretory potential and initiates transmitter release. Some cells do not have a steady resting potential and are spontaneously active. Moreover, despite similarity in principle, different neurons use different transmitters, have different receptors and channels in their membrane, and are therefore biochemically quite heterogeneous. These differences account for the fact that disease may strike neurons at very different points. As a result the brain is attacked by a greater number and variety of diseases (neurological and psychiatric) than any other organ in the body. For example, some diseases such as amyotrophic lateral sclerosis or poliomyelitis strike motor cells; other diseases such as tabes dorsalis affect sensory cells. Within neurons some diseases affect selectively the receptors of neurons, others affect the cell body of certain neurons, and still others affect the axon.

Nevertheless, the electrical signaling properties of all nerve cells are quite stereotyped. For instance, the long-range signaling varies only slightly from nerve cell to nerve cell. This feature was shown by Lord Adrian, who first approached the study of the nervous system on the cellular level in the 1920s. Adrian found that the action potential carried by a sensory axon into the nervous system is largely indistinguishable from the action potential of a motor axon carrying a command from the brain to muscles. Different sensory fibers convey information that gives rise to different sensory experiences, but they do so using the same types of action potentials. The type of signal (sensory or motor) is carried by specific sensory or motor channels, not by different action potential mechanisms. Similarly, the intensity of the signal is conveyed by changes in the frequency of action potentials and not by changes in the shape of the action potential (Figure 2–6). The only parameters of impulse firing in single sensory or motor neurons that are important for signaling are the number of action potentials and the intervals between action potentials. Considering the large number of nerve cells in the brain, this is immensely reassuring because it suggests that if we understand the mechanism for producing the various signals in any cell we shall be well along the way to understanding signaling in many cells.

We have seen how individual cells produce

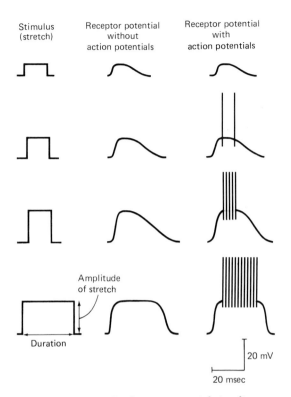

Stimulus (stretch) · · · Receptor potential without action potentials · · · Receptor potential with action potentials

Amplitude of stretch

Duration

20 mV

20 msec

2−6 Frequency code of action potential signaling. The mechanical stimulus due to stretch is transduced into an electrical signal, the receptor potential, which reflects both the amplitude and the duration of the stimulus. The receptor potential propagates passively to the initial segment, where it causes action potentials to be generated when it is sufficiently large. The graded nature of the receptor potential is then translated into a frequency code of spikes. The amplitude of the receptor potential determines the frequency with which the action potentials are generated. The duration of the receptor potential determines the duration of the train of action potentials.

simple behavior and how the activation of certain movements leads to the inhibition of others so that unity of purpose is achieved. How are we to relate the functioning of individual cells to more complex behavior? As we have noted in Chapter 1, in relation to language, a key strategy used by the nervous system is spatial organization. Specific functions are localized to particular regions or sets of regions within the brain. No function is carried out by a single neuron; rather, behavior is generated by a large number of cells all doing roughly the same types of operations. This redundancy of operation increases the reliability of function within the central nervous system. In

addition, as we have learned in Chapter 1, the brain contains distinctive regions designed to bring together neurons in various combinations in order to represent, in a precise topographical manner (and often repeatedly), the various sensory surfaces of the body: the skin, tendons and joints, retina, basilar membrane of the cochlea, and olfactory epithelium. There is also a topographical representation for muscles and for movements—a representation that is necessary for both voluntary and involuntary action. Thus, the brain contains at least two types of maps—one for sensory perceptions and the other for motor commands. The maps are interconnected in various ways.

Individual neurons within the two types of maps often do not differ greatly in their electrical properties. However, neurons with similar properties assume different functions because they are assigned embryologically to different positions in relation to the various maps, so that differences in input and output connections play a major role in determining a cell's role in behavior.

Selected Readings and References

Katz, B. 1966. Nerve, Muscle, and Synapse. New York: McGraw-Hill.

Peters, A., Palay, S. L., and Webster, H. De F. 1976. The Fine Structure of the Nervous System: The Neurons and Supporting Cells. Philadelphia: Saunders.

Other References

Adrian, E. D. 1932. The Mechanism of Nervous Action: Electrical Studies of the Neurone. Philadelphia: University of Pennsylvania Press.

The Brain. 1979. Sci. Am. 241(3).

Cajal, S. R. 1933. Histology. 10th ed. Baltimore: William Wood.

Kandel, E. R. 1976. Cellular Basis of Behavior: An Introduction to Behavioral Neurobiology. San Francisco: Freeman.

Kuffler, S. W., and Nicholls, J. G. 1976. From Neuron to Brain. Sunderland, Mass.: Sinauer Associates.

Penfield, W. (ed.) 1932. Cytology & Cellular Pathology of the Nervous System, Vol. 2. New York: Paul B. Hoeber.

Sears, E. S., and Franklin, G. M. 1980. Diseases of the cranial nerves. In R. N. Rosenberg (ed.), Neurology, Vol. 5 of The Science and Practice of Clinical Medicine. New York: Grune & Stratton, pp. 471–494.

Stevens, C. F. 1979. The neuron. Sci. Am. 241(3):54–65

Cell Biology of Neurons

II

In this part we shall consider the functional properties of nerve cells, the building blocks and elementary signaling units of the nervous system. The brain functions by combining these elementary signaling units—their electrical properties, biochemistry, and structure—in very specific and precise ways. One of the key ideas we would like to convey in this book is how this precise wiring gives rise to perception, motor action, and learning.

The nerve cell shares with other cells a number of common features. It has mitochondria, vesicles, and filaments—the general armamentarium for cellular function. Neurons are distinguished from other cells in the body by their remarkable ability to communicate with other cells. The chapters in this part will therefore place particular emphasis on the *synapses* of neurons (the foci in the nervous system where communication occurs) and on *synaptic transmission* (the process whereby one cell communicates with another). Each neuron forms about 1,000 synaptic connections (and receives even more). Given that the human brain has roughly 10^{12} neurons, these yield about 10^{15} synaptic connections—literally an astronomical number! There are many more synapses in the human brain than there are stars in the galaxy. It is therefore particularly fortunate that there are relatively few mechanisms for producing synaptic actions.

Neurons also differ from most other cells in the body in that neurons cannot divide. After the brain matures no new neurons are added. Moreover, serious injury to nerve cells often leads to their death, and therefore to a reduction in the total number of nerve cells. There is, in fact, a statement in the neurological literature (which faculty members think apocryphal) that after the age of 40 one loses about 1000 nerve cells a day. Although neurons cannot multiply, they have regenerative capabilities. Neurons, can, in certain cases, regrow parts of their axons after severance.

We shall also consider two aspects of the relationship of neuronal function to injury and disease. On the cell-biological level, we shall consider some of the morphological and functional consequences following injury of individual nerve cells. On the clinical level we shall consider the role of nerve cell injury in the diagnosis of neurological disease. The diagnosis of a neurological disease usually involves two steps. First, the anatomical site of the lesion in the nervous system is determined, and second, the cause of the lesion is inferred. Here we shall be primarily concerned with the first step. Because neurons make very specific connections with other cells and mediate specific functions, lesions of neurons produce specific deficits in functions that can be detected in a clinical examination and allow one to infer the site of the lesion.

John Koester

Resting Membrane Potential

3

The modern study of the physiology, pharmacology, and pathology of the nervous system is predicated on an understanding of the cellular properties of neurons. To describe neuronal function fully, we must be able to explain the mechanism by which signals are produced in nerve cells. Action potentials, synaptic potentials, and generator potentials are transient signals that convey information within and between the cells of the nervous system. All of these transient signals represent brief variations of the electrical potential difference across the membrane away from its resting value and are produced by alterations in the membrane properties that give rise to the resting potential. Thus, an understanding of how the resting potential is generated leads easily to an understanding of how the transient signals arise.

The Resting Membrane Potential Can Be Perturbed Experimentally

The membranes of all neurons have an electrical charge on them due to the clouds of positive and negative ions spread over their surfaces. There is a net excess of positive charges on one side of the membrane and negative charges on the other. This separation of charge gives rise to the *membrane potential*, V_m. A nerve cell at rest, which is not involved in signaling, is positively charged on the outside and negatively charged on the inside. This separation of charge is responsible for the *resting membrane potential, V_R*. All signaling involves changes in the potential difference across the membrane away from its resting value.

In most neurons the potential difference across the resting membrane is about 60 mV, with the inside negative with respect to the outside. Membrane potential *(V_m)* is defined as

$$V_m = V_{in} - V_{out}$$

where V_{in} is the potential on the inside of the cell and V_{out} the potential on the outside. Thus, for a cell that at rest is 60 mV more negative on the inside than on the outside, $V_R = -60$ mV.

To record the resting potential, one must place one electrode on each side of the membrane (Figure 3–1A). Although the size and shape of the extracellular electrode are not critical, the electrode inside the cell must have a very fine tip in order not to damage the cell membrane. The intracellular electrode is a glass pipette drawn out to a tip about 0.5 μm in diameter and is filled with a concentrated salt solution such as KCl. Contact with this intracellular microelectrode is made by a wire inserted into the salt solution. The leads from both the intracellular and the extracellular electrodes are connected to an amplifier, a voltage-sensing device. After amplification, the signal from the two electrodes is fed to an *oscilloscope*. This device displays the membrane potential as the vertical deflection of a spot of light on the face of a cathode ray tube. As the spot also moves at a constant rate in a horizontal direction across the screen of the oscilloscope, one obtains a trace that shows how the membrane potential varies with time. The spot of light on the oscilloscope screen is produced by a beam of electrons which, because of its low inertia, can accurately follow the most rapid changes in V_m.

With both electrodes outside the cell, no potential difference is recorded; but as soon as the microelectrode is inserted into the cell (Figure 3–1A), the oscilloscope will display a steady deflection of about −60 mV, the resting membrane potential.

To generate an action potential, the membrane potential must be made less negative by reducing the charge separation across the membrane. Because the cell is polarized in the resting state, charge must be removed so as to reduce the potential difference and excite the cell. We therefore call this process of removing charge, *depo-*

larization. A cell can be artificially depolarized in a graded fashion by using a second pair of current-passing electrodes (Figure 3–1B). Again, one electrode is put into the surrounding fluid and a second is inserted into the cell. These two electrodes are connected to a current generator that can pass current into or out of the cell. Assume that the current generator delivers a pulse of current with the polarity shown in Figure 3–1B: current flows into the neuron from the intracellular microelectrode and will now flow outward across its membrane. By convention, the direction of current flow is determined by the direction of net movement of positive charge. Thus positive charge accumulates within the cell from the intracellular electrode *(X)* and will be withdrawn from the outside of the membrane by the extracellular electrode *(Y)*. The result is a decrease in the normal charge separation across the membrane, which leads to a decrease in membrane potential. The net excess of internal negative charge and of external positive charge is reduced, and the cell is depolarized (Figure 3–1B).

Even if a steady rate of current injection is maintained, some of the positive charges forced into the cell will start to leak across the membrane. The greater the positive charge accumulation within the cell (that is, the greater the depolarization), the higher will be the rate of positive charge movement across the membrane because of the electrostatic forces between charges. Finally, after a relatively brief time, the rate of charge injection will be equaled by the rate of leakage of charge across the membrane, and the membrane potential will settle at a new steady-state value, remaining there until the current source is turned off (Figure 3–1B). Whenever a nerve cell is connected to an extrinsic current source in this way, passing an *outward current* across the membrane will always produce a depolarization. Reversing the direction of current flow results in an *inward current* across the membrane that leads to a greater than normal accumulation of negative charges within the cell. The increase in charge separation across the membrane makes the resting potential more negative, a change that is called *hyperpolarization* (Figure 3–1B). Such transient depolarizing or hyperpolarizing changes in membrane potential caused by current injection are called *electrotonic potentials*.

Within a certain range electrotonic potentials are graded. Thus a small outward current produces a small depolarization. If the outward cur-

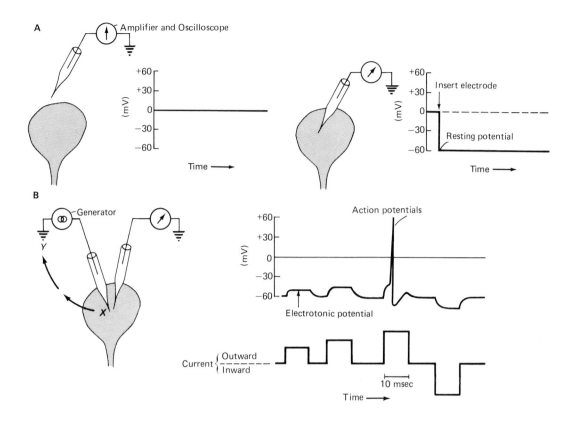

3-1 Resting potentials and action potentials in nerve cells. **A.** Measurement of resting potential. **B.** Passing outward current across a membrane depolarizes the cell. If the depolarization is large enough, an action potential is generated. Passing inward current across the membrane hyperpolarizes the cell.

rent pulse is larger, the depolarization will be proportionately larger. However, when V_m reaches a critical level, called the *threshold* (usually about 15 mV depolarized, from −60 mV to −45 mV), an action potential will be triggered (Figure 3–1B). The action potential differs from the electrotonic potential in its shape as well as in its origin.

The mechanisms by which action potentials are generated will be discussed in Chapter 6. It is first necessary to examine the membrane properties of the neuron that give rise to the resting potential. One can then easily understand the mechanism of action potential generation, as well as synaptic and generator potentials, in terms of variations in these resting membrane properties.

Resting Membrane Potential Is Generated by the Differential Distribution of Ions and Selective Permeability of the Membrane

No single ion species is distributed equally on the two sides of a nerve cell membrane. Of the four major ions in cells, Na^+ and Cl^- concentrations are lower inside the cell than on the outside, and

K^+ and organic anion (A^-) concentrations are higher inside than outside. The distribution of these ions across the membrane of the squid giant axon is shown in Table 3–1. As discussed below, the squid giant axon is widely used for experi-

Table 3–1. Intracellular and Extracellular Distribution of the Major Ions Across the Membrane of the Squid Giant Axon

Ion	Cytoplasm	Extracellular fluid	Nernst potential
K^+	400 mM	20 mM	−75 mV
Na^+	50	440	+55
Cl^-	52	560	−60
A^-	385	—	—

ments on nerve function because of its large size. Similar concentration ratios for each ion type are found for nerve cells in vertebrates, although the absolute values of ion concentration are in general three- to fourfold lower than in the squid.

There are two important questions to consider about these ionic distributions. First, how are they maintained; what prevents the ionic gradients from being dissipated by passive diffusion across the membrane? Second, how do these ionic gradients contribute to the resting potential? The answers to these questions are interrelated. We shall address these questions by considering two cases of increasing complexity.

The Nernst Equation Can Be Used to Calculate the Resting Potential of a Membrane That Is Permeable to Only One Ionic Species

The flow of ions in response to concentration gradients such as those in Table 3–1 is limited by the nerve cell membrane; it acts as a physical barrier to diffusion. Most of the ions that do diffuse across the membrane pass through intramembranous protein pores called *channels*. Each channel is selective for the type of ions that it will allow to pass, based on the size, charge, and hydration energy of the ions. The relative proportion of different types of ion-selective channels in a membrane will determine its net selectivity for the permeation of various ions.

The normal ionic gradient across a nerve cell membrane—to Na^+, K^+, Cl^-, and organic anions—could be maintained and a resting potential generated if the membrane were permeable[1] only to K^+ ions. For a cell with a membrane selectively permeable to K^+, the positively charged K^+ ions tend to diffuse out of the cell under the influence of the K^+ concentration gradient, thereby making the membrane slightly more negative on the inside than on the outside (Figure 3–2A). This internal negativity results from the net excess of nonpermeant anions that are left behind, inside the cell, when K^+ diffuses out. The electrostatic attraction between the excess cations on the outside of the membrane and the excess anions on the inner surface gives rise to a thin cloud

---

[1]The permeability of the membrane to an ion (P_i) is defined as the net flux (J_i) of that ion, divided by the product of the concentration difference (ΔC) of that ion across the membrane (ΔC_i) times the membrane area (A): $P_i = J_i/\Delta C_i A$.

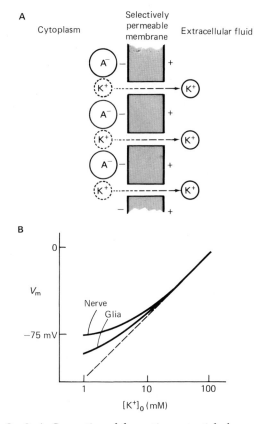

3–2 A. Generation of the resting potential of a nerve cell due to selective permeability to K^+. A^- represents impermeable anions, mostly organic molecules such as amino acids. **B.** Glial resting potential follows the K^+ equilibrium (Nernst) potential **(broken line)** more accurately than does the nerve cell resting potential.

of charge smeared over each surface of the membrane. Despite the electrostatic attraction between external K^+ and internal anions, there is no net movement of K^+ back into the cell because the K^+ concentration gradient continues to drive K^+ out of the cell. But the progressive buildup of positive charge outside the cell and negative charge inside does impede the further movement of the positively charged K^+ ions. Thus, there is an interaction of two opposing forces: (1) the force of the *concentration gradient*, which tends to push K^+ out of the cell, and (2) the force due to the charge separation, which results in an *electrical potential difference* that makes the outside of the cell membrane positive in relation to the inside and tends to push K^+ back into the cell.

As the charge separation due to K^+ diffusion continues, the electrical potential difference across the membrane increases, until the membrane potential eventually reaches a value that has an effect on K^+ equal and opposite to the effect of the concentration gradient. At this value of V_m, which in most cells is about -75 mV, K^+ ions are in equilibrium across the membrane. This K^+ *equilibrium potential* is therefore the resting membrane potential, V_R.

In a nerve cell that has a membrane permeable to only one ionic species, in this case K^+, no metabolic energy is required to maintain the ionic gradients shown in Table 3–1. The membrane potential automatically settles at a value where K^+ ions are in equilibrium—the efflux of K^+ is exactly balanced by the K^+ influx. The gradients for other ions are not important, because they cannot diffuse through the membrane. Thus, once the ionic gradients are established, they will persist indefinitely, with no expenditure of metabolic energy.

That the cell is truly at an equilibrium under these conditions can be appreciated by examining how V_m reacts to a transient deviation from its equilibrium value of -75 mV. For example, a depolarization caused by a brief current pulse will have no effect on the chemical potential because the concentration gradient for K^+ will not be altered significantly. But the electrical gradient drawing K^+ into the cell will decrease, and a net efflux of K^+ will develop. At the end of the current pulse the K^+ efflux will continue until V_m has returned to -75 mV, at which point K^+ ions are again in equilibrium. Conversely, a transient hyperpolarization will result in a self-correcting net influx of K^+; the influx will also gradually go to zero as V_m returns to the -75 mV, the equilibrium potential for K^+.

The membrane potential at which K^+ ions are in equilibrium can be calculated from an equation derived from basic thermodynamic principles by the German physical chemist Walter Nernst in 1888.

According to the Nernst equation,

$$E_K = \frac{RT}{ZF} \ln \frac{[K^+]_o}{[K^+]_i}$$

at 25°C. In this equation, E_K is the value of membrane potential at which K^+ is in equilibrium (K^+ Nernst potential), R is the gas constant, T the temperature in degrees Kelvin, Z the valence of K^+, F the Faraday constant, and $[K^+]_o$ and $[K^+]_i$ are the external and internal concentrations, respectively, of K^+. To be precise, chemical activities should be used in place of concentrations.

For K^+, $Z = +1$, and at 25°C RT/ZF is 26 mV. The constant for converting from natural logs to base 10 logs is 2.3. Substituting the values of K^+ concentration given in Table 3–1, we have

$$E_K = 26 \text{ mV} \times 2.3 \log_{10} \frac{20}{200} = -75 \text{ mV}$$

The Nernst equation applies not only to K^+ but can be used to find the equilibrium potential of any other ion that is present on both sides of a membrane permeable to that ion. The Na^+, K^+, and Cl^- Nernst potentials for the ion distributions across the squid axon are given in Table 3–1.

In 1902, Julius Bernstein used the Nernst equation to propose a theory of the resting potential based on a selective permeability of the membrane to K^+. Bernstein's theory could not be tested quantitatively until the 1940s, when techniques for intracellular recording were developed. It was then possible to compare the measured V_R to the value of E_K predicted from the Nernst equation (Figure 3–2B). Intracellular recording showed that for most neurons the observed values of V_m deviate from the theoretical curve for a Nernst K^+ electrode *(broken line)* at relatively low values of $[K^+]_o$. This suggests that neurons are permeable to one or more ions besides K^+. In contrast for glial cells the fit between theoretical and observed curves is much better, with good agreement down to quite low values of $[K^+]_o$ (Figure 3–2B). Thus glial cell membranes can be described to a first approximation as being selectively permeable to K^+.

Passive Fluxes of Na^+ and K^+ Are Balanced by Active Fluxes Driven by the Na–K Pump

Measurements of V_R with intracellular electrodes and flux studies using radioactive tracers indicate that nerve cells are permeable not only to K^+, but also to Na^+ and Cl^- ions. Of the major ionic species, only the large organic anions such as amino acids and proteins are nonpermeant. How then can concentration gradients for Na^+, K^+, and Cl^- all be maintained across the cell membrane, and how do these three concentration gradients interact to determine V_R?

To answer these questions, it is simplest to focus initially only on the trans-membrane concentration gradients for Na^+ and K^+. Various physiological control mechanisms act to keep extracellular K^+ and Na^+ concentrations constant:

[K$^+$]$_0$ is kept low, and [Na$^+$]$_0$ is high (Table 3–1). Particularly important is a metabolically dependent active transport process in the nerve cell membrane called the Na–K pump. This ion pump, which is an integral membrane protein, is a Na$^+$– and K$^+$–dependent ATPase. It extrudes Na$^+$ from the cell while taking in K$^+$, and is driven by the hydrolysis of ATP. Activity of this pump results in a low [Na$^+$]$_i$ and high [K$^+$]$_i$. Thus, the concentration gradients of these two ions across the membrane are fixed. Their permeabilities (P) in the resting membrane are also fixed: the permeability of K$^+$ (P$_K$)is high relative to that of Na$^+$ (P$_{Na}$). By definition, the resting potential, V_R, is also constant—it is the steady V_m that is maintained when the cell is not signaling. In order for V_m to remain at one value, there must be no *net* flux of charge across the membrane. For example, if there were a net flux of positive charge into the cell, V_m would become more positive. Thus V_R is the value of V_m at which the net flux of charge across the membrane is zero.

V_R, the value of V_m that corresponds to zero net charge flux, is neither E_K nor E_{Na}. For the example of the squid axon given in Table 3–1, E_K = −75 mV and E_{Na} = +55 mV. At +55 mV Na$^+$ ions are in equilibrium, but there is a net efflux of K$^+$ (Figure 3–3). Likewise, at −75 mV K$^+$ ions are in equilibrium, but there is a net influx of K$^+$. However, as V_m moves from −75 mV toward +55 mV, the fluxes of the two ionic species change in such a way that a steady-state is ultimately achieved. As V_m becomes more positive, the chemical forces (due to the concentration gradient) stay constant. But the electrical forces change in such a way that the *net* electrochemical forces affecting Na$^+$ and K$^+$ ions vary in opposite directions. The result is a continuously increasing K$^+$ efflux and a decreasing Na$^+$ influx as V_m is made more positive. Finally, when V_m reaches −60 mV, the two fluxes will be equal and opposite, so there will be no net flux of charge across the membrane. Thus, in this example, V_R is −60 mV.

The forces acting when the cell is at rest (V_m = V_R) are shown schematically in Figure 3–4. The large chemical and electrical forces driving Na$^+$ into the cell produce only a moderate Na$^+$ influx because P_{Na} is so small. The K$^+$ concentration gradient driving K$^+$ out of the cell is only slightly greater than the electrical force acting to hold it in the cell, but the small net outward force is enough to produce a moderate K$^+$ efflux because P_K is relatively large.

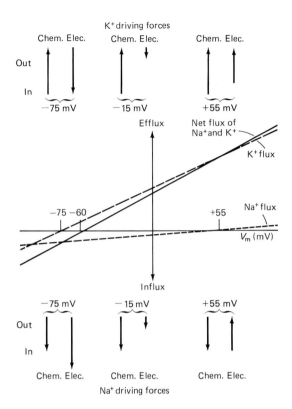

3–3 Chemical and electrical driving forces acting on Na$^+$ and K$^+$ ions at different values of V_m result in the flux curves shown by **broken lines.** The next flux curve of Na$^+$ and K$^+$ is shown by the **solid line.** The direction and amplitude of the chemical and electrical driving forces acting on Na$^+$ and K$^+$ are shown for three different values of V_m.

The change in driving force is about the same for Na$^+$ ions for a given change in V_m. The difference in the slopes of the Na$^+$ and K$^+$ flux curves reflects the fact that the resting membrane is more permeable to K$^+$ than to Na$^+$. The shapes of the Na$^+$ and K$^+$ flux curves as drawn here are simplified considerably. As described in Chapter 6, these curves become quite nonlinear for values of V_m more positive than about −50 mV.

Active Ion Pumping Balances Passive Fluxes

For the cell to have a steady V_R there must be a constant value of charge separation across the membrane; for, as noted above, a net flux of charge into or out of the cell would cause V_m to change. Therefore, in the cell at rest (Figure 3–4) the passive diffusion of K$^+$ out of the cell must be balanced by the passive diffusion of Na$^+$ ions into the cell. Although these steady ion

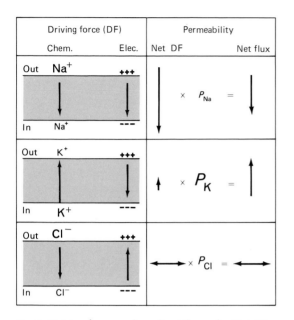

| Driving force (DF) | | Permeability | |
Chem.	Elec.	Net DF	Net flux

3–4 Driving forces and resultant fluxes for Na⁺, K⁺, and Cl⁻ ions for a cell with $V_m = -60$ mV and ion gradients as shown in Table 3–1.

leaks cancel each other, they cannot be allowed to continue unopposed. Otherwise, $[K^+]_i$ would be depleted, $[Na^+]_i$ would increase, and the ionic gradients would run down, thus abolishing V_R. Dissipation of ionic gradients is prevented by the Na–K pump. It transports steady streams of Na⁺ out of the cell and K⁺ into the cell (Figure 3–5). When the cell is at rest, the active and the passive fluxes of each of these two ions are balanced, so that the net fluxes of Na⁺ and of K⁺ are zero.

3–5 The cell at rest. The passive fluxes of Na⁺ and K⁺ ions down their electrochemical gradients are balanced by active transport driven in the opposite direction by the ATP-dependent Na–K pump.

Thus, at V_R the cell is not in an equilibrium, but rather in a *steady state*: metabolic energy (derived from ATP) must be used to maintain the ionic gradients across the membrane.

In most neurons the pump is electrogenic; it produces a net flux of charge across the membrane. For example, the pump typically extrudes three Na⁺ ions for every two K⁺ ions it brings in. As a result it tends to hyperpolarize the cell, because of the net efflux of positive charges it produces. In such a cell the passive Na⁺ and K⁺ fluxes are not equal, and three Na⁺ ions diffuse into the cell for every two K⁺ ions that diffuse out. For the example shown in Figure 3–3, the V_m at which this particular state occurs will be a few millivolts negative to -60 mV.

Cl⁻ Ions Are Passively Distributed

The contribution of Cl⁻ ions to the generation of V_R was not mentioned above. How can one ignore the role of this ion in determining V_R, especially as the P_{Cl} of most nerve cell membranes is relatively high? The answer is that V_R is ultimately determined by K⁺ and Na⁺ because their ionic concentrations are fixed by the Na–K pump. Cl⁻, on the other hand, is free to diffuse into or out of the cell; in most nerve cells Cl⁻ is not actively pumped. Because Cl⁻ ions are acted on only by passive forces (electrical and chemical gradients), they must be in equilibrium across the membrane. Thus the concentration ratio of Cl⁻ across the membrane settles at a value such that $E_{Cl} = V_R$. Because there is no net Cl⁻ flux at E_{Cl}, Cl⁻ ions have no effect on resting potential. Note that of the three major ions to which the membrane is permeable, only Cl⁻ is in equilibrium at V_R. Thus Cl⁻ is said to be *passively* distributed across the membrane, whereas K⁺ and Na⁺, which are pumped, are *actively* distributed.

The Net Charge Separation Across the Membrane Is a Small Fraction of the Total Charge in the Cell

The membrane potential is attributable to the separation of positive and negative charges across the membrane. For the example of a typical nerve cell considered above, there is a high permeability to K⁺ and a low permeability to Na⁺. Passive diffusion of K⁺ out of the cell leads

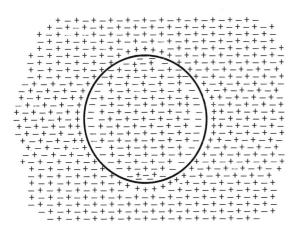

3–6 The net excess of positive charges outside and negative charges inside the membrane of a nerve cell at rest represents a small fraction of the total number of ions inside and outside the cell. (The ratio of the width of the region of charge separation to cell diameter is exaggerated here for purposes of illustration.)

to charge accumulation—an excess of cations outside the cell, and anions inside. Of course there is also a tendency for Na^+ to diffuse into the cell down its electrochemical gradient. One might expect this Na^+ influx to abolish the charge separation across the membrane and wipe out the resting potential. This depolarization does not occur, for (as shown in Figure 3–5) when the cell is at its resting potential there is a steady K^+ efflux that exactly balances the steady Na^+ influx.

V_m is directly proportional to the charge separation across the membrane. It has been found empirically that each increment of about 600 positive charges on one side of the membrane and of 600 negative charges on the other side, per square micrometer of membrane, will give rise to a 10-mV change in V_m. The number of positive and negative charges separated across the cell membrane to produce the resting potential represents an insignificant fraction of the total number of positive and negative charges inside the cell (Figure 3–6). The bulk of the cytoplasm and of the extracellular fluid is electrically neutral with an equal number of positive and negative charges. Charge separation exists only in a very narrow region, less than 1 μm wide on either side of the membrane.

The Resting Membrane Potential Can Be Quantified by the Goldman Equation

In the example above (Figures 3–3 and 3–4) the resting potential of a nerve cell with high P_K and P_{Cl} and relatively low P_{Na} was shown to be about -60 mV. As described above, Na^+ and K^+ ions set the resting potential value. V_R is equal to neither E_K nor E_{Na}, but rather lies between them. As a general rule, when V_m is determined by two or more ions, each ion will have an influence on V_m that is determined by its concentrations inside and outside the cell, and by the permeability of the membrane to that ion. This relationship is given quantitatively by the *Goldman equation*, which is sometimes also referred to as the Goldman–Hodgkin–Katz equation.

$$V_m = \frac{RT}{F} \ln \frac{P_K[K^+]_0 + P_{Na}[Na^+]_0 + P_{Cl}[Cl^-]_i}{P_K[K^+]_i + P_{Na}[Na^+]_i + P_{Cl}[Cl^-]_0}.$$

The Goldman equation applies only when V_m is not changing. Its derivation is rather complex and will not be given in detail here.[2] The equation states that the greater the concentration of a particular ionic species and the greater its membrane permeability, the greater will be its role in determining V_m. In the limiting case, when permeability to one ion is exceptionally high, the Goldman equation reduces to the Nernst equation for that ion. For example, if $P_K \gg P_{Cl}$, P_{Na}, the equation becomes

$$V_m \approx \frac{RT}{F} \ln \frac{[K^+]_0}{[K^+]_i}.$$

In 1949, Hodgkin and Katz were the first to apply the Goldman equation systematically to a nerve cell—the squid giant axon. They measured the variation of V_R with changing concentrations of Na^+, Cl^-, and K^+. Their results showed that $[K^+]_0$ and $[Cl^-]_0$, but not $[Na^+]_0$, had large effects on resting potential. Their data could be fit to the

---

[2]There are three basic steps in the derivation of this equation developed by Hodgkin and Katz:

1. Express the flux (*J*) of each species of ion (i) (Na^+, K^+, Cl^-) across the membrane as a function of V_m, concentration and membrane permeability: $J_i = f(V_m, conc_i, perm_i)$.
2. Convert these fluxes to membrane currents, *I* (e.g., an influx of Na^+ or an efflux of Cl^- is an *inward* membrane current). Since V_m is constant, the charge separation across the membrane is not changing, so $I_{Cl} + I_{Na} + I_{Na} + I_K = 0$.
3. Substitute the equations from step 1 into the equation in step 2; rearrange terms and solve for V_m. The result is the Goldman equation.

Goldman equation rather accurately by assuming that, for the membrane at rest:

$$P_K: P_{Na}: P_{Cl} = 1:0.04:0.45.$$

For the membrane at the peak of the action potential, however, they calculated a quite different set of membrane permeabilities. The variation of V_m at the peak of the action potential with external ionic concentrations could be fit best by assuming these relative membrane permeabilities.

$$P_K: P_{Na}: P_{Cl} = 1:20:0.45$$

For this set of permeabilities (P_{Na}, P_K, P_{Cl}), the Goldman equation reduces to

$$V_m \approx \frac{RT}{F} \ln \frac{[Na^+]_0}{[Na^+]_i} = +55 \text{ mV}$$

Thus at the peak of the action potential, when the membrane is much more permeable to Na^+ than to any other ion, V_m approaches E_{Na}, the Na^+ Nernst potential.

An Overall View

The membrane potential is determined primarily by three ions: K^+, Cl^-, and Na^+. In general, V_m will be closest to the Nernst potential of the ion or ions with the greatest concentrations inside and outside the cell and the greatest membrane permeability. Because the total concentrations of K^+, Cl^-, and Na^+ are roughly equal, the relative membrane permeabilities of these three ions are most important in determining V_m.

At rest, V_m is close to the Nernst potential of the ion to which the membrane is most permeable—K^+. However, because E_K is slightly more negative than V_R, there is a driving force that results in a steady efflux of K^+ from the cell. This outward K^+ flux is balanced by a steady Na^+ influx. These two passive fluxes are in turn balanced by active fluxes driven by the $Na^+–K^+$ pump. Cl^- ions are not pumped, and are therefore passively distributed such that they are at equilib-

rium. Under most physiological conditions the bulk concentrations of Na^+, K^+, and Cl^- inside and outside the cell are constant; the changes in V_m that occur during signaling (action potentials, synaptic potentials, and receptor potentials) are caused by changes in the relative membrane permeabilities to these three ions.

Selected Readings and References

Finkelstein, A., and Mauro, A. 1977. Physical principles and formalisms of electrical excitability. In E. R. Kandel (ed.), Handbook of Physiology; The Nervous System, Vol. 1, Part I. Bethesda, Md.: American Physiological Society, pp. 161–213.

Hille, B. 1977. Ionic basis of resting and action potentials. In E. R. Kandel (ed.), Handbook of Physiology; The Nervous System, Vol. 1, Part I. Bethesda, Md. American Physiological Society, pp. 99–136.

Hubbard, J. I., Llinás, R., and Quastel, D. M. J. 1969. Electrophysiological Analysis of Synaptic Transmission. Baltimore: Williams & Wilkins, chap. 3.

Khodorov, B. I. 1974. The Problem of Excitability. New York: Plenum, chap. 2.

Stevens, C. F. 1979. The neuron. Sci. Am. 241(3):54–65.

Other References

Bernstein, J. 1902. Investigations on the thermodynamics of bioelectric currents. Translated from Pflügers Arch. 92:521–562. In G. R. Kepner (ed.), Cell Membrane Permeability and Transport. Stroudsburg, Pa.: Dowden Hutchinson & Ross, 1979.

Goldman, D. E. 1943. Potential, impedance, and rectification in membranes. J. Gen. Physiol. 27:36–60.

Hodgkin, A. L., and Katz, B. 1949. The effect of sodium ions on the electrical activity of the giant axon of the squid. J. Physiol. (Lond.) 108:37–77.

Nernst, W. 1888. On the kinetics of substances in solution. Translated from Z. physik. Chemie 2:613–622; 634–637. In G. R. Kepner (ed.), Cell Membrane Permeability and Transport. Stroudsburg, Pa.: Dowden, Hutchinson & Ross, 1979.

John Koester

Passive Electrical Properties of the Neuron

4

Nerve cells generate electrical signals by changing the permeability of their membranes and allowing ions to diffuse down preestablished electrochemical gradients. Membrane permeability and ion diffusion can be measured directly by using radioactive isotopes. However, these methods lack the time resolution necessary to relate them to the rapidly occurring signals within the neuron. In most cases, therefore, a more convenient method is used that has better time resolution. Instead of measuring the permeability changes themselves, we record their consequences, the changes in *current flow* and the resulting changes in *membrane potential.* These data are then used to describe the excitability mechanisms of a neuron in terms of a mathematical model based on electrical circuits. The equations that describe the neuron in electrical terms are actually simpler than those dealing explicitly with membrane permeability and diffusion. Thus, in the next five chapters we shall develop a description of the nerve cell called the *equivalent circuit model.* With this model, all of the important functional properties of the neuron can be represented by a simple electrical circuit consisting only of batteries, resistors, and capacitors. An understanding of this equivalent circuit model leads to basic insights into the principles of nerve function and serves as a solid foundation for interpreting various clinical tests of nerve and muscle function.

The next five chapters deal with two subjects. This chapter and Chapter 5 deal with the *passive electrical properties* of the membrane, the properties that *do not* change during signaling. Chapters 6, 7, and 8 deal with *active electrical properties* of the membrane, the properties that *do* change during signaling. The active properties include those involved in action potential generation and transmitter release, as well as the chemically gated ionic channels that generate synaptic potentials. The active ionic pathways modulated by a variety of physical stimuli to produce receptor (generator) potentials in sensory cells will be discussed in Chapter 15.

The nerve cell has three types of passive electrical characteristics: electromotive force, resistance, and capacitance. This chapter will deal with the physical basis of these three properties, as well as their role in generating the resting membrane potential. In the next chapter we shall consider the function of passive membrane properties in the integration of synaptic signals and in the conduction of action potentials.

In order to follow the next five chapters, one should be familiar with some basic principles of electrical circuit theory on the level usually found in a high school physics course. The reader who is unfamiliar with this material will want to review it at this point by reading Appendix I.

The Membrane Has an Electromotive Force

On the microscopic level, the neuronal membrane has a mosaic structure (Figure 4–1). The lipid bilayer backbone is pierced by a variety of different types of ionic channels, or pores, made of intrinsic membrane proteins. Figure 4–1 is not drawn accurately to scale, for the distances between neighboring channels are actually several hundred times larger than the thickness of the membrane. Each channel can be characterized as being either *passive*—always open—or *active*—with a gate across its mouth that can be either open or closed. The gates of these active channels may be controlled by synaptic transmitters, by membrane potential, or, in the case of receptor cells, by various physical stimuli. Passive channels, which are not gated, are important in determining the resting membrane potential, as well as influencing synaptic integration.

Each ionic channel, whether active or passive, can also be characterized by its selectivity. Each channel behaves as if it contains a selectivity filter along its length that allows only one species of ion to pass through, usually Na^+, K^+, Cl^-, or Ca^{++}. For example, a K^+ channel will exclude virtually all ions except K^+. Most channels are not perfectly selective, however. For example, the K^+ channel lets one Na^+ ion go through for about every 12 K^+ ions that pass. For purposes of discussion, however, it is convenient to assume that each channel is completely selective.

Because there are unequal distributions of ions across the membrane, each open channel gives rise to an *electrical potential difference* across the membrane. For example, K^+ ions, which are present at a higher concentration inside than outside, will tend to diffuse out through each open K^+ channel, resulting in a net separation of charge: more positive charges on the outside and more negative charges inside. The result will be an electrical potential difference set up between the two ends of the channel, with the inside negative and the outside positive. As more and more charge separation occurs, the rate of K^+ efflux and the consequent rate of charge separation will rapidly go to zero. This occurs when sufficient positive charge has accumulated outside the membrane to generate an electrical potential difference equal and opposite to the chemical potential difference (concentration gradient) that drives K^+ out of the cell. The value of the electrical po-

4–1 Schematic diagram of active (gated) and passive (always open) channels that provide permeability pathways for ions through the membrane.

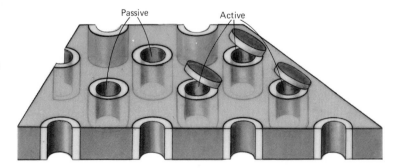

Passive   Active

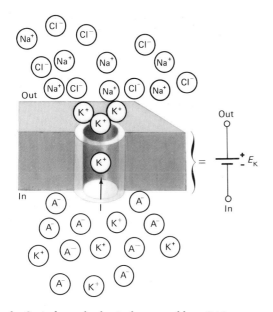

4–2 A channel selectively permeable to K⁺ ions gives rise to an EMF with a value equal to the K⁺ Nernst potential. In this and all subsequent figures the gates over the active channels have been eliminated to simplify the representation.

tential difference for K⁺ ions can be calculated from the Nernst equation:

$$E_K = \frac{RT}{ZF} \ln \frac{[K^+]_o}{[K^+]_i}.$$

The slight separation of charge across the channel will thus act as a constant source of potential difference. Such a potential source is called an *electromotive force* (EMF). The EMF generated in this way is the K⁺ Nernst potential. Because this EMF results from the passive diffusion of K⁺ ions through the K⁺ channel, we may represent the channel schematically with the symbol for a battery (Figure 4–2). The potential generated by this battery is equal to E_K, the K⁺ Nernst potential, which is typically about −75 mV.

The Membrane Has Resistive Properties

In addition to the EMF generated at K⁺ channels by diffusion of K⁺ ions down their concentration gradient, each K⁺ channel also has electrical *resistance*; that is, it resists the movement of electrical charge. Each K⁺ ion that travels through the channel gives up energy in the form of heat, due to collisions with the channel wall. The greater

the number of collisions, the greater the resistance of the channel. We may represent each channel, therefore, as the combination of a resistor and a battery in series (Figure 4–3). We call the resistor R'_K the K⁺ channel *resistance*. It is more common to use the term g'_K, the K⁺ channel *conductance*, which is the reciprocal of R'_K. This single-channel conductance is a measure of the ease with which K⁺ ions move through the channel.

The total K⁺ conductance (g_K) of the cell membrane is equal to the number of K⁺ channels (N_K) times the conductance of each individual channel (g'_K):

$$g_K = N_K \times g'_K.$$

Thus, we may lump all of the K⁺ channels of a given area of membrane into a single equivalent structure, consisting of a conductance g_K in series with a battery with the value E_K (Figure 4–4).

This K⁺ membrane conductance is related to the K⁺ membrane permeability. These two terms are not interchangeable, however; conductance varies with ionic concentration, whereas permeability does not. To understand this distinction better, consider a limiting case where K⁺ concentration is zero on both sides of the membrane. No matter how many K⁺ channels are open, g_K will be zero because no K⁺ ions are available to carry current across the membrane in response to a potential difference. At the same time, K⁺ permeability would be quite high, as it depends only on how many K⁺ channels are open. In other words, permeability is determined by the state of the membrane, whereas conductance depends on both the state of the membrane and the concentration of surrounding ions. Under most conditions, however, a membrane with high K⁺ permeability will also have a large K⁺ conductance.

4–3 A single K⁺ channel can be represented by the equivalent electrical circuit of a battery (E_K), in series with a resistor (R'_K).

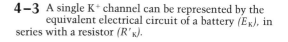

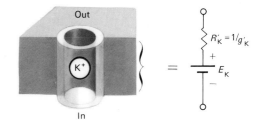

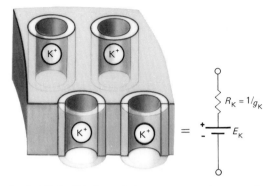

4–4 All the K$^+$ channels in a nerve membrane can be lumped into a single equivalent electrical structure: a series combination of a battery (E_K) and a resistor (R'_K/N_K).

The Resting Membrane Potential Can Be Calculated from the Equivalent Circuit of the Membrane

We have seen how all of the K$^+$ channels can be represented by a single resistor–battery combination. By analogy, it can be shown that all the passive Cl$^-$ channels can be represented by a similar resistor–battery combination, and likewise for the passive Na$^+$ channels (Figure 4–5). These three channels account for the bulk of the passive ionic pathways through the membrane.[1]

Using these electrical representations of the passive Na$^+$, K$^+$, and Cl$^-$ channels, we can easily

---

[1]Although there is good evidence that the membrane has separate active channels for Na$^+$, K$^+$, Cl$^-$, and Ca^{++}, it is not clear whether different ions have separate passive channels or share a common pathway. For the sake of convenience we shall assume separate channels.

calculate the resting membrane potential using a simple equivalent circuit model of the neuron. To construct this circuit, we need only connect the elements representing each type of channel at their two ends by elements that represent the extracellular fluid and the cytoplasm. Because these fluids both have relatively large cross-sectional areas with many available charge carriers, they have relatively low resistances. Thus extracellular fluid and cytoplasm, at least for the purposes of this discussion, may each be approximated by a *short circuit*—a conductor with zero resistance (Figure 4–6).

In order to simplify calculation of the membrane potential, one may ignore the Cl$^-$ channels initially. Thus we arrive at the circuit in Figure 4–7, with just two types of passive channels, K$^+$ and Na$^+$. As there are more passive channels for K$^+$ than for Na$^+$ ions, the resistance to current flow carried by K$^+$ ions is much lower than that for Na$^+$ current. In the example shown here, $R_K = 0.1 \times 10^6 \Omega$, 20 times lower than R_{Na}. Given these values, and the values of E_K and E_{Na}, one can calculate the membrane potential in four steps:

1. *Calculate the net EMF driving current around the loop.* This is the algebraic sum of E_{Na} and E_K. As we go around the loop, these two batteries have the same polarities, so that the net EMF is $75 + 55 = 130$ mV.

2. *Calculate the total resistance around the loop.* Given that batteries have zero resistance, this comes out to be

$$R_{Na} + R_K = 2.0 \times 10^6 \Omega + 0.1 \times 10^6 \Omega$$
$$= 2.1 \times 10^6 \Omega$$

4–5 Each type of ion-selective channel is represented by a series combination of a battery and a resistor.

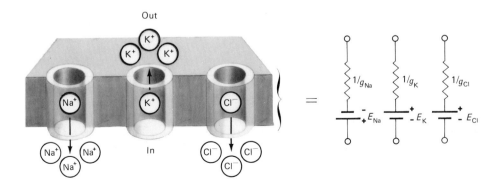

3. *Calculate the total current (I) flowing around the loop, and determine its direction.* From Ohm's law:

$$I = \frac{V}{R} = \frac{130 \times 10^{-3} \text{ V}}{2.1 \times 10^6 \, \Omega} = 62 \times 10^{-9} \text{ A}.$$

The direction of current flow, determined by the polarity of the net EMF, is counterclockwise. Note that current flow is the same in all parts of this circuit. Therefore, there will be an inward Na^+ current that is exactly balanced by an outward K^+ current. This current, as it flows inward through the Na^+ channels, is called I_{Na}, and as it flows outward through the K^+ channels it is called I_K.

4. *Calculate the membrane potential* $(V_i - V_o)$. This can be done by measuring the net sum of potential differences as you go across any part of the membrane.[2] For example, the net potential difference (V_m) across the Na^+ pore is

$$\begin{aligned} V_m &= E_{Na} + I_{Na} \times R_{Na} \\ &= +55 \text{ mV} + (-62 \times 10^{-9} \text{A})(2 \times 10^6 \Omega) \\ &= +55 \text{ mV} - 124 \text{ mV} = -69 \text{ mV}. \end{aligned}$$

This is a typical value for a nerve cell membrane. The same value is obtained if you calculate the sum of potential differences across the K^+ pore:

$$\begin{aligned} V_m &= E_K + I_K \times R_K \\ &= -75 \text{ mV} + (62 \times 10^{-9} \text{ A}) \times (0.1 \times 10^6 \, \Omega) \\ &= -69 \text{ mV}. \end{aligned}$$

This basic circuit can be used to calculate V_m under a variety of conditions, using the four steps outlined above. Note that the potential calculated for one leg of the circuit will always equal that for the other leg. This result follows simply from the basic rule that circuit elements in parallel always have the same potential difference across them.

A general rule for circuits with two ionic pathways in parallel is that the membrane potential will be closer to the Nernst potential of the ion with the larger conductance (lower resistance). The reason for this rule is easy to understand: the deviation of V_m from the EMF of either channel is equal to the potential difference $(I \times$

---

[2]Note that, because we have defined V_m as $V_{in} - V_{out}$, the following convention must be used for these equations: outward current (in this case I_K) is positive, inward current (I_{Na}) is negative; batteries with their positive poles toward the inside of the membrane (e.g., E_{Na}) are given positive values in the equations, and vice versa for batteries with their negative poles toward the inside.

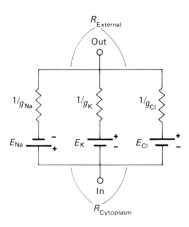

4–6 The neuron can be represented by an electrical circuit model that includes elements representing the ion-selective membrane channels, plus the short-circuit pathways provided by the cytoplasm and the extracellular fluid.

R) across the *resistance* of that channel. The current I has the same magnitude (but opposite polarity) for both paths, but the resistance R of the two paths differs—in this case by a factor of 20. Thus, the IR voltage drop is much greater for the Na^+ than for the K^+ pathway, so that the potential across the membrane is much further from E_{Na} than from E_K.

This rule can be illustrated with another example as we jump ahead briefly and consider what happens during the action potential. At the peak of the action potential total membrane g_K is essentially unchanged from its resting value, but g_{Na} increases by as much as 500-fold; in the example shown in Figure 4–7 it would go from $1/(2 \times 10^6 \, \Omega)$ to $1/(4 \times 10^3 \, \Omega)$, or from 5×10^{-7} siemens to 2.5×10^{-4} siemens. Substitute this

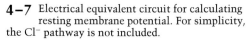

4–7 Electrical equivalent circuit for calculating resting membrane potential. For simplicity, the Cl^- pathway is not included.

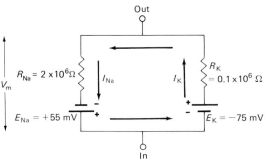

Chapter 4. Passive Electrical Properties of the Neuron **41**

new g_{Na} into Figure 4–7 and solve for V_m. You should get $V_m = +50$ mV, a value much closer to E_{Na} than to E_K. The reason V_m is closer to E_{Na} than to E_K at the peak of the spike is that g_{Na} is roughly 25-fold greater than g_K.

The tendency for V_m to be close to the Nernst potential of the ion with the greater conductance is also consistent with the Goldman equation, which deals with membrane permeability rather than conductance. Because conductance and permeability usually vary in the same direction, the ion with the greater permeability (or conductance) will dominate the membrane potential.

To complete the description of the basis for the resting membrane, we must now consider the contribution of the Cl^- channels to V_m. Because three pathways in parallel are much harder to deal with than two, let us condense the Na^+–K^+ combination shown in Figure 4–7. The net resistance of this pair is the parallel combination of $R_K + R_{Na}$:

$$R_{Na, K} = \frac{R_{Na} \times R_K}{R_K + R_{Na}}.$$

The net EMF is the potential difference across the parallel combination when it is isolated from other circuit components; it is the membrane potential calculated for Figure 4–7. This trick for combining two parallel pathways into one is often useful for simplifying circuits with two or more pathways in parallel. Let us now add the passive Cl^- channels to the circuit (Figure 4–8). g_{Cl} is typically within a factor of 2 to 4 of g_K, and E_{Cl} is usually rather close to E_K. If $E_{Cl} = -69$ mV, then including it in the equivalent circuit will have no effect on the calculated membrane potential. The algebraic sum of the batteries as one goes around the loop will be zero, thus no current will flow. Therefore, no IR voltage drop will occur across the resistive elements, and $V_m = -69$ mV, the value of the batteries. This descrip-

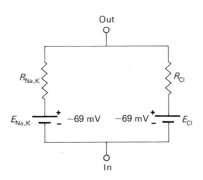

4–8 Electrical equivalent circuit model of a neuron in which Cl^- ions are passively distributed across the membrane.

tion is applicable to the actual situation in most nerve cells. The membrane potential is determined by the relative conductances and Nernst potentials of Na^+ and K^+. These Nernst potentials are, in turn, determined primarily by the Na–K pump, which maintains the ionic concentration gradients across the membrane by metabolically driven active transport. Cl^-, on the other hand, is usually passively distributed across the membrane, such that it is at equilibrium at the resting potential.

The Na–K Pump Should Be Included in the Equivalent Circuit

The important role of the Na–K pump in maintaining the Na^+ and K^+ concentration gradients is illustrated by the circuit shown in Figure 4–9. This equivalent circuit for the resting membrane shows not only the direction of current flow through the conductance channels, but also the ionic currents driven by the Na–K pump.

As mentioned above, there is a steady passive inward I_{Na} and outward I_K, even when the membrane is at resting potential. Clearly, if un-

4–9 Electrical equivalent circuit of a neuron at rest. Under steady-state conditions, Na^+ and K^+ currents through membrane channels are balanced by Na^+ and K^+ fluxes $(I'_{Na}$ and $I'_K)$ driven by the Na–K pump.

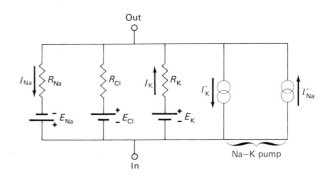

checked, these fluxes would result in Na$^+$ piling up inside the cell, with a concomitant loss of intracellular K$^+$. This would cause E_{Na} and E_K eventually to become zero, as their concentration gradients run down, and electrical signaling within the neuron would cease. To prevent the ionic batteries from running down, the Na–K pump continually extrudes Na$^+$ ions and pumps in K$^+$, even when the cell is at rest. The *actively* driven Na$^+$ and K$^+$ currents are exactly equal and opposite to the *passive* currents through the Na$^+$ and K$^+$ channels, respectively.

The Membrane Has Capacitive Properties

The third important passive electrical property of the neuron is membrane capacitance. In general, capacitance results whenever two conducting materials are separated by an insulating material. In the neuron, the conducting materials are the cytoplasm and the extracellular fluid. The insulation is the cell membrane, especially its lipid bilayer inner core. The capacitor portion of the membrane occupies at least 100 times the area of all of the ionic pores combined. A more complete equivalent circuit of the passive electrical properties of the membrane, with membrane capacitance included, is shown in Figure 4–10.

The fundamental property of a capacitor is its ability to store charges of opposite sign on its two surfaces. This maintained charge separation occurs whenever a potential difference exists between two sides of a capacitor. The net excess of positive and negative charge stored on the plates of a capacitor is given by the following equation:

$$Q = V \times C,$$

where Q is the net excess of positive or negative charges on each side of the capacitor, V is the potential difference between the two sides, and C is the capacitance.

A typical value of membrane capacitance for a nerve cell is about 10^{-6} F/cm^2 of membrane area. The net excess of positive and negative charges separated by the membrane of a cell with a resting potential of -70 mV can be calculated as follows:

$$Q = (70 \times 10^{-3} V) \times (10^{-6} F/cm^2)$$
$$= 7 \times 10^{-8} Coul./cm^2$$

We can convert charge measured in coulombs to units of electronic charge by using the appropri-

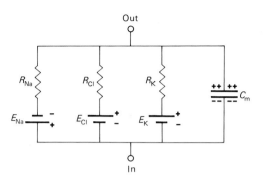

4–10 An electrical equivalent circuit of the passive membrane of a neuron that includes membrane capacitance (C_m).

ate conversion factor:

$$Q = (7 \times 10^{-8} Coul./cm^2)$$
$$\times (6.2 \times 10^{18} charges/Coul.)$$
$$= 4.3 \times 10^{11} charges/cm^2.$$

From this value of charge density and the membrane area, we can calculate the total amount of charge stored on the membrane capacitance. For a neuron with a 50-μm cell body diameter, the soma membrane area is 7.85×10^{-5} cm^2, so that the net charge separation across the soma membrane is

$$Q = (7.85 \times 10^{-5} cm^2)$$
$$\times (4.3 \times 10^{11} charges/cm^2)$$
$$= 34 \times 10^6 charges.$$

Although this number, 34 million, may sound quite large, it represents only a tiny fraction (1/200,000) of the *total* number of positive or negative charges within the cytoplasm of the cell.

Passive Electrical Properties of the Membrane Are Important for Signaling

The electrical equivalent circuit model of the neuron can be a great aid in the study of the cellular properties of neurons. With a few of the most elementary laws of physics, and some simple arithmetic, this basic model can be used to gain a fundamental understanding of the principles of electrical signaling in nerve and muscle cells.

The equivalent circuit model rests on a firm foundation of empirical data. The nerve cell actually does have resistive, capacitive, and EMF properties that are functionally indistinguishable from those of, for example, a television set.

Moreover, these parameters are experimentally measurable, and it was not until they were measured that it was possible to gain our current insights into the basic mechanisms of neuronal signaling.

Selected Readings and References

Finkelstein, A., and Mauro, A. 1977. Physical principles and formalisms of electrical excitability. In E. R. Kandel (ed.), Handbook of Physiology; The Nervous System, Vol. 1, Part I. Bethesda, Md.: American Physiological Society, pp. 161–213.

Hubbard, J. I., Llinás, R., and Quastel, D. M. J., 1969. Electrophysiological Analysis of Synaptic Transmission. Baltimore: Williams & Wilkins, chap. 2.

John Koester

Functional Consequences of Passive Electrical Properties of the Neuron

5

The passive resistive and capacitive properties of the membrane have important effects on the flow of information both within a neuron and between neurons. For example, the passive electrical properties of a nerve cell affect the time course of the postsynaptic potentials (PSPs) generated in it by other cells. The passive electrical properties of the postsynaptic cell also determine how efficiently PSPs are propagated within a cell from their site of origin to the trigger zone. These features of neuronal functioning contribute to *synaptic integration,* the process by which a nerve cell adds up all incoming signals to get some net value of synaptic input that determines whether or not the cell will generate an action potential. Once an action potential is generated, its speed of conduction from the trigger zone to axon terminals is also dependent on the passive electrical properties of the axon. Thus the passive electrical characteristics of a nerve cell affect both inter- and intracellular communication within the nervous system.

An understanding of the functional aspects of passive membrane properties is most easily achieved by considering the equivalent circuit model of the neuron developed in Chapter 4.

Membrane Capacitance Affects the Time Course of Signal Conduction
Simplified Equivalent Circuit Model

In order to examine the functional consequences of membrane capacitance, one can refer to the simplified equivalent circuit model of the membrane shown in Figure 5–1. In this diagram, the cell membrane is represented by a capacitor and a resistor in parallel. One can deal with only the passive membrane properties by considering the effects of depolarizing current pulses that are too small to open a significant number of the voltage-gated active Na^+ and K^+ channels. Therefore, the membrane resistance *(R)* in this example stands for the passive resistance channels, that is, the parallel combination of the nongated R_K, R_{Na}, and R_{Cl} elements (Figure 4–10, Chapter 4). The membrane "batteries" can also be ignored if one examines just the rate of change of membrane potential, rather than its absolute value.

Rate of Change of Membrane Potential

To understand the factors that determine how long it takes for membrane potential to change in response to a current pulse passed across the membrane, consider a nerve cell body. Specifically, what is the response of the membrane potential (V_m) to a rectangular pulse of current that is passed across the membrane from an intracellular electrode to an extracellular electrode in the bathing medium (Figure 5–2)?

Two types of current flow occur across nerve cell membranes: ionic (I_i) and capacitive (I_c). The total membrane current (I_m) is the sum of these two components:

$$I_m = I_i + I_c.$$

Ionic (or resistive) membrane current represents the actual movement of ions through the conductance channels of the membrane; for example, Na^+ ions moving from outside to inside the cell. *Capacitive* membrane current results in a change in the net charge stored on the membrane capacitance. Thus, if there is a net addition of positive charges to the inside of the membrane, and an equal number of positive charges are removed from the outside of the membrane, this charge movement is equivalent to an outward capacitive current (Figure 5–3).

This capacitance of the membrane has the ef-

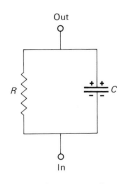

5–1 Electrical equivalent circuit for examining the effects of membrane capacitance on the response of a neuron to injected current. For simplicity, all resistive channels are lumped into a single element, and batteries representing the EMFs generated by ion diffusion are ignored.

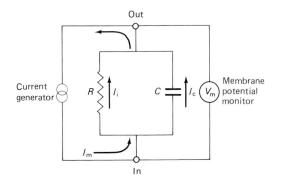

5–2 Experimental setup for the measurement of the rate of change of V_m in response to current injection.

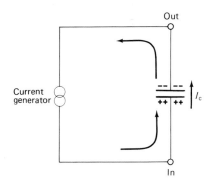

5–3 When capacitive current flows, positive charge builds up on one plate of the capacitor and leaves the other plate.

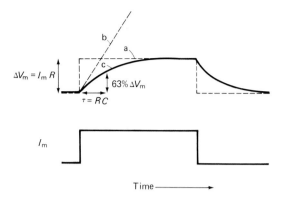

5-4 The time course (**c**) of the response of the membrane to a rectangular current pulse is intermediate between that of a pure resistive element (**a**) and that of a pure capacitive element (**b**).

fect of reducing the rate of change of the membrane potential in response to a current pulse. For example, if the membrane had only resistive properties, a step pulse of outward current passed across it would change the membrane potential instantaneously (Figure 5–4a). On the other hand, if the membrane had only capacitive properties, membrane potential would change in a ramplike manner in response to the same current waveform (Figure 5–4b). Because the membrane has both capacitive and resistive properties in parallel, the actual change in membrane potential resulting from a rectangular current pulse is intermediate between the two pure responses (Figure 5–4c): the initial slope of V_m versus time is the same as that for a purely capacitive element, whereas the final slope is the same as that for a purely resistive element.

To understand how the membrane capacitance results in a slowing of ΔV_m, recall that the potential across the capacitor is proportional to the charge stored on the capacitor:

$$V = \frac{Q}{C}.$$

For a change in potential (ΔV_m) to occur across the membrane, there must be a change in the charge (ΔQ) stored on the membrane capacitance:

$$\Delta V_m = \frac{\Delta Q}{C}. \tag{5-1}$$

This ΔQ is brought about by the flow of capacitive current (I_c). Current is defined as the net movement of positive charges per unit time. Thus the value of capacitive current is equal to

the rate of change of charge stored on the capacitor:

$$I_c = \frac{dQ}{dt}.$$

The total change in charge on the membrane capacitor will be equal to the product of the average value of I_c times its duration ($t_2 - t_1$). This product can be obtained by integrating I_c over the time t_1 to t_2:

$$\Delta Q = \int_{t_1}^{t_2} I_c \, dt.$$

By substituting back into Equation 5–1,

$$\Delta V_m = \frac{\int_{t_1}^{t_2} I_c \, dt}{C}.$$

Thus the larger the value of membrane capacitance, the smaller will be the change in V_m for a given amplitude and duration of I_c.

The reason for the gradual change in potential in Figure 5–4 is that the membrane capacitance and resistance are in parallel; therefore, the potential across these two elements must be equal at all times. The potential across the capacitor cannot change until the charge stored on its plates has changed ($\Delta V_m = \Delta Q/C$). Initially, all of the membrane current will flow into the capacitor, to change the charge on its plates. However, as the pulse continues and ΔQ increases, more and more current must flow through the resistance, because at any instant the voltage drop across the membrane resistance ($\Delta V_m = I_iR$) must be equal to the voltage across the capacitance ($\Delta V_m = \Delta Q/C$). As a larger fraction of the membrane current flows through the resistor, less is available for charging the capacitor; thus the *rate of change* of V_m decreases with time. When ΔV_m has reached its plateau value, all of the membrane current is flowing through the resistance and $\Delta V_m = I_m R$.

Membrane Time Constant

The waveform of the potential change shown in Figure 5–4 can be described by the following equation:

$$\Delta V_m(t) = I_m R (1 - e^{-t/\tau}).$$

In this equation, *e*, which has the value of 2.72, is the base of the system of natural loga-

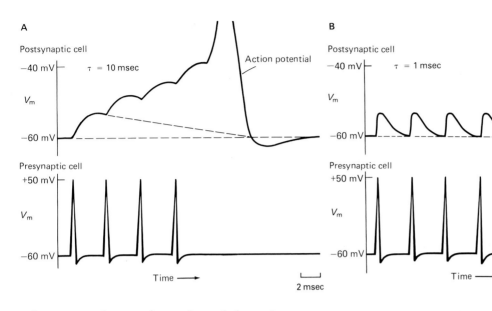

rithms; τ equals RC, the product of the resistance and capacitance of the membrane. The parameter τ is called the *membrane time constant.* It can be measured experimentally. For the response of the membrane to a rectangular step of current (Figure 5–4), τ is the time it takes for ΔV_m to reach 63% of its final value.[1] The time constants of different neurons typically range from about 1 to 20 msec.

The value of the time constant is especially important in its effect on integration of synaptic input. Most inhibitory and excitatory PSPs (IPSPs and EPSPs, respectively) are caused by brief synaptic currents triggered by neurotransmitters. The time course of the rising phase of a PSP is determined by both active and passive membrane properties (see Chapter 7). The falling phase is a passive process. Its time course is a function of the membrane time constant: the longer the time constant, the longer the duration of the PSP. PSPs that are not synchronous but that do partially overlap in time can add together in a process known as *temporal summation.* In this way individual EPSPs that in isolation might be too small to trigger an action potential can sum together to reach spike threshold (Figure 5–5). A long membrane time constant for the postsynaptic cell will mean longer PSP durations, and therefore more chance for temporal summation to occur. Temporal summation of generator potentials takes place in a similar fashion in receptor cells.

5–5 Temporal summation of PSPs in a postsynaptic cell occurs when spikes in the presynaptic cell are separated by a time interval less than the duration of the PSP. The longer the time constant of the postsynaptic cell, the longer will be the PSP duration, and the greater the extent of temporal summation. **A.** The time constant of the postsynaptic cell is 10 msec. **B.** It is 1 msec.

Membrane Resistance and Nerve Cell Geometry Affect the Efficiency of Signal Conduction
Threshold Dependence on Axon Diameter

When a peripheral nerve is stimulated with a pair of extracellular electrodes, the total number of axons that generate action potentials varies with the amplitude of the current pulse. In general, the *largest axons have the lowest current threshold.* To drive the cell to threshold, the current must pass through the cell membrane. But for any given axon, most of the stimulating current bypasses the fiber, passing instead through the low-resistance pathways provided by the other axons and by the extracellular fluid. Thus, only a small fraction of the total stimulating current crosses the membrane of any one axon. From there it flows along the axoplasmic core, and then out again through more distant regions of axonal membrane, to the second electrode in the extracellular fluid. The larger the diameter of the axon, the smaller will be the resistance of its axoplasm to longitudinal current spread because of the greater number of available intracellular charge carriers. As a result

---

[1]63% is equivalent to $(1 - 1/e) \times 100$.

of the increase in current spread, a greater fraction of total current enters and leaves the larger axon, thereby contributing to depolarization of the membrane.

Change of Membrane Potential with Distance

The *length constant* (also known as the *space constant*) is a measure of the distance that a potential difference can spread passively along a nerve cell process (axon or dendrite). To understand this parameter, we must consider the three-dimensional geometry of a neuron. Consider, for example, a dendrite. Because it has a relatively small cross-sectional area, the cytoplasmic core of a dendrite has a significant resistance to the longitudinal flow of current. Thus, as shown in Figure 5–6, the equivalent circuit of the dendrite may be represented as a series of identical patches of membrane, with each adjacent segment connected by a short segment of cytoplasm. In this diagram, r_a is the axial resistance of a given length of cytoplasmic core (Ω/cm); r_m is defined as the membrane resistance per unit length of membrane cylinder (Ω-cm), and c_m is the capacitance per unit length of membrane cylinder. Because of its greater volume, the extracellular fluid has a negligible resistance that may be ignored.

If a current is injected into the dendrite at one point, what will be the membrane potential distribution it produces with distance along the dendrite? For simplicity, let us consider the distribution after the current pulse has been on for some time ($t \gg \tau$). Under these conditions, the membrane potential will have reached a steady state, so that capacitive current will be zero. Because $I_c = 0$, all of the membrane current is now ionic, and $I_m = I_i$. The potential distribution is thus independent of c_m, and depends solely on the relative values of r_m and r_a. The current that is injected will flow out across the membrane by several possible pathways distributed along the length of the process (Figure 5–7A). Each of these pathways is made up of two components in series: a total axial resistance, R_a, and a membrane component, r_m. The total axial resistance (R_a) for each current pathway is the cytoplasmic resistance between the site of current injection and any site along the dendrite. Resistors in series add, so that $R_a = \sum r_a$, or $r_a \cdot x$, where x is the distance along the axon from the site of current injection. The membrane component, r_m, is the same for each of these current pathways. Because current always tends to follow the path of least resistance, more current will flow across the membrane near the site of injection than at more distant regions, for which R_a is larger (Figure 5–7A). Because $V_m = I_m r_m$, the change in membrane potential produced by the current, $\Delta V_m(x)$, becomes smaller as one moves down the dendrite, away from the current electrode. This decay with distance has an exponential shape (Figure 5–7B), expressed by the following equation:

$$\Delta V_m(x) = \Delta V_0 e^{-x/\lambda}$$

where λ is the membrane length constant, x is

5–6 A neuronal process (A), either axon or dendrite, can be represented by an electrical equivalent circuit (B).

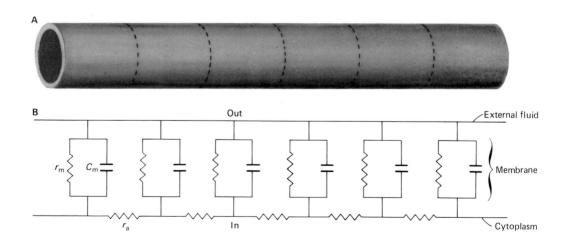

A

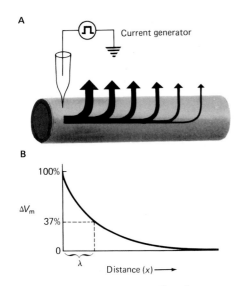

B

5–7 A. Current injected into a cell with a microelectrode follows the path of least resistance to the return electrode in the extracellular fluid. **B.** The change in V_m produced by focal current injection decays exponentially with distance along the length of the process.

the distance away from the site of current injection, and ΔV_0 is the change in membrane potential produced by the current flow at the site of the current electrode ($x = 0$).

This equation indicates that the change in potential (ΔV_m) decays with distance along the den-

drite, and the rate of decay with distance decreases as one moves away from the point $x = 0$. The *length constant*, λ, which is the distance along the dendrite to the site where ΔV_m has decayed to $1/e$, or 37% of its value at $x = 0$, is determined by the ratio of r_m to r_a where

$$\lambda = \sqrt{\frac{r_m}{r_a}}.$$

The better the insulation of the membrane (the higher the r_m), and the better the conducting properties of the inner core (the lower the r_a), the longer will be the length constant of the dendrite. The reason for this relationship is that the current will be able to spread further along the inner conductive core of the dendrite before leaking across the membrane. Typical length constant values fall in the range of about 0.1–1.0 mm.

Passive conduction of voltage changes along the neuron is called electrotonic conduction. The efficiency of this process, which is measured by the length constant, has two important effects on

5–8 Effect of length constant on electrotonic propagation of synaptic potentials. An action potential in cell A elicits synaptic potentials in cells B and C. At their sites of initiation, the two PSPs are equal in amplitude. But, since the length constant of the dendrites in cell B is much longer than that of cell C, the PSP is conducted to the trigger zone much more effectively in B than in C, even though the distance the PSP must travel is the same in both cells.

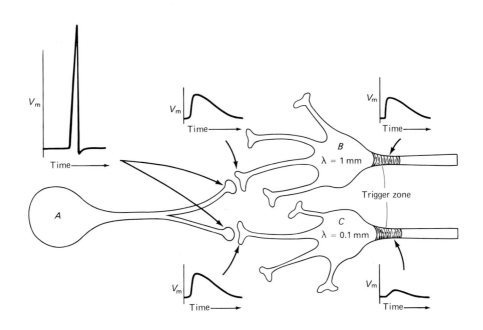

neuronal function. First, it determines how effectively PSPs or generator potentials will be conducted from their site of initiation to the trigger zone of the cell. This process, by which signals generated in different regions of the neuron are added together at the decision-making component of the neuron, is called *spatial summation.* The longer the length constant, the less such a signal will decrease during this passive conduction process (Figure 5–8).

A second important feature of the length constant is its role in the propagation of the action potential. Once the membrane at any point along an axon has been depolarized beyond threshold, active (voltage-sensitive) changes in the mem-

5–9 Conduction of depolarization to propagate action potentials. **A.** The waveform of an action potential propagating from right to left. **B.** The charge distribution across the membrane capacitance and the spread of depolarization from the active region (**2**) to the inactive region (**1**) ahead of the action potential results from local-circuit current flow. The spread of positive charge (current flow) along the inside of the axon from area 2 to area 3 also tends to depolarize the membrane behind the action potential. However, because g_K is increased in the wake of the action potential (see Chapter 6), this build-up of positive charge along the inner side of membrane capacitance is more than balanced by an efflux of K^+ through the membrane in area 3.

brane Na^+ permeability will occur, causing the generation of an action potential (see Chapter 6). For conduction to continue, this local depolarization must somehow cause the adjacent region of the membrane to reach the threshold for action potential generation (Figure 5–9). The mechanism for this spread of excitation is the passive, decremental conduction of depolarization along the axon cable. It is mediated by "local-circuit" current flow between the active and the inactive regions of the membrane. Once the inactive region of the membrane has reached threshold, it actively contributes to its own depolarization. The voltage-gated Na^+ channels in this region of membrane open up, Na^+ ions rush into the cell down their electrochemical gradient, and the depolarization becomes greater. This increment in depolarization causes more Na^+ gates to open, so that more Na^+ comes in, and so forth. Thus at threshold the depolarization of this local patch of membrane changes from a passive to an active, regenerative process. This actively generated depolarization now spreads by passive, local-circuit flow of current to the next region of membrane, and the cycle is repeated.

Passive Membrane Properties and Axon Diameter Affect the Velocity of Action Potential Propagation

The passive spread of depolarization during action potential conduction is not an instantaneous process. In fact, it is a rate-limiting factor in the process of action potential propagation. To understand this limitation, consider the simplified equivalent circuit of the axon shown in Figure 5–10. It represents two adjacent membrane segments, connected by a segment of axoplasm, r_a. In Figure 5–10A the two adjacent areas of membrane are both at rest. In Figure 5–10B, an action potential has been generated in one segment of membrane, and it is supplying depolarizing current to the adjacent membrane, causing it to depolarize gradually toward threshold.

According to Ohm's law, the larger the axoplasmic resistance, the smaller will be the current flow around the loop ($I = V/R$), and thus the longer it will take to change the charge on the membrane capacitance of this adjacent segment (recall that $\Delta Q = \int_{t_1}^{t_2} I_c \, dt$). Similarly, the larger the membrane capacitance, the more charge must be deposited on it to change the potential across the membrane. Therefore, the time it

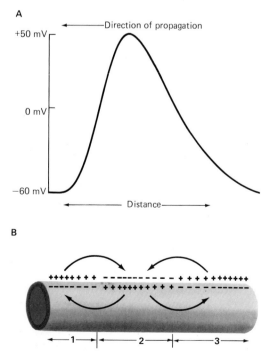

A

+50 mV

←——Direction of propagation

0 mV

−60 mV

←——— Distance ———→

B

←—1—→←——2——→←——3——→

A

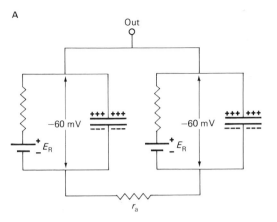

B

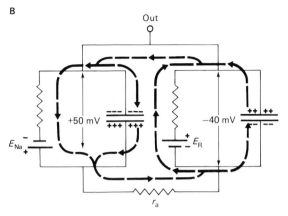

takes for depolarization to spread along the axon is determined by both r_a and c_m; it can be shown to depend on the product $r_a \times c_m$. If this product is reduced, the rate of passive spread of depolarization will increase, resulting in a faster rate of action potential propagation.

Speed of action potential propagation is functionally important, and during evolution two separate strategies have occurred to increase it. One is an *increase in the diameter of the axon core*. Because r_a decreases in proportion to the square of axon diameter, while c_m increases in direct proportion to diameter, the net effect of an increase in diameter is a decrease in $r_a c_m$. This adaptation has been carried to an extreme in the giant axon of the squid, which may be as large as 1 mm in diameter. However, because of the need to keep neuronal size small, this strategy has severe practical limitations.

A second strategy for reducing $r_a c_m$ is *myelination*. This process is functionally equivalent to increasing the thickness of the axonal membrane by as much as 100 times. Because the capacitance of a parallel-plate capacitor such as the membrane is inversely proportional to the thickness of the insulating material, myelination will decrease c_m, and thus also $r_a c_m$. The increase in *total* fiber diameter achieved by myelination causes a much larger percentage decrease in $r_a c_m$ than would the same increase in fiber diameter achieved by simply increasing the axon core diameter. For this reason, conduction velocity is typically greater in myelinated than in non-myelinated axons of the same diameter.

Because myelin is essentially a very thick insulating material, it prevents the flow of ionic currents across the axonal membrane. To keep

5–10 Electrical equivalent circuit for demonstrating the effects of r_a and c_m on action potential conduction velocity. **A.** Resting condition. **B.** An action potential is spreading from the left-hand membrane segment to the segment on the right.

the spike from dying out, there are bare "nodes" distributed every 1–2 mm along the axon, where no myelin is present (Figure 5–11A). Each node responds with an active, regenerative spike to the passive spread of depolarization from the preceding node. As each node in turn becomes active, the inward ionic current that flows across it spreads down the core of the axon to depolarize the next node, bringing it to spike threshold. This process, by which the action potential jumps rapidly from node to node, is called *saltatory conduction* (Figure 5–11B). Because ionic current flows only at the node in myelinated fibers, saltatory conduction is also favorable from a metabolic standpoint. Less energy must be expended by the Na–K pump in restoring the Na^+ and K^+ concentration gradients, which tend to run down as a result of spike activity.

Several diseases of the nervous system, such as multiple sclerosis or Guillain-Barré syndrome, cause demyelination. These diseases can have devastating effects on the control of behavior, because they cause slowing of action potential conduction. As an action potential goes from a region where myelin is present to a bare stretch of axon (Figure 5–11C), it encounters a region of relatively high c_m and low r_m. The inward current generated at the last node before this area will therefore have to flow for a longer time before it drives the adjacent membrane to threshold for ac-

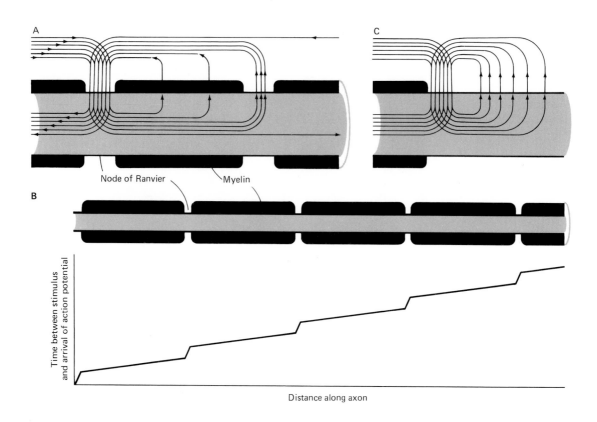

5–11 Saltatory conduction in myelinated nerves. **A.** Capacitive and ionic membrane current density is much higher at the nodes of Ranvier than that in the internodal regions of the axon. **B.** Because of the low capacitance of myelin, the action potential skips rapidly from node to node. **C.** Action potential conduction is slowed down or blocked at axon regions that have lost their myelin. The local circuit currents must charge a larger c_m, and because of the low r_m they do not spread as effectively along the length of the axon.

tion potential generation. In addition, this local circuit current will not spread as far as normal, because it is flowing into a segment of axon which, because of its low r_m, has a short length constant. These two factors will combine to slow down, and in some cases actually block, action potential conduction in the nerve.

Selected Readings and References

Barrett, J. N. 1975. Motoneuron dendrites: Role in synaptic integration. Fed. Proc. 34:1398–1407.

Graubard, K., and Calvin, W. H. 1979. Presynaptic dendrites: Implications of spikeless synaptic transmission and dendritic geometry. In F. O. Schmitt and F. G. Worden (eds.), The Neurosciences; Fourth Study Program. Cambridge, Mass.: MIT Press, pp. 317–331.

Hodgkin, A. L. 1964. The Conduction of the Nervous Impulse. Springfield, Ill.: Thomas, chap. 4.

Hubbard, I. L., Llinás, R., and Quastel, D. M. J. 1969. Electrophysiological Analysis of Synaptic Transmission. Baltimore: Williams & Wilkins, chap. 2; pp. 91–109, 257–264.

Jack, J. 1979. An introduction to linear cable theory. In F. O. Schmitt and F. G. Worden (eds.), The Neurosciences; Fourth Study Program. Cambridge, Mass.: MIT Press, pp. 423–437.

Jack, J. J. B., Noble, D., and Tsien, R. W. 1975. Electric Current Flow in Excitable Cells. Oxford: Clarendon Press, chaps. 1–5, 7; pp. 276–277.

Khodorov, B. I. 1974. The Problem of Excitability. New York: Plenum, chap. 3.

Rall, W. 1977. Core conductor theory and cable properties of neurons. In E. R. Kandel (ed.), Handbook of Physiology; The Nervous System, Vol. 1, Part I. Bethesda, Md.: American Physiological Society, pp. 39–97.

John Koester

Active Conductances Underlying the Action Potential

6

An important feature of the action potential is that it does not decrease in amplitude as it is conducted away from its site of initiation. The ability of nerve cells to conduct action potentials makes it possible for signals to be conveyed long distances within the nervous system. Knowledge of the self-regenerative mechanisms underlying the generation and propagation of action potentials is therefore important for understanding neuronal signaling. The generation of action potentials by nerve axons and muscle fibers was first described by DuBois-Reymond in 1849, but it was not until over 100 years later that it became possible to analyze its mechanism in terms of specific ionic conductances.

The Action Potential Is Due to an Increase in Membrane Conductance

One of the most important early clues about how action potentials are generated came from an experiment done in 1938 by K. C. Cole and Howard Curtis. Recording from the squid giant axon, they found that membrane conductance increases during the action potential. A decade later, Alan Hodgkin and Bernard Katz found that the amplitude of the action potential is reduced when external Na^+ concentration is lowered. They also found that the rate of repolarization during the falling phase of the action potential is reduced if the external K⁺ concentration is increased. Based on their own observations and those of Cole and Curtis, Hodgkin and Katz suggested a specific hypothesis to explain the generation of the action potential. The action potential is initiated by the opening of potential-sensitive gates of Na⁺ conductance channels in the membrane, which results in an increased Na⁺ influx into the cell. This increased Na⁺ influx produces the rising phase of the action potential. The falling phase of the action potential is caused by subsequent closing of these Na⁺ gates which reduces Na⁺ influx, and by an opening of gates of K⁺ conductance channels which results in an increase in K⁺ efflux from the cell.

To test this hypothesis, it is necessary to vary membrane potential and measure the resulting changes in Na⁺ and K⁺ conductances. This is difficult to do since there is mutual coupling between membrane potential and the Na⁺ and K⁺ conductance channels. For example, if the membrane is depolarized enough to open the gates of the active Na⁺ conductance channels, inward Na⁺ current will flow through them and cause additional depolarization. This depolarization will result in a greater increase in g_{Na}, and consequently induce more inward Na⁺ current. A regenerative cycle will therefore be initiated that makes it impossible to achieve a stable membrane potential. This cycle, which eventually drives V_m to the peak of the action potential, can be depicted as follows:

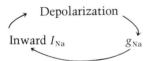

A similar difficulty hinders the study of the active K⁺ conductances that are responsible for the falling phase of the spike. An apparatus known as a voltage clamp was designed to overcome these problems.

Voltage-Dependent Channels Can Be Studied by Use of the Voltage Clamp

The basic function of the voltage clamp is to interrupt the mutual interaction between membrane conductance and membrane potential. When an axon is voltage clamped, membrane conductance still changes in response to changes in the membrane potential, but the clamp pre-

vents these conductance changes from influencing the membrane potential. Thus, the conductance of the membrane to different ions can be measured as a function of membrane potential.

The voltage clamp is essentially a current pump connected to two electrodes, one inside and the other outside the cell. The clamp has two functions. One is to step the membrane potential rapidly to various levels of depolarization in response to "commands" from the experimenter. These commanded depolarizations, which are produced by passing current across the passive membrane resistance and capacitance, turn on active Na⁺ and K⁺ conductance channels. The movement of Na⁺ and K⁺ across the membrane tends to change the membrane potential to a different level. This process then calls into play the other function of the voltage clamp, which is to "clamp" the membrane potential at its new level.

For example, an inward membrane current carried by Na⁺ ions would tend to depolarize the membrane by increasing the positive charge on the inside and reducing the amount of external

6–1 Voltage clamp of the squid axon. **A.** Basic flow diagram. **B.** Configuration of electronic components used in voltage clamping. CP—signal generator for producing different values of command potential.

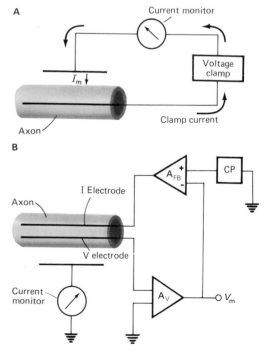

positive charge. The voltage clamp prevents the membrane potential from changing by simultaneously pumping positive charges out of the cell and into the external solution. Thus, the flow of any membrane current that would tend to change the resting membrane potential from its commanded value is automatically counteracted by an equal and opposite current generated by the voltage clamp circuit (Figure 6–1A). With regard to the regenerative cycle described above, the first two steps are not affected directly. Under voltage clamp conditions, depolarization still causes an increase in g_{Na}, which can still result in an increased inward Na^+ current. But the third step, the further depolarization caused by this extra I_{Na}, is prevented by the voltage clamp.

The current that must be generated by the voltage clamp to keep the membrane potential from changing is a measure of the membrane current. The membrane conductance can then be calculated from the membrane current and the membrane potential (see below). In describing the voltage clamp technique, we shall focus on the classical experiments done by Hodgkin and Huxley on the squid giant axon in the early 1950s. Their results led to the first complete description of the ionic mechanisms underlying the action potential.

The Voltage Clamp Employs Negative Feedback

The experimental apparatus used for voltage clamping a squid axon (Figure 6–1B) includes an intracellular electrode connected to an amplifier (A_v) for measuring the membrane potential. The membrane potential signal (V_m) is displayed on an oscilloscope and also fed into one terminal of the "feedback" amplifier (A_{FB}). The feedback amplifier is a differential amplifier. It has two inputs—one for the membrane potential, and another for the command potential (CP). The command potential, which comes from a signal generator, is selected by the experimenter. It can be of any desired amplitude and waveform. The feedback amplifier subtracts the membrane potential from the command potential. Any difference between these two signals appears amplified several thousand times at the output of the feedback amplifier. The output of this amplifier is connected to a thin AgCl wire, the current-passing electrode, which runs the length of the axon.

The voltage clamp is a negative feedback system.[1] Its configuration is such that the membrane potential *automatically follows* the command potential exactly. For example, if an inward Na^+ current causes the membrane potential to become more positive than the command potential, the output of the feedback amplifier will be negative. The resulting increased negativity of the internal current electrode will cause positive charges to be withdrawn from the cell through the voltage clamp circuit and deposited from the other current electrode into the external solution. The current flowing across the membrane will equal that generated by the feedback amplifier, so that there will be no *net* change in the amount of charge separated by the membrane and no significant change in V_m.

The current generated by the feedback circuit is recorded on the oscilloscope along with V_m. This current is the dependent variable in a voltage clamp experiment; membrane potential, which is set by the command, is the independent variable. Membrane potential is the same all along the length of the axon because the highly conductive current-passing wire short-circuits the axoplasmic resistance, reducing the axial resistance to zero. The presence of this low-resistance pathway along the inside of the axon makes it impossible for a potential difference to exist between different points along the axon core.

The membrane current that is recorded can be separated into ionic and capacitive components. The V_m at any time is proportional to the charge on the membrane capacitance (C_m). When V_m is not changing, the charge on C_m is constant, and no capacitive current is flowing. Capacitive current flows *only* when V_m is changing. Therefore, if the membrane potential is changed by means of a very rapid step of command potential, capacitive current will flow only at the beginning and the end of the step. This capacitive current is essentially instantaneous, and on the oscilloscope record it can be easily separated from the ionic currents by inspection (Figure 6–2).

---

[1]A *negative feedback system* is one in which the value of the output of the system (V_m in this case) is "fed back" to the input of the system, where it is compared to a command signal for the desired output. Any difference between the command and the output signal activates a "controller" device (in this case A_{FB}) that automatically reduces the difference. Negative feedback is also a widely used physiological mechanism, e.g., for the control of blood pressure, blood levels of hormones, and synthesis of various metabolites.

6–2 Typical squid axon voltage clamp records. **A.** A small depolarization is accompanied by capacitive and leakage currents (I_c and I_l, respectively). **B.** A larger depolarization also activates Na⁺ and K⁺ currents (I_{Na} and I_K) as the active Na⁺ and K⁺ channels open up. **C.** When the voltage step shown in part B is repeated in the presence of TTX and again in the presence of TEA, records of the pure K⁺ and Na⁺ currents are obtained by subtraction of I_c and I_l. When the axon is bathed in solution containing TTX, no Na⁺ current flows; only capacitive, leakage, and K⁺ currents flow. The leakage and capacitive currents can be eliminated by inspection, leaving a record of the pure K⁺ current. Similar analysis of the current measured with the axon exposed to TEA provides a record of the pure Na⁺ current.

I_{Na} and I_K Can Be Separated

We may now consider the results of a typical voltage clamp experiment. We shall start with the membrane potential clamped at its resting value. If a small, subthreshold depolarizing potential step is commanded, we observe the following waveform in the current trace (Figure 6–2A): an initial, very brief outward capacitive current (I_c), followed by a smaller, steady outward ionic current. At the end of the pulse there is a brief inward capacitive current, and the ionic current returns to zero. The steady ionic current is called the *leakage* current, I_l. It is the current that flows through the passive, nongated conductance channels of the membrane. These channels, which are always open, are responsible for generating the resting potential. In most neurons the leakage conductance channels, abbreviated g_l, are permeable primarily to K⁺ and/or Cl⁻ ions.

If larger depolarizing steps are commanded, the current records become more complicated (Figure 6–2B): the capacitive and leakage currents are both larger. Very shortly after the capacitive current and the start of the leakage current, an inward current develops; within a few milliseconds it reaches a peak, declines, and gives way to an outward current. This outward current reaches a plateau that is maintained for the duration of the pulse.

The simplest interpretation of this type of experiment is that the depolarizing voltage step sequentially turns on active conductance channels for two separate ions: one for inward current and another that carries outward current. Because these two oppositely directed currents overlap in time (as we now know), the most difficult part of a voltage clamp analysis is to determine their separate time courses.

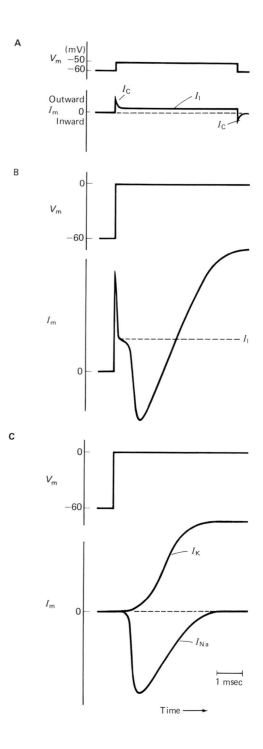

This separation was achieved by Hodgkin and Huxley using ion-substitution techniques. For example, by substituting a larger impermeable cation (choline) for Na⁺ in the external bathing solution, they found they could eliminate the inward current. Recently a simpler technique has been used to separate inward and outward currents. This method is based on the selective pharmacological blockade of the separate voltage-sensitive conductance channels: tetrodotoxin (TTX) blocks the inward Na^+ current, and tetraethylammonium (TEA) blocks the outward K^+ current.

To measure I_{Na} as a function of membrane potential, various command pulses are given to change V_m to different levels. If TEA is added to block the K^+ current, the total membrane current will consist of I_c, I_l, and I_{Na}. As g_l is constant and does not vary with V_m, I_l may be readily calculated and subtracted from I_m, leaving $I_{Na} + I_c$. Because I_c occurs only very briefly at the beginning and end of the pulse, it can be easily eliminated by inspection, leaving a pure I_{Na}. By a similar process, I_K may be measured in the presence of TTX (Figure 6–2C).

g_K and g_{Na} Are Calculated from I_K and I_{Na}

Once the currents have been separated (Figure 6–2C), it is possible to calculate the changes in the Na^+ and K^+ membrane conductance to Na^+ and K^+. This procedure may be illustrated with another, more complex equivalent circuit diagram of the membrane, which includes the passive membrane capacitance and leakage conductance (g_l), as well as the active, voltage-sensitive g_{Na} and g_K channels (Figure 6–3). E_l, the EMF of the leakage channels, is equal to the resting potential. The Na^+ and K^+ conductances are shown in series with the appropriate Nernst batteries.

The current through each conductance channel may be calculated from Ohm's law. Thus, for the K^+ channel (Figure 6–3):

$$V_m = E_K + I_K R_K \qquad (6-1)$$
$$I_K = \frac{V_m - E_K}{R_K} = g_K(V_m - E_K)$$

This equation simply states that I_K is equal to the product of two factors: a conductance factor, g_K, that is determined by the number of K^+ channels that are opened, and a driving force factor ($V_m - E_K$). The absolute value of the driving force is determined by the difference between V_m and E_K. The direction of the driving force depends on whether V_m is below or above E_K. If V_m equals E_K, I_K will be zero.

The derivation of equations for I_{Na} and I_{Cl} is analogous to the derivation of Equation 6–1:

$$I_{Na} = \frac{V_m - E_{Na}}{R_{Na}} = g_{Na}(V_m - E_{Na}) \qquad (6-2)$$
$$I_l = \frac{V_m - E_l}{R_l} = g_l(V_m - E_l). \qquad (6-3)$$

Equations 6–1 and 6–2 can be used to compute g_K and g_{Na}. To solve these equations for g_K and g_{Na}, one must know V_m, E_K, E_{Na}, I_K, and I_{Na}. Because V_m is the independent variable, set by the experimenter, it is readily determined. E_K and E_{Na} are constants. They can be calculated from the Nernst equation or measured empirically by finding the values of V_m at which I_K and I_{Na} reverse their polarities. For example, if V_m is stepped to very positive values, I_{Na} gradually becomes less inward. At E_{Na} it goes to zero, and for values of V_m more positive than E_{Na}, I_{Na} is out-

6–3 Electrical equivalent circuit of a nerve cell under voltage clamp conditions.

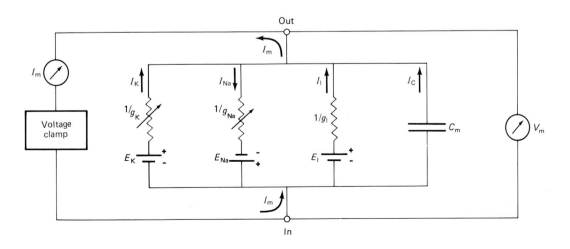

ward (Equation 6–1). I_K and I_{Na} are the dependent variables and can be obtained from the voltage clamp current records by the separation technique described above (Figure 6–2C). Thus one has all the data required to compute g_K and g_{Na}.

When g_{Na} and g_K are measured in this way at various levels of membrane potential, they show two basic similarities and two differences. They are alike in that both of them are turned on by depolarizing steps of membrane potential, and they both turn on more rapidly and to a greater extent for larger depolarizations (Figure 6–4). They differ, however, in two respects:

1. *Rate of onset and offset.* g_{Na} turns on more rapidly than g_K at all levels of membrane potential (Figure 6–4); it also turns off more rapidly when the depolarizing pulse is terminated (Figure 6–5,a).

2. *Inactivation.* With maintained depolarization, the Na^+ conductance channels begin to close down, or inactivate, resulting in a decay of inward current (Figures 6–4 and 6–5,b). The K^+ channels remain open as long as the membrane is depolarized. Na^+ channels that have been inactivated are refractory. They cannot be turned on again until the membrane has been repolarized to its resting level. Even then it takes a certain time for Na^+ inactivation to wane (Figure 6–6).

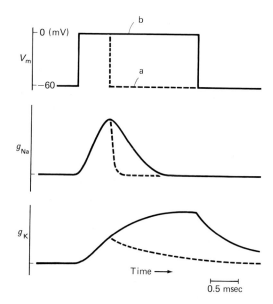

6–5 For a brief depolarizing step (a) both g_{Na} and g_K return to their initial values when the cell repolarizes. For a longer step (b), g_{Na} inactivates even though the depolarization is maintained, while g_K reaches a plateau level that is constant for the duration of the depolarization.

6–6 The second of two depolarizing pulses (*P₂*) produces a smaller increase in g_{Na} if the interval between P_1 and P_2 is brief, because Na^+ inactivation persists for a few milliseconds after the end of P_1.

6–4 Na^+ and K^+ conductance responses to a wide range of voltage clamp steps.

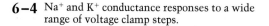

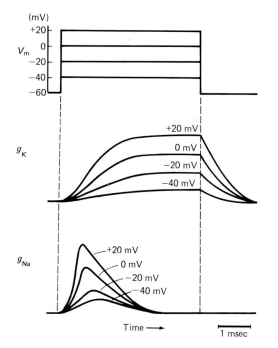

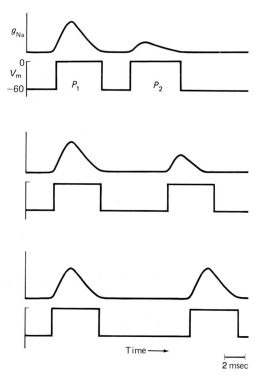

Reconstruction of the Action Potential

By analyzing the records of depolarizing pulses of various amplitudes and durations, Hodgkin and Huxley were able to obtain a complete set of empirical equations that described the variation of Na^+ and K^+ conductances with membrane potential and with time. Using these equations, plus the values of the passive properties of the axon, they were able to compute from their data the predicted shape and the conduction velocity of the propagated action potential. That this calculated waveform agreed almost perfectly with the action potential recorded in the unclamped axon indicates that their data described all the essential features of the voltage-dependent conductance channels.

According to Hodgkin and Huxley's results, an action potential involves the following sequence of events (Figure 6–7). A depolarization of the membrane causes a rapid increase in g_{Na}, resulting in an inward Na^+ current. This current causes further depolarization, which results in more inward current, and the regenerative process results in the generation of the action potential.[2] Two factors limit the duration of the spike: (1) As the depolarization continues, inactivation of g_{Na} proceeds; this inactivation contributes to the decline of g_{Na} during the falling phase of the action potential. (2) The depolarization also produces, with some delay, an increase in g_K; this increase results in an outward K^+ current that lags behind the Na^+ current and tends to repolarize the membrane. Repolarization in turn causes a further reduction of g_{Na}, due to its voltage dependence (Figures 6–4 and 6–5, a).

In most nerve cells action potentials are followed by a phasic hyperpolarization, the hyperpolarizing afterpotential. The brief increase in the negativity of the membrane potential results because the increase in g_K turned on during the later phase of the spike takes a few milliseconds

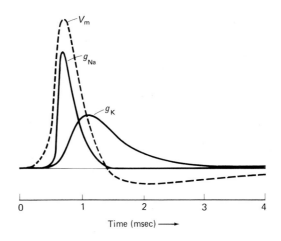

6–7 Reconstruction of g_{Na} and g_K changes during the action potential. (Adapted from Hodgkin, 1964.)

to decay back to its resting level, even after V_m has returned to its resting value (Figure 6–7). The residual increase in g_K, and the partial Na^+ inactivation that also persists for a few milliseconds (Figure 6–6), both contribute to the *absolute and relative refractory periods*, during which action potentials are either impossible to generate or have higher than normal thresholds.

Another feature of the action potential predicted by the Hodgkin–Huxley conductance data is the threshold. Action potentials are all-or-none in amplitude, and for depolarizations in the range of spike threshold an additional fraction of a millivolt may be the difference between a subthreshold stimulus and a stimulus that generates a full-blown action potential. This sensitivity may seem surprising when one considers that Na^+ conductance increases in a strictly graded manner as depolarization is increased (Figure 6–4). One must bear in mind, however, that although a small, subthreshold depolarization does increase the inward I_{Na}, it also increases the outward currents, I_K and I_l, by changing the driving forces that determine their values (see Equations 6–1 and 6–3 above). The increase in I_K is of course enhanced by the fact that depolarization also causes a slow increase in g_K (Figure 6–4). As I_K and I_l increase with depolarization, they tend to resist the depolarizing action of the Na^+ influx. The high voltage sensitivity of g_{Na} ensures that as the depolarization proceeds further it will eventually reach a point where the increase in inward I_{Na} will outstrip the increase in outward I_K and I_l. This value of V_m, at which the *net* ionic current

[2]It may at first seem paradoxical that to depolarize the cell experimentally one passes *outward* current across the membrane (see Figure 3–1), while the depolarization during the upstroke of the action potential is attributed to an *inward* Na^+ current. Actually, there is a simple explanation for this apparent inconsistency. In both cases *outward* current flows across the passive components, g_l and C_m of the membrane. This current is generated by placing an EMF that opposes the resting membrane potential in parallel with the passive components of the membrane. The EMF is either a battery connected to an intracellular and an extracellular electrode or it is the Na^+ Nernst potential generated across the open Na^+ conductance channels in the membrane (the Na^+ battery).

$(I_{Na} + I_K + I_l)$ just changes from outward to inward, is called the *threshold*.

The results of Hodgkin and Huxley also explain why a slowly rising stimulating current may fail to trigger a spike when it depolarizes the cell to its usual threshold membrane potential, V_T (Figure 6–8). It fails to do so because during a slow approach to V_T, inactivation of the g_{Na} channels and activation of g_K, the two dynamic processes that oppose the regenerative property of the membrane, have a chance to develop significantly before V_T is reached. Therefore, in order to turn on enough Na$^+$ channels to trigger a spike, one must depolarize the cell by a greater than normal increment (Figure 6–8B). The increase in threshold due to the application of a slowly rising current is called *accommodation*. By decreasing the rate of rise of current even more, one can produce a depolarization so slow that, regardless of how much the cell is depolarized, an action potential will not be elicited.

Molecular Properties of Na$^+$ Channels

Despite the remarkable success of the empirical equations derived by Hodgkin and Huxley in describing the conductance changes, they describe the process of excitation only on a phenomenological level. Their data give little information about the molecular nature of the conductance channels and the mechanisms by which they are activated. More recent work by other investigators has been directed along this line.

TTX Binding. An estimate of the density of voltage-gated Na$^+$ channels per area of axon membrane has been achieved by studying the binding of radioactively labeled TTX molecules to the axon membrane. The shape of the dose–response curve for the binding of TTX to the axon can be explained by assuming that some of the TTX molecules bind to a limited number of specific sites on the membrane. It is presumed that these specific sites represent the Na$^+$ conductance channels, because the binding constant and the kinetics of TTX binding to these sites correspond to the values determined by physiological measurement of Na$^+$ conductance blockade by TTX.

The number of Na$^+$ channels was estimated by measuring the total amount of TTX bound when these specific binding sites were saturated. It was found that, other things being equal, the greater the density of Na$^+$ channels in the membrane of

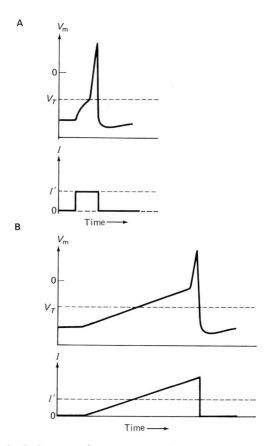

6–8 Accommodation. **A.** To reach threshold (V_T) for spike generation a rectangular current pulse need only have amplitude of I'. **B.** If depolarizing current is increased gradually, accommodation occurs and the stimulating current must surpass I' in order for a spike to be initiated.

an axon, the greater the speed at which it conducts action potentials (Chapter 5). The values obtained for nonmyelinated axons were about 2.5–500 molecules of TTX per square micrometer of axon membrane, depending on cell type.

The density of Na$^+$ channels is quite low— about 1 membrane surface molecule in 1 million in a Na$^+$ channel. In spite of this small number, quite large Na$^+$ currents can flow during the action potential. Thus, the current density through each channel must be rather high. In fact, a single Na$^+$ channel can pass up to 10^8 Na$^+$ ions/second. This is such a high rate that the only plausible mechanism for its generation would be flow of Na$^+$ ions through an aqueous pore. Both empirical data and theoretical calculations indicate that carrier molecules cannot transport ions at anything approaching this rate. The high specificity of binding of TTX to Na+ channels makes it possible to use TTX binding as an assay for the Na+ channel in attempts to purify it biochemically. Although it has not yet been totally isolated, studies to date make it clear that the Na+ channel is made primarily of protein.

Noise Analysis. An additional technique for gaining insight into the microscopic properties of the Na+ channels is called *noise analysis.* It is generally assumed that the smooth increase in g_{Na} measured during a depolarizing voltage clamp step (Figure 6–4) is due to a population effect: the average number of channels that are open increases during the initial period of depolarization. Each channel is thought to open in an all-or-none fashion; although individual channels may fluctuate randomly between the open and closed states, the probability that a given channel will be in the open state increases during the initial portion of a depolarizing step.

If this assumption is correct, one might expect to see some evidence of the random opening and closing of individual Na+ channels in the voltage clamp current records during a depolarization. With the cell at its resting potential, most of the Na+ channels are closed most of the time. When the cell is strongly depolarized, most of the channels are usually in the open state. For intermediate depolarizations, each Na+ channel spends a significant amount of time cycling back and forth between the open and the closed configurations. Thus, for intermediate depolarizations, one would expect an increase in the random noise in the Na+ current measured in a voltage clamp record. Such I_{Na} noise has been observed, and by using statistical theory it has been possible to calculate the conductance of individual Na+ channels from the relationship of the amplitude of

these random fluctuations of I_{Na} to the mean value of I_{Na}. The value of conductance calculated in this way is about 7×10^{-12} siemens. If rather than opening in all-or-none fashion, Na+ channels open in a graded fashion, one would expect the estimates of single-channel conductance to increase when measured at more depolarized potentials. This is not the case; the data are entirely consistent with the hypotheses that individual channels can have only two conductance states— fully open or fully closed.

Gating Currents. Hodgkin and Huxley suggested over 25 years ago that the Na+ and K+ conductance channels might be controlled by voltage-sensitive "gates" embedded in the membrane (Figure 6–9). Such a gating particle might, for example, consist of a molecule with a large dipole moment which is free to pivot about some point along its dipole axis. When the membrane is depolarized, the change in electric field would cause the molecule to rotate about this pivot (Figure 6–9B). Rotation would result in a small displacement of positive charge from near the inner surface to near the outer surface of the membrane capacitance (Figure 6–9C). This is equivalent to a reduction of the total charge separation across the membrane capacitance. Therefore, to keep

6–9 Hypothetical explanation for molecular events that underlie gating currents. **A.** Active membrane channel of a nerve cell at rest. **B.** Immediately after clamping to a depolarized V_m, the gating molecule starts to respond to the change in V_m by realigning its dipole moment with respect to the electric field. **C.** A short time later, the gate has opened and the effective charge distribution across the membrane has been altered. More positive charge must be pumped into the cell to produce the effective charge separation present in part B.

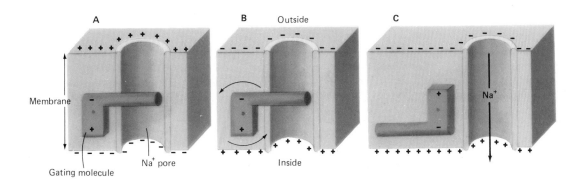

the potential constant in a voltage clamp experiment, a small, extra component of outward capacitive current would have to be generated by the clamp to maintain the net effective charge separation constant across the membrane.

For technical reasons this hypothesis could not be tested until a few years ago. When the membrane current was finally examined with very sensitive techniques, it was indeed found that such a capacitive gating current does flow at the beginning and at the end of a voltage clamp pulse that turns on g_{Na}. The properties of gating currents are now being intensively investigated to gain insight into the molecular processes underlying the action potential.

Membrane Conductance Properties Vary Among Cell Types and Among Different Regions of the Same Cell

Two general conclusions have emerged from studies designed to test the generality of the Hodgkin–Huxley model of action potential generation. First, almost every type of axon examined has conductance channels similar to the Na^+ and K^+ channels described by Hodgkin and Huxley in the squid axon. Second, most types of neurons have additional channels as well. Many neurons have voltage-sensitive Ca^{++} channels and additional species of K^+ channels that are activated either more rapidly or more slowly than the K^+ channels described in squid axon. The mixture of different types of voltage-sensitive channels found in a given neuron is particularly important in determining how that cell will respond to synaptic input. Some cells respond to a constant excitatory input with a decelerating train of action potentials. Others produce an accelerating firing pattern. In some cells, small changes in the strength of excitatory inputs produce a large increase in firing rate, whereas in other cells the increase in action potential frequency is relatively small. The marked diversity of input–output characteristics displayed by different neurons is explained by cell-to-cell variations in the mixtures of channel types.

In addition to variations in channel distributions between cells, important differences also occur in the topographic distribution of channel types between the different regions of an individual neuron. These topographic variations of membrane conductance properties between different regions of a cell have important functional effects. For example, Ca^{++} channels are typically most dense at axon terminals, where Ca^{++} influx is involved in release of transmitter. In addition, the membrane of the dendrites, cell body, and axon hillock has more types of conductance channels than does the axon membrane. Axons are relatively simple (in some nerve cells they lack even the active K^+ channels). Complexity in the types of channels is not required because axons serve as a simple relay line between the input and output zones of a cell.

Selected Readings and References

Almers, W. 1978. Gating currents and charge movements in excitable membranes. Rev. Physiol. Biochem. Pharmacol. 82:96–190.

Hille, B. 1978. Ionic channels in excitable membranes. Biophys. J. 22:283–294.

Hodgkin, A. L. 1964. The Conduction of the Nervous Impulse. Springfield, Ill.: Thomas.

Hodgkin, A. L. 1976. Chance and design in electrophysiology: An informal account of certain experiments on nerve carried out between 1934 and 1952. J. Physiol. (Lond.) 263:1–21.

Keynes, R. D. 1979. Ion channels in the nerve-cell membrane. Sci. Am. 240(3):126–135.

Khodorov, B. I. 1974. The Problem of Excitability. New York: Plenum, chaps. 3–9.

Llinás, R. 1980. Applicability of channel analyses in molluscs to vertebrate central neurons. In J. Koester and J. H. Byrne (eds.), Molluscan Nerve Cells: From Biophysics to Behavior. Cold Spring Harbor, New York: Cold Spring Harbor Laboratories.

Other References

Cole, K. S., and Curtis, H. J. 1939. Electric impedance of the squid giant axon during activity. J. Gen. Physiol. 22:649–670.

Hodgkin, A. L., and Huxley, A. F. 1952. A quantitative description of membrane current and its application to conduction and excitation in nerve. J. Physiol. (Lond.) 117:500–544.

Hodgkin, A. L., and Katz, B. 1949. The effect of sodium ions on the electrical activity of the giant axon of the squid. J. Physiol. (Lond.) 108:37–77.

Noble, D. 1966. Applications of Hodgkin-Huxley equations to excitable tissues. Physiol. Rev. 46:1–50.

Ritchie, J. M., and Rogart, R. B., 1977. The binding of saxitoxin and tetrodotoxin to excitable tissue. Rev. Physiol. Biochem. Pharmacol. 79:1–50.

Eric R. Kandel

Synaptic Transmission I: Postsynaptic Factors Controlling Ionic Permeability

7

Nerve cells differ from other cells in their ability to communicate rapidly with one another, sometimes over great distances and with great precision. Axonal conduction and synaptic transmission provide the means for this rapid and precise communication. An understanding of synaptic transmission is therefore central to an understanding of how the nervous system works. In this and the next four chapters we shall consider synaptic transmission at its most elementary level, the contacts made by a few presynaptic neurons on a single postsynaptic cell. We shall consider synaptic transmission from several perspectives. First, we shall view the physiology of synaptic function and analyze the postsynaptic and presynaptic contributions to synaptic transmission. Second, we shall discuss the fine structure of synapses. Third, we shall analyze the molecular machinery of synaptic actions. This background will permit us to examine how injury and disease disable function by interfering with one or another component of the synapse.

In this chapter, we shall consider the types of synapse found within the nervous system and examine how the fine structure determines their function. We shall then focus on the postsynaptic aspects of chemical synaptic transmission and examine three questions: (1) How are excitatory postsynaptic potentials (EPSPs) and inhibitory postsynaptic potentials (IPSPs) generated? What species of ionic channels are opened (or closed) when a chemical transmitter substance interacts with a receptor in the postsynaptic membrane? (2) What makes the excitatory postsynaptic potential excite and the inhibitory postsynaptic potential inhibit? (3) How does a neuron integrate inhibitory and excitatory synaptic actions coming from various sources?

In the next chapter, we shall consider the presynaptic mechanisms that control transmitter release from the terminals.

Synaptic Transmission Can Be Electrical or Chemical

Sir Charles Sherrington (who shared the Nobel Prize in Medicine with Lord Adrian in 1921) introduced the term *synapse* (Greek *synapsis*, junction) at the turn of the century to refer to the specialized contact zone, described histologically by Ramón y Cajal, where one neuron communicates with another. In the 1930s a great debate ensued between the physiologists (led by Sir J. C. Eccles) and the pharmacologists (led by Sir Henry Dale) about the mechanism of synaptic transmission. Both sides assumed that synaptic transmission had a single, universal mechanism. The physiologists argued that synaptic transmission was electrical—that it was due to current flow from the presynaptic neuron spreading directly to the postsynaptic cell. The pharmacologists argued that it was chemical—that it was due to a chemical mediator (or a transmitter substance) released by the presynaptic neuron that initiated current flow in the postsynaptic cell.

When physiological techniques improved in the 1950s and 1960s, it became clear that all synapses did not operate with one mechanism. The work of Eccles and his colleagues, of Paul Fatt and Bernard Katz, and of Edwin Furshpan and David Potter showed that both modes of transmission occur in the nervous system. Most synapses use a chemical transmitter. Some, however, operate by purely electrical means. Moreover, as it became technically possible to examine the fine structure of synapses, electron microscopists discovered that synaptic transmission does not occur at every point where neurons come close to one another; rather, transmission occurs only at certain critical points in the nervous system where specialized areas of the presynaptic and the postsynaptic neurons are brought into appropriate apposition. On the basis of the morphology of

the zone of apposition, it is possible to divide all synapses into two major morphological classes: bridged junction and unbridged junction. These two morphological classes correspond to and account for the two functional classes: the electrical and the chemical synapses.

The *bridged junctions* are *gap junctions* similar to those found in many other cells in the body. At these junctions the zone of apposition is bridged by channels that run from the cytoplasm of the presynaptic neuron to that of the postsynaptic cell. These junctions mediate electrical transmission. At electrical synapses the normal extracellular space separating the pre- and postsynaptic cells is narrowed. The outer limits of the junctional plasma membranes, when cut perpendicularly, are separated by a gap of only 2 nm (20 Å) (Figure 7–1A). This is about one-tenth the size of the separation between the membranes at non-gap junctional regions. Freeze-fracture studies show clusters of membrane particles that span the gap (Figure 7–1B and C). Because ions and small tracer molecules [up to 1000 daltons, or 1.5 nm in diameter; for example, cyclic adenosine 3′, 5′-monophosphate (cAMP), sucrose, fluorescein, or Procion yellow] can pass from one cell to another through the junction, the spanning structures are thought to be the walls of intercellular channels bridging two cells. Gap junctions can be isolated from homogenized tissue and are made up of hexagonal subunits called *connexons* (Figure 7–1A). These are composed of a protein called *connexin* of roughly 25,000 daltons.

Whereas gap junctions electrically couple adjoining cells, they do not occlude the extracellular space, as do tight junctions, nor do they provide adhesive coupling, as do desmosomes.

In the *unbridged junction*, or chemical synapse, the pre- and postsynaptic neurons are not in continuity (Figure 7–2). There is a discrete separation, the synaptic cleft, between the presynaptic and postsynaptic elements. This separation (30 nm) is typically slightly wider than the adjacent extracellular space (20 nm). In addition, the pre- and postsynaptic membranes are often specialized and the presynaptic terminals contain localized collections of vesicles (called *synaptic vesicles*).

The main functional properties of each type of synapse are summarized in Table 7–1. Many of these differences can be illustrated by injecting outward current into the presynaptic cell as shown in Figure 7–3. This current will deposit positive charge on the inside of the membrane

A

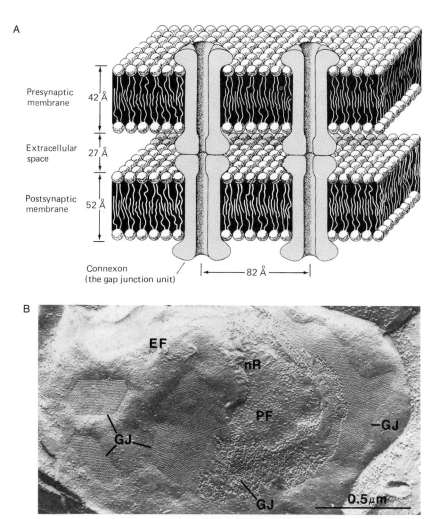

Presynaptic membrane   42 Å

Extracellular space   27 Å

Postsynaptic membrane   52 Å

Connexon (the gap junction unit)

|← 82 Å →|

B

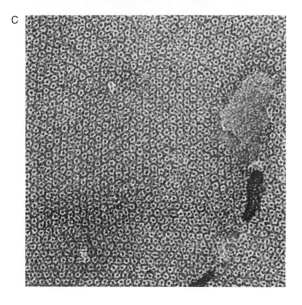

EF

nR

PF

GJ

GJ

GJ

0.5 μm

C

7–1 Electrical synapse: the bridged, or gap, junction.
A. Three-dimensional model of the connexon, the gap junctional unit that bridges the opposing membranes at an electrical synapse as revealed by X-ray diffraction studies. (Adapted from Makowski et al., 1977.) **B.** Freeze fracture preparation of gap junctions at an axosomatic synapse of a class of motor neuron in fish. The synapse shows much of the soma E face (**EF**). The gap junctions (**GJ**) show a highly ordered arrangement of pits. Two small gap junctions are seen to the left, and a large junction occupies much of the central region. The P face of the axonal membrane (**nR**) is exposed near the center. It displays the particulate face of the large gap junction. For details on freeze fracture see Figure 9–3. Primary magnification: 20,000 X. (Adapted from Bennett et al., 1978.) **C.** Negatively stained gap junctions isolated from rat liver. A regular hexagonal lattice with a periodicity of approximately 10 nm can be seen. This regularity corresponds to the lattice observed in thin sections. Magnification: 307,800 X. (Courtesy of N. Gilula.)

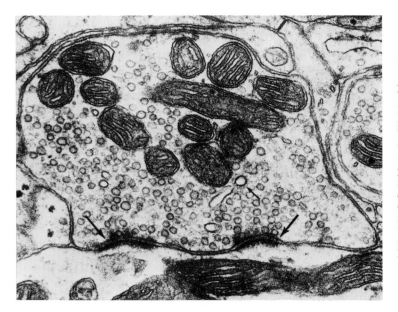

7–2 Chemical synapse: the unbridged junction. The presynaptic terminal occupies most of this electron migrograph. The large dark structures are mitochondria. The many round bodies are vesicles that hold transmitter. The cleft separating the presynaptic membrane from the postsynaptic is unbridged. The fuzzy dark thickenings (**large arrows**) along the presynaptic side of the cleft are thought to be active zones for the release of the transmitter. **Small arrows** point to cisternal element (Courtesy of Heuser and Reese.)

capacitance, depolarize the presynaptic neuron, and flow out across the presynaptic membrane resistance. At an electrical synapse some current will also flow into the low-resistance protoplasmic bridge between the pre- and postsynaptic cell. The current will now deposit positive charge on the inside of the membrane capacitance of the postsynaptic cell, depolarizing it as well, and will flow out across the postsynaptic cell (Figure 7–3A). In contrast, at a chemical synapse the outward current injected into a presynaptic cell will flow out across the presynaptic cell. However, because current seeks the path of lowest resistance, it will flow in the low-resistance pathway offered by the synaptic cleft and little or no current will cross the high resistance of the external membrane of the postsynaptic cell (Figure 7–3B).

Transmission across electrical synapses is very rapid. In addition, electrical synapses can cause a group of interconnected neurons to fire synchronously. They are usually rather inflexible in function, however. Consequently, they are thought to be used for interconnecting excitable cells that are responsible for stereotypic behavior, such as the rapid saccadic eye movements produced by the extraocular motor neurons. Chemical synapses (which are also much more numerous) are slower, but they are much more flexible, or plastic, and often reflect the history of their previous activity. Chemical synapses intercon-

Table 7–1. Main Functional Properties of Electrical and Chemical Synapses

Electrical synapses	Chemical synapses
1. Reduced extracellular space (2 nm); cytoplasmic continuity between pre- and postsynaptic cell	1. Increased extracellular space (typically 20–30 nm); no cytoplasmic continuity between pre- and postsynaptic elements
2. Mediating agent is ionic current	2. Mediating agent is a chemical transmitter (acetylcholine, norepinephrine, peptides, etc.)
3. Essentially no synaptic delay; transmission is limited only by the speed of electrotonic transmission across the short distance separating the presynaptic and postsynaptic elements at the synapse	3. Significant synaptic delay (at least 0.3 msec, sometimes 1–5 msec, or even longer); in some cells the delay is caused primarily by the time required for secretory process in the presynaptic terminals, in other cells the delay is due to the time required for the diffusion of the transmitter to the receptor
4. Typically bidirectional	4. Unidirectional

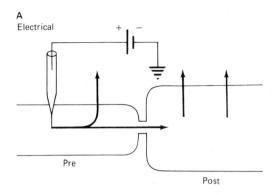

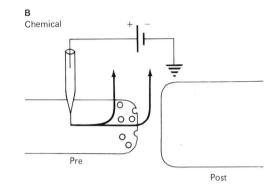

7-3 Outward current is injected into presynaptic cell to illustrate the difference between electrical and chemical synapses. **A.** In electrical synapses, current flows across the protoplasmic bridge and depolarizes the postsynaptic cell. **B.** In chemical synapses, no current crosses the membrane of the postsynaptic cell.

nect neurons for more variable and complex behavior. These distinctions are thought to be quite fundamental and may account for the preponderance of chemical or electrical synapses in various regions of the brain.

In the remainder of this chapter, we shall consider chemical transmission. From a physiological point of view, chemical transmission can be divided mechanistically into two processes: the *presynaptic processes* that determine the release of the chemical transmitter, and the *postsynaptic processes* whereby the interaction between the transmitter and the receptor molecule in the postsynaptic cell leads to the gating of specific ion channels, giving rise to the current flow that produces the various synaptic potentials. We shall focus here on postsynaptic mechanisms. There are two postsynaptic mechanisms for chemical synaptic actions: (1) an increase in the conductance of the membrane to one or more ion species, and (2) a decrease in the conductance to one (or more) ion species. Synaptic actions resulting from increased conductance are more common, and we shall consider them first in detail.

Some Synaptic Actions Are Due to an Increase in Membrane Conductance

Our understanding of the increased ionic conductance mechanisms of chemical synaptic action is based largely on the work of Eccles and his colleagues on spinal motor cells. This work, in turn, derives from the work of Fatt and Katz on the nerve–muscle synapses of crab and frog.

Experimental Background

Eccles and his colleagues obtained recordings with intracellular electrodes from spinal motor neurons, the large motor cells that lie in the ven-

tral portion of the spinal cord (the ventral horn), while stimulating either the excitatory inputs from nerves coming from the same or synergistic muscles, or the inhibitory input from nerves coming from antagonistic muscles. Among the first sets of synaptic connections that they analyzed were those that mediate the stretch reflex, the simple behavior we considered in Chapter 2 (Figure 7–4).

Eccles stimulated selectively the large axons of the stretch receptor neurons that innervate muscle-spindle stretch receptor organs in the gastrocnemius muscle (these are called Ia afferent fibers and are described more fully in Chapters 25 and 26). The same experiments can now be done by simply inserting a microelectrode into the cell body of one of these neurons as they lie in ganglia outside the spinal cord called the dorsal root ganglia. By passing stimulating current through the microelectrode, one can excite a single nerve cell to produce an action potential (Figure 7–5). Stimulation of a single stretch receptor neuron that comes from the gastrocnemius muscle produces an excitatory postsynaptic potential that depolarizes and excites the motor cells to that muscle (Figure 7–5, right-hand side). In contrast, stimulation of a stretch receptor neuron from the biceps, an antagonist muscle, produces an inhibitory postsynaptic potential that hyperpolarizes and inhibits the same motor neurons (Figure 7–5, left-hand side). The antagonist inhibitory pathway is disynaptic, involving an inter-

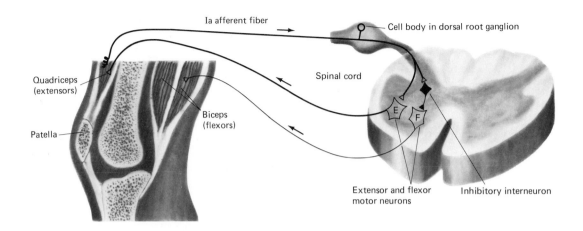

7-4 Connections of spinal neurons that mediate the stretch reflex used by Eccles and his colleagues in their study of synaptic excitation and inhibition.

posed inhibitory interneuron. Recently, these neurons have been identified and also can be recorded from and stimulated intracellularly (Figure 7-5).

The excitatory postsynaptic potentials reduce the membrane potential of the motor neurons,

7-5 Experimental arrangement for studying inhibition and excitation of motor neuron. In this hypothetical, idealized experiment the inhibitory interneuron from the biceps and receptor neuron from the gastrocnemius muscle are stimulated electrically with intracellular electrodes.

and if they are sufficiently large—because of the temporal and spatial summation produced by the action of a number of converging synaptic connections—the membrane potential will reach threshold and initiate an action potential. The inhibitory synaptic potentials, on the other hand, tend to counteract the excitatory actions by preventing the membrane potential from reaching threshold (Figure 7-6). In addition, inhibitory synaptic actions also exert powerful regulatory control over spontaneously active cells by suppressing the generation of action potentials and thereby determining the pattern of impulse activity. This function of inhibition is called the *sculpturing role* of inhibition (Figure 7-7).

We shall first consider inhibitory synapses because their ionic mechanisms are easier to understand.

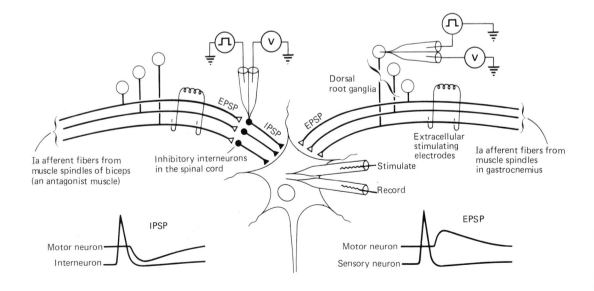

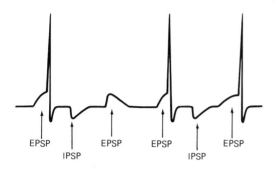

7 – 6 Interactions of excitatory and inhibitory
    synaptic actions in an otherwise silent cell.
Each of the synaptic potentials illustrated here is
usually produced by the synchronous action of many
presynaptic neurons.

Inhibitory Postsynaptic Potentials

Eccles and his colleagues found that inhibitory
postsynaptic potentials (IPSPs) inhibit by keeping
the membrane potential of the initial segment of
the axon (the integrative component) from reaching threshold for spike generation. Usually IPSPs
do this by increasing (hyperpolarizing) the membrane potential. IPSPs also reduce the synaptic actions produced by excitatory synapses in ways we
shall consider below. The binding of the transmitter to the receptors leads to a sudden increase in
the membrane permeability to Cl⁻ or K⁺ ions,
whose equilibrium potentials are usually between −65 and −75 mV. In most nerve cells, the
equilibrium potential for either of these ions is
more negative than the resting potential (about
−60 to −65 mV) and, more importantly, the equilibrium potential is more negative than threshold
(which is about −45 mV). In the motor neurons
studied by Eccles, the inhibitory transmitter increased the postsynaptic cell's permeability to
both K⁺ and Cl⁻. To simplify the discussion we

shall consider the elementary case, which is actually found in some synapses where the transmitter opens only K⁺ channels. Similarly, in
many neurons of the cerebral cortex and hippocampus, inhibitory transmitters open only Cl⁻
channels.

*Equivalent Circuit of the Inhibitory Synaptic
Action.* In the discussion below, we shall simplify
the analysis of the synaptic potential by considering the steady state of the synaptic actions and ig-
noring the resting membrane capacitance (C_m).
The reason that we can ignore the capacitance is
as follows. In the resting state the potential across
the membrane capacitance (V_c) equals the membrane potential; that is, $V_c = E_m$ (see Chapter 5
and Appendix I for discussion of capacitive current). As a result, no net current flows across the
membrane resistance R_m or into and out of the
membrane capacitance (Figure 7−8B, *1*). At the
onset of the inhibitory synaptic action (the dynamic phase), an outward current flows through
the synaptic channel due to the increased conductance to K⁺. This will cause current to flow that
is (1) inward (↓) in the nonsynaptic channel, and
(2) inward across the membrane capacitance,
changing the charge on the capacitor corresponding to the change in voltage. Initially, therefore,
the current due to inhibitory synaptic activity is
$I_{IPSP} = I_m + I_c$ (Figure 7−8B, *2*). As a result, the
IPSP leads to an increase in positive charge on the
outside and in negative charge on the inside of
the cell membrane (the outside and inside plates
of the membrane capacitor). Once the IPSP has
reached its peak, charge no longer flows into and

7 – 7 Sculpturing role of inhibition. Inhibition can
    produce changes in the firing pattern of a
spontaneously active neuron.

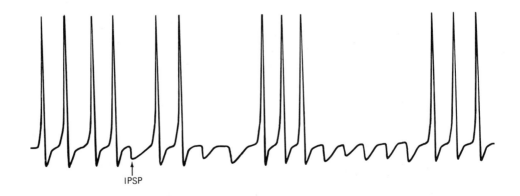

IPSP

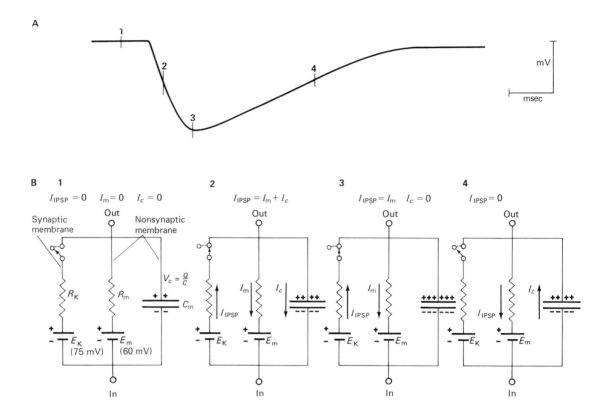

7–8 Relationship of capacitive current to ionic
current flow at a chemical inhibitory synapse
due to increased conductance to K$^+$ (g_K). **A.** Time
course of an IPSP. **B.** Various currents during the IPSP
at times **1, 2, 3,** and **4** indicated in part A.

out of the capacitor ($dV/dt = 0$) and I_{IPSP} is simply
equal to I_m, the current flowing through the resistive channels (Figure 7–8B, *3*). This is the
steady-state case that we shall consider in this
and all subsequent discussions of synaptic actions. During most of the declining phase of the
synaptic action (Figure 7–8A, *4*), no more current
flows through the synaptic membrane (the switch
is again open); current now flows only through
R_m and into and out of C_m.

As is the case for the passive properties of the
nerve cell membrane and the properties of the
membrane during the action potential, the inhibitory synaptic actions can be described in terms
of an equivalent circuit, or electrical model (Figure 7–9A). As illustrated in Figure 4–5, the pas-

sive (resting) membrane can be depicted as three
single resistor–battery combinations (for Cl$^-$,
Na$^+$, and K$^+$, respectively). In dealing with synaptic actions, these independent channels can be
lumped together and represented as a single resistor–battery combination—the membrane resis-
tance (R_m), with a value of $1.0 \times 10^8\,\Omega$, in series
with a single battery, which represents the rest-
ing membrane potential (E_m) of -60 mV. (For details on how this model can be obtained see
Chapter 4.) The battery for the membrane potential and the membrane resistance are in parallel
with the synaptic channel. It is important to realize that the synaptic and nonsynaptic channels
are interspersed; they do not represent different
areas on the postsynaptic cell surface, but different ionic pathways in the same area.

In the case of an inhibitory synapse that operates by increasing the conductance to K$^+$ (Figure
7–9A), the synaptic channels can be depicted by a
single K$^+$ channel ($R_K = 1/g_K$) in series with a K$^+$
battery (E_K). The value of this battery (-75 mV) is
determined by the Nernst potential for K$^+$. (A rea-

A

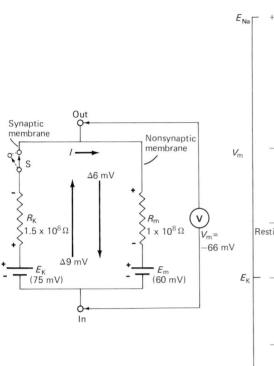

B

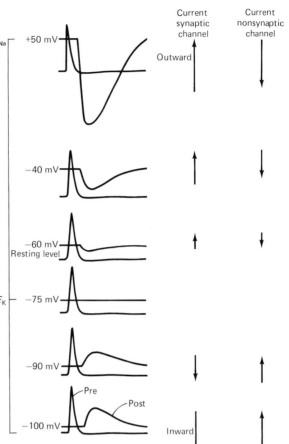

7–9 Chemical inhibitory synaptic action due to increased conductance to K^+ (g_K). **A.** Equivalent circuit of an inhibitory synapse and current flow during synaptic action. At rest, the synaptic channel is an open circuit and no current flows through it. The synaptic action is equivalent to closing the switch *(S)*, thereby placing the synaptic resistance pathway R_K = $1/g_K$ in parallel with the nonsynaptic resistance R_m. K^+ current will now flow out of the cell through the synaptic channel, and an equal current will flow into the cell through the nonsynaptic membrane, hyperpolarizing it by 6 mV from its resting level of −60 mV. The synaptic channels and the nonsynaptic channels are not located at different areas of the post-synaptic cell surface but are simply different ion pathways in the same area. [The current (I_c) through the membrane capacitance is ignored here; its effect is shown in Figure 7–8.] **B.** Reversal potential. In this hypothetical experiment two electrodes are placed in the presynaptic cell and two in the postsynaptic cell (Figure 7–5). One electrode is for passing current—in

the presynaptic cell to produce an action potential, and in the postsynaptic cell to systematically alter the membrane potential. The other electrode is for recording. At the resting value (−60 mV) a presynaptic spike produces a hyperpolarizing IPSP, which increases in amplitude as the membrane is artificially depolarized. However, as the membrane potential is hyperpolarized to −75, the IPSP first becomes nullified. This null potential is called the reversal potential for the IPSP. With further hyperpolarization the IPSP is inverted to a depolarizing synaptic potential (−90 and −100 mV). Even this depolarizing action is still inhibitory, however, because it only brings the membrane potential toward, but not beyond the reversal level, which is considerably below the firing level (−45 mV). The **arrows** on the right indicate the effects of changing V_m on the K^+ current through the synaptic channel and on the equal and oppositely directed current in the return pathway of the nonsynaptic channel. (The magnitude of the current is indicated by the size of the arrows.)

sonable value for R_K is $1.5 \times 10^8 \Omega$.) At rest, the synaptic channel is closed. The closed channel acts as an *open* circuit—no current flows through it. The interaction between the transmitter and the receptor is equivalent to closing the switch *(S)*, thereby placing the synaptic channel in parallel with the passive nonsynaptic channel (E_m in series with R_m). K^+ ions will now flow down their concentration gradient out of the cell ($\uparrow$). In order to complete the circuit, an equal current must flow into the cell ($\downarrow$) through the nonsynaptic membrane, thereby hyperpolarizing it (Figure 7–9B). (In the case shown in Figure 7–9, the synaptic current hyperpolarizes the cell by 6 mV from -60 to -66 mV.) Inward current across a passive element will be carried by a variety of ions: Na^+ influx and Cl^- efflux, as well as a reduction in steady state K^+ efflux.

The exact value of the synaptic potential can now be calculated using the four steps outlined in Chapter 4:

1. *Calculate the net EMF driving current around the loop.* This is the algebraic sum of E_K and E_m. Going around the loop, these batteries have opposite polarities, so that $75 - 60 = 15$ mV.

2. *Calculate the total resistance around the loop.*

$$R_K + R_m = 1.5 \times 10^8 + 1 \times 10^8 = 2.5 \times 10^8 \Omega.$$

3. *Calculate the total current flow around the loop.*

$$I = \frac{V}{R} = \frac{15 \times 10^{-3} \ V}{2.5 \times 10^8 \ \Omega} = 6 \times 10^{-11} \ A$$

4. *Calculate the synaptic potential.* This can be done by calculating V_m (as was done in Chapter 4) across either the synaptic or the nonsynaptic membrane (since they are in parallel) by simply adding the voltage drop across the resistor of the channel (R_m or R_K) to the battery (E_m or E_K) of the channel. Thus, the current across the nonsynaptic channel is:

$$
\begin{aligned}
V_m &= E_m + (I_m \times R_m) \\
&= -60 \times 10^{-3} V + (-6 \times 10^{-11} A) \times \\
&\quad (1 \times 10^8 \Omega) \\
&= -60 \times 10^{-3} V + (-6 \times 10^{-3} V) \\
&= -66 \text{ mV}
\end{aligned}
$$

The peak amplitude of the IPSP is then

$$\Delta V_{IPSP} = V_m - E_m = 6 \text{ mV}$$

Because the current flowing through the resistor makes the end it enters positive with respect to the other end (Figure 7–9A), the resulting potential change *adds* to the resting battery and

moves the potential of the nonsynaptic branch from -60 to -66 mV, which is still further below threshold (-45 mV) for spike generation.

Similarly we can calculate the V_m across the synaptic channel:

$$
\begin{aligned}
\Delta V_m &= E_K + (I_m \times R_K) \\
&= -75 \times 10^{-3} V + (+6 \times 10^{-11} A) \times \\
&\quad (1.5 \times 10^8 \Omega) \\
&= -66 \text{ mV}
\end{aligned}
$$

Here the resulting potential change of 9 mV opposes the synaptic battery of -75 mV and thereby also brings the synaptic branch of the circuit to -66 mV.

If additional parallel synaptic pathways were activated by the transmitter, the resistance of the synaptic branch would decrease further and more current would flow, producing a larger IPSP. With a larger conductance change, e.g., with $R_K = 10^6$ Ω, the IPSP amplitude would grow to almost 15 mV and the membrane potential would be transiently dominated by E_K. Thus synaptic inhibition due to an increased conductance to K^+ always drives the membrane potential toward E_K (-75 mV) and away from threshold (-45 mV).

Even when the IPSP due to increased conductance of K^+ does not hyperpolarize the membrane—because the membrane potential is already at -75 mV (E_K)—the inhibitory synaptic action due to an increased ionic conductance will still inhibit the cell from firing. By increasing the conductance to K^+, the inhibitory transmitter increases the overall conductance of the membrane. Because the conductance of the membrane (g_m) is equal to $1/R_m$, inhibition will decrease the overall resistance of the membrane. The amplitude of a synaptic potential produced by an EPSP is equal to $I_{EPSP} \times R_m$. The amplitude of an excitatory synaptic potential produced in the presence of inhibition when R_m is low will therefore be smaller than when R_m is normal, as it is in the absence of inhibition.

Thus, an IPSP due to increased conductance inhibits the postsynaptic cell in two ways. First, it invariably increases the membrane conductance. This action is called the *shunting* or *short-circuiting* action of inhibition due to increased conductance. Second, an increased-conductance IPSP usually hyperpolarizes the membrane potential and moves it further away from threshold (except in cells that have a high resting potential, where $V_m = E_K$).

The increase in the conductance to K^+ produced by the chemical transmitter has one other interesting property. The increase in conductance is independent of membrane voltage. A change in the membrane potential does not alter the number of K$^+$ channels opened by the transmitter. Thus, there is a fundamental difference between the K$^+$ channels gated by the action potential and those gated by the inhibitory synaptic action. The K$^+$ channels activated by the action potential are gated by changes in the membrane potential (see Chapter 5). These channels are therefore said to be *electrically* or *voltage gated*. The K$^+$ channels opened by a transmitter are not electrically gated; they are *chemically gated*. The two classes of K$^+$ channels are also different pharmacologically. For example, tetraethylammonium selectively blocks the voltage-gated K$^+$ channel but it does not generally affect the chemically gated channel.

Current That Flows During the IPSP. Just as we have used Ohm's law in Chapter 6 to describe the ionic currents flowing through different channels during a voltage clamp experiment, we can use it to describe the current flowing during the IPSP (I_{IPSP}). If we let $V_m - E_K$ represent the driving force for K$^+$, then

$$I_{IPSP} = \frac{V_m - E_K}{R_K}.$$

Since $\dfrac{1}{R_K} = g_K$

$$I_{IPSP} = g_K (V_m - E_K).$$

This equation illustrates that the current for the IPSP is determined by two factors: (1) a conductance (g_K) that varies with transmitter concentration, but usually not with V_m, and (2) a driving force ($V_m - E_K$) that does vary with V_m.

I_{IPSP} can best be determined in voltage clamp experiments. However, the number of K$^+$ channels opened (which determines the g_{IPSP}) does not vary with membrane potential. One can therefore gain considerable insight into I_{IPSP} by simply passing current across the membrane with a current generator and systematically changing the membrane potential (V_m), and thereby the driving force, and using the changes in the amplitude and sign of the IPSP as an index of changes in I_{IPSP} (Figure 7–9B).

The current illustrated with arrows in Figure 7–9B represents the current that flows through each of the two channels, the synaptic channel and the nonsynaptic channel, as a result of the synaptic action. Let us change V_m artificially by passing constant current through an intracellular electrode (Figure 7–9B). As the membrane potential is depolarized, the

IPSP gets larger because the driving force ($V_m - E_K$) becomes larger as V_m is moved further away from E_K. The force due to the concentration gradient moving K$^+$ from inside to outside the cell remains the same, but the force due to the electrical gradient moving K$^+$ from outside to inside is reduced, so that more K$^+$ flows outward across the synaptic channel and therefore more current flows inward through the nonsynaptic one. If the membrane potential is now increased by moving it in the hyperpolarizing direction to -75 mV, the IPSP is nullified. This null point is defined as the *reversal potential* for the IPSP (E_{IPSP}). In this case, it is E_K. At the null point, $V_m = E_K$, and the electrical driving force acting on K$^+$ is exactly equal to the force due to the concentration gradient. Even with g_K increased, there is no net current through the channel. If the membrane potential is further increased to -90 mV, the electrical driving force exceeds the driving force of the concentration gradient and K$^+$ begins to move inward from outside the cell. This is equivalent to current flowing into the cell through the synaptic channel and outward through the nonsynaptic membrane.

The ability to determine the reversal potential for a synaptic action is important because it indicates which ions are responsible for producing the synaptic action. When a new synaptic action is first encountered one does not know which of several ion species determines this particular synaptic potential. An important clue can be obtained by determining the reversal potential and seeing whether it describes a unique equilibrium for a specific ion species.

Excitatory Postsynaptic Potentials

Eccles and his colleagues also discovered that the excitatory synaptic potential depolarizes the membrane; if sufficiently large, the EPSPs bring the membrane potential of the initial segment (the integrative component) of the neuron to threshold for spike generation. By analogy to the inhibitory action produced by an increased conductance to K$^+$, one might have expected that the excitatory synaptic action simply involved an increase in conductance to Na$^+$. If that were so we would predict that the EPSP would have a reversal potential near E_{Na} ($+55$ mV). However, the reaction of the transmitter with the excitatory receptor leads to a simultaneous increase in both g_{Na} and g_K. This mechanism appears superficially similar to that of the action potential. Actually, it differs in several ways. First, the increase in g_{Na}

and g_K is simultaneous and not sequential, as in the action potential. Second, the increase in g_{Na} is not regenerative. The depolarization produced by the synaptic action does not lead to further increases in *synaptic* g_{Na} because (as we have seen for the K$^+$ channels activated by the inhibitory transmitter) the Na$^+$ channels activated by the excitatory transmitter are not voltage gated. This situation differs from that of the action potential, in which channels are sensitive to membrane potential, opening with depolarization and closing with hyperpolarization. (The time course of opening and closing the channels during the EPSP does show a very slight voltage dependence, but we can ignore that here.)

In addition, the channels opened by the transmitter's action are pharmacologically different from those opened by the action potential. The influx of Na$^+$ produced by excitatory transmission is not blocked by tetrodotoxin, which blocks the voltage-gated Na$^+$ channel activated by the action potential, nor is the K$^+$ efflux blocked by tetraethylammonium. Whereas Na$^+$ and K$^+$ move through separate channels during the action potential, the excitatory transmitters open up a special class of channels. These chemically gated channels are larger and less discriminating than the voltage-gated Na$^+$ channels and permit the simultaneous movement of Na$^+$ into and of K$^+$ out of the neuron. This finding is important because the fact that both g_{Na} and g_K increase simultaneously at excitatory synapses seems at first somewhat unexpected. Only the increase in g_{Na} leads to excitation. The increase in g_K actually dampens this excitatory action. This apparent paradox is explained by the finding that the size and shape of the channel gated by the transmitter allow *both* Na$^+$ and K$^+$ to pass. The channel is so large that it allows even larger cations, such as Ca^{++}, NH$_4^+$, and even certain organic cations, to pass. However, the channels will not allow anions to pass. This differentiation makes one think that the channel has some negative charge at its mouth that attracts a variety of cations below a certain maximum size and repels anions because of their charge.

Katz and Miledi and more recently Neher and Sakmann have developed elegant techniques for measuring the opening and closing of single conductance channels at the excitatory nerve–muscle synapse (Figure 7–10). Here also the transmitter (acetylcholine) increases both g_{Na} and g_K. They estimate that during the period (1 msec) a single channel is open, roughly 20,000 Na$^+$ ions flow into the cell and a somewhat smaller number of K$^+$ ions flow out. The opening of a single conductance channel produces a potential change of only 0.3 μV.

Equivalent Circuit of the Excitatory Synaptic Action. The excitatory synaptic membrane can be depicted as a parallel combination of a K$^+$ and a Na$^+$ battery (E_K and E_{Na}). The values of these batteries (−75 and +55 mV) are equal to the Nernst potential for K$^+$ and Na$^+$, respectively. Each of the batteries is in series with a resistance (R_K and R_{Na}) (Figure 7–11).

7–10 Response of a single membrane channel to acetylcholine. Acetylcholine-activated channels, which are present in postsynaptic membranes of skeletal muscle, allow the passage of roughly equal numbers of Na$^+$ and K$^+$ ions. This experiment shows that channels open on an all-or-none basis and stay open for random lengths of time. Downward deflection represents inward current. **A.** The record shows the flow of current through a single channel in the postsynaptic membrane of a frog muscle activated by acetylcholine. (Adapted from Neher and Sakmann, 1976.) **B.** The record shows the action of the compound suberyldicholine, which mimics the action of acetylcholine but keeps channels open longer. (Adapted from unpublished observations by Neher and Steinbach, after Stevens, 1979.)

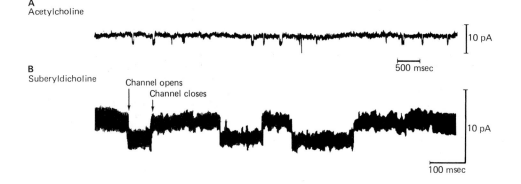

A
Acetylcholine

10 pA

500 msec

B
Suberyldicholine

Channel opens

Channel closes

10 pA

100 msec

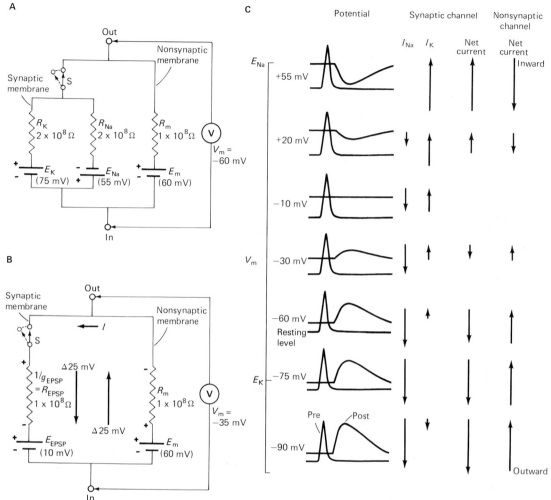

7-11 Chemical excitatory synaptic actions due to increased conductance to Na$^+$ and K$^+$ (g_{Na} and g_K). **A.** Equivalent circuit of an excitatory synapse. The synaptic membrane consists of a K$^+$ and a Na$^+$ battery (E_K and E_{Na}), each in series with a resistance (R_K and R_{Na}). The synaptic membrane is in parallel with the nonsynaptic membrane, consisting of the battery for the resting membrane potential (E_m) in series with the resting membrane leakage resistance (R_m). **B.** Simplified equivalent circuit achieved by collapsing the two synaptic pathways into one consisting of a synaptic battery E_{EPSP} in series with R_{EPSP}. At rest, the synaptic channel is an open circuit and no current flows through it. The synaptic action is equivalent to throwing the switch (S), thereby closing the circuit by placing the synaptic resistance pathway (R_{EPSP}) in parallel with the nonsynaptic membrane resistance (R_m). As a result, current flows inward through the synaptic channel and outward through the nonsynaptic membrane, depolarizing the membrane by 25 mV from a resting level of -60 mV. **C.** Reversal potential. When the membrane potential is at its

resting value (-60 mV) a presynaptic spike produces a depolarizing EPSP, which increases when the membrane potential is increased (hyperpolarized) to -90 mV. However, as the membrane potential is depolarized (made less negative) to -30 mV, the EPSP becomes smaller, and as the membrane potential reaches -10 mV, the EPSP becomes nullified. This null potential is called the *reversal potential* of the EPSP. Further depolarization to $+20$ mV inverts the PSP, making it a hyperpolarizing potential change. On either side of the reversal potential the synaptic action drives the membrane potential toward the reversal potential. The **arrows** on the right indicate how the individual ionic currents in the synaptic channel, due to Na$^+$ and K$^+$, are altered by changing V_m. The algebraic sum of the Na$^+$ and K$^+$ currents gives the net current that flows through the synaptic channel. This current is equal in size and opposite in direction to that flowing in the return pathway of the nonsynaptic channels. (The size of the arrows indicates the magnitude of current.)

Because the postsynaptic channel is permeable to *both* Na$^+$ and K$^+$, this equivalent circuit of the synaptic membrane can be simplified still further by collapsing the two parallel synaptic pathways (Figure 7–11A) into a single pathway (Figure 7–11B). Intuitively, what we have done is express the relationship between E_{Na} (which acts to depolarize the membrane) and E_K (which acts to hyperpolarize it) in an electrically equivalent term, a combined (lumped) battery of -10 mV which reflects the weighted algebraic sum of the Na$^+$ and K$^+$ batteries. The single pathway now consists of a single synaptic battery E_{EPSP}. In many cases, this resistance has a similar value to the resistance of the resting membrane (R_m), so that we can give it a resistance of 1.0×10^8 Ω.

At rest, the synaptic channel is closed. As a result of the synaptic action, current will flow inward ($\downarrow$) through the synaptic channel and outward ($\uparrow$) through the nonsynaptic channel, thereby depolarizing the membrane. The value of the synaptic potential can now be calculated to be 25 mV using the same four steps we used to examine the inhibitory synaptic current.

If additional parallel synaptic pathways were activated by the transmitter, the resistance of the synaptic branch would decrease further and more current would flow, producing a larger EPSP. With a larger conductance change, for example, with an R_{EPSP} of 10^6 Ω, the EPSP amplitude would grow to almost 50 mV and the membrane potential would be transiently dominated by E_{EPSP}.

Current That Flows During the EPSP. The flow of current due to the excitatory synaptic action (I_{EPSP}) can be inferred in a similar way to that of inhibition by artificially changing the membrane potential (V_m) and seeing how the changes affect the EPSP (Figure 7–11C). Thus the currents in Figure 7–11C again represent the current that flows through each channel as a result of the action by the transmitter.

As the membrane potential is increased from -60 to -75 mV, the EPSP increases in amplitude. This occurs because more inward current flows through the synaptic channels as the membrane potential is moved further away from the Na$^+$ equilibrium potential of $+55$ mV, thereby increasing the driving force on Na$^+$, whereas the outward (K$^+$) current is reduced (because V_m approaches E_K) and the driving force on K$^+$ is reduced. If V_m is moved to a more negative potential than -75 mV, the K$^+$ current will actually reverse.

However, as the membrane potential is pro-

gressively depolarized, the EPSP gets smaller, until it is abolished. The potential at which the EPSP is nullified (usually near 10 mV) is called the *reversal potential* of the EPSP (E_{EPSP}). Here, there is no net current flow through the synaptic channels: the inward I_{Na} is balanced by the outward I_K in the synaptic channel. Further depolarization produces a hyperpolarizing EPSP. Now, the driving force on K$^+$ is greater than on Na$^+$ because the membrane potential is closer to E_{Na} than to E_K. As a result, more K$^+$ leaves the cell than Na$^+$ comes in. The effects of changing V_m on I_{EPSP} are shown in Figure 7–11C, where the relative contributions of I_K and I_{Na} are compared to their sum $(I_K + I_{Na})$.

Thus, because g_{Na} and g_K increase simultaneously, the reversal potential for excitation (E_{EPSP}) is a *compound potential*, usually located midway between E_{Na} (55 mV) and E_K (-75 mV) at about -10 mV. The excitatory synaptic actions therefore tend to drive the membrane potential from its resting level (-60 mV) past threshold (-45 mV) in the direction of the reversal potential for the EPSP (E_{EPSP}).

Other Synaptic Actions Are Due to a Decrease in Membrane Conductance

We have thus far only considered the role of conductance increases in producing synaptic potentials. Work on the vertebrate sympathetic ganglion and various invertebrate neurons has shown that it is possible to produce synaptic inhibition by *decreasing* g_{Na}, and to produce synaptic excitation by *decreasing* g_K. We shall here consider only briefly the IPSPs due to a decrease in g_{Na}.

In some cells, the slight resting leakage of Na$^+$ (see Figure 4–7) is controlled by synaptic action. The transmitter can reduce that conductance and produce a hyperpolarization that will drive the membrane potential toward the E_m of the nonsynaptic membrane (Figure 7–11).

This type of synaptic action can be depicted with the equivalent circuit shown in Figure 7–12A. At rest, the nonsynaptic membrane $(R_m$ and $E_m)$ is in parallel with the synaptic membrane $(R_{Na}$ and $E_{Na})$. There is a constant Na$^+$ leak. At rest, inward current flows through R_{Na} and outward current flows through R_m, and the membrane potential is depolarized by 10 mV to a level of -50 mV. The synaptic action is equivalent to *opening* a switch removing the Na$^+$ battery and its series resistance $(E_{Na}$ and $R_{Na})$ from the membrane circuit. As a result, the negativity of the membrane potential is increased (by 10 mV) from

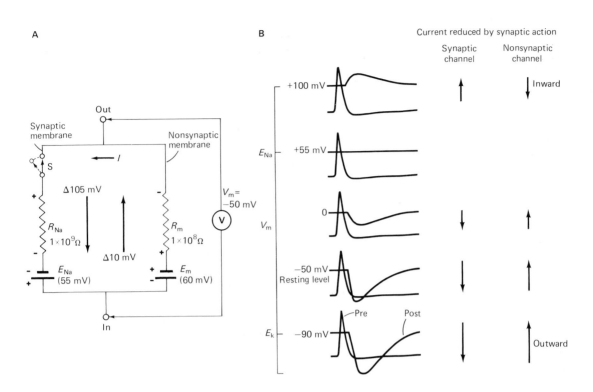

7–12 Chemical inhibitory synaptic actions due to decreased conductance to Na^+ (g_{Na}).
A. Equivalent circuit of an inhibitory synapse and current flow during rest. At rest, current flows outward through R_m and inward through R_{Na}. The synaptic action is equivalent to opening a switch (S); this turns off the slight Na^+ leak that normally keeps V_m away from E_m. As a result, the membrane hyperpolarizes and moves to E_m. **B.** Reversal potential. At the resting level (−50 mV) the presynaptic spike produces a hyperpolarizing IPSP, which increases in amplitude as the membrane potential is hyperpolarized (−90 mV). However, as the membrane potential is decreased to 0, the IPSP becomes smaller. When the membrane potential is reversed and brought to the equilibrium potential for Na^+, the IPSP becomes nullified. Further depolarization (to +100 mV) reverses the IPSP to a depolarizing potential. The arrows on the right indicate how the Na^+ current in the synaptic channel is altered by changes in V_m. This current is equal in size and opposite in direction to that flowing in by return pathway of the nonsynaptic channel. (The size of the arrows indicates the magnitude of the current.)

−50 to −60 mV, which is E_m. You can understand this intuitively, if you appreciate that in the resting state V_m is a compromise between the weak depolarizing action of the Na^+ battery and the strong hyperpolarizing action of the K^+ battery. When the small Na^+ conductance is transiently diminished (by the transmitter closing the leaky Na^+ channels), the influence of E_{Na} is reduced, and K^+ can exert more influence over V_m and hyperpolarize it.

When the membrane potential is altered, the behavior of the decreased-conductance PSPs is opposite from that of increased-conductance PSPs. Thus, when the membrane potential is artificially hyperpolarized, the IPSP due to decreased conductance actually becomes larger (Figure 7–12B). The reason for this is that at hyperpolarized levels, the driving force on Na^+ is increased and more inward current flows through the Na^+ pathways at rest, driving current outward through the adjacent "leakage" pathways. This depolarizing current counteracts the effects of the hyperpolarizing current that is artificially generated through the intracellular current-passing electrode. Turning off g_{Na} decreases the inward current and hyperpolarizes the membrane potential. However, when the membrane potential is depolarized to E_{Na}, the synaptic potential becomes nullified. If it is depolarized beyond E_{Na} the IPSP becomes inverted to a depolarizing synaptic potential. At this level, the resting leakage conductance of Na^+ generates an outward current that hyperpolarizes the cell; turning that conductance off causes depolarization.

An important problem for a decreased-conductance mechanism is that the channels that are closed by the synaptic actions—in our exam-

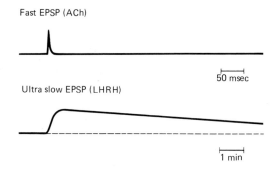

Fast EPSP (ACh)

50 msec

Ultra slow EPSP (LHRH)

1 min

7–13 Time course of an EPSP (induced by luteinizing hormone-releasing hormone, *LHRH*) is very slow (10 min) compared to that (20 msec) of increased-conductance EPSP (induced by acetylcholine, *ACh*). (Adapted from Jan, Jan, and Kuffler, 1979.)

ple, the leaky Na^+ channels—need to be accessible to the transmitter. There is now some evidence that at some synapses these channels are not located under the synaptic terminals, but appear to be distributed over the surface of the cell body. In these cases, the transmitter may trigger the synthesis of a second messenger (possibly a cyclic nucleotide) that diffuses throughout the inside of the cell body to act on widely distributed channels.

Another feature of decreased-conductance synaptic actions is their time course; these synaptic potentials are much slower—in one known case 10,000 times slower—than those due to increased conductance. Stephen Kuffler and his colleagues Yuh Nung Jan and Lily Yeh Jan have described a decreased-conductance EPSP in a sympathetic ganglion produced by presynaptic neurons that use a peptide hormone (LHRH) as a transmitter substance. This EPSP lasts 10 minutes; in contrast, the increased-conductance EPSP on the same neurons lasts 20 msec (Figure 7–13).

Ionic Mechanisms for Signaling Have Features in Common

The resting potential, action potential, generator potentials, IPSPs, and EPSPs all have certain common features (Table 7–2). They are all due to ions moving down their concentration gradients, but these various types of potentials differ in the specific ions involved, whether increases or decreases in ionic conductances are triggered, whether there is a regenerative link between voltage and conductance, and the nature of the stimulus that produces the change in conduc-

tance (voltage for the action potential, transmitter chemical for synaptic actions, pressure for Pacinian corpuscle receptors, light for rods, etc.). In addition, when two ionic conductances are activated, different potentials are produced when they are turned on simultaneously or sequentially. For example, both the action potential and certain EPSPs involve an increase in g_{Na} and g_K; but during an EPSP, Na^+ and K^+ move through the same channels and are gated simultaneously, whereas in the action potential the two ion species move through different channels and Na^+ is gated first, with K^+ turned on later. In addition, the PSP channels are not voltage gated and lack the regenerative link between conductance and voltage that is critical for the explosive all-or-none nature of the action potential.

The synaptic potentials we have considered here account for most synaptic actions. In the next chapter, we shall analyze the factors that control transmitter release from the presynaptic terminals. There we shall encounter an interesting exception wherein the ionic channels activated by the synaptic transmitter are actually voltage dependent.

Integration of Signals Determines Firing of Action Potential

To discharge an action potential, the membrane potential has to reach a certain critical level, the threshold for spike generation. This usually is −45 mV. As we have seen, EPSPs excite because they drive the membrane potential toward threshold. In most cases the synaptic potentials produced by a single presynaptic neuron are small. For example, most sensory neurons connected to a muscle spindle produce synaptic potentials of 200 μV in a motor cell. To reach threshold a motor neuron requires a depolarization of about 15 mV. If the synaptic potentials were to sum linearly (which they do not), at least 75 sensory neurons would have to fire to discharge a motor neuron. The summing of synaptic inputs from different neurons is called *spatial summation* because each synaptic input occupies a slightly different area on the membrane of the postsynaptic cell. The degree of spatial summation is determined by the *time constant* and the *space constant* of the postsynaptic cell. We have considered the importance of these passive properties in Chapter 5. A presynaptic neuron can also increase its effect on the postsynaptic neuron's membrane potential by firing repeatedly, giving rise to *temporal summation*. The degree of tem-

Table 7–2. Common Features of Signaling Potentials

Potentials	Channel specificity	Gating mechanism	Properties
Resting potential	Mostly nongated K^+ and Cl^- channels; some nongated Na^+ channels	None	Usually steady, ranging in different cells from -35 to -70 mV
Action potential	Independently gated Na^+ and K^+ channels	Voltage	All or none, about 100 mV in amplitude, 1–10 msec in duration
Receptor potential	Modality-specific gating of Na^+ and K^+ channels	Sensory stimulus	Graded, fast, several milliseconds in duration, several millivolts in amplitude
Electrical PSP	None	None	Passive propagation of presynaptic potential change
Increased-conductance EPSP	Simultaneous gating of a single class of non-voltage-gated cation-selective channels for Na^+ and K^+	Chemical	Graded, fast, several milliseconds to seconds in duration, several millivolts in amplitude
Increased-conductance IPSP	Non-voltage gating of K^+ or Cl^- channels (channel is thought to be selective for small ions)	Chemical	Graded, fast, several milliseconds to seconds in duration, several millivolts in amplitude
Decreased-conductance EPSP	Closure of leakage channels for K^+	Chemical (? intracellular messenger)	Graded, slow, seconds to minutes in duration, 1 to several millivolts in amplitude
Decreased-conductance IPSP	Closure of leakage channels for Na^+	Chemical (? intracellular messenger)	Graded, slow, seconds to minutes in duration, 1 to several millivolts in amplitude

poral summation is determined by the time constant of the postsynaptic cell.

In addition to excitation, a postsynaptic cell also includes inhibitory synaptic input in the summation, which can reduce the effectiveness of even large EPSPs. All told, a single cell such as a motor neuron receives a total of 1000 or more synapses from presynaptic neurons, some capable of exciting it some of inhibiting it. At different times different numbers and combinations of presynaptic neurons will be active. On the basis of this input, the motor neuron must decide whether to discharge an action potential, and if so what the frequency and pattern of the action potential will be.

As Lord Adrian first pointed out, once a series of action potentials is initiated in a cell, such as a motor neuron, "the messages are scarcely more complex than a succession of dots in the Morse Code." The amplitude of the action potential is all or none. Therefore, the information for signaling the next cell is contained in the number of spikes in a train and the interval between spikes.

The cell bodies of some neurons cannot generate an action potential. Even in neurons whose cell bodies can trigger an action potential, the threshold in the cell body for spike generation is usually high (-30 mV), while that of the trigger zone in the initial segment of the axon is relatively low (-45 mV). As a result, the decision to discharge an impulse is made at the trigger zone, a point often remote from the synaptic region. The trigger zone is called the integrative component of the neuron because the integrative action of the neuron takes place there. The integrative action essentially reduces to the control of the membrane potential of the trigger zone by means of the summation of the synaptic excitation. The cell will fire if, and only if, excitation exceeds inhibition by a critical minimum.

Selected Readings and References

Bennett, M. V. L. 1977. Electrical transmission: A functional analysis and comparison to chemical transmission. In E. R. Kandel (ed.), Handbook of Physiology; The Nervous System, Vol. 1, Part I. Bethesda, Md.: American Physiological Society, pp. 357–416.

Eccles, J. C. 1964. The Physiology of Synapses. Berlin: Springer.

Eccles, J. 1976. From electrical to chemical transmission in the central nervous system. The closing address of the Sir Henry Dale Centennial Symposium. Notes Rec. R. Soc. Lond. 30:219–230.

Fatt, P., and Katz, B. 1951. An analysis of the end-plate potential recorded with an intra-cellular electrode. J. Physiol. (Lond.) 115:320–370.

Furshpan, E. J., and Potter, D. D. 1959. Transmission at the giant motor synapses of the crayfish. J. Physiol. (Lond.) 145:289–325.

Katz, B., and Miledi, R. 1970. Membrane noise produced by acetylcholine. Nature (Lond.) 226:962–963.

Other References

Bennett, M. V. L., Sandri, C., and Akert, K. 1978. Neuronal gap junctions and morphologically mixed synapses in the spinal cord of a teleost, *Sternarchus albifrons* (gymnotoidei). Brain Res. 143:43–60.

Cajal, S. R. 1894. La fine structure des centres nerveux. Proc. R. Soc. Lond. 55:444–468.

Cajal, S. R. 1911. Histologie du Système Nerveux de l'Homme & des Vertébrés, Vol. 2. L. Azoulay (trans.). Paris: Maloine. Republished in 1955. Madrid: Instituto Ramon y Cajal.

Coombs, J. S., Eccles, J. C., and Fatt, P. 1955. The specific ionic conductances and the ionic movements across the motoneural membrane that produce the inhibitory post-synaptic potential. J. Physiol (Lond.) 130:326–373.

Dale, H. 1935. Pharmacology and nerve-endings. Proc. R. Soc. Med. 28:319–332.

Eccles, J. C. 1936. Synaptic and neuro-muscular transmission. Ergeb. Physiol. Biol. Chem. Exp. Pharmakol. 38:339–444.

Furshpan, E. J., and Potter, D. D. 1957. Mechanism of nerve-impulse transmission at a crayfish synapse. Nature (Lond.) 180:342–343.

Jan, Y. N., Jan, L. Y., and Kuffler, S. W. 1979. A peptide as a possible transmitter in sympathetic ganglia of the frog. Proc. Natl. Acad. Sci. U.S.A. 76:1501–1505.

Makowski, L., Caspar, D. L. D., Phillips, W. C., and Goodenough, D. A. 1977. Gap junction structures. II. Analysis of the X-ray diffraction data. J. Cell Biol. 74:629–645.

Neher, E., and Sakmann, B. 1976. Single-channel currents recorded from membrane of denervated frog muscle fibres. Nature (Lond.) 260:799–802.

Sherrington, C. S. 1897. The Central Nervous System. Part III of M. Foster, A Text Book of Physiology. 7th ed. London: Macmillan.

Sherrington, C. 1947. The Integrative Action of the Nervous System. 2nd ed. New Haven: Yale University Press.

Stevens, C. F. 1979. The neuron. Sci. Am. 241(3):54–65.

Takeuchi, A. 1977. Junctional transmission. I. Postsynaptic mechanisms. In E. R. Kandel (ed.), Handbook of Physiology; The Nervous System, Vol. 1, Part I. Bethesda, Md.: American Physiological Society, pp. 295–327.

Eric R. Kandel

Synaptic Transmission II: Presynaptic Factors Controlling Transmitter Release

Some of the most remarkable properties of the brain, such as memory and learning, seem ultimately to derive from the properties of chemical synapses. The distinctive feature of chemical synapses is that the action potentials in the presynaptic terminals lead to the secretion of a chemical substance. In this chapter, we shall consider how the electrical events in the presynaptic terminals are coupled to the secretory process for the release of chemical transmitter.

Certain Ion Species Are Necessary for Transmitter Release

Much of what we know about transmitter release comes from the work of Bernard Katz and his collaborators, who examined in detail the intermediary steps between the action potential and transmitter release. As you have learned, the action potential is the result of two sequential steps. There is first an increased conductance to Na⁺, with the voltage-gated Na⁺ channels opening and Na⁺ moving into the cell, followed by an increased K⁺ conductance, resulting in the voltage-gated K⁺ channels opening and K⁺ moving out of the cell.

Is either of these two processes responsible for triggering the release of the transmitter substance? This question was successfully approached by using two agents that selectively block one, but not the other, ion channel: Tetrodotoxin (TTX) selectively blocks the Na⁺ channel; and tetraethyl-ammonium (TEA) selectively blocks the K⁺ channel. As we have seen in Chapters 6 and 7, these agents are amazingly selective. For example, tetrodotoxin does not affect K⁺ permeability and indeed it does not affect the slight resting leak of Na⁺ that normally occurs through the membrane. Tetrodotoxin also does not interfere

8–1 Effect of Na⁺ channel blockage by TTX on presynaptic action potential and PSP at the squid giant (stellate ganglion) synapse. (Adapted from Katz and Miledi, 1967a.) **A.** Experimental arrangement with recording electrodes in both the pre- and postsynaptic fibers of the giant synapse. A current-passing electrode has also been inserted in the presynaptic terminal. **B.** Transmitting effectiveness of the nerve impulse during the gradual development of TTX paralysis. **1:** 7 min after TTX is added, the presynaptic spike still produces a suprathreshold EPSP that triggers an action potential in the postsynaptic cell. **2** and **3:** 14–15 min after TTX is added, the presynaptic spike gradually becomes smaller and produces smaller EPSPs. **4:** When the presynaptic spike is reduced to 40 mV it fails to produce a synaptic action. **C.** Input–output curve for different size action potentials in the presence of TTX (**curve 2**). The EPSP has a definite threshold; in this experiment the presynaptic spike had to be 40 mV to produce an EPSP. Beyond this threshold the relationship of presynaptic height to EPSP is logarithmic; usually a 10-mV increase in the presynaptic spike produces a tenfold increase in the EPSP. A semilog plot of this relationship is shown (**curve 1**).

with properties of the postsynaptic receptors of the channel that it controls. Thus, at a cholinergic synapse, tetrodotoxin will block the presynaptic Na⁺ spike, but acetylcholine will still produce an excitatory postsynaptic potential when applied directly to the postsynaptic receptors. This is not surprising since, as we saw in the last chapter, the Na⁺ channel activated by the action potential is distinct from that activated by the EPSP. These drugs thus illustrate in capsule form a key principle of neuropharmacology: the ability of certain drugs to act selectively at specific regions of the neuron and, in those regions, on specific molecular processes. As a corollary there is reason to believe that the molecular alterations produced by disease states are similarly selective.

Na⁺ Influx Is Not Necessary

Katz and Miledi utilized the giant synapse of the squid because it is large enough to put two electrodes (one for stimulating and one for recording) in the presynaptic terminal and a recording electrode in the postsynaptic cell (Figure 8–1A).

Before treatment with tetrodotoxin, the presynaptic cell produces a full-blown action potential, which in turn leads to transmitter release and the generation of a large synaptic potential in the postsynaptic cell. In the presence of TTX, the presynaptic action potential becomes progressively smaller with time and the postsynaptic po-

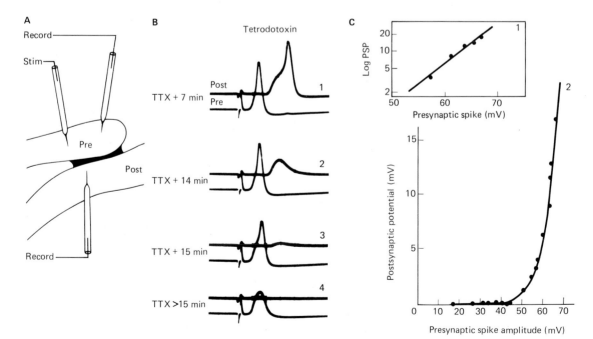

tential is reduced (Figure 8–1B). As the presynaptic spike is reduced below 25–40 mV, the synaptic potential disappears. From these results alone it might appear that Na⁺ influx is essential for transmitter release. However, in the absence of Na⁺ influx, Katz and Miledi now artificially depolarized the presynaptic membrane in steps of up to 150 mV and found that after a certain threshold (25–40 mV), there was a progressive increase in the amount of transmitter release (as judged by the appearance and amplitude of the postsynaptic potential; Figure 8–2B). In the range of depolarization where more transmitter is released (25–110 mV), a 13-mV depolarization produces a tenfold increase in transmitter release (Figure 8–1C). Thus, in the absence of Na⁺ influx, the presynaptic terminal can still release transmitter substance. A passive potential change in the terminal that is matched in size and shape to the normal action potential is no less effective in releasing transmitter and producing a postsynaptic response. Hence, the cause of the transmitter release is not the regenerative Na⁺ entry that occurs during the action potential but some other event associated with the presynaptic depolarization.

K⁺ Efflux Is Not Necessary

The K⁺ conductance increase is unaffected by TTX. This is evident in Figure 8–2B by the decrease in the presynaptic potential during the

long current pulse. To examine the contribution of the K⁺ current to transmitter release, Katz and Miledi blocked the K⁺ conductance, in addition to blocking the Na⁺ conductance, by using both tetraethylammonium and tetrodotoxin together (Figure 8–2). They then passed a depolarizing current through the presynaptic terminals and

8–2 Effect on transmitter release of blockage of the Na⁺ and the K⁺ channels in the presynaptic terminals by TTX and by TEA. (Adapted from Katz and Miledi, 1967a.) **A.** Recording arrangement as in Figure 8–1. **B.** The action potentials have been blocked with TTX. The three traces in each group represent (from bottom to top) the current injected into the presynaptic cell. *(I):* the current pulse in the presynaptic neuron. **(Pre):** the electrotonic potential produced by the current pulse in the presynaptic neuron. **(Post):** the PSP generated in the postsynaptic cell. Progressively larger depolarizations of the presynaptic terminal generated by intracellular current pulses produce progressively larger synaptic potentials in the postsynaptic cell (1–4). **C.** Traces as in part B. After the action potential was blocked with TTX, TEA was injected into the presynaptic terminal. This results in an increase in the duration of the EPSP in response to long current pulses. Progressively larger presynaptic depolarizations still produce larger postsynaptic potentials (1–4). **D.** Input–output curve based on the experiment illustrated in part C. The initial level of the presynaptic membrane potential was −69 mV. In this experiment the threshold for transmitter release (as indicated by the appearance of an EPSP in the postsynaptic cell) was about 40 mV. In other experiments the threshold was lower, about 25 mV.

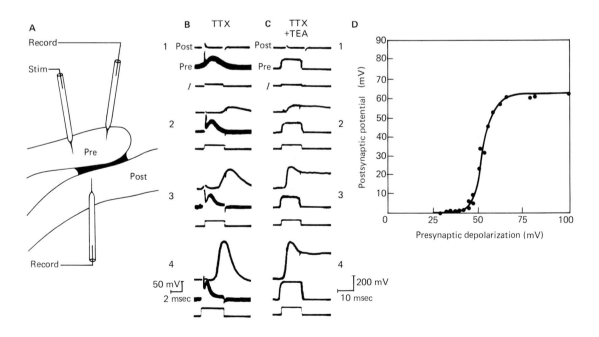

found that they still obtained transmitter release and in amounts comparable to that produced by the normal action potential. Transmitter release was now even prolonged because the effective depolarization was maintained (Figure 8–2C), but otherwise the input–output curve of the synapse was unaltered (Figure 8–2D). Katz and Miledi therefore concluded that neither Na^+ nor K^+ is required for release.

Ca^{++} Influx Is Necessary

Earlier, Katz and del Castillo had found that Ca^{++} is essential for transmitter release. Lowering the extracellular Ca^{++} concentration reduces and ultimately blocks synaptic transmission. Conversely, increasing the extracellular Ca^{++} concentration enhances transmitter release. The facilitatory effect of Ca^{++} on synaptic transmission is blocked by Mg^{++}. In the squid giant axon, Hodgkin and Baker had found that a very small amount of Ca^{++} moves into the axon with each action potential through voltage-gated channels that are fairly selective for Ca^{++}. These channels, however, are very sparsely distributed. Katz and Miledi therefore proposed that these Ca^{++} channels might be much more abundant at the terminal than they are in the axon and that Ca^{++} is not simply a carrier of charge (as are Na^+ and K^+), but Ca^{++} influx is the critical agent for coupling the action potential to transmitter secretion. Consistent with this prediction, Katz and Miledi found that with the Na^+ and K^+ channels blocked in the presence of TTX and TEA, Ca^{++} influx actually produces a secretory potential in the terminals— a regenerative Ca^{++} action potential! This is not present in the preterminal part of the axon because the axon lacks sufficient density of Ca^{++} channels. As the Ca^{++} currents are small even in the terminal region, they are normally masked by the Na^+ and K^+ currents, which are 10–20 times larger. Recently Rodolfo Llinás and his colleagues have voltage-clamped the presynaptic terminals in the presence of TTX and TEA and shown directly that the graded depolarizations of the terminals activate an inward Ca^{++} current in a graded manner and this current in turn leads to graded release of transmitter (Figure 8–3).

In order to find out at what stage of transmitter release external Ca^{++} is involved, Katz and Miledi used a nerve–muscle preparation bathed in TTX and Ca^{++}-free Ringer's solution. In addition to the normal microelectrode for recording inside the muscle fiber, they also used two external electrodes. One electrode, filled with NaCl, served as a stimulating electrode that depolarized the terminals, and the other electrode, filled with $CaCl_2$, was used to raise the local Ca^{++} concentration at a critical moment before or after the depolarizing pulse (Figure 8–4). By this means Katz and Miledi found that Ca^{++} must be present during the depolarization to produce transmitter release. When the Ca^{++} pulse is delayed until the end of the depolarization no release occurs. This suggests that the depolarization of the action potential in the terminals opens the Ca^{++} channels so that Ca^{++}

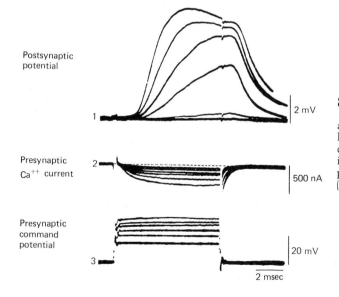

Postsynaptic potential

1   2 mV

Presynaptic Ca^{++} current

2   500 nA

Presynaptic command potential

3   20 mV

2 msec

8–3 Voltage clamp of the presynaptic terminal in the presence of TTX and TEA and the responses evoked postsynaptically. Six levels of presynaptic depolarization (presynaptic command potential) are accompanied by an inward Ca^{++} current, which in turn leads to the production of the postsynaptic responses. (Adapted from Llinás, 1977.)

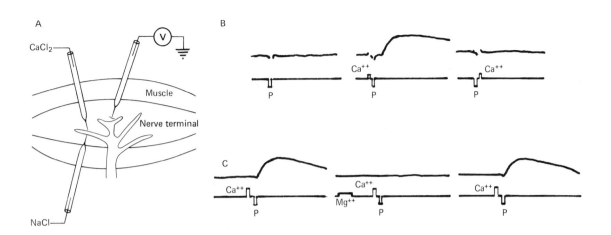

8–4 Effect of Ca^{++} on transmitter release. (Adapted from Katz and Miledi, 1967b.) **A.** Experimental setup for studying the role of Ca^{++} at the nerve–muscle synapse of the frog. **B.** Timing of Ca^{++} influx. A brief depolarizing pulse (**P**) is presented alone, just after a pulse of Ca^{++}. Only when the Ca^{++} pulse precedes the depolarizing pulse by a critical interval is transmitter released. Thus, the utilization of Ca^{++} must occur during or perhaps *immediately* after the depolarization. **C.** Mg^{++} is capable of blocking the Ca^{++} action in producing release.

can move down its steep concentration gradient into the cell and reach the critical sites involved in transmitter release.

But where are the critical sites at which Ca^{++} exerts its effect? In order to understand how Ca^{++} works, we have to examine some additional features of the release process.

Transmitter Is Released in Packets Called Quanta

The release of synaptic transmitter substance has been shown to be quantized at all chemical synapses examined thus far. Small elementary units of fixed size called *quanta* make up the synaptic potential. The reason the synaptic potentials and the input–output curves of Figures 8–1 and 8–2 appear graded is that each quantum is small and the number of quantal units released is graded. Fatt and Katz discovered the quantal nature of transmission when they recorded at the nerve–muscle synapse of the frog in the absence of presynaptic stimulation. They observed small, spontaneously occurring potential changes of about 0.5–1.0 mV in amplitude; similar results have been obtained in mammalian muscle (Figure 8–5A). As the synaptic potentials at vertebrate nerve–muscle synapses are called *end-plate potentials* (because the postsynaptic region has a specialization called the end-plate region), Fatt and Katz called these small spontaneously occurring potentials *miniature end-plate potentials*. The time course of the miniature end-plate potentials and the effects of various drugs on them are almost indistinguishable from those seen when the end-plate potential is evoked by nerve stimulation. This synapse uses acetylcholine (ACh) as its transmitter and, like the end-

plate potentials, the miniature end-plate potentials are enhanced and prolonged by prostigmine, a compound that inhibits the hydrolysis of ACh by acetylcholinesterase. The miniature end-plate potentials are also abolished by agents that block the ACh receptor, such as *d*-tubocurarine. In the absence of stimulation the miniature end-plate potentials occur at random intervals. The frequency of their occurrence can be increased by depolarizing the presynaptic terminal; they disappear following degeneration of the presynaptic nerve and reappear with reinnervation, a pattern indicating that they are caused by the random release of ACh from the presynaptic nerve terminal.

What could account for the fixed size of the spontaneous miniature synaptic potentials? One possibility that had been suggested was that these potentials represent the responses of the receptor to single ACh molecules, and that the receptor response is quantized. Del Castillo and Katz tested this hypothesis by applying ACh iontophoretically to the frog muscle end-plate: a positive potential source was applied to an electrode containing acetylcholine chloride and the positively charged ACh was passed out of the pipette in controlled amounts as a function of current. They failed to find quantized receptor re-

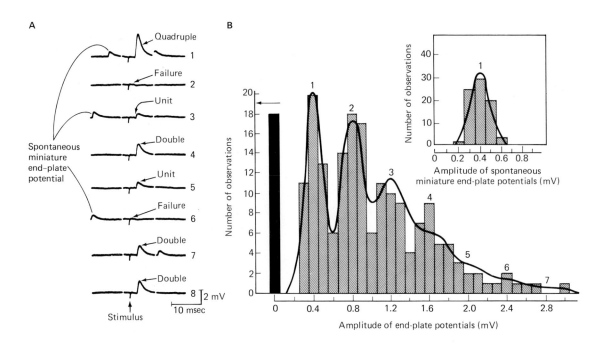

8-5 Quantal nature of synaptic transmission.
  A. Intracellular recording from a rat nerve–muscle synapse, showing a few spontaneous minature end-plate potentials and the synaptic responses (end-plate potentials) to a single impulse in the phrenic nerve in a Ca^{++}-deficient and Mg^{++}-rich solution. The end-plate potentials show considerable fluctuations; two impulses produced failures and two traces (**3** and **5**) produced a unit potential; others produced responses that are two or four times the amplitude of the unit potential. Note the stimulus artifact produced by current flowing between the stimulating and recording electrodes in the bathing solution. (Adapted from Liley, 1956.) **B.** Histogram illustrating the distribution of amplitudes of evoked end-plate potentials at a mammalian end-plate. Synaptic transmission has been reduced with a high-Mg^{++} solution. Peaks occur at **1, 2, 3,** and **4** times the mean amplitude of the spontaneous potentials (0.4 mV). A Gaussian curve is fitted to the spontaneous miniature end-plate potentials and is used to calculate the theoretical (Poisson) distribution of the evoked end-plate potential amplitudes (**continuous line**). The actual number of failures (**black bar at 0 mV**) was only slightly lower than the theoretically expected number of failures (**arrow above black bar**). Inset: The distribution of the spontaneous miniature end-plate potentials. (Adapted from Boyd and Martin, 1956.)

sponses that resembled miniature end-plate potentials. The potential change produced by the interaction of the postsynaptic receptor with a small number of ACh molecules is much smaller than the 0.5 mV potential change produced by the miniature end-plate potential.

As we learned in Chapter 7, Katz and Miledi were subsequently able to estimate the elementary ionic conductance event—the opening of a single synaptic channel due to the interaction of one ACh molecule (or at most a very few) with a single ACh receptor. They did this by analyzing the fluctuations in membrane potential (ACh noise) caused by applying small amounts of ACh to the receptor membrane. On the basis of a model in which the electrical noise of the membrane produced by ACh represents the sum of many randomly occurring channel openings and closings, they estimated that the elementary ACh potential produced by the opening of a single conductance channel is only about 0.3 μV. Therefore, about 1000 elementary depolarizations would have to summate in order to produce a miniature end-plate potential of 0.5 mV. This, however, is only a lower limit. The collisions necessary to produce an elementary conductance change probably involve 1 or 2 ACh molecules. In addition, some of the released ACh is lost by diffusion in the synaptic cleft or by hydrolysis and does not interact with receptor molecules at all. Thus, it is likely that between 10^3 and 10^4 molecules are necessary to produce a miniature end-plate potential. This number is similar to that estimated on the basis of direct chemical measurement of the ACh released. These measurements suggest that a miniature synaptic potential is produced not by 1 molecule, but by a packet containing up to 5×10^3 ACh molecules. As we shall see below, there is good reason to believe that these multimolecular packets of ACh are stored and released from the terminal by specialized organelles called *synaptic vesicles*, which are abundant in electron-microscopic pictures of synaptic terminals.

Amount of Ca++ Influx Affects the Number of Quanta Released

We can now ask the following questions: What happens during normal transmission? Is ACh released in quanta or in continuously graded amounts? If ACh is released in quanta, how does Ca++ exert its action? Does Ca++ influence the size of each quantum by determining the number of ACh molecules packaged into each vesicle or, alternatively, does Ca++ influence the probability that a quantum will be released? These questions can be answered by decreasing the external concentration of Ca++ and determining whether Ca++ acts on the amplitude of the quantum or on the number of quanta released. Del Castillo and Katz found that by bathing the preparation in low Ca++ solutions, the evoked end-plate potential (normally 40 mV) was reduced markedly (0.5–2.5 mV) and often failed. The minimum response above zero (the unit synaptic potential) was, however, identical in size and shape to the spontaneously occurring miniature end-plate potential, and the larger end-plate potentials were integral multiples of the unit potential. Thus, in an amplitude histogram of the responses to a large number of stimuli, there is a peak of failures (zero responses) followed by a multimodal response distribution. The first response peak occurs at the voltage of the unit potential: this voltage is also identical to the amplitude of the spontaneous miniature end-plate potential. The voltage of each subsequent peak is an integral multiple of the value of the first response peak; that of the second response peak is twice that of the first; and that of the third peak is three times that of the first (Figure 8–5B). The series of peaks is broad rather than sharply defined because of the statistical variation in the size of the individual miniature end-plate potentials (Figure 8–5B, inset). Thus, alterations in external Ca++ concentration do not affect the *number* of ACh molecules packaged into each quantum but the *probability* that a given quantum is released.

The dramatic stepwise fluctuations in the amplitude of the end-plate potentials at low

levels of release and the finding that the unit potential has the same mean amplitude as the spontaneously released miniature end-plate potentials prompted del Castillo and Katz to propose the quantal hypothesis for synaptic transmission. According to this hypothesis, the normal end-plate potential (40–50 mV) is caused by the release of more than 300 quanta. The fluctuation in amplitude of the end-plate potential in response to consecutive stimuli results from the fact that the exact number of quanta released varies slightly from stimulus to stimulus.

Morphological studies indicate that in the resting state the presynaptic terminal contains accumulations of synaptic vesicles, which are thought to serve as packages for transmitter (discussed in Chapters 9 and 10). Each vesicle contains one quantum (several thousand molecules) of transmitter. The vesicles are thought to fuse to the inside surface of the presynaptic terminal at specific release sites. The membrane then opens transiently so as to allow the vesicle to extrude its entire contents, in an all-or-none fashion, into the extracellular space of the synaptic cleft by a process of exocytosis (reverse pinocytosis). Katz and Miledi proposed that Ca++ (brought into the terminal by the action potential) interacts with release sites inside the terminal, where it causes or facilitates a transient fusion of the vesicular membrane with the terminal membrane, thereby

8–6 An action potential in the presynaptic terminal membranes of a neuron opens a number of Ca++ channels (**squares**) in parallel with the Na+ channels of the membrane (**hexagons**), leading to an increase in the conductance to Ca++, and an influx of Ca++. In the presynaptic terminals Ca++ is thought to be important in allowing the vesicles to bind to release sites, therefore increasing the probability of vesicles being released.

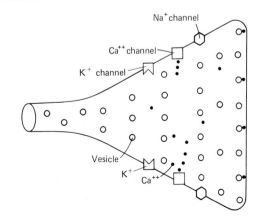

enhancing the probability of a given quantum of transmitter being released (Figure 8–6).

Amount of Ca⁺⁺ Influx Affects Synaptic Effectiveness

As we saw in Chapter 7, one advantage that chemical synapses have over electrical synapses is that chemical synapses are flexible and are sensitive to their previous history. The process whereby chemical synapses can change their effectiveness as a result of the previous pattern of activity is called *synaptic plasticity*. Three factors can produce changes in synaptic effectiveness by altering the amount of Ca^{++} that comes into the terminals: the membrane potential, the activity within the neuron itself, and the synaptic actions of other neurons.

Membrane Potential

In some cells there is a small steady influx of Ca^{++} across the membrane of the presynaptic terminals. This influx is enhanced by depolarization and decreased by hyperpolarization. Because of the steep dependence of transmitter release on intracellular Ca^{++} concentration, small changes in this steady-state Ca^{++} influx into terminals produce significant changes in the amount of transmitter released. Thus, a slight decrease in membrane potential (depolarization)—produced artificially by current or naturally by transmitter substances—which increases the steady-state Ca^{++} influx will enhance the amount of transmitter release by subsequent action potentials. A slight increase in membrane potential has the opposite effect (Figure 8–7).

The amount of Ca^{++} influx into the presynaptic neuron can thus make an effective synapse inoperative or a weak synaptic connection highly effective (Figure 8–7).

Intrinsic Governors: Activity Within the Neuron

The *intrinsic governors* reflect the changes in Ca^{++} influx produced by a cell itself. In many cells a train of high-frequency action potentials will lead to a heightened Ca^{++} influx and will be followed by a period during which each subsequent spike produced will produce a larger PSP than normal (Figure 8–8). The high rate of stimulation of the presynaptic neuron (which in some cells can be 50–100/sec or even higher) is

called a *tetanus*; the increase in PSP during the tetanus is called *facilitation*. The facilitation persisting after the tetanus is called *posttetanic potentiation*; this enhancement usually lasts several minutes but it can persist for 1 hr or more in some cells.

This process has been shown to result from a transient saturation of the Ca^{++} buffering systems in the terminals (the mitochondria and the endoplasmic reticulum) owing to the relatively large influx of Ca^{++} that occurs during a train of action potentials. This *residual Ca^{++}* increases the concentration of free Ca^{++} in the terminals and thereby enhances synaptic transmission for many minutes.

Here then is the simplest case of memory! This neuron remembers that it has generated a train of impulses by increasing the intracellular concentration of Ca^{++} in its terminals, and now each action potential in the presynaptic neuron, playing upon this memory, produces more transmitter release than before.

Extrinsic Governors: Presynaptic Inhibition and Facilitation

The *extrinsic governors* reflect the influence of other cells that synapse on the presynaptic terminals of the neuron. Thus neurons can innervate other cells not only at the cell body and dendrites (where they can control impulse activity), but also at their terminals (where they can control transmitter release). The synapses that one presynaptic terminal makes with another are called *axo-axonic* or *presynaptic*. Axo-axonic synapses can exert their actions because the presynaptic terminals contain receptors for various transmitters (presynaptic receptors). In some cases neurons have receptors to their own transmitter on their terminals; these are called *autoreceptors*. Presynaptic receptors are thought to exert their action by controlling the Ca^{++} current of the terminals.

The presynaptic actions of neurons can either depress (presynaptic inhibition) or enhance (presynaptic facilitation) transmitter release (Figure 8–9). Presynaptic inhibition in particular has been extensively documented in the mammalian brain and spinal cord. For example, in the spinal cord these inhibitory interactions occur between the presynaptic terminals of afferent fibers connected to stretch receptors from muscle and afferents from mechanoreceptors in skin. However, the best analyzed instances of presynaptic inhibition and facilitation are in certain invertebrate

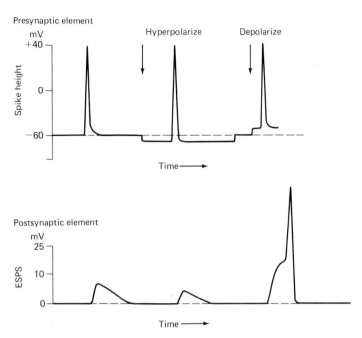

8–7 Changes in membrane potentials of the presynaptic terminal affect the amplitude of the PSP. At the normal resting potential of the presynaptic terminal an action potential produces a PSP of about 8 mV. When the membrane potential of the presynaptic terminal is hyperpolarized by 10 mV, the steady-state Ca^{++} influx is decreased and the presynaptic spike produces a PSP of only 5 mV. When the membrane potential of the presynaptic neuron is returned to the resting level and then depolarized by 10 mV, the Ca^{++} influx is increased and the resulting action potential produces a PSP of 15 mV, which triggers an action potential.

8–8 Posttetanic potentiation: simultaneous recordings from a presynaptic neuron and its postsynaptic target cell. (In order to show events that occur over a long time, the sweep speed of this experiment has been compressed so that each presynaptic potential and the postsynaptic potential it produces appear as a simple line.) During the control period the presynaptic neuron is stimulated at a rate of 1/sec and produces a PSP of about 1 mV. The presynaptic neuron is then stimulated for several seconds at a higher rate of 5/sec. During this tetanus the PSP increases in size. After several seconds of tetanus, the presynaptic neuron is returned to its control rate of firing of 1/sec; however, the PSP it produces continues to be facilitated for many minutes and in some cells for several hours.

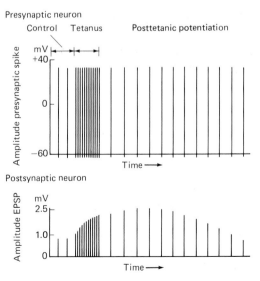

ganglia and dissociated vertebrate mechanoreceptor sensory neurons (dorsal root ganglion cells) studied in tissue culture. These indicate that presynaptic inhibition is due to a decrease in influx of Ca^{++} into the terminal and presynaptic facilitation is due to enhanced influx of Ca^{++}.

The distinction between the pre- and postsynaptic actions of neurons is important, so let us make sure it is understood. We will use inhibition as an example, as illustrated in Figure 8–9. *Post*synaptic inhibition is a process whereby one neuron (cell *A*) hyperpolarizes the cell body or dendrites of another (cell *B*), thereby decreasing the likelihood of cell *B* firing. In contrast, during *pre*synaptic inhibition, a neuron (cell C_1) may have no effect on the membrane potential of the presynaptic terminals of another cell (cell *D*), and therefore no effect on its probability of firing; however, it can reduce the amount of transmitter released by cell *D* to another cell (cell *B*). This action is presynaptic because it is exerted on the presynaptic terminals rather than in the trigger zone of cell *D*; it is inhibitory because it interferes with transmitter release. In the terminals, this synaptic action leads to a reduction of the Ca^{++} influx produced by the action potential.

Presynaptic actions are useful because they allow selective control of the actions of individual branches of a neuron. Presynaptic actions are also interesting because they can produce their actions on the voltage-sensitive Ca^{++} channels of the terminals. In these actions, a novel

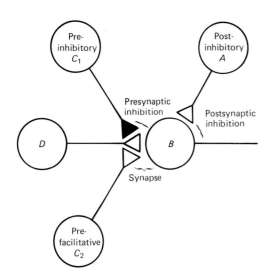

8–9   Axo-axonic synapses that act as governors modulating transmitter release. In presynaptic actions the inhibitory neuron *(C₁)* or facilitating neuron *(C₂)* acts on the terminals of the presynaptic neuron *(D).* In postsynaptic inhibition of the inhibitory neuron *(A)* acts on the cell body or dendrite of the postsynaptic neuron *(B).*

mechanism of synaptic transmission is involved, whereby a transmitter modulates a voltage-dependent ionic channel. Presynaptic actions tend to be found at sensory inflow points. Thus presynaptic inhibition is found in the retina, spinal cord, and dorsal column nuclei.

By modulating the Ca^{++} concentration in its terminals, the neuron alters its release on the basis of its previous history. By modulating the Ca^{++} channels of the presynaptic terminals of other neurons, one neuron can influence transmitter release by another. These processes are interesting because they have a time course of minutes or even hours—bestowing upon chemical synapses a short-term memory. In Chapter 52 we shall see that under certain circumstances synaptic actions can be altered for a much longer period of time; this is exactly what is needed in a brain that is capable of learning and remembering.

Selected Readings and References

Katz, B. 1969. The Release of Neural Transmitter Substances. Springfield, Ill.: Thomas.

Katz, B., and Miledi, R. 1967a. A study of synaptic transmission in the absence of nerve impulses. J. Physiol. (Lond.) 192:407–436.

Llinás, R. R. 1977. Calcium and transmitter release in squid synapse. In W. M. Cowan and J. A. Ferrendelli (eds.), Approaches to the Cell Biology of Neurons. Soc. Neurosci. Symp., Vol. II, pp. 139–160.

Martin, A. R. 1977. Junctional transmission. II: Presynaptic mechanisms. In E. R. Kandel (ed.), Handbook of Physiology; The Nervous System, Vol. 1, Part I. Bethesda, Md.: American Physiological Society, pp. 329–355.

Other References

Baker, P. F., Hodgkin, A. L., and Ridgway, E. B. 1971. Depolarization and calcium entry in squid giant axons. J. Physiol. (Lond.) 218:709–755.

Boyd, I. A., and Martin, A. R. 1956. The end-plate potential in mammalian muscle. J. Physiol. (Lond.) 132:74–91.

Del Castillo, J., and Katz, B. 1954. The effect of magnesium on the activity of motor nerve endings. J. Physiol. (Lond.) 124:553–559.

Fatt, P., and Katz, B. 1952. Spontaneous subthreshold activity at motor nerve endings. J. Physiol. (Lond.) 117:109–128.

Katz, B., and Miledi, R. 1967b. The timing of calcium action during neuromuscular transmission. J. Physiol. (Lond.) 189:535–544.

Liley, A. W. 1956. The quantal components of the mammalian end-plate potential. J. Physiol. (Lond.) 133:571–587.

Llinás, R. R., and Heuser, J. E. 1977. Depolarization-release coupling systems in neurons. Neurosci. Res. Program Bull. 15:555–687.

Michael D. Gershon, James H. Schwartz, and Eric R. Kandel

Morphology of Chemical Synapses and Patterns of Interconnection

9

Physiology is concerned primarily with the analysis of function *in time*; in contrast, morphology is concerned with the analysis of function *in space*. Thus morphological studies have revealed that the communication between nerve cells or between neurons and effector cells is mediated by one of two types of spatially discrete membrane specializations. Both types are called synapses, but ontogenetically the two types are not related. Electrical synapses, which correspond to the gap junctions found in many other epithelial cell types in the body, interconnect the cytoplasm of two adjacent cells and permit the flow of small molecules between the connected cells. On the other hand, chemical synapses are regions of the neuron specialized for the release and reception of neurotransmitter. Ontogenetically the presynaptic specializations of chemical synapses can be thought of as differentiating from subcellular components used in the universal process of secretion.

In this chapter we shall focus on the fine structure of chemical synapses. Morphological studies have revealed several subclasses of chemical synapses. In addition, these studies have provided new insight into how vesicles are released and how vesicle membrane is recycled.

Chemical Synapses Can Be Classified into Directed and Nondirected Types

The modern definition of a chemical synapse starts with the requirement that it include the region of the transmitting neuron where neurotransmitter is released and the receptor region of the target cell. In many instances, the transmitting region of a neuron is a well-differentiated structure occurring at the end of an axonal process, but there are many variations. For example, release of transmitter can occur directly from cell bodies or even from dendrites. Thus, the usual histological division of a neuron into receptive and transmitter poles may not always apply. The dendritic arbor may be both receptive and transmitting. Although the geometries of terminal axons vary greatly, subcellular features within the presynaptic element are characteristic. Essentially invariable is a high concentration of vesicles, not always uniform in size, but usually with diameters ranging from 30 to 150 nm. Mitochondria are consistently observed at synapses. Frequently observed, but not always present, are specializations at the plasma membrane to be described later in this chapter.

Chemical synaptic transmission is a form of neurosecretion in which the *area* of the postsynaptic target and its *distance* from the presynaptic site of transmitter vary. This variability is physiologically significant and accounts for an important feature of chemical synapses—their degree of *directedness*. The most directed synapses signal a postsynaptic area of less than 1 μm^2 at a distance of 25 nm from the release site; these dimensions vary greatly in other types of synapse. The least directed neurons, neuroendocrine cells, release hormones into the blood stream that signal distant targets. Autonomic synapses are probably an intermediate form, working over a large, but local area.

The synaptic cleft of directed synapses is sometimes filled with a meshwork of fibrous materials that are only now being characterized morphologically and biochemically. The postsynaptic element is the most difficult part of the synapse to typify. Greatly dependent upon the cell type and the region of the cell on which the connection occurs, the receptor area can be simple—showing no morphological differences from noninnervated regions of the same cell—or complex—showing many specialized membranous features not seen in surrounding noninnervated regions.

To appreciate the importance of distance and target area as physiological features we shall next consider two well-studied peripheral synapses that have served as models for directed and relatively nondirected synapses: the neuromuscular junction (the synapse between motor neurons and skeletal muscle), and the synapse between autonomic postganglionic neurons and their effectors. We shall then consider the synapses in the central nervous system, where similar forms as well as a family of transitional types of synapse are encountered.

The Nerve–Skeletal Muscle Synapse Is an Example of a Directed Synapse

The neuromuscular junction (and other chemical synapses) can be conveniently divided into two components: (1) the presynaptic terminal, which is secretory; and (2) the postsynaptic component, which is receptive and transductive. The synaptic cleft lies between them. Using primarily the nerve–muscle synapse (Figure 9–1) as a well studied prototype, we shall examine each of these components in detail.

9–1 Vertebrate neuromuscular junction: a highly directed chemical synapse.

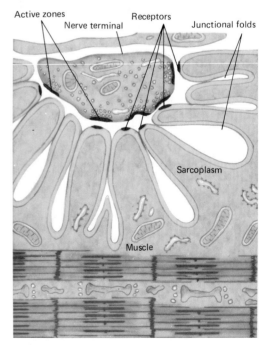

The Presynaptic Terminal: Vesicles, Exocytosis, and the Concept of the Active Zone

An essential feature of the presynaptic terminal is an accumulation of vesicles. The discovery of this array of vesicles in terminals in the first electron micrographs of synapses corresponded nicely in timing and appearance with physiological observations of del Castillo and Katz that transmitter release is quantal. This finding suggested to del Castillo and Katz, in 1957, that vesicles are the structural unit of quantal release. They imagined that the whole extent of presynaptic membrane contains release sites and that the vesicles mill around the nerve terminals in Brownian motion; when a vesicle strikes a release site it initiates the exocytotic process.

The idea that release sites are distributed along the whole presynaptic membrane is consistent with Sherrington's original view of the synapse as an extensive area of functional contact between cells—regions where the electrical activity of one neuron is brought to bear upon another.

Active Zones. Within several years of the proposal by del Castillo and Katz, Palay obtained high-resolution electron micrographs of adequately fixed central nervous system synapses. These pictures revealed that synaptic vesicles are not uniformly clustered along the entire length of the presynaptic membrane, but rather are collected at regions where the neighboring membranes of two neurons appear thicker and more dense than elsewhere.

Using tissue treated with phosphotungstic acid, a method first introduced to stain contractile proteins in muscle and in neurons, Couteaux found that the presynaptic thickening is not an increased thickness of the plasma membrane itself, but a series of dense bars attached to the internal face of the membrane (Figure 9–2A). These dense bars are located directly above the postsynaptic folds in the muscle. The synaptic vesicles collect in rows along the edges of these bars, where Couteaux occasionally found images that he interpreted to be vesicles undergoing exocytosis. Couteaux therefore called the transverse dense bar and the lined-up vesicles the *active zone,* the term now used to describe the specialized regions within synapses where transmitter is actually released.

The discovery of the dense bars indicated that synaptic vesicles collect preferentially around

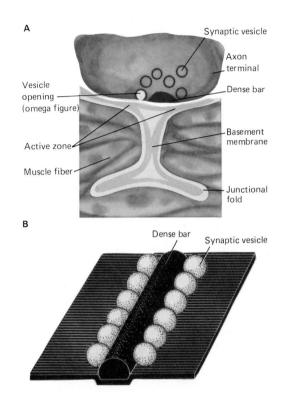

9–2 The synaptic vesicles are clustered near active zones, which are opposed to receptor patches on the surface of the postsynaptic membrane and separated from them by about 250 Å. The active zone at the neuromuscular junction shown in cross (**A**) and longitudinal (**B**) sections to illustrate the arrangement of the synaptic vesicles along each side of the dense bar. (Adapted from Couteaux et al., 1977.)

specific points in the presynaptic membrane where they seem to be destined to discharge, but are these sites the only points where exocytosis occurs? This question is difficult to investigate in conventionally fixed tissue as the chance of finding a discharging vesicle is extremely small.

Freeze Fracture Reveals the Panoramic Interior of Synaptic Membranes. Because only small areas of synaptic membrane can be examined in the ultrathin sections (50–100 nm) required for transmission electron microscopy, many workers in the 1970s began to use freeze-fracture techniques. With these techniques, frozen tissue is fractured or broken open in a high vacuum, and the freshly exposed surface is replicated by evaporating platinum and carbon on it. The advantage of this approach is that the fracture tends to split the frozen membranes through their hydrophobic interiors between the bimolecular layer of lipids. Fracture occurs here because the bilipid membrane is weakest in the middle, where the bimolecular leaflets of lipid are held together only by van der Waals forces between the hydrophobic ends of lipid molecules. Because freeze-fracture normally exposes *not* the true surface of the cell, but an intramembranous view, deformations of the plasma membrane that occur where synaptic vesicles are attached are readily apparent and easily mapped (Figure 9–3).

Using freeze-fracture, Reese and Heuser have made four key observations: First, the dense bars

9–3 Exposure of the interior of the membrane during freeze-fracture. Deformation of the membrane indicates sites of vesicle attachment. (Adapted from Peters, Palay, and Webster, 1976.)

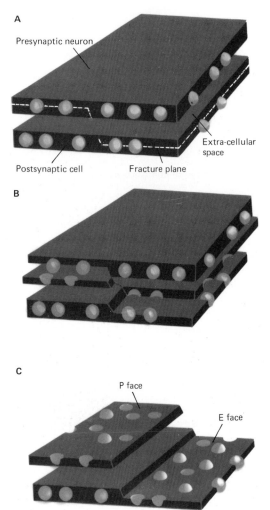

A

Presynaptic neuron

Postsynaptic cell   Fracture plane

Extra-cellular space

B

C

P face

E face

described by Couteaux are easily identified because they displace the plasmalemma slightly toward the mouth of the subadjacent transverse fold. Second, one or two rows of unusually large intramembranous particles are found to lie along both margins of each bar (Figures 9–4B and 9–5A). These large intramembranous particles seem to be permanent specializations involved in the vesicle discharge. Their function is not yet known. It is attractive to think that they may represent the Ca^{++} channels. This would be consistent with the voltage clamp data obtained by Llinás (discussed in Chapter 8), which indicate that the synaptic delay between the onset of the Ca^{++} current and the release of transmitter at the squid giant synapse is very short. This short latency suggests that the Ca^{++} channels and the vesicle release sites are near each other. Third, during synaptic activity, deformations become apparent alongside the rows of intramembranous particles (Figure 9–5B), which is exactly the region of nerve terminal where electron-microscopic thin sections show invagination of the plasmalemma. Fourth, these deformations do not seem to persist after the transmitter has been released; rather, they seem to be transient distortions that occur only at the very moment of vesicle discharge.

Thus, morphological traces of the exocytotic process are visible in the presynaptic membrane when the nerves are fixed during stimulation (under conditions of enhanced quantal release) and are absent when the nerves are fixed at rest. These results are consistent with the idea that vesicles are vehicles for quantal transmission, but these experiments did not provide compelling quantitative evidence.

To catch vesicles in the act of exocytosis, a quick-freezing machine has been constructed that shoots tissue onto a copper block cooled by liquid helium. This device also allows stimulation of the presynaptic axon in flight so that the tissue is frozen at precisely defined intervals after nerve stimulation. The neuromuscular junction can thus be caught just as the nerve action potential invades the terminal and exocytosis occurs. Using this device and the drug 4-aminopyridine (a tetraethylammonium-like substance that blocks K^+ channels, broadens the action potential, and increases the number of quanta discharged with each nerve impulse), Heuser, Reese, and their colleagues have studied exocytosis quantitatively.

Their observations of vesicles during exo-

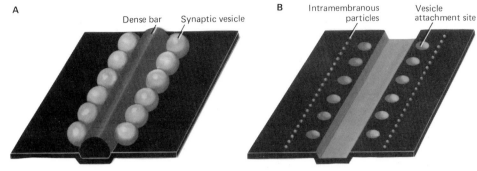

A

Dense bar   Synaptic vesicle

Thin section

B   Intramembranous   Vesicle
particles   attachment site

Freeze–fracture
P face

9–4 Comparison of the active zone at the neuromuscular junction as reconstructed from thin sections (**A**) and as seen on the P face following freeze-fracture (**B**).

9–5 Freeze-fracture replicas of the presynaptic membrane of the frog neuromuscular junction. **A.** The membrane 3 msec after the muscle had been stimulated. Running across the axon membrane is a double row of intramembranous particles; these membrane proteins may be Ca^{++} channels or structural proteins to which vesicles attach. **B.** The membrane 5 msec after stimulation. The stimulation has caused synaptic vesicles to fuse with presynaptic membrane and form pits. (Courtesy of Heuser and Reese.)

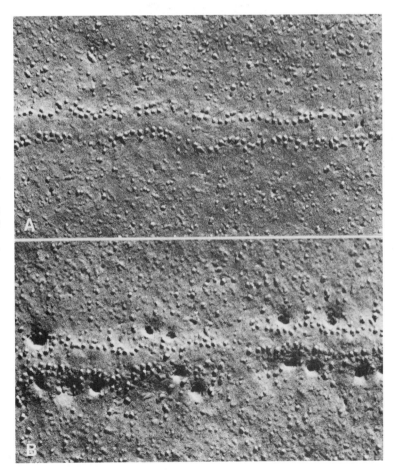

cytosis indicate that one vesicle undergoes exocytosis for each quantum of transmitter that is discharged. Statistical analyses of the spatial distribution of synaptic vesicle discharge sites along the active zones show that individual vesicles fuse with the plasma membrane independently of one another. This result is expected from physiological studies that show that quanta are discharged independently. These studies thus provide independent and direct morphological evidence that the synaptic vesicle is the transmitter storage organelle and that exocytosis is the release mechanism.

The Vesicle Membrane Can Recycle. If no process compensated for exocytosis, the membrane of the terminal would be enlarged as a result of nerve stimulation, as vesicle membrane would add to the plasmalemma. The expected increase does not occur, however, because the vesicle membrane added to the terminal membrane is recycled. The precise mechanism by which recycling takes place has not yet been determined. One hypothesis, that of Heuser and Reese, is shown in Figure 9–6. According to their view, vesicle membranes flatten into the plasma membrane and are then recycled by one of two routes. Under normal physiological circumstances the vesicles are recycled directly (route *1*). The pieces of membrane *(1a)* flow away from the active surface *(1b)* to be removed by endocytosis as coated vesicles *(1c)*. The coats are shed and the vesicles are reused *(1d)*. Under conditions of intense stimulation (route *2*) the presynaptic membrane invaginates *(2a)*, cisternae form *(2b)*, coated vesicles bud off the cisternae *(2c)*, the coats are shed, and the vesicles are reused *(2d)*.

Nerves stimulated extensively show a depletion of vesicles but a conservation of membrane. The total amount of membrane in vesicles, cisternae, and plasma membrane remains constant. In addition, the recycling of membranes is supported by studies using the enzyme horseradish peroxidase (HRP), the reaction product of which can be located by electron microscopy. In the presence of horseradish peroxidase, stimulated axons first show uptake of HRP by coated vesicles, but not by synaptic vesicles. Tracer eventually appears in cisternae, and, finally, after a period of rest, in synaptic vesicles. It is subsequently released from these loaded synaptic vesicles when the nerve is again stimulated.

Other workers (for example, Pappas and Ceccarelli) believe recycling happens in a different

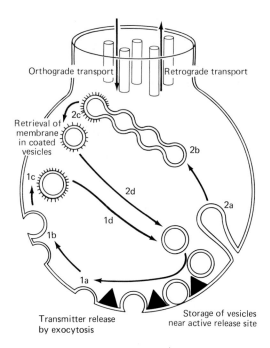

Orthograde transport   Retrograde transport

Retrieval of membrane in coated vesicles

Transmitter release by exocytosis

Storage of vesicles near active release site

9–6 Vesicle membrane recycling according to Heuser and Reese. Recycling takes place by either of two routes (*1* or *2*).

way. They envision a rapid exocytosis–endocytosis, or fusion–fission. Instead of vesicle membrane being incorporated into the plasma membrane, they think the vesicle simply fuses, opens, and then is withdrawn. It cannot be stated with certainty which view is correct because the actual processes cannot be visualized; moreover, recycling may be different at different synapses. However, one additional feature of this process deserves emphasis. Vesicle membrane is not reused indefinitely. Some vesicle membrane is not recycled into functioning vesicles but is degraded. Studies with HRP have shown that during synaptic activity much of the tracer ultimately winds up in cell bodies in lysosomes. Therefore, synaptic vesicle membrane turnover involves retrograde axonal transport of membranes (Figure 9–6) to neuronal perikarya for further processing including lysosomal degradation. The old and used vesicles are replaced by new vesicles brought into the terminals by orthograde axonal transport (a process we shall consider in Chapter 11).

Synaptic vesicle exocytosis and membrane retrieval can be divided into the stages illustrated in Figure 9–7: The vesicles initially approach the active zone (*1*), perhaps by some energy-requiring

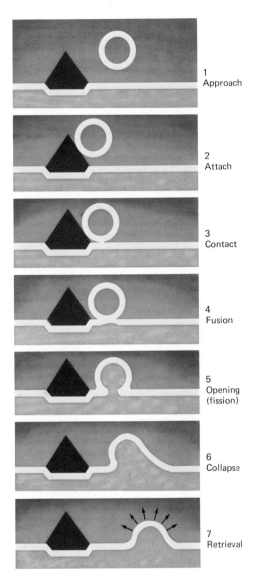

9–7 Stages in exocytosis of synaptic vesicles and vesicle membrane retrival at the active zone. (Adapted from Llinás and Heuser, 1977.)

process that may involve contractile proteins. Vesicles closest to the dense projections attach to these projections *(2)* and can be seen in thin-section electron micrographs to hover close to the presynaptic membrane even in the absence of a nerve impulse. The entry of Ca^{++} with each nerve impulse (perhaps through channels provided by the intermembranous particles next to the dense projections) leads to contact *(3)* and fusion *(4)* of the vesicle membrane and the external (plasma) membrane by an as yet unknown mechanism.

Fusion is followed by a fission *(5)* of all the intervening membrane components, which opens up the synaptic vesicle. The vesicle membrane then collapses *(6)*, presumably as a consequence of membrane fluidity by coalescence between components of the two membranes. Finally, some vesicle membrane is retrieved for reuse *(7)*, and some leaves the terminals within lysosomes to be degraded and returned to the cell body.

Postsynaptic Component

The postsynaptic receptors for ACh at the neuromuscular junction are highly localized to the plasma membrane of the junctional folds, although they spread to nonjunctional membrane of the muscle cell after denervation. The receptor molecules can be localized by autoradiography after application of labeled snake neurotoxins (α-bungarotoxin or cobra venom), which bind to nicotinic acetylcholine receptors (see Chapter 10).

The structure of the postsynaptic membrane, containing the receptors, has been analyzed in detail by freeze-fracture techniques. This analysis has been done more extensively in the electrocyte (electrical cell) of elasmobranch electric organs than in vertebrate neuromuscular junctions, but the two cholinergic synapses are similar. A new technique of quick-freezing tissue, followed by freeze-fracturing, shallow freeze-drying, and covering the dry tissue with platinum deposited in many directions simultaneously (rotary replication) permits visualization of the external surface of the membrane as well as the P and E faces of the fractured membrane (Figure 9–8). The E face and the true surface of the postsynaptic membrane contain a geometrical lattice of 8.5-nm projections rising out of the membrane surface. These projections look like small doughnuts. These structures, which are also seen in negatively stained images or in freeze-fracture views of isolated postsynaptic membranes, appear to be ACh receptors. There are about 10,000 receptors per square micrometer of membrane. The receptors are arranged in dimers, tetramers, and ordered rows. In addition, there is a morphologically identifiable structure in the form of a distinct web. Both this web and the basal lamina interposed between the nerve and the postsynaptic membrane make contact with the postsynaptic membrane, the web from below the membrane and the basal lamina from above. These contacts probably support the membrane but may also help position proteins within it.

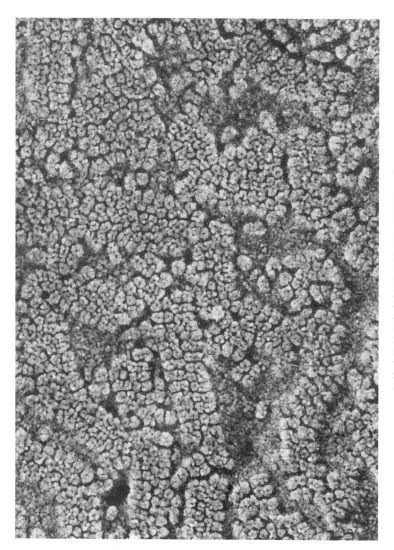

9–8 Acetylcholine-activated channels are densely packed in the postsynaptic membrane of a cell in the electric organ of a torpedo, a fish that can administer an electric shock. This electron micrograph shows the platinum-plated replica of a membrane that had been frozen and etched. The size of the platinum particles limits the resolution to features larger than about 2 nm. According to recent evidence the channel protein molecule, which measures 8.5 nm across, consists of five subunits surrounding a channel whose narrowest dimension is 0.8 nm. (Courtesy of Heuser and Salpeter.)

Autonomic Postganglionic Synapse Is an Example of a Nondirected Synapse

The presynaptic structures that constitute the active zone can be thought of as part of the directional apparatus of the synapse, ensuring that vesicles arrive at the right site for exocytosis. Many, but not all, chemical synapses function in this way. There is a major type of synapse that lacks this specialization. In these synapses transmitter release appears not to be directed. These nondirected synapses often use a biogenic amine as their transmitter. A particularly good example of this type of synapse is that of the postganglionic neuron of the autonomic nervous system.

The axon terminals of these neurons arborize diffusely, and the branches have the appearance of beads on a string (Figure 9–9). The terminal branches have this appearance because they consist of a series of piriform swellings or varicosities connected by thin intervaricose segments (Figure 9–9). Transmitter is released from the varicosities, but there are no recognizable presynaptic dense projections, and the vesicles in the varicosities show no preferred orientation toward any surface membrane. In addition, in contrast to directed synapses, the synaptic gap may be as wide as 400 nm, and the postsynaptic membrane is not modified.

The autonomic synapse appears to be specialized to ensure a widespread effect of the transmitter. The extensive system of varicosities, the wide synaptic gap, and overlapping axons (autonomic ground plexus) contribute to this diffuse

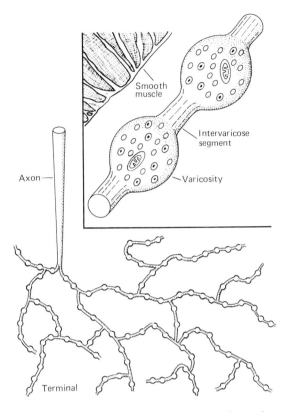

9–9 Peripheral autonomic synapse: a nondirected chemical synapse.

shows few. In the central nervous system both extremes and many intermediate forms are encountered. Like autonomic adrenergic neurons of the peripheral nervous system, adrenergic and serotonergic neurons in the central nervous system have varicosities distributed over relatively broad target areas. Active zones seem rare in these varicosities, but they do occur.

More typically, central synapses display prominent modifications of the plasma membrane of presynaptic elements consisting of dense projections. As in directed synapses in the peripheral nervous system, these dense projections are ar-

9–10 Dense projections and active zone at a gray type I synapse. **A.** Schematic drawing of an electron microscope section of a central synapse stained with phosphotungstic acid. **B.** Arrangement of vesicles around the dense projections at the active zone.

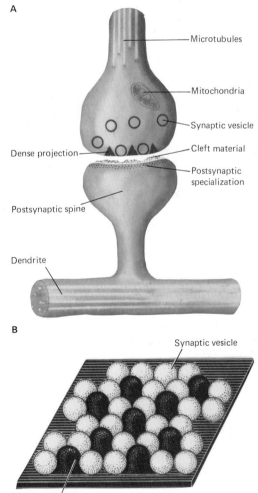

action in the peripheral autonomic nervous system. Thus, sympathetic stimulation affects large areas of blood vessels; it does not lead simply to the twitches of one smooth muscle cell in a single artery.

Central Synapses Have Diverse Morphologies

Although they adhere to the general principles we have considered above, central synapses vary greatly in detail. Variation occurs in the extent of presynaptic specializations, in the types of vesicles the presynaptic terminals contain, in the geometry of the zone of apposition, and in the site of the pre- and postsynaptic cells that contact one another.

Extent of Presynaptic Specialization

The neuromuscular synapses and the synapses of autonomic postganglionic neurons represent extremes in synaptic specialization: the first shows prominent specializations, whereas the latter

ranged in more or less trigonal arrays, each of which extends from the presynaptic membrane into the cytoplasm for some distance and is typically surrounded by synaptic vesicles (Figure 9–10A). This close spatial relationship suggests that vesicles adhere to the dense projections in preparation for discharge. The dense projections are interconnected by fine strands forming a "presynaptic grid" (Figure 9–10B). The spacing of adjacent dense projections is just far enough apart so that the synaptic vesicle can nestle between them and thus reach the presynaptic membrane. The spacing between the dense projections is narrower in synapses that contain smaller synaptic vesicles.

Examples of the more directed type of synapse are two common classes referred to as Gray type I and type II (after E. G. Gray, who described them) (Figure 9–11). In the type I synapse the cleft is slightly widened to approximately 30 nm, the active zone is 1–2 μm^2 in area, dense projections are prominent, and the vesicles tend to be round. In addition, there is an extensive postsynaptic density, and amorphous dense material appears in the synaptic cleft. In the type II synapse the cleft is 20 nm across. The active zone is smaller (less than 1 μm^2), the presynaptic dense projections and the postsynaptic density are modest, and there is no material in the cleft. Characteristically, the vesicles of type II synapses tend to be oval, with a flattened appearance.

Types of Synaptic Vesicles

There are other variations in the size and electron density of the synaptic vesicles in central synapses. As a general rule, ACh and the amino

acid transmitters are stored in electrolucent and relatively small vesicles, 30–60 nm in their largest diameter. In contrast, vesicle populations appear heterogeneous in neurons that secrete peptides. These neurons contain both larger vesicles (70–150 nm), which have electron dense cores of varying sizes, and smaller vesicles, which vary in electron density. Axons that release biogenic amines also have both large and small vesicles at their terminals.

Geometry of the Zone of Apposition

The zone of apposition can be flat and relatively simple (of the sort we have considered up to this point), or it can be indented, whereby the postsynaptic process typically protrudes into the presynaptic one (Figure 9–12). The functional differences between these two types are not as yet known. Perhaps the indented appositions (which in some synapses contain more vesicles per area of active zone than do flat appositions) are more effective than the flat appositions.

Site of Contact

The site on the postsynaptic cell that is contacted by the presynaptic terminal can vary greatly. Among the known sites of contact are the following (by convention, the presynaptic element is named first):

1. Axo-somatic
2. Axo-dendritic (axospinous)
3. Axo-axonic
4. Dendro-dendritic
5. Soma-somatic

Some of these contacts are illustrated in Figure 9–13.

Does the region of a neuron where synaptic contact is made have any functional significance?

9–11 Comparison of the Gray type I and type II central synapses

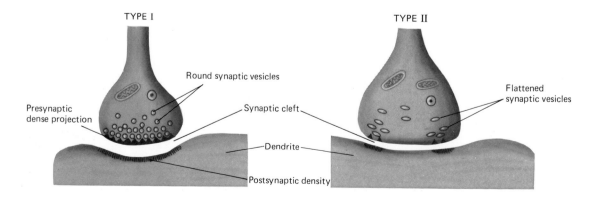

TYPE I

TYPE II

Round synaptic vesicles

Presynaptic dense projection

Synaptic cleft

Flattened synaptic vesicles

Dendrite

Postsynaptic density

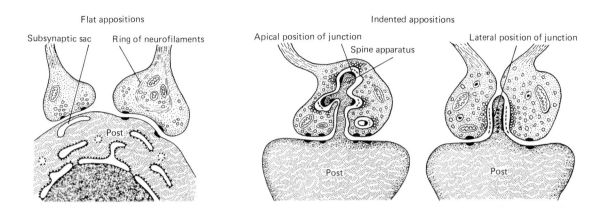

The proximity of a synapse to the trigger zone of the postsynaptic cell is obviously important. Axo-somatic contacts tend to be closer to the trigger zone than do remote axo-dendritic contacts. As a result, a given synaptic current generated by an axo-somatic input will have a greater effect on the trigger zone than will distant inputs on the dendrites. Axo-axonic synapses have no direct effect on the trigger zone of the postsynaptic cell that they innervate. They produce their actions not by affecting the threshold of the neuron, but by controlling the amount of transmitter released by the presynaptic terminal.

Inputs onto a Neuron Can Be Highly Segregated

We have previously considered synapses as individual entities. Neurons typically have many synaptic inputs. A cerebellar Purkinje cell, for example, may have as many as 80,000. Some of these inputs are excitatory, others are inhibitory; some are strong, others are weak. Clearly, in cells with many inputs, no one synapse is likely to be capable of exciting the cell above its threshold for firing.

9–12 Flat and indented zones of apposition in central synapses. In the flat apposition the pre and postsynaptic membranes are parallel to one another with only a slight widening at the synaptic cleft. At indented apposition the postsynaptic cell sends a finger-like process into the presynaptic terminal.

Function depends not only on the existence of excitatory and inhibitory synapses, but also on their strategic location, size, shape, terminal diameter, relationship to glial insulation, and the proximity of other synapses. Certain principles bear on these relationships between cells.

The synapses made by different afferents are consistent in position and structure. Consider, as an example, the pyramidal cells of the hippocampus, which have a consistent dendritic structure. These cells receive seven major categories of inputs, and six of these are rigidly segregated. The synapses of each of the six categories are restricted to different parts of the dendritic tree.

9–13 Various sites of contact at synapses. (Presynaptic neurons are shown on top of postsynaptic neurons.)

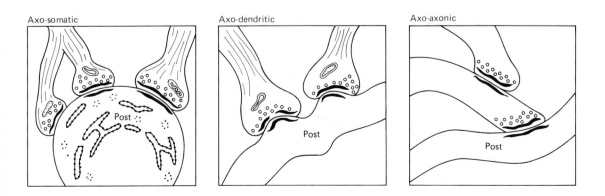

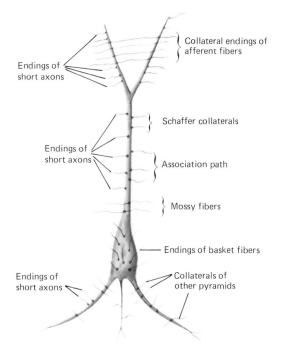

Endings of short axons

Collateral endings of afferent fibers

Schaffer collaterals

Endings of short axons

Association path

Mossy fibers

Endings of basket fibers

Endings of short axons

Collaterals of other pyramids

9–14 Segregation of inputs onto a single hippocampal pyramidal cell.

The seventh input from neurons with short axons (presumably a diffuse modulatory one) innervates the dendritic tree throughout its extent (Figure 9–14).

Another example is the cerebellar Purkinje cell. These cells receive input from four principal sources:

1. General weak excitation comes from as many as 8×10^5 granular cell axons (known as parallel fibers) that end on dendritic spines.
2. Weak inhibition comes from stellate cells that contact primary and secondary dendrites.
3. Strong inhibition comes from the combined terminals or 10–20 basket cell axons that form a basket-shaped cluster around the axon hillock.
4. Finally, very strong excitation, overriding everything else, is exerted by a single climbing fiber that runs over the soma and the entire dendritic tree and synapses repeatedly over much of that huge area of contact.

The importance of this segregation is that the position of a synaptic input along a dendritic arbor determines its interaction with other synapses and its effect on the firing pattern of the cell. Although there are exceptions, dendrites of

most cells do not generate spikes. They serve as passive conductors of synaptic potentials to the cell body, where integration occurs and the *net* effect is read out at the axon hillock. Therefore, for any given conductance change, synaptic inputs near the soma are more effective than more distant inputs. Synapses relegated to the branches of apical dendrites are less effective than those placed on the apical dendrite itself. Inhibitory endings, which generally increase membrane conductance to K^+ or Cl^-, are more effective when they make contact near the site of action potential generation. Their short-circuiting action way out on dendrites only affects nearby excitatory synapses on the same dendrite. Perhaps for this reason many inhibitory inputs end on the cell soma, the axon hillock, or the most proximal parts of the dendritic arbor.

Interconnections Give Rise to Local Processing of Information

Most of the discussion in this chapter has focused on the polarized model of the neuron. The dendritic arbor constitutes the receptive pole of this model, the axon, the conducting portion, and the axon terminal (long, varicose, and branched, as in the autonomic nervous system or a terminal bouton) the transmitting pole. With this model in mind, we naturally think of the nervous system as being composed of coordinating centers (or nuclei) made up of cell bodies and dendritic arbors receiving information, and tracts of axons acting as pathways connecting the centers. Some brain centers, however, function in the processing and integration of information in addition to their role in relaying information from place to place. These centers are characterized by neurons with short axons that do not project out of the centers. These short-axoned cells are classified as interneurons or Golgi type II neurons. (The long-axoned principal cells whose axons project out of the nucleus—such as the Purkinje cells—are classified as Golgi type I cells.) The processing of information is also accomplished in some regions by dendro-dendritic interactions among the dendritic arbors themselves. The existence of dendro-dendritic synapses indicates that (1) dendrites can have active release zones, (2) the dendritic arbor is not always strictly receptive, and (3) impulse activity (action potentials) is not always necessary for transmitter release because many dendrites release transmitters without having spike-generating capability. Large EPSPs gener-

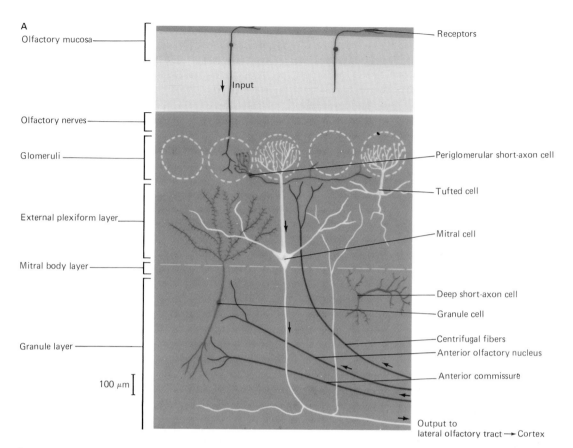

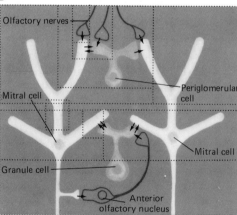

9–15 Mammalian olfactory bulb. **A.** Neuronal elements. Inputs: afferent fibers (from above) from olfactory receptors; and central fibers (from below) from three sources—centrifugal fibers from the nucleus of the horizontal limb of the diagonal band, ipsilateral fibers from the anterior olfactory nucleus, and contralateral fibers from the anterior commissure. Principal neurons: mitral cell (1') and tufted cell. Intrinsic neurons: periglomerular short-axon cell, deep short-axon cell, and granule cell. Adapted from Shepherd, 1974.) **B.** Organization of functional units. **Dotted lines** enclose "functional units," each defined as the morphological substrate for a specific function. The units differ in size and complexity: single synapse with its pre- and postsynaptic terminals; reciprocal synapses and other patterns involving dendritic terminals and axonal inputs; parts of dendritic trees with their associated input–output ensembles of processes; and long-distance "loop units" through neighboring structures (anterior olfactory nucleus). **Arrows** indicate functional polarity of synapses. (Adapted from Rakic, 1975.)

ated near active release zones in dendrites can activate sufficient Ca^{++} influx to initiate transmitter release.

An example of a region where dendro-dendritic connections are important in processing is the olfactory bulb (Figure 9–15). Here, the input and output of the center are separate. The input comes to the bulb from olfactory receptors. The output is directed to the olfactory cortex. Cells in the bulb are located in discrete layers. The principal cell in the bulb is the *mitral cell.* This Golgi type I cell receives an input from olfactory receptors in complex synaptic structures called *glomeruli* and sends its axons to the cortex. Other types of neuron are interneurons (Golgi type II) and are confined within the olfactory bulb. These include the *periglomerular* cell, which sends a small dendritic tuft into a glomerulus and has a short axon that terminates nearby. Another cell is the granule cell, which as two long vertical dendrites covered with spines but *this cell has no axon at all.*

If the axon of the mitral cell fires an action potential, long-lasting recurrent inhibition of the mitral cell results. This is due to retrograde invasion of the mitral cell body by the spike generated in the axon, which in turn leads to electrotonic invasion of the dendritic arbor. The mitral dendritic arbor then excites granule cells, which, reciprocally and in an orthograde manner, now inhibit the mitral cell (as well as neighboring mitral cells). All of this is made possible by dendro-dendritic synapses. The periglomerular cells contact the mitral cell's dendrites inside the glomerulus, and these two cell types also make reciprocal dendro-dendritic inhibitory synapses with one another.

These dendro-dendritic connections are a logical and economical way to organize synaptic interactions in a minimum space. The reciprocal dendro-dendritic circuit is as compact a synaptic circuit as exists. It has therefore been called a *microcircuit* (or local circuit). Such circuits have been found in parts of the brain other than the olfactory bulb. These include the retina, basal ganglia, cerebral cortex, thalamus, fifth nerve nucleus, and suprachiasmatic nucleus.

An Overall View

Synaptic contacts between cells range in complexity from the most simple, the electrical synapse, to more complex directed chemical synapses. Electrical synapses are ideal for synchronizing cellular events but permit little flexibility and integration. Chemical synapses appear to have evolved to fulfill the latter functions. The simplest of these is the autonomic postganglionic terminal axon, a long-branched chain of vesicle-filled varicosities. These structures disperse transmitter by means of exocytosis over a wide area and are not suited for discrete control. For discrete directed release of transmitter, a more complex chemical synapse has evolved. This synapse has a well-defined active surface with pre- and postsynaptic membrane specializations. The synaptic vesicles are directed to the active zone, where exocytosis occurs. Exocytosis necessitates membrane recycling. Either membrane is recycled locally in terminals or, in a process that involves retrograde axonal transport, retrieved membrane is degraded in cell bodies in lysosomes. The directed synapse, producing highly localized excitatory or inhibitory responses, makes possible a great deal of integration through the spatial distribution of synapses on receptive cells. Directed synapses can be segregated and meaningfully arranged on a single postsynaptic neuron. In much of the nervous system the dendritic arbor is specialized as the receptive pole of the neuron and the axon terminal is the transmitting pole; however, in certain instances microcircuits utilize dendro-dendritic synapses.

Selected Readings and References

Bennett, M. V. L., and Goodenough, D. A. 1978. Gap junctions, electrotonic coupling, and intercellular communication. Neurosci. Res. Program Bull. 16:371–486.

Burnstock, G. Hökfelt, T., Gershon, M. D., Iversen, L. L., Kosterlitz, H. W., and Szurszewski, J. H. 1979. Non-adrenergic, non-cholinergic autonomic neurotransmission mechanisms. Neurosci. Res. Program Bull. 17:377–519.

Heuser, J. E., and Reese, T. S. 1977. Structure of the synapse. In E. R. Kandel (ed.), Handbook of Physiology; The Nervous System, Vol. 1, Part I. Bethesda, Md.: American Physiological Society, pp. 261–294.

Llinás, R. R., and Heuser, J. E. 1977. Depolarization-release coupling systems in neurons. Neurosci. Res. Program. Bull. 15:555–687.

Palay, S. L., and Chan-Palay, V. 1977. General morphology of neurons and neuroglia. In E. R. Kandel (ed.), Handbook of Physiology; The Nervous System, Vol. 1, Part I. Bethesda, Md.: American Physiological Society, pp. 5–37.

Peters, A., Palay, S. L., and Webster, H. de F. 1976. The Fine Structure of the Nervous System: The Neurons and Supporting Cells. Philadelphia: Saunders.

Shepherd, G. M. 1978. Microcircuits in the nervous system. Sci. Am: 238(2):92–103.

Other References

Cajal, S. R. 1911. Histologie du Système Nerveux de l'Homme & des Vertébrés. L. Azoulay (trans.). Vol. 2. Paris: Maloine. Republished in 1955. Madrid: Instituto Ramon y Cajal.

Ceccarelli, B., Hurlbut, W. P., and Mauro, A. 1973. Turnover of transmitter and synaptic vesicles at the frog neuro-muscular junction. J. Cell Biol. 57: 499–524.

Couteaux, R. 1974. Remarks on the organization of axon terminals in relation to secretory processes at synapses. Adv. Cytopharmacol. 2:369–379.

Couteaux, R., Akert, K., Heuser, J. E., Reese, T. S. 1977. Ultrastructural evidence for vesicle exocytosis. Neurosci. Res. Program Bull. 15:603–607.

Couteaux, R., and Pécot-Dechavassine, M. 1970. Vésicules synaptiques et poches au niveau des "zones actives" de la jonction neuromusculaire. C. R. Hebd. Séances Acad. Sci. Sér. D. Sci. Nat. 271:2346–2349.

Del Castillo, J., and Katz, B. 1957. La base "quantale" de la transmission neuro-musculaire. In Microphysiologie comparée des éléments excitables. Colloq. Int. Cent. Natl. Rech. Sci. 67:245–258.

Geffen, L. B., and Livett, B. G. 1971. Synaptic vesicles in sympathetic neurons. Physiol. Rev. 51:98–157.

Gray, E. G. 1963. Electron microscopy of presynaptic organelles of the spinal cord. J. Anat. 97:101–106.

Heuser, J. E., Reese, T. S., Dennis, M. J., Jan, Y., Jan, L., and Evans, L. 1979. Synaptic vesicle exocytosis captured by quick freezing and correlated with quantal transmitter release. J. Cell Biol. 81:275–300.

Holtzman, E. 1977. The origin and fate of secretory packages, especially synaptic vesicles. Neuroscience 2:327–355.

Palay, S. L. 1958. The morphology of synapses in the central nervous system. Exp. Cell. Res. Suppl. 5:275–293.

Pappas, G. D., and Waxman, S. G. 1972. Synaptic fine structure-morphological correlates of chemical and electrotonic transmission. In G. D. Pappas and D. P. Purpura (eds.), Structure and Function of Synapses. New York: Raven Press, pp. 1–43.

Pfenninger, K., Sandri, C., Akert, K., and Eugster, C. H. 1969. Contribution to the problem of structural organization of the presynaptic area. Brain Res. 12:10–18.

Rakic, P. 1975. Local circuit neurons. Neurosci. Res. Program Bull. 13:289–446.

Shepherd, G. M. 1974. The Synaptic Organization of the Brain. An Introduction. New York: Oxford University Press.

Sherrington, C. S. 1897. The Central Nervous System. Part II of M. Foster, A Text Book of Physiology. 7th ed. London: Macmillan.

Vrensen, G., Nunes Cardozo, J., Muller, L., and Van Der Want, J. 1980. The presynaptic grid: a new approach. Brain Res. 184:23–40.

James H. Schwartz

Chemical Basis
of Synaptic Transmission

10

What is the molecular machinery that underlies synaptic transmission? To what degree can we explain the structural and functional features of synaptic transmission in terms of specific molecules? As a class, neurons are distinguished from other cells of the body by certain molecular properties. Many of these characteristic properties are responsible for the signaling activities of neurons considered in previous chapters. These primary activities include (1) responding to specific chemical transmitter substances by altering membrane permeability to common ions (Na^+, Cl^-, K^+, Ca^{++}), (2) conducting electrical impulses, and (3) communicating with other, postsynaptic cells by the process of synaptic transmission. Underlying each of these three physiological functions are biochemical processes and cellular components that are currently being characterized and understood at the molecular level. Thus, a neuron's specific responsiveness to certain substances results from various intrinsic membrane proteins called *receptors*. Membranes of different neurons contain different receptors; this fact is very important for understanding neuronal diversity.

The alteration of membrane permeability to ions, so important to signaling, is also mediated by a number of distinct protein complexes embedded in the nerve cell membrane. The protein channels and pumps for any one ion differ from those for other ions, as would be expected, because the sizes and shapes of the ions are different. On the other hand, there is some indication that the ion channels (e.g., voltage-gated Na^+ channels) of different neurons are chemically similar to one another. Although information about the molecular structure of the proteins that constitute these channels is still scanty, it is likely that ion channels of neurons are chemically similar to those in other cells. Thus, neuronal Ca^{++} channels may be homologous to Ca^{++} channels of the sarcoplasmic reticulum of muscle and to similar channels in the protozoan amoeba.

The release of transmitter substances from presynaptic terminals is another physiological function that is composed of many biochemical processes; some are characteristic of specific neurons, whereas others are pathways and mechanisms that are familiar to us from the study of other cell types. In this and the next chapter we shall consider synaptic transmission in biochemical terms. In this chapter we shall focus on transmitter substances, their storage, release, disposal, and receptors; in the next chapter we shall discuss three regulatory mechanisms that govern synaptic transmission.

A General Scheme Describes Chemical Synaptic Transmission

Chemical transmission can be divided into four steps: (1) synthesis of transmitter substance; (2) storage and release of transmitter; (3) interaction of transmitter with receptor in the postsynaptic membrane; and (4) removal of the transmitter from the synaptic cleft. These steps are diagrammed in Figure 10–1, which shows the sequence of events that takes place within nerve terminals. Even though synaptic transmission occurs at nerve terminals, it is important to realize that other parts of a neuron contribute significantly to the process. The terminal is dependent upon the cell body for all of the macromolecular components needed for transmission—biosynthetic and degradative enzymes, proteins of synaptic vesicles (both those in membranes and those that may be contained within the vesicle in soluble form), and most (but not all) of the lipid. These components are rapidly exported after being synthesized in the cell body and move along axons to nerve terminals by fast axonal transport.

Before the biochemical processes involved in

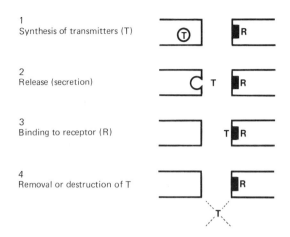

1
Synthesis of transmitters (T)

2
Release (secretion)

3
Binding to receptor (R)

4
Removal or destruction of T

10–1 Four biochemical steps in synaptic transmission: (1) synthesis of the neurotransmitter substance (**T**), (2) release of transmitter into the synaptic cleft, (3) binding of the transmitter to the postsynaptic receptor, and (4) removal or destruction of the transmitter substance.

synaptic transmission are described in detail, it is important to make clear what is meant by *transmitter.* The concept had become familiar by the early 1930s, after Otto Loewi demonstrated the release of ACh from vagus terminals in frog heart and Sir Henry Dale reported his work on cholinergic and adrenergic transmission. It has been continually modified since that time to accommodate new information about the cell biology of neurons and the pharmacology of receptors.

As a first approximation we can define a *transmitter* as a substance that is released synaptically by one neuron and that affects another cell (neuron or effector organ) in a specific manner. As with many other operational concepts that emerge in biology, the concept of a transmitter is quite clear at the center but can be somewhat fuzzy at the edges. Thus, most neuroscientists would agree that eight substances can indisputably function as transmitters, but there are many others about which there are varying degrees of uncertainty. Moreover, it is often difficult to prove in all instances that one of the accepted eight substances is a transmitter at any given synapse. Because of these (often, but not always, scholastic) difficulties, a set of experimental criteria has been developed: strictly speaking, a substance will not be accepted as the transmitter at a particular synapse of a neuron unless the following four criteria are met:

1. It is synthesized in the neuron.
2. It is present in the presynaptic terminal and is released in amounts sufficient to exert its supposed action on the affected neuron or effector organ.
3. When applied exogenously (as a drug) in reasonable concentrations, it mimics exactly the action of the endogenously released transmitter (for example, it activates the same ionic channels in the postsynaptic cell).
4. A specific mechanism exists for removing it from its site of action (the synaptic cleft).

Needless to say, it is often impossible experimentally to demonstrate *all* of these features at a given synapse; this has resulted in the very cautious use of the word *transmitter*.

Despite the foregoing words of caution, a great many nerve cells have been characterized with respect to their transmitter biochemistry, and an important generalization has emerged: *A mature neuron makes use of the same transmitter substance at all of its synapses.* This generalization, attributed to the great British pharmacologist, Sir Henry Dale, was actually formulated as a principle in 1957 by Sir John Eccles. Eccles had been studying the motor neuron of the spinal cord, which has a cholinergic peripheral synapse; he correctly predicted—on the basis of Dale's discussions of work on cholinergic and adrenergic neurons in the autonomic nervous system, dating from the early 1930s—that the synapse from the recurrent central branch (onto the Renshaw cells of the cord) would also be cholinergic. During the intervening years, much more information on the chemistry and cell biology of synaptic transmission has been obtained, and the number of accepted transmitter substances has increased from the two recognized in the 1930s, ACh and norepinephrine (NE). As a general rule, available evidence indicates that the vast majority of neurons use only one transmitter substance, and Dale's principle has come to be a doctrine of neuronal specificity.

It is certain that the spirit of Dale's law is *not obeyed in some developing neurons* that have been shown to synthesize, and to release, more than one transmitter substance; moreover, there are recent reports of the coexistence of two potential transmitter substances in the terminals of some (unusual) neurons. Nevertheless, the current view is that most, if not all, adult neurons are differentiated so that only the biochemical apparatus specific to one transmitter is present; consequently, a mature neuron contains an ex-

clusive set of biochemical processes that together endow that neuron with its differentiated character. In this respect, neuronal differentiation is thought to resemble the specialization of cells in other body tissues: thus, some cells differentiate to make albumin but not insulin, fibrinogen but not immunoglobulin, etc.

Biosynthesis of the Eight Canonical Transmitter Substances

One set of molecules that is of obvious importance in determining which transmitter a neuron uses is that of biosynthetic enzymes, for without them, the characteristic transmitter would not be made (Table 10–1). A specific set of biosynthetic enzymes is a necessary but not a sufficient determinant of transmitter specificity, however, because other specific biochemical processes intervene between synthesis of the transmitter and its release at synapses: for example, packaging of the transmitter into storage vesicles and synaptic vesicles that mediate synaptic release (described below).

In any biosynthetic pathway, there is some controlling element; in *all* transmitter pathways there is an enzymatic step at which the overall synthesis of the transmitter is regulated; this enzyme ordinarily is characteristic of or specific to the neuron, and therefore endows that cell with the property of being cholinergic, norepinephrinergic (noradrenergic), dopaminergic, serotonergic, etc.

Acetylcholine

As an example, the biosynthetic pathway for ACh has only one enzymatic reaction, that of choline acetyltransferase [*(1)* in reaction below]; this enzyme is the determining and characteristic enzyme in ACh biosynthesis. The biosynthesis of the cosubstrate, acetyl coenzyme A (acetyl CoA), is not specific to cholinergic neurons, since acetyl CoA participates in many metabolic pathways.

Acetyl CoA + choline

$$(1) \quad CH_3-\overset{\overset{\displaystyle O}{\|}}{C}-O-CH_2-CH_2-\overset{+}{N}-(CH_3)_3 + CoA$$
$$ACh$$

ACh is the transmitter used by the motor neurons of the spinal cord, and therefore at all nerve–skeletal muscle junctions in vertebrates. It is important in the autonomic nervous system,

Table 10–1. Canonical Transmitter Substances and Their Key Biosynthetic Enzymes

Transmitter	Enzymes
Acetylcholine	Choline acetyltransferase (specific)
Biogenic amines	
Dopamine	Tyrosine hydroxylase (specific)
Norepinephrine	Tyrosine hydroxylase and dopamine β-hydroxylase (specific)
Serotonin	Tryptophan hydroxylase (specific)
Histamine	Histidine decarboxylase (specificity uncertain)
Amino acids	
γ-Aminobutyric acid (GABA)	Glutamic acid decarboxylase (probably specific)
Glycine	General metabolism (specific pathway undetermined)
Glutamate	General metabolism (specific pathway undetermined)

being the transmitter for all preganglionic neurons and for the parasympathetic post-ganglionic neurons as well. In the central nervous system ACh is diffusely localized throughout the brain, but is highly concentrated in neurons of the basal ganglia. The large Betz cells of the motor cortex that send their axons into the pyramidal tract are also cholinergic.

Amine Transmitters

Dopamine and norepinephrine (NE), two important transmitter substances, are synthesized in a common pathway that consists of several enzymatic steps. Not all of the enzymes are specific to this pathway, however. Tyrosine hydroxylase *(1)*, an oxidase which converts tyrosine (Tyr) to L-di-hydroxyphenylalanine (L-DOPA), is rate limiting in both dopamine and NE synthesis and is a characteristic enzyme of dopaminergic cells. It requires a reduced pteridine (Pt) cofactor, which is reoxidized by another enzyme, pteridine reductase *(4)*. This reductase is not specific to neurons.

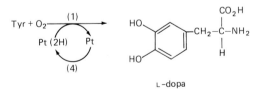

L-DOPA is next decarboxylated by a decarboxylase *(2)* to give dopamine and CO_2.

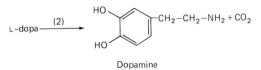

Dopamine β-hydroxylase *(3)*, which converts dopamine to NE, is characteristic of noradrenergic cells.

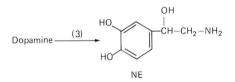

In the central nervous system, norepinephrine-containing nerve cell bodies are prominent in the locus ceruleus, a nucleus of the brain stem; these cells are unusual because, while few in number, they project diffusely throughout the cortex, cerebellum, and spinal cord. In the peripheral nervous system NE is the transmitter in the post-ganglionic neurons of the sympathetic nervous system.

Dopamine-containing cells are located in three regions: the substantia nigra, where the cells project to the striatum; the midbrain, where they project to the limbic cortex; and the hypothalamus, where they project to the pituitary stalk. Sympathetic ganglia also contain small intensely fluorescent (SIF) cells that are dopaminergic.

The synthesis of serotonin (5-hydroxytryptamine, 5-HT) involves two enzymes: tryptophan hydroxylase *(1)*, an oxidase similar to tyrosine hydroxylase, which puts a hydroxyl group on the indole ring in the 5 position; and 5-hydroxytryptophan (5-HTP) decarboxylase *(2)*, which forms serotonin.

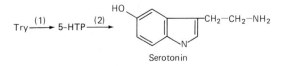

The controlling step is tryptophan hydroxylase, the first enzyme in the pathway. Interestingly, L-DOPA decarboxylase and 5-hydroxytryptophan decarboxylase seem to be identical; this enzyme activity, L-aromatic amino acid decarboxylase, is present in many tissues, including organs outside the nervous system.

Serotonergic cell bodies are found in the midline raphe nucleus of the brain stem; these cells (like the NE cells of the locus ceruleus) send fibers throughout the brain and spinal cord.

Histamine has been convincingly shown to be a transmitter in invertebrates, and binding sites for certain kinds of antihistaminic drugs have been localized to neurons in the vertebrate brain. This putative transmitter substance is concentrated in the hypothalamus. It is synthesized from the amino acid histidine (His) by decarboxylation. Although not extensively characterized, the decarboxylase (1) catalyzing this step appears to be characteristic of histaminergic neurons.

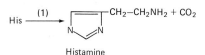

Several other naturally occurring amines may also be transmitters: tyramine and octopamine have both been found to be active in invertebrate nervous systems.

NE and dopamine are catecholamines, containing, a 3,4-dihydroxylated (adjacent) benzene ring. Tyramine and octopamine, possible transmitter substances, are derived from catecholamines. Serotonin is an indoleamine. Catecholamines, indoleamines, and histamine all can be referred to as *biogenic amines*.

Amino Acid Transmitters

Acetylcholine and the biogenic amines are substances that are not intermediates in general biochemical pathways. Consequently, their production occurs only in certain neurons and not in others. In contrast, there is a group of amino acids that are released as neurotransmitters and also are universal cellular constituents. Glycine, glutamate, and aspartate are 3 of the 20 common amino acids that are incorporated into the proteins of all cells; glutamate and γ-aminobutyric acid (GABA) also serve as substrates in the major cycles of intermediary metabolism.

Glutamate and aspartate are synthesized in familiar metabolic pathways that need not be reviewed here. The case for glutamate as a transmitter in the cerebellum and the spinal cord is fairly strong; aspartate's role is more controversial.

Glycine, which is probably synthesized from serine (its specific biosynthesis in neurons has not been studied, but its pathways in other tissues are well known), is thought to be one of the inhibitory transmitters in spinal cord interneurons.

Gamma-amino butyric acid (GABA) is synthesized from glutamate (Glu) in a reaction catalyzed by glutamic acid decarboxylase (1):

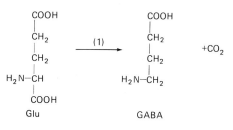

GABA is present in neurons in the basal ganglia which project to the substantia nigra; the Purkinje cells of the cerebellum are GABAminergic, as are certain inhibitory interneurons in the spinal cord.

It might at first seem puzzling how common amino acids can act as a transmitter in some neurons but not in others. This phenomenon can be taken as an indication that the presence of a substance, even in substantial amounts, is insufficient evidence that the substance is a transmitter. To illustrate this point, let us consider the following example. GABA is the inhibitory transmitter at the neuromuscular junction of the lobster (and of other crustacea and insects as well), and glutamate is the excitatory transmitter. Edward Kravitz and his co-workers at Harvard showed that the concentration of GABA in inhibitory cells is about 12 times greater than that in excitatory cells and this supports the idea that GABA is the inhibitory transmitter. On the other hand, the concentration of glutamate (the excitatory transmitter) was found to be the same in both the excitatory and inhibitory cells. Glutamate must be compartmentalized within these neurons: *transmitter* glutamate is somehow kept separate from *metabolic* glutamate. What mediates the compartmentalization of the amino acid transmitters is not yet certain. With ACh and the biogenic amines it has been convincingly demonstrated that the transmitter substances are packaged in specific and characteristic membranous vesicles. Similar vesicles are present in neurons that use the amino acid transmitters, and, although it has not yet been proved, it is likely that these vesicles constitute the *transmitter* compartment.

Neuroactive Peptides

In recent years, about 25 short peptides have been found to be localized in neurons (primarily by immunocytochemical techniques) and also to be pharmacologically very active, causing inhibition, excitation, or both when applied iontophoretically on neurons (Table 10–2). Some of these peptides were previously identified as hormones with known targets outside the brain (for example, angiotensin and gastrin) or as products of neurosecretion [for example, oxytocin, vasopressin, somatostatin, luteinizing hormone (LH) and thyrotropin-releasing hormone (TRH)]. Neuronal or regional localization in the brain on the one hand, and specific target action on the other, has spurred the idea that, in addition to being hormones in some tissues (i.e., substances released at

Table 10–2. Neuroactive Peptides

Gut-brain peptides
  Vasoactive intestinal polypeptide (VIP)
  Cholecystokinin octapeptide (CCK-8)
  Substance P
  Neurotensin
  Methionine enkephalin
  Leucine enkephalin
  Insulin
  Glucagon
Hypothalamic-releasing hormones
  Thyrotropin-releasing hormone (TRH)
  Luteinizing hormone-releasing hormone (LHRH)
  Somatostatin (growth hormone release-inhibiting
    factor, SRIF)
Pituitary peptides
  Adrenocorticotropin (ACTH)
  β-Endorphin
  α-Melanocyte-stimulating hormone (α-MSH)
Others
  Angiotensin II
  Bradykinin
  Vasopressin
  Oxytocin
  Carnosine
  Bombesin

Source: S. H. Snyder, Brain peptides as neurotransmitters, Science 209:976–983, 1980.

a considerable distance from their intended sites of action), in other tissues these peptides may act as neurotransmitters (i.e., substances that are released essentially directly onto the site of intended action). The study of neuroactive peptides has become popular, possibly because certain peptides are localized in regions of the brain thought to be involved in the perception of pain, pleasure, feeling, and emotion.

There are two families of peptides that possess opiate-like actions, the endorphins and the enkephalins. The opioid peptides are involved in a variety of functions including the modulation of pain (see Chapter 18 and Table 10–3). These peptides contain a common tetrapeptide sequence:

Try-Gly-Gly-Phe.

There are three known pharmacologically active endorphins, all derived from a large precursor peptide with 91 amino acid residues (see Figure 18–3), called β-lipotropin: α-endorphin (residues 61–76 of β-lipotropin); γ-endorphin (residues 61–77); and β-endorphin (residues 61–91). All of the active endorphin fragments bind to the same receptors as do opiate analgesics. The most active and the only one known to act physiologically is β-endorphin, which is synthesized in the arcuate nucleus of the hypothalamus, as well as in the pituitary.

The enkephalins are two pentapeptides:

Try-Gly-Gly-Phe-Met (Met-enkephalin)

and

Try-Gly-Gly-Phe-Leu (Leu-enkephalin).

The enkephalins are also produced by cleavage of a larger precursor protein that has multiple copies of both the Met- and Leu-enkephalin sequences. The enkephalins are synthesized only in neurons and in the adrenal gland. The precursor is synthesized in the cell body on ribosomes and transported within secretory vesicles to nerve terminals. During transport, enkephalin molecules are produced by proteolytic cleavage. Unlike β-endorphin, the enkephalins are widely distributed in the brain. The distribution matches that of the opiate receptor. In brain the opiate receptor appears to correspond to the enkephalin receptor.

Substance P is an undecapeptide concentrated in certain neurons of the dorsal root ganglia, basal ganglia, hypothalamus, and cerebral cortex. It acts at low concentrations to depolarize neurons and has been proposed as the transmitter for primary afferent sensory fibers of the dorsal root

Table 10–3. Localization and Possible Function of Opiate Receptors[a]

Location	Functions influenced by opiates
Spinal Cord	
Laminae I and II	Pain perception in body
Brain Stem	
Substantia gelatinosa of spinal tract of caudal trigeminal	Pain perception in body
Nucleus of solitary tract, nucleus commissuralis, nucleus ambiguus	Vagal reflexes, respiratory depression, cough suppression, orthostatic hypotension, inhibition of gastric secretion
Area postrema	Nausea and vomiting
Locus ceruleus	Euphoria
Habenula-interpenducular nucleus-fasciculus retroflexus	Limbic, emotional effects, euphoria
Pretectal area (medial and lateral optic nuclei)	Miosis
Superior colliculus	Miosis
Ventral nucleus of lateral geniculate	Miosis
Dorsal, lateral, medial terminal nuclei of accessory optic pathway	Endocrine effects through light modification
Dorsal cochlear nucleus	
Parabrachial nucleus	Euphoria in a link to locus coeruleus
Diencephalon	
Infundibulum	ADH secretion
Lateral part of medial thalamic nucleus, internal and external thalamic laminae, intralaminar (centromedian) nuclei, periventricular nucleus of thalamus	Pain perception
Telencephalon	
Amygdala	Emotional effects
Caudate, putamen, globus pallidus, nucleus accumbens	Motor rigidity
Subfornical organ	Hormonal effects
Interstitial nucleus of stria terminalis	Emotional effects

Source: From Miller, R. J., and Pickel, V. M., The distribution and functions of the enkephalins. J. Histochem. Cytochem. 28:903–917, 1980.
[a]Courtesy of Dr. S. H. Snyder.

ganglion cells that project into the substantia gelatinosa of the spinal cord and are involved in mediating pain. In the brain, there is some indication that substance P is a transmitter in the striatonigral fiber system, presumably involved in the modulation of motor movement.

Whether these peptides should be regarded as neurotransmitters is an interesting question that has not yet been answered. Many of the established criteria for neurotransmitters have been met by some peptides, but no peptide has met all of them. Moreover, certain features of their metabolism and their action differ from those of the accepted (low molecular weight) transmitters. Although peptides have been shown to be present in some neurons at relatively high concentrations, unlike the low molecular weight transmitters that are synthesized locally at terminals, the peptides can be formed only in the cell body because their synthesis requires peptide-bond formation on ribosomes. Furthermore, although synaptic release of some peptides has been demonstrated, the resulting action of peptides differs somewhat from those of the classical neurotransmitters already described. The chief difference is that the effects of the peptides last longer. This difference, which could have profound consequences on the type and quality of the information transmitted, may result from two features characteristic of the peptides. First, they are effective at much lower concentrations than are the classical transmitter substances. Second, there do not appear to be specific and rapid mechanisms available for terminating the

Table 10–4. Co-Existence of a Transmitter Substance with Neuroactive Peptides

Transmitter	Peptide
Acetylcholine	Vasoactive intestinal peptide (VIP)
Norepinephrine	Somatostatin
	Enkephalin
	Neurotensin
Dopamine	Cholecystokinin (CCK)
	Enkephalin
Adrenalin	Enkephalin
Serotonin	Substance P
	Thyrotropic-releasing hormone (TRH)

Evidence for the co-existence of a classical transmitter substance with a neuroactive peptide has been reported for these combinations. With the information thus far available, it is not yet possible to determine the specificity of the pairs and their physiological significance.

action of these peptides. (Although the brain contains a great variety of peptidases, most of these are intracellular degradative enzymes.) It is as yet unclear to what extent these differences between peptides and classical transmitter substances imply differences in synaptic mechanism.

Hökfelt and his collaborators have recently proposed the interesting idea that a peptide and a low molecular weight (classical) transmitter might co-exist in the same neuron and be released together during synaptic transmission (Table 10–4). Coordinate release of two substances with potentially different postsynaptic activities suggests many new possibilities about how neurons can signal their targets.

Vesicles Store and Release

Synthesis of the transmitter is only one aspect of the biochemistry of synaptic transmission. The storage and release of transmitters have also been extensively investigated. There is considerable evidence that much of the transmitter within a neuron is packaged in storage granules or synaptic vesicles. These vesicles are thought to be required for two physiological functions: they accumulate and store the transmitter, and they mediate the synaptic release of transmitter by the process of exocytosis.

Evidence for a Storage Role

There is abundant evidence for the association of transmitters with vesicles within the neuron. Supply of transmitter is an important factor in regulating synaptic transmission. Vesicular

stores constitute a large reserve of transmitter protected from intracellular degradative enzymes. A family of enzymes of this type that degrade biogenic amines is situated in the outer membrane of mitochondria; they are called *monoamine oxidases*. At least two types (A and B) can be distinguished on the basis of their substrate specificity. If the transmitter is packaged in vesicles, it is safe from these intracellular enzymes.

Association of neurotransmitters with vesicles has been shown with a variety of experimental approaches. Nerve cells viewed by electron microscopy reveal characteristic vesicular profiles that are greatly concentrated at nerve endings (see electron micrographs in Chapter 9). The morphological appearance of these vesicles varies in different neurons but the diameters of all of them range between 30 and 150 nm.

Histochemical Studies. With the biogenic amines it is possible to show that vesicles contain transmitter by using specific histochemical or autoradiographic techniques. Catecholamine and serotonin, when reacted with formaldehyde vapor, form fluorescent derivatives. The Swedish neuroanatomists Falck and Hillarp found that under properly controlled conditions the reaction can be used to localize transmitters on histochemical sections under the fluorescence (light) microscope. Because individual vesicles are too small to be resolved by the light microscope, histofluorescence can localize only transmitters to particular regions of nerve cells. Vesicular localization can be inferred by comparing the distribution of fluorescence under the light microscope with the localization of vesicles under the electron microscope. Histochemical analysis can be extended to the ultrastructural level: fixation of nervous tissue under special conditions intensifies the electron density of vesicles containing biogenic amines. Thus fixation in the presence of potassium permanganate, chromate, or silver salts brings out dense-core vesicles that are characteristic of aminergic neurons.

Direct localization of transmitter substances to vesicles can also be accomplished by electron-microscopic autoradiography and by immunocytochemistry. A necessary condition for autoradiography is that the labeled transmitter is not washed out of the tissue during preparation for microscopy. Amino acid transmitters and biogenic amines can be successfully localized by autoradiography because they have a primary amino group that permits their covalent fixation in place within the neuron by cross-linking to proteins by glutaraldehyde or formaldehyde, the usual fixatives used in microscopy. For immuno-histochemical localization, specific antibodies to the transmitter substance are necessary. Specific antibodies have been raised that combine with serotonin and with many of the neuroactive peptides. Under the light microscope these antisera can localize antigens to regions of individual neurons (e.g., cell bodies, axons, and sometimes terminals) by immunohistofluorescence using antibody labeled with fluorescein. Ultrastructural localization is achieved by immunohistochemical techniques (usually involving a peroxidase–antiperoxidase system developed by the American immunologist Ludwig Sternberger).

Subcellular Fractionation Studies. Additional biochemical evidence for transmitter vesicles comes from subcellular fractionation. This is usually accomplished by means of differential centrifugation. Transmitter vesicles can be separated from other subcellular organelles because they differ in size, density, or shape. Isolation of synaptic vesicles is facilitated by an artifact of homogenization of nervous tissue. The gentle grinding of neurons in an isotonic medium can result in pinching off of entire synaptic terminals. These artifactual sacs were named *synaptosomes* by Victor Whittaker, the British neurochemist who first described them and who has subsequently developed techniques for their preparation. They are fairly stable and are quite a bit larger (about 1 μm across) then most subcellular membrane structures. They therefore can be isolated by differential centrifugation using either step or continuous density gradients created by layering or mixing viscous solutions of inert, impermeable substances such as sucrose or polysaccharide polymers. Centrifugation is carried out at high speeds in the ultracentrifuge: this method has been used for over 2 decades for separating subcellular organelles and viruses. Once separated from the smaller cellular components, the isolated synaptosomes can be broken by osmotic shock when diluted into water. This process releases synaptic vesicles, which in turn can be separated from all the other constituents of synaptosomes by another differential centrifugation step because they are considerably smaller.

Isolation of vesicles allows their biochemical characterization. Neurophysiological evidence for packaging of transmitters has been described

in Chapter 8, where the quantal hypothesis was considered. Biochemical estimates of the amount of ACh in a single vesicle (2000 molecules) match quite well with the neurophysiological evidence (fewer than 10,000 molecules per quantum). Studies of vesicles isolated from adrenergic neurons show that at least two populations of vesicles exist—large and small. Less extensive work suggests that other aminergic neurons similarly have more than one type of transmitter vesicle. The large aminergic vesicle contains both a higher concentration and more transmitter than does the smaller vesicle. In aminergic neurons precise measurements of quantal size by electrophysiological methods are more difficult to do than in cholinergic neurons, and they have not yet been closely correlated to the biochemical determinations of vesicle content.

Isolated synaptic vesicles contain other substances in addition to neurotransmitter. Both cholinergic and aminergic vesicles contain ATP. The large adrenergic vesicles also contain at least two soluble proteins, called *chromogranins*; large and small adrenergic vesicles also contain the enzyme dopamine β-hydroxylase, partly in a soluble state within the vesicle and partly bound to the membrane of the vesicle. Within vesicles, ATP and the chromogranins possibly serve to form complexes with transmitter, thereby decreasing the osmotic activity that would otherwise result from the high intravesicular concentration of free transmitter.

Mechanisms of Transmitter Storage

How do the vesicles concentrate transmitter? What is the driving force? The best information available suggests that the biogenic amines move into aminergic vesicles because of a pH gradient. pH gradients also underlie the formation of ATP in mitochondria. This "chemiosmotic" mechanism, proposed by Peter Mitchell in 1961 to explain oxidative phosphorylation, has only recently been shown to apply to accumulation of amines by aminergic storage vesicles. Vesicle membrane contains a pump that drives out OH^- or brings in H^+, making the inside of the vesicle more acid than the cytoplasm. The pH of the vesicle is 5.5; that of the cytoplasm is 7. This pH gradient established, it requires only a few more assumptions to understand how the process would work.

Biogenic amine transmitters exist as charged and uncharged species. The pK of the primary amine group in catecholamines is about 9: therefore, at the neutral pH of cytoplasm, about 0.5% of the amine exists in uncharged form. It can be assumed that only this unprotonated species can pass through the vesicle's membrane. Because the pH of the inside of the vesicle is 5.5, the proportion of uncharged amine inside is about 70-fold lower than in the cytoplasm. Consequently, when a molecule of uncharged amine comes into the vesicle, it is protonated and cannot escape. Thus the transmitter is driven into the vesicle by ion trapping and by the formation of complexes with ATP and internal proteins. In addition to passive entry, some evidence also indicates that there is an active and specific exchange of H^+ with transmitter molecules. This would bring about even greater accumulation than by passive ion trapping alone.

Evidence for Involvement in Release

Although there is still some debate, the vesicle hypothesis has been generally accepted, and there is little doubt that synaptic vesicles are directly involved at the site in the synaptic membrane at which transmitter molecules are released from the neuron. Morphological examination of tissue under the electron microscope has shown that overstimulation of a synapse (that results in failure of transmission as determined electrophysiologically) is accompanied by depletion of vesicles at the stimulated synapse. Moreoever, as reviewed in Chapter 9, convincing evidence that synaptic vesicles undergo exocytosis has been obtained by freeze-fracture techniques.

Biochemical Evidence for Exocytosis

The best biochemical evidence that exocytosis is involved in transmitter release comes from experiments in which the cells of the adrenal medulla (which embryologically can be thought of as postganglionic adrenergic neurons of the sympathetic nervous system) were stimulated to release their content of biogenic amine (NE and adrenalin) into the circulation. When the materials released with the hormones were assayed, it was found that ATP, the chromogranins, and dopamine β-hydroxylase were released into the blood, in addition to the amines; furthermore, these constituents were present in the same molar ratios as they occurred in isolated chromaffin granules. Only the soluble fraction of dopamine β-hydroxylase was released: no membrane proteins were lost from the gland. Historically, this experiment has been quite persuasive, and is often cited as proof of exocytosis. More recent morphological and biochemical observations suggest that synaptic transmission, although an exocytotic process, differs in certain respects from glandular release and neurosecretion. Release by the adrenal medulla is mediated by large vesicles that contain high concentrations of amine complexed to core proteins; these large vesicles interact slowly with the external membrane of the gland cell. Synaptic transmission, on the other hand, involves smaller vesicles that contain less transmitter and little if any core proteins. Interaction of synaptic vesicles with the synaptic membrane is facilitated by specialized membrane structures built into the presynaptic membrane. These membrane specializations constitute the *active zone*. In contrast to the slower, massive type of release of hormone from glands and neurosecretory neurons, synaptic transmission of neurotransmitter is rapid, sustained, and repetitive because the membrane interactions are mediated by the special synaptic apparatus at the active zone described in Chapter 9.

Basis of Neuronal Specificity

The biochemical make-up of storage and synaptic vesicles differs in neurons of different transmitter type. In addition to a specific biosynthetic pathway, each type of neuron has a characteristic system of membranes involved in packaging its particular transmitter substance. This vesicular apparatus is also the vehicle by which transmitter is released into the synaptic cleft by exocytosis. It is generally believed that a potential transmitter cannot be used unless it is packaged; thus, in addition to the specificity built into the biosynthetic enzymatic pathway, there is a *specificity to the packaging apparatus* in these cells. These various specificities are interesting not only theoretically, but also practically, because whenever a biological system has a specificity it can be interfered with pharmacologically.

Any specificity recognition system within neurons can easily discriminate between ACh and serotonin because they are dissimilar chemically. However, there are drugs that are sufficiently similar to the normal transmitter substance that they can act as *false transmitters*; these are packaged in the vesicles and released as if they were true transmitters. They often have less potency in interacting with the receptor than the true transmitter; therefore, their release decreases the efficacy of transmission at specific synapses. A clinically important example is α-methyl DOPA (Aldomet), which is used in the treatment of high blood pressure. α-Methyl DOPA is converted to α-methyl NE in adrenergic neurons. It is taken up adrenergic vesicles and acts as a false transmitter when released.

Structure and Function of Receptors

Once released, a transmitter molecule is effective only if it interacts with a receptor. *A given transmitter does not always open the same ionic gates or bring about the same biochemical change in the postsynaptic neuron.* For example, ACh can excite some synapses, inhibit others, and do both at the same time at others; catecholamines (e.g., NE) may excite at some synapses, while at others they bring about changes in cAMP; at still others, they may do both. These effects are not specifically characteristic of the transmitter *as a chemical* but result from its interactions with specific receptors; for example, it is the receptor that determines whether a synapse will be excitatory or inhibitory. Although this dictum is in principle true, within a group of closely related animals (for example, vertebrates) a given transmitter substance will usually be associated with specific physiological functions. Thus ACh is *the* transmitter at the vertebrate neuromuscular junction, and is there associated with excitatory synaptic transmission. ACh slows the vertebrate heart; excitatory transmission to the heart is adrenergic. As we shall see in later chapters (see especially Chapters 50 and 51), emotional affect is related to central biogenic amines.

This close association between transmitters and physiological functioning is somewhat deceptive. Muscle, heart, and mind are each quite similar in all vertebrates from the standpoint of evolution. It is therefore not surprising that organs in similar species share common modes of innervation. In contrast, heart and muscle of phylogenetically distant animals are not necessarily excited or inhibited by the same transmitter substances.

At first the notion of a receptor was a mental construct or operational model proposed to account for the site on a membrane which is sensitive to a transmitter substance. Following the Roman philosopher Lucretius, who postulated that matter must come in contact in order to interact, Paul Ehrlich introduced the concept of a receptor to explain the selectivity of pharmacological agents and the specificity of antibody–antigen reactions. A receptive substance in skeletal muscle sensitive to curare and nicotine was postulated by J. N. Langley in 1906. This substance has now been isolated and characterized as the cholinergic receptor of the neuromuscular junction. Receptor theory was subsequently developed by British pharmacologists and was greatly influenced by the study of both enzyme kinetics and cooperative interactions between ligands and proteins (an historically important example of which is the binding of O_2 to hemoglobin).

General Characteristics

All receptors for transmitters have two common biochemical features:

1. Their location is in the membrane facing outward; this is important for their interaction with the transmitter arriving from across the synaptic cleft.
2. They are proteins that have active sites that bind transmitter substance.

In a few instances, progress has been made in the isolation of receptor molecules. Some receptors can be localized in tissues autoradiographically or assayed in isolated preparations of membranes radiochemically by binding studies using radiolabeled ligands. Most often, specific pharmacological antagonists are used because of their high affinity for the receptor. Neurotoxins have turned out to be most useful because they bind specifically with great avidity, but transmitter analogues have also been used. A variety of receptors have begun to be characterized by experimentally convenient binding assays on filter disks, but biochemically the most completely characterized example is the nicotinic cholinergic receptor from the electric organ of electric fish. Although there is still some disagreement among the laboratories working on this receptor, it is agreed that the cholinergic receptor (AChR) is a multimeric intrinsic membrane protein that traverses the postsynaptic membrane.

The nicotinic AChR of the electric organ of *Torpedo californica,* which is a rich source, can be isolated by extraction in solutions containing a relatively mild (nonionic) detergent, Triton X-100, and purified by affinity chromatography on columns containing gels substituted with quaternary ammonium groups (for example, immobilized choline carboxymethyl groups). The receptor has a molecular weight of 250,000 daltons and contains two ACh binding sites. When sulfhydryl groups are reduced and the complex is dispersed in the strong ionic detergent sodium dodecyl sulfate, four protein subunits can be separated by polyacrylamide gel electrophoresis. These are polypeptide chains with apparent molecular weights (in daltons) of 39,000 (α), 48,000 (β), 58,000 (γ) and 64,000 (δ). (Disagreement between laboratories involves these values; differences appear to arise because of proteolytic degradation of the polypeptides during isolation.) The two ACh-binding sites are situated on polypeptide α, and the composition of the receptor complex is $\alpha_2\beta\gamma\delta$. The snake venom toxin α-bungarotoxin binds specifically and essentially irreversibly to the receptor, also on the α-subunit. This toxin has been used extensively as a probe for the isolation and characterization of cholinergic receptors in a variety of tissues because it can be radiolabeled with iodine or made fluorescent by derivatization with rhodamine or fluorescein (Figure 10–2).

Current ideas about mechanism suggest that the complex consists of two portions, a *binding component* (described above) and an *ionophore component*. The ionophore is a channel in the membrane through which ions flow. Increased permeability to ions would be the result of a cooperative rearrangement of the subunits brought about by interaction of the binding portion with transmitter molecules. This in turn causes the ionophore to open a wider channel through the membrane, thereby permitting the inflow of ions (Figure 10–3). Accelerated degradation or turnover of AChR in the presence of autoantibodies is thought to cause the neurological disorder myasthenia gravis (see Chapter 12).

Receptors are categorized first by the transmitter substance to which they respond, and then by their behavior with specific drugs (either activation by agonists or inhibition by blocking agents). Further characterization might include a determination of whether specific ion species are involved, as some ionophores are quite specific and will carry only Na^+, or Cl^-, and some are permissive and will allow passage of any cation or anion. This type of characterization is most conveniently done with isolated nervous tissue because the ionic environment can be manipulated experimentally (see Chapter 8). It should be noted that not all receptors for transmitters mediate changes in ionic conductances. An important class of receptors responds by changing the metabolic machinery of the postsynaptic cell. Important examples are those receptors that provoke the intracellular synthesis of the second messengers, cAMP or cyclic guanosine 5'-monophosphate (cGMP).

The mechanism described for the cholinergic receptor explains the activity of that class of receptors which change membrane permeability. Receptors that bring about intracellular metabolic changes are thought in principle to behave in an analogous manner. There are again at least two components involved. One, on the outer surface of the membrane, serves to bind the transmitter substance. The other subunit, *transducer,* rather than forming a channel, activates an enzyme on the inner face of the membrane, which catalyzes the synthesis of a second messenger within the cell. This type of receptor–effector–enzyme complex has been postulated for adenylate cyclase, which synthesizes cAMP from ATP in response to NE.

In addition to specificity subunits (binding components), ionophore subunits (channel components), and transducing subunits (components linking the binding function to a biochemical or enzymatic process), there are indications for regulatory subunits that can control the activity of the other functions. Suggestive evidence for this type of subunit in the receptor for GABA was obtained by studying the binding to nervous tissue of a group of psychoactive drugs, the benzodiazepines [diazepam (Valium) and chlordiazepoxide (Librium) belong to this group]. The biochemical results obtained can be explained by the following hypothesis: the drugs bind to and block a regulatory subunit in the GABA receptor, thereby permitting GABA to interact with its binding site more effectively. These biochemical results are consistent with the pharmacology of the benzodiazepines, which are tranquilizers that are physiologically inhibitory.

Receptors and Neuronal Interactions

The rules by which neurons interact synaptically are important for an understanding of how information is processed by the nervous system. Dale's law, already cited as a guiding hypothesis of the biochemical specificity of neurons, implies that a neuron can release only one transmitter. It is necessary to stress that a neuron may have any number of receptors for a wide variety of transmitter substances. Thus, although a neuron's output is essentially unique, it can be influenced by many inputs. This informational feature is

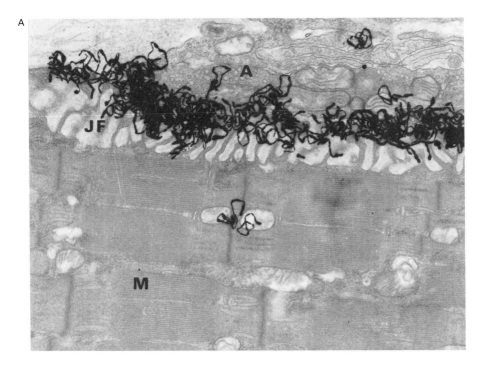

10–2 Labeling the cholinergic receptor with radioactive α-bungarotoxin. **A.** Electron microscope autoradiograph of an endplate from mouse sternomastoid muscle incubated with ^{125}I-labeled α-bungarotoxin until all neurally evoked muscle contractions were blocked. The autoradiograph is overexposed (i.e., the emulsion saturated with developed grains) in order to show that the label is not uniformly distributed throughout the postjunctional membrane but is concentrated near the axonal interface. **JF**, junctional folds; **A**, axon; **M**, muscle. × 21,000. **B.** Autogradiograph of an endplate labeled as in **A** but not overexposed. Note the subneural location of the developed grains, again concentrated at the postjunctional membrane nearest the primary cleft, and not distributed throughout the folds. × 37,500. **Inset:** Section after lead citrate staining (the autoradiograph are not lead stained) emphasizes that postsynaptic membrane densities are concentrated near the muscle surface and dip partly down into the folds **(arrows)**. These densities may be related to the receptor specializations. **JF**, junctional folds; **A**, axon. × 21,000. (Adapted from Fertuck and Salpeter, 1974.)

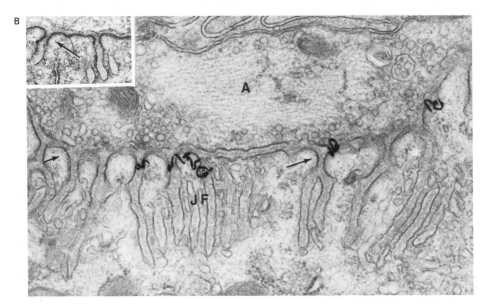

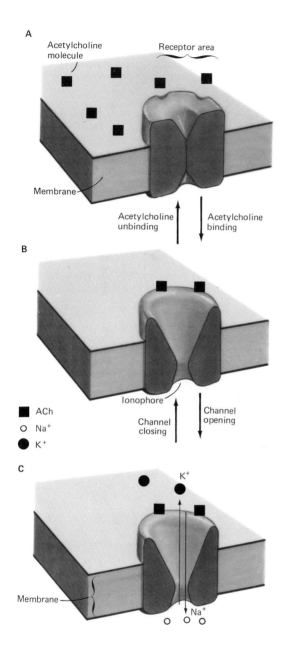

10–3 A model of the nicotinic acetylcholine receptor in the postsynaptic membrane. Two molecules of ACh bind rapidly to the receptor component to form a receptor–ACh complex **(A, B)**. The complex then changes its conformation, and this change results in the opening of a channel (formed by the ionophore component). The channel now allows Na$^+$ and K$^+$ to rush into the cell, causing the postsynaptic changes in membrane potential. Interaction of the binding component of the receptor with transmitter (in this case, ACh) causes the ionophore component to open a wider channel through the membrane, permitting the inflow of ions (in this case, Na$^+$). (Adapted from Stevens, 1979.)

especially important in the central nervous system. In the final common pathway, less complexity may be needed, and consequently, as in vertebrate muscle, the postsynaptic cell is receptive to only one transmitter substance, ACh. This is not true for all muscle, as invertebrate muscle and vertebrate heart and smooth muscle respond to at least two transmitters—one excitatory, the other inhibitory.

Removal of Transmitter from the Synaptic Cleft and the Termination of Synaptic Transmission

The way in which a neuron disposes of transmitter to end the signal is critical to synaptic transmission, because if a released transmitter substance persisted for a very long time, a new signal could not get through. There are three mechanisms by which a neuron may dispose of soluble or unbound transmitter substance:

1. Diffusion
2. Enzymatic degradation
3. Re-uptake.

Diffusion will remove some transmitter substance; it is an important means by which the synaptic cleft gets rid of transmitter.

Enzymatic degradation of transmitter substance is used primarily by the cholinergic system and the extracellular enzyme involved is acetylcholinesterase. While this enzyme is important in synaptic transmission, its chief role is probably to make possible the recapture of choline, which is readily taken up by the neuron from the extracellular space, whereas ACh is not.

There are a number of enzymatic pathways which degrade transmitter substances *within* the neuron and in nonneural tissues of the body. While these are of obvious importance in controlling the concentrations of the transmitter within the neuron or in detoxifying escaped transmitters, they probably are not specifically involved in terminating synaptic transmission. Many of these pathways are important chemically, however: they provide sites for drug action. Thus monamine oxidase inhibitors, which are currently used for the control of hypertension and in psychiatry, potentiate adrenergic transmission. The intracellular enzyme catechol-O-methyltransferase is an important factor in the degradative pathway of biogenic amines. It is found in the cytoplasm of most cells, including neurons, but is most prominent in liver and kidney. Concentrations of this enzyme's metabolites in body fluids serve as an indirect or diagnostic indication of the efficacy of drugs which affect the synthesis or degradation of the biogenic amines in nervous tissue.

Re-uptake of the transmitter substance from the cleft is probably the most widely used mechanism for inactivation of transmitter substance. At synaptic junctions there are high-affinity uptake mechanisms for released transmitter. Specific uptake of choline has already been discussed. Biogenic amines are also taken up into the presynaptic terminal by specific concentrating mechanisms. Certain powerful psychotropic drugs act by blocking these uptake processes (for example, cocaine and imiprimine). Amino acid transmitters are also taken up from the synaptic cleft by glial cells, as well as by neurons, in the central nervous system. For biogenic amines and GABA, application of appropriate drugs that block uptake prolongs and enhances the action of the transmitter. Even with this pharmacological evidence, it is difficult to assess the quantitative importance of uptake (as compared to diffusion) for terminating transmission. Thus, as with other aspects of the biochemistry of synaptic transmission, our understanding is not yet complete.

Selected Readings and References

Cooper, J. R., Bloom, F. E., and Roth, R. H. 1978. The Biochemical Basis of Neuropharmacology. 3rd ed. New York: Oxford University Press.

Hökfelt, T., Johansson, O., Ljungdahl, Å., Lundberg, J. M., and Schultzberg, M. 1980. Peptidergic neurones. Nature (Lond.) 284:515–521.

Karlin, A. 1980. Molecular properties of nicotinic acetylcholine receptors. Cell Surface Rev 6:192–260.

Kelly, R. B., Deutsch, J. W., Carlson, S. S., and Wagner, J. A. 1979. Biochemistry of neurotransmitter release. Annu. Rev. Neurosci. 2:399–446.

Kuhar, M. J., and Murrin, L. C. 1978. Sodium-dependent, high affinity choline uptake. J. Neurochem. 30:15–21.

McGeer, P. L., Eccles, J. C., and McGeer, E. G. 1978. Molecular Neurobiology of the Mammalian Brain. New York: Plenum.

Other References

Dale, H. 1935. Pharmacology and nerve-endings. Proc. R. Soc. Med. 28:319–332.

Eccles, J. C. 1957. The Physiology of Nerve Cells. Baltimore: Johns Hopkins Press.

Ehrlich, P. 1913. Chemotherapeutics: Scientific principles, methods, and results. Lancet 2:445–451.

Falck, B. 1962. Observations on the possibilities of the cellular localization of monoamines by a fluorescence method. Acta Physiol. Scand. Suppl. 197.

Falck, B., Hillarp, N.-Å., Thieme, G., and Torp, A. 1962. Fluorescence of catechol amines and related compounds condensed with formaldehyde. J. Histochem. Cytochem. 10:348–354.

Fertuck, H. C., and Salpeter, M. M. 1974. Localization of acetylcholine receptor by ^{125}I-labeled α-bungarotoxin binding at mouse motor endplates. Proc. Natl. Acad. Sci. U.S.A. 71:1376–1378.

Jan, Y. N., Jan, L. Y., and Kuffler, S. W. 1979. A peptide as a possible transmitter in sympathetic ganglia of the frog. Proc. Natl. Acad. Sci. U.S.A. 76:1501–1505.

See the following papers in E. R. Kandel (ed.), 1977, Handbook of Physiology; The Nervous System, Vol. 1, Part I. Bethesda, Md.: American Physiological Society.

Collier, B. Biochemistry and physiology of cholinergic transmission, pp. 463–492.
Geffen, L. B., and Jarrott, B. Cellular aspects of catecholaminergic neurons, pp. 521–571.
Gershon, M. D. Biochemistry and physiology of serotonergic transmission, pp. 573–623.
Obata, K. Biochemistry and physiology of amino acid transmitters, pp. 625–650.

Kravitz, E. A. 1967. Acetylcholine, γ-aminobutyric acid, and glutamic acid: physiological and chemical studies related to their roles as neurotransmitter agents. In G. C. Quarton, T. Melnechuk, and F. O. Schmitt (eds.), The Neurosciences: A Study Program. New York: Rockefeller University Press, pp. 433–444.

Langley, J. N. 1906. On nerve endings and on special excitable substances in cells. Proc. R. Soc. Lond. B. Biol. Sci. 78:170–194.

Loewi, O. 1960. An autobiographic sketch. Perspect. Biol. Med. 4:3–25.

Mitchell, P. 1979. Keilin's respiratory chain concept and its chemiosmotic consequences. Science (Wash., D.C.) 206:1148–1159.

Otsuka, M., Kravitz, E. A., and Potter, D. D. 1967. Physiological and chemical architecture of a lobster ganglion with particular reference to gamma-aminobutyrate and glutamate. J. Neurophysiol. 30:725–752.

Snyder, S. H. 1980. Brain peptides as neurotransmitters. Science (Wash., D.C.) 209:976–983.

Sternberger, L. A. 1974. Immunocytochemistry. Englewood Cliffs, N.J.: Prentice-Hall.

Stevens, C. F. 1979. The neuron. Sci. Am. 241(3):54–65.

Whittaker, V. P., Michaelson, I. A., and Kirkland, R. J. A. 1964. The separation of synaptic vesicles from nerve-ending particles ("synaptosomes"). Biochem. J. 90:293–303.

James H. Schwartz

Biochemical Control Mechanisms in Synaptic Transmission

11

We have thus far considered the molecular properties of neurons in static terms, but biochemical systems in cells are characteristically highly modulated and under the control of many regulatory processes. In the neuron regulation poses special problems. In addition to regulating the concentration of a particular molecule at a given locus within the cell, the neuron also has to provide for the distribution of materials over substantial distances, and this involves movement of molecules and organelles from one site in the cell to another. In this chapter we shall describe three types of control mechanisms that govern the distribution and amounts of molecules within the neuron: axonal transport, axoplasmic flow, and the control of transmitter biosynthesis.

Three classes of molecules directly participate in the process of synaptic transmission: biosynthetic enzymes, membrane constituents (components of synaptic vesicles, receptor proteins, and the molecules of the high-affinity uptake processes), and the transmitter substance itself. These classes of molecules are metabolized in different ways. Because regions of the neuron are typically differentiated, the region involved in synthesis of a constituent may be distantly separated from the region where that constituent is meant to function. Axonal transport is the principal mechanism by which macromolecules are distributed from their site of synthesis in the cell body. Future synaptic vesicles, proteins involved in high-affinity uptake, and the precursors of receptors are conveyed by fast axonal transport to the regions of the neuron where they are destined to function. In contrast, biosynthetic and other soluble enzymes move from the cell body to the terminal by slow axoplasmic flow.

In addition to spatial or regional aspects, synthesis and metabolism of transmitters have temporal and environmental controlling features. The low molecular weight transmitter substances themselves generally can be formed in all regions of the neuron, unlike their biosynthetic enzymes and the membrane proteins involved in their storage and release. The rate of transmitter synthesis, however, is dependent upon the concentrations of biosynthetic enzymes and substrates (which, in turn, can depend on high-affinity uptake proteins) and on the availability of vesicular depots for storage of the transmitter once synthesized. The rate of transmitter synthesis is regulated by a variety of mechanisms. We will therefore also consider the mechanisms that control transmitter biosynthesis, which ultimately determine the adaptability of the neuron and modify its response and output of transmitter substance.

Axonal Transport and Axoplasmic Flow Control Intracellular Distribution of Materials

Neurons are secretory cells. The biochemical processes underlying synaptic transmission can be understood if the general plan of secretion in other cells is kept in mind. Like gland cells, in which secretory granules are assembled in the region of the Golgi apparatus, neurons have transmitter storage granules (precursors of synaptic vesicles) that are formed in the internal membrane systems in the nerve cell body. In gland cells, the granules must be moved to a particular region of the plasmalemma (for example, the apical region of the gland cell that abuts the lumen of a duct), where exocytosis of the granule's contents occurs. Although formally similar, the process in neurons may appear quite different because of the extreme regional differentiation of the nerve cell. Nerve cells can be schematically divided into cell body (perikaryon), dendrites, axons, and terminals. Typically, these regions are at considerable distances from each other. Consider, for example, a spinal motor-neuron that originates in the sacral region of a 6-ft man that

innervates a toe muscle, or the phrenic nerve of a giraffe. In terms of the secretory process, this separation implies a great distance between that part of the plasmalemma specialized for exocytosis (the active zone of the presynaptic terminal membrane) and the site of origin of the synaptic or secretory vesicle (the endoplasmic reticulum and Golgi apparatus in the perikaryon) (Figure 11–1, step 1).

Once it is recognized that almost all macromolecular synthesis occurs in the perikaryon, the functional significance of rapid *anterograde* (or *orthograde*, away from the cell body) axonal transport becomes obvious. Essentially all membranous subcellular organelles in axons, dendrites, and terminals must originate in the cell body, if not fully assembled, then at least in some precursor form. We are particularly interested in transport at this point because the membranes of synaptic vesicles are synthesized in the cell body and must be brought to the terminals. In the process of exocytosis at nerve terminals, this membrane is recycled many times for reuse in synaptic transmission (Figure 11–1, step 3) (see Chapter 9). Membrane is constantly being renovated by new components arriving from the cell body. At a compensating rate, existing membrane components are removed from the nerve terminals and returned to the cell body for degradation or reuse (Figure 11–1, step 4). Thus, although the neurotransmitter substance itself can be synthesized at the nerve ending, membrane cannot. Therefore, synaptic transmission depends on axonal transport (Figure 11–1, step 2).

Ever since the cell theory became histological dogma, there has been considerable speculation about the factors that maintain the far-flung structure of the neuron. One interesting (though incorrect) theory is that the three-dimensional structure of the neuron is maintained by a hydro- or aerodynamic mechanism: the perikaryon acts as a pressure head which keeps the cell's processes extended. This notion prompted the first modern experiment in axon transport. In 1948, Paul Weiss tied off a nerve and observed that axoplasm accumulated behind the ligature. The amounts accumulated increased with time, and Weiss concluded that axoplasm moves distally at a slow, constant rate from the cell body toward terminals in a process he called *axoplasmic flow.*

Since this discovery, at least two processes have been distinguished, one fast (now named *axonal transport*), which in warm-blooded animals has a rate of about 400 mm/day, and the other slow (axoplasmic flow), with a rate of 0.5–3

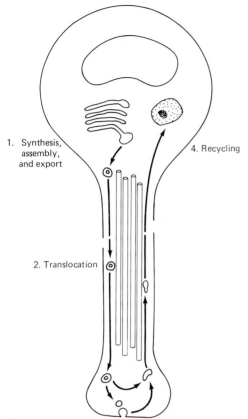

1. Synthesis, assembly, and export

4. Recycling

2. Translocation

3. Maturation and release

11–1 The life history of synaptic vesicles and other membranous organelles involved in synaptic transmission. Proteins and lipids are synthesized and incorporated into membranes within the endoplasmic reticulum and Golgi apparatus of the neuron's cell body. Organelles are then assembled from these components and exported from the cell body into the axon where they are rapidly moved toward terminals by fast axonal transport. Some of the material is deposited along the axon to maintain the axolemma. Synaptic vesicles and their precursors reach the neuron's terminals to participate in the exocytotic release of transmitter substances. The membranes of synaptic vesicles are used many times over in the release process. At random, a small amount of the membrane becomes degraded by lysosomes, and this material is returned to the cell body by fast retrograde axonal transport. The degraded membrane is partly recycled; its residue is progressively accumulated in large, end-stage lysosomes that are characteristic of neuronal cell bodies.

mm/day. (Cold-blooded animals also have fast and slow transport.)

Rapid transport also occurs from nerve endings toward the cell body in the retrograde direction, presumably returning worn out materials from terminals to the cell body either for degradation or for restoration and reuse (Figure 11–1, step *4*). The rate of fast retrograde transport appears to be about one-half to two-thirds that of orthograde transport, but it has been difficult to approach quantitatively. Although a scavenger function for transport in the retrograde direction is its most obvious role, there are other, clinically important physiological roles for movement of materials from nerve endings back to the cell body. It has been suspected that some neurotropic viruses reach the central nervous system by ascending from peripheral nerve terminals to cell bodies by fast retrograde transport. This has been demonstrated for herpes simplex, but is likely also to occur with rabies and polio viruses. Tetanus toxin has been shown to be taken up at nerve endings and to be moved by fast retrograde transport to the cell body. Another interesting example is the fast retrograde transport of nerve growth factor, of which we shall learn more in Chapter 42. Retrograde transport provides one possible physiological route for an exogenous trophic substance to reach its target. There is considerable speculation in developmental neurobiology concerning a possible signaling role of retrograde transport in informing the cell body (the site of macromolecular synthesis) about events that occur at the distant ends of axonal processes.

As anterograde transport can be viewed as an analogue to a first step in the secretory process, so retrograde transport may be an analogue of the last step of secretion: the recovery and turnover of membranes by lysosomes. All of the components that are transported in the retrograde direction obtain access to the cell by being taken up into terminals. Particles and substances not bound are not taken up to any great extent. Adsorbed components are readily engulfed and packaged into lysosomes in terminals that presumably function normally to return used membrane components back to the cell body. Unadsorbed particles ("fluid-phase" particles) can also be taken up into terminals by pinocytosis and transported back to the cell body within lysosomes. Experimentally, the most familiar example of an unadsorbed particle is the enzyme horseradish peroxidase (HRP), which is useful histochemically because its position within tissue sections prepared either for light or electron microscopy can be localized histochemically by the distribution of the enzyme's reaction product (Figure 11–2).

Although both adsorbed and fluid-phase materials are apparently transported by the same axonal system, the amounts transported are quite

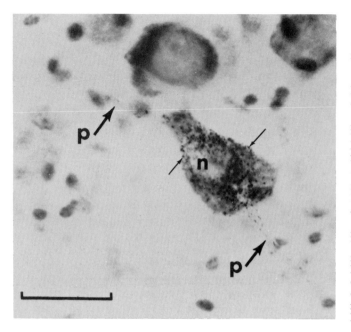

11–2 Use of fast retrograde axonal transport to study the axon distribution of a neuron in the central nervous system. This photomicrograph is taken from an experiment investigating the sources of afferents to the inferior parietal lobule of the cerebral cortex (association cortex, Brodmann's area 7) in the rhesus monkey. A cell body in the magnocellular nucleus of the basal forebrain was found to be labeled 2 days after injection of horseradish peroxidase into the cortex. The HRP, taken up by the cell's terminals in the cortex, was transported in the retrograde direction, to mark the cell body. **Small arrows** indicate HRP reaction product in the cell body; **large arrows** indicate processes (**p**) in which some reaction product can be seen. The neuron's nucleus (**n**) does not contain any label. The bar is about 25 μm. This neuron in the limbic forebrain is part of a neural pathway that H. G. M. Kuypers has suggested provides a channel by which the forebrain can influence directly the cortex in accordance with motivational and emotional states. (From Divac, LaVail, Rakic, and Winston, 1977.)

different. Much more specifically adsorbed material is transported. Less HRP is taken up and transported, but, unlike transport of specifically absorbed substances, these small amounts of the fluid-phase material are dramatically increased during nerve stimulation. This change in uptake and transport reflects the increase in exocytosis–pinocytosis that occurs during the process of synaptic transmission (described in Chapter 9).

Techniques for Observing Transport

Destination Analysis. There have been two major approaches to the experimental observation of transport. In the first approach the parameters of the process are inferred from the time at which material from one region of the neuron arrives at another region. Weiss's ligature experiments described above are a good example of this approach. Several weeks after a nerve had been ligatured, axoplasm ballooned out proximal to the constriction. From the amount of material accumulated, the time of observation, and the distance from cell body to ligature, the rate of flow was estimated. Later, the process of fast orthograde transport was revealed when some cellular components were found to accumulate proximal to the ligature much more rapidly. The process of fast retrograde transport was also de-

11–3 Fast transport of radioactively labeled proteins in the optic system of the goldfish. Fast transport of proteins in axons was measured after administering a radioactively labeled amino acid to the retina of a goldfish, which contains the cell bodies of optic neurons. Sections of the optic tectum, where the neurons terminate, were obtained at various times and covered with a photographic emulsion. The greatest number of silver grains develop in the emulsion overlying areas of the brain that contain the highest concentration of radioactively labeled material. In this autoradiograph, made by Bernard W. Agranoff of the University of Michigan 24 hours after the injection of the amino acid into the eye, the brightness of the area at the right (the tectum) indicates that much of the protein that took up the labeled material while being synthesized in the cell bodies of retinal neurons had been delivered to terminals. Bar is 1 mm. (From Springer et al., 1977.)

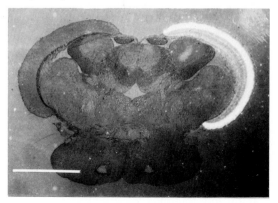

tected in this manner, since material also accumulated on the distal side of the constriction. Another example of destination analysis is the study of the optic system of the goldfish. Here material synthesized in the retina after intraocular injection of radioactive precursors is monitored at its destination, the projections of the optic nerve in the brain (tectum) (Figure 11–3).

Direct Kinetic Analysis. Direct microscopic analysis of the movement of unidentified large particles (presumably mitochondria) in living axons in culture was initiated as early as 1920, but has more recently been used to examine movement of particles in a variety of nerves. Continuous direct microscopic observation has revealed that large particles move in a saltatory fashion in both the orthograde and the retrograde direction.

One of the most useful kinetic preparations is the sciatic nerve. Transport, primarily of labeled proteins synthesized in dorsal root ganglion cells after injection of radioactive amino acids, is counted in uniform sequential segments taken along the nerve. Transport profiles showing the distribution of labeled protein with distance along the nerve are obtained from different animals at various times after the injection (Figure 11–4). Using this system it has been shown that fast axonal transport depends critically on oxida-

11–4 Distribution of radioactive proteins along the sciatic nerve of the cat at various times after injection of ^{3}H-leucine into dorsal root ganglia in the lumbar region of the spinal cord. Radioactivity is measured by scintillation counting of sequential segments of the sciatic nerve. In order to display the transport curves from the sciatic nerve of the cats killed at 2, 4, 6, 8, and 10 hours after the injection together in one figure, several ordinate scales had to be used. Note that they are in logarithmic units. Large amounts of labeled protein remain in the ganglion cell bodies (**G**) where they were synthesized just after the injection of the ^{3}H-amino acid. With time, some of the protein moves out along axons in the sciatic nerve. Note that the advancing front of the labeled protein (**arrows**) is displaced progressively farther from the cell body with time. The velocity of transport can be calculated from the distances displaced at the various times; from experiments of this kind, Sidney Ochs has found that the rate of fast transport is constant at 410 mm/day at body temperature. (Adapted from Ochs, 1972.)

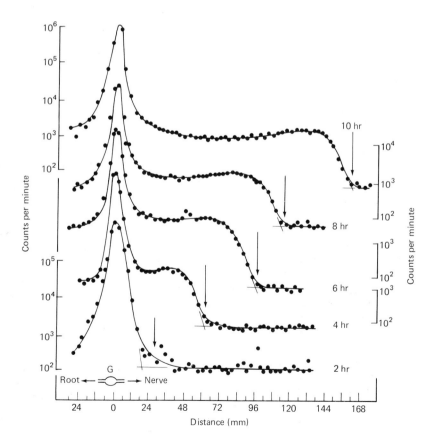

tive metabolism, is not affected by inhibitors of protein synthesis (once the precursor is incorporated), and, in fact, is independent of the cell body, since it occurs in nerves actually severed from the ganglion.

Fast Transport and Neuroanatomical Tracing

In the past decade, use of the phenomenon of fast axonal transport has revolutionized neuroanatomy. Previously, the projections of neurons were ascertained by cutting axons, allowing degeneration to occur, and then locating the position of the affected cell bodies and process. These studies (described in Chapter 13) relied on difficult and sometimes unreliable histochemical staining procedures. Making use of anterograde transport, the neuroanatomist can localize the axons and terminals of specific nerve cell bodies by finding the accumulation of labeled protein autoradiographically soon after administering to those cell bodies labeled amino acids (precursors of protein), certain labeled sugars (fucose or amino sugars, precursors of glycoprotein), or specific transmitter substances (Figure 11–5). Similarly, the location of the cell bodies belonging to specific terminals can be identified by making use of particles that are readily taken up at nerve terminals and transported in the retrograde direction to cell bodies. HRP has been most widely used for this type of study because it readily undergoes retrograde transport, and its reaction product is conveniently localized histochemically (Figure 11–2).

There are several other methods for localizing neurons in the brain and for tracing their axonal connections without creating lesions in the nervous system. The uptake of radioactive transmitter substances by nerve terminals mediated by specific high-affinity uptake mechanisms (see Chapter 10) is often selective enough for autoradiographic identification of nerve endings by transmitter type. A similar strategy is also used with radiolabeled ligands to identify neurons containing specific receptors. Many of the interesting transmitter substances or specific receptor ligands have primary amines as functional groups and therefore can be fixed in place with the aldehyde fixatives (formaldehyde or glutaraldehyde) used for preparing tissue for both light and electron microscopy. An important and new autoradiographic procedure (that so far can be used only in the light microscope) makes use of ^{14}C-deoxy-glucose. This analogue of glucose is phosphorylated by hexokinase within nerve cells but cannot be metabolized further. Increased functioning results in marked enhancement of energy metabolism at the site of activity, presumably by the numerous mitochondria in those terminals where synaptic transmission is occurring. Thus, in frozen tissue sections, deoxyglucose can light up autoradiographically an entire functioning neuronal pathway. The analogue accumulates because, unlike glucose, it cannot enter into the glycolytic pathway; once phosphorylated, deoxyglucose cannot escape from the neuron as it is no longer permeable to the external membrane.

Characterization of Transported Materials

Biochemical, histochemical, and electron-microscopic analyses show that material moving along the axon by rapid transport is mainly particulate, consisting primarily of membranous organelles. Considerable evidence indicates that synaptic vesicles (or their precursors) involved in the storage and release of the neurotransmitters are functionally a most important constituent of fast axonal transport. Membrane-associated proteins (for example, acetylcholinesterase and dopamine β-hydroxylase) also move by rapid transport.

Material moving in the retrograde direction is also particulate. The organelles, however, differ from those moving in the orthograde direction in that they are somewhat larger, on the average. Consequently, in experiments in which transport is studied in thin living nerve fibers using light microscopy (with Nomarski or phase-contrast optics), those particles visualized are seen principally to be moving in the retrograde direction. This is something of an illusion, however, because synaptic vesicles and other small particles moving toward nerve endings are too small to be resolved in the light microscope. The large particles have been identified as lysosomes and mitochondria.

Slow transport occurs only in the anterograde direction, carrying predominantly soluble macromolecules and small molecules that are not packaged within vesicles. These include most of the biosynthetic enzymes for neurotransmitters. In addition, axoplasmic flow also contains the fibrillar constituents of axoplasm (or their subunits): these include neural actin and myosin, the components of neurofibrils, and tubulin. These

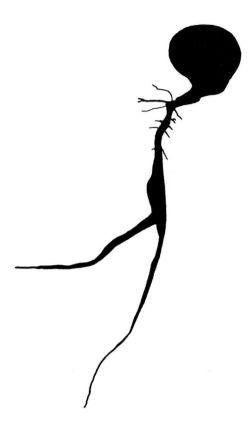

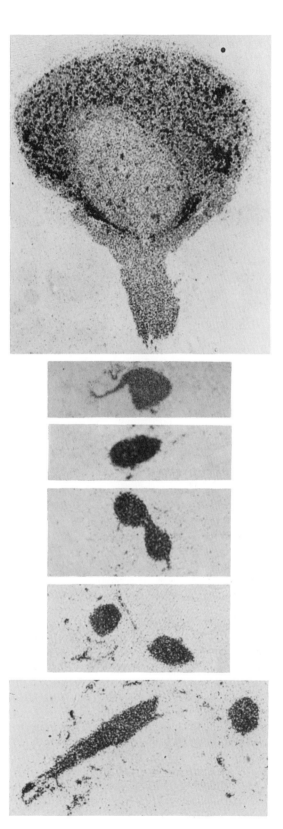

11–5 Use of a radioactive serotonin to study the fast axonal transport of transmitter storage vesicles in a giant neuron of the marine mollusk, *Aplysia.* Invertebrate neurons are experimentally useful for biochemical studies because of their large size. When ^{3}H-serotonin is injected into the cell body of a giant serotonergic neuron (measuring about 250 μm in diameter), the labeled transmitter is taken up into vesicles. These are exported from the cell body and move along the axons of the neuron by fast transport. The figure shows a montage of serial sections that have been coated with photographic emulsion for autoradiography. **At left:** diagram of the cell body and main axon that is approximately 1 mm long. The main axon bifurcates into axon branches that are approximately equal in diameter. Silver grains reveal the location of storage vesicles within the neuron 3 hr after injection of the labeled transmitter. From the micrographs it can be estimated that the label has moved at least five cell body diameters out along the axons at this time. A more precise rate of transport can be measured by scintillation counting of sequential segments as already described for the sciatic nerve experiment in Figure 11–4. In this neuron from a poikilothermic invertebrate, serotonergic vesicles were found to move at a rate of 130 mm/day at room temperature. (Autoradiographs by L. J. Shkolnik and J. H. Schwartz; camera lucida drawing by K. R. Weiss.)

proteins constitute a substantial proportion of the neuroplasm: actin and tubulin alone account for more than 10% of the proteins in neural tissue. They are thought to be important for providing structure and may also be involved directly in the mechanism of axonal transport.

Hypotheses of Transport Mechanisms

The mechanisms of transport are not yet known. There are two popular theories of fast axonal transport. In one, it is suggested that microtubules provide an essentially stationary and passive track on which specific organelles move in a stepwise fashion (Figure 11–6A). Translocation is the result of a local (but sequential) energy-dependent reaction, involving either conformational changes occurring as a result of the interaction of the organelle with a subunit of the track (rachette mechanism), or a sliding-filament mechanism in which the tracks function as actin and the organelles contain myosin.

In the other theory, it is postulated that organelles are moved *between* tracks by intratubular convection. Formally, this hypothesis involves specific channels within the axon through which organelles are translocated essentially by peristalsis or by microstreams of axoplasm (perhaps moved by hypothetical cilia) (Figure 11–6B). In support of this mechanism are morphological studies which suggest that the axoplasmic reticulum is continuous from the cell body to the nerve terminal. Always considered an extention of the smooth endoplasmic reticulum of the perikaryon, this tubular membrane system in the axon, if indeed continuous, could provide the specific channels postulated.

There is strong pharmacological evidence that microtubules are involved in transport: the antimitotic alkaloids, colchicine and vinblastin, which are known to disrupt microtubules, interfere with fast transport. Neural actin and myosin are likely candidates for providing motive force in the transport process, but conclusive experimental evidence for their participation is lacking thus far. Although other hypotheses can make use of microtubules and the contractile proteins, a bone and muscle mechanism now seems attractive.

The postulated muscle-like filament would be attached at one end to the organelle to be moved, and at the other to a microtubule serving as skeletal support running in the long direction in the axon. Shortening of the filament, like con-

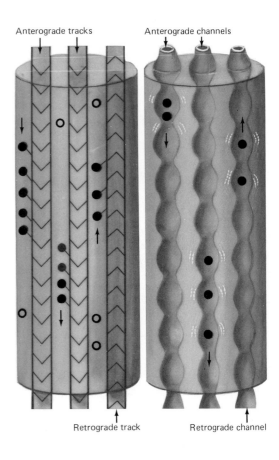

● Moving organelles

○ Stationary organelles

11–6 Two possible mechanisms of fast axonal transport. In the first (**A**), organelles move along continuous tracks through the axoplasm when attached by filaments. Unattached organelles are stationary. One end of each filament is linked to the organelle being moved and the other to the track. The chemical makeup of the tracks and filaments is not certain, but it might be microtubules and actin. In the second (**B**) mechanism, organelles are moved passively within tubular channels of a continuous smooth axoplasmic reticulum, possibly by peristalsis. In both track and channel mechanisms, the movement is limited to one direction; the tracks or channels are polar, some going in the anterograde direction, and the rest in the retrograde direction.

traction of actomyosin, could result in the displacement of the organelle along the microtubule. Sequential or continued displacement might be achieved if the organelle reattached to the next filament, and the process repeated. Alternatively, a vesicle might retain its association with the same filament throughout its passage. If so, the muscle-like filament could make new insertions on the microtubule as the complex moves along the cytoskeletal element.

The mechanism of slow transport is quite different. Unlike the fast process, it is dependent on the cell body and requires the synthesis of bulk constituents. It can occur only in the anterograde direction.

Transport, both fast and slow, appears to be independent of the electrical activity of the neuron. Although there are changes in rates and amounts of transport during development and in response to injury, the functional activity of a neuron has not been shown to influence transport.

Transmitter Biosynthesis Is Controlled by Three Mechanisms

The amount of transmitter substance a neuron can release is important to the functioning of a synapse. Neuronal plasticity (in which synaptic activity is altered by previous experience or activity) often involves changes in amount of transmitter released at the plastic synapse. One way in which the neuron might change the amount of transmitter released is by modifying its rate of synthesis. There are three formal mechanisms by which the rate of a biochemical pathway can be altered.

1. Alter the availability of substrates to the pathway.
2. Inhibit or stimulate the activity of enzymes (usually the rate-limiting ones) in the pathway. Often the end-product of the pathway is the governing element; this is called *feedback* or *end-product inhibition*.
3. Increase the synthesis of enzymes (usually the rate-limiting ones); this is called *induction*.

It should be evident from the discussion on the regional differentiation of the neuron that any *rapid* changes in transmitter concentration at synapses cannot involve the synthesis of new enzyme. Because the synapses are separated from the cell body and materials must be moved over relatively great distances, changes in protein synthesis are effective only after considerable delay. In a warm-blooded animal it takes about 18 hr to move an organelle 1 ft by fast transport, and most transmitter biosynthetic enzymes move by slow transport, which is at least 100 times slower.

We shall examine two pathways to illustrate our current understanding of how neurons modulate their content of neurotransmitter substances: one in the noradrenergic neuron, and the other in the cholinergic neuron.

Catecholamine Biosynthesis

The formation of norepinephrine is extraordinarily plastic. Under normal conditions, the amount of norepinephrine available for release remains constant in nonadrenergic terminals despite moderate variation in functional activity. This steady level of transmitter is regulated by *short-term* mechanisms. On the other hand, under stressful conditions that result in intense sympathetic activity (for example, cold, forceful immobilization of the animal, and the administration of the drug reserpine), *long-term* processes come into play. Both types of regulatory mechanisms have been studied in greatest detail in the autonomic nervous system (adrenergic neurons of sympathetic ganglion cells and in the adrenal medulla), but most of the processes have also been shown to occur in the central nervous system (principally in neurons whose cell bodies are situated in the locus ceruleus).

Short-term regulatory mechanisms involve modulation of the first enzyme in the pathway, tyrosine hydroxylase, and occur primarily at nerve terminals. The activity (V_{max}) of the hydroxylase in extracts has been shown to be about 50 times lower than that of aromatic amino acid decarboxylase and 1000 times lower than that of dopamine β-hydroxylase. In addition to being dependent on the concentration of the substrate, tyrosine, the enzyme also requires a pteridine cofactor, for example, tetrahydrobiopterin. In the adrenal medulla, the concentration of tetrahydrobiopterin is one-half that of the enzyme's Michaelis constant (20 μM); consequently, tyrosine hydroxylase activity there should normally be limited by the availability of the cofactor. Indeed, addition of a pteridine to isolated sympathetic tissue has been found to increase the enzyme's activity. At normal plasma concentrations of tyrosine, tyrosine hydroxylase is saturated, indicating that availability of the substrate is not a critical factor under physiological conditions. Enzyme activity is reversibly inhibited, however, by norepinephrine and dopamine, the end-products of the pathway. These feedback inhibitors may act by competing with the binding of the oxidized form of the pteridine cofactor. Two other mechanisms may be important in regulating the activity of tyrosine hydroxylase. Cyclic AMP-dependent protein phosphorylation of the hydroxylase has been shown to increase the enzyme's affinity for both tyrosine and the pteridine cofactor and diminish the effects of end-product inhibition. Finally, tyrosine hydroxylase activity is influenced by the enzyme's subcellular localization. If free in the cytoplasm, it is less active than when bound to membranes. Fractionation studies have revealed that most of the enzyme is soluble, but some is recovered bound to membrane, and transient association may occur within nerve terminals.

Thus a rather large number of possible mechanisms have been described that could account for the observed short-term regulation of catecholamine biosynthesis. All of the mechanisms have been postulated to influence tyrosine hydroxylase in the animal, and all of them may in fact be controlling factors under different physiological circumstances.

Whereas the short-term increases in production of norepinephrine occur within minutes, and are rapidly reversible, severe stress to the animal results in a long-term change which takes days to occur. These changes are observed within hours in cell bodies (in the autonomic nervous system, in sympathetic ganglia and adrenal medulla; in the central nervous system, in the locus ceruleus). Only much later (several days to 1 week) are they seen in terminals. Increased production of transmitter in this instance has been shown to result from the induction of new enzyme protein. This has been shown immunologically with antiserum prepared against purified tyrosine hydroxylase, both in the central and autonomic nervous systems. Synthesis of the hydroxylase, like all proteins, occurs in the cell body. The delay between the provoking environmental stimulus and the expression of the effect at synaptic terminals is a reflection of the time it takes for the newly synthesized enzyme to reach nerve terminals by axoplasmic flow. Stimulation

of synthesis of the hydroxylase is specific: the formation of other proteins, including aromatic amino acid decarboxylase and monoamine oxidase, is not affected.

ACh Biosynthesis

In contrast to the process described above, choline acetyltransferase appears to be controlled through the availability of its substrate, choline. The concentration of choline at nerve terminals depends upon a high-affinity uptake process which accumulates choline from the extracellular space. This process is present only in cholinergic axons and terminals; it is absent in cell bodies and neurons that are not cholinergic. Recent evidence indicates that uptake of choline by this process—which depends on the presence of Na^+, as do many other uptake processes—is enhanced when cholinergic terminals are depolarized. Coupling of choline uptake and depolarization, perhaps through an effect on the conductance of Na^+, would serve to bring more substrate into the neuron when it is most needed: depolarization triggers the synaptic release of the transmitter. Unlike the situation in the catecholamine pathway, no changes in the amount of enzyme protein have been described in response to increased utilization of cholinergic pathways.

Selected Readings and References

Schwartz, J. H. 1980. The transport of substances in nerve cells. Sci. Am. 242(4):152–171.

Tuček, S. 1978. Acetylcholine Synthesis in Neurons. London: Chapman and Hall.

Usdin, E., Weiner, N., and Youdim, M. B. H. (eds.). 1977. Structure and Function of Monoamine Enzymes. New York: Marcel Dekker.

Other References

Divac, I., LaVail, J. H., Rakic, P., and Winston, K. R. 1977. Heterogeneous afferents to the inferior parietal lobule of the rhesus monkey revealed by the retrograde transport method. Brain Res. 123:197–207.

Kievit, J., and Kuypers, H. G. J. M. 1975. Basal forebrain and hypothalamic connections to frontal and parietal cortex in the rhesus monkey. Science (Wash., D.C.) 187:660–662.

Grafstein, B., and Forman, D. S. 1980. Intracellular transport in neurons. Physiol. Rev. 60:1167–1283.

Ochs, S. 1972. Fast transport of materials in mammalian nerve fibers. Science (Wash., D. C.) 176:252–260

Schwartz, J. H. 1979. Axonal transport: components, mechanisms, and specificity. Annu. Rev. Neurosci. 2:467–504.

Springer, A. D., Heacock, A. M., Schmidt, J. T., and

Agranoff, B. W. 1977. Bilateral tectal innervation by regenerating optic nerve fibers in goldfish: a radio-autographic, electrophysiological and behavioral study. Brain Res. 128:417–427.

Weiss, P., and Hiscoe, H. B. 1948. Experiments on the mechanism of nerve growth. J. Exp. Zool. 107:315–395.

Lewis P. Rowland

Diseases of Chemical Transmission at the Nerve–Muscle Synapse: Myasthenia Gravis and Related Syndromes

12

In previous chapters we have described the synaptic structures that participate in chemical transmission and have analyzed the electrical and molecular events that occur both in the presynaptic nerve terminal and at the receptor in the postsynaptic membrane of the target organ. This is the first chapter in which a disease is discussed to illustrate a specific function. Several human diseases are due to disordered function of chemical synapses. The best understood of these diseases is myasthenia gravis, a disorder of function at the synapse between the cholinergic motor neuron and skeletal muscle. Scientists have probed synaptic transmission experimentally, using pharmacological and electrophysiological tools. Myasthenia gravis is a disease that illuminates the normal process.

Myasthenia gravis is an autoimmune syndrome caused by antibodies to the acetylcholine receptor, which reduce the number of functional receptors or otherwise impede the interaction of ACh with the receptors. This results in muscle weakness that has special characteristics:

1. The weakness is especially likely to affect cranial muscles (eyelids, eye muscles, oropharyngeal muscles) as well as limb muscles.
2. Unlike any other disease of muscle or nerve, there is a tendency for the weak-

ness to vary in severity within the course of a single day, from day to day, or for longer periods (remissions and exacerbations).

3. There are no conventional signs of denervation.
4. The weakness is partially reversed by cholinergic drugs.

To understand this disease, it is useful to trace the historical evolution of ideas concerning it in two periods: the first, from the delineation of the syndrome in the 19th century to about 1970; and the second, from the first steps in the development of new ideas in 1973 to the present. During these two periods it is important to follow two themes that are intertwined—one physiological, the other immunological.

Essential Characteristics Define the Disease in the First Period (1865–1970)

By 1900, the essential clinical characteristics of the disease had been described. At that time, diseases were defined primarily in terms of postmortem lesions rather than in physiological or etiological terms. The gross and histological appearance of the brain, spinal cord, peripheral nerves, and muscle seemed normal in myasthenia; the disease was therefore considered a disorder of function or physiology.

Physiological Approach: A Disorder of Neuromuscular Transmission

By the mid-1930s, two discoveries in England provided the information essential to identify myasthenia as a disease of neuromuscular transmission. First, Dale, Feldberg, and Vogt applied the theory of neurohumoral or chemical synaptic transmission to the neuromuscular junction, specifically identifying ACh as the transmitter. Second, Mary Walker demonstrated that physostigmine and neostigmine were effective in treating the symptoms of myasthenia gravis. These drugs are inhibitors of acetylcholinesterase, the enzyme that hydrolyzes ACh and thereby terminates its action.

In the years between 1945 and 1960, at Johns Hopkins Hospital, A. M. Harvey and several illustrious colleagues established the basis of the physiological disorder. When a human motor nerve is stimulated electrically at rates of 2–

5/sec, the amplitude of the action potential evoked in muscle, which represents the sum of many muscle fiber action potentials, remains constant in normal individuals but the amplitude decreases rapidly in myasthenia. This abnormality resembles the abnormality induced in normal individuals by d-tubocurarine (curare), and is reversed by neostigmine.

The myasthenic abnormality might be explained by one of three possibilities: (1) cholinesterase activity in myasthenia is excessively high; (2) the motor nerve terminals release inadequate amounts of ACh; or (3) the postjunctional receptor is blocked by an endogenous curarelike factor. For several reasons, a curarelike factor seemed most likely. However, in 1964, Elmqvist, Thesleff, and their associates reported what seemed to be the definitive microelectrode study of human intercostal muscle. These Swedish neurophysiologists found that the amplitude of miniature end-plate potentials was greatly reduced in myasthenia. Prolonged washing failed to remove any curarelike substance. Application of K^+ caused the release of a normal amount of ACh, indicating that there was no abnormality of release mechanisms. Similarly, the store of ACh was normal. Depolarization of the end-plate by the ACh agonists, carbachol or decamethonium, was also normal, implying normal postjunctional responses. Because these tests did not indicate that the response of the postsynaptic receptor was reduced, they concluded that myasthenia is due to subnormal amounts of ACh in each quantum released. The abnormally low amounts of ACh might be explained either by defective binding of ACh in each vesicle or by the presence of some false transmitter in the vesicles.

Immunological Approach: An Autoimmune Disease

Soon after the clinical syndrome had been identified, it was recognized that benign tumors of the thymus occur in about 15% of adult patients with myasthenia. In 1939, Alfred Blalock first reported improvement of myasthenia after removal of a thymoma. After World War II, he and A. M. Harvey systematically performed thymectomy on patients with the disease and initiated what has now become standard therapy. (There has never been a controlled trial of thymectomy, but it is generally agreed that about 66% of patients improve after surgery, and that patients with thymoma do not do as well as those without the tumor.)

Why these tumors are associated with myasthenia and why thymectomy is beneficial remained mysteries because the immunological role of the thymus was not established until 1960. By that time, Simpson, a neurologist in Scotland, suggested that myasthenia is due to immunological abnormality because the disease frequently occurs in patients who also have other presumably autoimmune diseases, such as rheumatoid arthritis. The strongest experimental evidence indicating that an antibody might be involved was provided at Columbia University College of Physicians and Surgeons by William Nastuk and Arthur Strauss, who was then a medical student. Using the indirect immunofluorescence method they demonstrated antibodies to muscle striations in the serum of about one-third of all patients with myasthenia, and in almost all patients with both myasthenia and thymoma. Serum that reacted with muscle also reacted with thymus, presumably with *myoid* (striated) cells in the gland.

It was soon evident, however, that the muscle antibodies of Strauss and Nastuk could not be the immediate cause of symptoms for the following reasons: (1) These antibodies were not present in all patients. (2) There was no correlation between titer of antibodies and severity of symptoms. (3) Antibodies that bind to striations in muscle could not explain the abnormality of junctional transmission. (4) There was no correlation between the presence or absence of antibodies and the occurrence of neonatal myasthenia in infants born to myasthenic mothers. (5) Some patients with thymoma had antibodies but no symptoms of myasthenia and no evidence of latent myasthenia (no abnormal response to repetitive stimulation and no sensitivity to *d*-tubocurarine). (6) It was (and still is) not known what components of the skeletal muscle fibril those antibodies react with; some seem to react with A-band proteins (myosin), others with the I-band (actin, tropomyosin), and still others with surface or internal membranes.

Therefore, in 1969, myasthenia seemed to be an ill-defined autoimmune disease and the best evidence suggested that the physiological disorder was presynaptic, despite the lingering impression that there was a curarelike postsynaptic abnormality. This uncomfortable and confused state of affairs was rapidly reversed in the next few years.

Identification of Antibodies to AChR Initiates the Modern Period (1973–Present)

With the isolation and characterization of the nicotinic AChR, the modern concept of myasthenia emerged. Langley and Dale, in England, and Nachmansohn, at Columbia University, had proposed that ACh exerts postsynaptic effects by interacting with a specific receptor, but numerous early attempts failed to isolate the receptor. In 1967, two Taiwanese chemists, Chang and Lee, were concerned with a local public health problem—poisonous snakebite. One of the toxins they isolated from snake venom, α-bungarotoxin, was found to interact essentially irreversibly with the motor end-plate, thereby causing paralysis. By 1971, Miledi and Potter, in England, and Changeux and Lee, in France, had used the toxin to isolate and purify AChR from the electric organ of the electric eel or *Torpedo* (see Chapter 10). In 1973, Fambrough and Drachman used ^{125}I-α-bungarotoxin in an autoradiographic study of human end-plates; in myasthenia, the number of reacting sites was significantly decreased (Figure 12–1). In the same year, Patrick and Lindstrom of the Salk Institute injected AChR purified from eel electroplax into rabbits, intending to use antibodies to study the properties of eel AChR. When the expected antibodies appeared the rabbits became "myasthenic." They became weak, and the weakness was reversed by edrophonium or neostigmine. The animals were

12–1 Drawing of autoradiograms of human muscle fibers after incubation in ^{125}I-labeled α-bungarotoxin. **A.** Normal fibers show a dense accumulation of silver grains over a limited junctional area and a paucity of grains outside this region. **B.** In myasthenic fibers the number of grains is markedly reduced, but grains are mostly localized over the end-plate region, indicating a reduced number of functional reacting sites. (Adapted from Fambrough, Drachman, and Satyamurti, 1973.)

A

B

sensitive to *d*-tubocurarine, and the response of the summated action potentials in muscle decreased with repetitive stimulation, as it does in human patients with myasthenia gravis.

Between 1973 and 1975, workers in several laboratories demonstrated that all essential characteristics of human myasthenia gravis were reproduced in experimental autoimmune myasthenia gravis. In addition to the observations of Lindstrom and Patrick already listed, these included reduced amplitude of the miniature endplate potentials, simplification of postjunctional folds, loss of AChR from the tips of postjunctional folds, and deposition of antibody (immunoglobulin G, IgG) and complement at postjunctional sites. AChR from electric eel or *Torpedo* induced experimental autoimmune myasthenia gravis in guinea pigs, rats, goats, and monkeys. In inbred rats, antibodies to syngenic AChR were demonstrated and the disease could be transferred by thymus-derived (T) cells. Thymectomy in early life prevented induction of experimental autoimmune myasthenia gravis.

After the demonstration of experimental autoimmune myasthenia gravis, similar antibodies to AChR were demonstrated in human myasthenia by several methods: serum from patients (1) interferes with the binding of ^{125}I-α-bungarotoxin to purified AChR, (2) fixes complement when incubated with purified eel AChR, (3) prevents interaction of α-bungarotoxin with human AChR in frozen muscle sections in a peroxidase-immunocytochemical reaction, and (4) binds to ^{125}I-α-bungarotoxin–labeled human AChR, or similarly labeled AChR from denervated rat muscle, as demonstrated by a precipitin reaction when the complex is precipitated by anti-human IgG. By use of this precipitation technique and human AChR as antigen, antibodies were demonstrated in 75–94% of patients in different studies. When thymus cells from patients were cultured, antibodies against AChR were produced in the culture.

The idea that the human antibodies actually cause the symptoms of myasthenia was suggested by several observations: Drachman and his co-workers at Johns Hopkins showed that repeated injection of human myasthenic serum into mice reproduced electrophysiological abnormalities and reduced the number of α-bungarotoxin–binding sites in skeletal muscle. Antibodies were found in infants with neonatal myasthenia; as the clinical syndrome abated, the level of antibodies declined. In adults, drainage of lymph from the

thoracic lymph duct improved symptoms, which recurred when the lymph fluid was returned to the patient, but not when cells were replaced. Symptoms improved and antibody levels declined when patients were subjected to *plasmapheresis,* a procedure in which blood is removed from a patient, cells are separated from plasma, and then the cells are returned to the patient but the plasma is discarded. Furthermore, clinically typical myasthenia seemed to be inordinately frequent in patients taking penicillamine (usually to treat rheumatoid arthritis); these patients also had antibodies to AChR. When penicillamine therapy was discontinued, the myasthenic symptoms remitted and the antibodies disappeared.

Finally, in 1976, Albuquerque and his associates at the University of Maryland resolved the electrophysiological difficulties of the Elmqvist–Thesleff experiments. Repeating the intercostal muscle studies with improved techniques, they found decreased postjunctional receptor responsiveness in myasthenic muscle.

Unsolved Problems Remain

The central role of antibodies to AChR in the pathogenesis of myasthenia seems to be established, so much so that myasthenia is now the prototype of human autoimmune disease. Nevertheless, there are important unsolved problems.

1. It is not known how the process starts, that is, *what initiates the production of antibodies* to AChR. One possibility is that a persistent viral infection could alter surface-membrane properties, rendering them immunogenic.

2. It is not known *how the antibodies cause symptoms*. Simple blockade of ACh-binding sites on the receptor seems improbable because the antibodies clearly react with sites on the antigen other than the α-bungarotoxin–binding site (and therefore the ACh-binding site); this property is actually the basis of the immunoprecipitation test to detect the antibodies. Steric hindrance of the interaction of ACh and its receptor might play a role. The most likely possibility is that the antibodies cause increased turnover of AChR (and a decreased number of functioning sites).

3. Circulating antibodies cannot be demonstrated in all patients; when they are present there is *no strict relationship between antibody titer and severity of symptoms*. This was dramatically emphasized by a woman who recovered

from myasthenia and was in complete remission when she became pregnant. The mother had very high levels of antibodies although she was asymptomatic; the infant had both high antibody levels and severe symptoms. A similar situation can be produced in experimental animals. As already described, experimental autoimmune myasthenia gravis is produced by immunizing animals with the native receptor. Immunization with *denatured* AChR, however, results in the formation of high titers of antibody but no symptoms of experimental autoimmune myasthenia gravis.

4. The *role of the thymus* remains uncertain, and it is not clear why, when improvement occurs after thymectomy, the improvement may be delayed for months or years. It is not clear whether thymectomy removes the cells that produce antibody, the antigenic stimulus, both, or neither.

5. If the disease is due to circulating antibodies, it is not clear *why some muscles should be affected and others spared.*

6. The *nature of remissions and exacerbations* is not known.

7. *Abnormal lymphocyte responses* to AChR have also been identified in human myasthenia, but the role of altered cell-mediated immunity is uncertain.

8. The *relationship of the antibodies to AChR and the striation-binding antibodies* of Nastuk and Strauss is uncertain.

Therapy

Despite the truly revolutionary impact of the recent immunological advances, treatment is still a problem, although progress has been considerable. Twenty-five years ago, the mortality rate of the disease was about 33%. Now, few patients die of myasthenia itself; other complicating diseases are much more likely to cause death. Years ago, hospital respiratory-care units were usually populated by patients with myasthenia; that number seems to have decreased dramatically. The cause of these changes is not clear. Some investigators attribute the improvement to widespread use of thymectomy and steroid therapy; skeptics point to improved respiratory care, so that the disease is not fatal and a new type of natural history emerges.

There are two types of therapy: anticholinesterase medication, and measures that are de-

signed to alter the course of the disease by immunological manipulation. Drugs that inhibit cholinesterase provide symptomatic relief but do not alter the course of the disease; moreover, they rarely relieve symptoms completely. For more prolonged treatment, the clinician must choose among thymectomy, steroids, immunosuppressive drugs (azathioprine and cyclophosphamide are most popular), and plasmapheresis. The best sequence and combination of these choices are currently being debated.

Other Disorders of Neuromuscular Transmission
Antibiotic Neuromuscular Block

Aminonucleoside antibodies (kanamycin and gentamycin) cause a block of transmission that resembles the disorder in myasthenia gravis. This is not just of theoretical interest, for clinical disorders may result when these drugs are given in high dosages to patients who have poor kidney function (and cannot excrete the drug effficiently) or otherwise have impaired disposition of the drugs.

Facilitating Neuromuscular Block

In some patients with carcinoma, weakness is associated with a neuromuscular disorder that is the opposite of myasthenia. Instead of a myasthenic response that declines with repetitive stimulation, there is an incremental response or "facilitating neuromuscular block." The first response is abnormally small. Subsequent responses increase with repetition, so that the final summated action potential in a train at 5/sec is two to four times the amplitude of the first potential. This syndrome is called the Eaton-Lambert syndrome, after the investigators at the Mayo Clinic who identified it. A similar abnormality is found in human botulism, and experimental studies have indicated that botulinum block is due to impaired release of ACh. The clinical syndromes are helped by calcium gluconate and by guanidine, agents that promote the release of ACh.

An Overall View

Myasthenia gravis, a disease in which the number of AChR is reduced, is improved by drugs that inhibit cholinesterase and thereby prolong the action of the transmitter. Facilitating neuromuscular block, in which the number of transmitter quanta is reduced, is improved by calcium gluconate, which presumably is effective because it enhances release. These findings suggest a primary insight into the treatment of diseases of synaptic function. It is essential to determine first whether the cause of a disorder of transmission is presynaptic (a disease of transmitter release) or postsynaptic (a disease of the receptor). Once the cause is identified, the treatment most likely to give symptomatic relief is one which corrects the diseased step in transmission. This insight emphasizes the importance of a theoretical understanding of synaptic transmission for analyzing and treating some human diseases of the nervous system.

Selected Readings and References

Dau, P. C. (ed.). 1979. Plasmapheresis and the Immunobiology of Myasthenia Gravis. Boston: Houghton Mifflin.

Drachman, D. B. 1978. Myasthenia gravis. N. Engl. J. Med. 298:136–142, 186–193.

Grob, D. (ed.). 1976. Myasthenia Gravis. Ann. N.Y. Acad. Sci. 274:1–682.

Lindstrom, J. 1979. Autoimmune response to acetylcholine receptors in myasthenia gravis and its animal model. Adv. Immunol. 27:1–50.

Lindstrom, J. M., and Lambert, E. H. 1978. Content of acetylcholine receptor and antibodies bound to receptor in myasthenia gravis, experimental autoimmune myasthenia gravis, and Eaton-Lambert syndrome. Neurology 28:130–138.

Rowland, L. P. 1977. Myasthenia gravis. In E. S. Goldensohn and S. H. Appel (eds.), Scientific Approaches to Clinical Neurology, Vol. 2. Philadelphia: Lea & Febiger, pp. 1518–1554.

Rowland, L. P. 1978. Myasthenia gravis. In W. B. Matthews and G. H. Glaser (eds.), Recent Advances in Clinical Neurology, Number 2. Edinburgh: Churchill Livingstone, pp. 25–46.

Other References

Albuquerque, E. X., Rash, J. E., Mayer, R. F., and Satterfield, J. R. 1976. An electrophysiological and morphological study of the neuromuscular junction in patients with myasthenia gravis. Exp. Neurol. 51:536–563.

Blalock, A., Mason, M. F., Morgan, H. J., and Riven, S. S., 1939. Myasthenia gravis and tumors of the thymic region. Report of a case in which the tumor was removed. Ann. Surg. 110:544–561.

Changeux, J.-P., Kasai, M., and Lee, C.-Y. 1970. Use of a snake venom toxin to characterize the cholinergic receptor protein. Proc. Natl. Acad. Sci. U.S.A. 67:1241–1247.

Dale, H. H., Feldberg, W., and Vogt, M. 1936. Release of acetylcholine at voluntary motor nerve endings. J. Physiol. (Lond.) 86:353–380.

Eaton, L. M., and Lambert, E. H. 1957. Electromyography and electric stimulation of nerves in diseases of motor unit. Observations on myasthenic syndrome associated with malignant tumors. J.A.M.A. 163:1117–1124.

Elmqvist, D., Hofmann, W. W., Kugelberg, J., and Quastel, D. M. J. 1964. An electrophysiological investigation of neuromuscular transmission in myasthenia gravis. J. Physiol. (Lond.) 174:417–434.

Fambrough, D. M., Drachman, D. B., and Satyamurti, S. 1973. Neuromuscular junction in myasthenia gravis: decreased acetylcholine receptors. Science (Wash., D.C.) 182:293–295.

Harvey, A. M., and Masland, R. L. 1941. The electromyogram in myasthenia gravis. Bull. Johns Hopkins Hosp. 69:1–13.

Lee, C. Y. 1972. Chemistry and pharmacology of polypeptide toxins in snake venoms. Annu. Rev. Pharmacol. 12:265–286.

Miledi, R., Molinoff, P., and Potter, L. T. 1971. Isolation of the cholinergic receptor protein of Torpedo electric tissue. Nature (Lond.) 229:554–557.

Nachmansohn, D. 1959. Chemical and Molecular Basis of Nerve Activity. New York: Academic.

Patrick, J., and Lindstrom, J. 1973. Autoimmune response to acetylcholine receptor. Science (Wash., D.C.) 180:871–872.

Simpson, J. A. 1960. Myasthenia gravis: a new hypothesis. Scott. Med. J. 5:419–436.

Strauss, A. J. L., Seegal, B. C., Hsu, K. C., Burkholder, P. M., Nastuk, W. L., and Osserman, K. E. 1960. Immunofluorescence demonstration of a muscle binding, complement-fixing serum globulin fraction in myasthenia gravis. Proc. Soc. Exp. Biol. Med. 105:184–191.

Toyka, K. V., Drachman, D. B., Pestronk, A., and Kao, I. 1975. Myasthenia gravis: passive transfer from man to mouse. Science (Wash., D.C.) 190:397–399.

Walker, M. B. 1934. Treatment of myasthenia gravis with physostigmine. Lancet 1:1200–1201.

Walker, M. B. 1935. Case showing the effect of prostigmin on myasthenia gravis. Proc. R. Soc. Med. 28:759–761.

James P. Kelly

Reactions of Neurons to Injury

13

In this chapter we shall consider the responses of neurons to physical trauma. To simplify matters, we shall use the neurons of the spinal cord and the associated dorsal root ganglia as models for analyzing the consequences of cutting the axon, also known as *axotomy*. Damage to nervous tissue is particularly serious because neurons in the adult central nervous system have withdrawn from the mitotic cycle and are no longer capable of cell division. Consequently, any physical injury that causes neurons to die will bring about permanent change in the structure of the nervous system, and this structural change is usually accompanied by long-lasting alterations in the functions of the affected areas.

Cutting an axon interrupts the mechanisms that carry materials synthesized in the cell body to the axon terminals, both rapid transport and axoplasmic flow (see Chapter 11). Therefore, the axon and synaptic terminals are deprived of their normal metabolic connection with the cell body and degenerate. Because axonal transport occurs in both directions along the axon, it would be logical to predict that changes might also occur in the cell body after axotomy: *retrograde* changes are found quite frequently after axotomy; in some instances they are quite severe and can result in death of the neuron.

In previous chapters we have seen that synapses between neurons process sensory input, and that synaptic interactions lead eventually to the generation of the motor output which constitutes a behavioral act. Important for understanding the consequences of nerve injury is the fact that synapses mediate not only electrical signals but also nutritive (or *trophic*) interactions between neurons. The mechanisms underlying trophic interactions between neurons are not as well understood as those underlying the synaptic interactions, yet trophic factors are very important. Deprived of its synaptic terminals, a neuron may shrink, atrophy, or degenerate. Therefore, if a bundle of axons in the central nervous system is severed, degenerative changes may be found not only in the damaged neurons, but also in subsequent neurons that *receive* synapses from the damaged neurons. In some injuries the presynaptic neurons that synapse upon the damaged cells are also affected. Such reactions are called *transsynaptic* or *transneuronal* because they cross from one neuron to the next via the synapse. These influences range from subtle ones to drastic ones that cause the degeneration of the affected neurons. Transneuronal changes of various kinds are important in explaining why a lesion at one site in the central nervous system can have effects on sites distant to the lesion, sites that are distributed according to the connections interrupted by the lesion.

Degenerative reactions after injury have been studied in detail by neurologists over the past century. As a result, anatomical methods have been devised—some still in active use—that utilize these reactions to trace synaptic connections within the brain. These anatomical methods are useful adjuncts to the modern cell labeling techniques such as the deoxyglucose method and rapid orthograde and retrograde transport of electron-dense and radio-labeled markers that we considered in Chapter 11. We shall consider some of the applications of these tracing procedures later in this chapter.

In addition to neurons, nervous tissue contains glial cells (oligodendrocytes, astrocytes, ependymal, and microglia) and Schwann cells. These cells play an important role in healing. On the one hand, certain types of supporting cells absorb cellular debris resulting from neuronal injury by phagocytosing toxic products of degeneration. On the other hand, the proliferation of supporting cells may effectively block restoration of severed synaptic connections within the brain and spinal cord. Therefore, the healing processes that are activated in the central nervous system by neuronal injury are both helpful (phagocytosis) and

troublesome (blocked regeneration), a rule that holds true for many of the restorative processes employed by the body.

Axotomy Causes Changes in the Axon and Cell Body and in Glial Cells

If a bundle of axons is cut, either by sectioning a tract within the brain or by sectioning a peripheral nerve, the site where the lesion is located is termed the *zone of trauma*. The part of the axon still connected to the cell body is the *proximal segment,* and the part isolated from the rest of the cell is the *distal segment.* The cut ends of both parts of the axon seal off the axoplasm almost immediately after injury, retract from one another, and begin to swell. These swollen *retraction bulbs* are formed largely by materials carried along the axon by axonal transport. Mitochondria, vesicles, multivesicular bodies, neurofilaments, and neurotubules pile up in the sealed end of each axon segment. Both the proximal and the distal segments swell because axonal transport occurs in two directions.

In the zone of trauma there is rapid degeneration locally of the axon and myelin sheath. Because blood vessels are usually interrupted by the lesion, macrophages from the general circulation can enter the area and phagocytose axonal debris. Glial cells (*astrocytes* and *microglia*) also proliferate and act as phagocytes. In the central nervous system, the proliferation of fibrous astrocytes leads to the formation of a *glial scar* around the zone of trauma. Scarring can block the course taken by regenerating axons and may become an effective barrier against the reformation of central connections. *Microglia* are probably undifferentiated glial cells that proliferate in response to injury. In undamaged tissue they divide at a lower rate, and differentiate into oligodendrocytes and astrocytes to replace cells lost during normal life.

Degeneration spreads in both directions along the axon from the zone of trauma, but only for a short distance in the proximal segment, usually up to the point of origin of the first axon collateral. After 2–3 days, a retrograde reaction is seen in the cell body. If the entire cell body dies, then degeneration spreads from the axon hillock down along the remainder of the proximal segment. In the distal segment, outside the zone of trauma, degeneration first appears in the axon terminal about 1 day after the occurrence of the lesion. In approximately 2 weeks, the synapses formed by the distal segment degenerate completely; this process is called *terminal degeneration.* Degeneration of the distal axon itself, termed *Wallerian degeneration,* takes place over a time span of 2–3 months. Eventually, cells that are either pre- or postsynaptic to the injured neuron may also be affected. This transneuronal degeneration may be orthograde or retrograde: it is orthograde if the affected cell receives synapses from the injured neuron and retrograde if the affected cell makes synapses on the injured neuron. The various types of reaction to a neural lesion are depicted in Figure 13–1. We shall consider each of them in turn.

Terminal Degeneration Leads to the Rapid Loss of the Presynaptic Terminal

The axon terminal is very sensitive to interruption of contact with the parent cell body. Within 1 day after axotomy, the terminal and mitochondria within it begin to swell. In some cases the terminal becomes filled with sworls of neurofilaments surrounding a central packet of disrupted mitochondria. Alternatively, the terminal may become filled with more homogeneous electron-dense products of degeneration (Figure 13–2). After 6–7 days, the terminal is pushed away from its contacts with postsynaptic neurons by invading glial cells and is eventually phagocytosed by them. At the neuromuscular junction, after the motor axon is severed, Schwann cells invade the junctional cleft and surround the presynaptic terminal. The terminal then degenerates totally and is phagocytosed.

Wallerian Degeneration Leads to the Slow Loss of the Distal Axon Segment

About 1 week after the appearance of the initial degenerative changes in the axon terminal, degeneration begins in the entire distal axon. The myelin sheath draws away from the axon and breaks apart (Figure 13–3B). The axon swells and then becomes beaded. Neurofilaments and neurotubules (collectively termed *neurofibrils* by light microscopists) soon fill the axon. Fragments of the axon and the myelin sheath are absorbed by *local* phagocytes derived from the glial cell population in the central nervous system or from Schwann cells in the peripheral nervous system (Figure 13–3C). Invading macrophages do not absorb the debris produced by Wallerian degeneration, as they do in the zone of trauma.

The sequence of axonal degeneration in the peripheral nervous system differs from the sequence that occurs in the central nervous system.

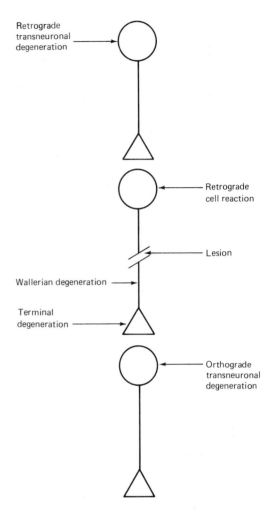

13–1 Various reactions to axotomy.

If the *peripherally* directed process of a dorsal root ganglion cell is cut, or if a motor axon is cut, then the distal segment of the severed axon will degenerate. However, the connective tissue sheath through which the severed nerve ran originally may often remain intact. In many instances, depending upon the nature of the injury, a severed axon can regenerate back to its previous synaptic sites as long as its cell body remains alive. The regenerating axon runs along the connective tissue sheath, which acts like a conduit leading the growing axon back to the peripheral target. If the *centrally* directed branches of dorsal root ganglion cells are cut, the glial scar that forms around the degenerating axons in the dorsal aspect of the spinal cord prevents any regenerating axon that might arise from reaching its central target.

The disappearance of myelin from degenerat-

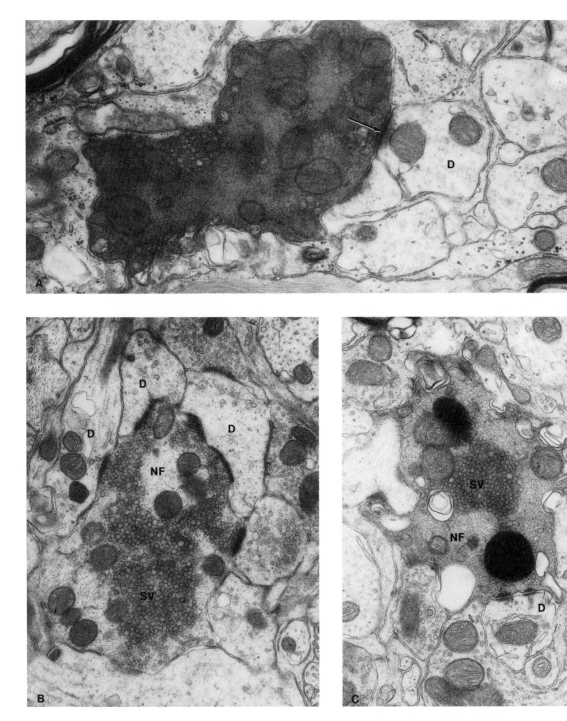

13–2 Neurofilamentous degeneration of synaptic profiles in the spinal cord dorsal horn of the monkey following lesions of the dorsal roots. **A.** Advanced neurofilamentous degeneration resulting in a very electron dense appearance of the synaptic profile. The degenerating profile forms a synapse at the arrow with a dendrite (**D**). **B.** Early filamentous degeneration in which neurofilaments (**NF**) appear among clumps of synaptic vesicles (**SV**). The altered profile forms synaptic contacts on several adjacent dendrites (**D**). **C.** Advanced neurofilamentous degeneration in which neurofilaments (**NF**) form a dense matrix adjacent to a clump of synaptic vesicles (**SV**). The degenerating profile contacts a dendrite (**D**). Magnification approximately × 40,000. (Courtesy of H. J. Ralston III.)

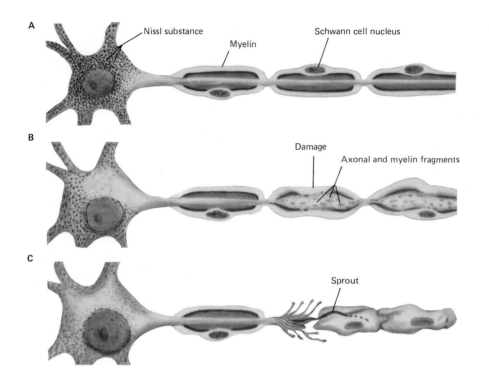

13–3 Sequence of changes in Wallerian degeneration and the retrograde cell reaction in a damaged neuron.

ing fibers in the central nervous system provides a means of tracing neural pathways. Normal myelin can be stained a dark blue with the *Weigert method* using a combination of chromium salts and hematoxylin. If a tract in the brain is cut, the myelin wrapping the distal portions of the fibers will disappear. These degenerating fibers will not be stained by the Weigert method, thus providing a negative image of the route taken by the interrupted pathway. Because the loss of myelin persists indefinitely after a lesion, plotting fiber loss with the Weigert stain is often the only method available for tracing pathways in human pathological material. The Weigert method was one of the first techniques used to study the central connections of dorsal root ganglion cells, and a large part of what is known about the anatomical organization of afferent pathways in the spinal cord has come from observations made with the use of this technique.

The hypertrophy of neurofilaments or of electron-dense products of degeneration in damaged axons also provides a means of tracing connections. For example, neurofilaments found in

the axons and cell bodies of normal neurons bind silver selectively. If the staining of normal fibers is suppressed with an oxidizing agent, the degenerating fibers can still be stained intensely because of their increased content of argyrophilic neurofibrils. Degenerating axons appear as black-beaded profiles against a pale background. This is in part the basis of the *Nauta method*, a procedure for tracing fiber degeneration that is widely used today in experimental studies of the anatomy of the brain because it stains both unmyelinated and myelinated degenerating axons.

The Neuronal Cell Body Also Reacts to Axotomy

There is considerable variety in the way the cell bodies of different classes of neurons respond to axotomy. Cutting of the peripheral processes of dorsal root ganglion cells or the axons of spinal motor neurons causes chromatolysis (see below) in the parent neurons within 2 or 3 days (Figure 13–3B). The cells first begin to swell; they may double in size. The nucleus moves to an eccentric position, usually opposite the axon hillock, and also begins to swell. Finally, the rough endoplasmic reticulum in the cell body breaks apart and moves to the periphery of the swollen cell (Figure 13–3C). Rough endoplasmic reticulum in the cell bodies of normal neurons can be stained a bright blue with basic dyes, such as thionin, that bind to the acidic proteins in ribosomes. Clumps of endoplasmic reticulum stained in this way are termed *Nissl substance. Chromatolysis*, or the dissolution of Nissl substance, indicates that the axons of the chromatolytic neurons have been severed. In experimental animals, or in human pathological nervous tissue, chromatolysis can therefore be used to identify which cells in the central nervous system give rise to peripheral nerves. In fact, observations of the distribution chromatolytic neurons in the anterior horn of the spinal cord after motor nerve lesions provided the first anatomical maps of the motor neuron pools that innervate particular muscle groups.

Chromatolysis commonly lasts for 1–3 weeks. During this period the number of free polysomes in the cell body increases, as does the total amount of protein. Ribonucleic acid (RNA) synthesis in the nucleus increases as well. These changes suggest that chromatolysis involves massive synthesis of proteins involved in regenerating the severed parts of the axon. If proper connections are restored after regeneration of the axon, chromatolysis ceases and the cell body usually regains its normal appearance. If proper connections are not restored, the cell may atrophy or degenerate totally.

Many cells do not undergo chromatolysis after axon section. Thalamic neurons, for example, undergo a rapid degeneration after their axons are cut; they may either degenerate completely or remain shrunken indefinitely. Purkinje cells of the cerebellum do not undergo chromatolysis at all after axotomy. Furthermore, if the centrally directed processes of spinal ganglion cells or cells in the sensory ganglia of the cranial nerves are sectioned, ganglion cell bodies show no change. Two reasonably safe generalizations can be made about the process of chromatolysis despite its variability. (1) Chromatolysis is always more pronounced in young animals, where axotomized neurons commonly undergo chromatolysis and then degenerate completely, as if they were unable to regenerate their axons. A similar population of adult neurons may undergo chromatolysis after axotomy, regenerate, and return to its former state. (2) Chromatolysis is more prolonged if the site of the lesion is close to the cell body. If a peripheral nerve is cut very close to its site of origin in the central nervous system, a substantial proportion of the injured neurons degenerates rapidly, and if the nerve is forcefully ripped apart,

the number of degenerating neurons increases even more. Consequently, the age of the animal, the site of the lesion, and the nature of the injury are important considerations in judging the potential for functional recovery after nerve section.

Neurons with processes confined to the central nervous system may undergo chromatolysis after axotomy, but they then degenerate or remain in a state of severe atrophy. This is presumably because they cannot restore appropriate synaptic connections. The deformation induced by the glial scar may block regrowth, or the injured central neurons may be metabolically unable to regenerate an axon. Whatever the reason, the prognosis for the recovery of axotomized neurons within the brain is very poor. Finding the causes that prevent damaged neurons from regrowing their axons and reinnervating their target cells is one of the key problems in experimental neurology. Solving of this problem might eventually lead to relief from the disability and often tragic effects of stroke or trauma of the nervous system.

Glial Cells Absorb the Debris Caused by Injury

It is important to recognize the role played by glial cells in normal function as well as in response to disease or damage of the central nervous system. Two types of glial cells, astrocytes and oligodendrocytes, vastly outnumber neurons. Astrocytes predominate in gray matter. They have small (3–5-μm) cell bodies that are packed with fascicles of glial filaments about 100 nm in diameter. Numerous processes radiate out from the cell body in various directions, and many of these come into close contact with blood vessels. The physiological importance of astrocytes is not known. They are often found wrapping individual synaptic profiles in electron micrographs, and this has given rise to the idea that they may insulate synaptic terminals from their neighbors. In the damaged brain, however, it is known that astrocytes phagocytose neuronal debris. Oligodendrocytes, which form myelin in the central nervous system, predominate in white matter. They have smaller cell bodies (1–3 μm in diameter) and give off fewer processes than astrocytes, and each process appears to participate in forming myelin for a single axon (Figure 13–4). In the central nervous system, each oligodendrocyte contributes to the myelin sheath of several (as

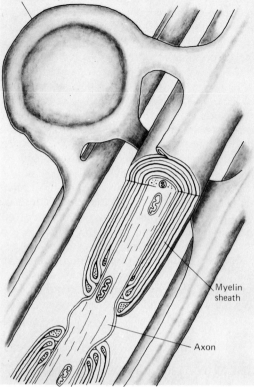

Oligodendrocyte

Myelin sheath

Axon

13–4 Processes of an oligodendrocyte sheathing myelinated, not unmyelinated fibers in the central nervous system. (Adapted from Bunge, 1968.)

many as 20) axons by means of its different processes. Oligodendrocytes do not sheath unmyelinated fibers in the central nervous system, (Figure 13–4), astrocytes do.

Glial cells proliferate around chromatolytic neurons and assume the appearance of phagocytes. Reactive glial cells have been observed displacing presynaptic terminals along the proximal dendrites and cell bodies of axotomized motor neurons. The pre- and postsynaptic elements of the synapse appear to be pushed apart by the invading glial cells. This stripping of synapses has been confirmed by intracellular recording from cell bodies of chromatolysing motor neurons. Damaged neurons receive reduced synaptic inputs, and the evoked EPSPs are smaller in amplitude, as if synapses on the cell body and proximal dendrites were removed by encroachment of glial cells. Even though somatic synapses are displaced, chromatolysing motor neurons can still be activated because remote synapses on their dendritic tree that are normally ineffective begin

to excite the cell. After the normal input to the soma is removed, new trigger zones develop on the cell body and along the axon. A reorganization of this type may enable the cell to maintain normal activity in the absence of a normal number of synapses. If appropriate connections with muscles are established by the regenerating motor axons, then the normal input to the cell body of the motor neuron returns. The reason synapses are shed in the first place, however, is still unknown.

It would be interesting to know the signal for chromatolysis. It is likely that axotomy interrupts the flow of some trophic substance moving back along the axon from the terminal to the cell body. Cutting the axon might deprive the cell body of this essential substance and elicit chromatolysis.

Transneuronal Degeneration Leads to Changes in Cells to Which the Damaged Neuron Connects

As noted earlier, transneuronal degeneration is one facet of a broad class of trophic interactions known to occur between neurons that are in synaptic contact as well as between neurons and their peripheral target organs. The clearest example of this type of trophic interaction is found at the neuromuscular junction. To understand the nature of this interaction, consider what happens when the axons of a group of anterior horn motor cells, also called *lower motor neurons,* are cut. The muscles innervated by the cut axons are paralyzed, and their reflexes are lost. The affected muscles also show a distinct decrease in tone (hypotonia), so that they display little or no resistance to passive movement. After a short period of time (a few weeks) the muscles deprived of innervation atrophy, or lose bulk. Spontaneous contractions, termed *fasciculations,* also appear in small groups of muscle fibers within the affected muscles. For some reason, muscles are dependent upon their normal innervation to maintain normal metabolism; when the innervation is removed the denervated muscles waste away. The alterations that take place in the cell membranes and in the biochemistry of denervated muscles will be considered in Chapter 43. For our present purposes, it is important to emphasize that damage to a lower motor neuron interrupts the trophic interactions between nerve and muscle, and the clinical sequelae observed in affected muscles after motor nerve section reflect the absence of normal trophic influences.

The phenomenon of transneuronal degeneration was first observed in the visual system. The axons of the retinal ganglion cells join together to form the optic nerve, which terminates in the lateral geniculate nucleus of the thalamus. The postsynaptic neurons in this nucleus send their axons to the visual cortex of the occipital lobe. When the optic nerve is sectioned, the retinal terminals in the lateral geniculate nucleus degenerate rapidly. After several months, the postsynaptic neurons in the nucleus undergo a severe atrophy (Figure 13–5). This type of reaction to injury is called *orthograde transneuronal degeneration* (Figure 13–1). It does not occur in all brain pathways. When transneuronal degeneration does occur, the degree of atrophy is related to the percentage of total input removed from a population of neurons by a lesion. Other sources of input can reduce the severity of transneuronal degeneration.

Two speculative mechanisms have been proposed to explain transneuronal degeneration. The first is that neurons require a certain amount of stimulation to survive. Cutting the axons that provide input to a population of cells could reduce activity below a critical level, and the deafferented cells might atrophy as a consequence of this reduced activity. However, activity may not be the sole factor (see Chapter 43). The second is that some trophic substance, necessary for the normal survival of neurons, is released by synaptic terminals. Degeneration of the terminals removes this substance and leads eventually to the atrophy of the postsynaptic cell. Of course, the two mechanisms could be related if the release of the trophic factor is tied to the level of activity in the presynaptic fiber.

Transneuronal degeneration may cross more than one synapse. For example, some changes are seen in the neurons of the visual cortex after optic nerve section. Cutting of the optic nerve causes neurons in the lateral geniculate nucleus to atrophy, and they subsequently induce degeneration in cortical cells receiving input from the thalamus. Transneuronal degeneration can also move along a neural pathway in a retrograde direction. Lesions in the visual cortex cause neurons in the lateral geniculate nucleus to undergo severe retrograde degeneration. The retinal ganglion cells that synapse upon the affected

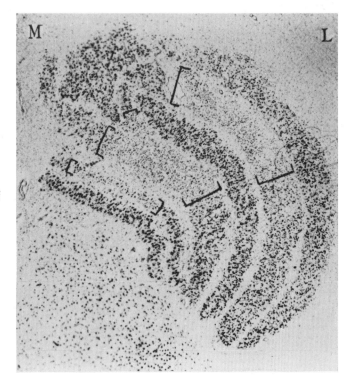

13–5 Photomicrograph of a Nissl preparation showing transneuronal degeneration of the nerve cells in three of the laminae of the lateral geniculate body of a monkey after a retinal lesion. **M**, medial; **L**, lateral. (Adapted from Le Gros Clark and Penman, 1934.)

neurons in the lateral geniculate nucleus may then atrophy after a few months. Evidence of this kind reveals the degree to which neurons are dependent upon one another for survival, and illustrates the widespread changes brought about by damage confined to a small part of the brain.

Lesions of Nerve Cells and Behavior

As we have seen, the behavioral role of a nerve cell is determined by its location in the brain and by its connections, its input–output relationships. As a result, a similar injury will have very different behavioral consequences depending upon which neuron it strikes. For example, severance of the axons of motor neurons that innervate skeletal muscle (lower motor neurons) will result in the paralysis of individual muscles on the side of the lesion. These muscles will undergo a reduction in mass (atrophy), tone, and reflex activity. In contrast, a lesion will produce a very different disorder of behavior when it severs axons of cortical motor cells (upper motor neurons) as they run in the pyramidal tract soon after they leave the cerebral cortex. In this case, groups of muscles rather than individual muscles will be disturbed and the disturbance will be on the side opposite the lesion (since the axons of the upper motor neurons cross to the other side of the brain during their descent, at the level of the brain stem). The muscle mass will be reduced only slightly, and muscle tone and reflex activity will be increased. This example demonstrates that the importance of specific nerve cells for behavior is determined largely by their location in the brain and their pattern of interconnection.

Selected Reading and References

Brodal, A. 1981. Neurological Anatomy, 3rd ed. New York: Oxford University Press, pp. 3–44.

Lieberman, A. R. 1971. The axon reaction. Int. Rev. Neurobiol. 14:49–124.

Mendell, L. M., Munson, J. B., and Scott, J. G. 1976. Alterations of synapses on axotomized motoneurones. J. Physiol. (Lond.) 255:67–79.

Other References

Bunge, R. P. 1968. Glial cells and the central myelin sheath. Physiol. Rev. 48:197–121.

Le Gros Clark, W. E., and Penman, G. G. 1934. The projection of the retina in the lateral geniculate body. Proc. R. Soc. Lond. B Biol. Sci. 114:291–313.

Lewis P. Rowland

Diseases of the Motor Unit: The Motor Neuron, Peripheral Nerve, and Muscle

14

The reactions of nerve cells to injury and other principles of cellular neurobiology enable clinicians to diagnose and to understand the manifestations of neurological disease. Conversely, the manifestations of particular diseases in humans help us to understand how the nervous system functions. Nowhere is this reciprocal benefit more evident than in diseases of the motor unit.

The Motor Unit Is the Functional Element of the Motor System

Each mature mammalian skeletal muscle fiber is innervated by only one motor neuron. However, a motor neuron innervates more than one muscle fiber. Synaptic transmission at the nerve–muscle synapse is normally so effective that every action potential in the motor neuron leads without fail to the contraction of every muscle fiber innervated by that neuron. Sherrington introduced the term *motor unit* to refer to the motor neuron in the spinal cord and the population of muscle fibers that it innervates (Figure 14–1). The motor unit therefore is composed of three components: (1) the cell body of the motor neuron, (2) its axon that runs in the peripheral nerve, and (3) the muscle fibers innervated by that neuron. In theory, the neuromuscular junction should also be included, but diseases of

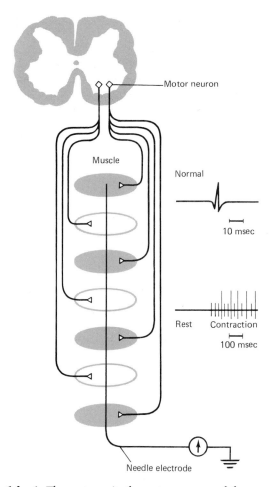

14–1 The motor unit: the motor neuron and the population of muscle fibers it innervates. The muscle fibers innervated by a single motor neuron do not usually lie adjacent to one another. A needle electrode inserted into the muscle will record an all-or-nothing motor unit potential when a unit fires because the highly effective transmission at the neuromuscular junction ensures that each action potential in the nerve produces a contraction in every fiber innervated by the motor neuron. The unit potentials vary in size as a function of the number of muscle fibers that contribute to them. Muscular contraction will usually recruit smaller units first and then the larger ones. On the right the action potential from a single unit is shown on a fast time base (**top**). Two units are displayed on a slow time base during a contraction (**bottom**).

junctional transmission, such as myasthenia gravis, are best considered separately because of their special manifestations (see Chapter 12).

The number of muscle fibers innervated by a single motor neuron varies greatly according to its function. Motor units that control fine movements, for example, those of the extraocular

muscles of the eye or the small muscles of the hand, consist of only three to six muscle fibers. In contrast, motor units of the gastrocnemius, a muscle involved in coarse movements of the leg, and of other muscles involved in postural control, may contain 2000 muscle fibers.

The motor units can be considered to be the elementary units of behavior in the skeletal motor system—the quantum of movement. Variations in the range, force, or type of movement are determined by the pattern of recruitment and the frequency of firing of different motor units.

Most diseases of the motor unit cause weakness and wasting of skeletal muscles because muscle function is the final expression or "readout" of the motor system. The diseases may differ in other features, however, depending upon which of the three components of the motor unit the disease primarily affects.

The distinctions among diseases were originally established by postmortem examination. When pathologists of the nineteenth century studied patients who had died from diseases characterized by progressive weakness and wasting of limb muscles, they found different pathological changes in different patients. In some patients there were pronounced pathological changes in the nerve cell bodies of the motor neuron, but relatively minor changes in the muscle *(motor neuron diseases)*. In contrast, other patients had advanced degeneration of muscle, with little change in motor neurons *(myopathies)*. A third group of patients had changes that affected primarily the axons of peripheral nerves *(peripheral neuropathy)*. These pathological findings show two important features of neurological disease. First, diseases can be functionally selective: some affect only sensory systems, others only motor systems. Second, a disease can be regionally selective, affecting only one functional component of the neuron (for example, the axon rather than the cell body). Thus the distinctions among the different components of the neuron have important clinical implications; reciprocally, clinical observations can also provide invaluable insights into the functional significance of these components.

There Are Two Major Classes of Motor Unit Disease

Diseases of the motor unit are commonly divided into two classes on the basis of which components of the motor unit are affected: (1) *neurogenic diseases* primarily affect the cell body (motor neuron diseases) or the peripheral axon (peripheral neuropathy); and (2) *myopathic diseases* primarily affect muscle itself.

Atrophy (literally, lack of nourishment) means wasting away of a once normal muscle. Perhaps by historical accident, atrophy appears in the names of several diseases, all thought to be neurogenic. Therefore, in describing the appearance of a patient's muscles, it is best to use the word *wasting* unless the condition is known to be neurogenic.

A clinical consequence of neuropathy, denervation of muscle, is seen most clearly when a peripheral nerve is accidentally severed. The muscles innervated by that nerve are immediately paralyzed and then waste progressively. Since severance of a nerve interrupts sensory as well as motor fibers, there is also immediate loss of sensation in the area innervated by sensory fibers in the nerve and the stretch reflexes are lost. Similar effects on muscle appear more slowly in diseases that affect the motor neuron.

Myopathies are diseases in which there is dysfunction of muscle without evidence of denervation. The disorder is usually revealed by weakness, but other muscle symptoms may occur. These include the inability to relax *(myotonia)*, cramps, pain *(myalgia)*, or the appearance in the urine of the protein that colors the muscle red *(myoglobinuria)*. The *muscular dystrophies* are a group of inherited myopathies manifested only by weakness. The weakness becomes progressively more severe. In muscular dystrophy there is no evidence of storage of abnormal metabolities within the muscle.

Neurogenic and Myopathic Diseases Can Be Distinguished

Clinical Evidence

Both neurogenic and myopathic diseases are characterized by weakness and wasting of muscle. Neurogenic disorders tend to cause distal limb weakness and myopathic disorders tend to cause proximal limb weakness, but there are many exceptions; therefore, location of weakness cannot be regarded as a reliable differential sign. Some signs, however, are restricted to neurogenic diseases. Perhaps because of denervation supersensitivity, denervated muscle fibers tend to fire spontaneously. This process gives rise to spontaneous twitches of muscle called *fasciculations*. For reasons that are not clear, fasciculations are characteristic of slowly progressive diseases of

the motor neuron and are uncommon in peripheral neuropathies. The combination of overactive reflexes (evidence of disease of upper motor neurons) in a weak, wasted, and twitching limb (evidence of disease of the lower motor neuron) is virtually pathognomonic of *amyotrophic lateral sclerosis,* a condition that involves both the upper and lower motor neurons (Figure 14–2). When the sole manifestation of a disease

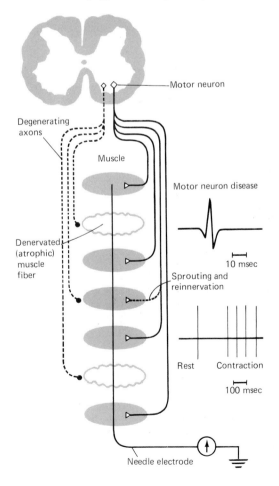

14–2 Motor neuron disease. The motor neuron on the left is undergoing degeneration. Its muscle fibers have become denervated and atrophic and this unit no longer produces a unit potential. However, the remaining neuron on the right has sprouted an axonal branch that has reinnervated one of the denervated muscle fibers. The motor unit potential from the remaining motor neuron is therefore larger than normal. In addition, this residual motor unit fires spontaneously even at rest, giving rise to fasciculations, another characteristic of motor neuron disease. On the right the unit potential is shown on a fast (**top**) and a slow (**bottom**) time base.

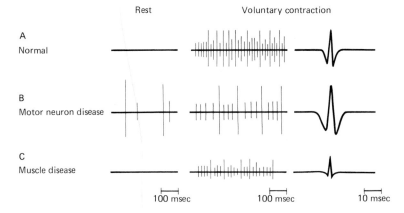

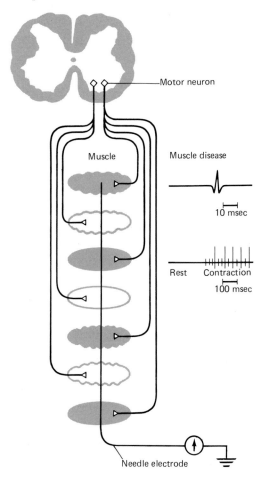

14–3 Some characteristic features in the electromyogram in normal subjects (**A**) and in patients with neurogenic (**B**) and myogenic (**C**) diseases.

14–4 Muscle disease (myopathy). Some muscle fibers innervated by each of the two motor neurons have shrunk and become nonfunctional. Therefore, each motor unit potential is reduced. The unit potentials, shown on the right on a fast (**top**) and a slow (**bottom**) time base, are now smaller than normal in amplitude and shorter in duration.

is limb weakness, as often happens, clinical criteria alone rarely suffice to distinguish between neurogenic and myogenic diseases. To assist in this differentiation, clinicians rely upon several laboratory tests.

Laboratory Evidence

The sarcoplasm of muscle is rich in soluble enzymes. Low concentrations are also found in the serum. In muscle diseases, the serum level of these *sarcoplasmic enzymes* is increased, presumably from alteration of the muscle surface-membrane properties that ordinarily retain soluble enzymes within the sarcoplasm. Slight increases are also found in some denervating diseases, but the amounts differ. The enzyme activity most commonly measured for this purpose is creatine phosphokinase (CPK), an enzyme important in the energetics of muscle, but serum glutamic oxaloacetic transaminase (SGOT) and lactate dehydrogenase (LDH) are also used.

Some abnormalities can be diagnosed by *electromyography* (EMG), a routine clinical procedure (Figure 14–3) in which a small needle is inserted into a muscle to record the electrical activity of several neighboring motor units. Attention is given to three measurements: spontaneous activity at rest, number of motor units under voluntary control, and the duration and amplitude of each motor unit potential. Because each motor unit fires in an all-or-none fashion, it gives rise to an all-or-none motor unit potential. Normally, there is no activity in a resting muscle (Figure 14–3A). During a weak voluntary contraction, a series of motor unit potentials is recorded as different motor units are recruited. Normal values have been established for the amplitude and dura-

Table 14–1. Differential Diagnosis of Neurogenic and Myopathic Diseases

Finding	Neurogenic	Myopathic
Weakness	+	+
Wasting	+	+
Loss of reflexes	+	+
Fasciculation	+(ALS)	0
Sensory loss	+(PN)	0
Hyperreflexia, Babinski	+(ALS)	0
Cerebrospinal fluid protein increased	+(PN)	0
Slow nerve conduction velocity	+(PN)	0
Electromyography		
Duration of potentials	Increased	Decreased
Fibrillation, fasciculation	+	0
Number of potentials	Decreased	Normal
Serum enzymes increased	±	++++
Muscle biopsy	Group atrophy, fiber-type grouping	Necrosis and regeneration

Abbreviations. ALS, Amyotrophic lateral sclerosis; PN, peripheral neuropathy.

tion of these unit potentials. For example, the amplitude of the unit potential is determined by the number of muscle fibers within the motor unit. In denervated muscle (Figure 14–3B), there is spontaneous activity even at rest (fibrillation and fasciculation). On volitional movement few motor units contract (because the motor axons have been lost and there are fewer units under voluntary control). In addition, the amplitude and duration of individual potentials may be increased (presumably because remaining nerve fibers sprout and reinnervate denervated fibers, so that surviving units contain more than the normal number of muscle fibers) (Figure 14–2). In myopathic diseases (Figure 14–3C), there is no activity at rest and no change in the number of units during a contraction, but because there are fewer surviving muscle fibers in each motor unit, individual motor unit potentials are smaller and the duration is shorter (Figure 14–4).

Electrical stimulation and recording can also be used to measure the *conduction velocities* of peripheral motor and sensory nerves. Motor conduction velocity is slowed in demyelinating neuropathies. In neuropathies without demyelination *(axonal neuropathies)*, conduction is normal.

Finally, muscle can be biopsied and the muscle fibers examined histologically. Normally, at least two different types of muscle fiber can be identified histochemically. Normal muscle appears like a checkerboard, because fibers of the two types lie side by side. Muscle fibers supplied by a single neuron are of the same histochemical type. In chronic denervating diseases, muscle fibers innervated by a dying neuron become atrophic and disappear; axons of surviving neurons tend to sprout and innervate some of the muscle fibers left by the dying neuron. Because histochemical type is determined by the neuron, these reinnervated muscle fibers all become the same histochemical type. As a result, instead of a normal checkerboard pattern, there is fiber-type grouping. Because the surviving motor unit is larger than normal, the motor unit potential is also larger than normal (Figure 14–2). When these neurons are ultimately affected, atrophy occurs in groups of muscle fibers all of the same histochemical type (group atrophy).

In myopathies, fibers are affected in a more or less random fashion by signs of cell death (necrosis) and regeneration, sometimes with an inflammatory cellular response, and sometimes with prominent infiltration of the muscle by fat and connective tissue.

The clinical and laboratory features upon which differential diagnosis of the motor unit is based are listed in Table 14–1.

Common Clinical Syndromes

The major diseases affecting the motor neuron, axons, and muscle are listed in Table 14–2. We shall consider each of these in turn.

Diseases of the Motor Neuron

The best known disorder of motor neurons is *amyotrophic lateral sclerosis.* "Amyotrophy" is another word for neurogenic atrophy of muscle.

Table 14–2. Neurogenic and Myopathic Diseases

Neurogenic		Myopathic	
Motor neuron	Peripheral nerve	Inherited	Acquired
ALS	Guillain-Barré syndrome	Duchenne dystrophy	Dermatomyositis
		FSH dystrophy	Polymyositis syndromes
	Chronic peripheral	LG dystrophy	Endocrine myopathies
	neuropathy	Myotonic dystrophy	Myoglobinurias

Abbreviations. ALS, amyotrophic lateral sclerosis; FSH, facioscapulohumeral; LG, limb–girdle.

"Lateral sclerosis" refers to the hardness to the touch of the spinal cord at autopsy, which results from the proliferation of astrocytes and scarring of the lateral columns of the spinal cord. Scarring is caused by disease of the corticospinal tracts that carry the axons of upper motor neurons whose cell bodies lie in the cortex and in the brain stem. There is progressive degeneration of upper motor neurons in the cortex, and of lower motor neurons in the brain stem and spinal cord. The cause is unknown.

The symptoms usually start with painless weakness of the arms or legs. Typically, the patient, most often a man in his 40s, discovers that he has become awkward in executing fine movements of the hands (typing, playing the piano, fingering coins, or working with tools). This weakness is associated with wasting of the small muscles of the hands and feet and fasciculations of the muscles of the forearm and upper arm. These signs of lower motor neuron disease are often paradoxically associated with *hyperreflexia,* the increase in tendon reflexes that is characteristic of upper motor neuron disease. Sensation is always normal. There is no treatment for this uniformly fatal condition from which several distinguished athletes have died in the prime of life.

There are other variants of motor neuron disease. Sometimes the first symptoms are restricted to muscles innervated by cranial nerves, with resulting *dysarthria* (difficulty in speaking) and *dysphagia* (difficulty in swallowing). When cranial symptoms occur alone, the syndrome is called *progressive bulbar palsy.* (The term "bulb" is synonymous with "brain stem.") If only lower motor neurons are involved, the syndrome is called *spinal muscular atrophy;* there is weakness, wasting, loss of reflexes, and fasciculation, but no hyperreflexia or other signs of disease of the upper motor neuron. This spinal muscular atrophy is probably the same disease as amyotrophic lateral sclerosis, because at autopsy there is usually demyelination in descending cortico-spinal tracts even though that was not manifest in life, presumably because the more advanced degeneration of the lower motor neurons did not permit detection of upper motor neuron signs.

Amyotrophic lateral sclerosis and its variants are restricted to motor neurons of skeletal muscle. The disease does not affect sensory neurons, or motor neurons to viscera, and therefore illustrates dramatically the individuality of nerve cells in the central nervous system. The motor neuron is also selectively vulnerable to polio virus, which causes an acute disease restricted to motor neurons. Although the basis of this selectivity is not yet understood, it might be explained in both acute (polio) and chronic diseases (amyotrophic lateral sclerosis) by characteristic biochemical components in the membrane of motor neurons which act as receptors for specific neurotropic viruses.

Diseases of Peripheral Nerves (Peripheral Neuropathies)

Disorders of peripheral nerves usually cause symptoms of both motor and sensory dysfunction. Patients with sensory dysfunction often report abnormal sensory experiences, frequently unpleasant. Similar sensations are recognized by normal individuals after local anesthesia for dental work and are variously called "numbness," "pins-and-needles," or "tingling." The latter, occurring spontaneously without a proximate sensory stimulus, are called *paresthesias.* Patients may lack discrimination of hot and cold. Lack of pain perception may lead to painless injuries. On examination, patients with paresthesias may demonstrate impaired perception of cutaneous modalities of sensation (pain and temperature) due to selective loss of the small myelinated fibers that carry these sensations; the sense of touch may or may not be involved. Proprioceptive sensations (position and vibration) may be lost without loss of cutaneous sensation. The sensory disorders are always more prominent distally—the glove-and-stocking pattern—presumably because the distal portions of the nerves are most remote from the cell body and therefore more susceptible to disorders that interfere with axonal transport of essential metabolites and proteins. This concept of "dying back" is invoked to explain the distal weakness as well as sensory loss.

The motor disorder is first manifested by weakness, which may be predominantly proximal in acute cases, but is usually distal in chronic cases. Reflexes are usually depressed or lost. Fasciculation is only rarely seen, and atrophy does not ensue unless the weakness has been present for many weeks. Protein content in the cerebrospinal fluid is often increased, presumably because of altered permeability of the nerve roots within the subarachnoid space.

Neuropathies may be acute or chronic. The best known acute neuropathy is the Guillain-Barré syndrome, which achieved notoriety in 1976 when many cases seemed to follow vaccination against the swine influenza virus. Most cases, however, follow a more banal respiratory infection or occur without preceding illness. This condition may be mild, or so severe that mechanical ventilation is required. The cranial nerves may also be affected, with paralysis of ocular, facial, and oropharyngeal muscles. Although the condition may be life-threatening, some improvement occurs in every case and return to normal function is possible no matter how severe the original state. Many patients, however, are left with some disability. The disorder is believed to be due to an autoimmune cellular attack on peripheral nerves. It is therefore often treated with corticosteroids, although the efficacy of this treatment has not been proven. Guillain-Barré syndrome may occur with other viral infections, especially infectious mononucleosis.

The chronic neuropathies also vary from the mildest manifestations to incapacitating or even fatal conditions, and the list of possible causes seems almost endless, including genetic diseases (acute intermittent porphyria, Charcot-Marie-Tooth disease), metabolic disorders (diabetes, B_{12} deficiency); intoxications (lead); nutritional disorders (alcoholism, thiamine deficiency); carcinomas (especially carcinoma of the lung); and immunological disorders (plasma cell diseases, amyloidosis). Some are amenable to therapy, such as the neuropathy of B_{12} deficiency in pernicious anemia. The variety of different conditions associated with neuropathy implies a variety of different pathogenetic mechanisms.

In addition to being acute or chronic, neuropathies can be demyelinating or axonal. Demyelinating neuropathies are more common. As might be expected from the role of the myelin sheath in saltatory conduction, demyelinated axons that have lost myelin have a slowed conduction velocity. In axonal neuropathies where the myelin sheath is not affected, there is a normal conduction velocity and no loss of myelin.

Diseases of Muscle (Myopathies)

The muscle diseases are conveniently divided into those that are inherited and those that seem to be acquired.

Inherited. The best known inherited diseases are the muscular dystrophies, and these are separated on the basis of clinical and genetic patterns (Table 14–3). Of those characterized by weakness alone, two can be distinguished clearly. The *Duchenne* type starts in the legs, affects boys only (because it is transmitted as an X-linked recessive trait), and progresses relatively rapidly, so that the boys are in wheelchairs by age 12, and they usually die in the third decade. The concentration of sarcoplasmic enzymes in serum is markedly increased. The *facioscapulohumeral* type differs in genetic pattern (autosomal domi-

Table 14–3. Major Forms of Muscular Dystrophy

Features	Duchenne	Facioscapulohumeral	Limb–girdle
Sex	Male	Both	Both
Onset	Before age 5	Adolescence	Adolescence
Initial symptoms	Pelvic	Shoulder–girdle	Either
Face involved	No	Always	No
Pseudohypertrophy	80%	No	Rare
Progression	Rapid	Slow	Slow
Inheritance	X-linked recessive	Autosomal dominant	Autosomal recessive
Serum enzymes	Very high	Normal	Slight increase

nant), affects the two sexes equally, starts later (usually in adolescence), affects the shoulder girdle and face early, and may be much milder, compatible with an almost normal life span. These clinical and genetic differences imply different biochemical abnormalities, which have not been identified. However, increasing evidence suggests that Duchenne dystrophy is due to a genetic fault of the muscle surface membrane. Forms of muscular dystrophy that do not fit either of these major types are lumped as *limb– girdle dystrophy*, which probably includes more than one type since families differ in distribution of weakness, age at onset, and genetic patterns.

A fourth type of muscular dystrophy, called *myotonic muscular dystrophy*, has, in addition to weakness, a characteristic feature—*myotonia*, which is a delayed relaxation of muscle after voluntary contraction, percussion of muscle, or electrical stimulation of muscle. The delayed relaxation is apparently due to repetitive firing of the muscle action potentials and is independent of nerve supply because it persists after nerve block or curarization. The molecular fault is not known and may involve an abnormality of the membrane conductance to Cl^-. In addition to myotonia, the dystrophy itself has special characteristics in that it involves cranial muscles and the limb weakness is primarily distal rather than proximal. The symptoms are not confined to muscles; for instance, cataracts are found in all patients and testicular atrophy is common.

Acquired. The prototype of an acquired myopathy is *dermatomyositis*, defined by two clinical features, each with special characteristics. The rash has a predilection for the face, chest, and extensor surfaces of joints, including the fingers. The myopathic weakness primarily affects proximal limb muscles. Both rash and weakness usually appear simultaneously and become worse in a matter of weeks. The weakness may be mild or life threatening, and the disorder affects children or adults. The cause is not known, but about 10% of the adult cases are associated with malignant neoplasm. The pathogenesis is not known either, but the prominence of lymphocytic infiltration of muscle suggests a cell-mediated autoimmune disorder. Corticosteroid therapy is therefore used routinely, but its effects are unproven because the disease may remit spontaneously.

An Overall View

At the moment there is no treatment for most diseases of muscle. However, muscle represents a target of nerve cell action that is accessible for biochemical study or for culture. It is likely that the cell-biological approaches to muscle and its neural control will yield, in the near future, substantial insights into the mechanisms of various muscle diseases—a useful step toward development of rational treatment.

Selected Readings and References

See the following papers in P. B. Beeson, W. McDermott, and J. B. Wyngaarden (eds.), 1979. Cecil Textbook of Medicine, 15th ed. Philadelphia: Saunders.

Dyck, P. J. Diseases of the peripheral nervous system, pp. 899–913.

Rowland, L. P. Diseases of muscle and neuromuscular junction, pp. 914–930.

Brooke, M. H. 1977. A Clinician's View of Neuromuscular Diseases. Baltimore: Williams & Wilkins.

Rowland, L. P., and Layzer, R. B. 1977. Muscular dystrophies, atrophies, and related diseases. In A. B. Baker (ed.), Clinical Neurology, Vol. 3. New York: Harper & Row, pp. 1–109.

Sensory Systems of the Brain: Sensation and Perception

III

The brain functions both to perceive and to initiate action. These two aspects of the nervous system are considered in the next two sections: Part III on Sensory Systems and Part IV on Motor Systems.

Familiar to all of us are the perception of incoming information in the form of sensation (sight, sound, smell, taste, and touch), the perception of our own bodies in movement (position sense and kinesthesia), and the awareness of harmful stimuli arising both in the external world and from within as pain.

The modern study of sensory systems begins with *psychophysics*, the establishment of quantitative correlations between specific physical stimuli and the sensations that they evoke. Important information can be obtained about the various classes of receptors, their specificity, the stimuli they respond to, and the major sensory pathways that carry information from these receptors to the cortex. Thus physiological events can be related to stimulus events, and both can be correlated with quantitative assessments of discriminative sensory behavior. As a result, we can begin to understand how the myriad sensory events that impinge upon us alter the activity of the brain so as to generate specific perceptions.

Sensory neurons—both peripheral receptors and central cells—often show remarkable specificity for a stimulus. This specificity is related to the locus of the stimulus and its quality, dynamic properties, and configuration. Specificity provides an important means for encoding some attributes of sensations within the nervous system. For encoding other attributes of sensation, however, the pattern of activity in a population of neurons seems to be equally important.

A major task of current sensory physiological research is to determine, for each sensory pathway, the extent to which either specificity or pattern codes are utilized. We know, for example, that receptor specificity for sweet, sour, bitter, or salty is very important in coding for different tastes. In contrast, auditory coding depends, in large part, on pattern coding. Many other sensory systems are more complicated and involve combinations of sensory neuron specificity and response pattern. In addition, both serial and parallel processing occur in each sensory system. It is important to learn which aspects of a given sensation are analyzed in the several cortical and subcortical regions devoted to that sensibility.

John H. Martin

Somatic Sensory System I: Receptor Physiology and Submodality Coding

15

We believe that our perceptions are always precise and direct. We shall learn in these nine chapters on sensory systems that this belief is an illusion—a perceptual illusion. We shall see that we confront the world neither directly nor precisely, but, as Vernon Mountcastle has pointed out:

> . . . from a brain linked to what is "out there" by a few million fragile sensory nerve fibers, our only information channels, our lifelines to reality. They also provide what is essential for life itself: an afferent excitation that maintains the conscious state, the awareness of self.
>
> Sensations are set by the encoding functions of the sensory nerve endings and by the integrated neural mechanics of the central nervous system. Afferent nerve fibers are not high fidelity recorders, for they accentuate certain stimulus features, neglect others. The central neuron is a story-teller with regard to the nerve fibers, and it is never completely trustworthy, allowing distortions of quality and measure . . . *Sensation is an abstraction, not a replication, of the real world.*[1]

Our contact with the external world occurs through specialized neural structures called *sensory receptors*. At these receptor organs, various natural stimuli that impinge upon our bodies are transformed into neurally relevant signals. We receive information not only from the external world, but also from within our bodies: from the blood, the viscera, and the movement of skeletal muscles. In order to distinguish the systems that convey signals from these different sources the sensory systems are divided into three categories: (1) exteroceptive, (2) proprioceptive, and (3) interoceptive.

Exteroceptive systems are sensitive to stimuli from the external environment. These include vision, audition, skin sensation, and some chemical senses. *Proprioceptive systems* provide information about the relative position of body segments to one another and the position of the body in space. *Interoceptive systems* signal internal bodily events such as the blood glucose level and blood pressure.

The somatic sensory system, which is the subject of this and the next three chapters, receives and processes stimuli that impinge on the body surface or originate from within the deeper tis-

---

[1]Mountcastle, V. B. The view from within: Pathways to the study of perception. Johns Hopkins Med. J. 136:109, 1975.

sues and viscera. Thus, unlike the visual system, which is entirely exteroceptive, the somatic sensory system serves all three classes of stimulus reception (exteroceptive, proprioceptive, and interoceptive). We may therefore view the somatic sensory system as comprising several different perceptual *submodalities*, or subclasses, each related to different stimuli. There are four major submodalities:

1. *Touch–pressure sensation* is elicited by mechanical stimulation applied to the body surface.
2. *Position sense* is elicited by mechanical disturbances in the muscles and joints; this submodality has two components, the sense of static limb position and the sensation of limb movement (kinesthesia).
3. *Thermal sensations* include separate cold and warm sense.
4. *Pain sensation* is elicited by noxious stimuli.

Each of the major submodalities is mediated by a particular class of receptors.

Interoceptive signals (such as those keeping our brain informed about blood pressure or the concentration of glucose in the blood) often do not reach consciousness; however, we are typically aware of exteroceptive and proprioceptive stimuli. The relationship between the physical dimensions of sensory stimuli and our perception of them is the basis of psychophysics. In this chapter we shall first illustrate how psychophysical studies can provide major insights into receptor function and neural processing. We shall then consider the mechanisms whereby stimulus energy is encoded into neural signals. Finally, we shall examine the nature of receptor specificity and survey the types of known somatic receptors and their general physiological properties. In Chapters 16–18 we shall consider how the sensory submodalities, which are initially processed by separate afferent information channels, converge in the spinal cord, then project to the thalamus, and finally reach the somatic sensory cortex.

Sensory Psychophysical Studies Have Correlated Behavior with the Physiology of Neurons

Sensory psychophysics is an area of experimental psychology concerned with the quantification of sensory experiences. Psychophysical investigation allows one to establish the limits of performance and overall function of the neural machinery comprising a sensory system. In addition, by providing quantitative methods for investigating sensory phenomena, psychophysics provides a powerful experimental tool for correlating behavior with the physiological properties of neurons. To illustrate this correlation we shall consider two psychophysical observations that can be explained by the physiological properties of afferent fibers: sensory threshold and evaluation of stimulus intensity.

Sensory Thresholds for Perception and for Afferent Fibers May Be Equal

The *absolute sensory threshold* is defined as the lowest stimulus intensity a subject can detect. The determination of this threshold is a statistical process. If a subject is presented several series of stimuli of different intensities, the intensity at which the stimulus is first detected in each series (i.e., threshold) will differ slightly. Moreover, if a subject is presented a series of stimuli whose intensity is close to the average threshold, he or she will typically fail to detect a certain proportion. It is therefore convenient to define threshold as that stimulus intensity detected in 50% of the trials. This is shown as curve *b* in Figure 15–1. In this

figure, probability of detection is graphed as a function of stimulus intensity.

This definition of threshold does not take into consideration the fact that subjects frequently report a sensory experience (i.e., detection) when no stimulus is actually presented; this is referred to as a *false positive* or *false alarm*. It is possible to reconcile the occurrence of a false alarm with the sensory threshold by means of the theory of *signal detection* developed by W. P. Tanner and J. A. Swets. According to this theory a subject's stimulus-detecting capabilities can be divided into two components, each of which can be measured separately: (1) the absolute *detectability* of the sensory system under examination; and (2) the *criterion* the subject uses to evaluate the presence (or absence) of a stimulus. In certain behavioral circumstances it may be functionally advantageous to report the presence of a stimulus even when the stimulus is absent. Consider the soldier in a fox hole who might duck at the slightest *mention* of gunfire! This anxiety due to the danger of battle would manifest itself as a decrease in the observed threshold (Figure 15–1, curve *a*). Similarly, threshold increases are observed, such as heightened pain thresholds during competitive events (Figure 15–1, curve *c*).

In addition to measuring a subject's threshold for detecting a stimulus, we can also measure the threshold of a particular class of afferent fibers to the same stimulus. Such psychophysical observations are typically obtained from human subjects and the afferent fiber recordings are usually obtained from experimental animals. Recently, Vallbo and colleagues recorded from afferent fibers in alert (i.e., unanesthetized) humans and were able to combine the psychophysical and physiological experiments in a single subject. The advantage of this method is that the subject is able to communicate verbally an objective and subjective appraisal of the stimulus while afferent fiber response patterns are assessed. The relationship between afferent fiber threshold and perceptual threshold is exemplified by the recent work of Vallbo suggesting that the afferent fiber threshold is approximately equal to the perceptual threshold. He showed in human subjects that detection of a mechanical stimulus corresponded to the presence of activity in a single afferent fiber!

The comparison of psychophysical and electrophysiological results is essential for assigning roles to particular afferent fiber types in the mediation of particular sensations.

15–1 Absolute sensory threshold, curve **b**, is an idealized representation of the relationship between stimulus intensity and the probability of stimulus detection. Curve a is that which would be observed if either the detectability of the sensory system increased or response criterion decreased; curve **c** illustrates the converse.

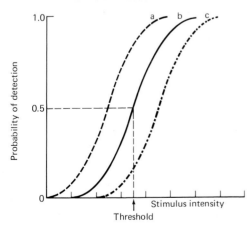

Stimulus Discrimination and Intensity Evaluation Are Correlated with the Discharge Rate of Afferent Fibers

Not only is the somatic sensory system remarkably sensitive in detecting the occurrence of stimuli, but the system also provides information concerning the magnitude of the stimulus. This is important for our ability to discriminate between stimuli and to estimate stimulus intensity.

Our capacity to distinguish stimuli that differ only in magnitude depends upon how large the stimuli are. In considering perception of weight, for example, we perceive a 1-kg weight as obviously different from a 2-kg weight, but it is very difficult to tell the difference between a 50- and a 51-kg weight; yet both sets differ by only 1 kg! This problem was examined in the nineteenth century by E. H. Weber (see Boring), who developed a quantitative description of the relationship between stimulus intensity and discrimination, now known as Weber's law, whereby

$$\Delta S = K \cdot S$$

where ΔS is the minimal intensity difference that can be perceived relative to a reference stimulus S (i.e., background), and K is a constant. Thus, as the reference stimulus intensity increases, the magnitude of the increment in intensity necessary to perceive the stimulus as different also increases.

In 1860, Gustav Fechner applied Weber's law to sensory experience (see Boring). Fechner found that the intensity of the sensation experienced by a subject is proportional to the logarithm of the strength of the stimulus:

$$I = K \log \frac{S}{S_0}$$

where I is the subjectively experienced intensity, S_0 is the threshold, S is the suprathreshold stimulus used in the estimation of stimulus magnitude, and K is a constant.[2]

Subsequently, in 1953, S. S. Stevens at Harvard noted that subjective experience is proportional not to the logarithm but to the nth power of the suprathreshold stimulus. In these cases the

sensory experience is best described by a power rather than a logarithmic relationship:

$$I = K \cdot (S - S_0)^n.$$

Without concerning ourselves with the details of these formulations, the important point is that Fechner believed that the relationship between subjective sensation and the physical magnitude of a stimulus is a *log* function, whereas Stevens felt it is a *power* function. The power function has been shown to be more accurate over an extended range for describing the relation between stimulus intensity and sensation. In general, a graph of subjective estimates of magnitude as a function of stimulus intensity typically parallels the intensity function of afferent fibers (see Figure 15–3)—a function that is achieved by plotting fiber discharges as a function of stimulus intensity. In fact, a correlation can be made between the perceived magnitude of stimulus intensity and the rate at which afferent fibers discharge. Therefore, a comparison of psychophysical and electrophysiological data can provide important insights into sensory functions by describing the overall limits of performance of the sensory systems. As we shall see in later sections of this chapter, an analysis of our sensory capacities is essential for understanding how the nervous system encodes the various stimulus dimensions that we can perceive.

Sensory Transduction Provides the First Step for the Extraction of Stimulus Features

The function of somatic receptors is to convert (or transduce) natural stimuli into electrical signals. We shall consider stimulus transduction in a particularly well-understood mechanoreceptor, the Pacinian corpuscle (Figure 15–2A).

Receptor activation requires that the stimulus be of suitable intensity (greater than threshold) as well as of suitable quality. (The latter requirement will be discussed in detail later in this chapter.) The area of skin within which stimuli evoke activity in a receptor is called the *receptive field*. Receptive field dimensions typically exceed the regions of tissue directly innervated since stimulus energy can be transmitted through body tissue.

The key to understanding sensory transduction lies in the analysis of the receptor (or generator) potential. As discussed in Part II, the receptor potential is a local (nonpropagated) depolarizing potential that is restricted to the receptive mem-

---

[2]The subject's ability to rate the intensity of a stimulus can be quantified through a psychophysical technique called *magnitude estimation*. A subject is presented stimuli differing only in magnitude and asked to assign a numerical (i.e., 1 to 10) or subjective (i.e., weak to strong) index to each stimulus intensity.

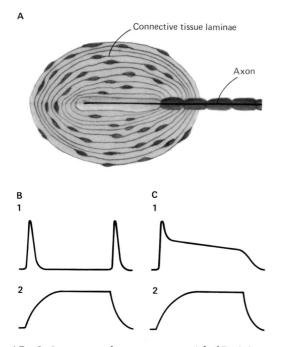

A

Connective tissue laminae

Axon

B
1

C
1

2

2

15–2 Structure and generator potential of Pacinian corpuscle. **A.** Cross section of Pacinian corpuscle. Note the concentrically arranged layers of connective tissue which surround the sensory nerve terminal and first node of Ranvier of the stem axon. **B.** Generator potential (1) evoked in intact Pacinian corpuscles in response to mechanical stimulation (2). **C.** Same as part B, but after removal of outer laminae. Note the prominent rapidly adapting on–off response in part B and the slowly adapting response in part C.

brane. It is due to an increase in conductance to the cations Na$^+$ and K$^+$ and is similar to an excitatory postsynaptic potential, which is also due to an increase in ionic conductance (see Chapter 7).

An important feature of all somatic receptors is the property of *adaptation*, a property whereby the generator potential decreases in amplitude in response to a maintained and constant stimulus. The Pacinian corpuscle is a *rapidly adapting receptor*. It responds only transiently at stimulus onset and sometimes also at the termination of a continuous stimulus (Figure 15–2B). The rate at which the generator potential of the Pacinian corpuscle adapts depends on an accessory structure surrounding a central axon. This accessory structure consists of concentric layers of connective tissue, much like the layers of an onion, surrounding an afferent nerve fiber terminal (Figure 15–2A). A steady stimulus applied to the outermost layer deforms the inner myelinated stem

axon, but transverse slippage between the layers of the accessory structure then takes place and the effective stimulus reaching the core decreases with time. Hence, the receptor serves to filter steady or slow components of mechanical stimuli. As a result, the receptor responds only to rapid changes in pressure (Figure 15–2B). Removal of the connective tissue accessory structure transforms the Pacinian corpuscle into a slowly adapting receptor (Figure 15–2C). Other receptors are slowly adapting or exhibit intermediate properties between rapid and slow adaptation. We shall consider other examples in later sections of this chapter.

Transduction processes in the other somatic receptors are in principle quite similar (as are such processes in the visual and auditory receptors). The appropriate stimulus produces an ionic conductance change in the receptive portion of the afferent fiber, which leads to a graded recep-

15–3 Relationship between stimulus intensity and discharge frequency. **A.** Stimuli of increasing intensity evoke greater generator potentials and more frequent action potentials. **B.** Plot of discharge frequency as a function of stimulus intensity. Note the absolute physiological threshold (S_0). (Adapted from Zimmermann, 1978.)

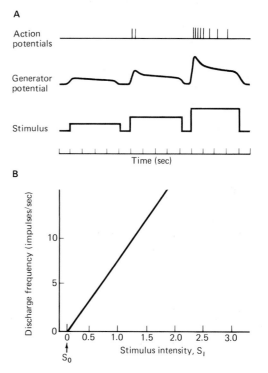

A

Action potentials

Generator potential

Stimulus

Time (sec)

B

Discharge frequency (impulses/sec)

10

5

0

0   0.5   1.0   1.5   2.0   2.5   3.0

S_0

Stimulus intensity, S_I

tor potential. Stimuli of larger amplitude evoke greater receptor potentials (Figure 15–3). When the amplitude of the receptor potential reaches the threshold of the trigger zone, an action potential is generated (see Chapter 6). In the Pacinian corpuscle, the trigger zone is at the first node of Ranvier. Greater suprathreshold stimuli lead to receptor potentials that exhibit a faster rate of rise and larger amplitude and evoke trains of action potentials at progressively higher frequencies.

Rapid adaptation in the Pacinian corpuscle is an example of a very simple form of selective detection by sensory neurons of certain features of a stimulus. This property of neural elements in sensory systems is called *stimulus feature extraction.* In the case of a steady and maintained stimulus the duration is uniquely defined by stimulus onset and offset. The intervening neural discharges are redundant and carry no additional information (see Werner).

Stimulus Intensity Is Encoded by Frequency and Population Codes

Lord Adrian first noted in the 1920s that the discharge frequency of any given afferent fiber increases with increasing stimulus intensity. This is known as the *frequency code* for stimulus intensity. Stimuli of greater amplitude evoke larger generator potentials, which cause not only a greater number of action potentials but also action potentials at higher frequencies. A graph of discharge frequency as a function of stimulus intensity *(intensity function)* often is similar to the psychophysical magnitude estimation function (see below).

A stimulus of increasing intensity also activates a greater number of receptors. This is called the *population code* for stimulus intensity. Therefore, as the intensity becomes greater, stimulus intensity is encoded in two ways: (1) there is an increase in the number of action potentials in each afferent fiber, and (2) there is an increase in the number of active afferent fibers. (As we shall see in Part IV, these principles also apply to the motor system, in which an increase in both the size of the population of active neurons and their frequency of firing determines the strength of muscle contraction.) Because all sensory information reaches the central nervous system via the afferent fibers connected to the receptors, we can view these fibers as information channels or lines of communication.

Afferent Fibers Conduct Action Potentials at Different Rates

It is a general principle that a single afferent fiber in a peripheral nerve always terminates on receptors of only one anatomical type, often located at the terminal portion of several branches. The terminal portion of the afferent fiber is sensitive to stimulation, whereas the more proximal portion of the fiber is specialized for conduction of action potentials to the spinal cord and brain stem. In later sections of this chapter we shall consider those properties of afferent fibers that are related to the type of receptor to which they are connected. Here we shall consider the conduction of action potentials to the central nervous system.

The speed at which an afferent fiber conducts action potentials is related to its diameter (see Chapter 5). For the larger myelinated fibers, the conduction velocity (in meters per second) is approximately equal to six times the diameter (in micrometers). The factor is somewhat smaller for smaller myelinated fibers and still smaller for unmyelinated fibers. In order to investigate the composition of afferent fibers in peripheral nerves it is essential that all efferent fibers are accounted for. The simplest way to accomplish this is to *de-efferent* the peripheral nerve. The ventral roots and gray rami, which respectively contain the somatic and autonomic motor supply, are transected in experimental animals. The animals are allowed to recover for approximately 4 months to ensure that the motor fibers distal to the transection undergo Wallerian degeneration. The nerves, which are thought to contain only afferent fibers because the motor fibers have degenerated, are then examined histologically.[3] The fibers are counted, diameters measured, and a frequency distribution histogram of fiber diameter is constructed. Conduction velocities (and axonal diameters) of afferent fibers innervating muscle are not the same as those of the fibers innervating the skin. The frequency distribution histogram for conduction velocity and axonal diameter in a muscle nerve is presented in Figure 15–4A and that for a cutaneous nerve is shown in Figure 15–4B. Note that the former histogram has four peaks, corresponding to the large myelinated

---

[3]Recently it has been shown that there are *afferent* fibers in ventral roots. However, for our purposes the "ventral root afferents" are not important because there are very few of them.

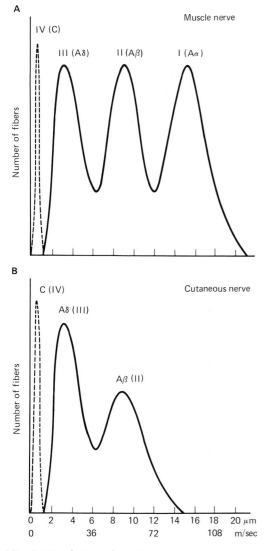

15-4 Distribution of conduction velocities and axon diameters of muscle (**A**) and skin (**B**) nerves.

Table 15-1. Afferent Fiber Groups

Muscle nerve	Cutaneous nerve	Fiber diameter (μm)	Conduction velocity (m/sec)
I	Aα	13–20	80–120
II	Aβ	6–12	35–75
III	Aδ	1–5	5–30
IV*	C*	0.2–1.5	0.5–2

*Unmyelinated.

ered in detail in Chapter 25. In Table 15-1 the two classification schemes are compared and the fiber diameters and conduction velocities are given for each group.

The conduction velocity of a fiber has important functional significance. The faster a fiber conducts action potentials, the quicker the central nervous system receives the information. Consider that a stimulus delivered to a fingertip activates receptors that are located quite a distance from the spinal cord. A C fiber, conducting at the rate of 0.5 m/sec, will take 2 sec or more to convey information to the central nervous system. In contrast, an A fiber will convey its information in 0.2 sec. If the stimulus is noxious and only carried by the C fibers, damage to the tissue can begin long before the central nervous system receives the information. There are also time delays for the central processing of a stimulus, which further increases the possibility of damage. Such conduction and processing delays are equally critical in determining the response to nonnoxious stimuli.

Stimulus Quality Is Encoded by a Labeled Line Code

How do afferent fibers encode stimulus quality? Does perception of stimulus quality depend on *receptor specificity* (so that only a particular receptor responds selectively to one type of stimulus), or does quality depend on the *temporal pattern of activity* in a single class of relatively nonspecific receptors? Modern electrophysiology has discriminated between these two possibilities by demonstrating that single receptors and the afferent fibers to which they connect exhibit specificity of response. Whether a receptor or its afferent is activated by a natural (or *adequate*) stimulus or artificially (i.e., by electrical stimulation) it will always elicit the same sensation. An excellent illustration of this prin-

(I), small myelinated (II), smaller myelinated (III), and unmyelinated (IV) fibers. The numerical classification identifying these peaks (I, II, III, IV) was first used for muscle afferents, but physiologists studying cutaneous nerves chose an alternative nomenclature (Aα, Aβ, Aδ, C). The cutaneous nerve histogram has only three peaks because the group I afferents are from the muscle spindle primaries and from the Golgi tendon organs, and thus are not represented in cutaneous nerves. The physiological properties of muscle spindle primaries and Golgi tendon organs will be considered

ciple is that electrical stimulation of the optic nerve produces a sensation similar to that produced by a brief flash of light. This specificity was first proposed by Johannes Müller in 1826 (see Boring) and forms the basis for what we now call a *labeled line code*, in contrast to a *pattern code*, in which the same pathway can signal different sensations by using different patterns of firing. Pattern codes do not seem to be important in the coding of stimulus quality by the afferent fiber in the somatic sensory system.

On the basis of their selective response to stimuli, four major classes of somatic receptors can be distinguished: nociceptors, thermoreceptors, chemoreceptors, and mechanoreceptors.

Pain Is Mediated by Nociceptors

Certain receptors respond selectively to damaging stimuli. These are called *nociceptors* (from the Latin *nocere,* to injure) and are connected to axons belonging to two fiber classes: Aδ and C. There are three major types of nociceptors. *Mechanical nociceptors* are activated only by very strong mechanical stimulation, most effectively by sharp objects. A striking example of this feature of nociceptors is illustrated in Figure 15–5. Figure 15–5A shows that no response is evoked when a blunt probe is pressed firmly into the skin. On the other hand, a pin prick (Figure 15–5B) or a pinch with a pointed instrument (Figure 15–5C) causes a very brisk response. The response in Figure 15–5C indicates that this is an intermediately adapting receptor. *Heat nociceptors* begin firing when the receptive field is heated to temperatures greater than 45°C, the heat pain threshold in humans. *Mixed nociceptors* respond to various types of noxious stimuli. Many of the latter receptors are connected to unmyelinated fibers and respond only to great pressure or to extreme temperatures that typically produce pain.

We recognize two different types of pain: fast and slow. *Fast pain* is an abrupt and sharp sensation that is carried by Aδ fibers. *Slow pain,* carried by C fibers, is a sickening burning sensation. Short latency fast pain followed by longer latency slow pain occurs, for example, when the web between the fingers is pinched hard and very quickly between the fingernails. Some C-fiber nociceptors are known to be chemoreceptors. The stimulus for activating these fibers is the release of some chemical substances by tissue injury, but the identity of these substances is not yet estab-

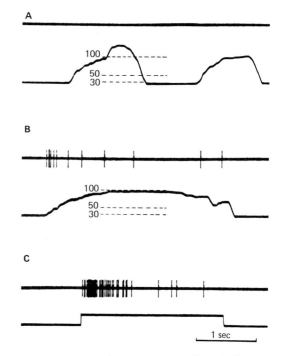

15–5 Responses (**upper trace** in each part) of a mechanical nociceptor with a myelinated afferent fiber to graded mechanical stimuli (**lower trace** in each part). In parts A and B, lower trace shows output of calibrated probe in grams. **A.** Blunt tip of 2 mm. **B.** Needle tip. **C.** Pinch to receptive field with a serrated forceps. (Adapted from Perl, 1968.)

lished. Morphologically, the nociceptors are free nerve endings.

Thermal Sensation Is Mediated by Cold and Warm Receptors

Temperature sensitivity is punctate: separate spots on the skin (approximately 1 mm in diameter) correspond to discrete zones of innervation where thermal stimulation elicits the sensation either of warmth or of cold. The threshold for eliciting a thermal sensation at these spots is considerably lower than at surrounding regions.

Cold receptors are connected to fibers that belong to the same bands of the fiber spectrum as the pain fibers: the Aδ and C fibers. The cold fibers discharge intensely when a cold stimulus is delivered and the frequency of firing is proportional to the rate and extent of temperature lowering, as are the psychophysical responses (Figure 15–6).

A curious sensory illusion can be demonstrated by applying a heat stimulus of 45°C to a

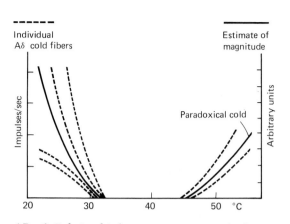

15–6 Relationship between temperature, discharge of individual monkey Aδ cold fiber (**broken lines**), and human verbal magnitude estimation (**solid lines**) of cold stimuli of comparable intensities and durations.

cold spot on the skin (Figure 15–6). This stimulus is ordinarily painful when applied to diffuse areas of skin, but when applied to a single cold spot it will be experienced by the subject not as hot, but as cold. This is called the sensation of *paradoxical cold*. Neurophysiological experiments have explained the neural substrate for this illusion. The heat stimulus excites cold receptors even though normally they would be selectively excited by decreasing temperature within a more modest range of temperature change. As a result, cold fibers increase their firing rate. This is another example of a labeled line code. Regardless of the mode of activation,

15–7 Similar to Figure 15–6, but shows discharge of individual monkey C warm fibers (**broken lines**) and human estimation (**solid line**) of the magnitude of warm and hot stimuli.

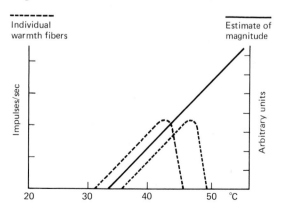

activity in the cold fiber population (or subpopulation) elicits the sensation of cold.

The role of warm receptors in the psychophysics of warmth and heat pain is illustrated in Figure 15–7. The correlation is strong between warm fiber discharge properties and estimations of warm stimuli (less than 45°C), but weak for hot stimuli (greater than 45°C). Therefore, we can state that warmth is mediated by unmyelinated (C) warm fibers. The initial pain associated with intense heat is mediated by heat nociceptors. Thermal receptors, like nociceptors, are free nerve endings.

Touch–Pressure Is Mediated by Rapidly and Slowly Adapting Mechanoreceptors
Rate of Adaptation and Receptor Morphology

Two different groups of receptor types mediate the response to mechanical stimuli: the slowly adapting mechanoreceptors, which respond continuously to an enduring stimulus, and the rapidly adapting mechanoreceptors, which respond only at the onset (and perhaps the termination) of such a stimulus (Figure 15–8). These two kinds of cutaneous mechanoreceptors have somewhat different fiber diameter spectra.

The rapidly adapting receptors have fibers in both Aβ and Aδ bands. The morphological types of receptors that connect to rapidly adapting Aβ afferent fibers have been identified. In hairy skin, the fibers are connected by free nerve endings at the base of the hair follicles (Figure 15–9A). Glabrous, or hairless, skin (such as that on the palms of the hands) contains rapidly adapting fibers of the Aβ fiber group that are connected to Meissner endings, an important rapidly adapting receptor. The hair and Meissner afferents are examples of cutaneous rapidly adapting receptors. The Pacinian corpuscle (Figure 15–9) is a rapidly adapting receptor that is located in subcutaneous tissue; in our earlier discussion of its morphology it was shown that rapid adaptation of the generator potential can be explained by the properties of the accessory structure.

The slowly adapting receptors that innervate the skin are confined to the Aβ band. Two kinds of slowly adapting afferent fibers in the hairy skin, called type I and type II, have been studied in detail (Figure 15–9). The *type I* afferent fibers have punctate receptive fields (corresponding to the small touch dome, Figure 15–9A). These receptors tend to fire in an irregular fashion when a maintained indentation stimulus is applied. They may only serve reflex functions since in humans they do not seem to generate touch sensations upon stimulation. The *type II* touch receptor gives rise to a more steady pattern of discharge in response to maintained pressure on the skin. It can also be excited by lateral stretch of the skin some distance from the point of maximum sensitivity. Ainsley Iggo, a leading sensory physiologist, has found that in the hairy skin this type of afferent fiber innervates the *Ruffini end-organ*. This is a structure in which the afferent fiber terminal branches, which are located in a connective tissue capsule, run parallel to the skin surface (Figure 15–9A). This receptor type seems to be concerned with the sensation of steady skin indentation.

Flutter and Vibration: Comparison of Psychophysics and the Electrophysiological Properties of Receptors

Rapidly adapting mechanoreceptors are particularly sensitive to *sinusoidal* mechanical stimuli which indent (and withdraw from) the skin at rapid rates (Figure 15–10A). Low-frequency sinusoidal mechanical stimulation evokes a light, fluttering feeling in human subjects, which they can localize well to the skin surface. This sensation is termed *flutter*. The sensation in response to high-frequency sinusoidal mechanical stimu-

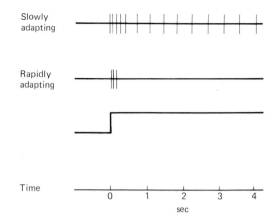

15–8 Responses of slowly and rapidly adapting mechanoreceptors to a step indentation of the skin.

15–9 Morphology of mechanoreceptors of the hairy and glabrous skin. **A.** Hairy skin. Rapidly adapting (**RA**) receptor, the Pacinian corpuscle, is located in the border region between the dermal and subcutaneous tissue. Other rapidly adapting receptors have fibers that are connected by free nerve endings at the base of the hair follicles. The type I slowly adapting (**SA**) receptors correspond to the touch dome. The type II slowly adapting receptors are located in the Ruffini end-organ. **B.** Glabrous skin. Meissner corpuscles, which are rapidly adapting receptors, are located in dermal papillae. Pacinian corpuscles are located beneath glabrous skin as well as hairy skin.

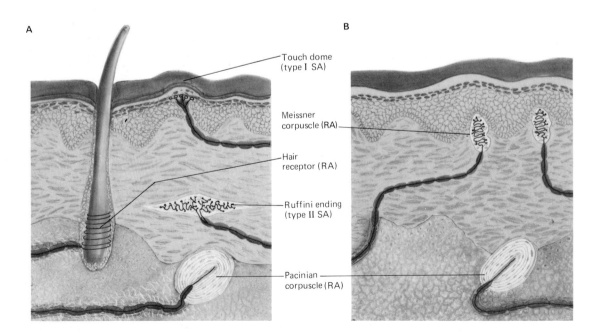

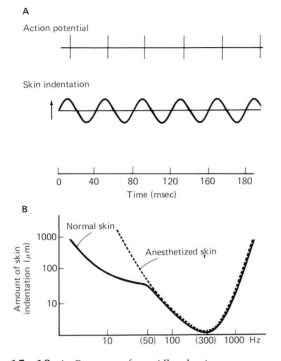

15–10 **A.** Response of a rapidly adapting mechanoreceptor to sinusoidal mechanical stimuli. Note that the afferent fiber response is a single action potential for each phase of the stimulus. **B.** Idealized threshold relationships for flutter and vibration psychophysical experiments. The abscissa shows frequency of sinusoidal mechanical stimulus and the ordinate indicates the magnitude of the threshold stimulus.

lation, called *vibration,* is a diffuse humming feeling localized to deeper tissues.

If the psychophysical thresholds for detection of flutter and vibration stimuli are plotted as a function of frequency of indentation, sensitivity is found to be greatest in the 200–300-Hz range, and falls off (i.e., increases in threshold) with both lower and higher frequencies (Figure 15–10B, *solid line*). Anesthesia of the *skin* causes an elevation only in the threshold to low-frequency (flutter) stimulation (Figure 15–10B, *broken line*). Vibratory sense is unchanged. This result suggests that the receptors responsible for flutter are located within the skin and those responsible for vibration are located in the deeper tissues, which are not affected by anesthesia.

Vernon Mountcastle and co-workers were able to explain these psychophysical data by the electrophysiological properties of mechanoreceptors. In hairy skin, the afferents responsible for low-

frequency flutter sensations are those innervating hair follicles (Aβ afferent fibers); in glabrous skin, functionally similar afferents end as Meissner corpuscles in the dermal papillae. High-frequency vibration is detected by deeply located Pacinian corpuscles.

Position Sense and Kinesthesia Are Mediated by Muscle Afferent Fibers and Joint Afferents

Position sense typically refers to two kinds of sensations: (1) kinesthesia (joint movement), and (2) static limb position. What afferents mediate static limb position? In 1900, Sherrington argued that the joint afferent fibers and muscle afferent fibers cooperate in the determination of static limb position. Over the past few years, Burgess and his colleagues have examined the role of joint afferents by carrying out systematic psychophysical studies of limb position sense, and of the static and dynamic properties of joint afferent fibers innervating the knee. They found, for example, that knee joint afferents are not sensitive to joint angle over the midrange, where static position sense is well developed. Moreover, anesthesia of the joint capsule often leaves subjects with good static limb position sense and individuals with artificial joints can have good static limb position sense. This evidence suggests that the joint afferents may not play a dominant role in the sense of static limb position.

Matthews and his colleagues conducted psychophysical experiments on kinesthesia which involved illusions of limb movement that occur when muscles of the limb are vibrated. Muscle vibration (i.e., vibrating the skin over a muscle at larger amplitudes than those discussed for vibration sense) causes the length of the muscle to vary by a small amount. Vibration powerfully excites specialized receptors in muscle called muscle spindles. Not surprisingly, vibration of a muscle activates muscle spindle organs, as muscle spindles are stretch receptors (see discussion in Chapters 2 and 25). This is similar to (but not as effective as) tugging on the tendon of a muscle. Because the muscle spindle afferents excite the motor neurons innervating the muscle, this stimulus causes the muscle to contract (tonic vibration reflex) and the limb to move. Matthews found that there is a considerable disparity between the actual limb position and the perceived position that a subject reported when the limb was vibrated (Figure 15–11). The illusion shown in Figure 15–11 is in the direction of extension,

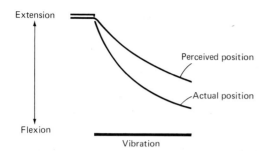

15–11 Illusion of limb movement after stimulation of the biceps tendon. Upon vibration of the biceps tendon the subject perceives his forearm to be somewhat more extended than the actual position. Note that the illusion is in the direction of limb extension.

which would be expected if muscle spindles mediate the illusion. Vibration of the biceps increases muscle spindle activity within the biceps. Normally, these receptors would exhibit an increase in their rate of discharge when the biceps is stretched (i.e., extension). The experiments of Matthews and Burgess suggest that we estimate joint angle from muscle length information provided by muscle spindle receptors. Unlike joint afferents, muscle spindle receptors have complex properties that are also controlled by efferent signals from the central nervous system. The joint afferents may also play a role in signaling the extremes of limb position and pressure changes within the joint capsule.

An Overall View

We have at present rather complete knowledge, extending from receptor identification to correlative sensory quantification, of four mechanoreceptors. Nonneural accessory structures, fast fiber conduction, and receptor specificity are important in discriminative mechanoreception. In contrast, free nerve endings and slower fiber conduction characterize the sensations of pain and temperature (Table 15–2).

Each of these sensory receptors is optimally tuned to different stimulus characteristics, ranging from steady indentation to high-frequency vibration for mechanosensation, and from cold to warm for thermal sensation. Thus, a complex stimulus would generate activity that is fractionated into relatively independent sensory channels by the filtering properties of the different receptors. The sensory message is transformed in a way that foreshadows the more radical central feature abstraction of the central nervous system.

Selected Readings and References

Burgess, P. R., and Perl, E. R. 1973. Cutaneous mechanoreceptors and nociceptors. In A. Iggo (ed.), Handbook of Sensory Physiology, Vol. 2, The Somatosensory System. New York: Springer, pp. 29–78.

Goodwin, G. M., McCloskey, D. I., and Matthews, P. B. C. 1972. The contribution of muscle afferents to kinaesthesia shown by vibration induced illusions of movement and by the effects of paralysing joint afferents. Brain 95:705–748.

Iggo, A. 1974. Cutaneous receptors. In J. I. Hubbard (ed.), The Peripheral Nervous System. New York: Plenum, pp. 347–404.

Mountcastle, V. B. 1975. The view from within: Pathways to the study of perception. Johns Hopkins Med. J. 136:109–131.

Stevens, S. S. 1961. The psychophysics of sensory function. In W. A. Rosenblith (ed.), Sensory Communication. Cambridge, Mass.: MIT Press, pp. 1–33.

Vallbo, Å. B., Hagbarth, K.-E., Torebjörk, H. E., and Wallin, B. G. 1979. Somatosensory, proprioceptive, and sympathetic activity in human peripheral nerves. Physiol. Rev. 59:919–957.

Other References

Adrian, E. D., and Zotterman, Y. 1926. The impulses produced by sensory nerve endings. Part II. The response of a single end organ. J. Physiol. (Lond.) 61:151–171.

Boring, E. G. 1942. Sensation and Perception in the History of Experimental Psychology. New York: Appleton-Century.

Table 15–2. Receptor Types Active in Various Sensations

Receptor type	Fiber group	Submodality
Hair follicle	$A\beta$	Flutter
Meissner corpuscle	$A\beta$	Flutter
Ruffini end-organ	$A\beta$	Steady skin indentation
Pacinian corpuscle	$A\beta$	Vibration
Free nerve ending	$A\delta$, C	Pain and temperature sense

Chambers, M. R., Andres, K. H., von Duering, M., and Iggo, A. 1972. The structure and function of the slowly adapting type II mechanoreceptor in hairy skin. Q. J. Exp. Physiol. 57:417–445.

Iggo, A., and Muir, A. R. 1969. The structure and function of a slowly adapting touch corpuscle in hairy skin. J. Physiol. (Lond.) 200:763–796.

Knibestöl, M., and Vallbo, Å. B. 1976. Stimulus-response-functions of primary afferents and psycho-physical intensity estimation on mechanical skin stimulation in the human hand. In Y. Zotterman (ed.), Sensory Functions of the Skin in Primates with Special Reference to Man. Oxford: Pergamon, pp. 201–213.

LaMotte, R. H., and Campbell, J. N. 1978. Comparison of responses of warm and nociceptive C-fiber afferents in monkey with human judgments of thermal pain. J. Neurophysiol. 41:509–528.

Loewenstein, W. R., and Mendelson, M. 1965. Components of receptor adaptation in a Pacinian corpuscle. J. Physiol. (Lond.) 177:377–397.

See the following papers in V. B. Mountcastle (ed.), 1980, Medical Physiology, 14th ed., Vol. 1. St. Louis: Mosby.

Mountcastle, V. B. Sensory receptors and neural encoding: Introduction to sensory processes, pp. 327–347.

Mountcastle, V. B. Neural mechanisms in somesthesis, pp. 348–390.

Mountcastle, V. B. Pain and temperature sensibilities, pp. 391–427.

Perl, E. R. 1968. Myelinated afferent fibres innervating the primate skin and their response to noxious stimuli. J. Physiol. (Lond.) 197:593–615.

Schmidt, R. F. 1978. Somatovisceral sensibility. In R. F. Schmidt (ed.), Fundamentals of Sensory Physiology. New York: Springer, pp. 81–125.

Sherrington, C. S. 1900. The muscular sense. In E. A. Schäfer, Text-book of Physiology, Vol. 2. Edinburgh & London: Pentland, pp. 1002–1025.

Stevens, S. S. 1953. On the brightness of lights and the loudness of sounds. Science (Wash., D.C.) 118:576.

Tanner, Jr., W. P., and Swets, J. A. 1954. A decision-making theory of visual detection. Psychol. Rev. 61:401–409.

Werner, G. 1974. Introduction to feature extraction by neurons and behavior. In F. O. Schmidt and F. G. Worden (eds.), The Neurosciences. Third Study Program. Cambridge, Mass.: MIT Press, pp. 93–94.

Zimmermann, M. 1978. Neurophysiology of sensory system. In R. F. Schmidt (ed.), Fundamentals of Sensory Physiology. New York: Springer, pp. 31–80.

John H. Martin

Somatic Sensory System II: Anatomical Substrates for Somatic Sensation

16

The somatic receptors are the first neurons in a chain of neurons that reaches from the periphery to the cerebral cortex. Second-order neurons in the spinal cord and medulla transmit the sensory information to the thalamus, where it is then conveyed (by third-order cells in the thalamus) to the cerebral cortex.

In the last chapter we learned that different sensory receptors are sensitive to different stimulus qualities. This specificity is shared by central neurons. Afferent fibers from receptors that are functionally specific for a particular submodality connect to anatomically discrete regions in the spinal cord and in the brain stem. In this chapter we shall consider the structural organization of the peripheral and central neuronal pathways for somatic sensation. We shall consider only the projection from the body (via the spinal cord). The projection from the face (via the trigeminal nerve) is discussed in Chapter 33 in the context of the brain stem.

Organization of the Peripheral Nerves

Information from the periphery is transmitted to the central nervous system by the afferent nerve fibers. Bundles of these afferent fibers join efferent fibers to form the *peripheral nerves.* As the peripheral nerves approach the spinal cord they become known as *spinal nerves.* Here, the afferent fibers separate from the efferent ones and enter the spinal cord as the dorsal root, each root innervating a peripheral region (Figures 16–1 and 16–2). The extent of this region cannot be inferred simply by summing the innervation areas of the various peripheral nerves that send afferent fibers into the dorsal root. At various points, called *plexuses,* located between the cord and the periphery, the afferent fibers are regrouped so that each spinal nerve receives afferents from several peripheral nerves. As a result of this overlap, the area innervated by a dorsal root is less well defined than that of a peripheral nerve. In fact, the innervation areas of adjacent dorsal roots overlap a good deal. Therefore, section of the distal portion of a peripheral cutaneous nerve will result in a highly circumscribed area of sensory loss in the skin. In contrast, section of a spinal nerve or a

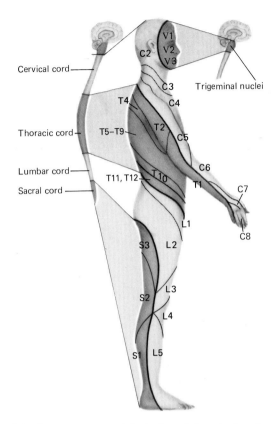

16–2 Dermatomes of the body and the spinal cord segments to which the dorsal roots project. (Adapted from Zimmermann, 1978.)

16–1 Relationship between the area of skin innervated by peripheral nerves and dorsal roots.

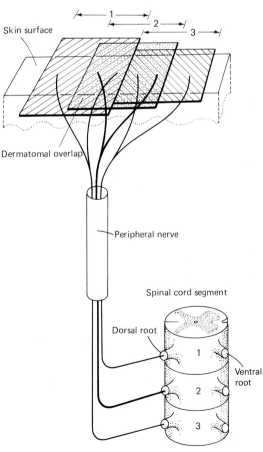

dorsal root often results in only a modest sensory loss.

The sensory innervation of a dorsal root is called a *dermatome.* The dermatomes are arranged in a highly ordered way on the body surface. Studies of the sensibility and responsiveness that remain after systematic lesioning of the various dorsal roots have outlined the dermatomal distribution of the peripheral cutaneous fields for each of the spinal dorsal segments (Figure 16–2). Maps of the dermatomes provide a diagnostic tool for localizing injury to the spinal cord and dorsal roots. Such a map of the human forearm is shown in Figure 16–3. One can see that injury to C8 and T1 may give rise to sensory changes limited to the distal forearm and fourth and fifth digits of the hand. The segmental organization of the dorsal roots is preserved in the various ascending systems and will be considered in detail in Chapter 17. This is an example of one of the key principles of sensory organization: there is an orderly

Dermatomes

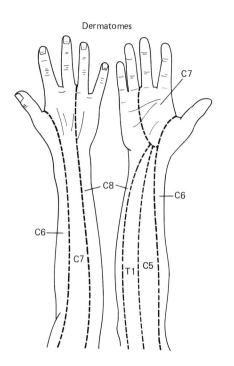

Peripheral nerves

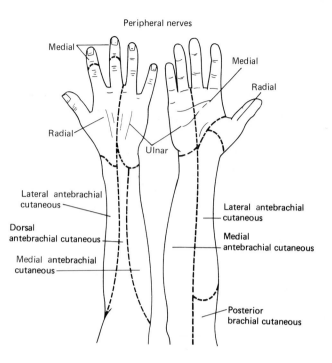

16–3 Relationship of dermatomes and peripheral nerves in the human forearm.

arrangement between regions of the receptive sheet and those of the various central structures receiving sensory projections. This orderly mapping of the body surface onto central neural structures is called *somatotopy*. There are analogous organizational schemes for the visual system (retinotopy) and the auditory system (tonotopy).

Organization of the Spinal Cord

The spinal cord has three readily identifiable functions:

1. It is a relay point for sensory information.
2. It is a conduit for all ascending afferent pathways and descending motor tracts.
3. It contains the interneurons and motor neurons that mediate body and limb movement.

The spinal cord is organized into a butterfly-shaped central area, where the cell bodies of neurons are located, and a surrounding region of afferent and efferent axons, most of which are myelinated (Figure 16–4A).

Spinal Gray Matter

The central cellular region is referred to as the gray matter of the spinal cord because it appears gray in unstained material (as does the cellular region of the cerebral cortex). Size and shape of the gray matter vary as a function of the size of the spinal nerve roots (see Figure 16–6). The cervical and lumbar spinal segments that serve the limbs are larger than the thoracic and lumbar segments that serve the trunk because the arms and legs are more densely innervated than the trunk.

The spinal gray matter is divided into a dorsal horn, an intermediate zone, and a ventral horn (Figure 16–4B). Each of these zones can be subdivided into nuclei. Six nuclei are particularly important:

1. The *posterior marginal nucleus,* which serves as an important relay for pain and temperature sense
2. The *substantia gelatinosa,* which integrates afferent information
3. The *nucleus proprius,* which integrates sensory information in conjunction with descending control
4. *Clarke's nucleus* or cell column, which relays limb position to a motor structure, the cerebellum

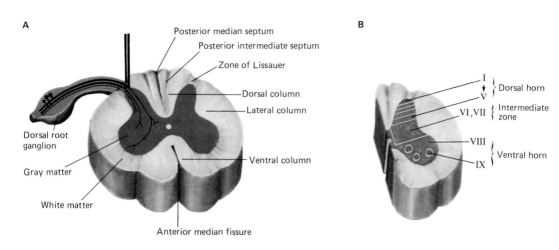

A

Posterior median septum
Posterior intermediate septum
Zone of Lissauer
Dorsal column
Lateral column
Ventral column
Dorsal root ganglion
Gray matter
White matter
Anterior median fissure

B

I } Dorsal horn
V
VI, VII } Intermediate zone
VIII
IX } Ventral horn

5. The *intermediolateral nucleus* or cell column, which contains autonomic preganglionic neurons
6. The *motor nuclei,* which contain motor neurons that innervate the skeletal muscles.

The locations of these nuclei are shown in Figure 16–5A.

A functionally important classiflcation scheme

16–4 A. General organization of a spinal segment.
B. Schematic view of the spinal gray matter including the laminae of Rexed.

16–5 Nuclei and laminae of the spinal gray matter. In each part, the left-hand section is a low lumbar segment and the right-hand section is a thoracic segment. **A.** The important nuclei. **B.** Rexed's laminae. Note that lamina VI is not ordinarily present in thoracic segments.

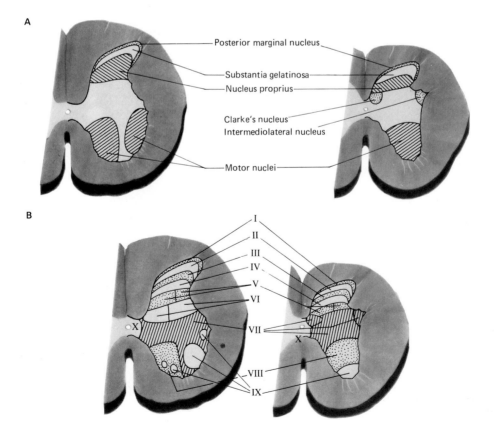

A

Posterior marginal nucleus
Substantia gelatinosa
Nucleus proprius
Clarke's nucleus
Intermediolateral nucleus
Motor nuclei

B

I
II
III
IV
V
VI
VII
VIII
IX
X

Table 16–1. Major Spinal Cord Nuclei and Corresponding Laminae and Regions

Nuclei	Laminae	Regions
Posterior marginal nucleus	I	Dorsal horn
Substantia gelatinosa	II, III	Dorsal horn
Nucleus proprius	IV, V	Dorsal horn
Clarke's nucleus (T1–L2)	VII	Intermediate zone
Intermediolateral nucleus	VII	Intermediate zone
Motor nuclei	IX	Ventral horn

was established by Bror Rexed in 1952. He divided the spinal gray matter into 10 horizontally oriented layers or laminae (Figures 16–4B and 16–5B). Laminae I–V are roughly equivalent to the dorsal horn, laminae VI and VII are equivalent to the intermediate zone, and laminae VIII and IX are equivalent to the ventral horn. Lamina X refers to the gray matter surrounding the central canal. The laminar organization and the more common spinal cord nuclei found in these laminae are presented in Table 16–1.

Spinal White Matter

The area surrounding the gray matter is called the white matter of the spinal cord because myelinated axons are white in unstained sections. Located in the white matter are the major ascending and descending tracts as well as pathways made up of the short axons that connect local regions of the cord (these interconnecting tracts are called the *fasciculus proprius*). The white matter is divided into three bilaterally paired columns or funiculi (Figure 16–4A):

1. The ventral columns (which lie medial to the ventral horns)
2. The lateral columns
3. The dorsal columns.

Like the gray matter, the white matter varies considerably in size along the spinal cord (Figure 16–6). Most dramatic is the increase from caudal to rostral levels. This increase reflects the increasing number of fibers that ascend to higher levels as additional contingents of afferent fibers from the periphery arrive at the spinal cord at each segment. In addition, there are more descending fibers rostrally, since those destined for caudal segments have not yet left the white matter to terminate within the gray matter.

16–6 Cross-sectional shape of various spinal segments. (Adapted from Ranson and Clark, 1953.)

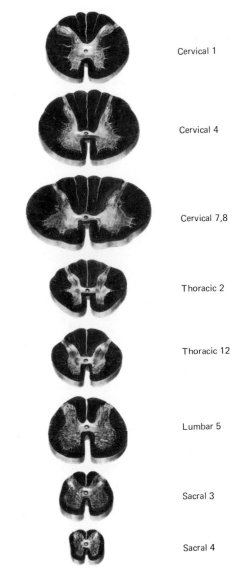

Cervical 1

Cervical 4

Cervical 7,8

Thoracic 2

Thoracic 12

Lumbar 5

Sacral 3

Sacral 4

Termination of Dorsal Root Fibers

Dorsal root fibers enter the spinal cord at its dorsolateral margin. These fibers have their cell bodies in the dorsal root ganglion. The largest cells have myelinated axons up to 20 μm in diameter. The smallest cells have unmyelinated axons less than 1 μm in diameter. The large-diameter myelinated fibers enter the spinal cord medially and the smaller fibers (thinly myelinated or unmyelinated) enter more laterally (Figure 16–4A).

Fibers that enter the spinal cord send branches that ascend and descend in the cord and arborize in the spinal gray matter. In some cases the ascending branch may project to the medulla. Again, the axons from large and small cells, carrying information from different submodalities, have different distributions. Collaterals of small-diameter fibers do not enter the gray matter immediately but pass into the zone of Lissauer (located dorsal and lateral to lamina I of the dorsal horn; Figure 16–4). There the fibers bifurcate into branches that ascend and descend one to two segments and terminate superficially in the posterior marginal nucleus or pass through the superficial dorsal horn to terminate in the nucleus proprius. Only a few fine fibers terminate in the substantia gelatinosa. Collaterals of large-diameter fibers do not pass into the zone of Lissauer but enter the lateral aspect of the dorsal columns (Figure 16–4) and enter the dorsal horn from its medial aspect. Large-diameter fibers have been observed to terminate throughout the spinal gray matter and some even terminate directly in motor nuclei (lamina IX). These fibers mediate the stretch reflex, which was described in Chapter 2. Collaterals entering the dorsal horn at the same level of entrance in part provide the anatomical basis for *intrasegmental reflexes.* Collaterals associated with the ascending and descending branches mediate *intersegmental reflexes.*

Two Major Ascending Systems Convey Somatic Sensory Information

There are two major ascending systems for somatic sensation: (1) the dorsal column–medial lemniscal system, and (2) the anterolateral system. These systems relay afferent information to the brain for perception, arousal, and motor control. The dorsal columns, which are made up of large diameter axons from dorsal root ganglion cells, ascend ipsilaterally to the medulla and carry discriminative touch sensation, vibration sense, and information about joint and limb position. The anterolateral pathways originate from cells of the dorsal horn, cross at the spinal level, and ascend in the lateral columns. These pathways carry information about pain, temperature sense, and crude touch. Also located in the lateral columns are the spinocerebellar tracts, but the information they carry does not contribute to the perception of somatic stimuli. The spinocerebellar tracts are important in the cerebellar control of movement and will therefore be considered with the motor system in Chapters 28 and 30. The distinction between the information carried by the spinocerebellar tracts and that carried by the dorsal columns and the anterolateral system is important. It illustrates that *all ascending information does not give rise to sensation.* It is therefore useful to distinguish afferent pathways that carry information about proprioception, which is relevant for movement, from sensory pathways that carry information which contributes to perception.

The Dorsal Column–Medial Lemniscal System Mediates Touch, Pressure, and Position Sense

The dorsal columns are primarily made of the central branches of dorsal root ganglion cells (i.e., primary afferent fibers), which ascend to the caudal medulla without synapsing. It has recently

16–7 Cross-section through a high cervical spinal section showing the somatotopic organization of the dorsal column.

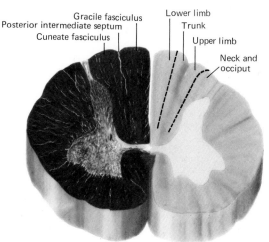

Gracile fasciculus
Posterior intermediate septum
Cuneate fasciculus

Lower limb
Trunk
Upper limb
Neck and occiput

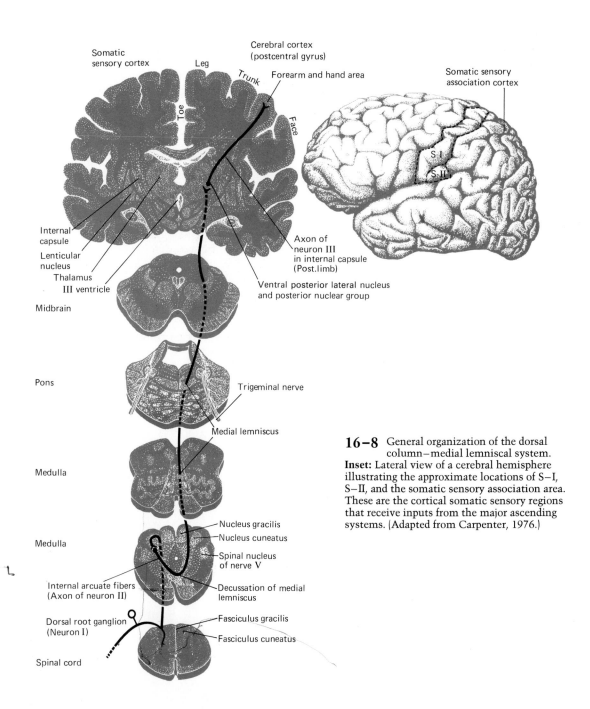

16–8 General organization of the dorsal column–medial lemniscal system. **Inset:** Lateral view of a cerebral hemisphere illustrating the approximate locations of S–I, S–II, and the somatic sensory association area. These are the cortical somatic sensory regions that receive inputs from the major ascending systems. (Adapted from Carpenter, 1976.)

been shown, however, that some fibers are actually ascending axons of dorsal horn neurons, and therefore are second-order cells. At upper spinal levels, the dorsal columns can be divided into two fascicles, the *gracile fasciculus* and the *cuneate fasciculus* (Figure 16–7). Input from the ipsilateral sacral, lumbar, and low thoracic segments ascends medially in the gracile fasciculus.

This fascicle terminates at the level of the lower medulla, in the *gracile nucleus* (Figure 16–8). Input from the upper thoracic and cervical segments ascends laterally in the dorsal columns in the cuneate fasciculus, which terminates in the *cuneate nucleus* of the lower medulla (Figure 16–8). The cuneate and gracile nuclei are located at about the same level in the caudal medulla and

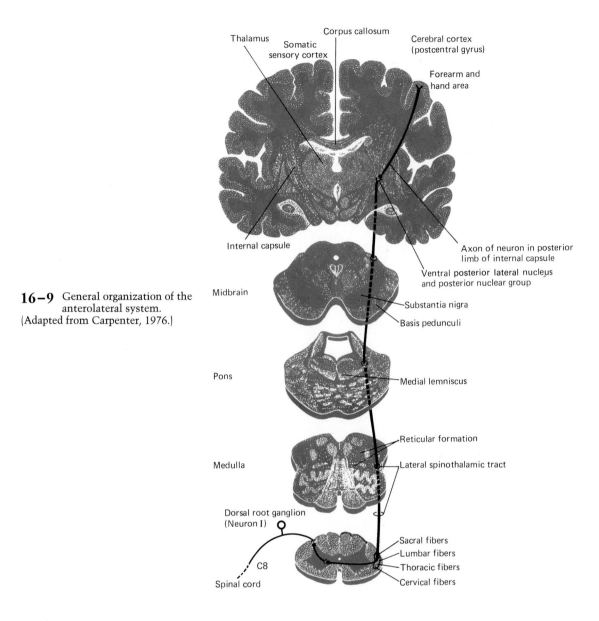

16–9 General organization of the anterolateral system. (Adapted from Carpenter, 1976.)

are referred to collectively as the *dorsal column nuclei*. The fibers that leave the dorsal column nuclei cross the midline of the medulla as the *internal arcuate fibers* (Figure 16–8) and ascend through the contralateral lower brain stem as the *medial lemniscus* to terminate in the thalamus (see below).

The Anterolateral System Mediates Pain and Temperature Sense

The anterolateral pathways differ from the dorsal column–medial lemniscal system in at least two respects: (1) they are primarily crossed in the spinal cord, and (2) their cells of origin (in the dorsal horn) are postsynaptic to the primary afferent fibers. In addition, the incoming afferent fibers ascend one or two segments before synapsing on cells that project to the brain stem or thalamus.

The major termination of the pathways in the anterolateral columns is in the thalamus. This is the *spinothalamic tract* (Figure 16–9). The anterolateral pathways also project to the lower brain stem and the midbrain. The termination in the lower brain stem is rather diffuse and is also called the *spinoreticular tract* because it terminates in a region of the central core of the brain stem known as the *reticular formation*. (The reticular formation will be discussed in Chapter 32.) The termination in the gray matter of the midbrain in the region surrounding the aqueduct of Sylvius, called the *mesencephalic periaqueductal gray*, is thought to be important in endogenous mechanisms for pain inhibition and we shall return to it in Chapter 18.

Thalamic Nuclei

The thalamus plays a key role in transforming information that reaches the cerebral cortex. With rare exception, all afferent pathways projecting to

16–10 Major thalamic nuclei and the cortical regions to which some of them project. (Adapted from Brodal, 1981.)

the cerebral cortex do so through a relay nucleus in the thalamus. Thus, the thalamus is composed of numerous nuclei, each presumably serving a different function (Figure 16–10). The nuclei are classified into three main groups on the basis of their location: (1) the medial thalamic nuclei, (2) the lateral thalamic nuclei, and (3) the anterior thalamic nucleus. These nuclear groups are separated by white matter laminae made up of axons (which overall appear Y-shaped in frontal sections). A number of smaller nuclei, collectively called the *intralaminar nuclei*, are located within the laminae.

The importance of the connections between the thalamus and the cortex is evident from the fact that ablation of the cortex gives rise to atrophy of cells in many thalamic nuclei. This atrophy is due to retrograde degeneration (see Chapter 13) of cell bodies of the thalamocortical

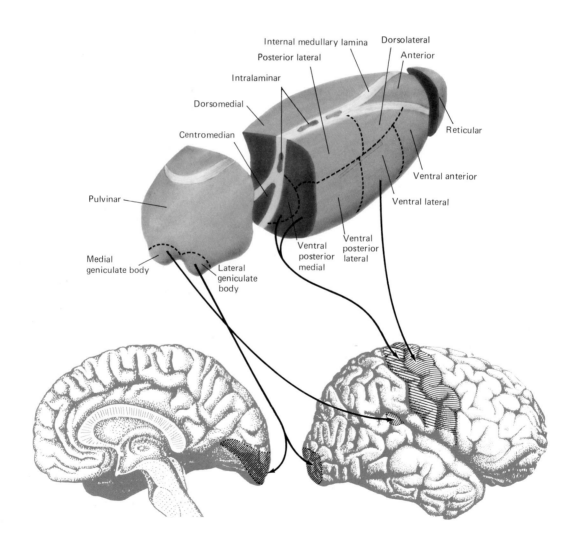

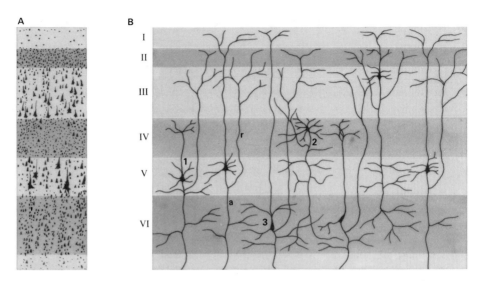

16–11 Cell layers and shapes in the cerebral cortex.
A. Drawing of Nissl-stained section illustrating the various densities and shapes of neuronal cell bodies forming the six layers. **B.** A small number of neurons with their dendritic and axonal branching patterns. **1**, pyramidal cell; **2**, stellate cell; **3**, fusiform cell; **a**, pyramidal cell main axon; **r**, pyramidal cell recurrent axon. (Adapted from Brodmann, 1909; Carpenter, 1976.)

relay neurons after destruction of their axon terminals located in the cortex.

Our understanding of thalamic projections was hampered until recently by the limited number of techniques available for mapping pathways. All were dependent upon changes in degenerating neurons following injury. Recently, cellular tracers have been developed that do not depend on neuronal injury and allow normal unperturbed connections to be mapped. For example, radioactive labeled amino acids are readily taken up by nerve cells, incorporated into protein, and transported to the axon terminal. As a result of transsynaptic transport (discussed in Chapter 13), labeled material can even be seen in neurons a number of synapses away. Thus, after an injection of a radioactive amino acid into a dorsal column nucleus, labeled proteins are rapidly transported into thalamic nuclei and from there to the cerebral cortex receiving inputs from those thalamic nuclei. In contrast to labeled amino acids, which are carried by anterograde transport (soma to terminal), a second label, horseradish peroxidase, is carried by retrograde transport. Horseradish peroxidase injected into a restricted cortical region is taken up by local presynaptic terminals and transported to cell bodies lying in the thalamus.

These mapping techniques have shown that not every thalamic nucleus projects to the cortex. The more important thalamic nuclei and the cortical regions to which they project are shown in Figure 16–10.

The anterolateral system and the dorsal column–medial lemniscal system converge at the thalamus. The somatic inputs originating from the body converge upon the *ventral posterior lateral nucleus*, a nucleus to which the medial lemniscus and anterolateral system both project heavily. These afferent pathways also project to the *posterior nuclear group*, a group of thalamic nuclei located posterior to the ventral posterior lateral nucleus. Many neurons in the posterior nuclear group receive converging projections from different sensory modalities (somesthesis, vision, and audition).[1] In addition, the anterolateral system projects to the *intralaminar nuclei*. This nuclear group is thought to play a role in arousal because it projects not to a specific cortical sensory area but widely, to many different regions of the cortex.

Organization of the Cerebral Cortex

The cerebral cortex is the neural structure most important for perception, thought, and other higher functions. It has six cell layers (Figure 16–11A). Layer I, the *molecular layer*, is closest

---

[1]In the primate the posterior nuclear group includes parts of the magnocellular portion of the medial geniculate nucleus, the suprageniculate nucleus, and the pulvinar.

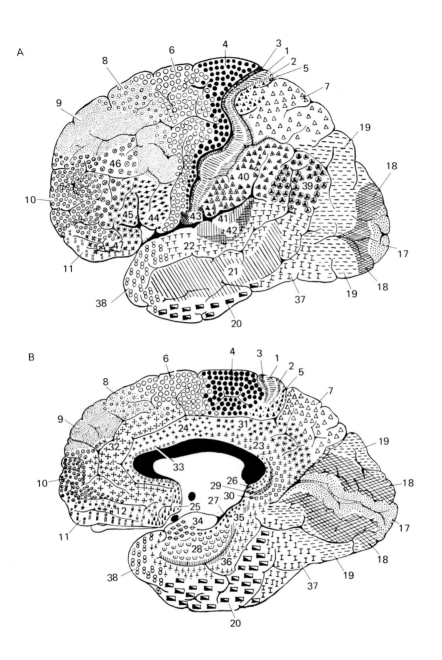

16–12 Map of cerebral cortical cytoarchitectonic regions. **A.** View of lateral convexity of cortex. **B.** Medial view. (Adapted from Brodmann, 1909.)

to the pial surface. This layer contains relatively few cell bodies; it contains primarily dendrites from cells lying in deeper layers and fibers from other areas.

Layer II is called the *external granular layer* and layer III is called the *pyramidal cell layer.*

These layers contain many tightly packed, small pyramidal and stellate (star-shaped) cells. The pyramidal cells have two types of dendrites: basilar dendrites that arborize near the layer of origin of the cell, and apical dendrites that ascend perpendicularly toward the surface of the cortex (Figure 16–11B). Cells of layers II and III project to deeper cortical layers and out of the local cortical area. The cells in these layers in turn receive inputs from cells of the deeper layers and from other cortical areas.

Layer IV is the *granular cell* or *internal granular layer* and receives the major direct projection from thalamic nuclei (i.e., the ventral posterior lateral nucleus for the somatic sensory cortex and the lateral geniculate nucleus for the visual cortex, Figure 16–10). Layer IV is best developed in the primary sensory cortices and least developed in the motor cortex. The cells in layer IV are small and very densely packed and project to layers above and below. They represent an early stage in the intracortical processing of information.

Layer V is the *giant pyramidal* or *ganglionic layer.* This layer contains the large pyramidal cells of the motor cortex (Betz cells). These cells have long apical dendrites that may ascend 1 mm or more to layers I and II. Typically, the pyramidal cells of layer V send their main axon out of this cortical area to another area. Pyramidal cells also give off recurrent collateral branches from the main axon, which turn back toward the cortex, where they synapse on other cortical cells.

Layer VI is the *fusiform* or *multiform cell layer.* This layer contains spindle-shaped cells. The large spindle cells have dendrites that rise to the superficial layers and the smaller spindle cells have dendrites that ramify only in the layers below layer IV.

Since the microscopic anatomy of the cortex is not uniform, a knowledge of cortical layering is important for understanding how the cortex processes information. Different regions have a different morphological pattern or *cytoarchitecture.* Brodmann, in the late 19th century, used cell density, size, and type and the varying thickness of the different layers as criteria to divide the cerebral cortex into approximately 50 different cyto-

architectonic regions called Brodmann's areas (Figure 16–12).

How do the different architectonic regions relate to different functions? Particularly good progress in answering this question has been made in the somatic sensory system. Several cytoarchitectonic regions in the anterior part of the parietal cortex have been identified as receiving somatic inputs. The *primary somatic sensory cortex* (S-I), located in the postcentral gyrus and in the depths of the central sulcus, corresponds to Brodmann's areas 1, 2, and 3 (Figure 16–13). Lateral and somewhat posterior is the *secondary somatic sensory cortex* (S-II), lying in the upper bank of the Sylvian fissure. (S-I was identified before S-II; the designation "primary" and "secondary" cortical regions does not indicate order of processing.) S-II corresponds to the preinsular portion of area 2 (area 2 pri of Brodmann).

Both S-I and S-II are somatotopically organized. The afferent inputs to S-I derive entirely from the contralateral body, whereas the inputs to S-II are bilateral. Direct thalamic projections to S-I and S-II arise chiefly from the ventral posterior lateral nucleus and the posterior nuclear group. A third cortical region that receives somatic inputs is located in the posterior parietal cortex (Brodmann's areas 5 and 7). This region is referred to as

16–13 Somatic sensory cortices. **A.** Lateral view of cerebral hemisphere illustrating somatic sensory receiving areas. **B.** Idealized section taken at level B of part A, perpendicular to the cortical surface. Brodmann's areas are shown for S–I (areas **3, 1, 2**), part of the motor cortex (area **4**), and the posterior parietal association area (Brodmann's areas **5** and **7**; only **5** is illustrated).

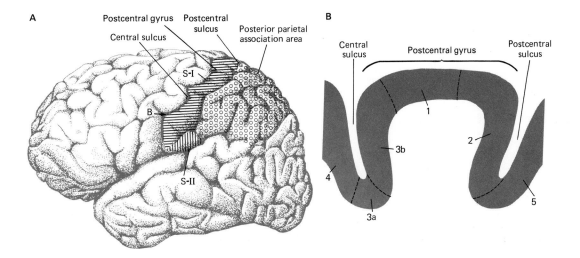

the *somatic sensory association area* (Figure 16–13) because complex associations between different sensory modalities necessary for perception are thought to be made here.

Cortical neurons make four types of connections: (1) intracortical, (2) association, (3) callosal, and (4) subcortical. Intracortical connections connect neurons within the same cortical region. Cells connecting different cortical regions on the same side give rise to *association fibers*. Thus, there are connections between the cytoarchitectonic regions of S-I (Brodmann's areas 3, 1, and 2), and in turn there is a projection from S-I to the somatic sensory association cortex. There are also reciprocal association connections between S-I and S-II and between these two cortices and the motor cortex (which is located in the precentral gyrus). In general, cortical areas (including the somatic sensory cortices) of each cerebral hemisphere are connected to the symmetrical area in the other hemisphere via a thick fiber tract called the *corpus callosum*. Exceptions exist, however; for example, the cortical regions in each hemisphere that receive inputs from the distal limbs are not connected via the corpus callosum. Fibers that course through the corpus callosum to connect the two cerebral hemispheres are called *callosal fibers*. The fourth class of connections originating from cortical neurons are projections to subcortical structures. The fibers are called *projection fibers*. Two major projections of the primary somatic sensory cortex are to the dorsal column nuclei and the intermediate zone of the spinal cord.

Association, callosal, and projection fibers distribute processed information to other regions of the cortex and subcortical structures. The recent work of Jones and co-workers indicates that the

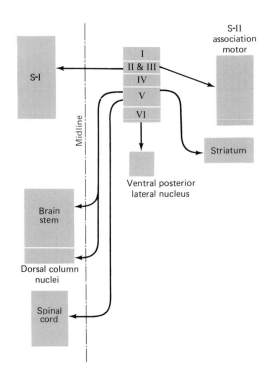

16–14 Projections from the six layers of the cerebral cortex.

various layers of the cerebral cortex give rise to different projection pathways (Figure 16–14). In the primary somatic sensory cortex, for example, cells located in layers II and III project to S-II, to the somatic sensory association area, and to the motor cortex. These cells also give rise to callosal fibers destined for the contralateral cortex. Cells in layer V give rise to the projection fibers. Finally, layer VI gives rise to fibers that project to the ventral-posterior lateral nucleus.

TABLE 16–2. Major Ascending Somatic Sensory Systems

Ascending system	Submodalities	Location in spinal cord	Level of decussation	Brain stem terminations	Cerebral terminations
Dorsal column Medial Lemniscus	Touch–pressure Vibration Position sense– kinesthesia	Dorsal column	Medulla	Ventral posterior lateral nucleus and Posterior nuclear group of thalamus	Primary and secondary somatic sensory cortices and somatic sensory association area
Anterolateral	Pain Thermal Crude touch	Anterolateral column	Spinal cord	Brain stem reticular formation Ventral posterior lateral nucleus and posterior nuclear group of thalamus	Primary and secondary somatic sensory cortices and somatic sensory association area

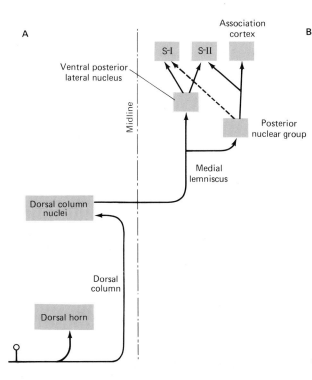

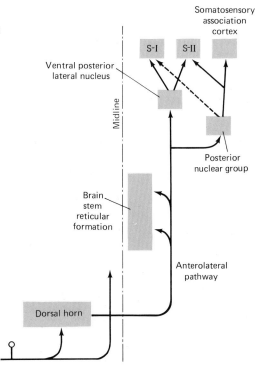

16–15 Summary diagram of the major ascending somatic sensory systems. **A.** Dorsal column–medial lemniscal system. **B.** Anterolateral system.

An Overall View

Afferent information from the body is relayed to the cerebral cortex by two major ascending systems: the dorsal column–medial lemniscal system and the anterolateral pathways (Figure 16–15). These systems, which serve different functions, converge in the thalamus (Table 16–2). Here, the ventral posterior lateral nucleus and the posterior nuclear group mediate the projection to the somatic sensory cortices, which include S-I, S-II, and the somatic sensory association area. In the somatic sensory cortices, afferent information is further processed for somatic perception.

Selected Readings and References

Boivie, J. 1979. An anatomical reinvestigation of the termination of the spinothalamic tract in the monkey. J. Comp. Neurol. 186:343–369.

Jones, E. G., and Powell, T. P. S. 1973. Anatomical organization of the somatosensory cortex. In A. Iggo (ed.), Handbook of Sensory Physiology, Vol. 2, The Somatosensory System. New York: Springer, pp. 579–620.

Jones, E. G., and Wise, S. P. 1977. Size, laminar and columnar distribution of efferent cells in the sensory–motor cortex of monkeys. J. Comp. Neurol. 175:391–437.

Other References

Brodal, A. 1981. Neurological Anatomy. 3rd ed. New York: Oxford University Press.

Brodmann, K. 1909. Vergleichende Lokalisationslehre der Grosshirnrinde. Leipzig: J. A. Barth.

Carpenter, M. B. 1976. Human Neuroanatomy. 7th ed. Baltimore: Williams & Wilkins.

Kuypers, H. G. J. M. 1973. The anatomical organization of the descending pathways and their contributions to motor control especially in primates. In J. E. Desmedt (ed.), New Developments in Electromyography and Clinical Neurophysiology, Vol. 3. Basel: Karger, pp. 38–68.

Ranson, S. W., and Clark, S. L. 1953. The Anatomy of the Nervous System. 9th ed. Philadelphia: Saunders.

Rexed, B. 1952. The cytoarchitectonic organization of the spinal cord in the cat. J. Comp. Neurol. 96: 415–495.

Whitsel, B. L., Rustioni, A., Dreyer, D. A., Loe, P. R., Allen, E. E., and Metz, C. B. 1978. Thalamic projections to S-I in macaque monkey. J. Comp. Neurol. 178:385–409.

Zimmermann, M. 1978. Neurophysiology of sensory systems. In R. F. Schmidt (ed.), Fundamentals of Sensory Physiology. New York: Springer, pp. 31–80.

Eric R. Kandel

Somatic Sensory System III: Central Representation of Touch

17

The somatic sensory system allows us to perceive and recognize objects through touch, to read braille, to experience pain or a change in temperature. This system is distinctive for two reasons. One, the receptors for somatic sensibility are not restricted to a small, well-delineated organ like the eye for vision or the cochlea for hearing, but are spread throughout the body. For this reason the somatic sensibilities are called the *skin* or the *body senses*. Second, the sensations mediated by the somatic sensory system are remarkably diverse; they include not only the five relatively elementary submodalities —touch, pressure, heat, cold, and pain— but also various compound sensations such as vibration, itch and tickle that are achieved by combining elementary submodalities in different ways.

In this chapter we shall consider how neuronal activity within a specific submodality gives rise to perception by focusing on the mechanisms underlying tactile discrimination. We shall first explore how we make tactile discriminations and why we do so better with our fingertips than with our toes or with the skin of our back. We shall next examine the degree to which the various submodalities of somatic sensibility are segregated. Because this is the first system whose central projections we shall study, the chapter will also provide us with an initial opportunity to see how the brain and particularly the cerebral cortex are organized and how they handle information coming from the outside world.

Sensory Systems Transform Information at Specific Relay Points

Normal human somatic sensibility is usually subdivided into 4 major types: (1) *discriminatory tactile sensibility* (fine touch and pressure); (2) *position sense* (static position and kinesthesia); (3) *pain* (slow and fast); and (4) *temperature sense* (warm and cold). Lesions of systems concerned with discriminatory tactile sensibility often reveal a fifth submodality: crude touch.

Most aspects of tactile sensibility (except for crude touch) and position sense are carried by the dorsal column medial lemniscal system and are therefore also called dorsal column–medial lemniscal modalities. Pain, warmth, cold, and a crude tactile sensibility are carried by the anterolateral system. Here we shall focus on the medial lemniscal sensibilities, in particular, touch. In the next chapter we shall consider the anterolateral system and the perception of pain.

As we have seen, the anatomical plan of tactile sensation is simple and can be briefly recapitulated. There are specific receptors for each submodality. For example, Meissner's corpuscles mediate superficial (phasic) touch, and the Pacinian corpuscles mediate vibration. Large myelinated afferent fibers from these receptors in skin, subcutaneous tissues, and deep tissue enter the spinal cord via the dorsal roots. Here each axon divides and sends a long ascending branch into the dorsal columns to synapse in the medulla with cells in the dorsal column nuclei (the gracile and cuneate nuclei). Somatic sensory information from the face and head is carried by the trigeminal nerve, which will be treated separately in Chapter 33. Axons of second-order sensory cells in the dorsal column nuclei cross the midline in the medulla. These axons then ascend the brain stem on the opposite side as the medial lemniscus and form synapses with cells in the *ventral posterior lateral nucleus* of the thalamus (Figure 17–1A).

The third-order neurons in the thalamus send axons to the cerebral cortex (together with those from certain other thalamic nuclei) in the extensive thalamocortical projection or radiation. These fibers run through the internal capsule and terminate in the postcentral gyrus of the parietal

cortex in four distinct cytoarchitectural regions designated 1, 2, 3a, 3b in the subdivisions of the cortex made by Brodmann (Figure 17–1B). This area is called the primary somatic sensory region (S-I). Most of the thalamic fibers terminate in area 3, which then projects to 1 and 2. Third-order neurons from the thalamus also project to the adjacent cortex, called the secondary somatic sensory region (S-II). Unlike S-I, which receives input only from the contralateral part of the body, S-II receives input from both parts of the body. We shall focus below primarily on S-I.

As the anatomical plan of the somatic sensory system illustrates, a sensory system consists of a series of relay points within the brain. To understand what function these relays serve, it is necessary to combine the longitudinal analysis illustrated in Figure 17–1 with a segmental or cross-sectional analysis (Figure 17–2) that shows what happens to the flow of neural activity within each relay point.

At each relay nucleus the principal relay cells—the cells that project out of the nucleus to the next relay point—receive synaptic input from many afferent fibers; each afferent cell ends on many relay cells. There is convergence and divergence of sensory input on the relay cells. In addition to relay cells, the afferent fibers activate both excitatory and inhibitory interneurons. As a result, the sensory information can be processed by passage from the principal neurons of one nucleus to those of the next. In some nuclei the information may be transformed into a new, more abstract, pattern of activity; in others, the afferent message will ascend to the next level without change.

The process at a sensory relay nucleus does not differ in principle from that at a motor relay nucleus. In fact, we can gain additional insight into what happens at a sensory relay nucleus by examining a cross section of a motor nucleus in the spinal cord. Here we encounter, in addition to the convergence and divergence of the excitatory synaptic input, two types of inhibitory pathways: reciprocal inhibition and feedback (recurrent) inhibition (Figure 17–3).

Reciprocal inhibition ensures that excitation of a synergist group of neurons (such as flexor motor neurons in a motor nucleus) leads to inhibition of the antagonist neurons (such as extensor motor neurons). Reciprocal inhibition is functionally economical and permits what Sherrington called a "singleness of action," ensuring that only one of two (or more) competing re-

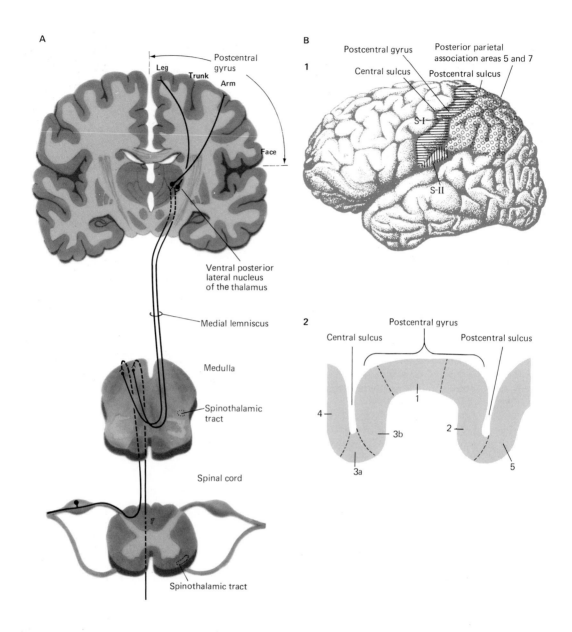

17–1 A. Longitudinal analysis: Simplified diagram of the main features in the medial lemniscal components of the somatic sensory pathways. (Adapted from Brodal, 1981) **B.** Somatic sensory cortex (parietal lobe). **1:** Surface of the cortex, showing the relationship of S–I to S–II and to the posterior parietal association area (areas **5** and **7.**) **2:** Saggital section, showing the subdivisions of S–I into the four distinct cytoarchitectural regions of Brodmann (areas **3a, 3b, 1,** and **2;** area **4** is motor cortex and area **5** is parietal association cortex).

sponses is expressed. Whereas reciprocal inhibition occurs only between antagonist groups of neurons, *feedback* or *recurrent inhibition* limits the spread of excitation among adjacent units, thereby functionally isolating cells that are anatomically near each other. The interesting feature of both types of inhibition is that both create contrast; there is a central excitatory zone of active neurons surrounded by an inhibitory annulus of less active neurons.

These inhibitory interactions—first noted in the analysis of motor nuclei in the spinal cord—

turn out to be quite general: they will be encountered repeatedly in the analysis of relay sensory nuclei in the sensory systems. Consider, for
example, the dorsal column nuclei, the first relay
we encounter in the somatic sensory systems.
There is no synaptic inhibition at the level of the
peripheral receptor in the somatic sensory system. In contrast, in the dorsal column nuclei
there are at least two types of feedback inhibition: (1) *local feedback inhibition* (of both the
postsynaptic and presynaptic variety) results
from activity in relay cells within the dorsal column nuclei and leads, by means of collaterals

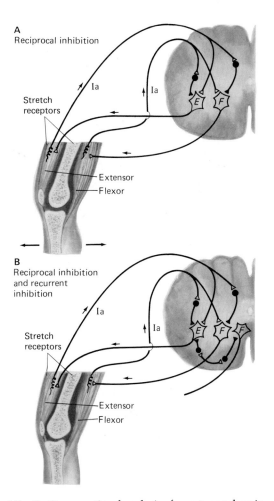

A Reciprocal inhibition

B Reciprocal inhibition and recurrent inhibition

17–3 Cross-sectional analysis of a motor nucleus in
the spinal cord, illustrating excitatory and
inhibitory interactions. These interactions are similar
to those that occur in sensory relay nuclei.
A. Reciprocal inhibition. **B.** Reciprocal and recurrent
inhibition. **Ia,** afferent fibers; **E** and **F,** extensor and
flexor motor neurons.

17–2 **Cross-sectional analysis** of neural activity at
sensory relay: a dorsal column nucleus. The
principal relay cells of this nucleus project to the
thalamus. These cells receive convergent and
divergent excitatory input from axons traveling in the
dorsal columns. The relay cells also receive pre- and
postsynaptic inhibitory input from interneurons
activated by recurrent collateral axons as well as from
neurons in the cerebral cortex.

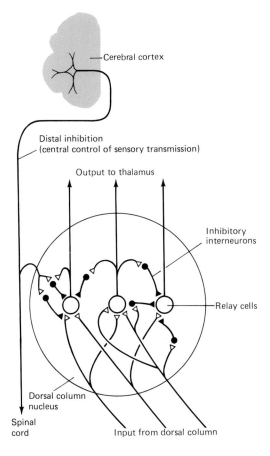

from these cells, to inhibition of the surrounding
relay cells; and (2) *distal feedback inhibition*
(mostly presynaptic), which is exerted on the input coming into the relay cells from the dorsal
columns. This inhibition is produced by the axons of neurons in the motor and somatic sensory
cortex as well as in the brain stem. Distal feedback illustrates still another principle in the organization of the sensory system: *central control of
sensory transmission.* Higher areas of the brain
are able to control the sensory inflow from the
peripheral receptors into relay nuclei.

The Body Surface Is Mapped onto the Brain

Early Functional Analyses of Somatic Sensation

Early knowledge about the function of the somatic sensory system came from the analysis of traumatic injuries of the spinal cord and disease states. Until penicillin became available, during the 1940s, syphilis was a common infectious disease and a frequent cause of admission to psychiatric hospitals. One of the late consequences of syphilitic infection of the nervous system is a syndrome called *tabes dorsalis.* Patients with tabes display loss of tactile and vibratory sensibility as well as position sense but show much less deficit in temperature or pain perception. The symptoms of tabes dorsalis are similar to the effects of experimental lesions in animals and traumatic injuries in humans. Transsection of the dorsal columns results in a chronic deficit in certain tactile discriminations such as two-point discrimination (the minimum stimulus separation necessary for a subject to perceive two stimuli). There is also an impairment of position sense, and the deficit is ipsilateral to the lesion (and of course below the lesion).

Similarly, removal of S-I cortex produces deficits in position sense and in the ability to discriminate size, roughness, and shape. Thermal and pain sensibilities are not abolished but thresholds may be elevated. Removal of S-II cortex results in no obvious abnormalities, but damage to the posterior parietal association cortex produces complex abnormalities in spatial orientation for the contralateral half of the body and extrapersonal space.

Conversely, transsection of the dorsal columns does not change the threshold to painful stimuli, whereas transsection of the anterolateral system results in prolonged (but not necessarily permanent) loss of pain sensation. This alteration in sensory capacity begins a few segments below the level of the lesion because the dorsal root fibers ascend a few segments before synapsing on anterolateral projection neurons.

Modern Electrophysiological Studies

Modern interest in the somatic sensory system started in the early 1930s with the classic work of Wade Marshall, Clinton Woolsey, and Philip Bard at the Johns Hopkins Medical School. This important series of experiments began with a chance observation made in the course of studying the

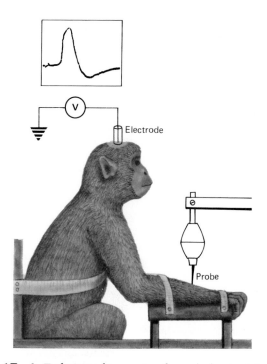

17–4 Techniques for mapping the evoked potentials produced on the surface of the left postcentral gyrus of the cerebral cortex by stimuli applied to the body surface on the opposite side.

electrical activity of the cerebral cortex in the cat. Using gross surface electrodes that recorded the activity of several thousand cells in an area of cortex several millimeters in extent, Marshall found that when a part of the animal's body surface was touched, a deflection could be recorded on the oscilloscope, indicating that neurons over a particular part of the cortex were activated (Figure 17–4). These evoked potentials represent the electrical activity of populations of neurons activated by stimulating a point on the skin.

Later, Marshall joined Woolsey and Bard to map the representation of the body surface on the cortex systematically. By connecting the points of maximal activity (that is, by relating a position on the body surface to a position in the cortex), they could produce a coherent map of the body surface (Figures 17–5 and 17–6). This and subsequent studies showed that the outline of the body form is repeatedly represented in each of the two somatic sensory receiving areas of the brain (S-I and S-II). For example, there are four independent and fairly complete maps in S-I alone, one for each of the Brodmann areas: 3a, 3b, 1, and 2 (Figure 17–1B). Representations of body surface

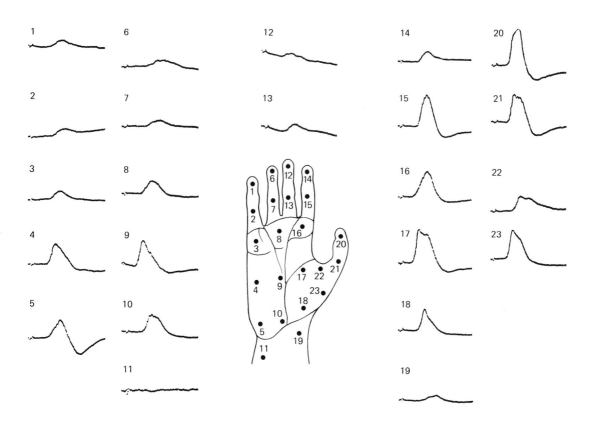

exist not only in the cortex but also in the thalamus and the dorsal column nuclei, as was found later by others.

Similar representations were found in the human cortex by the neurosurgeon Wilder Penfield during operations for epilepsy and other brain lesions. Working with local anesthesia, Penfield stimulated the surface of the postcentral gyrus at various points in the area of S-I and asked the patients what they felt. This protocol was necessary to ascertain the focus of the epilepsy. Penfield found that stimulation produced tactile sensations—paresthesias (numbness, tingling) and pressure—in the corresponding part of the opposite side of the body. A transverse section through the somatic cortex of the human brain based on these studies is shown in Figure 17–7; it illustrates the representation of the body in one hemisphere. The lower extremity is represented most medially, followed by the upper extremity, the face, and finally, most laterally, the teeth, tongue, and esophagus.

Penfield's observations were important. First, they provided independent confirmation in humans of Marshall, Woolsey, and Bard's experimental mapping technique based on evoked po-

17–5 Drawing based on a series of evoked potential recordings from single spot in the hand area of the left postcentral gyrus of a monkey when a light tactile stimulus is applied to various points on the right palm. (Adapted from Marshall, Woolsey, and Bard, 1941; Bard, 1938.)

tentials in animals. Second, Penfield's findings explained how a disturbance within the somatic sensory system can be readily localized clinically. The findings illustrated why neurology has been a precise diagnostic discipline while using (for many decades) only the simplest tools—a wad of cotton, a safety pin, a tuning fork, and a hammer: the reason is that the brain is precisely organized in space and many aspects of that space correspond to a particular function. By knowing that function, one can extrapolate back to that space. To take a particularly dramatic example, before Penfield, Hughlings Jackson, the great British neurologist, had described a characteristic sensory epileptic attack that now bears his name. This attack has as its early and sometimes only feature a characteristic sensory progression of numbness and paresthesia that begins at one locus and spreads throughout the body. The

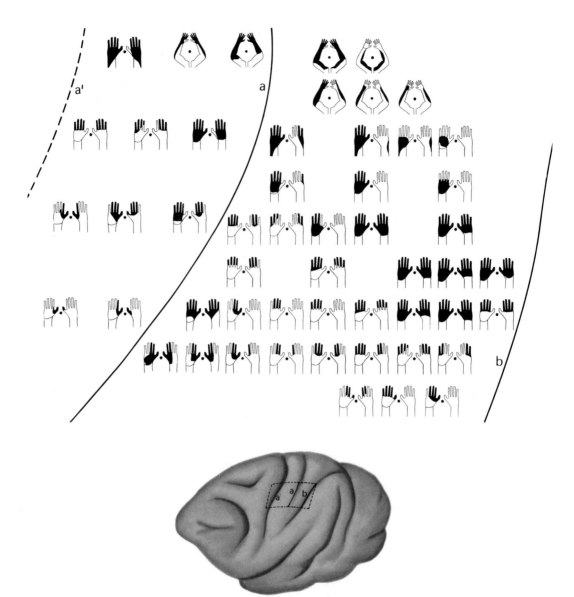

17—6 Drawing based on the recorded points on the left postcentral gyrus of a monkey responding to tactile stimulation of right palm and right dorsal surface. Each **dot** indicates the pairing of the two surfaces in a single hand. (Adapted from Marshall, Woolsey, and Bard, 1941.)

tion in the brain. The irritative focus of the seizure is in the opposite hemisphere, in this case the left, and specifically in the precentral gyrus. In this gyrus the seizure is first set up laterally in the hand area and propagates medially in an orderly fashion.

Potentials from the somatic sensory cortex can now be recorded from the surface of the scalp in humans in a completely noninvasive manner by using computers to obtain an average of many evoked signals so that the evoked response can be distinguished from background electrical ac-

numbness might begin on the right side at the tip of the finger, spread to the hand, up the arm, down across the shoulders, into the back, and down the ipsilateral leg. This sensory seizure can now be understood by its topographical localiza-

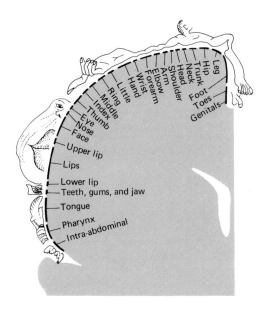

17–7 The orderly projection of the body surface onto the human brain. (Adapted from Penfield and Rasmussen, 1950.)

tivity. These evoked potentials provide information not only about the somatic sensory cortex, but also about the ascending pathways in the spinal cord, brain stem, and thalamus. For example, the evoked potentials in the cortex will reveal a delay in demyelinating disease due to slowing of conduction in the spinal cord and brain stem. (As we have seen in Chapter 14, demyelination also causes slowing of conduction in peripheral nerves due to interference with the saltatory propagation of action potentials.) A common cause for demyelination in the central nervous system is multiple sclerosis. Conduction can be slowed at an early stage of the disease when sensation is still normal. Thus, evoked responses can provide *clinical* information about sensory deficits that may not be detectable in a routine neurological examination.

Why Is the Map So Distorted?

The representation of the body surface found in the evoked responses illustrates another important principle. The map in Figure 17–7 is drawn to scale and illustrates that the different parts of the body are represented in brain areas of different sizes. The face is large compared to the back of the head; the index finger is gigantic compared to the big toe.

As the homunculus in the human brain is a distorted picture of man, so is the body image of other species. Comparative studies by Woolsey and his colleagues show that the distortions parallel the importance of a particular part of the body surface for tactile sensibility (Figure 17–8). In humans the hand and the tongue predominate, and both representations are large. Moreover, the caricature of humans and animals emerges only if one connects the points of maximal response. Each area in neural space is involved in both convergent and divergent relationships.

These findings also raise a number of paradoxes: Given the relatively poor resolution illustrated in the map of Figure 17–7, how do we achieve the extraordinarily precise tactile sensibility of which we are capable? In addition, the maps for the various submodalities of somatic sensory sensibility (deep versus superficial touch, touch versus position sense) were found to be superimposable. All the receptors from each part of the body seem to project to the same area of cortex. However, perceptually, one can discriminate deep from superficial sensations or touch from position sense. This finding was also paradoxical, and suggested that here too some information must be missing in maps obtained by evoked potentials.

17–8 Highly schematic drawings of the body representation for somatic sensibility in the thalamus and cortex of the rabbit, cat, monkey, and man as determined by evoked responses.

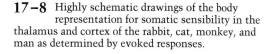

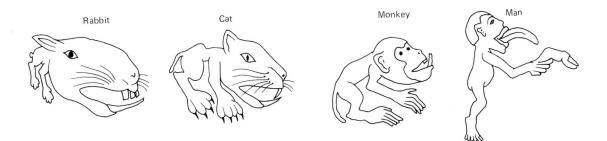

Each Central Neuron Has a Specific Receptive Field

To try to resolve these questions, Vernon Mountcastle, Jerzy Rose, and their colleagues began to examine the somatic sensory system at the cellular level using extracellular microelectrodes (which became available in the late 1940s) to record the electrical responses of individual neurons. It is difficult to record intracellularly in the brain. The cells are relatively small and intracellular electrodes cause damage to the cell. Fortunately, it is possible to record from cells extracellularly for several hours without damage. Extracellular recordings reveal only the action potentials of the cell; they do not show synaptic activity except under rare circumstances. Nevertheless, a great deal has been learned by studying how sensory stimuli modulate the firing patterns of single cells.

Mountcastle found that neurons in the somatic sensory system are not silent but spontaneously active. Sensory stimuli therefore act to modulate ongoing neuronal activity in central nuclei and in the cerebral cortex. Moreover, a given cell's activity cannot be modulated by stimuli applied at any point on the body surface. Rather, for each cell there is a specific area of the skin that can alter its firing rate. Mountcastle called that area the *receptive field* of the cell, following the tradition established in the study of peripheral receptor cells. The receptive field is probably the single most important concept of sensory physiology. The receptive field of a cell is *that area on any receptive sheet which upon stimulation will either excite or inhibit the firing of the specific cell being recorded from.* In anatomical terms, this refers to the area on the receptive sheet (in the somatic sensory system that would be the skin, in the visual system the retina) that projects (directly or indirectly) onto the particular cell. In physiological terms, it refers to the area which, when stimulated, will either increase or decrease the firing rate of the cell.

There are important functional consequences of the restricted areas of a neuron's receptive field. If we apply a probe to a point in the skin, the excited neurons are those connected to the afferent fibers that innervate the point on the skin being stimulated. If we now move the probe to a new point, we activate a different population of neurons. Thus we know that one point rather than another is being stimulated on the skin because one rather than another population of neurons in the brain is active.

Mountcastle next described two other interesting features of receptive fields: their size distribution on the body surface and their fine structure.

Sizes of Receptive Fields Vary

The size of the receptive field varies, corresponding precisely to the distortion of the body surface in the map (Figure 17–9A). The areas of the skin that are most sensitive to touch and therefore have the greatest cortical representation—the tips of the fingers and the tongue—have the smallest receptive fields and the largest number of receptive fields per unit area of skin. As one moves proximally along the arm, there is a gradient of receptive field sizes and density that parallels the gradient of innervation and is reflected in tactile sensibility. The distortions in the map of the body representation in the cerebral cortex (Figures 17–5, 17–6, and 17–7) are therefore due to innervation density; there is relatively more neural innervation and more cortical representation going to areas of greater sensibility. It is now easy to understand why fingertips can be used for reading braille, whereas the elbows or shoulders cannot.

Receptive Fields Have a Fine Structure

Each receptive field has a fine structural organization. First, there is a gradient within the excitatory portion of the receptive field that is reflected in the brain as a gradient of activity at each relay point, including the cortex. The discharge of the cell is greatest when a stimulus is applied to the center of the excitatory part of the receptive field; the discharge is weakest at the periphery. This gradient is reflected as a gradient of nerve cell activity at each relay point. Superimposed upon this excitatory gradient is a gradient of inhibition. The inhibitory gradient is also greatest at the center and decreases toward the edge of the excitatory zone of the receptive field. Inhibition sometimes extends beyond the excitatory receptive field, giving rise to an *inhibitory surround* (Figure 17–9B–D). Under these circumstances, stimulation of the area surrounding the excitatory portion of the receptive field inhibits the cell. Thus, a stimulus in the excitatory portion of the receptive field sets up a gradient of activity in the brain and activates a population of cells—some greatly, some moderately, and some slightly. This active population is surrounded by a population of less active cells that serves to sharpen the peak of activity within the brain.

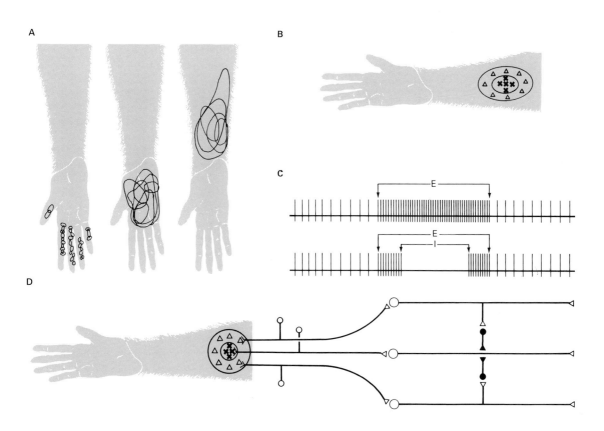

A Model for Two-Point Discrimination

Reading braille involves discriminating shape and contour. We can understand how this is accomplished by considering the simplest example of spatial discrimination: the ability to distinguish two closely placed point stimuli as two discrete points rather than as one fused point. Clinically, this discrimination test is called two-point discrimination.

Mountcastle proposed a model for two-point discrimination based on the reconstruction of the neural events in the postcentral gyrus of the cortex produced by a light tactile stimulus delivered to the skin. According to this model, two stimuli applied to separate positions on the skin will set up two excitatory gradients of activity at every relay point in the somatic sensory system. The activity in each population of cells will have a discrete peak. The inhibitory surround will sharpen each peak and further enhance the distinction between the two peaks.

Consider a single-point stimulus. This stimulus will activate a number of touch receptors that will produce short trains of impulses in each of several first-order afferent fibers activated. These afferent fibers will in turn provoke a discharge in

17–9 Properties of the tactile receptive fields of
cells in the monkey thalamus and cortex.
A. The size of receptive fields carries along the arm.
The fields are small in the finger tips and become large
proximally. **B.** Topographical relationship of the
excitatory (**X**) and inhibitory (Δ) zones of the receptive
fields for a neuron in the postcentral gyrus. Often the
excitatory and inhibitory zones are coextensive so
there is no inhibitory surround of the sort illustrated.
C. Extracellular recordings from a single cell in the
cortex illustrate the interaction of excitatory (**E**) and
inhibitory (**I**) portions of the receptive field.
D. Schema for producing an excitatory zone and
inhibitory surround in a dorsal column nucleus. A
stimulus applied to the skin activates a group of
receptors that excite a group of cells in the nucleus.
This central area of skin is part of the excitatory
portion (**X**) of the receptive field of these cells.
Stimulating surrounding skin activates other cells
that end on inhibitory interneurons and suppress the
firing of the cells activated by the excitatory portion
of the receptive field.

a group of cells in a dorsal column nucleus, and those cells will activate another group of cells in the ventrobasal complex of the thalamus, which will in turn discharge a group of cells in the cortex. At each level the cells that discharge impulses will be limited to a restricted zone by two factors: (1) excitatory anatomical connections, and (2) lateral inhibition. This inhibition is *not present at the level of the receptor but comes in at the dorsal column nuclei and is found at each subsequent relay step, so that in the brain the population excited by the stimulus is also surrounded by a belt of inhibition.* As a result of these two factors, the activated cells at each level may be regarded as forming an excitatory discharge zone.

The *location* of the stimulus on the body surface is thus signaled in the nervous system by the firing of specific populations of neurons activated by the stimulus. Those populations are located at specific points in each relay nucleus as well as in the cerebral cortex. The *intensity* of the stimulus is signaled by the frequency of firing of the specific populations and by the size of the active populations because strong depression of the skin causes a higher frequency of firing and a wider excitation profile than weak depression. Not all cells in this population will respond in an identical manner. Cells at the center, which have the most powerful connections with the area being stimulated, will be caused to discharge most effectively. These cells at the center of discharge zones respond with great security and short latency. Cells just off the center discharge fewer

17–10 Possible role of inhibition in two-point discrimination. **A.** Distribution, in the three-dimensional neural space of the brain, of a population of cells activated by stimulation of a single point of the skin. **B.** Distribution of cells activated by stimulation of two adjacent points with (curve **1**) and without (curve **2**) the presence of lateral inhibition. (Adapted from Mountcastle and Darian-Smith, 1968.)

impulses with longer latency and with less certain probability.

Because each point on the skin sets up a gradient of activity at each level in the nervous system, we can begin to see how the evolution of the receptive field along the ascending system can give rise to two-point discrimination. Each stimulus will excite a set of cells that will have a receptive field with a central excitatory zone surrounded by a weaker excitatory zone (Figure 17–10A). The weaker excitatory zone will be further depressed by the inhibitory surround. When two stimuli are brought close together there will be a summation of the surround inhibition of each field in the neurons activated in the area of the skin between the two stimuli. This summation of inhibition will retard fusion of the excitatory zones set up by the two stimuli, thus preserving peaks of activity at the cortical level and enhancing the contrast between the two points (Figure 17–10B). Lateral inhibition—a form of feedback inhibition—occurs in all sensory and motor systems. In each case it functions to enhance contrast. It is easy to see how a neural organization such as this might lead to pattern and contour recognition.

Modality-Specific Labeled Communication Lines Are Organized into Columns

In addition to inhibition, another feature of cortical organization was revealed with microelectrodes that could not have been found with evoked responses. This feature explained the puzzling observation that the maps of the various

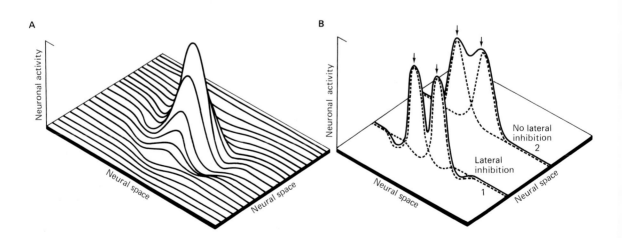

submodalities for touch–pressure and position sense are topographically often the same. Cellular techniques have made it possible to investigate whether there is segregation on the cellular level; that is, are single cells sensitive to one or to several submodalities? Work has now been carried out on single neurons in the dorsal column nuclei, in the thalamus, and in the cortex. In each region, cells are found to respond to only one submodality: cells respond specifically either to superficial touch stimuli or to deep pressure stimuli. There is even segregation between the superficial modalities, such as hair and steady skin indentation. Moreover, cells responding to one submodality are located together and are segregated from cells responding to other submodalities. The most remarkable example of this grouping is evident in the cerebral cortex.

Because the cortex consists of six major cellular layers (see Chapter 16), Mountcastle first examined the distribution of the various submodalities as a function of cell layers, but found no correlation. He then examined the submodalities as a function of vertical position in the cortex and found, to his surprise, that the cortex is organized into narrow vertical columns running from the cortical surface to the white matter (Figure 17–11): Each neuron in such a vertical column is activated by the same single submodality; some columns are activated by position of the joints, some by touch, and some by movement of hairs. In addition, the neurons of the column have receptive fields that are almost identical. Neurons lying within a narrow vertical column therefore make up the elementary topographical and modality-specific unit of function. We shall soon see that columnar organization is quite general and reflects a basic organizational principle of the cerebral cortex. The modality-specific columns are intermingled in the space of the cerebral cortex, although there is a strong tendency for grouping of columns into domains. Thus, in any one part of the cortex, input from one submodality or another tends to dominate. (For example, Brodmann's area 3a cells respond primarily to deep input from muscle stretch, Brodmann's area 3b cells respond primarily to slowly adapting cutaneous stimuli, and Brodmann's area 2 cells respond primarily to deep pressure.) The reason the maps for the various submodalities seemed to be similar is that a gross electrode will record the activity of many columns representing different submodalities.

In view of the columnar organization of the

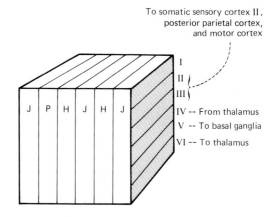

17–11 The cerebral cortex is organized vertically and horizontally. Vertically, the cortex is organized into columns that run from surface to white matter. Each column is specific for a submodality. The examples shown here are for joint (**J**), pressure (**P**), and hair (**H**) stimulation. The columns are intermingled in a mosaic fashion, although there is some tendency for grouping. Horizontally, the cortex is organized into layers that receive inputs from certain regions of the brain and project to other regions. (Adapted from Mountcastle, 1957.)

cortex, what is the function of the six cell layers that, as we have seen in the last chapter, are so prominent in the cross section of the cortex? Anatomical studies with various tracers such as horseradish peroxidase and ^{3}H-amino acids that are delivered by retrograde and fast orthograde axonal transport have shown that different layers project to different parts of the brain: layer VI projects back to the thalamus, layer V to subcortical structures, and layers II and III to other somatic cortices. Thus, as we shall see again in the visual system, the cortical columns are computational modules that transform information coming from a particular point on the skin and distribute that transformed information to various regions of the brain.

Dynamic Properties of Receptors Are Matched to Those of Central Neurons

The finding that neurons of a given modality are grouped together suggests that there are specific communication lines or sensory channels for various submodalities. Submodality-specific receptors are connected to submodality-specific cells in the dorsal column nuclei and in the thalamus, and these then project to a submodality-specific column in the cortex.

We can now ask: how do the properties of the receptor at the beginning of the sensory channel relate to the properties of the subsequent neurons in the brain to which the receptors connect? As we have seen in Chapters 15 and 16, the various mechanoreceptor cells differ in their dynamic response properties: some receptor cells are rapidly adapting, others adapt slowly. Mountcastle found that the various receptors are well matched to their central neurons. Rapidly adapting hair receptors connect to rapidly adapting neurons in the thalamus and the cortex. Slowly adapting joint receptors connect to neurons in the brain that adapt slowly. As a result, the dynamic response of a central neuron corresponds to that of the receptors to which it is connected, ensuring high fidelity in the transmission of neural information along communication lines. The response of the receptor is faithfully transmitted to the cortex.

Thus, for certain intensity dimensions, the sensitivity of the receptor sets the sensitivity for the whole communication line. In these cases, the major transformations of the stimulus are determined by the peripheral receptor. We might therefore predict that stimulation of a *single* receptor neuron might give rise to the quantum— the elementary unit—of tactile perception. The ability of humans to perceive the activation of a single receptor has indeed been recently demonstrated. In addition, psychophysical studies show that several types of tactile perceptions in humans are determined by the response properties of the receptors. The subsequent points in communication channels serve to preserve this initial abstraction.

Some Cells Have Complex Properties

In the hand area of the monkey cortex a few cells (about 6%) have properties that are more complex than those we have so far considered. These cells do not respond well to punctate stimuli on the receptive field, but respond briskly to movement of a mechanical stimulus within the receptive field. Many of these cells are *directionally sensitive* and respond better to movement along the skin in one direction than in the reverse direction (Figure 17–12). Some neurons respond well to an edge placed on the skin in a certain (optimal) direction. These complex cells are not found in Brodmann's area 3, the primary target for the axons that project from the ventral posterior lateral nucleus of thalamus; rather, the complex cells are found in

the two posterior cortical regions in area 1 and, particularly, in area 2. This suggests that these complex properties arise not from the receptor but from cortical processing of the incoming sensory information. (We shall encounter this idea again in considering the visual system.)

What is the function of cortical neurons with complex receptive field properties? Hyvärinen and Poranen suggest that these cells become active during movements of the hand designed to explore the shape of an object and that they have a role in *stereognosis*—the capacity to perceive three-dimensional structure.

As we shall see in Chapter 48, all of the sensory areas of the cerebral cortex project to adjacent regions in the cortex called *association areas.* Each association area receives information from several sensory areas. These association regions are thought to bring together and associate information from two or more senses. The somatic sensory cortical areas project to the posterior association areas 5 and 7 of the parietal cortex (Figure 17–1B). In these parietal cortex association areas, cells have very complex properties, receive convergence from several separate modalities, and are often related to movement. Here the mechanisms for tactile discrimination and position sense are integrated with visual information and used to probe *extrapersonal space,* the environment immediately surrounding the subject. It is here that the picture that we have of our body is thought to arise.

Parallel Processing and Feature Detection

Thus studies of the somatic sensory system on the cellular level reveal a detail of organization that was not apparent from evoked response mapping. First, the system is organized topographically. There are repeated maps of our body surface in every relay point in our brain. Neighborhood relationships are preserved. Second, the system maintains in its early stages an organization for each submodality. Third, some neural transformations—aspects of feature detection—occur at the very first level, that of the receptor. Although many important transformations, such as the detection of movement and orientation, occur in the cortex, it is surprising nonetheless that, for some intensity dimensions of sensation, cells in Brodmann's area 1 of the primary somatic cortex follow the sensory input faithfully with little distortion or abstraction.

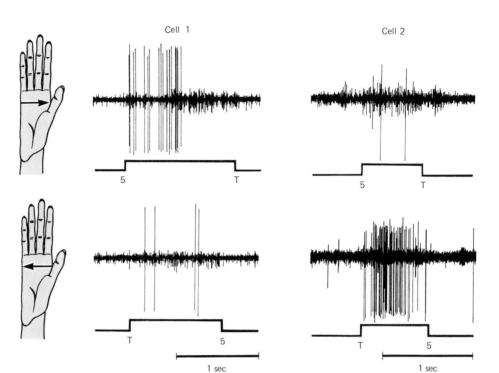

17–12 Recordings from two neurons in the hand area of the monkey cortex that have the same receptive field but opposite direction preferences. (Recordings came from the same electrode penetration.) **Upper records:** responses to movement of a sable hair brush from fifth digit (**5**) to thumb (**T**) across the interdigital pads of the palm. **Lower records:** responses to the same stimulus moving across the pads from T to 5. For cell **1,** movement from 5 to T evoked a strong response, while movement from T to 5 evoked a very weak response. The converse was true for cell **2.** (Adapted from Constanzo and Gardner, 1980.)

In discussing the central representation of touch we have focused on the medial lemniscal pathway. However, for touch as for other sensory and motor modalities, signals from the periphery reach the cortex by several parallel pathways, each carrying information that is at once partly similar and partly different. As a result, lesions of the medial lemniscus do not abolish all tactile perception. Patients with these lesions still retain the capability for crude tactile discrimination, through pathways that ascend in the anterolateral column, although aspects of discriminative touch are lost or seriously impaired.

The relative resistance of sensory function to disruption of components of the somatic afferent pathway is an example of parallel processing in the brain, a form of processing we shall encounter again later. This processing is characteristic of all sensory and motor systems; it is not to be confused with redundancy, which it resembles. Redundancy is an engineering term that is used to denote duplication of components—such as multiple lighting, tracking, or ignition systems—designed to ensure the security that one system will operate when the other breaks down. Although parallel processing also achieves a measure of security in case of disease, this is not its primary purpose. Parallel processing is not de-signed to achieve multiplication of identical circuitry but to allow different neuronal pathways and brain relays to deal with the same sensory information in slightly different ways. It is parallel processing that allows simple neuronal transformations to give the richness to our perception.

Selected Readings and References

Brodal, A. 1981. Neurological Anatomy. 3rd ed. New York: Oxford University Press, pp. 46–147.

Hyvärinen, J., and Poranen, A. 1978. Movement-sensitive and direction and orientation-selective cutaneous receptive fields in the hand area of the postcentral gyrus in monkeys. J. Physiol. (Lond.) 283: 523–537.

Kaas, J. H., Nelson, R. J., Sur, M., Lin, C.-S., and Merzenich, M. M. 1979. Multiple representations of the body within the primary somatosensory cortex of primates. Science (Wash., D.C.) 204:521–523.

Mountcastle, V. B. 1975. The view from within: Pathways to the study of perception. Johns Hopkins Med. J. 136:109–131.

Mountcastle, V. B. 1976. The world around us: Neural command functions for selective attention. Neurosci. Res. Program Bull. 14:Suppl.

Starr, A. 1978. Sensory evoked potentials in clinical disorders of the nervous system. Annu. Rev. Neurosci. 1:103–127.

Werner, G., and Whitsel, B. L. 1973. Functional organization of the somatosensory cortex. In A. Iggo (ed.), Handbook of Sensory Physiology, Vol. 2, The Somatosensory System. New York: Springer, pp. 621–700.

Other References

Bard, P. 1938. Studies on the cortical representation of somatic sensibility. Harvey Lect. 33:143–169.

Costanzo, R. M., and Gardner, E. P. 1980. A quantitative analysis of responses of direction-sensitive neurons in somatosensory cortex of awake monkeys. J. Neurophysiol. 43:1319–1341.

Jackson, J. H. 1931–1932. Selected Writings of John Hughlings Jackson. J. Taylor (ed.). 2 vol. London: Hodder and Stoughton.

Marshall, W. H., Woolsey, C. N., and Bard, P. 1941. Observations on cortical somatic sensory mechanisms of cat and monkey. J. Neurophysiol. 4:1–24.

Mountcastle, V. B. 1957. Modality and topographic properties of single neurons of cat's somatic sensory cortex. J. Neurophysiol. 20:408–434.

Mountcastle, V. B., and Darian-Smith, I. 1968. Neural mechanisms in somesthesia. In V. B. Mountcastle (ed.), Medical Physiology, Vol. II. St. Louis: Mosby, pp. 1372–1423.

Norrsell, U. 1980. Behavioral studies of the somatosensory system. Physiol. Rev. 60:327–354.

Penfield, W., and Rasmussen, T. 1950. The Cerebral Cortex of Man. A Clinical Study of Localization of Function. New York: Macmillan.

Woolsey, C. N. 1958. Organization of somatic sensory and motor areas of the cerebral cortex. In H. F. Harlow and C. N. Woolsey (eds.), Biological and Biochemical Bases of Behavior. Madison: University of Wisconsin Press, pp. 63–81.

Dennis D. Kelly

Somatic Sensory System IV: Central Representations of Pain and Analgesia

18

Pain is a primitive, protective experience that we share with almost all living organisms. Because there is such an urgent and primordial quality about the array of sensations we label as painful (such as pricking, burning, aching, stinging, and soreness), it is often difficult for us to appreciate scientifically that the neural activity associated with pain is probably the most easily modified of any sensory system. Pain can be modified not only by opiates and by surgery, but also by such emotions as joy of childbirth or fear of a dentist, by social context, by stress, by hypnosis, and by many other forms of stimulation and ritual, including acupuncture. The extraordinary plasticity of human pain suggests that neural mechanisms must exist to modulate either transmission in primary pain pathways or the organism's emotional reaction to pain. As we shall see, there is now firm evidence for both types of inhibitory interactions in the nervous system. We shall also find that not only is afferent information concerning pain localized within certain populations of neurons, but so is neural activity associated with the relief of pain.

Pain is more than a conspicuous sensory experience that warns of danger. When pain becomes chronic, it represents a massive social problem and sustains a major industry. In the United States more than 2 million workers are incapacitated by pain at any given time, and compensation payments for pain exceed 2.5 billion dollars each year. Despite these social dimensions and the fact that millions have suffered for centuries, the scientific study of pain, apart from clinical observations, is only decades old.

Until recently there was very little systematic animal experimentation dealing with pain and its relief. In part this may be attributable to a lag in the development of accurate psychophysical methods for assessing pain in animals. However, there were also serious misgivings voiced by a number of clinical researchers about the fundamental relevance of animal research to human pain, given the extraordinary psychological maleability of the human pain response and a reluctance to acknowledge similar nonsensory factors in the pain experience of animals. To some it seemed that the subjective relief of pain reported by some patients under placebo medication represents a unique property of the human nervous system. On the other hand, practiced veterinarians had long recognized the value of stroking an animal's head before examining an injured limb. In fact, there has been a recent convergence of neurobiological evidence that establishes the existence in both man and lower animals of an endogenous pain inhibitory system. This system appears to be composed of a set of phylogenetically ancient structures that line the medial and caudal portions of the ventricular system.

In this chapter we shall concentrate first upon the parts of the nervous system involved in the perception of pain and then upon those involved in pain suppression. Although it is true that an aversive sensation can be aroused in any modality if the stimulus is sufficiently intense, this discussion will deal only with somatic pain.

Pain Is Transmitted by Select Neural Pathways
Transduction of Pain by Receptors

In the peripheral nervous system painful stimulation has been associated with activity in the network of free nerve endings in the skin. Although these small nerve endings can be depolarized directly by strong mechanical pressure, the most common belief is that the peripheral stimulus for pain is some chemical released into the extracellular fluid as a result of tissue damage. Extracts from damaged tissue cause intense pain

when injected into normal skin. A variety of substances are known to cause pain when similarly injected into skin, and, at times, each has been proposed as the putative chemical mediator of pain. Pain can be induced by low pH (acidic) solutions, as well as by histamine, bradykinin, serotonin, acetylcholine, and even by substance P (which, as we shall see below, is also the transmitter substance released by primary pain afferents at their first central synapse in the spinal cord). It has also been demonstrated that a relationship exists between pain intensity and local K^+ ion concentration, which may prove to be a significant fact, since most tissue damage results in an extracellular increase in K^+ concentration.

Primary Pain Afferents Are Coded by Size and Terminate in the Dorsal Horn of the Spinal Cord

As we have seen in Chapter 15, pain in humans appears to be subserved by two distinguishable populations of peripheral afferent fibers. One set is found among small, finely myelinated Aδ fibers conducting at about 5–30 m/sec and is associated with sensations of sharp, pricking pain. Aδ fibers are distributed only to skin and mucous membranes. The other set of nociceptive fibers is found among the small unmyelinated C fibers conducting at 0.5–2 m/sec. The peripheral ends of these bare axons are activated by high-intensity mechanical, chemical, and thermal ($>45°C$) stimulation, for which reason they are known as polymodal nociceptors. Unmyelinated C fibers are very widely distributed in deep tissues as well as skin (and in the latter they occur in much greater density than do Aδ fibers). C fibers appear to mediate long-lasting, burning pain. A similar duality exists in peripheral populations of trigeminal neurons.

Upon entering the spinal cord in the more lateral aspects of the individual dorsal roots, the first-order Aδ and C fibers most often branch longitudinally for one to three segments as Lissauer's tract before synapsing on neurons in the marginal zone (lamina I), substantia gelatinosa (laminae II and III) and, to a lesser extent, the deeper lamina V of the dorsal horn. It has recently been discovered that the mediating substance released by C-fiber afferents at their central synapses is the undecapeptide, substance P (H-Arg-Pro-Lys-Pro-Gln-Gln-Phe-Phe-Gly-Leu-Met-NH$_2$).   Thomas

Hökfelt, using immunohistochemical techniques, has localized substance P in the skin, in the smallest cells of the dorsal root ganglion, in the tract of Lissauer, and in laminae I, II, and III of the dorsal horn—in other words, virtually wherever small unmyelinated primary pain afferents extend. In addition, T. L. Yaksh has found recently that, after injections of the neurotoxin, capsaicin, into the cerebrospinal fluid surrounding the spinal cord, substance P neurons in the dorsal horn degenerated and this was accompanied by significant elevations in pain thresholds.

Two Populations of Pain-Transmission Neurons Exist in the Spinal Cord

Second-order connections of pain afferents are not well understood. Some second-order neurons (particularly from lamina I) decussate immediately in the anterior white commissure before ascending in the lateral spinothalamic tract in the anterolateral quadrant of the cord (Figure 18–1). Other neurons receiving Aδ- and C-fiber input, principally cells in the substantia gelatinosa, simply project deeper into the dorsal horn. There, these interneurons synapse on cells (often in lamina V) whose ascending axons enter either the contralateral or ipsilateral anterolateral funiculus. While the spinothalamic tract is primarily crossed in humans, the existence of a small but significant ipsilateral component is well established. These uncrossed fibers may be the reason pain returns in some patients despite an initially successful surgical section of anterolateral fibers.

Electrophysiological analysis of dorsal horn cells that receive nociceptive input and whose axons ascend in the anterolateral funiculi suggests that there are two populations of nociceptive neurons (Figure 18–2): (1) marginal neurons in lamina I that are selectively activated by high-threshold polymodal nociceptors, and (2) lamina V neurons that also have polymodal nociceptive input but display a significantly wider range of thresholds. We shall consider these in order.

Edward Perl has found that among the relatively large cells at the periphery of the dorsal horn comprising lamina I are a number of specific nociceptive neurons. These are vigorously excited by high-intensity thermal and mechanical stimuli (polymodal) but are unaffected by touch or movement of hairs (hence, they are specific

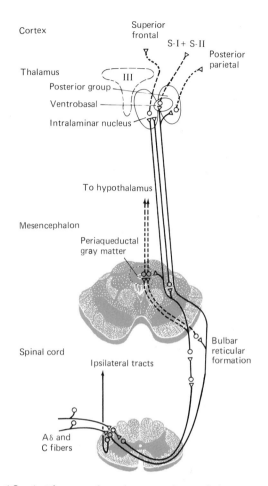

18–1 The anterolateral system of spinothalamic, spinoreticular, and spinotectal fibers, which convey information about pain to broad regions of the brain stem and diencephalon.

nociceptors). Moreover, these neurons can be excited antidromically from the anterolateral portion of the contralateral cervical cord and from the thalamus. As indicated in Figure 18–2, these direct spinothalamic axons of marginal cells form the *neospinothalamic* component of the anterolateral system and, as we shall see later, may be responsible for the good localization of sharp or acute pain on the body surface. Although this is the type of pain most often studied in the laboratory, it is not the type that normally prompts patients to seek medical attention.

The second group of ascending dorsal horn nociceptors shown in Figure 18–2 is located primarily in lamina V. These large cells respond

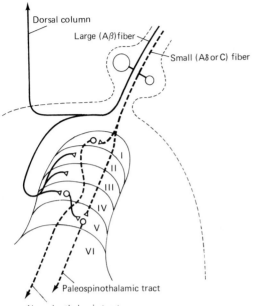

18-2 Simplified diagram of somatic sensory input to the dorsal horn of the spinal cord and of the laminar organization of nociceptive neurons whose axons form the ascending anterolateral system. Note that while neurons in the marginal layer (lamina I) receive input primarily from small Aδ and C fibers, there is greater convergence of large- and small-fiber input upon nociceptive neurons in lamina V. This difference is reflected in the electrophysiology of these cells. Many nociceptive neurons in the marginal layer do not respond to nonpainful touch stimuli, while those in the deeper layers display a wider dynamic range.

to activity of all three of the main fiber components of the cutaneous nerves: Aβ, Aδ, and C fibers. As might be expected, they respond to both nonnoxious and noxious stimuli, and hence are called *wide dynamic range nociceptors*. However, the type of response to each fiber group differs. Threshold touch stimuli produce a brief burst of firing in lamina V cells followed by brief inhibition. However, when large-fiber touch input is suppressed, there is a remarkable build-up in the activity of the same cell following C-fiber stimulation, that is, prolonged afterdis-charges and facilitation ensue. As will be emphasized later, the axons of these cells contribute to the paleospinothalamic and spinoreticular components of the anterolateral system, which

seem to subserve the more diffuse, chronic types of pain that are of most importance to the practice of medicine.

Spinal Pain Projections to the Brain Stem Are Widespread

Walle Nauta has pointed out that the classical name for the spinothalamic system is in reality a *pars pro toto* term, that is, a collection of pathways named after only a portion of its constituent neurons, in that only a small proportion of the fibers ascend directly to the thalamus. Instead, most fibers tend to synapse at brain stem levels below the thalamus, largely in the tegmental reticular formation. Therefore, the vast majority of anterolateral fibers are actually spinoreticular neurons. Fiber counts by David Bowsher suggest that in man only about 12% of the 2–4-μm and 36% of the 4–7-μm anterolateral fibers found at the first cervical level can be accounted for in the rostral midbrain. Others have estimated that direct spinothalamic fibers in man number only 1500 in the midbrain, as compared with about 1,000,000 in the medial lemniscus. While these estimates, made some years ago, are undoubtedly low, the lopsided ratio of through fibers to the thalamus in the lemniscal versus anterolateral system is probably correct. Thus, the anterolateral system of the cord is characterized by a great divergence of terminations throughout the brain stem.

At the level of the mesencephalon, a number of anterolateral, pain-activated fibers from the cord end in the lower layers of the superior and inferior colliculi (spinotectal tract), although this possible pain projection has been largely ignored in recent years. Nevertheless, noxious stimuli give rise to evoked potentials in the tectum, and electrical stimulation of this area in humans, as in lower animals, has been reported to be particularly painful. Moreover, from a comparative standpoint the reptilian midbrain roof represents a well-developed somatic sensory relay nucleus, not unlike the mammalian thalamus.

An even larger number of anterolateral fibers enter the mesencephalic periaqueductal gray matter (*broken line* projection in Figure 18-1), which has strong reciprocal connections with the periventricular region of the diencephalon (through the dorsal longitudinal fasciculus of Schutz) and, via the hypothalamus, with the limbic system. In 1900, on purely architectural grounds, Bechterew suggested prophetically that the central gray substance might function as a nodal point in conducting pathways. As we shall see later, current theories of pain describe the mesencephalic central gray as a probable convergent area of limbic forebrain and sensory impulses which may play an important role in the integration of the emotional aspects of pain sensations and, conversely, in the modulation of pain input by prior emotional states.

Thalamic Relays Preserve the Duality of Ascending Pain Projections

The limited number of truly spinothalamic fibers in the anterolateral system terminate in two thalamic areas which generally reflect the separate projections of the neospinothalamic and paleospinothalamic neurons.

The first area of somatotopically arranged neospinothalamic terminations has been referred to in the physiological literature by Poggio and Mountcastle as the *posterior nuclear group.* This region overlaps in part the *ventrobasal complex,* as Rose and Mountcastle termed the zone of lemniscal termination which coincides closely, but not exactly, with the ventral posterior nucleus. Therefore, this part of the thalamus represents not only a gateway to the somatic sensory cortical areas, S-I and S-II, but also a site of convergence between the medial lemniscal system conveying touch and proprioceptive information and the neospinothalamic component of the anterolateral system, which probably contributes the rapidly felt quality of sharpness to pain. This anatomical overlap in thalamic terminations of the two systems is particularly marked within the ventral posterior lateral nucleus, where, in monkeys and man, many spinothalamic fibers appear to be arranged in a spotty, archipelago fashion as discrete clusters of terminals interspersed among the more regularly spaced somatotopical terminations of lemniscal fibers from the dorsal column nuclei.

One physiological property of posterior nucleus neurons that can be activated only by noxious stimuli is particularly interesting. Although specifically responsive to pain, they show exceptionally large receptive fields. Because such cells are not likely to provide information concerning the localization of the painful stimulus, Poggio and Mountcastle suggested that simultaneous stimulation of mechanoreceptors may provide the information by which pain is localized. This assumption is supported by clinical observations in humans who have suffered interruption of the lemniscal system: these patients display a diminished capacity to localize painful stimuli.

A second important termination of spinothalamic fibers is found in the nonspecific intralaminar nuclei, particularly the paracentral and central lateral nuclei. These medial polysynaptic spinothalamic fibers have been referred to as the *paleospinothalamic* system and may be homologous to the spinodiencephalic system of lower vertebrates. Mountcastle has proposed that these projections upon the intralaminar nuclei may subserve slow-burning pain. In addition to spinothalamic fibers, the intralaminar nuclei also receive projections from the cerebellum and from the brain stem reticular tegmentum and project diffusely to the cortex.

Stereotaxically placed surgical lesions in the thalamus have been attempted often during the past 20 years to relieve the pain of patients suffering from advanced cancer. In one particularly informative study by Mark, Ervin, and Yakovlev, damage to the sensory relay nuclei (the ventrobasal complex) produced a loss of cutaneous touch and sharp pain (pinprick), but left deep chronic pain unaffected. Lesions of the intralaminar nuclei successfully relieved chronic deep pain but not cutaneous pain. These observations seem to confirm the finding that the duality of pain initially noted in separable populations of peripheral afferents may be preserved even at the thalamic level.

These investigators also noted the interesting fact that electrical stimulation of the thalamus never resulted in reports of pain, nor did the patients report any recognizable sensory experience such as touch, temperature, or vibration. Instead, thalamic stimulation was most often appreciated as a tingling sensation of pins and needles. This suggests that the temporospatial patterning of somatic sensory afferents to the thalamus is probably as important a determinant of pain as is the specific pathway over which the information is conducted. Blunt excitation of thalamic neurons is insufficient to mimic the sensory quality of pain. In fact, electrical stimulation of the intralaminar nuclei in patients has been discovered to be analgesic and relaxing, provided it remains at low frequencies (10–20 Hz) and low amplitude. Increases in either frequency or amplitude lead to aversive effects; although the patients still never report specific pain, they describe arousal, anxiety, and a need to escape.

Role of the Cerebral Cortex in Reactions to Pain

It is unlikely that the cortical projections from either the nonspecific or specific thalamic nuclei mentioned above are critical for the appreciation of pain, since large neocortical ablations, including all of both S-I and S-II, leave chronic clinical pain undiminished and experimental pain thresholds normal.

However, there are two documented examples in which cortical surgery has alleviated suffering in chronic pain patients, although neither cortical region receives direct projections from the thalamic nuclei innervated by pain afferents. The first observation, which dates from the extensive psychosurgical treatment of mental patients following World War II, is that frontal lobotomized patients with prior histories of chronic pain still reported the perception of pain but were no longer bothered by it. A similar dissociation between the perception and tolerance of pain has subsequently been noticed following lesions in the dorsomedial and anterior thalamic nuclei that project to the prefrontal cortex. The second, more recent and less drastic procedure involves the bilateral destruction of the anterior portion of the cingulate gyrus and bundle (the latter contains fibers that connect the frontal lobes with medial limbic structures). In fact, this operation, called *cingulotomy*, was cited as possibly the most efficacious of current psychosurgical procedures in the 1976 report on psychosurgery of the National Commission for the Protection of Human Subjects of Biomedial and Behavioral Research. It is interesting that several rigorous follow-up studies of cingulotomy patients, performed at the request of the Commission, found that successful relief of pain was greatest among patients with pain accompanied by depression. Unlike frontal lobotomized patients, patients with successful cingulotomies reported that they no longer felt the pain that once afflicted them.

Gate Control Theory of Pain

This frequently cited theory was developed in the early 1960s by Melzack and Wall to account for some of the ways in which pain differs from other sensations. In particular, they were interested in the mechanisms by which other cutaneous

stimuli and emotional states can alter the level of pain felt. One site of interaction suggested by the theory is among the interneurons of the substantia gelatinosa in the spinal cord (laminae II and III; Figure 18–2). Melzack and Wall suggested that collateral input from the large myelinated Aβ touch fibers and collateral input from the smaller Aδ and C fibers have antagonistic effects on cells in the substantia gelatinosa. These gate cells, in turn, are presumed to regulate the firing of cells deeper in the dorsal horn, presumably lamina V, that give rise to the paleospinothalamic tract. A higher central decoding mechanism is hypothesized which subsequently monitors spinothalamic activity for a critical level at which, and above, pain is felt. The brain is also assumed to exert descending control on this system since cognitive factors are known to influence even spinal withdrawal reflexes. For example, if a person picks up a very hot cup of tea, he or she may drop it. However, if the cup is made of fine Dresden china, one is not so likely to drop it, but may well manage jerkily to put it back on the table, and *then* shake the hand.

Although the anatomical possibility exists for large- and small-fiber interactions in the dorsal horn (Figure 18–2), there is relatively little, and conflicting, physiological evidence for the gate control theory. At a spinal level, the gate control theory predicts that somatic stimulation should produce presynaptic inhibition on both the small- and large-diameter dorsal root fibers that synapse upon spinothalamic neurons. To test this, Whitehorn and Burgess stimulated both Aα and Aδ fibers and looked for evidence of presynaptic inhibition on C fibers. They found none. Only when C fibers themselves were stimulated by noxious stimuli was any presynaptic inhibition seen on C fibers. Similarly, presynaptic inhibition of large-diameter fibers was found only with gentle mechanical stimulation, the quality mediated by these fibers. Although disappointing for the gate control hypothesis, these negative results are probably not definitive. C fibers are too small to penetrate intracellularly and their size also makes it difficult for their individual firing patterns to be extracted with precision from dorsal root potentials. On the other hand, Hentall and Fields have been able to track the thresholds of single C afferents stimulated by intraspinal microelectrodes in the region of their terminals. They found indirect evidence of what may represent a large-to-small fiber presynaptic inhibition. Innocuous mechanical stimuli (brushing) in the vicinity of the receptive field of the C fiber (which did not fire the C fiber) often reduced its antidromic threshold for firing.

As several studies have failed to provide empirical support for the gate-control theory, it is appropriate to ask why the theory should be mentioned if it is not correct. There are two reasons. First, even if the theory is incorrect in detail, some of its clinical predictions have proven empirically useful—for example, the suggestion that stimulation of the large-diameter dorsal column fibers should close the gate and thus diminish pain. Direct, or even transcutaneous, electrical stimulation of sensory nerves, particularly the dorsal columns, which by itself is felt as tingling, can provide clinical pain relief for long periods during and after stimulation. Admittedly, this technique is not successful in all hands, and in some it is even too successful, as in the case of the Boston patient who failed to hook up his batteries before gaining relief! The second reason is that the gate control theory reversed the historical research emphasis upon pain as solely an afferent sensory experience. Pain also disrupts ongoing behavior, demands immediate attention, and serves as a primary negative reinforcer in a variety of situations. It suppresses behavior when made contingent upon it and supports a broad repertoire of avoidance and escape responses. To emphasize only the sensory features of pain in the study of its neural bases and to ignore its unique affective and motivational properties is to confront only part of the problem. Similarly, to treat pain only by trying to cut down the sensory input by pharmacological or surgical blocks denies us several useful modalities of treatment and can only delay the understanding of how the brain itself is organized to inhibit the perception of pain.

Pain Is Also Inhibited by Select Neural Pathways: The Mechanisms of Analgesia

It was once believed that sensory systems were all quite reliable in their afferent transmission of signals and that central ascending pathways conveyed to the cortex with minimal transformations whatever messages were generated by sensory end-organs. Only when sensory impulses reached the cortex were they then believed accessible to perceptual processing and modification by psychological factors. However, we now know that, despite the apparent urgency of information concerning pain, it, like all other sensory systems, can be modulated from its very point of origin through successive synaptic junctions in its central pathway. The endogenous mechanism for pain inhibition most likely evolved and survived to be represented even in man because it offered a significant selective advantage to its possessors. While there are many conceivable instances when an organism's normal reactions to pain could be seriously disadvantageous, we must admit that little is actually known about the normal biological role of the built-in neural system for pain relief. This is still a new and exciting area of research. To outline the physiological properties of the system, we shall briefly summarize four convergent lines of research concerning pain inhibition: the analgesia produced by direct brain stimulation, the mapping of morphine-sensitive sites in the brain, the characterization of the opiate receptor, and the discovery of endogenous opiates.

Stimulation-Produced Analgesia

Although it has been known for at least 2 decades that central stimulation can elicit pain, it is only within the past decade that intracranial stimulation of certain other sites has been shown to be capable of inhibiting pain. Stimulation of an irregular string of sites along the medial periventricular–periaqueductal axis results in a profound surface analgesia, sufficient for abdominal surgery to be performed without apparent discomfort in an unanesthetized rat. Stimulation-produced analgesia is an extremely specific antinociceptive effect and not a generalized sensory, motivational, or motor deficit. The most convincing evidence is that stimulation-produced analgesia often exhibits a restricted peripheral field. Subjects respond normally to noxious stimuli in the unaffected body areas. Moreover, subjects still respond to nonpainful stimuli such as touch and temperature within the circumscribed area of analgesia.

Stimulation-produced analgesia also exhibits several unusual properties for an electrically induced phenomenon. In cats and monkeys analgesia from stimulation of midbrain reticular sites has been found to develop gradually over a period of about 5 min, which could represent either the build-up of a functional neurochemical pool or the release of an agent that requires time to exert its effects upon adjacent neurons or at more distant neural sites. Stimulation-produced analgesia may also outlast the period of stimulation by many minutes or even hours. Fortunately, in human patients analgesic relief of chronic clinical pain has (after an initial latent period of 10–15 min) been seen to outlast a period of periaqueductal gray stimulation by over 24 hr. The determinants of the asynchronous time course of stimulation-produced analgesia remain one of the major unresolved questions surrounding the phenomenon, and perhaps hold the key to its mechanism of action.

The best examples of pure analgesia unaccompanied by other behavioral reactions have been obtained from electrodes placed in the caudal mesencephalic periaqueductal gray (particularly the region of the serotonin-rich dorsal raphe nucleus) and in the medullary nucleus raphe magnus. As previously noted, the periaqueductal gray receives anterolateral projections from dorsal horn laminae known to contain cells uniquely or differentially responsive to noxious stimuli. However, neither destruction of the periaqueductal gray nor microinjections of procaine (Novocain), a local anesthetic, into the region increase pain thresholds. This suggests that stimulation-produced analgesia does not result from a temporary disruption of pain afferents. The stimulation appears to exert its effects through active inhibition of afferent volleys elsewhere in the nervous system, specifically in the cord and the fifth nerve nucleus.

As an example of the selectivity of this inhibition, responses to intensely noxious peripheral stimuli of lamina V type cells of the dorsal horn of the cat have been completely inhibited by stimulation of the periaqueductal gray, while lamina IV type cells, apparently unrelated to pain, were unaffected. Furthermore, dorsolateral funiculus lesions in the cord, which interrupt serotonin-containing axons descending from cells in the medullary nucleus raphe magnus and terminating in the dorsal horn, block analgesia elicited from the periaqueductal gray. Periaqueductal sites that support analgesia in the rhesus monkey also suppress neurons located in nucleus oralis and nucleus caudalis of the fifth nerve that respond selectively to facial pinching or burning. Stimulation-produced analgesia blocks both pain-evoked potentials and spontaneous firing rates in these trigeminal cells for 3–5 min. Stimulation-produced analgesia from the periaqueductal region also selectively blocks the digastric jaw-opening reflex elicited by noxious toothpulp stimulation, but leaves the same response unaffected when elicited by mild taps on the tooth or gingiva.

Stimulation-Produced Analgesia Is Related to Opiate Analgesia

A number of recent studies have suggested possible parallels between the sites and mechanisms of morphine's analgesic action and the sites and mechanisms of stimulation-produced analgesia. Narcotic analgesic drugs are known to exert a powerful, lamina-specific inhibition on spinal cord sensory interneurons, remarkably similar to that just described for periaqueductal stimulation. Furthermore, recent work on stereospecific receptor binding of opiate agonists and antagonists (outlined below) reveals that these opiate-sensitive sites are broadly and unevenly distributed throughout the brain; their distribution overlaps extensively with the areas whose stimulation results in analgesia. It has also been found in a number of studies that microinjections of morphine directly into many of these sites, particularly the periaqueductal gray, result in profound analgesia, while identical injections just a few millimeters removed in the midbrain tegmentum do not. Intracranial morphine injections do not appear to block transmission of pain impulses at this level; like stimulation-produced analgesia, the effects appear to be exerted more caudally, presumably via the same efferent pathway.

Depletion of serotonin produced by prior administration of parachlorophenylalanine or by lesions of the raphe nuclei blocks the ability of both intracranial and systemic narcotics to diminish pain; stimulation-produced analgesia is similarly blocked by depletion of serotonin. Intracranial morphine analgesia also shows an impressive cross tolerance to systemic morphine injections, as does stimulation-produced analgesia. Simultaneous administration of weak brain stimulation and low doses of morphine, each insufficient to inhibit pain, will summate to produce analgesia. Perhaps the most impressive evidence linking stimulation-produced analgesia and opiate mechanisms is that naloxone, a specific narcotic antagonist, blocks not only morphine analgesia, but stimulation analgesia as well, although somewhat less reliably. Thus, to study either of these mechanisms may advance our understanding of the other.

Opiate Receptors

Morphine and related opiates appear to exert their analgesic effects by interacting with specific postsynaptic receptors. Because the opiates demonstrate such extreme chemical specificity, the existence of specific opiate receptors had long been assumed by pharmacologists before they were recently demonstrated almost simultaneously in the laboratories of Lars Terenius in Sweden, Solomon H. Snyder at Johns Hopkins, and Eric Simon at New York University. Their procedures were similar. Brain tissues were homogenized, and synaptosomes were extracted by means of differential centrifugation. These samples were then incubated in a solution of labeled opiates or antagonists with high specific activity and subsequently washed to remove loosely bound and unbound radioactivity. The binding that occurred, like the pharmacological activity of opiates, showed high stereospecificity. There was also an extraordinary correlation between the pharmacological potency of various opiates in producing or antagonizing analgesia and their affinity for the binding sites. Potent opiates, such as morphine and levorphanol, demonstrated affinities in the nanomolar range, whereas weak opiates, such as meperidine, did not bind at these concentrations.

The identification in vitro of a cellular component, with which opiates most likely combine to produce their characteristic analgesic and euphoric effects, posed the inevitable question concerning the normal physiological role of these receptors. It seemed unlikely that such highly specific receptors should have evolved in nature fortuitously only to interact with alkaloids from the opium poppy. On the contrary, the history of pharmacology had suggested that most drug receptors were really receptors for endogenous ligands. The current study of this group of naturally occurring substances, collectively named *endorphins* (for endogenous morphine-like substances), is one of the most interesting and potentially important areas of research in the neurosciences.

Endorphins and Enkephalins Serve Many Functions in the Brain

At present at least nine distinguishable substances that possess opiate-like properties have been isolated from either brain or pituitary tissue. These include a family of six structurally related peptides (dynorphin, the two enkephalins and α-, β-, and γ-endorphin), two pituitary peptides of still unknown structure that are apparently unrelated to the others (the morphine-like factors isolated by Terenius and by Spector), and a low molecular weight peptide found in blood (anodyn-

in). All mimic at least some of the pharmacological actions of opiates in in vitro assays, but as yet not all have been tested for their presumed analgesic properties in vivo.

The first endorphins to be characterized were the enkephalins, two small peptides isolated from pig brains by John Hughes and Hans Kosterlitz in Scotland. These turned out to be two pentapeptides with identical amino acid sequences save for the last position: H-Tyr-Gly-Gly-Phe-Met-OH (Met-enkephalin) and H-Tyr-Gly-Gly-Phe-Leu-OH (Leu-enkephalin). The small size of the enkephalins allowed them to be rapidly synthesized and prompted some initial hope that an analgesic agent might be produced that would be as effective as opiates but without their addictive potential. However, when tested in vivo, the enkephalins turned out to be only mildly analgesic and strongly addictive. When injected directly into the cerebral ventricles, enkephalin produced a very brief analgesia (10 min in rats), probably due to its rapid degradation by polypeptidases present in the cerebrospinal fluid and in brain tissue. One D-alanine[2] analogue of Met-enkephalin, upon intravenous administration in rats, has been reported to produce a more profound naloxone-reversible and dose-dependent analgesia that lasts for approximately 1 hr, but this is accompanied by stupor and severe catatonia. Rabi Simantov (see Snyder and Childers) confirmed the presence of both enkephalins in many species, but found that the ratio of Met- to Leu-enkephalin was not constant in all species of animals. This suggested to Snyder and Simantov that the two peptides may have separate regulatory roles. The distribution of the two enkephalins is similar and closely parallels that of opiate receptors. In turn, several sites which show high concentrations of enkephalin-containing neurons correspond to areas from which stimulation-produced analgesia can be best obtained.

Most recently, a group headed by Avram Goldstein of Stanford University has identified another brain peptide that incorporates the entire sequence of Leu-enkephalin in its structure and that is 200 times more potent than morphine in standard in vitro assays. Because it is so potent, the substance has been named dynorphin, from dynamis (the Greek word for *power*) and endorphin. Dynorphin is a tridecapeptide (13 amino acids long) with the structure: H-Tyr-Gly-Gly-Phe-Leu-Arg-Arg-Ile-Arg-Pro-Lys-Leu-Lys-OH. Its effectiveness as an analgesic agent in living animals has not yet been determined.

Another striking structural feature of the en-

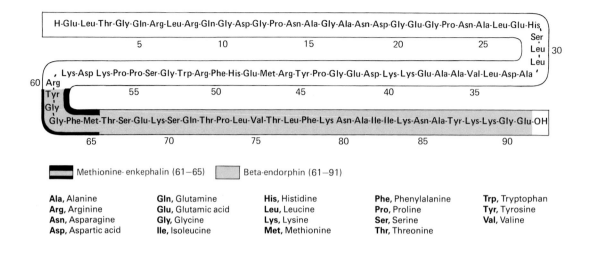

Ala, Alanine **Gln,** Glutamine **His,** Histidine **Phe,** Phenylalanine **Trp,** Tryptophan
Arg, Arginine **Glu,** Glutamic acid **Leu,** Leucine **Pro,** Proline **Tyr,** Tyrosine
Asn, Asparagine **Gly,** Glycine **Lys,** Lysine **Ser,** Serine **Val,** Valine
Asp, Aspartic acid **Ile,** Isoleucine **Met,** Methionine **Thr,** Threonine

18–3 Structure of β-lipotropin, a pituitary peptide hormone that is 91 amino acids long. Contained within this chain is the entire sequence of Met-enkephalin in positions 61–65. The sequence 61–91 is that of β-endorphin, a peptide present in both the pituitary and brain, which has potent analgesic effects when injected intravenously or directly into the brain.

kephalins is that the same sequence of amino acids is also found in an oligopeptide known as *β-lipotropin*. This hormone, whose structure is shown in Figure 18–3, had been isolated over 15 years ago from camel pituitary and was so named because it promotes the breakdown of fats (as do many other hormones). The recognition that the sequence of 91 amino acids comprising β-lipotropin contains the sequence of Met-enkephalin (61–65) prompted a series of experiments to determine whether β-lipotropin possessed opiate activity. While the whole molecule was found to be virtually devoid of opiate activity, a number of its peptide fragments, also found in the brain, did prove extremely active, namely, α-endorphin (61–76), β-endorphin (61–91), and γ-endorphin (61–77). The most active of these is β-endorphin, which is shaded in Figure 18–3. It demonstrates an even higher affinity for the opiate receptor than does morphine and it is itself highly analgesic; it is 48 times more potent than morphine when injected intraventricularly and 3 times more potent when given intravenously. Unfortunately, chronic administration of β-endorphin produces progressively weaker analgesic effects (tolerance) and also gives rise to withdrawal signs comparable to those of morphine (dependence). Nevertheless, the potential

role of the enkephalins and endorphins in the therapeutic control of pain is of great interest to researchers.

In addition to their addictive liability, the relatively brief duration of the analgesia induced by these naturally occurring opiates is presently a major obstacle to their practical application. The enkephalins also appear to have epileptogenic effects (which are naloxone reversible) on the rat's cerebral cortex, and intracerebral β-endorphin injections lead to a pronounced catatonic posturing. The latter observation has prompted the dramatic, but probably premature speculation that the endorphins may be involved in schizophrenia. However, there are many experimental manipulations that can cause catatonia in laboratory animals, and relatively few schizophrenic patients who exhibit the symptom.

Descending Control of Spinal Pain-Transmission Neurons

The evidence summarized in the preceding sections suggests that opiate, stimulation-produced, and endorphin analgesias may share a common physiological substrate. As noted before, an optimal site for eliciting stimulation-produced analgesia appears to be the midbrain periaqueductal gray matter in or near the serotonergic dorsal raphe nucleus, as well in the gray matter that extends rostrally into the diencephalic periventricular area. These observations may be relevant clinically since Giesler and Liebeskind have shown that visceral, as well as somatic pain can be inhibited from this region. Moreover, anterograde transport and autoradio-

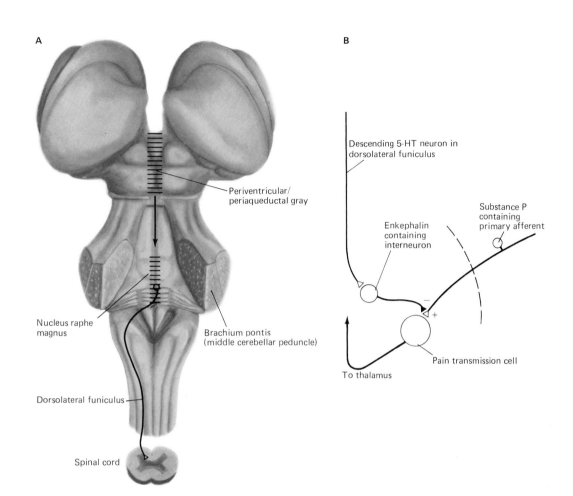

graphic anatomical studies by Mary Ann Ruda have demonstrated widespread projections from this periventricular–periaqueductal area, of which the following are of particular interest: (1) descending connections to the medullary reticular nuclei and to the nucleus raphe magnus (another important site for stimulation-produced analgesia), both of which project to the spinal cord; and (2) ascending projections to the intralaminar nuclei of the thalamus in a pattern very similar to that known for the spinothalamic tract. As illustrated in Figure 18–4A, the former fibers probably form part of a descending control system that modulates pain transmission in the dorsal horn of the cord via the raphe nuclei in the midline of the medullary reticular formation. From the nucleus raphe magnus, serotonergic fibers (which use 5-hydroxytryptamine as a transmitter) descend through the dorsolateral funiculus of the spinal cord to end in the substantia gelatinosa. Here the raphe spinal neurons synapse with enkephalinergic interneurons that

18–4 **A.** Descending pain modulatory system described by Fields and Basbaum (1978). Neurons in the periventricular and periaqueductal gray matter excite those in the nucleus raphe magnus in the medullary reticular formation. From here serotonergic fibers descend in the dorsolateral funiculus of the spinal cord to terminate in the substantia gelatinosa, where they are believed to activate (or disinhibit) enkephalinergic inhibitory interneurons. **B.** Cellular model proposed by Leslie Iversen to account for modulation of pain-transmission neurons in the dorsal horn of the spinal cord by descending serotonergic neurons of the brain stem. Enkephalinergic interneurons may exert presynaptic inhibitory control over incoming substance P-containing primary afferent fibers concerned with pain. **5-HT,** 5-hydroxytryptamine (serotonin).

inhibit neurons normally responsible for the on-ward transmission of noxious information (Figure 18–4B). This process would explain why electrodes implanted in the periaqueductal gray matter are able to block the upward transmission of pain and why transsection of the dorsolateral funiculus can both block stimulation-produced analgesia and attenuate analgesia induced by systemic morphine injections. (However, there is some evidence that morphine can produce mild analgesia by acting directly upon enkephalinergic neurons or opiate receptors in the dorsal horn.)

Leslie Iversen has suggested that enkephalinergic neurons in the substantia gelatinosa may modulate pain transmission by inhibiting primary afferent $A\delta$ and C fibers presynaptically at their first central synapse. The evidence for this hypothesis, illustrated in Figure 18–4B, is that when the dorsal root is sectioned (at the *broken line*) the opiate receptors previously present in the dorsal horn of the cord disappear, while there is a slight build-up in enkephalin concentrations. This finding suggests that the opiate receptors are on the primary afferent cells themselves and that enkephalin-containing neurons, intrinsic to the dorsal horn and thus spared by dorsal root section, may make presynaptic contact upon them.

Stress-Induced Analgesia: A Nonopiate Phenomenon

There is evidence that at least one pain inhibitory system does not involve endorphins. Exposing an animal to a novel stressful situation produces a long-lasting analgesia (1–2 hr) that shows no cross tolerance with morphine and is only marginally affected by opiate antagonists. Repeated exposures to the same environmental stressor result in a progressive decline of the analgesic response, in much the same manner as other physiological stress responses (such as pituitary–adrenal activation) adapt. The anterior pituitary is known to release β-endorphin concomitantly with adrenocorticotropin during periods of extreme stress, albeit in amounts far too small to induce analgesia when administered intravenously. However, removal of the pituitary (specifically the anterior lobe) attenuates stress-induced analgesia, which suggests that the phenomenon is hormone-mediated, if not by β-endorphin.

Despite the ambiguity surrounding its mechanism, the phenomenon of stress-induced analgesia may bear upon the major unanswered question concerning the biological significance of central pain inhibitory pathways. In light of the strong evidence outlined in this chapter, the existence of such pathways, whose normal purpose is to dampen the warning signals of pain, is no longer in doubt. However, the reasons this neural, and hormonal, capability evolved and apparently survived so as to be represented even in humans is still a matter of conjecture. There are few clues. Stimulation of the periaqueductal gray results not only in analgesia, but, at adjacent electrode sites, in aggressive and defensive behaviors. Is it possible that the analgesic mechanisms are related to the suppression of pain when such behaviors are being performed? If so, there are many behavioral situations in which an organism's normal reactions to pain, prompting withdrawal, rest, and other recuperative behaviors, could prove disadvantageous—for instance, during predation, defense, intraspecific confrontations for dominance, and virtually any adaptation to an extreme environmental demand. These are normally defined as times of stress.

A number of experimental questions remain to be answered before the laboratory phenomenon of stress-induced analgesia can be accepted as a model for human stress reactions. This form of analgesia has been studied only in rodents, not in higher species, and mostly in response to stressors that are themselves very painful. Only the most severe stressors induce analgesia; there are many standard laboratory procedures, such as prolonged physical exertion and exposure to loud noise, that elicit maximal adrenal corticosteroid responses but do not produce analgesia. Nor has it been proved that the sensory deficit induced by severe stress is limited to the modality of pain.

Nevertheless, there is strong intuitive support for the existence of stress-induced analgesia in humans. Soldiers wounded in battle and athletes injured in sports sometimes report that they do not feel pain. Are these examples of a natural response of the body to a novel stressor, or are they complicated exceptions to the rule? Why do most soldiers and athletes feel pain? Pain as a warning of serious physical damage can represent vital information that in normal, even stressful, circumstances ought not to be ignored. Perhaps, as in the laboratory, stress induces analgesia only in the most extreme, life-threatening situations. If so, we can find an extraordinary and century-old expression of this idea in the writings of David Livingstone, the Scottish missionary and explorer of Africa. On an early journey to find the source of the Nile, Livingstone was attacked by a lion that crushed his shoulder. The experience haunted Livingstone for over 20 years:

. . . I heard a shout. Starting, and looking half round, I saw the lion just in the act of springing upon me. I was upon a little height; he caught my shoulder as he sprang, and we both came to the ground below together. Growling horribly close to my ear, he shook me as a terrier does a rat. The shock produced a stupor similar to that which seems to be felt by a mouse after the first shake of the cat. It caused a sort of dreaminess in which there was no sense of pain nor feeling of terror, though quite conscious of all that was happening. It was like what patients partially under the influence of chloroform describe, who see all the operation, but feel not the knife. This singular condition was not the result of any mental process. The shake annihilated fear, and allowed no sense of horror in looking round at the beast. This peculiar state is probably produced in all animals killed by the carnivora; and if so, is a merciful provision by our benevolent creator for lessening the pain of death.

(David Livingstone, *Missionary Travels*, 1857)

Selected Readings and References

Bodnar, R. J., Kelly, D. D., Brutus, M., and Glusman, M. 1980. Stress-induced analgesia: Neural and hormonal determinants. Neurosci. Biobehav. Rev. 4:87–100.

Bowsher, D. 1976. Role of the reticular formation in responses to noxious stimulation. Pain 2:361–378.

Cannon, J. T., Liebeskind, J. C., and Frenk, H. 1978. Neural and neurochemical mechanisms of pain inhibition. In R. A. Sternbach (ed.), The Psychology of Pain. New York: Raven Press, pp. 27–47.

Fields, H. L., and Basbaum, A. I. 1978. Brainstem control of spinal pain-transmission neurons. Annu. Rev. Physiol. 40:217–248.

Hughes, J., Smith, T. W., Kosterlitz, H. W., Fothergill, L. A., Morgan, B. A., and Morris, H. R. 1975. Identification of two related pentapeptides from the brain with potent opiate agonist activity. Nature (Lond.) 258:577–579.

Kerr, F. W. L., and Wilson, P. R. 1978. Pain. Annu. Rev. Neurosci. 1:83–102.

Mayer, D. J., and Price, D. D. 1976. Central nervous system mechanisms of analgesia. Pain 2:379–404.

Snyder, S. H. 1977. Opiate receptors and internal opiates. Sci. Am. 236(3):44–56.

Snyder, S. H., and Childers, S. R. 1979. Opiate receptors and opioid peptides. Annu. Rev. Neurosci. 2:35–64.

Other References

Christensen, B. N., and Perl, E. R. 1970. Spinal neurons specifically excited by noxious or thermal stimuli: Marginal zone of the dorsal horn. J. Neurophysiol. 33:293–307.

Giesler, Jr., G. J., and Liebeskind, J. C. 1976. Inhibition of visceral pain by electrical stimulation of the periaqueductal gray matter. Pain 2:43–48.

Gintzler, A. R., Levy, A., and Spector, S. 1976. Antibodies as a means of isolating and characterizing biologically active substances: Presence of a nonpeptide, morphine-like compound in the central nervous system. Proc. Natl. Acad. Sci. U.S.A. 73:2132–2136.

Goldstein, A., Tachibana, S., Lowney, L. I., Hunkapiller, M., and Hood, L. 1979. Dynorphin-(1–13), an extraordinarily potent opioid peptide. Proc. Natl. Acad. Sci. U.S.A. 76:6666–6670.

Hentall, I. D., and Fields, H. L. 1979. Segmental and descending influences on intraspinal thresholds of single C-fibers. J. Neurophysiol. 42:1527–1537.

Hökfelt, T., Kellerth, J. O., Nilsson, G., and Pernow, B. 1975. Substance P: Localization in the central nervous system and in some primary sensory neurons. Science (Wash., D.C.) 190:889–890.

Jessell, T. M., and Iversen, L. L. 1977. Opiate analgesics inhibit substance P release from rat trigeminal nucleus. Nature (Lond.) 268:549–551.

Mark, V. H., Ervin, F. R., and Yakovlev, P. I. 1963. Stereotactic thalamotomy. III. The verification of anatomical lesion sites in the human thalamus. Arch. Neurol. 8:528–538.

Melzack, R., and Wall, P. D. 1965. Pain mechanisms: A new theory. Science (Wash., D.C.) 150:971–979.

Nauta, W. J. H. 1975. Anatomical organization of pain pathways in the central nervous system. In S. H. Snyder and S. Matthysse (eds.), Opiate Receptor Mechanisms. Neurosci. Res. Program Bull. 13:84–87.

Poggio, G. F., and Mountcastle, V. B. 1960. A study of the functional contributions of the lemniscal and spinothalamic systems to somatic sensibility. Bull. Johns Hopkins Hosp. 106:266–316.

Poggio, G. F., and Mountcastle, V. B. 1963. The functional properties of ventrobasal thalamic neurons studied in unanesthetized monkeys. J. Neurophysiol. 26:775–806.

Rose, J. E., and Mountcastle, V. B. 1952. The thalamic tactile region in rabbit and cat. J. Comp. Neurol. 97:441–489.

Ruda, M. A. 1976. Autoradiographic Study of the Efferent Projections of the Midbrain Central Gray in the Cat. Ph.D. Dissertation, University of Pennsylvania, Philadelphia.

Simon, E. J., Hiller, J. M., and Edelman, I. 1973. Stereospecific binding of the potent narcotic analgesia [³H] etorphine to rat-brain homogenate. Proc. Natl. Acad. Sci. U.S.A. 70:1947–1949.

Terenius, L. 1973. Characteristics of the "receptor" for narcotic analgesics in synaptic plasma membrane fraction from rat brain. Acta Pharmacol. Toxicol. 33:377–384.

Teuber, H.-L., Corkin, S. H., and Twitchell, T. E. 1977. Study of cingulotomy in man: A summary. In W. H. Sweet, S. Obrador, and J. G. Martín-Rodríguez (eds.), Neurosurgical Treatment in Psychiatry, Pain, and Epilepsy. Baltimore: University Park Press, pp. 355–362.

Whitehorn, D., and Burgess, P. R. 1973. Changes in polarization of central branches of myelinated mechanoreceptor and nociceptor fibers during noxious and innocuous stimulation of the skin. J. Neurophysiol. 36:226–237.

Yaksh, T. L., Farb, D. H., Leeman, S. E., and Jessell, T. M. 1979. Intrathecal capsaicin depletes substance P in the rat spinal cord and produces prolonged thermal analgesia. Science (Wash., D.C.) 206: 481–483.

Craig H. Bailey

Visual System I:
The Retina

The sight in my opinion is the source of the greatest benefit to us, for had we never
seen the stars, and the sun, and the heaven, none of the words which we have
spoken about the universe would ever have been uttered.

Plato, *Timaeus*

19

In this chapter, the first of four devoted to
the visual system, we shall explore a rather
remarkable sensory structure—the retina.
We shall concentrate on two aspects of retinal function: (1) the biochemical processes
involved in photoreception, and (2) the
physiological events and (wherever possible) the morphological substrates involved
in the processing of visual information.

The retina differs from the somatic receptor structures of the skin, such as the
touch corpuscles, or even the ear, because it
is not a peripheral organ but a direct extension of the central nervous system. Embryologically, skin receptors derive from ectoderm. In contrast, the retina derives from
neuroectoderm, the part of the ectoderm
that gives rise to the brain. Indeed, the
structural organization and physiological
diversity of the cellular components of the
retina are sufficiently complex to warrant
our considering the retina as a small brain.

There Are Two Types
of Photoreceptors
Rod and Cone Systems

A highly schematic illustration of the eye
and retina is presented in Figure 19–1. One
of the surprising features of the human
retina is that it appears to be built upside
down. Light must travel through the most
proximal layers of the retina before it

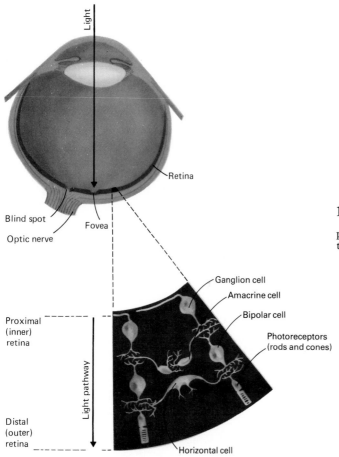

19-1 Retinal inversion. Light entering the eye must first travel through the proximal layers of the retina before reaching the photoreceptors.

strikes the first neural element in the visual pathway, the photoreceptors. (The terms proximal or inner and distal or outer are used in relation to the center of the eye.) This unusual organization might appear to be counterproductive. Fortunately, the layers of nerve cells and neural processes that lie proximal to the photoreceptors only affect the sensitivity of the retina in one discrete region—the optic disc or blind spot. In fact, under ideal conditions, rod photoreceptors are so sensitive that one receptor can be excited by the absorption of a single quantum of light.

The human retina contains two types of photoreceptors: *cones,* which mediate color vision at higher light intensities, and *rods,* which are utilized in nocturnal vision. Rods provide great sensitivity—especially to blue-green light (scotopic vision)—whereas cones provide visual acuity for pattern detection as well as color vision. The existence of different photoreceptors

that perform different functions was formulated as the *duplicity theory* of photoreception by Schultze in the nineteenth century.

These different characteristics are in part due to the specific pattern of connections that rods and cones make with other neural elements in the retina. (The properties of the rod and cone systems are summarized in Table 19–1.) For example, the rod system is characterized by extensive convergence of the photoreceptors on retinal ganglion cells, permitting adequate excitation and

Table 19-1. Properties of Rod and Cone Systems

Rod system	Cone system
Convergent pathway	Direct pathway
High sensitivity	Low sensitivity
Low visual acuity	High visual acutity

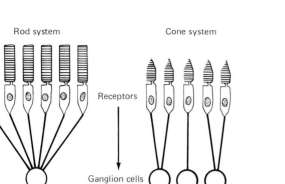

19–2 Connections of rods and cones to retinal ganglion cells.

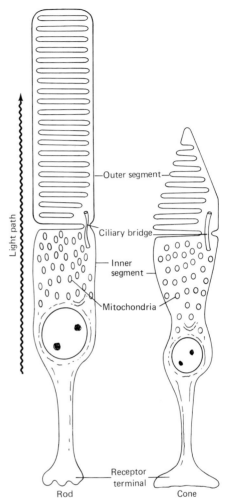

19–3 Structure of photoreceptors. Both rod and cone cells are differentiated into inner and outer segments connected by a ciliary bridge. The inner segments of both cell types contain the nucleus and most of the biosynthetic machinery and are continuous with the receptors' terminals. The membranous discs in the outer segments of rod cells (unlike those in cone cells) are not connected with the plasma membrane.

therefore optimum sensitivity but poor spatial resolution (large receptive fields) (Figure 19–2). In contrast, the cone cells are connected more directly to the retinal ganglion cells, endowing the cone system with less sensitivity but greater spatial resolution (smaller receptive fields). In addition, the two receptors differ in their distribution along the retina. In humans, a modified region called the *fovea* is adapted for high visual acuity. This region contains only cones. At all other points along the retina rods greatly outnumber cones. The significance of this differential distribution of receptors is most evident in low illumination. For example, on a dark night the fovea is essentially blind and vision depends almost exclusively on the more peripheral, rod-laden regions of the retina. As a result, our nocturnal vision is endowed with great sensitivity but poor pattern or spatial discrimination.

Functional Organization of Photoreceptors

What are the structural differences between the rods and cones? Both photoreceptors are differentiated into an *inner segment* and an *outer segment* (Figure 19–3). Using electron microscopy, de Robertis showed that the inner and outer segments of both rod and cone cells are connected by a thin cytoplasmic bridge containing a cilium. The inner segment contains a nucleus, numerous mitochondria, and a normal complement of other cytoplasmic organelles; it is continuous with the terminal portion of the receptor cell, which forms synaptic contacts with the next neural elements

in the retinal pathway. The outer segments of rods and cones differ from the inner segments developmentally and morphologically. Both rods and cones contain an elaborate system of stacked membranous discs that arise during development as a series of invaginations of the cell's plasma or outer membrane. In rods, most of these sacs eventually become separated from the outer membrane, whereas cone discs remain connected with the surface membrane. In addition, the outer segments of rod cells undergo constant renewal. Young examined this process with tritiated amino acids and autoradiography. His studies have shown that the membranous sacs of rods disintegrate near the apical surface of the receptor (where cellular debris is removed by phagocytosis by the overlying pigment epithelial cells) and are gradually replaced by the upward migration of newly formed discs located near the basal pole. In contrast, the membranous discs of cone cells apparently do not migrate and their renewal mechanism appears to be more diffuse and probably less efficient than that found in rod cells. The normal turnover of rod outer segments may be impaired in retinitis pigmentosa and other retinal diseases. This has been found to be the case in the rat, where retinal dystrophy is characterized by extensive amounts of cellular material between the distal tip of the receptors and the pigment epithelium, suggesting a disturbance in the normal phagocytotic and digestive activity of the epithelial cells.

What is the functional advantage of these elaborate morphological specializations found in the outer segments of the photoreceptors? The membranes of the outer segment discs contain the visual photopigments. These visual pigment molecules are positioned within the disc membranes in such a fashion as to maximize the probability of their interacting with the path of incident light. The light-catching potential of rods and cones is therefore greatly enhanced by both of these functional adaptations; that is, the extensive invagination of membrane increases the total surface area available for photopigment, and the spatial orientation of pigment molecules within disc membranes maximizes their interaction with light.

Photoreceptor Stimulation

Now that we have an idea of how the photoreceptors are built, let us next consider how they are excited by light. How is light absorbed and subsequently transduced into electrical signals? The excitation of the rod cells will be considered first.

Excitation of Rod Cells. The rod cells are sensitive to light because they contain a visual pigment, called *rhodopsin,* which is capable of trapping photons. Rhodopsin is arranged in single molecular layers in the discs of the outer segment and is composed of two essential parts. One com-

ponent is a light-absorbing molecule known as *retinal* (or *retinene*). This component is chemically closely related to vitamin A. Retinal is attached to the second moiety of rhodopsin, a protein found in different chemical forms and therefore called by the generic term *opsin.* Retinal can assume several three-dimensional configurations. Two significant retinal isomers in the visual cycle are (1) the all-*trans* form, which has a straight carbon–carbon backbone, and (2) the 11-*cis* isomer (the retinal form found in rhodopsin), which is bent at the 11th carbon in the tail and retains this configuration provided it remains in the dark (Figure 19–4).

The absorption of light by rhodopsin causes it to break down into opsin and retinal. In the first step of this series of reactions—the understanding of which was worked out by George Wald and his colleagues at Harvard—light causes the transformation or *isomerization* of 11-*cis*-retinal to the all-*trans* form. *This reaction is the only light-dependent stage in visual excitation.* Once the all-*trans* isomer is formed, it proceeds through a series of unstable intermediates that are unable to conform to opsin sites, allowing the opsin to change its shape. These transformations proceed spontaneously and finally produce all-*trans*-retinal and opsin (Figure 19–5).

The constant breakdown of rhodopsin by light requires an efficient restoration mechanism to ensure regeneration of the visual pigment. Rhodopsin can be recovered by (1) isomerization of all-*trans*- to 11-*cis*-retinal or (2) reduction of all-*trans*-retinal to all-*trans*-retinol (vitamin A). In the latter case, the all-*trans*-retinol is then converted to 11-*cis*-retinol; this intermediate is subsequently altered to form 11-*cis*-retinal. The spontaneous combination of opsin with 11-*cis*-retinal produces rhodopsin and also provides the energy required to produce more retinal from vitamin A. One of the limiting factors in the resynthesis of 11-*cis*-retinal is the availability of the protein opsin. The primary role of vitamin A in the visual cycle is that of a precursor pool for retinal. A nutritional deficiency in vitamin A can therefore reduce vision in dim light.

Excitation of Cone Cells. Like rhodopsin, the visual pigments found in cone cells are composed of two parts. The light-absorbing molecule appears to be similar to retinal. Unlike rod cells, however, in the primate retina there are three types of cone cells and each photoreceptor is sensitive to blue, or green, or red light. The sensitivi-

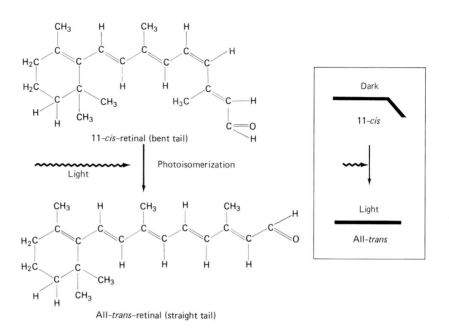

11-*cis*-retinal (bent tail)

Light → Photoisomerization

All-*trans*-retinal (straight tail)

ty of the retinal molecule in each cone cell to a particular wavelength is determined by the specific type of protein (opsin) to which it is bound. These cone opsins are collectively referred to as *iodopsin*. Each of the three types of cone opsin provides its own unique electrical environment for retinal. The number of electrical charges and their distribution help to define the absorption spectrum characteristics of the retinal in each type of cone. The decomposition and regeneration of the cone visual pigments are believed to occur in essentially the same way as described above for rhodopsin.

19–4 Structure of retinal isomers. The net effect of light is the transformation of 11-*cis*-retinal to the all-*trans*-isomer. (Adapted from Wald, 1968; Case, 1966; Uttal, 1975.)

19–5 The absorption of light by rhodopsin produces the all-*trans*-retinal isomer. This molecule is no longer capable of binding to opsin and proceeds through a series of unstable intermediate forms (illustrated collectively here) with the ultimate production of separate retinal and opsin moieties. These steric changes lead to a decrease in the Na^+ conductance of the outer segment plasma membrane. (Adapted from Case, 1966; Wald, 1968.)

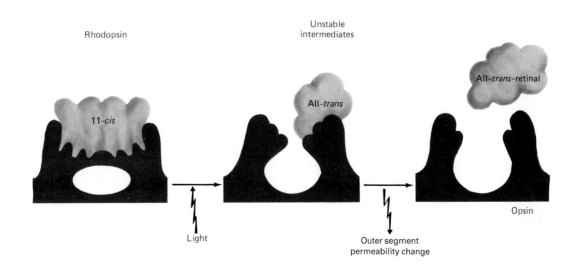

Light Is Transduced into Electrical Energy

The conformational changes resulting from the breakdown of rhodopsin ultimately produce a change in the permeability of the outer segment plasma membrane, specifically a decrease in Na^+ conductance. The biophysical and biochemical mechanisms which link photon absorption by rhodopsin with this decreased Na^+ conductance remain unclear. There are two current hypotheses for the molecular events that may underlie transduction in rod cells.[1] According to the first hypothesis, a cyclic nucleotide, cGMP, achieves signal amplification enzymatically. In the dark, cGMP acts on a cGMP-dependent protein kinase that phosphorylates a protein, which in turn maintains the Na^+ channels in an open configuration so that ions flow freely. Light splits rhodopsin, which initiates the breakdown of cGMP by activating a phosphodiesterase. The lower concentration of cGMP results in the dephosphorylation of channel proteins and consequent closing of the Na^+ channels.

The second hypothesis suggests a role for Ca^{++} in receptor transduction. According to this model, originally proposed by Hagins and his colleagues in the early 1970s, Ca^{++} is sequestered in the outer segment discs of dark-adapted rods. Rhodopsin is postulated to exist as a transmembrane protein in the discs, and exposure to light transforms this molecule into a Ca^{++} channel (by a conformational change). The effect of light in this hypothesis would be to release the stored Ca^{++} ions, which would flow from within the disc, through the rhodopsin-formed Ca^{++} channel, into the cytoplasm. The free Ca^{++} is then postulated to bind to the Na^+ channel and thereby block the channel.

The decrease in Na^+ conductance ultimately leads to the production of an electrical response (a slow hyperpolarizing receptor potential) in the photoreceptor cells. In the resting or dark state, there is constant leakage of some ion (undoubtedly Na^+), which keeps the resting membrane potential measured in photoreceptor cells at a relatively low value (-30 mV). At the onset of the light stimulus, the membrane's permeability to Na^+ (the primary ion responsible for the "dark current") is reduced. The decrease in Na^+ conduc-

tance removes the depolarizing influence of inwardly flowing Na^+ ions and allows the membranes to go toward the equilibrium potential of other ions (primarily K^+). The net result is a hyperpolarizing response in the photoreceptor (see Figure 19-7). The response of the photoreceptors to light may seem somewhat surprising; here is a receptor built to detect light which, in fact, remains excited (partially depolarized) in the dark. We shall next consider how the retina signals excitation utilizing predominantly hyperpolarizing or inhibitory responses.

Five Classes of Neurons in the Retina Process Visual Information

The subsequent synaptic events involved in the transfer of information from the receptor cells to other neurons in the retina have been well documented, both physiologically and morphologically. Here we shall pay particular attention to the way in which specific synaptic connections influence the response properties of retinal cells and how the various interactions between the nerve cells of the retina contribute to the final pattern of nerve impulses that carry the information in the optic nerve to the brain.

The vertebrate retina consists of five classes of neurons: receptor, bipolar, horizontal, amacrine, and ganglion cells. The cell bodies of these neurons are found in three layers: the outer nuclear layer, the inner nuclear layer, and the ganglion cell layer. Their synaptic fields are restricted to two zones: the *inner* and *outer plexiform layers* (Figure 19-6).

The arrows appearing in Figure 19-6 represent two of the major pathways available in the retina for information transfer from receptor to ganglion cells. The *on-line pathway* is the simplest and represents a direct receptor–bipolar–ganglion cell route that serves to carry information from nearby receptors to ganglion cells. The *off-line pathway* involves a receptor–horizontal–bipolar–ganglion cell circuit and illustrates how laterally oriented interneurons, in this case horizontal cells, can integrate and transfer information from distant receptor cells to a bipolar–ganglion cell connection. Using these two pathways as our guide, we shall examine information processing in the retina by exploring an organizational scheme outlined primarily by John Dowling and his colleagues at Johns Hopkins and Harvard, who have used the experimentally advantageous amphibian retina as a model system for de-

---

[1]For a detailed discussion of the experiments leading up to both hypotheses, see the 1979 review article by Hubbell and Bownds listed in the Selected Readings and References at the end of the chapter.

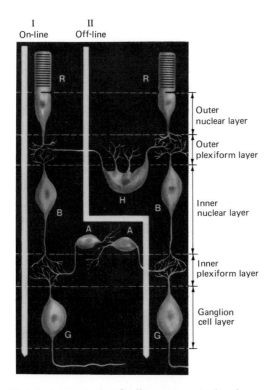

19–6 Arrangement of cell types in retinal pathways. The outer nuclear layer contains the cell bodies of receptors (**R**) and the inner nuclear layer the somata of horizontal (**H**), bipolar (**B**), and amacrine (**A**) cells. The cell bodies of ganglion cells (**G**) are restricted to the ganglion cell layer. The processes of these cell types interact in two distinct synaptic layers: the outer plexiform layer contains the processes of receptor, bipolar, and horizontal cells; the inner plexiform later contains the processes of bipolar, amacrine, and ganglion cells. (Adapted from Dowling, 1970.)

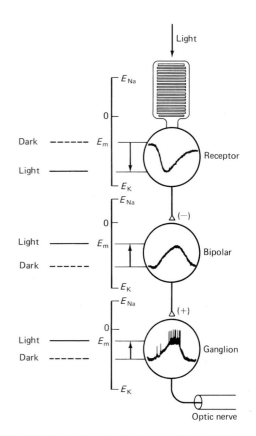

19–7 Polarization of cells in the on-line retinal pathway involving a depolarizing bipolar cell. In the dark a constant leakage of Na^+ ions keeps the resting membrane potential (E_m) of the photoreceptor relatively low. A flash of light (**arrow**) presented to the receptor results in decreased Na^+ conductance and a net hyperpolarization. The light-induced receptor hyperpolarization decreases the release of inhibitory transmitter (−) at the receptor–bipolar cell synapse. This disinhibition of the bipolar cell produces an increase in the release of excitatory transmitter (+) at the bipolar–ganglion cell synapse, resulting in excitation of the ganglion cell. (Adapted from Dowling, 1979.)

picting the functional organization of the vertebrate retina.

On-Line Pathway

We have considered above how light produces a decreased Na^+ conductance in photoreceptors and how this permeability change results in the production of slow, graded, hyperpolarizing responses. We shall now consider how these hyperpolarizing receptor potentials are transmitted synaptically to the next elements in the visual pathway and how excitation is generated in the ganglion cells (the neurons ultimately responsible for transmitting information to the brain). Some of the essential features of retinal function can be best illustrated by examining the events in

the on-line pathway involving a depolarizing (see below) bipolar cell (Figure 19–7). The photoreceptors do not generate action potentials. They are one of the exceptions to the general model of the neuron we have considered in Chapter 2; they are nonspiking neurons. Their synaptic terminal (the output component where transmitter is released) is close to the input component, so that slight changes in membrane potential affect transmitter release. In the dark the photoreceptor is depolarized and the terminal continually releases a transmitter that hyperpolarizes (inhibits) the bipolar cell. Since the bipolar cell, which is also a nonspiking neuron, is hyperpolarized in the dark, it is restricted from releasing its excitatory transmitter at the synapse with the ganglion cell, and consequently the ganglion cell is not excited. Light produces a decrease in the Na^+ conductance of the photoreceptor membrane, resulting in hyperpolarization. This decreases the amount of inhibitory transmitter released at the synapse with the bipolar cell, leading to depolarization of the bipolar cell. The depolarization of the bipolar cell in turn increases the amount of excitatory transmitter released at the bipolar–ganglion cell synapse, exciting the ganglion cell. *Disinhibition* or the removal of inhibition to produce excitation (in this case at the bipolar cell level) is a fundamental mechanism in the nervous system.

The vertebrate retina contains two types of bipolar cells, each of which responds differently to the transmitter released by the receptor cell. The *depolarizing bipolar cell* depolarizes in response to central (direct) illumination of its receptive field and hyperpolarizes in response to surround (indirect) illumination. (This is the type whose action is described above and in Figure 19–7). The second type, the *hyperpolarizing bipolar cell*, hyperpolarizes in direct illumination and depolarizes in surround illumination. Both types of bipolar cells in turn form specific connections with ganglion cells. Depolarizing bipolar cells connect with *on-center ganglion cells.* These cells have the same response properties as the depolarizing bipolar cells. Direct illumination produces a depolarization, whereas indirect lighting results in a hyperpolarization. Conversely, hyperpolarizing bipolar cells connect with *off-center ganglion cells*, which hyperpolarize in a central light stimulus and depolarize in surround illumination.

Recent morphological findings confirm this organizational pattern. Utilizing the intracellular injection of fluorescent dyes into ganglion cells in the cat, Nelson and his colleagues have shown that the dendritic arbor of off-center ganglion cells is confined to the upper regions of the inner plexiform layer, whereas the dendritic processes of on-center ganglion cells branch primarily within the lower levels of the inner plexiform layer. This layering of on- and off-center ganglion cell processes parallels the differential distribution of the terminals of depolarizing and hyperpolarizing bipolar cells.

In a direct on-line pathway involving the hyperpolarizing bipolar cell and off-center ganglion cell, the following synaptic events occur. The photoreceptor continuously releases transmitter at its synapse that, in this case, depolarizes or excites the bipolar cell. As was the case with the depolarizing bipolar cell, the hyperpolarizing bipolar cell releases transmitter that excites the ganglion cell. Light will reduce the amount of transmitter released at the receptor–bipolar cell synapse, thereby hyperpolarizing (inhibiting) the bipolar cell. This will decrease the amount of transmitter released at the bipolar–ganglion cell synapse, resulting in hyperpolarization of the ganglion cell.

Four unusual features of neuronal organization emerge from this survey of retinal function:

1. The specific response of receptor cells to light is a hyperpolarization mediated by decreased Na^+ conductance. Photoreceptors are normally excited (i.e., tonically depolarized) in the dark, and light modulates this dark current to produce a hyperpolarizing response.

2. Synapses of photoreceptors and bipolar cells *do not* have a clear threshold for transmitter release: they constantly release their transmitter, and slight changes in membrane potential produce small perturbations in spontaneous release. Thus retinal synapses demonstrate spontaneous transmitter release, just as some nerve cells have spontaneous activity. This establishes a background of activity that can be modulated by information from other cells. Very small voltage changes at the photoreceptor terminals can affect transmitter release. This sensitivity is probably due to the tonic depolarization of these cells in the dark.

3. A single transmitter released by the photoreceptors will inhibit certain bipolar cells (depolarizing bipolar cells) and excite others (hyperpolarizing bipolar cells). Thus the retina illustrates nicely a principle we encountered earlier (Chapter 7): the sign of transmitter action is determined not by the chemical nature of the transmitter but by the properties of the receptor in the postsynaptic membrane and the ion channels the receptor controls.

4. All of the distal cells in the visual pathway (i.e., receptors, bipolars, and, as we shall see below, horizontal cells) carry their information without the aid of action potentials. The primary function of action potentials is to carry information rapidly, in an unfailing fashion, over long distances. The distances between different retinal cells are relatively minor compared to the length constants of the retinal cells; therefore, informa-

tion does not need to be transferred over long distances and can be carried by the passive or electrotonic spread of current along the cell.

Synaptic Organization

The retina contains both chemical and electrical synapses. There are gap junctions between receptor neurons both at their terminals and between their inner segments. The electrical coupling between similar receptors is stronger than the coupling between different receptor types.

As in the rest of the brain, the predominant class of synapses found in the retina is chemical. Particularly interesting is a variant called the *ribbon synapse,* which is found at the terminals of photoreceptors (Figure 19–8). Three characteristics distinguish ribbon synaptic contacts from most of the synapses considered thus far. First, the photoreceptor terminal contains an unusual presynaptic modification—the *presynaptic ribbon* (Figure 19–8B, *arrows*). This electron-dense bar is oriented perpendicular to the presynaptic membrane and is intimately associated with synaptic vesicles. The bar at the ribbon synapses may be analogous to the dense bar at the nerve–muscle synapse (or the dense projections at other conventional synapses). These paramembranous densities serve to delineate that portion of the presynaptic membrane (the active zone) specialized for the positioning and binding of vesicles prior to their exocytotic release. Second, the ribbon photoreceptor synapse involves three postsynaptic elements (a triad). Typically, this precise three-membered arrangement consists of horizontal cell processes occupying the two lateral positions and a single bipolar cell process situated centrally. Finally, these postsynaptic processes invaginate, to varying degrees, the presynaptic photoreceptor membrane. Ribbon synapses can also occur in the inner plexiform layer, where bipolar cells are the presynaptic neurons. These contacts typically exhibit only two postsynaptic elements: either a pair of amacrine cell processes, or an amacrine process and a ganglion process.

The physiological types of bipolar cells (hyperpolarizing or depolarizing) are morphologically recognizable. One morphological class of bipolar cell is activated at the photoreceptor ribbon synapse. Each synaptic contact contains a single bipolar process as part of the postsynaptic invagination; another name for this class of bipolar cells is therefore *invaginating bipolar cells.* The invaginating bipolar cells are thought to correspond

to the depolarizing type. The second morphological class of bipolar cells is activated at *superficial* or *flat contacts.* These also occur at the receptor terminal, but, unlike the receptor ribbon synapse, they have no presynaptic ribbon and only a single (noninvaginating) postsynaptic element (Figure 19–8A). The flat bipolar cells are thought to be hyperpolarizing bipolar cells. In addition, fine structural analyses (including freeze-fracture) of synaptic architecture support the pharmacological and electrophysiological evidence suggesting that the receptor to flat bipolar cell synapses is excitatory and the receptor to invaginating bipolar cell synapses is inhibitory.

The activation of bipolar cells at photoreceptive terminals (either ribbon synapses or flat contacts) and their subsequent connections with ganglion cells in the inner plexiform layer account for the physiological events we have considered in the on-line pathway. In addition, it has been suggested that the bipolar cells can not only be activated by nearby receptors, but may also be affected by more distant receptors via the interconnections of horizontal cells. In Figure 19–8B, the considerable lateral projections of a single horizontal cell are shown forming conventional synapses with the processes of bipolar cells. Electrical connections found between horizontal cells probably add to their lateral distribution, increasing their effective receptive field.

Horizontal and Amacrine Cells Are the Local-Circuit Neurons of the Retina

Horizontal and amacrine cells are both examples of a broad class of cells known as local-circuit neurons (see Chapter 9). This concept distinguishes between neurons possessing long axons that project considerable distances (all principal relay cells) and cells with short or no axons that interact extensively with their immediate neighbors. In the retina, the process of horizontal cells (outer plexiform layer) and amacrine cells (inner plexiform layer) modulate and transform visual information that is conveyed to the brain.

Although there are classes of amacrine cells which respond to illumination with sustained responses, in many species the amacrine cells are the first cells in the visual pathway that respond transiently to illumination. The transient amacrine cells connect to ganglion cells and endow them with similar on–off response properties. These *on–off ganglion cells* form the second ma-

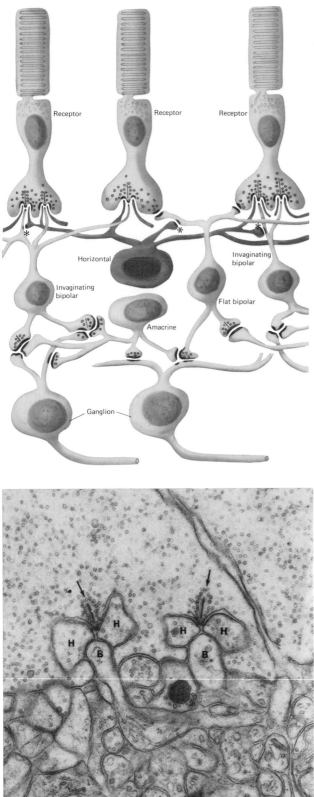

A

19–8 Organization of retina synapses. **A.** The retina of most vertebrates contains three basic forms of chemical synapses: (1) ribbon synapses, (2) superficial or flat contacts, and (3) conventional synapses. The most unusual are the ribbon synapses, which occur in the outer plexiform at photoreceptor terminals and in the inner plexiform layer at bipolar terminals. The ribbon synapses at the receptor terminals (see also Part B) are characterized by a presynaptic ribbon positioned perpendicular to the membrane and surrounded by vesicles. Multiple postsynaptic elements (typically three) invaginate the terminal at these junctions; horizontal cell processes occupy the lateral positions and a single, bipolar cell process is located centrally. The activation of invaginating bipolar cells occurs at these sites. Flat bipolar cells are activated at the receptor terminal at flat contacts. These junctions lack a presynaptic ribbon and have a single noninvaginating, postsynaptic element. The two types of bipolar cells contact ganglion cells and amacrine cells at ribbon synapses in the inner plexiform layer. These synaptic contacts mediate on-line pathways by which direct illumination affects ganglion cell activity. The effects of light on more distant ganglion cells are carried by the off-line pathway and are mediated via the interconnections of horizontal cells. The extensive lateral domain of the horizontal cell (**shaded**) is well suited for this function and allows communication between receptor cells and distant bipolar cells. The horizontal–bipolar cell interactions probably occur at the conventional synapses (*) found between horizontal terminals and bipolar cell dendrites. **B.** Ribbon synapses at the photoreceptor terminal are characterized by an electron-dense presynaptic ribbon (**arrows**) and an invagination by one bipolar cell (**B**) and two horizontal cell (**H**) processes. (Adapted from Dowling, 1979.)

B

jor class of ganglion cells found in the retina (remember, the first were defined as either *on* or *off* and had receptive field organizations similar to their respective bipolar cells). The transient responses of amacrine cells seem well suited for conveying dynamic or temporal aspects of illumination and may, in part, be responsible for motion and direction selectivity in the retina. Recently Harvey Karten has found that the amacrine cells can be divided into seven different subtypes based on the peptide that they contain. Some cells contain enkephalin, others substance P, neurotensin, somatostatin, vasoactive intestinal polypeptide, or glucagon. These results indicate that as biochemical resolution increases many subtypes will be recognized among the major classes of retinal neurons.

Off-Line Pathway: Antagonistic Surround Receptive Field

The transformation of visual information in the retina is reflected to a large degree by the complexity of ganglion cell receptive fields. The basis for much of our current understanding of ganglion cell receptive field organization has come from Stephen Kuffler's pioneering cellular studies of single ganglion cells published in 1953. His classification of receptive field properties will be considered in detail in Chapter 21. In the present discussion we have already considered the response properties of retinal ganglion cells to direct illumination and how these central response properties are mediated by the direct receptor–bipolar–ganglion cell connections found in the on-line pathway. Ganglion cells can also display more complex response properties. One such response is referred to as *surround antagonism*.

The *antagonistic surround receptive field* is mediated by receptor–horizontal–bipolar–ganglion cell connections and can best be understood by considering the second major pathway in the retina—the *off-line pathway* (Figure 19–9). In this discussion we shall consider the hyperpolarizing bipolar cells and the off-center ganglion cells.

The bipolar cell on the left-hand side of Figure 19–9 hyperpolarizes in response to direct light, reflecting a direct receptor–bipolar interaction. When the receptor on the left is illuminated, however, it can also produce a depolarizing response in a distant bipolar cell (at the right in Figure 19–9). Thus, there is an *antagonistic*

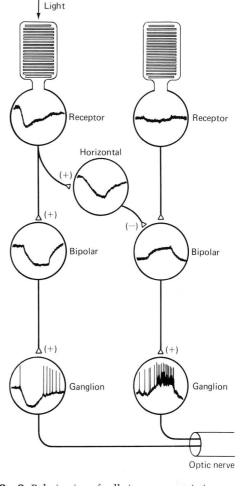

19–9 Polarization of cells in an antagonistic surround receptive field. A direct on-line pathway is shown on the left, and an off-line pathway mediated by the laterally oriented horizontal cell is shown on the right. The flash of light (**arrow**) produces a large hyperpolarizing response only in the receptor directly beneath it, reflecting the relatively narrow receptive field found at the receptor level in many retinas. The small deflection observed in the distant receptor on the right may be due to electrical coupling between the receptor cells. The horizontal cell mediates an antagonistic surround receptive field at the level of the bipolar cells and stimulates the hyperpolarizing bipolar cell on the right. This receptive field organization is transferred to the ganglion cell, where its expression is utilized to accentuate visual contrast. **+**, excitatory transmitter; **−**, inhibitory transmitter. (Adapted from Dowling, 1979.)

center–surround receptive field organization at the bipolar cell level. The surround antagonism is mediated by the laterally spread processes of horizontal cells. What is the importance of this receptive field organization for information processing? How does it affect the output of the ganglion cells?

These questions can be answered by examining the synaptic events of the off-line pathway. We have already seen how direct illumination of a receptor can ultimately lead to hyperpolarization of the on-line ganglion cell. Now let us consider how the illumination of the same receptor affects the electrical activity of a distant ganglion cell. The receptor on the left in Figure 19–9 hyperpolarizes in response to light, producing a hyperpolarization of the horizontal cell. This response reduces the release of an inhibitory transmitter at the horizontal–bipolar synapse, resulting in depolarization of the distant bipolar cell. This horizontal–bipolar cell interaction probably takes place at the conventional synapses between horizontal processes and bipolar dendrites. The effect of this interaction (in this specific example utilizing hyperpolarizing bipolar cells) is the increased release by the distant bipolar cell of transmitter onto a distant ganglion cell, producing excitation of the ganglion cell. Thus, the antagonistic center–surround receptive field found at the bipolar cell level is transferred to the ganglion cell level where it ultimately results in an enhancement of the information carried by some ganglion cells by producing an opposite signal in their neighbors. This is a common property of the brain and was discussed in Chapter 17 as providing a fine-point discrimination. The antagonistic surround or spatially opponent mechanism is used by the retina to sharpen visual contrast.

An Overall View

The absorption of light and its subsequent transduction into electrical signals occurs at the photoreceptors. Visual information is then transferred from the receptors to the ganglion cells via the bipolar cells. The ganglion cells project to the brain. Two types of laterally disposed interneurons (horizontal cells and amacrine cells) participate in local circuits to integrate and modulate the activity of both the bipolar neurons and the ganglion cells. The retina is elegantly simple: it works with only five basic neuronal types, yet it can generate complicated receptive field properties that allow considerable transformation of visual information before it reaches the brain.

Selected Readings and References

Baylor, D. A., and O'Bryan, P. M. 1971. Electrical signaling in vertebrate photoreceptors. Fed. Proc. 30: 79–83.

Dowling, J. E. 1979. Information processing by local circuits: The vertebrate retina as a model system. In F. O. Schmitt and F. G. Worden (eds.), The Neurosciences; Fourth Study Program. Cambridge, Mass.: MIT Press, pp. 163–181.

Hubbell, W. L., and Bownds, M. D. 1979. Visual transduction in vertebrate photoreceptors. Annu. Rev. Neurosci. 2:17–34.

Kaneko, A. 1979. Physiology of the retina. Annu. Rev. Neurosci. 2:169–191.

Rodieck, R. W. 1973. The Vertebrate Retina—Principles of Structure and Function. San Francisco: Freeman.

Other References

Brecha, N., Karten, H. J., and Davis, B. 1980. Localization of neuropeptides, including vasoactive intestinal polypeptide and glucagon, within the adult and developing retina. Soc. Neurosci. 6:346.

Brecha, N., Karten, H. J., and Laverack, C. 1979. Enkephalin-containing amacrine cells in the avian retina: Immunohistochemical localization. Proc. Natl. Acad. Sci. U.S.A. 76:3010–3014.

Brown, K. T. 1980. Physiology of the retina. In V. B. Mountcastle (ed.), Medical Physiology, 14th ed., Vol. 1. St. Louis: Mosby, pp. 504–543.

Case, J. 1966. Sensory Mechanisms. New York: Macmillan.

De Robertis. E. 1960. Some observations on the ultrastructure and morphogenesis of photoreceptors. J. Gen. Physiol. 43 Suppl. 2:1–13.

Dowling, J. E. 1970. Organization of vertebrate retinas. Invest. Ophthalmol. 9:655–680.

Dowling, J. E. 1974. Synaptic arrangements in the vertebrate retina: The photoreceptor synapse. In M. V. L. Bennett (ed.), Synaptic Transmission and Neuronal Interaction. New York: Raven Press, pp. 87–103.

Hagins, W. A. 1972. The visual process: Excitatory mechanisms in the primary receptor cells. Annu. Rev. Biophys. Bioeng. 1:131–158.

Kuffler, S. W. 1953. Discharge patterns and functional organization of mammalian retina. J. Neurophysiol. 16:37–68.

Nelson, R., Famiglietti, Jr., E. V., and Kolb, H. 1978. Intracellular staining reveals different levels of stratification for on- and off-center ganglion cells in cat retina. J. Neurophysiol. 41:472–483.

Schultze, M. 1866. Zur Anatomie und Physiologie der Retina. Arch. Mikrosk. Anat. 2:175–286.

Uttal, W. R. 1975. Cellular Neurophysiology and Integration. An Interpretive Introduction. Hillsdale, N.J.: Lawrence Erlbaum Associates.

Wald, G. 1959. The photoreceptor process in vision. In H. W. Magoun (ed.), Handbook of Physiology, Vol. 1, Neurophysiology. Washington D.C.: American Physiological Society, pp. 671–692.

Wald, G. 1968. Molecular basis of visual excitation. Science (Wash., D.C.) 162:230–239.

Young, R. W. 1970. Visual cells. Sci Am. 223(4):80–91.

James P. Kelly

Visual System II:
Anatomy of the Central Visual Pathways

20

In this chapter we shall examine the structure of the visual pathway from the retina to the thalamus and then to the visual cortex. We shall begin by considering the different types of retinal ganglion cells, and how the visual field is projected upon the retina. We shall next consider how the retinal ganglion cell axons are arranged in the optic nerve and in the optic tract, and the topographic manner in which these axons terminate in the lateral geniculate nucleus of the thalamus. The topography is critical because lesions in different parts of the visual pathway produce characteristic deficits of sight in the visual field. Once the topography of the visual pathway is understood, it is possible to predict the location of a lesion in the central nervous system that could produce particular types of visual field aberrations. Finally, we shall discuss the structure of the primary visual cortex, where the axons from the lateral geniculate nucleus terminate. To appreciate the role of the visual cortex in visual perception it is necessary to understand its three-dimensional structure. In addition, studies of the visual cortex have provided important hints about the mechanisms used by the cerebral cortex in processing sensory input of all types and in generating a perception of the world around us.

There Are Several Populations of Ganglion Cells

Although it might not be obvious at first glance, the ganglion cell layer of the retina is far from being a homogeneous sheet of cells. There are clear differences in the populations of retinal ganglion cells from point to point in the retina. In the area surrounding the fovea, the density of cells is greatest. Here ganglion cells with small dendritic fields, presumably engaged in high-acuity vision, predominate. In the periphery of the retina the ganglion cell density is much lower, and cells with larger dendritic fields capable of integrating input from a larger sample of receptors are more common.

In Golgi preparations of the cat's retina, Boycott and Wässle found three classes of ganglion cells: (1) large cells (cell bodies 30–40 μm in diameter) with enormous dendritic trees spreading 500 μm or more across the retina; (2) medium-size cells (measuring 10–15 μm in diameter) with dendritic fields restricted to a small part of the inner plexiform layer; and (3) small cells (less than 10 μm in diameter) with thin dendrites that spread over a relatively wide zone. As we shall see, these differences in ganglion cell type and cell density have important consequences for the central connections of the retina: (1) different types of ganglion cells process different aspects of the visual input and relay this input to separate sites in the brain; and (2) ganglion cell density determines the extent of the central nervous system devoted to the representation of particular points in the retina and hence the topography of the visuotopic map in the brain.

The Visual Field Projects upon the Retina in an Orderly Way

The axons of all types of ganglion cells stream toward the *optic disc*, where they exit from the retina, become myelinated, and join other axons to form the *optic nerve*. The optic nerves from each eye join at the *optic chiasm*. Here an important sorting of fibers destined for particular regions in the brain stem takes place. This sorting process can best be understood in terms of projection of the visual fields upon the retina (Figure 20–1). Imagine that the foveas of both eyes are fixed on a single point in space. It is then possible to define a *left* and a *right* half of the visual field.

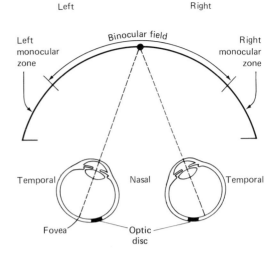

20–1 Organization of the visual field. Light from the binocular zone strikes both eyes; light from the left or right monocular zone will strike only that eye. The regions of the retina are referred to as the temporal and nasal hemiretinas.

Light originating from the central region of the visual field will strike *both* eyes; this is termed the *binocular zone* of the visual field. In either half of the visual field there is also a *monocular zone*, where light will strike only the eye on the same side. The regions of the retina are named with reference to the midline: the *nasal hemiretina* lies medial to the fovea, while the *temporal hemiretina* lies lateral to the fovea. Each half of the retina can also be divided into a *dorsal* and a *ventral* quadrant.

There are two important sets of terminology for the visual system that should be clarified at the outset. Confusion might occur because the lens of the eye inverts the visual world upon the retina. Figure 20–2 is a schematic view of the eye from a lateral perspective. Notice that the optical property of the lens inverts the projection of the visual field upon the retina, so that the superior half of the visual field is projected upon the inferior (or ventral) half of the retina, while the inferior visual field is projected upon the superior (or dorsal) half of the retina. We see the world in its correct orientation because higher levels of the brain take this inversion into account and compensate for it. When speaking about the visual system, however, one must be specific in referring to either a region of the *visual field* or a region of the *retina*. As an example, suppose an individ-

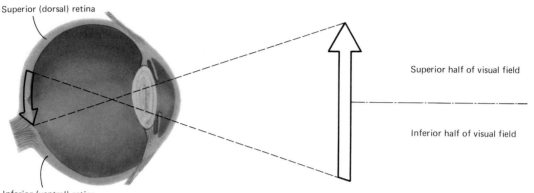

Superior (dorsal) retina

Superior half of visual field

Inferior half of visual field

Inferior (ventral) retina

20–2 Inversion of the visual field upon the retina.

ual sustained direct damage to the *inferior* half of the retina of one eye. This would cause a monocular deficit in the *superior* half of the visual field. One must also be careful to speak about the nasal and temporal halves of the retina, or the nasal and temporal halves of the visual field to avoid confusion.

To understand the importance of this distinction, consider the projection of a point in the binocular half of the right visual hemifield upon the two retinas (Figure 20–3). Light originating from this point falls upon the temporal retina on the left side and the nasal retina on the right side. The optic nerves from each side join at the optic chiasm, where the fibers from the nasal half of each retina cross to the opposite side. The axons arising from ganglion cells in the temporal retina remain uncrossed. The left optic tract therefore is composed of axons from the left temporal retina and the right nasal retina. In other words, the *left optic tract* contains a complete representation of the *right hemifield* of vision. The axons in the optic tract synapse in the lateral geniculate nucleus of the thalamus, a structure that will be considered in some detail below. Cells in the lateral geniculate nucleus, in turn, send their axons to the visual cortex. At this point it is important to remember that at the initial stages of visual processing in the central nervous system each half of the brain is concerned with the contralateral hemifield of vision. This pattern of organization begins with the segregation of axons in the optic chiasm, where fibers from the two eyes dealing with homonymous parts of the visual field are brought together.

Let us now examine the projection of the monocular portion of each hemifield (Figure

20–4). The temporal portion of the left hemifield projects only upon the nasal retina of the left eye. This monocular portion of the visual field is called the *temporal crescent,* because it constitutes the crescent-shaped temporal extreme of each visual field.

20–3 Light from the right binocular field falls on the left temporal retina and the right nasal retina. Because fibers from the nasal retina of each eye cross to the opposite side at the optic chiasm, the left optic tract carries axons from the left temporal retina and the right nasal retina and therefore contains a complete representation of the right hemifield of vision.

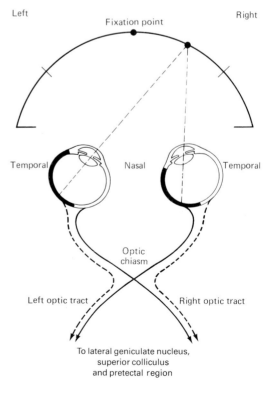

Left   Right

Fixation point

Temporal   Nasal   Temporal

Optic
chiasm

Left optic tract   Right optic tract

To lateral geniculate nucleus,
superior colliculus
and pretectal region

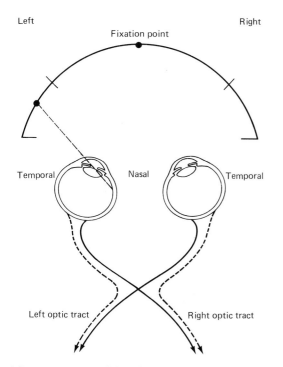

20–4 Projection of the left monocular crescent upon the retina.

The Lateral Geniculate Nucleus Is Composed of Six Cellular Layers

A substantial number of the fibers in the optic tract terminate in the *lateral geniculate nucleus,* a knee-shaped structure in the posterior aspect of the thalamus. In this nucleus there is an orderly representation of the contralateral visual hemifield. Ganglion cells at different loci in the retina project upon distinct visuotopic points in the lateral geniculate nucleus. However, all parts of the retina are not represented equally; there is proportionally much more of the nucleus devoted to the representation of the central area than to the periphery of the retina. Regions with increased ganglion cell density send more axons to the brain and consequently dominate a greater portion of the central representation of the retina.

In primates, the lateral geniculate nucleus of the thalamus consists of six layers of neurons separated by intervening layers of axons and dendrites. The layers are numbered from 6 most dorsally to 1 most ventrally (Figure 20–5). An individual layer in the nucleus receives input from one eye only: fibers from the contralateral nasal retina contact layers 6, 4, and 1; fibers from the ipsilateral temporal retina contact layers 5, 3, and

2. Thus, the complementary halves of the retina in both eyes each contact individual layers in a topographically ordered way, so that each layer contains a precise representation of the contralateral visual field. These representations are stacked on top of one another in the layers of the nucleus, which contains six maps of the contralateral hemifield as a result.

Let us concentrate on a single layer of the nucleus—for example, the most dorsal one, layer 6. It contains two types of cells: *principal cells,* which send their axons on to the visual cortex, and *local interneurons,* whose axons terminate within the borders of the layer. Using the electron microscope it is possible to determine the types of synapses formed by retinal ganglion cell axons in the lateral geniculate nucleus. This is done by placing a lesion in the appropriate part of the retina and then searching for the types of synapses that degenerate in the lateral geniculate nucleus. One particular type, a large, pale terminal containing round synaptic vesicles, has been found to be of retinal origin. When the retina is removed, this type of terminal is separated from its parent

20–5 Projection of the retinas upon the lateral geniculate nucleus.

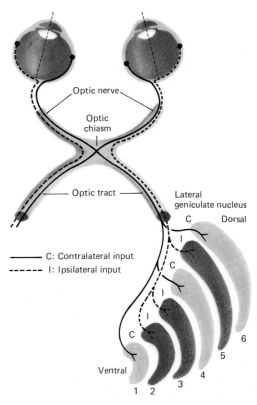

cell body and soon becomes filled with electron-dense products of degeneration. The large, pale terminal contacts the dendrites of a small number of principal cells. The retinal terminal and associated dendrites are encased in a *glomerulus* by the processes of nearby glial cells. This illustrates one important function of glial cells—the segregation of synaptic input.

To complete our understanding of this set of connections between the retina and the thalamus, we need to know which classes of retinal ganglion cells project to the lateral geniculate body. It should be mentioned that the retina also projects to other sites in the brain stem in addition to the thalamus, notably the superior colliculus of the midbrain, a structure important for the control of eye movements. Differential projections from the retina have been identified by means of a newly developed technique that utilizes the transport of the marker enzyme horseradish peroxidase (see Chapter 10). When this low molecular weight enzyme is deposited extracellularly at a site within the central nervous system, it is taken up by active nerve terminals in association with coated vesicles during the process of vesicle recycling. The enzyme is then transported back along the axon to the cell body and dendrites of the parent neurons. By appropriate histochemistry, these cells and their processes can be labeled with a reaction product resulting from the action of the enzyme. The structure and location of the labeled neurons can then be studied in detail. In this way it is possible to trace synapses back to their cells of origin.

The ganglion cells projecting to the most dorsal layers of the lateral geniculate body have been identified with the peroxidase method in the cat. It was found that the medium-size cells, with restricted dendritic fields, project exclusively to the lateral geniculate nucleus. This confirms the idea that the nucleus is concerned with high-acuity aspects of visual perception. The large ganglion cells also project to the lateral geniculate nucleus, but at least half of them have branching axons that go to the superior colliculus as well. The smallest retinal ganglion cells in the cat, in contrast, project only to the superior colliculus. These cells, as mentioned earlier, always have long, thin dendrites. Available evidence suggests that the largest and smallest types of ganglion cells, both with broad dendritic fields, respond best to stimuli moving in the visual field. Moving stimuli of this kind elicit tracking movements of the eyes in a normal animal. Similar eye movements can also be produced by direct electrical stimulation of the superior colliculus.

The Superior Colliculus and Pretectum Are Visual Reflex Centers
Connections of the Superior Colliculus

The superior colliculus is known to receive direct visual input from the retina. Certain cells in the visual cortex also send their axons to the superior colliculus, so that it has at least two distinct sources of visual input. The location of the superior colliculus is shown in Figure 20–6. Axons from cells in the superior colliculus are distributed to several areas. Some of these axons cross the midline and descend in the brain stem adjacent to the ventricle as the *tectospinal tract* (in Latin *tectum* means "roof," and is another term used to describe the *colliculi* or "mounds" that make up this roof). This tract is probably important for the reflex control of head and neck movements. Other, *tectopontine*, axons synapse upon cells in the pontine nuclei and are part of the mechanism for relaying visual input to the cerebellum. Finally, although there are few direct connections between neurons in the superior colliculus and the motor nuclei innervating the extraocular muscles, it is clear that the superior colliculus has a profound influence upon the activity of these motor nuclei; however, the pathways mediating this influence have not been identified definitively.

Pretectal Region

There is another important visual reflex center lying just rostral to the superior colliculus, where the midbrain fuses with the thalamus (Figure 20–7). This is the *pretectal area*, a region that mediates pupillary light reflexes. Pupillary reflexes are significant clinically, so it is necessary to understand the pathways that underlie them. Light shone upon one eye causes a constriction of the pupil in that eye (the *direct response*) as well as a constriction of the pupil in the other eye (the *consensual response*). Certain retinal ganglion cells respond to the change in overall luminance of the visual field. These cells send their axons through the optic nerve and tract to synapse in the pretectal region. The pretectal area then projects to the Edinger-Westphal nuclei bilaterally. Preganglionic neurons in the Edinger-Westphal nucleus send axons out of the brain

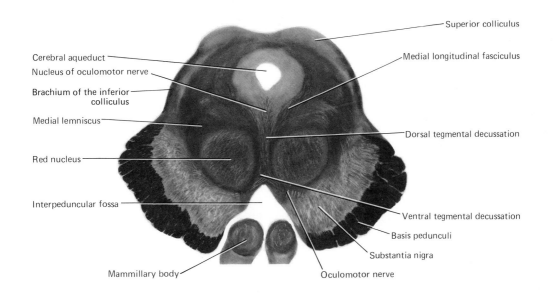

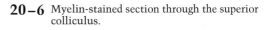

Cerebral aqueduct

Nucleus of oculomotor nerve

Brachium of the inferior colliculus

Medial lemniscus

Red nucleus

Interpeduncular fossa

Mammillary body

Superior colliculus

Medial longitudinal fasciculus

Dorsal tegmental decussation

Ventral tegmental decussation

Basis pedunculi

Substantia nigra

Oculomotor nerve

with the third nerve to innervate the *ciliary ganglion*, where the postganglionic neurons innervating the smooth muscle of the pupillary sphincter are found.

Testing of pupillary reflexes provides important information about the functional state of the afferent and efferent pathways mediating them. As an example, let us imagine that light shone in the left eye of a patient elicits a consensual response, but not a direct one. This means that the afferent limb of the reflex is intact, but the efferent limb to the left eye is damaged, possibly by a lesion of the third nerve. If the optic nerve is

20–6 Myelin-stained section through the superior colliculus.

lesioned unilaterally, light shone in the affected eye will cause no change in either pupil, while light shone in the intact eye will elicit both a direct and consensual response.

20–7 Myelin-stained section through the junction of the midbrain and thalamus, showing the location of the pretectal region. (Adapted from Carpenter, 1976.)

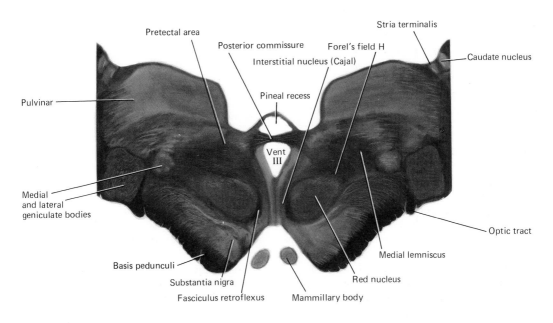

Pretectal area

Posterior commissure

Interstitial nucleus (Cajal)

Pineal recess

Stria terminalis

Forel's field H

Caudate nucleus

Pulvinar

Vent III

Medial and lateral geniculate bodies

Optic tract

Basis pedunculi

Substantia nigra

Fasciculus retroflexus

Mammillary body

Red nucleus

Medial lemniscus

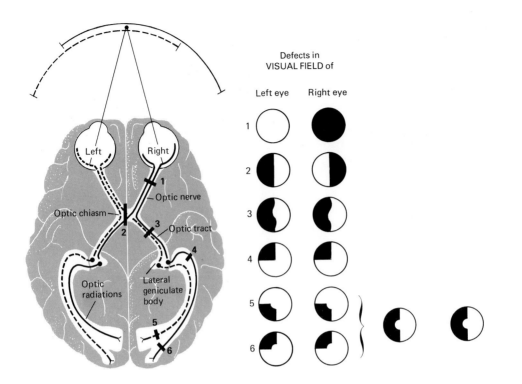

20-8 Visual field deficits caused by lesions at various levels of the visual pathway.

Lesions in the Visual Pathway Cause Predictable Changes in Sight

Before considering the structure of the visual cortex in detail, let us consider the visual deficits produced by lesions at various levels along the visual pathway leading up to the visual cortex. After section of the *optic nerve*, the visual field is seen monocularly via the eye on the intact side. The far periphery of the temporal half of the visual field is normally seen only by the nasal retina on the same side; this region of the visual field is called the temporal crescent (Figure 20–4). An individual with optic nerve section would therefore be blind in the temporal crescent on the lesioned side. Removal of binocular input in this way would also affect *stereopsis*, or depth perception, which is based upon binocular interactions.

Destruction of the fibers crossing in the *optic chiasm* would remove input from the temporal portions of both halves of the visual field. The deficit produced by such a lesion is termed *bitemporal hemianopsia*. It should be remembered that this deficit occurs because fibers aris-

ing from the nasal half of each retina have been destroyed.

Destruction of the *optic tract* will produce a complete *homonymous hemianopsia*, that is, a loss of vision in the entire contralateral visual field. Finally, a lesion of the *visual cortex*, where the fibers are more spread out, produces an *incomplete hemianopsia* in the related part of the contralateral half of the visual field.

The visual field deficits caused by lesions at various levels of the visual pathway are summarized in Figure 20–8.

The Primary Visual Cortex Has Characteristic Cellular Architecture

The primary visual cortex, also called the striate cortex (area 17 of Brodmann), located in the occipital lobe, receives the axons from the principal cells of the lateral geniculate nucleus. These axons are collectively termed the *optic radiation*. After sweeping around the ventricle, the fibers of the optic radiation are found on the lateral surface of both the temporal and occipital horns of the ventricle (Figure 20–9). Fibers representing the inferior parts of the retina swing in a broad arc over the temporal horn of the ventricle and loop into the temporal lobe before turning caudally to

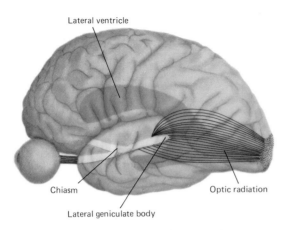

20–9 Course of the fibers in the optic radiation. (Adapted from Brodal, 1981.)

reach the occipital pole. This group of fibers, termed *Meyer's loop*, accounts for the fact that unilateral lesions in the temporal lobe affect vision in the *superior* quadrant of the contralateral hemifield. The geniculocortical fibers relaying input from the inferior half of the retina terminate in the inferior bank of the cortex lining the calcarine fissure, while the fibers relaying input from the superior half of the retina terminate in the superior bank (Figure 20–10). Consequently, a lesion in the *inferior* bank of the calcarine cortex causes a deficit in the *superior* half of the contralateral visual field.

20–10 Representation of the superior and inferior halves of the calcarine cortex.

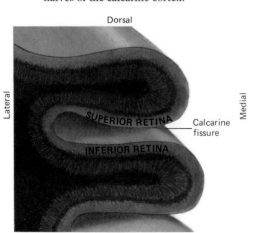

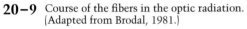

Anatomy

The visual cortex is about 2 mm in thickness and consists of several alternating layers of fibers and cells stretching from the pial surface to the underlying white matter (Figure 20–11). The separate layers of the visual cortex carry out different tasks. In the primate visual cortex, input from the lateral geniculate nucleus terminates in layer IV. We can study the pattern of termination by utilizing the process of *transneuronal transport* of radioactively labeled proteins. If a tritiated amino acid is injected into the eye, it is incorporated into proteins by the retinal ganglion cells, and some of these proteins are transported along the axon to the synaptic terminals in the lateral geniculate nucleus. A small fraction of the labeled material in the retinal terminals reaches the postsynaptic neurons of the lateral geniculate nucleus and is transported to the geniculate terminals in the cortex. After an eye injection, therefore, the regions of the cortex receiving input from the injected eye can be demonstrated in autoradiographs. Experiments of this type have

20–11 Laminar organization of the visual cortex.

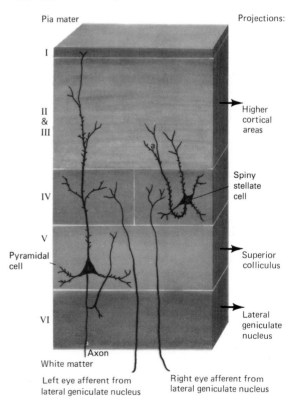

shown that the geniculate terminals relaying input from each eye are clustered in patches within layer IV (Figure 20–11). Each patch represents a zone dominated by one eye, and the patches dominated by either eye alternate regularly with one another. Cells in layer IV therefore receive input from either one eye or the other via the separate layers of the lateral geniculate nucleus; the output from layer IV goes to the layers above and below it, where signals from both eyes converge upon individual cells. The fact that the geniculate terminals relaying input from each eye are clustered in separate zones within layer IV is the anatomical basis for the ocular dominance columns to be described in Chapter 21.

The layers of the visual cortex contain a variety of cell types. The two most common are the *stellate cell* and the *pyramidal cell* (Figure 20–11). Stellate cells are small (10–20 μm in diameter) and usually circular in outline, with dendrites radiating from all aspects of the cell body like the arms of a many pointed star. The axons of stellate cells terminate in the local cortical area. Pyramidal cells tend to be larger (sometimes reaching 30 μm in diameter). Their cell bodies are triangular in outline; the apex of the triangle points toward the pial surface and gives rise to a long apical dendrite, and the base of the triangle gives rise to a number of basal dendrites. All of these dendrites are studded with dendritic spines. The axons of pyramidal cells leave the local cortical area after emitting one or two collaterals.

Efferent Connections

Pyramidal cells are the sources of the projections from the cortical layers in Brodmann's area 17 to other sites in the brain. They are the only cell types labeled in the peroxidase experiments to be described below. Stellate cells appear to be concerned with the local integration of visual input. The majority of axons from the principal cells of the lateral geniculate nucleus terminate upon the spiny stellate cells of layer IV. Unlike most stellate cells, this special class bears dendritic spines where the geniculate axons synapse. The stellate cell axons then project to other layers within area 17 to disseminate input.

We know that layer IV receives input from the thalamus. What are the connections of the other layers in the visual cortex? The connections of the other layers have been studied with the peroxidase method and the results can be summarized as follows:

1. Cells in layers II and III are labeled with peroxidase when injections of this marker enzyme are made in certain "higher" visual areas in the same cerebral hemisphere. These higher visual areas (such as Brodmann's areas 18 and 19) do not receive direct connections from the thalamus, but rather receive the output of area 17.

2. Cells in layer V are labeled when injections of peroxidase are made in the superior colliculus. The superior colliculus, therefore, integrates visual input received directly from the retina with input derived from the visual cortex.

3. Cells in layer VI are labeled when peroxidase injections are made in the lateral geniculate nucleus. This layer therefore exerts a feedback control over visual input reaching the cortex from the thalamus.

The connections of the cortical layers in the primary visual area are summarized diagrammatically in Figure 20–11. Visual input arrives in layer IV, and, after intracortical processing (as described in the next chapter), is forwarded to higher cortical areas via layers II and III, to the superior colliculus via layer V, and back to the lateral geniculate nucleus via layer VI. Layer I contains mostly axons running parallel to the surface of the cortex. Its function is to relate separate parts of area 17.

An Overall View

The degree of specificity in the central connections of the visual system is quite astounding. Separate regions in the retina project upon the lateral geniculate nucleus in such a way that a complete representation of the contralateral visual hemifield is established in the thalamus. Furthermore, distinct cell types occupying the same retinal locus project their axons upon different targets in the brain stem; some cells project to the thalamus, some to the midbrain, others to both. The lateral geniculate nucleus is mapped onto the visual cortex (Brodmann's area 17) in a point-to-point manner, since each geniculate axon contacts only a small part of layer IV. Cells in the layers of area 17 have their own highly stereotyped patterns of connections. One of the central problems in neurobiology is to understand how these intricate networks of synaptic connections arise during development. To get a feeling for the magnitude of the problem, remember that there are more than 1 million fibers in each optic nerve. An individual fiber must find its small target in the midst of the several million cells in the lateral geniculate nucleus. The geniculate neurons must then find their targets among the billions of cortical cells. The processes governing the formation of these specific connections remain a mystery.

Selected Readings and References

Brodal, A. 1981. Neurological Anatomy. 3rd ed. New York: Oxford University Press, Chap. 8.

Hubel, D. H., and Wiesel, T. N. 1972. Laminar and co-lumnar distribution of geniculo-cortical fibers in the macaque monkey. J. Comp. Neurol. 146:421–450.

Hubel, D. H., and Wiesel, T. N. 1977. Functional architecture of macaque monkey visual cortex. Proc. R. Soc. Lond. B Biol. Sci. 198:1–59.

Other References

Boycott, B. B., and Wässle, H. 1974. The morphological types of ganglion cells of the domestic cat's retina. J. Physiol. (Lond.) 240:397–419.

Carpenter, M. B. 1976. Human Neuroanatomy. 7th ed. Baltimore: Williams & Wilkins.

Eric R. Kandel

Visual System III: Physiology of the Central Visual Pathways

21

How do we recognize visual images? And, how do we do so independent of the exact position the image occupies on our retina? In this chapter we shall describe research that is addressed to these two questions.

Most of what we know about the functional organization of the visual system derives from experiments using first evoked responses and then single-cell recording methods similar to those used by Marshall, Woolsey, and Bard and by Mountcastle in investigating the somatic sensory system. We are therefore in a good position to compare these two sensory systems. The similarities may in turn lead us to some general principles governing the transformation of sensory information in the brain and the organization and functioning of the cerebral cortex. We should also look for differences between the two systems. For example, the visual system is numerically the most complex of all sensory systems. Whereas the auditory nerve contains about 30,000 fibers, the optic nerve contains 1 million. There are more optic nerve fibers than there are dorsal root ganglion cells in all the segments of the spinal cord!

The Retina Projects to the Colliculus and to the Lateral Geniculate Nucleus

As described in Chapter 20, the retina projects to both the superior colliculus and the lateral geniculate nucleus by means of three classes of output neurons: small cells, medium-size cells, and large cells. The large and small cells of the retina project to the superior colliculus, the large cells (and a few small cells) also project to the lateral geniculate nucleus. The medium-size cells project almost exclusively to the lateral geniculate nucleus.

Colliculus Projection

Small and large ganglion cells in each retina project to the contralateral superior colliculus. In the colliculus, visual information is brought together with somatic sensory and auditory information so that sensory responses are coordinated with movements of the head, ears, and eyes toward a stimulus in the environment. Thus, in addition to the visual representation, the colliculus also contains maps of the body surface and of the cochlea. However, the map for somatic sensation in the colliculus is quite different from that in the somatic sensory cortex. In the colliculus the size of the central representation is not determined by tactile importance, i.e., by peripheral innervation density, but rather by the visual map. Structures close to the eye receive greater representation than do structures specifically concerned with fine tactile discrimination. A given location in the colliculus is thought to represent a given point in space around the animal. All three modalities can activate that point and result in movement oriented toward the stimulus.

Geniculate Projection

The *right hemiretina of each eye* (the nasal hemiretina of the left eye and the temporal hemiretina of the right eye) projects to the *right lateral geniculate nucleus* via the optic nerve and tract (the left hemiretinas project to the left lateral geniculate nucleus) (Figure 21–1). From the lateral geniculate nucleus, neurons project via the *optic radiations to the primary visual cortex* (Brodmann's area 17, or visual area I). This area is also called the *striate cortex*. From the striate cortex, neurons project to the *peristriate cortex* (Brodmann's areas 18 and 19, or visual areas II and III). Neurons from area 17 also project to the superior colliculus, and back to the lateral geniculate nucleus (another example of central control of sensory input). From the peristriate cortex, neurons project to the *infratemporal cortex*. The infratemporal cortex also receives input from the *pulvinar* of the thalamus.

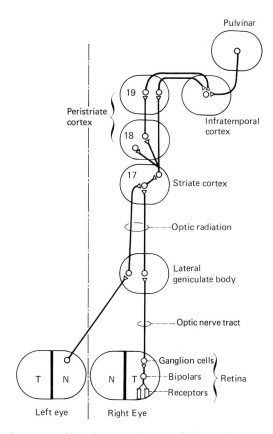

21–1 Highly schematic diagram of the visual projections to the cortex.

There Is a Map of the Retina in Various Relays in the Visual System

Modern physiological studies of the visual system began in 1941 with the experiments of Wade Marshall and Samuel Talbott. They used small spots of light projected through an operating ophthalmoscope to stimulate various parts of the retina (now spots and bars of light are projected on the retina more conveniently by means of a light source projected onto a tangent screen mounted in front of the subject as illustrated in Figure 21–2). Marshall and Talbott found that the striate cortex contains a map of the retina. Neighborhood relations are preserved. Continuous areas of the retina are represented as continuous areas of cortex. Subsequently, similar maps were found within each relay point in the geniculate projection. Here we see again a principle encountered in the somatic sensory system. The visual brain is able to recreate a map of its receptive sheet and thereby perceive the external world. As in the somatic sensory system, there is

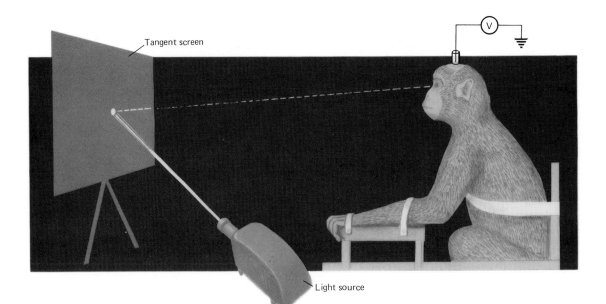

21–2 Stimulation of the retina with patterns of light. The eyes of an anesthetized, light-adapted monkey focus on a screen onto which various patterns of light are projected. An electrode records the responses from a single cell in the visual pathway.

distortion in the retinal projection. For example, the fovea, the area of the retina with the greatest acuity, is represented in enormous detail: 80–90% of the neural mass in the lateral geniculate nucleus or visual cortex is devoted to the fovea. The peripheral portions of the retina are much less well represented.

Receptive Fields of Neurons in Various Parts of the Visual System Have Different Properties

The next stage in the study of the visual system came in 1952 when Stephen Kuffler, then at Johns Hopkins University, recorded the activity of single retinal ganglion cells. He found that these cells were never silent, even in the dark; light simply modulated their spontaneous activity. Each cell responded to light, the most effective stimulus being a spot placed in a specific area of the retina. This area Kuffler called the *receptive field* of the cell. The receptive field of a single cell in any part of the visual system is *that area in the retina which, upon stimulation with light, causes either excitation or inhibition of the cell's firing pattern.*

The Ganglion Cells of the Retina

Using small spots of light to probe the properties of the receptive field, Kuffler found that the receptive fields of the retinal ganglion cells are roughly circular, covering about 4–8° of visual field. The field is not homogeneous throughout but has a fine structure. On the basis of their fine structure Kuffler classified the cells into two large groups: on-center and off-center ganglion cells (Figure 21–3). The two types of cells are about equally common. On-center fields have a central excitatory zone and an inhibitory surround. Shining a spot of light on the center of the field causes an increase in the spontaneous firing of an on-center retinal ganglion cell. In contrast, shining an annulus of light around this central zone inhibits the cell's firing. Thus, the most effective excitatory stimulus for this cell is a spot of light on the center of its receptive field and the most effective inhibitory stimulus is a doughnut of light on the surround of the receptive field. The opposite is true of off-center fields, which consist of an excitatory surround and an inhibitory center. Diffuse light over the whole of either type of receptive field (center plus surround) is ineffective. We see here, on the level of the retinal ganglion cells, a key principle in the organization of the visual system: *the cells in the visual system read contrasts.* There is an antagonistic or opponent organization in the center–surround structure of the receptive field. We shall encounter this organization again in considering color vision in the next chapter.

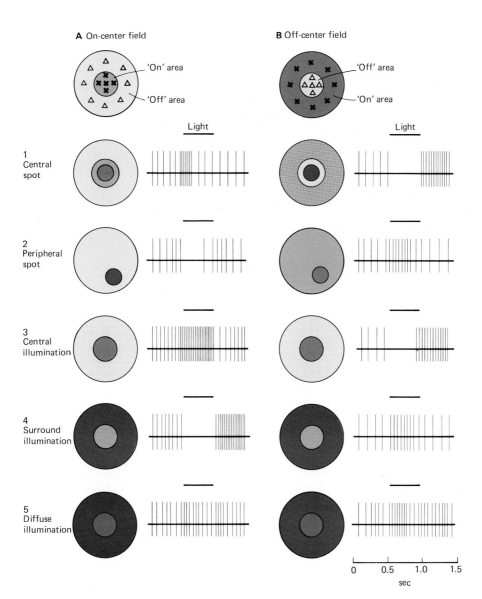

A On-center field

'On' area
'Off' area

B Off-center field

'Off' area
'On' area

Light

Light

1
Central
spot

2
Peripheral
spot

3
Central
illumination

4
Surround
illumination

5
Diffuse
illumination

| 0 | 0.5 | 1.0 | 1.5 |

sec

Kuffler also found that the receptive fields vary in size across the retina. In the center of the retina in the foveal region, where visual acuity is greatest, the receptive fields are very small with a field center of a few minutes of arc; at the periphery of the retina, where the acuity is low, the fields are large with a field center of 10–20° (1° on the retina is equal to about 0.25 mm).

In more recent studies first initiated by Christina Enroth-Cugell of Northwestern University, each of the center–surround categories has been subdivided into two classes: X and Y. In addition, a small number of cells seem to be organized according to principles other than center–surround. For example a third group of cells, W cells, seem

21–3 Responses of on-center and off-center retinal ganglion cells to different types of illumination. (**X**, excitatory zone; Δ, inhibitory zone.) **A.** An on-center cell responds best to a spot of light shone onto the central part of its receptive field *(1)*. Illumination (**bar** above records) of the surrounding area with a spot *(2)* or an annulus *(4)* of light reduces or suppresses the discharges and causes a response when the light is turned off. Diffuse illumination of the entire receptive field *(5)* elicits a relatively weak discharge because center and surround oppose each other's effects. **B.** A cell with off-center receptive field has its spontaneous firing suppressed when the central area of its field is illuminated *(1, 3)* and accelerated when the light is turned off. Light shone onto the surround of an off-center receptive field area excites *(2, 4)*. (Adapted from Kuffler, 1952.)

to be designed to detect moving stimuli. The X, Y, and W cells correspond to the three types of ganglion cells described earlier (see also Chapter 20). W cells (40% of the total) have small cell bodies, small-diameter axons, and extensive dendrites. Most of these cells project to the superior colliculus. X cells (55% of the total) have medium-size cell bodies and axons and a small dendritic arborization. They project to the lateral geniculate nucleus. Y cells (5% of the total) have large cell bodies and axons and a large dendritic tree and project to both the geniculate and the superior colliculus. These findings illustrate another principle that we have encountered earlier: *parallel processing.* Here this is accomplished when a single locus in the retina abstracts several types of information from the visual world and projects this information to different regions in the central nervous system.

As seven to eight relay points have been analyzed in the visual system, a more detailed longitudinal analysis can be carried out here than in the somatic sensory system. Knowing the organization of the receptive fields in the retina, we can now determine how the receptive fields are transformed at each sequential relay point in the higher reaches of the visual system. This is the task that David Hubel and Torsten Wiesel at the Harvard Medical School set for themselves.

Lateral Geniculate Nucleus

Hubel and Wiesel first examined the lateral geniculate nucleus. As you will recall from the last chapter, each layer of the lateral geniculate is fairly simple in its organization. It receives input only from one eye. The receptive fields in the lateral geniculate nucleus are also concentric and fairly straightforward and resemble those found in the retina (Figure 21–4A). The cells have concentric receptive fields that are several degrees in diameter. There are on-center and off-center fields. The most effective stimuli are small spots of light, and diffuse light is ineffective.

Striate Cortex

The structure of the striate cortex is more complex than that of the lateral geniculate nucleus. Large numbers of cells are arranged in several different ways. Most of the input from the geniculate comes into layer IV of the cortex and then is conveyed to the cortical layers above and below. Paralleling the increase in anatomical complexity, Hubel and Wiesel found an increase in complexity of the stimulus requirements needed for cells to respond. Small spots of light that are effective in the retina and the lateral geniculate are not as effective in the striate cortex. To be effective, a stimulus must have linear properties (Figures 21–4 and 21–5). It must be a line, a bar, or something that has a clear edge. Hubel and Wiesel categorized the cortical cells in area 17 into two major groups, simple and complex. Both respond to linear stimuli.

Simple cells have discrete excitatory and inhibitory zones that are larger than those of retinal and ganglion cells or geniculate cells (Figure 21–4). For example, a cell may have a rectangular excitatory zone (with its long axis running from 12 to 6 o'clock) flanked on each side by rectangular inhibitory zones (Figure 21–5A). The effective stimulus for this field must have the right position on the retina, the right linear properties—in this case a bar—and, in addition, it must have a specific axis of orientation—in this case vertical—running from 12 to 6 o'clock. A horizontally or obliquely placed stimulus is ineffective. Other cells in the cortex have similar retinal positions and receptive field shapes, but their axes of orientation are horizontal or oblique. By this means, every retinal position is represented for

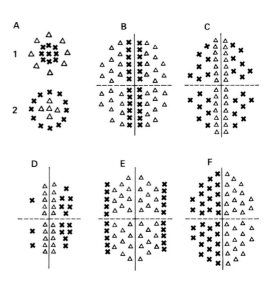

21–4 Comparison of receptive fields of various simple cells of the striate cortex (**B–F**) to those of the retina and lateral geniculate (**A**). Only receptive fields with a vertical axis of orientation are shown. Each has a rectilinear configuration with a vertical axis and clearly defined excitatory (**X**) and inhibitory (Δ) zones. (Adapted from Hubel and Wiesel, 1962.)

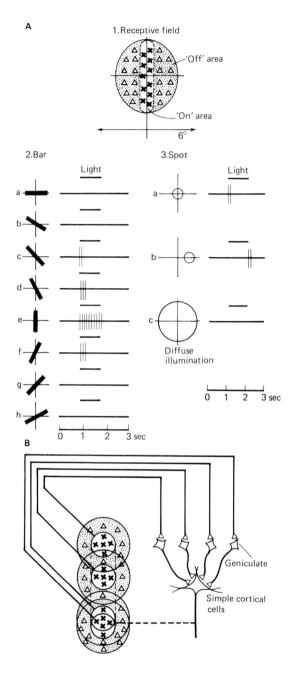

21–5 Receptive field of a simple cell in the striate cortex. **A.** *1:* The receptive field has a narrow central "on" area (**X**) flanked by symmetrical antagonistic "off" areas (Δ). *2:* The best stimulus for this cell is a vertically oriented light bar (1° × 8°) in the center of its receptive field (record **e**). Other orientations (rotated clockwise) are less effective or ineffective. *3:* In contrast to a vertical bar, a small spot of light in the "on" center of the field (record **a**) gives only a weak excitatory response. A small spot in the inhibitory flanks of "off" areas (record **b**) gives a weak inhibitory response. Diffuse light (record **c**) is ineffective. (Period of illumination is marked by a **bar** above each record.) (Adapted from Hubel and Wiesel, 1959, after Kuffler and Nicholls, 1976.) **B.** Hubel and Wiesel's scheme for explaining simple receptive fields. According to this scheme, a simple cortical neuron such as that illustrated here, receives convergent excitatory connections from one or more cells in the lateral geniculate nucleus that have similar center surround organization and similar retinal positions but but that are slightly displaced along a vertical line in the retina. The receptive field of the cortical cell will then have an elongated "on" region indicated by the interrupted rectangular outline in the receptive field diagram. A bar of light that falls on this elongated excitatory region of the simple cortical cell will activate several geniculate cells and this will excite the cortical neuron. **X**, excitatory portion of the receptive field; Δ, inhibitory portion. (Adapted from Hubel and Wiesel, 1962.)

every axis of orientation. Hubel and Wiesel suggest that the properties of a simple receptive field could be generated by appropriate connections from geniculate cells (Figure 21–5B).

The receptive fields of *complex cells* are larger than those of simple cells (Figure 21–6A) and also have a critical axis of orientation. Position of the stimulus within the receptive field is not critical, however, because there are no clearly defined excitatory or inhibitory zones. For certain cells movement is a particularly good stimulus. Although some complex cells receive their connections from geniculate cells, Hubel and Wiesel have proposed that a significant input to the

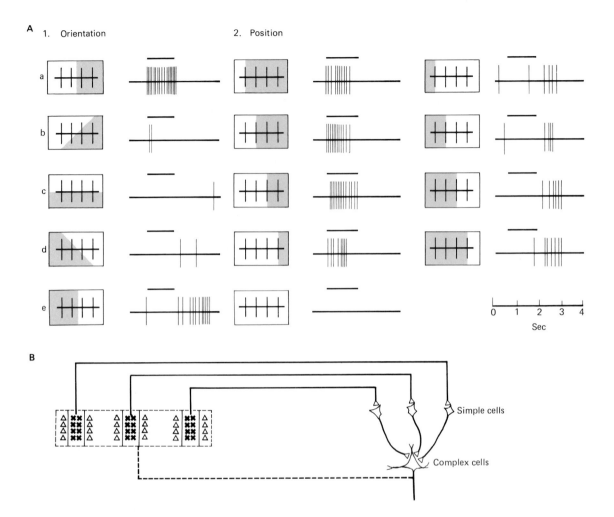

21–6 Receptive field of a complex cell in the striate cortex. **A.** The cell responds best to a vertical edge; orientation is important but position within the field is not critical. *1:* Orientation. With light on the left and dark on the right (record **a**), there is an "on" response. With light on the right (record **e**), there is an "off" response. Orientation other than vertical is less effective. *2:* Position of border within field. Illumination of entire receptive field (record **e**) gives no response. (Illumination is indicated by **bar** above records.) **B.** Hubel and Wiesel's hierarchical scheme for explaining the properties of complex receptive fields. According to this scheme a complex cortical neuron such as the one illustrated here receives convergent excitatory connections from several simple cortical cells that have a vertical axis of orientation and central excitation zone and two flanking inhibitory regions and that have retinal positions that are slightly displaced along a horizontal line in the retina. **X**, excitatory portion of the receptive field, Δ, inhibitory portion. (Adapted from Hubel and Wiesel, 1962.)

complex cells comes from simple cells (Figure 21–6B).

The Striate Cortex Is Organized into Columns

Some support for the hypothesis that complex cells are connected to simple ones comes from the finding by Hubel and Wiesel that the visual cortex is organized into narrow columns (much as is the somatic sensory cortex), running from the surface to the white matter. Each column is about 10–30 μm wide and 2 mm deep, and in each column there are many simple cells with almost identical retinal position and identical axes of orientation. In any column there are also complex cells. The properties of these complex cells in a column could most easily be explained by pos-

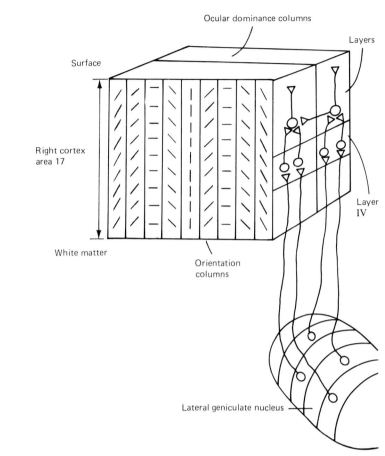

21−7 Orientation columns and ocular dominance columns in area 17 of the visual cortex.

tulating that each complex cell receives direct connections from the simple cells in the column. This finding gives us a completely new insight into the importance of cortical columns. In the visual system columns seem to serve as anatomical devices for bringing cells together so as to interconnect them and to generate, by means of these interconnections, a new level of abstraction of visual information. For example, the columns allow cortical cells to generate *linear* receptive field properties from a geniculate input that responds best to small spots of light.

The discovery of columns in the various sensory systems is perhaps the most important single advance in cortical physiology in the past several decades and has led to a number of related discoveries. For example, given that cells with the same axis of orientation tend to be grouped into columns, how are columns of cells with *different* axes of orientation organized in relation to

one another? Detailed mapping of adjacent columns by Hubel and Wiesel, using tangential microelectrode penetrations, has revealed a very orderly shift of axis orientation. Every 20–50 μm, the electrode encounters a new column and a shift in axis of orientation of about 10° (Figure 21–7).

In addition to columns devoted to axis of orientation there are columns devoted to eye preference or ocular dominance (properties related to binocular interaction), which we shall consider later (Chapter 52). Figure 21–7 illustrates in schematic form the relationship between the orientation columns and the independent ocular dominance columns. Hubel and Wiesel have designated the term *hypercolumn* to refer to the whole set of columns for analyzing lines of all orientations from a particular region in space via *both eyes*. From these studies it is apparent that the striate cortex carries out two major functions: (1)

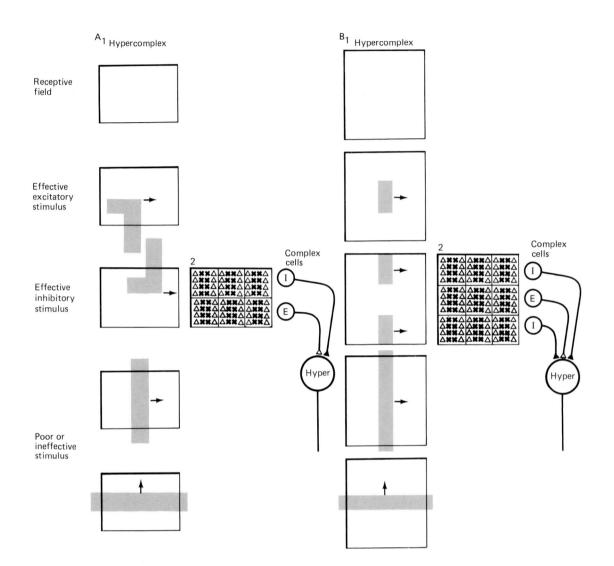

21–8 Receptive fields of hypercomplex cells in the peristriate cortex. **A.** A single-stopped (lower order) hypercomplex cell. *1:* Receptive field properties. *2:* Hubel and Wiesel's scheme for generating the hypercomplex receptive field. According to this scheme two complex cells that have similar receptive field properties and axes of orientation, but that are lined up one below the other, converge on a common lower order hypercomplex cell. One complex cell excites the hypercomplex cell, the other complex cell inhibits it. **B.** Double-stopped (higher order) hypercomplex cell. *1:* Receptive field properties. *2:* Hubel and Wiesel's scheme for generating the receptive field. Three complex cells with similar receptive field properties, lined up one below the other, converge on a common higher order complex cell. Two of the complex cells are inhibitory, the central one is excitatory. **Gray area:** light. (Adapted from Hubel and Wiesel, 1965.)

it combines the input from the two eyes, a step in a sequence of transformations necessary for depth perception; and (2) it decomposes the visual world into short line segments of various orientations, an early step in the process thought to be necessary for pattern discrimination.

Hubel and Wiesel suggest that the interaction between simple and complex cells may be important for the issue raised at the beginning of this chapter: the perception of patterns irrespective of where they fall on the retina. Take a vertical line—or an object with vertical edges—that is located in front of you. The vertical edge (or the line) will excite a population of simple cells and a population of complex ones, each with a vertical axis of orientation. A slight (saccadic) movement of your eye or of the object will call into play a new population of simple cells (because these cells are very sensitive to the exact position of the line in the receptive field). However, for a small movement the stimulus will still excite the original population of complex cells (because these cells are less sensitive to movement within the receptive field).

Peristriate Cortex

Hubel and Wiesel have also examined the peristriate cortex, areas 18 and 19. These areas receive input from area 17 and elaborate the information further. Here the stimulus requirements are sometimes even more complex. Some cells in areas 18 and 19 have been classified as *hypercomplex cells* (Figure 21–8). (A few of these cells have now also been found in area 17.)

Lower order hypercomplex cells respond well to a bar of light in the excitatory part of the receptive field as long as it is stopped—so that it does not extend beyond the excitatory receptive field in one direction (Figure 21–8A). Hubel and Wiesel suggested that lower order hypercomplex cells receive the convergent input from two complex cells with similar properties, one being excitatory, the other inhibitory (Figure 21–8A, 2).

Higher order hypercomplex cells (Figure 21–8B) respond best to a bar of light that passes over the middle of the receptive field but does not extend to either of the two lateral inhibitory areas (Figure 21–8B). A narrow bar will cause the higher order hypercomplex cell to discharge. But if the bar is increased in size in either direction it will decrease the discharge of the cell because it encroaches on the inhibitory areas. Thus, whereas the lower order hypercomplex cells deal with edges that stop in one direction—they can signal a corner moving in one direction over part of the retina—the higher order cell is even more specific and signals that there is a small bar moving over a part of the retina which is not wider than an amount specified by the inhibitory component of the receptive fields. Hubel and Wiesel have suggested that these higher order cells might receive convergence from three cells with a complex receptive field having the same axis of orientation (a central excitatory one and two lateral inhibitory ones), which are lined up one below the other (Figure 21–8B, 2). We consider only two representative examples here. Within each category of hypercomplex cells there are actually many subtle distinctions and a large variety of subtypes.

Some Feature Abstraction Could Be Accomplished by Progressive Convergence

On the basis of these data, Hubel and Wiesel have proposed that the cells in areas 17, 18, and 19 are the early building blocks of perception and that they work by a principle of increasing convergence. Looked at in its simplest form, this scheme would suggest that each second-order hypercomplex cell surveys several lower order hypercomplex cells. These, in turn, survey the activity of a group of complex cells, which survey the activity of a group of simple cells. The simple cells survey the activity of a group of geniculate cells, which in turn survey the activity of a group of ganglion cells. The ganglion cells survey the activity of bipolar cells, which in turn survey the activity of a group of receptors. *At each level, each cell sees a greater perspective than at an earlier level, and its ability to abstract is increased.*

Hubel and Wiesel postulated that as a first approach one can view that part of the visual system which they have analyzed as a hierarchy of relay points, each of which is involved in increasing visual abstraction (Figure 21–9). At the lowest level of the system, at the level of the retinal ganglion and the lateral geniculate cells, neurons respond primarily to brightness contrast. As we move up the hierarchy to the simple and complex cells of the cortex, cells begin to respond to line segments and boundaries. The hypercomplex cells respond to changes in boundaries. Thus, as we progress up the system, the stimulus requirements necessary to activate the cell become more complex. In the retina and the lateral geniculate, position is important. In simple cells, in addition to position, the axis of orientation is important. In complex cells, the axis of orientation is important, but we now have generalized the property of position. In hypercomplex cells, edges and corners become important.

Visual Perception Must Also Involve Parallel Processing

An unresolved question that is now receiving increasing attention is, how far can this hierarchy go? Is there a special supercomplex cell or cell group on top of the hierarchical processing for each familiar face? (Is there a grandmother cell?) Is there a group of cells that observe the hyperhypercomplex cells and make one aware of the total pattern? If so, is there a still higher group in

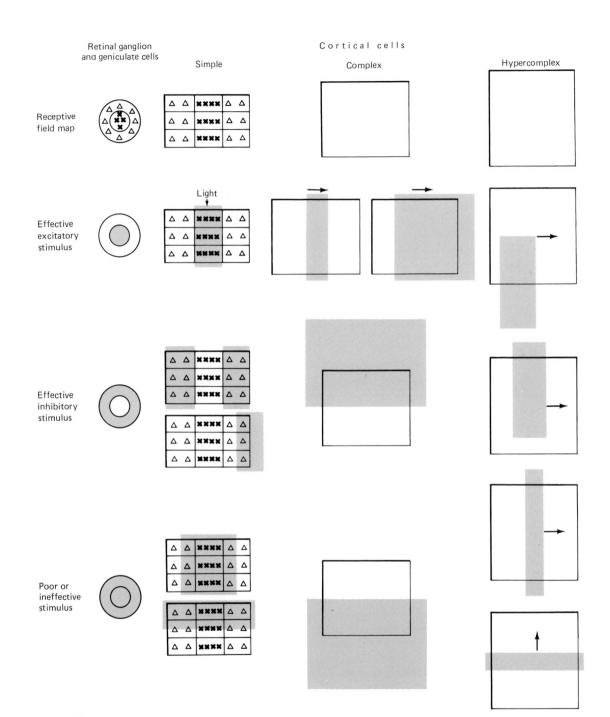

21–9 Summary of the receptive field properties of neurons in the retina and lateral geniculate nucleus and those in the striate cortex. Retinal ganglion and lateral geniculate cells respond mainly to brightness contrast; simple and complex cortical cells respond to shapes, lines, edges, and boundaries. **X**, excitatory zone; Δ, inhibitory zone; **gray area**, light. (Adapted from Hubel and Wiesel, 1962; Kuffler and Nicholls, 1976.)

the hierarchy that looks at combinations of complex patterns as these enter our awareness?

There may indeed be other higher order cells combining the computational results of the inferotemporal, peristriate, and striate cortices to produce even more elaborate abstractions. However, to discern the relatively simple features we have thus far considered has already required an enormous proportion of visual brain. It would appear curious to attribute progressively more important processing to a relatively small group of cells and expect of them this enormously complex abstraction. An alternative to this supposition would be that at higher levels the mechanism of transformation changes, so that single units no longer serve to represent feature states but represent only selected aspects of the percept. To represent a familiar face or a landscape may require *parallel processing,* that is, activity in cells in different areas in the inferotemporal, peristriate, and striate cortices, with the cells in each area coding for a particular aspect of the stimulus. At this higher level of representation cells in many parallel visual areas are likely to be involved, and their simultaneous activity may serve as the feature detector. The states of the parts taken separately may not represent the whole; rather, it is the relationship among them that may be important. One can draw an analogy to the individual silver halide grains of a photograph: these do not represent the photograph of a face, but the ensemble of grains does.

There is in fact some support for this view. We have seen that even as early as the retina, visual information is carried to the lateral geniculate nucleus and then to area 17 of the cortex by two parallel systems, the X and Y cells. Moreover, we described area 17 above as if it sent one main projection to areas 18 and 19. Actually, S. M. Zeki at University College London has found that area 17 sends five separate projections to area 18 alone. Zeki found that the cells in each of the five regions that receive input from area 17 have different functional properties, a finding that supports the idea that each region handles a different aspect of visual information. For example, several regions in area 18 contain cells that code for color, and other regions contain cells that code for movement. Interconnections among these various regions could generate a very large variety of response types suitable for analyzing in almost endless detail the intricacies of the visual world.

An Overall View

In conclusion, let us consider some similarities and differences between the somatic sensory and visual systems. Both are modality specific, topographically organized, and have a columnar organization. However, in the somatic sensory system the receptor at the periphery sets the sensi-

tivity for the system—at least for certain dimensions of the stimulus. There is relatively little change in the receptive field until we go beyond the first somatic cortex. In contrast, in the visual system there is complex transformation of neural information at all levels in the system and progressively greater abstraction as information ascends into the higher centers. Thus, whereas aspects of tactile perception literally reside in the hand of the perceiver, visual perception resides largely in the abstracting capabilities of the neurons of the brain.

Selected Readings and References

Hubel, D. H., and Wiesel, T. N. 1977. Ferrier Lecture: Functional architecture of macaque monkey visual cortex. Proc. R. Soc. Lond. B Biol. Sci. 198:1–59.

Hubel, D. H., and Wiesel, T. N. 1979. Brain mechanisms of vision. Sci. Am. 241(3):150–162.

Kuffler, S. W. 1952. Neurons in the retina: Organization, inhibition and excitation problems. Cold Spring Harbor Symp. Quant. Biol. 17:281–292.

Stone, J., Dreher, B., and Leventhal, A. 1979. Hierarchical and parallel mechanisms in the organization of visual cortex. Brain Res. Rev. 1:345–394.

Van Essen, D. C. 1979. Visual areas of the mammalian cerebral cortex. Annu. Rev. Neurosci. 2:227–263.

Zeki, S. M. 1976. The functional organization of projections from striate to prestriate visual cortex in the rhesus monkey. Cold Spring Harbor Symp. Quant. Biol. 40:591–600.

Other References

Enroth-Cugell, C., and Robson, J. G. 1966. The contrast sensitivity of retinal ganglion cells of the cat. J. Physiol. (Lond.) 187:517–552.

Hubel, D. H., and Wiesel, T. N. 1959. Receptive fields of single neurones in the cat's striate cortex. J. Physiol. (Lond.) 148:574–591.

Hubel, D. H., and Wiesel, T. N. 1962. Receptive fields, binocular interaction and functional architecture in the cat's visual cortex. J. Physiol. (Lond.) 160: 106–154.

Hubel, D. H., and Wiesel, T. N. 1965. Binocular interaction in striate cortex of kittens reared with artificial squint. J. Neurophysiol. 28:1041–1059.

Kuffler, S. W., and Nicholls, J. G. 1976. From Neuron to Brain: A Cellular Approach to the Function of the Nervous System. Sunderland, Mass.: Sinauer Associates.

Marshall, W. H., and Talbot, S. A. 1942. Recent evidence for neural mechanisms in vision leading to a general theory of sensory acuity. In H. Klüver (ed.), Visual Mechanisms. Lancaster, Pennsylvania: Cattell, pp. 117–164.

Marshall, W. H., Woolsey, C. N., and Bard, P. 1941. Observations on cortical somatic sensory mechanisms of cat and monkey. J. Neurophysiol. 4:1–24.

Mountcastle, V. B. 1975. The view from within: Pathways to the study of perception. Johns Hopkins Med. J. 136:109–131.

Mountcastle, V. B. 1976. The world around us: Neural command functions for selective attention. Neurosci. Res. Program Bull. 14:Suppl.

Talbot, S. A., and Marshall, W. H. 1941. Physiological studies on neural mechanisms of visual localization and discrimination. Am. J. Ophthalmol. 24: 1255–1264.

Peter Gouras

Visual System IV:
Color Vision

22

Color is a remarkable sensation, greatly enriching our visual experience. Far beyond its esthetic value, color vision is of great practical value for detecting patterns and objects which would be elusive in a world devoid of color.

Although color depends upon the physical parameters of light, its perception, like the perception of pattern, is a sophisticated abstraction of the physical parameters by neurons within the brain which create the experience of color and project it into the objects we see. This operation has evolved to enhance contrast by utilizing wavelength differences between the light reflected from an object and its background in an environment where gradients of light energy are often small. Color vision does not simply detect the wavelength composition of light reflected from an object's surface but also analyzes an object in relation to its background. This is why one does not experience color when the eye is bathed in an absolutely uniform and edgeless field of color devoid of any pattern. The best example of this is "graying out," a temporary but total absence of vision experienced by pilots in cockpits under a cloudless, blue sky. Furthermore, totally different wavelength combinations can often produce identical colors (a mixture of red and green can totally match a spectrally different yellow), and different colors can sometimes be produced by identical combinations of wavelengths (white objects can appear to be pink, pale green, or other contrasting colors in the proper background). *The colors we see in objects are those that best set them off from their background under the existing lighting conditions.*

In this chapter we shall first consider the photoreceptor systems that are required to produce color discrimination and then review the spectrophotometric and psychophysical data indicating that we use three different cone systems to see all colors. We shall then consider the physiological mechanisms involved in color vision and the diseases that produce color blindness.

Cones Have Three Different Pigments

The eyes of humans are sensitive to wavelengths that range from 400 to 700 nm. Throughout this range, the colors change gradually from blue, through green, to red. At the beginning of the 19th century Thomas Young, a practicing English physician, proposed a trichromatic theory of color vision based upon the perception of three color sensations: blue, green, and red. He argued that there are three classes of light-absorbing substances and that excitation of each of these is transmitted separately to the brain, where they are combined to generate the variety of colors that we encounter in the world. Young's simple but sophisticated hypothesis received independent support 50 years later when James Clerk Maxwell (then in his twenties) and, independently, Hermann von Helmholtz, demonstrated that all the colors we see can be completely matched by mixtures of three suitably chosen spectral lights. A wide assortment of three such lights can be used.

This hypothesis of color vision was confirmed in 1964 when Edward MacNichol, Jr., and his colleagues at Johns Hopkins and George Wald and his colleagues at Harvard actually measured the absorption spectrum of visual pigments of single cones in humans, the first stage in color vision. They found that individual cones contain only one of three pigments: a pigment primarily sensitive to blue with a maximum absorption at 445 nm; another for green with a maximum at 535; and a third for red with a maximum at 570 (Figure 22–1). Similar results were obtained from psychological experiments that measured the spectral properties of these three mechanisms by using the subject's response to visual stimuli, the final stage of color vision (Figure 22–2). To obtain the best psychophysical data, subjects who had

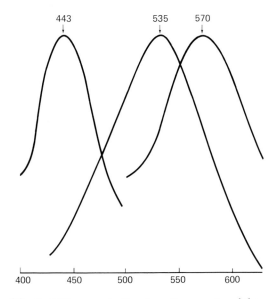

22–1 Differences in the absorption spectra of the three types of human cones. (Adapted from Marks, Dobelle, and MacNichol, Jr., 1964.)

specific genetic defects in their photoreceptors were examined. As we shall see later, some people have only two cone mechanisms (dichromats), and others only one cone mechanism (monochromats). In people with these genetic defects, the psychophysical measurement of the spectral sensitivities of the remaining mechanisms is greatly facilitated. These three mechanisms have been called red (R), green (G), and blue (B) because each is largely activated by the corresponding color sensation. Nevertheless, these three cone mechanisms are not each responsible singly for red, green, and blue because the visual system can mix and contrast the effect of the channels activated by the individual cone mechanisms; therefore, the three cone mechanisms are responsible for *all* the colors that we see in broad daylight.

The blue mechanism (at 445 nm) is spectrally remote from the other two mechanisms, which have their peak sensitivities near one another (535 and 570 nm) in the yellow region of the spectrum. This gives blue cones a greater latitude for spectral contrast. Chromatic aberration, however, blurs the optical image in this spectral region (see Appendix III). Consequently, nature has kept the blue mechanism out of the central fovea, where resolution of fine detail is maximal (due to the fine grain of foveolor cones). Thus, in the central fovea, color vision is dichromatic. Handi-

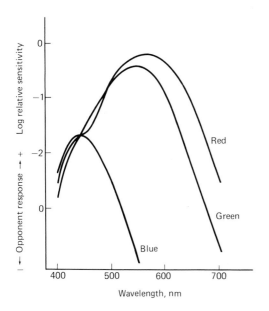

22-2 Spectral curves of human perception come very close to representing the relative spectral sensitivities of the red-, green-, and blue-absorbing photopigments (see Figure 22-1). (Adapted from Smith and Pokorny, 1972.)

capped by chromatic aberration, the retinal mosaic of blue cones has been kept much coarser than that of the other cones, so that color vision becomes dichromatic everywhere when objects are small. If objects become small enough, color vision deteriorates completely, since single photoreceptors are color blind. Optimal color vision has not been designed to discriminate fine spatial detail but to detect relatively large objects in backgrounds that could make these objects invisible.

Thus, to code for color, the retina uses three different sets of cone photoreceptors, each responding best to a different part of the visible spectrum. The perception of color involves not simply the action of the sensory receptors, but also the interaction between them. A fourth set of photoreceptors, the rods, are nocturnal receptors that do not function in broad daylight, where color vision is optimal.

Good Color Discrimination Requires Three Photoreceptor Systems

Why do we need three cone pigments for color? Why would one not do? With one set of cones, we would detect an object only if it reflected more (or less) light energy than its background. A single type of photoreceptor cannot distinguish between different wavelengths of light, even though it might be more sensitive to some wavelengths than to others. Such a system is color blind and is unable to distinguish changes in energy from changes in wavelength (Figure 22-3A). You can simulate a single photoreceptor system with your own eyes by adapting to moonlight. All the objects you see have brightnesses different from their background but are achromatic (colorless) because you are only using a single set of photoreceptors, rods. Many objects that reflect spectrally different wavelengths from their background but have identical brightnesses will be invisible under these conditions. A full moon may itself look pink only because its brightness is sufficient to excite cones.

This disadvantage of a one-receptor system can be reduced greatly by using two sets of photoreceptors. What may be an identical stimulus for one set will usually not be for the other. A two-receptor, or dichromatic, system may have been a first step in the evolution of color vision. Many spectral combinations between object and background can nevertheless be invisible to even a dichromatic system. An object reflecting both ends of the spectrum in a midspectral background could be undetectable (Figure 22-3B). This object could produce the same output from both types of photoreceptors as does the background stimulus. It would therefore be invisible to these photoreceptors. Theoretically, there are infinite combinations of these possibilities. A three-receptor, or trichromatic system reduces such ambiguities to a much greater degree (Figure 22-3C). Although some birds employ tetrachromacy, the evolutionary evidence suggests that any further augmentation of receptor systems yields diminishing returns.

Hue, Saturation, and Brightness

The use of three photoreceptors to detect objects is not equivalent to using them to see colors. For example, the honeybee and other animals detect objects using three photoreceptor systems but may never see the colors of these objects if the input from these receptors is not mixed to allow for color contrast, the essential feature of color perception in higher animals. For example, a neuron designed to detect an object brighter (or darker) than the background could be excited by activity in any one of the three photoreceptor systems. Such a cell would be sensitive to the presence of an object in the external world and would

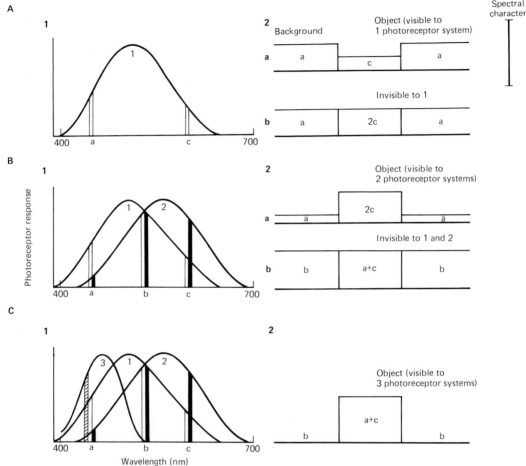

22–3 Discrimination of objects by one-, two-, and three-receptor system. **Left-hand side of each part (1):** the spectral response function of each photoreceptor system, with wavelength on the abscissa (400 nm, violet, to 700 nm, deep red) and relative response on the ordinate. **Right-hand side of each part (2):** hypothetical spectral reflectances (color) of an object (**middle rectangle**) and the background (**flanking regions**) against which it can be seen (the color of the object is different from its background). In all cases the spectral characteristic of this reflected signal is shown by its position on the abscissa on the left. **A.** Single-photoreceptor system. *1.* Object c affects photoreceptor 1 about one-half as much as the background a. *2a:* Therefore, photoreceptor 1 will be stimulated about one-half as much by the object as by the background; consequently, object c will appear dark in a bright background. *2b:* If object c reflects sunlight about twice as much as the background, however, it will become totally invisible to photoreceptor 1 since the response will be about 2c, which is identical to the response generated by

background a. Even though this object (2c) is spectrally quite different from its background, it cannot be detected by a single-photoreceptor system under these particular conditions. **B.** Two sets of photoreceptors, each with a different spectral response. *1:* Objects invisible to receptor 1 are usually visible to photoreceptor 2. *2a:* An object 2c, which is invisible to photoreceptor 1, is strongly visible to photoreceptor 2. *2b:* There is, however, a possibility that some unusual objects could be bispectrally reflectant, such as object (a+c). Such an object would stimulate both photoreceptors 1 and 2 exactly the same as background b and consequently be invisible to both photoreceptors. One can work this out by showing that a + c = b for both photoreceptors 1 and 2. **C.** Trichromatic system. This system would detect object (a + c) when the dichromatic system failed. This system would be much tougher to fool than the others, at least under natural lighting. b and c both affect receptors 1 and 2, but only a affects receptor 3; therefore object a+c will be a bright object in a dark background to receptor 3.

share the benefits of a trichromatic detector system but might not contribute to color vision. A color detector must be able to distinguish how much each of the three cone mechanisms is activated by the object. *Color vision requires that neurons compare the three inputs.* In humans, the neurons do both, but it is the unique esthetic experience of color in the mind's eye that has fascinated humans throughout the ages.

Animals with color vision simply have great perceptual capability, and this presumably has great survival value. Think for a moment of a black and white version of a work by a colorist such as Turner, Monet, or Renoir; almost a million nuances of contrasting shapes are lost by an achromatic rendition of one of their works. This high degree of discrimination in color vision can actually be understood in quantitative terms. The subjective experience of color can be broken down into three semi-independent sensibilities: (1) hue, (2) saturation, and (3) brightness. All color experience is composed of these three psychological impressions.

Hue has the strongest effect on color and is the major determinant of principal colors such as red, yellow, green, and blue. It is what we ordinarily mean by "color." This impression is determined by the proportion in which the three cone mechanisms are activated by the object and its background. The brain must keep track of how much *each* of the three photoreceptor systems contributes to the detection of an object. Most of us have names for only a family of hues, but actually about 200 varieties can be distinguished. The second distinct quality of color is *saturation*, which reflects how much a hue has been diluted by grayness; this is determined by the degree to which all three cone mechanisms are stimulated in common by the object and by the background. There are about 20 distinguishable steps of saturation for each hue.

The third quality of color, *brightness*, is a sensation shared with achromatic visual systems. It is due to the total effect on all three cone mechanisms of an object relative to its background. We shall see later that one of the three cone mechanisms (the so-called blue mechanism) makes little or no contribution to brightness. It is the brightness factor that turns orange into brown and gray into black or white. There are about 500 distinguishable steps of brightness for every hue and grade of saturation. In contrast to achromatic vision with only 500 steps, color vision has more than 1 million gradations with which to detect the contours of shapes in the external world [500 (brightness) $\times$ 200 (hue) $\times$ 20 (saturation)]. It is no wonder that natural selection uncovered its power.

By the latter part of the eighteenth century it was realized that the ability to experience myriad different colors might not be due to an equivalent number of detectors in the retina but to a minimum number—three—with every color determined by the proportions in which each of these three detectors responds to light.

Neural Mechanisms in Color Vision

As we have seen in Chapter 21, the cells that code for pattern in the retina, the lateral geniculate nucleus, and the visual cortex are sensitive to brightness contrast. They use a spatially opponent mechanism. Two sets of cones (or two sets of rods) containing the same visual pigment are connected to a single cell in a spatially separate concentric center–surround fashion, so that the system is designed to detect contrast between light and dark. Simultaneous stimulation of the center and surround leads to mutual antagonisms; diffuse light is a poor stimulus.

Color is similarly coded by an opponent mechanism. Although the cones contain three independent receptor systems, each with its own pigment, these receptor systems do not project to the brain by means of independent communication channels; rather, the cells of the brain that respond to color invariably receive information from two types of cones—one that excites and one that inhibits the cell. Color is therefore abstracted by an opponent mechanism in which one wavelength of light drives the cell, and another wavelength inhibits it. The ganglion cells of the retina and the cells of the lateral geniculate nucleus that code for color have concentric receptive fields consisting of a center connected to one type of cone and a surround connected to another type of cone. If a cell is excited by one class of cone (red cones, for example), it is inhibited by another class of cone (green cones, for example). These cells are consequently strongly excited by red light and strongly inhibited by green light (Figure 22–4). Other ganglion cells show the reverse arrangement; they are excited by green cones and inhibited by red cones. Consequently, they are excited best by green light and inhibited best by red light. A third variety is excited by blue cones and inhibited by both red and green cones; these cells are best excited by blue light and best inhibited by yellow light. Thus, the retina and geniculate consist of parallel systems of

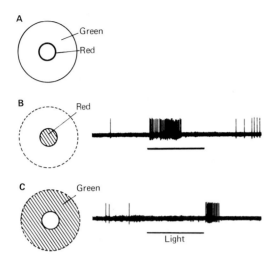

22–4 Responses of a concentric cell in the retina to a monochromatic stimulus. **A.** The cell has a concentric red–green receptive field; the center is excitatory and sensitive to red; the surround is inhibitory and sensitive to green. **B.** A red light shown on the center produces an excitatory "on" response. **C.** A green light shown on the surround is inhibitory. There is an "off" discharge when it ceases. (Illumination is indicated by the **bar** below each record.)

22–5 Color-coded cortical cells with concentric receptive fields. **A.** Responses of a light-adapted concentric cell to monochromatic stimuli. The field center was 0.5° in diameter; the total diameter of the field was 8°. Stimuli were a 0.5° spot, a 0.5° inner diameter and −8° outer diameter annulus, and an 8° spot. *1:* A centered red spot produced an "on" outer diameter discharge. *2:* A centered green spot produced an "off" discharge. *3:* A red annulus evoked an "off" response. *4:* A green annulus evoked an "on" response. *5,* and *6:* Larger monochromatic spots were without effect. The 1-sec stimulus duration is indicated by the **bar** below each oscilloscope trace. Duration of each sweep was 3 sec.; wavelengths were 630 nm for red and 500 nm for green. **B.** Proposed synaptic mechanism to explain the response properties and receptive field organization of the concentric cells. *Solid circles:* receptive fields of the geniculate fibers; *broken circles:* center and surround of the concentric cortical cell's field. A single geniculate afferent has a circular receptive field (in this case green on, red off) which coincides with the cell's field center. Encompassing in an annular fashion the field of the central afferent are the circular fields of a large group of geniculate fibers, only two of which are shown here. Fields of these units, which collectively form the surround of the cell's field, are all of the same opponent-color type and are the same diameter. The central fiber and the surround group have the opposite opponent-color organization. All synapses are excitatory. (Adapted from Michael, 1978a.)

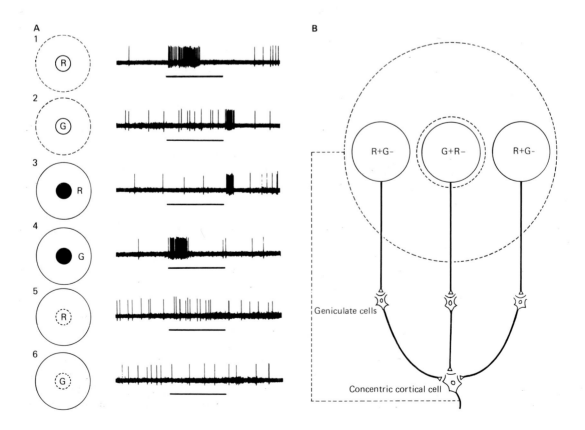

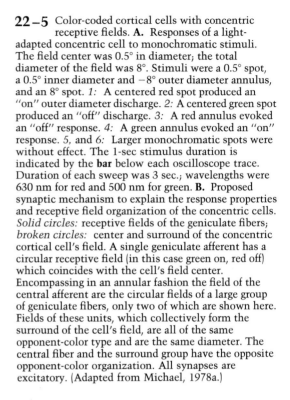

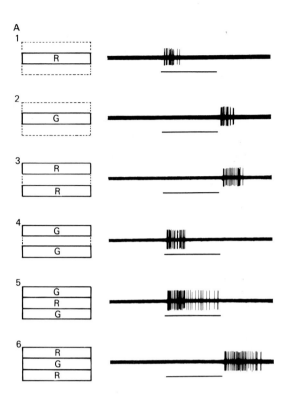

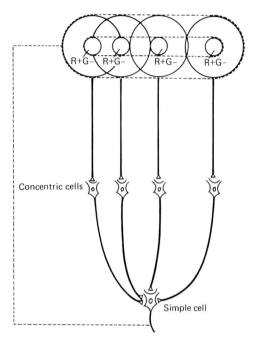

cells. Some cells have spatial opponency and are best excited by local brightness (or darkness) and by white or yellow light, which strongly activates most cones. Others have spectral opponency and are best excited by the red or the green or the blue part of the spectrum.

In the striate cortex (area 17) Charles Michael at Yale and Peter Gouras and Jurgen Krüger at Columbia have found separate classes of neurons that simultaneously process either color or brightness contrast from these geniculate cells. The color-contrast cells form a distinct population quite separate from the cells concerned with brightness contrast (which Hubel and Wiesel described and we considered in Chapter 21). As with the cells concerned with brightness discrimination, the color-contrast cells can be divided into simple, complex, and hypercomplex cells.

The most elementary group of color-contrast cells in the cortex has *concentric* receptive fields. There is one red–green opponent color system in the center of the field and an opposite organization in the surround. These cells differ from geniculate cells, however, in that they are most sensitive to simultaneous color contrast (Figure 22–5). Such cells are best excited when one type of cone (red cones, for example) is stimulated in the center and another type of cone (green

22–6 Color-coded cortical cells that respond to bars and rectangles of one opponent-color system. **A.** Responses of a light-adapted simple cell to monochromatic bars of light. The central band was 0.5″ wide and 3° long, the overall receptive field was 1.5° wide. The stimulus bars were 0.5° wide and 3″ long; they were oriented horizontally along the receptive field axis of the cell (9 o'clock to 3 o'clock). *1:* A red bar covering the central strip produced an "on" discharge. *2:* A green bar produced an "off" discharge. *3:* Two red bars covering the antagonistic flanks evoked an "off" response. *4:* Two green bars evoked an "on" response. *5:* A red bar flanked by two green ones elicited a strong, maintained "on" response. *6:* A green bar flanked by two red ones evoked a vigorous "off" discharge. The 1-sec stimulus duration is indicated by the *bar* below each oscilloscope trace. Duration of each sweep was 3 sec. **R,** red, 620 nm; **G,** green, 500 nm. Background, 1.1 log cd/m². **B.** Proposed synaptic mechanism to explain the response properties and receptive field organization of the color-sensitive simple cells. (Adapted from Michael, 1978b.)

cones, for example) is stimulated in the surround of the cell's receptive field. The cells with concentric receptive fields probably serve as the input stage to the cortex. The next phase in processing of color information involves simple cells that respond to bars and rectangles of one (red–green) opponent-color system and have two antagonistic flanking regions with reverse opponent arrangement (Figure 22–6). Next there are complex and hypercomplex cells in which there are no clear inhibitory and excitatory zones, in which orientation is important but exact position in the receptive field is less critical. As with the cells concerned with brightness contrast, the color-contrast cells can also be thought of as being arranged in a hierarchical manner (Figures 22–5B and 22–6B). In addition, there are columns devoted to color contrast that are independent of those concerned with axis of orientation and ocularity.

Beyond the striate cortex, evidence suggests that cells coding for color may still be kept separate. The work of S. M. Zeki suggests that there may be specific areas that deal predominantly with color, although the importance of color contrast for contour detection implies that it participates in most visual functions.

Color Blindness Can Be Caused by Genetic Defects in the Photoreceptor or by Retinal Disease

Although most of us agree on the colors we see because we are using similar neural circuits to see them, some people disagree and have been called color defective by the rest of us. This deficit can result from either inherited or acquired factors. Most forms of color blindness are listed in Table 22–1. In general, they involve either a loss of one or more of the three cone mechanisms or a

change in the absorption spectrum of one or more of the photopigments within these cones. The adjectives *protan, deutan,* and *tritan* refer to the red, green, and blue mechanisms, respectively. The suffixes *-opia* and *-omalous* refer, respectively, to a total loss or a moderate defect of each of these three mechanisms. Some people lose two (usually the red and green) or all three cone mechanisms and consequently have no color vision at all (achromats). It is noteworthy that the genes for the red and green cone mechanisms are on the X (sex-linked) chromosome, while that for the blue is autosomal. Acquired defects of color vision are more complex but an old clinical rule, occasionally disobeyed, states that diseases of the outer retinal layers tend to produce tritanopia, whereas diseases of the inner layers and optic nerve produce protan–deutan defects. The protan–deutan defects are presumably associated with disease of the inner layer because of the great number of axons that subserve the red and green cones, many of which are very fine and are likely to be affected by any disease state of the inner layer.

Although color vision involves larger numbers of extraretinal than retinal cells, most of the defects, especially the genetic ones, involve only photoreceptors. This is undoubtedly due to the fact that the genes that code for photoreceptors are more specific to color vision than those that code for the neural circuitry that processes the information provided by these photoreceptors. The

Table 22–1. Classification and Incidence of Defects in Color Vision

Classification	Incidence (% males)
Congenital	
Trichromats (three cones present)	
Normal	91.2
Anomalous	
Protanomaly (red cone pigment reduced)	1.3
Deuteranomaly (green cone pigment reduced)	5.0
Tritanomaly (blue cone pigment reduced)	0.001
Dichromats (two cones present)	
Protanopia (red cone absent)	1.3
Deuteranopia (green cone absent)	1.2
Tritanopia (blue cone absent)	0.001
Monochromats (achromats)	
Typical (all cones absent)	0.00001
Atypical (two cones absent)	0.000001
Acquired	
Tritanopia: outer retinal layer disease	
Protan–deutan defects: inner retinal layer disease	

genes involved in this neural circuitry must code for mechanisms common to much of the brain, and consequently mutations in them have a greater chance of being lethal. In this respect the neural basis of color vision shares many principles common to all sensory neurobiology.

Selected Readings and References

Boynton, R. M. 1979. Human Color Vision. New York: Holt, Rinehart and Winston.

Hurvich, L. M. 1972. Color vision deficiencies. In D. Jameson and L. M. Hurvich (eds.), Handbook of Sensory Physiology, Vol. 7, Part 4. New York: Springer, pp. 582–624.

Land, E. H. 1977. The retinex theory of color vision. Sci. Am. 237(6):108–128.

Stiles, W. S. 1978. Mechanisms of Colour Vision. New York: Academic.

Wald, G. 1964. The receptors of human color vision. Science (Wash., D.C.) 145:1007–1016.

Other References

Gouras, P., and Krüger, J. 1979. Responses of cells in foveal visual cortex of the monkey to pure color contrast. J. Neurophysiol. 42:850–860.

Marks, W. B., Dobelle, W. H., and Mac Nichol, Jr., E. F. 1964. Visual pigments of single primate cones. Science (Wash., D.C.) 143:1181–1183.

Michael, C. R. 1978a. Color vision mechanisms in monkey striate cortex: Dual-opponent cells with concentric receptive fields. J. Neurophysiol. 41:572–588.

Michael, C. R. 1978b. Color vision mechanisms in monkey striate cortex: Simple cells with dual opponent-color receptive fields. J. Neurophysiol. 41: 1233–1249.

Rubin, M. L., and Walls, G. L. 1969. Fundamentals of Visual Science. Springfield, Ill.: Thomas.

Smith, V. C., and Pokorny, J. 1972. Spectral sensitivity of color-blind observers and the cone photopigments. Vision Res. 12:2059–2071.

Zeki, S. 1980. The representation of colours in the cerebral cortex. Nature (Lond.) 284:412–418.

James P. Kelly

Auditory System

23

Well over 100 years ago, G. S. Ohm, who gave his name to Ohm's law, recognized the basic principle governing the function of the ear. He proposed that complex sounds, such as speech, are broken down by the ear into simple and discrete vibrations for subsequent analysis by the brain. In effect, Ohm suggested that the ear performs a Fourier analysis on complex, air-borne sound waves by breaking them down into a number of basic frequency components of different amplitudes and phases. The results of modern research on the auditory system support Ohm's original idea, and a major segment of this chapter will be devoted to the mechanisms used by the ear to perform this Fourier transformation on incoming sounds. It should be made clear at the outset, however, that the auditory system does much more than carry out a frequency analysis. To appreciate this, consider the following situation. Imagine that you are viewing the surface of a pond through a narrow tube of the same diameter as the external auditory meatus. If two individuals were then to drop small rocks in different regions of the pond, you would see a resultant complex wave through the tube. It would be very difficult for you to say where the rocks were being tossed into the pond, and at what rate. This is just the kind of analysis the ear performs on complex sound waves propagated through air. In a concert hall, for example, the sound of musical instruments, the voices of men and women, the movement of clothing, all intermingle. However, the auditory system can distinguish the separate constituent parts of this complicated auditory environment. The way in which the brain carries out this task is the subject of this chapter.

We shall begin by considering the peripheral conductive apparatus associated with the middle ear, then go on to study the cochlea of the inner ear, and, finally, the organization and function of pathways associated with hearing in the central nervous system. (Other aspects of the auditory system will be considered in Chapter 35 in the discussion of the vestibular system.)

The Conductive Apparatus Is Necessary for Normal Hearing

To understand the nature of sound itself, consider a simple sinusoidal wave (Figure 23–1). The sinusoid consists of regularly alternating condensations and rarefactions of the air that could be produced, for example, by the vibration of a speaker cone. The *frequency* of the wave measured in cycles per second or hertz (Hz) determines its pitch. Low-frequency waves correspond to tones of low pitch; for reference, middle C is a tone with a fundamental frequency of 512 Hz. The *amplitude* of the wave is correlated with its loudness, and a special scale, the decibel scale, is used to measure this aspect of sound. A decibel (db) is defined as follows:

$$1\text{dB} = 20 \log P_t/P_r.$$

where P_t is the test pressure and P_r is the reference pressure (2×10^{-4} dynes/cm²). This log scale

was devised by Alexander Graham Bell, the inventor of the telephone, and is used because we are sensitive to sound over an enormous range of different amplitudes. The *reference pressure (P_r)* in the equation above is that sound pressure which is required to make a sound of 3,000 Hz (human hearing is most acute near this frequency) just audible. A test sound *(P_t)* 10 times louder than this *($P_t = 10 \ P_r$)* would have a pressure level 10 times greater, and would be a sound of 20 dB (dB = $20 \log P_t/P_r = 20 \log 10 \ P_r/P_r = 20 \log 10 = 20$). A test sound 100 times P_r *($P_t = 100 \ P_r$)* in pressure would be a sound of 40 dB (dB = $20 \log P_t/P_r = 20 \log 100 \ P_r/P_r = 20 \log 100 = 40$). A sound 1000 times P_r would be 60 dB, and so on. It is important to note the enormous range of sound intensity detectable by the human ear. The dynamic range of the ear is about 120 dB, so that the faintest sound we can detect is about one-millionth the amplitude of the loudest sound the ear could process without actual discomfort.

The human ear is sensitive to a limited range of sound frequency from about 20 to 20,000 Hz. Air-borne sounds strike the *tympanic membrane* at the end of the external auditory meatus, and the resultant motion of the membrane is conveyed to the *oval window of the cochlea* by a lever system composed of three ossicles: the mal-

23–1 Sinusoidal sound wave. The ambient pressure in the air is measured with a microphone probe at a fixed point as a sound wave propagates through space. The speed of sound is a constant in air (approximately 1100 ft/sec) and is related to both the wavelength and frequency of the wave as shown in the equation above. The tympanic membrane of the ear moves in response to the alternating condensations (peaks) and rarefactions (troughs) of the sound wave.

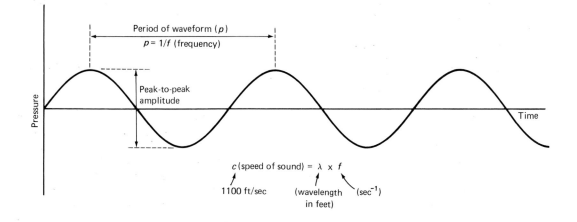

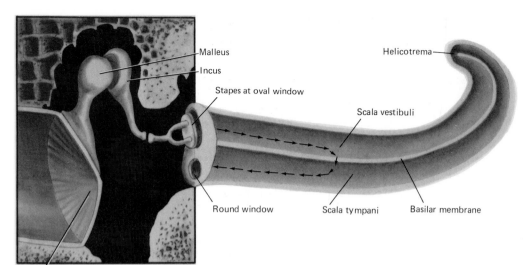

Malleus

Incus

Stapes at oval window

Helicotrema

Scala vestibuli

Round window

Scala tympani

Basilar membrane

Tympanic membrane

23–2 Schematic view of the auditory periphery. The tympanic membrane is joined to a chain of three ossicles in the middle ear, the malleus, incus and stapes. Motion of the tympanic membrane eventually causes motion of the stapes and sets up a propagated wave in the fluid-filled cochlea. Changes in fluid pressure in the cochlea are possible because both the oval window, where the stapes sits, and the round window, are flexible membranes, so that pushing the oval window inward would cause the round window to bulge into the middle ear cavity. The two scalae of the cochlea communicate with each other at the helicotrema.

leus, incus, and stapes (Figure 23–2). This baroque arrangement of membranes and bones has an important function. If sound were to strike the oval window (where the stapes sits) directly, most of the energy in the sound wave would be reflected and lost since the cochlea is fluid filled. In other words, there is an impedance-matching problem between air-borne sounds and fluid motion within the cochlea. Both the tympanic membrane and the ossicles are arranged to counteract this matching problem. First, the area of the tympanic membrane is 25 times greater than the area of the oval window, and as a consequence the force striking the relatively large tympanic membrane is concentrated on the smaller oval window. There is thus a net increase in the force of the movement caused initially by air-borne sound, but the amplitude of the movement at the oval window is decreased. Second, the ossicular chain acts as a lever system that also decreases the amplitude of movement, but increases its

force by a factor of 1.3 to 1. The total gain in force/unit area achieved by the conductance mechanism of the middle ear is a factor of about 18 times. This increase in force enables air-borne sound waves to propagate effectively through the fluid-filled cochlea. It should be pointed out that middle ear structures have a *resonant frequency* of about 3,000 Hz, which accounts in large part for the fact that human hearing is most acute in this range.

Sounds may reach the cochlea directly by *bone conduction,* that is, by vibration of the entire temporal bone, but this is an inefficient means of sound transfer and it becomes important only if the middle ear ossicles are malfunctioning. In *otosclerosis,* for example, the footplate of the stapes becomes locked in situ due to an abnormal growth of the annular ligament (this ligament binds the stapes to the oval window). Patients with otosclerosis actually hear better by bone conduction than by the normal route of air conduction.

The Cochlea Transduces Sound Waves into Electrical Potentials

The motion of the stapes causes a wavelike motion of the fluid in the scalae of the cochlea and in turn initiates the motion of the *basilar membrane* (Figure 23–2). The pressure wave eventually exits at the *round window.* The fluid motion caused by the pressure wave in the cochlea also affects the *organ of Corti,* which rests on top of the basilar membrane. The structure of the organ of Corti is quite complicated (Figure 23–3). How-

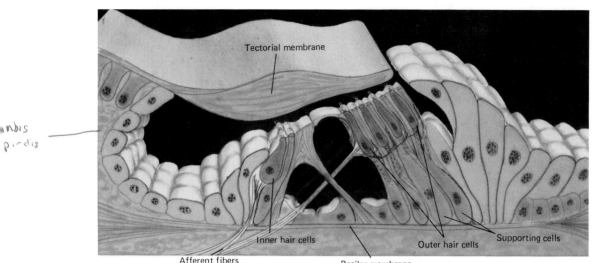

Tectorial membrane

Inner hair cells

Outer hair cells

Supporting cells

Afferent fibers

Basilar membrane

23-3 Reconstruction of the organ of Corti. Afferent fibers innervate the bases of the inner and outer hair cells. These nerve fibers have cell bodies in the spiral ganglion. The whole organ of Corti rests on the basilar membrane, and contains hair cells that are surrounded by an elaborate network of supporting cells. The hair cells project their apical microvilli or hairs toward the overlying tectorial membrane and make contact with it. (Adapted from Wersäll et al, 1965.)

ever, since the functional roles of many facets of this structure are not completely understood at this time, we shall concentrate on a few morphological features that are most likely to be of significance for the transduction process. A simple model of the cochlea shows that rows of hair cells rest upon the basilar membrane. The apical surface of each hair cell is thrown into a number of microvilli or "hairs," and hence the name of this cell type (Figure 23–4). There are four rows of hair cells, one inner and three outer, but the physiological differences between them remain unknown. Each hair cell projects its apical hairs into the overlying *tectorial membrane*. One theory of cochlear function suggests that as the basilar membrane moves, a net shearing force is produced upon the microvilli of the hair cells since the tectorial membrane does not move to the same degree (Figure 23–5). A potential change occurs in the hair cells, probably as a result of this shearing motion. This potential change then leads to activity in the fibers of the eighth nerve, which synapse at the bases of the hair cells.

The basilar membrane itself is not a uniform physical structure; it is narrow (100 µm) and taut near the stapes, and wider (500 µm) and more floppy near the apex of the cochlea (Figure 23–6). In the 19th century Helmholtz noted this variation in structure and, with characteristic insight (he formulated the law of conservation of energy while he was a surgical resident in the army), proposed that different portions of the basilar membrane resonate with different frequencies of

sound, much as piano strings do. The taut part of the basilar membrane near the oval window would, in this view, resonate with high frequencies (approximately 15,000 Hz), while the loose, wider part of the membrane near the apex would vibrate with low frequencies (approximately 200 Hz). Between these extreme points, a continuous resonance spectrum would exist, running from high frequencies at the base of the cochlea to low frequencies nearer the apex. In 1960, Georg von Békésy proved that this viewpoint was not precisely correct. By direct observation of the motion of the basilar membrane in response to sound, he showed that a *traveling wave* moves along the membrane, starting at the oval window. However, the *peak motion* of the basilar membrane in response to sounds of different frequencies does occur at the points predicted by Helmholtz (Figure 23–7). Therefore, there is a *mechanical processing* of signals in the cochlea. A signal composed of many frequencies will cause several different points along the basilar membrane to vibrate and will excite hair cells at these points. The variation in the mechanical properties of the

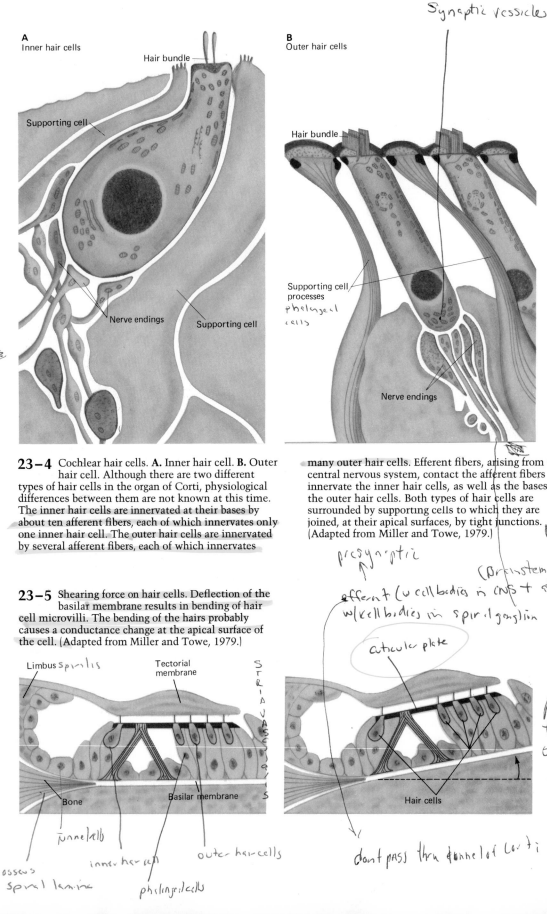

A Inner hair cells

Hair bundle

Supporting cell

Nerve endings

Supporting cell

B Outer hair cells

Synaptic vessicles *(handwritten)*

Hair bundle

Supporting cell processes

phalangeal cells *(handwritten)*

Nerve endings

23–4 Cochlear hair cells. **A.** Inner hair cell. **B.** Outer hair cell. Although there are two different types of hair cells in the organ of Corti, physiological differences between them are not known at this time. The inner hair cells are innervated at their bases by about ten afferent fibers, each of which innervates only one inner hair cell. The outer hair cells are innervated by several afferent fibers, each of which innervates many outer hair cells. Efferent fibers, arising from the central nervous system, contact the afferent fibers that innervate the inner hair cells, as well as the bases of the outer hair cells. Both types of hair cells are surrounded by supporting cells to which they are joined, at their apical surfaces, by tight junctions. (Adapted from Miller and Towe, 1979.)

presynaptic (handwritten)

post synaptic (handwritten)

efferent (w cell bodies in CNS + afferent VIII (Brainstem) w(cell bodies in spiral ganglion (handwritten)

cuticular plate (handwritten)

pass thru tunnel of corti (handwritten)

23–5 Shearing force on hair cells. Deflection of the basilar membrane results in bending of hair cell microvilli. The bending of the hairs probably causes a conductance change at the apical surface of the cell. (Adapted from Miller and Towe, 1979.)

Limbus *spiralis (handwritten)*

Tectorial membrane

S T R I A V A S C U L A R I S

Bone

Basilar membrane

Hair cells

Tunnel cells (handwritten)

inner hair cell (handwritten)

outer hair cells (handwritten)

osseus spiral lamina (handwritten)

phalangeal cells (handwritten)

dont pass thru tunnel of corti (handwritten)

VIII (handwritten, left margin)

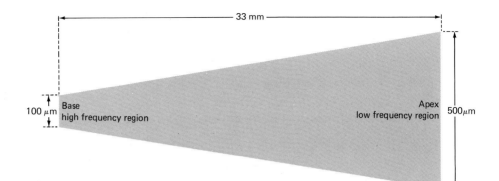

23-6 Dimensions of the basilar membrane. In this surface view, the basilar membrane is shown diagrammatically as if it were uncoiled and stretched out flat.

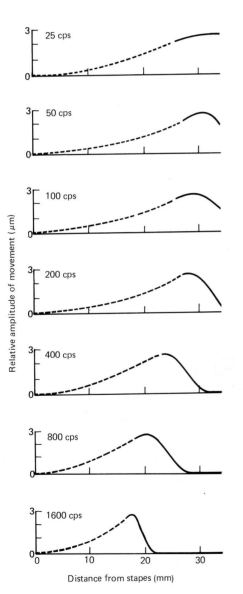

23-7 Peak motion of the basilar membrane in response to sounds of different frequencies. Even though the stimuli used by von Békésy were very loud (approximately 120 dB) the peak motion of the basilar membrane was only 3 μm or so. The actual data observed in the experiment are indicated by the smooth line; the dashed line is an extrapolation based on the observed measurements. Note that a very broad region of the basilar membrane moves in response to stimulation at a single frequency. As the frequency of the stimulus increases, the peak motion moves progressively toward the base of the cochlea. Because these measurements were made in cadavers, they may not be a completely accurate reflection of the type of movement occurring in the living cochlea. (Adapted from von Békésy, 1960.)

basilar membrane along its length accounts for the fact that different regions of it vibrate maximally at different frequencies.

The Cochlea Is Innervated by Fibers of the Eighth Nerve

The *spiral ganglion* is unusual. It is composed of myelinated bipolar neurons lying in the *modiolus*, or bony hub of the cochlea. There are about 30,000 spiral ganglion cells in the human cochlea. The peripheral processes of these cells run toward the organ of Corti. Most (90%) of the fibers innervate the inner hair cells; each inner hair cell (there are approximately 3000 in total) receives contacts from about 10 fibers and each fiber contacts only 1 inner hair cell. The remaining 10% of the peripherally directed processes innervate the outer hair cells; each of these fibers diverges to innervate many outer hair cells. Efferent fibers coming from the central nervous system also synapse upon outer hair cells and upon the afferent axons innervating inner hair cells, but the function of the efferent fibers remains unknown.

Given that the majority of spiral ganglion cells innervate a restricted portion of the basilar membrane only a single hair cell in width, it is not surprising that eighth-nerve fibers, the centrally directed branches of the ganglion cells, display a frequency-dependent response to sound. A *tuning curve* can be established by measuring the number of impulses produced by a single eighth-nerve fiber in response to brief pulses of sound at various frequencies. This is a plot of the amplitude of sound required to produce a detectable response versus the frequency of the sound stimulus. An individual fiber will respond to a range of frequencies since a substantial portion of the basilar membrane moves in response to a single frequency of sound even at moderate intensities (Figure 23–7). A single fiber, however, is most sensitive to a particular frequency, called its *characteristic frequency*. This is directly related to the region of the basilar membrane the fiber innervates; fibers innervating the part of the basilar membrane near the oval window have high characteristic frequencies, while those innervating the part of the basilar membrane near the apex of the cochlea have low characteristic frequencies. A sample tuning curve for an eighth-nerve fiber with a 2-kHz characteristic frequency is shown in Figure 23–8.

The time structure of the response to a brief tone burst at the characteristic frequency is very similar from one eighth-nerve fiber to the next.

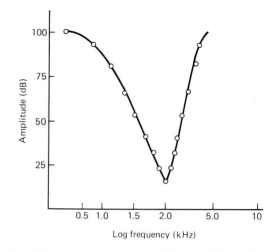

23–8 Tuning curve for an eighth nerve fiber with a characteristic frequency of 2 kHz. The fiber will give a response that is just detectable when stimulated with a 2 kHz tone at about 15 dB. If the amplitude of the 2 kHz tone is increased then the fiber will give a more pronounced response. At other frequencies, at about 1.5 kHz, a much louder sound of nearly 55 dB is required to get a just detectable response.

There is an initial phasic increase in firing above the spontaneous level, followed by a maintained tonic discharge that persists for the duration of the tone. When the tone is turned off, there is a transient decrease in firing below the spontaneous level before the fiber returns to its resting state (Figure 23–9).

An interesting feature of the individual neuronal responses is that they are probabilistic in occurrence. A particular stimulus will not always elicit precisely the same response upon re-

23–9 Time structure of an eighth nerve fiber response to a pure tone.

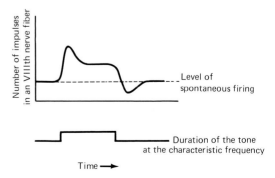

Tone burst level in dB

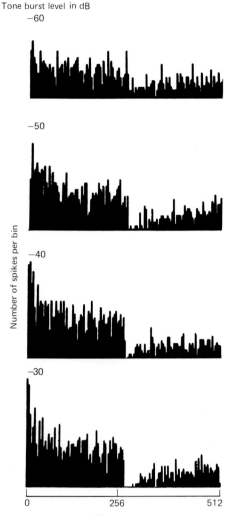

-60

-50

-40

-30

Number of spikes per bin

0   256   512

Time, msec

23–10 Poststimulus time histograms showing
response patterns of a unit to tone bursts as a
function of stimulus level. Zero time of each
histogram is 2.5 msec before the onset of the electrical
input to the earphone. Stimuli: tone bursts, 5.8 kHz
(the characteristic frequency of the unit), 250-msec
duration, 2.5-msec rise–fall time. The stimulus is
followed by a quiet period lasting 250 msec, then
repeated again, and this is done for a period of 2 min.
The important pattern to observe is the initial phasic
increase in firing correlated with the onset of the
stimulus, the maintained discharge during the course
of the stimulus, and the decrease in activity following
termination. There is a gradual return to baseline
activity during the inter-stimulus interval. (Adapted
from Kiang, 1965.)

peated presentation. A useful way to study these
responses, therefore, is to indicate their average
characteristics. This can be done by preparing a
poststimulus time (PST) histogram of the averaged responses of a single eighth-nerve fiber to
many stimuli. A poststimulus time histogram is
a plot of the number of spikes versus time, relative to the beginning of the stimulus. Each
stimulus is repeated many times in order to study
the average response. A sample poststimulus
time histogram is shown in Figure 23–10. The
stimulus was a 5.8-kHz tone, 250 msec in duration, which was repeated a large number of times
during a 2-min period to produce each histogram.
The amplitude of the stimulus was decreased in
successive 10-dB steps from the lowest histogram
to the uppermost. Note that the envelope of the
histogram in the lowest frame is similar to the
model curve of Figure 23–9; i.e., there is an initial onset burst, followed by a constant level of
firing, and finally a period of inhibition after the
tone is turned off. The response of the cell becomes progressively degraded in its time structure and magnitude as the amplitude of the
stimulus is decreased.

Some fibers with low characteristic frequencies (less than 2 kHz or so) can actually *phase
lock* to a pure tone stimulus. These neurons tend
to fire at a particular time during each cycle of the
sinusoid. Consequently, such fibers can indicate
the frequency of a stimulus on the basis of a *place
principle*, because they innervate the apex of the
cochlea, and also on the basis of a *volley principle*, since their discharges occur in a predictable
way relative to the stimulating waveform.

The Central Auditory Pathways Are
Organized Tonotopically

Auditory fibers in the eighth nerve terminate in
the *cochlear nucleus*, lying on the external aspect
of the restiform body (Figure 23–11). The
cochlear nucleus is divided into a *dorsal division*
and a *ventral division*. The entering auditory
nerve fibers pierce the ventral division of the
cochlear nucleus at about the middle of its rostrocaudal extent, thereby separating the ventral
division into an anteroventral cochlar nucleus
and a posteroventral cochlear nucleus. Each auditory nerve fiber branches as it enters the
cochlear nucleus. An *ascending branch* innervates the anteroventral nucleus, and a *descending branch* innervates the posteroventral cochlear
nucleus along with the dorsal cochlear nucleus.

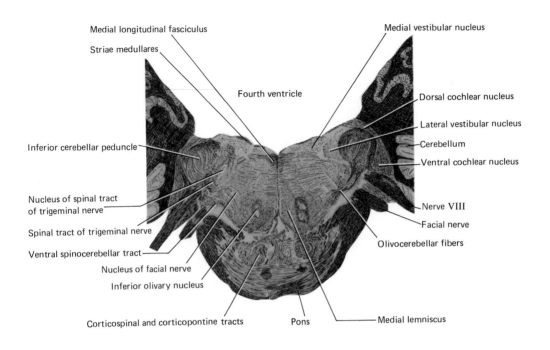

Medial longitudinal fasciculus

Striae medullares

Fourth ventricle

Medial vestibular nucleus

Dorsal cochlear nucleus

Lateral vestibular nucleus

Cerebellum

Ventral cochlear nucleus

Inferior cerebellar peduncle

Nucleus of spinal tract of trigeminal nerve

Spinal tract of trigeminal nerve

Ventral spinocerebellar tract

Nucleus of facial nerve

Inferior olivary nucleus

Corticospinal and corticopontine tracts

Pons

Nerve VIII

Facial nerve

Olivocerebellar fibers

Medial lemniscus

23–11 Myelin-stained section through the lower pons, showing the location of the cochlear nucleus. It lies on the external aspect of the restiform body. (Adapted from Ranson and Clark, 1953.)

23–12 Organization of the cochlear nucleus. The three divisions of the cochlear nucleus receive input from the eighth nerve. The nerve fibers are arranged in an orderly sequence, so that a tonotopic map is established in the nucleus.

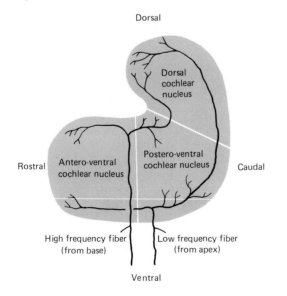

Dorsal

Dorsal cochlear nucleus

Rostral

Antero-ventral cochlear nucleus

Postero-ventral cochlear nucleus

Caudal

High frequency fiber (from base)

Low frequency fiber (from apex)

Ventral

The various subdivisions of the cochlear nucleus contain different cell types. It appears that each auditory nerve fiber makes a morphologically different type of contact with distinct cell types in each division of the cochlear nucleus.

In view of the cellular diversity of the cochlear nucleus, it is reasonable to expect a variety of physiological response types to be found within the confines of the nucleus. In addition to cells that respond to tone bursts in a manner very similar to the primary eighth-nerve fibers, there are cells that respond only to the *onset* of the stimulus, some whose rate of firing *builds up* slowly during the course of the stimulus, and others that *pause,* showing no response at all to the onset of the stimulus. These different physiological cell types are located in different parts of the cochlear nucleus. Therefore, it is likely that they correspond to particular morphological cell types, but hard proof of this correspondence at the cellular level is not yet available.

Probably the most important principle governing the topography of the cochlear nucleus is the *tonotopic organization* of its cells and fibers (Figure 23–12). Primary auditory fibers from the base of the cochlea penetrate deeply into the nucleus before branching to terminate in its three principal divisions. Primary fibers from the apex of the cochlea branch at more superficial levels in the nucleus. Consequently, each part of the nucleus shows a *tonotopic order.* This can be studied by making a long penetration with a microelectrode through the nucleus while recording the characteristic frequency of each cell encountered. If the path of the electrode is marked, then each cell recorded from can be assigned a particular location in the nucleus. Such experiments have demonstrated that each division of the cochlear nucleus possesses a regular tonotopic organization. All of the central auditory nuclei, including the auditory cortex, appear to be organized on this basis.

There Is Bilateral Representation of Each Cochlea in the Brain

The ascending connections of the cochlear nuclei are somewhat bewildering to the beginning student because of the enormous number of brain stem auditory nuclei and the myriad possibilities for interconnections among them. In the following account, the essential points will be stressed at the expense of fine detail.

As shown in Figure 23–13, the axons of cells in the cochlear nucleus stream out along three pathways, the *dorsal acoustic stria*, the *intermediate acoustic stria*, and the *trapezoid body*. By far the most important route is the trapezoid body. It contains fibers destined for *superior olivary complex* on both sides of the brain stem. The *medial superior olive* is an interesting structure. It is composed of spindle-shaped cells with one medial and one lateral dendrite; these dendrites receive input from the contralateral and ipsilat-

eral cochlear nuclei, respectively. These *binaural cells* are exquisitely sensitive to differences in the time of arrival of auditory stimuli to the two ears. Because this *time difference* cue is one of the cues used to localize sounds in space, the medial superior olive is most probably concerned with this physiological task. The *lateral superior olive*

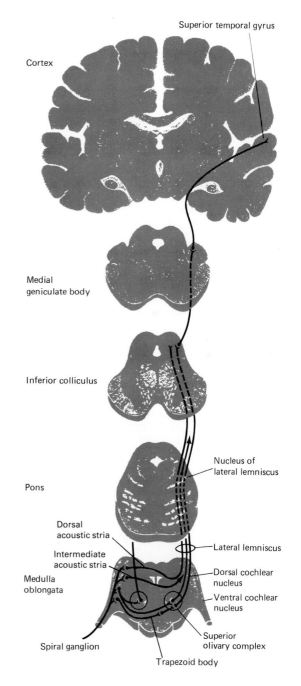

23–13 Organization of the central auditory pathways. Postsynaptic neurons in the cochlear nucleus send their axons to other centers in the brain via three main pathways: (1) the dorsal acoustic stria, (2) the intermediate acoustic stria, and (3) the trapezoid body. The first binaural interactions occur in the superior olivary complex, which receives input via the trapezoid body. The medial and lateral divisions of the superior olivary complex are probably involved in the localization of sounds in space. The neurons of the medial division receive direct input from both cochlear nuclei and compare interaural differences in the time of sound arrival, one of the cues used in localization. Postsynaptic axons from the superior olive, along with axons from the cochlear nuclei, form the *lateral lemniscus*, which ascends to the midbrain. Axons relaying input from both ears are found in each lateral lemniscus. The axons synapse in the inferior colliculus, and postsynaptic cells in the colliculus send their axons to the medial geniculate body of the thalamus. The geniculate axons terminate in the superior temporal gyrus (Brodmann's areas 41 and 42), also called the primary auditory cortex. (Adapted from Brodal, 1981.)

is also concerned with localizing sounds in space. Cells in this nucleus detect interaural *differences in sound intensity,* a cue used to localize high-frequency sounds.

Axons arising from the superior olivary complex, along with crossed and uncrossed axons from the cochlear nucleus, run together to form the *lateral lemniscus.* From the onset there is extensive bilateral representation of each ear in the central nervous system. Consequently, *lesion of the central auditory pathway does not give rise to monoaural deficits.* The lateral lemniscus courses through the *nuclei of the lateral lemniscus,* where some fibers synapse. Here again there is extensive crossing between the two sides via *Probst's commissure.* All fibers in the lateral lemniscus eventually synapse in the *inferior colliculus.* The cells of the inferior colliculus receive binaural input and show a very orderly tonotopic organization. Most of them send their axons to the *medial geniculate body* of the thalamus on the same side of brain, but some project contralaterally. The cells in the medial geniculate body send their axons to the homolateral *auditory cortex* located in the superior temporal gyrus. The auditory cortex also shows a relatively precise tonotopic organization. Unilateral lesions of this part of the cerebral cortex do not disrupt auditory perception dramatically, as one might suspect because of the bilateral representation of each ear, but such lesions do affect the ability to localize sounds in space.

The auditory cortex of each hemisphere uses the cues of interaural differences in sound intensity and interaural differences in the time of sound arrival to localize the position of a sound source. An individual hemisphere is concerned principally with localizing sounds coming from the contralateral auditory hemifield; i.e., the auditory cortex on the right side is important for localizing sounds arising from the left hemifield. Only large lesions of the auditory cortex affect sound-localizing ability to a significant extent. The auditory cortex is therefore somewhat different from the visual cortex, where even small lesions produce noticeable deficits *(scotomata)* in the perception of the visual field.

Finally, there is an extensive set of *distal feedback connections* in the auditory system. Some cells in the auditory cortex send their axons back to the medial geniculate body, and some back to the inferior colliculus. The inferior colliculus in turn sends recurrent fibers to the cochlear nucleus. In the region around the superior olivary complex, there are cells that give rise to the efferent *olivocochlear bundle,* which terminates either on the hair cells of the cochlea directly, or on the afferent fibers, innervating them. Although the function of the recurrent connections is not yet understood, they could provide a basis for selective attention to particular sounds.

Selected Readings and References

Brodal, A. 1981. Neurological Anatomy. 3rd ed. New York: Oxford University Press, Chap. 9.

Goldstein, Jr., M. H. 1980. The auditory periphery. In V. B. Mountcastle (ed.), Medical Physiology, 14th ed., Vol. 1. St. Louis: Mosby, pp. 428–456.

Helmholtz, H. L. F. 1877. On the Sensations of Tone. 2nd Eng. ed. New York: Dover, 1954.

Kiang, N. Y.-S. 1965. Discharge Patterns of Single Fibers in the Cat's Auditory Nerve. Cambridge, Mass.: MIT Press.

Other References

Miller, J. M., and Towe, A. L. 1979. Audition: Structural and acoustical properties. In T. Ruch, and H. D. Patton (eds.), Physiology and Biophysics. 20th ed. Philadelphia: Saunders, pp. 339–375.

Ranson, S. W., and Clark, S. L. 1953. The Anatomy of the Nervous System. 9th ed. Philadelphia: Saunders.

von Békésy, G. 1960. Experiments in Hearing. New York: McGraw-Hill.

Wersäll, J., Flock, Å., and Lundquist, P.-G. 1965. Structural basis for directional sensitivity in cochlear and vestibular sensory receptors. Cold Spring Harbor Symp. Quant. Biol. 30:115–132.

Motor Systems of the Brain: Reflex and Voluntary Control of Movement

IV

This section is concerned with what Sherrington called the "integrative action" of the nervous system. To Sherrington, one of the most important features of nervous function was the way that motor output is regulated so that an organism can effectively achieve a *single purpose* at any given time (even when presented with conflicting stimuli). He was therefore interested in the mechanisms responsible for functionally yoking together diverse parts of the nervous system to give this highly focused and purposeful mode of action. Sherrington correctly recognized that intrinsic spinal reflexes provide the simplest expression of this integration, and he devoted much of his long career to analyzing their interactions and basic principles of operation.

As we have seen in Part III, the spinal cord is an important sensory structure. Through its motor neurons and their associated interneuronal circuits, the spinal cord also provides the final output for voluntary as well as reflex actions. Thus, spinal mechanisms are critical for refined execution of all movements of the segmental musculature.

Physiological studies on the motor cortex have, in turn, revealed some of the detailed relationships between general cortical organization and motor cortical function in the quantitative control of voluntary movements. Moreover, the many important functions of the basal ganglia and their disturbance by disease are now beginning to be understood in terms of transmitter pharmacology and biochemistry. From this, we are learning that other neurological and psychiatric disorders may also originate in the altered functioning of different components of specific chemical transmitter systems such as transmitter synthesis, transport, release, and interaction with the postsynaptic receptor.

Claude Ghez

Introduction
to the Motor Systems

The motor systems of the brain and spinal cord provide us with the ability to move and thereby to act upon our ever changing environment. In the section on sensory systems we saw how physical energies are translated by receptors and neurons into a language of impulses and synaptic potentials. This language allows the different parts of the brain to communicate with each other and to abstract and analyze the features of the physical world. The motor systems of the brain and spinal cord are in a sense concerned with the reverse process. Here, according to the purpose to be achieved, computations performed by the brain on current and previously stored information lead to sets of instructions or commands that are translated into physical energy. This transformation is accomplished at the neuromuscular junction and in muscles that generate contractile force in response to nerve impulses ending in motor neurons. Thus, all processing and commands arising in the brain must be conveyed to a single target: the large alpha motor neurons located in the brain stem and spinal cord. To emphasize their importance Charles Sherrington called the alpha motor neurons the "final common path." The activity of the alpha motor neurons in the ventral horn of the spinal cord alone governs the state of contraction of our skeletal muscles. As Sherrington, the founder of modern motor physiology, has put it: "To move is all mankind can do and for such, the sole executant is muscle, whether in whispering a syllable or in felling a forest."

Although perception and movement are distinct goals of neural integration, the underlying sensory and motor mechanisms are intimately related and functionally interdependent. Sensation provides us with the information necessary to direct our movements toward particular points in space and can trigger complete sequences of motor responses. In addition, the state of activity of different sensory receptors keeps the central nervous system informed about the position of the body and limbs. In a larger sense, the major function of neural processing is to articulate the transfer of sensory information from afferent pathways to motor neurons in order to accomplish a particular purpose. We therefore need to understand how the central nervous system integrates information impinging upon it and coordinates its output to produce our varied repertoire of motor abilities. In this and subsequent chapters we shall examine the various components of the motor system and learn how these components are acted upon by sensory input to produce both postural adjustments and skilled movements.

There Are Three Requirements for Neural Integration in Motor Systems

Before dealing with the various components of the motor systems and the neural circuits responsible for different movements, let us consider the tasks accomplished by neural integration. These are evident in three basic requirements.

First, information arising either from sensory receptors or from memory stores must ultimately be channeled to appropriate motor neurons; that is, sites on the body surface must be mapped topographically onto the different motor neuron pools innervating specific muscles. Because in different circumstances we are required to make different movements in response to stimuli applied at a particular location, the motor system must be able to *select* and to *switch* the direction of information flow (or impulse traffic).

Second, the nervous system must control accurately the degree of contraction of each muscle according to the intended purpose. Thus, when we are reaching for an object, sensory cues must tell us just how much to contract each one of our arm muscles.

Finally, the activities of a variety of different muscles must be coordinated. To bring a limb segment to a desired position it is not enough to contract a single group of muscles acting as prime movers (agonist muscles); antagonist muscles must also relax so that movement can take place with the least expenditure of energy. In addition, postural muscles must also contract: some to fix the proximal joints and others to prevent loss of balance. This overall spatiotemporal pattern of muscle activity is known as a *synergy*. Most activities of muscles occur without our being aware of them. For example, when one is in an upright position and one lifts an arm, muscles of the legs contract before those of the arm; this prevents a sudden shift in our center of gravity from causing us to fall over.

The Reflex Is an Elementary Model of Behavior

A particularly fruitful approach to understanding the basic principles of neural integration in motor systems has been the study of *reflexes.* These automatic, machinelike behavioral responses that are elicited by particular types of sensory stimuli have preoccupied scientists since Descartes. An example is the *knee jerk*, a contraction of the quadriceps muscle after a sharp tap to a point just below the kneecap. In this reflex the tap produces a sudden stretch of the quadriceps and transient activation of receptors in the muscles. This results in a sudden barrage of impulses into the central nervous system that is conveyed directly to the motor neurons of the same muscle and to its synergists (*synergists* are muscles acting together at the same joint and having similar mechanical action). In other reflexes, one or more interneurons may be interposed between the primary afferent fibers and the motor neurons. Interneurons are present in all reflexes produced by stimulation of cutaneous mechanoreceptors. An example is the abdominal reflex, in which stroking of the skin of the abdomen evokes a brief contraction of the underlying muscles.

Since the time of Descartes it has been conventional to distinguish reflexes from voluntary responses. In general, reflexes are characterized by a fixed spatial relationship between the locus of a stimulus and the particular muscles that contract. This specific topographic relationship is known as *local sign*. In addition, the intensity of the stimulation governs that of the response. In voluntary actions the relationship between the location of a sensory stimulus and the particular muscles that contract may be arbitrary and the quantitative relationship between the two depends only on the purpose to be achieved. For example, if an object that we are holding suddenly moves in a given direction, we can either resist the movement imposed on our arm or follow the stimulus, contracting different muscle groups.

By the end of the last century, after a variety of reflexes had been identified, Sherrington began a systematic analysis of their properties. Studies of the mechanisms of reflex function are still pursued today, but at a cellular level. These cellular studies, especially those of Sir John Eccles in Australia and Anders Lundberg and his colleagues in Sweden, have shown that spinal interneurons constitute an important set of networks for processing both peripheral inputs and commands descending from higher brain centers. The properties of these networks ultimately determine the pattern and sequence of impulses distributed to different pools of motor neurons. These networks can, for example, transform a steady input (i.e., at steady frequency) into rhythmic patterns of im-

pulses conveyed to different muscle groups. Such a situation occurs in locomotor rhythms, which we shall consider in Chapter 28. Because these networks are shared by a variety of input systems (both peripheral and central), central commands can also select the action a given peripheral input may have at a given time. For example, cutaneous stimuli applied to the foot during walking can have different reflex effects depending upon when they occur relative to the rhythmic lifting and lowering of the leg. Reflex actions are dependent not only on current context, but also on the subject's recent experience. A most striking example is the recent discovery that the direction of the vestibulo-ocular reflex (which produces movement of the eyes when the head is turned and maintains gaze on a target; see Chapter 34) may be changed when a subject has been adapted to wearing spectacles with reversing prisms (which reverse right and left visual fields). The mechanisms by which such adaptive changes (or motor learning) take place present fascinating problems that are now being studied (see Chapters 30 and 34). Because reflexes are not necessarily as stereotyped as they were once thought to be, the distinction between reflexes and instinctive and voluntary acts has become blurred.

Interneuronal networks in the spinal cord which are involved in reflex actions, as well as other components of the motor systems which contribute to voluntary movement, give rise to *central motor programs*. These central programs can produce complex sequences of commands to different muscles. Once initiated, central programs can operate without further peripheral input. Nevertheless, the central programs responsible for a variety of motor acts can also utilize and incorporate ongoing sensory information effectively.

Neuronal Connections Can Form Both Divergent and Convergent Patterns

Most axons of individual neurons send off multiple branches, known as *collaterals*, that form connections with several target neurons (Figure 24–1A). This pattern of *divergence* allows individual neurons to influence the activity of many other neurons to different degrees since the number of synaptic terminals on each of the target neurons may be different.

Similarly, all neurons receive converging inputs from a variety of different sources and their activity reflects the sum of excitatory and in-

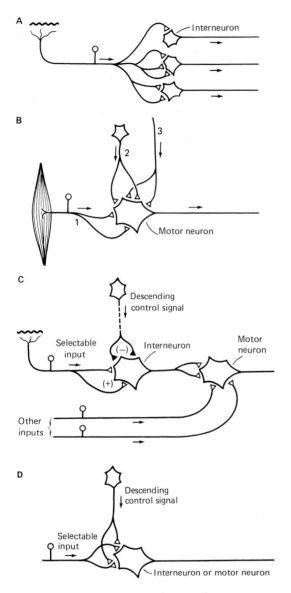

24-1 Elementary patterns of neuronal connections.
A. Divergence. Collaterals of a single neuron synapse on several target neurons. **B.** Convergence. The activity of a single neuron, for example a motor neuron shown here, depends upon the sum of inputs from afferent fibers *(1)*, interneurons *(2)*, and descending fibers from supraspinal regions *(3)*.
C. Gating by interneurons. Inhibitory command, direct or via an intercalated inhibitory interneuron (not shown), can prevent peripheral input from discharging interneuron acting on motor neuron. **D.** Gating by presynaptic inhibition. Descending command can control afferent input by acting on presynaptic terminals of afferent fibers.

hibitory influences (postsynaptic potentials) prevailing at the time. Thus the activity of spinal motor neurons and interneurons depends on the sum of the several inputs impinging upon them from afferent fibers, from interneurons, and from descending fibers from supraspinal regions (Figure 24–1B).

The presence of converging peripheral and descending synapses on spinal neurons allows for a great deal of flexibility in the way that the central nervous system can influence motor neuron activity. Subliminal excitatory influences from descending pathways on a motor neuron (which depolarize the cell without making it fire) can facilitate the action of a concurrent peripheral input. In this way the strength of a reflex can be increased. Descending inhibitory influences on motor neurons have the opposite effect and lead to a decrease in reflex strength.

The control descending pathways exert on the final motor response (reflected in muscle tension) differs fundamentally when that control is exerted through interneurons from when it is exerted directly on motor neurons. For example, when a constant peripheral input produces a steady resting discharge of a population of motor neurons, any change in the level of excitatory or inhibitory descending drive to the motor neurons will result in a change in motor neuron activity and in a corresponding change in muscle tension. In contrast, descending pathways that engage spinal interneurons can either enhance or suppress specific reflex actions without a change in muscle tension. For example, a descending inhibitory control signal, acting as a command, can be switched on or off without affecting the motor neuron output. Here the group of interneurons can act as a gate which either enables or prevents peripheral input from having an effect on motor neuron output (Figure 24–1C). The descending command only implements the inherent capability to respond in the presence of an input. Gating by interneurons allows the automatic control of a variety of responses without the need for processing information or making decisions in the brief time interval between stimulus and response. Similar gating can be achieved by presynaptic actions on the terminals of afferent fibers (Figure 24–1D). Indeed, the axons composing many descending pathways terminate as axo-axonic contacts with primary afferent fibers and can inhibit presynaptically the transmission of afferent information.

The Major Components of the Motor Systems

The major components of the motor systems and their interrelationships are shown schematically in Figure 24–2. Incoming volleys arising from the activation of sensory receptors enter the spinal cord carried by primary afferent fibers. The axons act on segmental interneurons and motor neurons and thus generate reflex outputs mediated by the spinal cord. The neuronal networks of each segment connect to those of other segments through propriospinal neurons. Ascending pathways convey both raw and segmentally processed information to motor centers of the brain stem and, via the thalamic nuclei, to the cerebral cortex. Both the brain stem and cortical centers project back to the segmental networks and thereby both control reflex activity and produce skilled voluntary movements. The output of these supraspinal centers is influenced and ultimately integrated by the cerebellum and basal ganglia.

24–2 Major motor systems of the brain. Note that in this scheme **arrows** denote strong influences; they do not imply direct (monosynaptic) connections. Converging arrows do not necessarily imply convergence on the same individual neurons of the target structure. Crossing of pathways is not indicated.

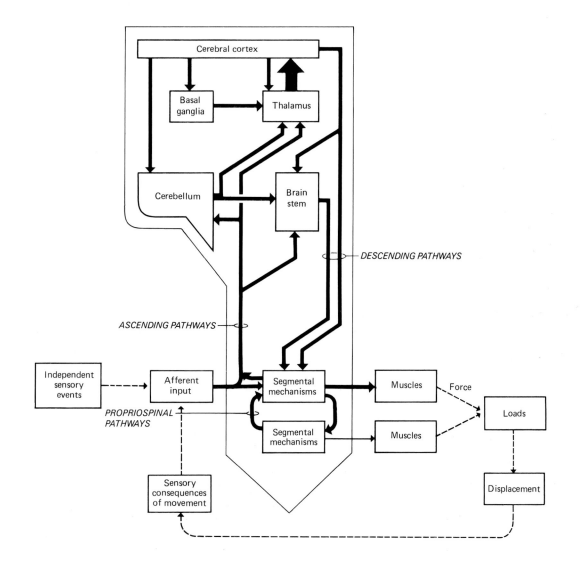

The only mechanical action that the nervous system can control directly is muscle tension or force. From a mechanical perspective, muscles can be represented as springs with some viscosity. When activated they act as springs whose stiffness has increased and whose resting length is shortened. The amount of displacement that will occur following a given neural excitation of a muscle is therefore strictly dependent on the nature and amount of opposing forces or loads. A variety of receptors (to be discussed in Chapter 25) sense the displacement of muscles and limbs and can influence the output at segmental or higher levels. Now we shall briefly consider each of the main components of the motor system.

Spinal Cord

Input and Output: Afferent Fibers and Motor Neurons

On entering the spinal cord, the axons of the dorsal root ganglion cells send terminal branches to all laminae of the dorsal horn except lamina II (Figure 24–3A). Some fibers continue within the intermediate zone and a small number of these reach the motor neuron cell groups of the ventral horn. There, the afferent fibers bifurcate and travel in rostral and caudal directions, sending off terminals at various segmental levels.

Within the ventral horn lie the motor neurons. Those innervating a single muscle are called a *motor neuron pool*. The various motor neuron pools are segregated into *longitudinal columns* extending through two to four spinal segments (Figure 24–3A). The dendrites of the motor neurons are also oriented rostrocaudally within the respective cell columns. This longitudinal orientation of motor neurons and their dendrites matches that of the primary afferent terminals in this zone. Thus, impulses in a given axon tend to be distributed to motor neurons innervating the same muscle or to muscles with similar function (this set of connections gives rise to the well-known stretch reflex discussed earlier). This anatomical arrangement correlates well with the physiological observation that the only afferent fibers synapsing directly on motor neurons (and arising from muscle spindle receptors) focus their action exclusively on motor neurons of a single muscle and on those of its synergists that are located nearby.

Two groups of motor neuron pools can be distinguished morphologically. One is located in the medial part of the ventral horn; the other, much larger, lies more laterally. Individual pools of motor neurons are spatially distributed in the spinal cord according to a strict functional rule: *those projecting to proximal muscles are located medially* and *those projecting to distal muscles are located dorsolaterally* within the ventral horn (Figure 24–3B). Thus, the motor neurons of the medial division of the motor neuron cell group innervate the axial muscle of the neck and back. The most medial motor neuron pools within the lateral division tend to innervate the muscles of the shoulder and pelvic girdles, while motor neuron pools located more dorsolaterally go to distal muscles of the extremities and the digits. In addition, motor neurons innervating extensor muscles tend to lie ventral to those innervating flexors (Figure 24–3B).

Interneurons and Propriospinal Neurons of the Intermediate Zone

The connections of the interneurons within the spinal intermediate zone produce a clear-cut polarization of the impulse traffic that courses through them (Figure 24–3B). The lateral parts of the intermediate zone project to the ipsilateral dorsolateral motor neuron cell groups that innervate distal limb muscles. The medial regions of the intermediate zone project bilaterally to the medial motor neuron cell groups innervating axial muscles on both sides. The areas in between project to the motor neurons innervating girdle muscles.

Some interneurons in the lateral, ventral, and medial portions of the intermediate zone give origin to axons that course up and down the spinal cord and terminate in homologous regions several segments away. These interconnecting interneurons are known as *propriospinal neurons* (Figure 24–3B). The corresponding propriospinal axons in the lateral columns (deriving from interneurons in the lateral parts of the intermediate zone) are short and extend only a few segments. Those in the ventral and ventromedial columns are longer (especially those arising from cervical segments) and may extend the entire length of the spinal cord.

Apart from the overall topographic organization, the connections made by the interneurons are precisely specified. *Particular populations of interneurons receive inputs from particular classes of afferent fibers* (group Ib, II, joint receptors, etc.) *which mediate specific reflexes*. Many of these interneurons also receive characteristic

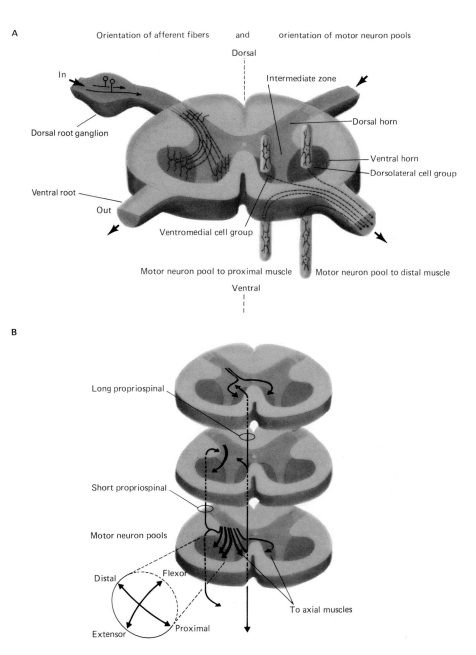

A

Orientation of afferent fibers   and   orientation of motor neuron pools

Dorsal

In

Intermediate zone

Dorsal horn

Dorsal root ganglion

Ventral horn

Dorsolateral cell group

Ventral root

Out

Ventromedial cell group

Motor neuron pool to proximal muscle   Motor neuron pool to distal muscle

Ventral

B

Long propriospinal

Short propriospinal

Motor neuron pools

Distal   Flexor

To axial muscles

Extensor   Proximal

connections from descending pathways (discussed in further detail in Chapters 32–36.) Recent evidence obtained by Lundberg and his colleagues indicates that in the cat short propriospinal neurons play a crucial role in mediating descending commands for quick limb movement.

All descending pathways ultimately terminate on neurons in the dorsal horn and intermediate zone and upon the motor neurons themselves. We shall first review the pathways originating from brain stem nuclei, which were the first to

24–3 Intrasegmental and intersegmental connections. **A.** Input–output organization of spinal segments and interconnections between segments. **B.** Projection patterns of interneurons and propriospinal neurons.

develop phylogenetically and have persisted with little change in different mammalian species. We shall then consider the pathways originating from the cortex. From a functional standpoint, as has been stressed by H. G. J. M. Kuypers, it is most useful to consider these pathways in relation to the mediolateral distribution of their terminations in the spinal cord. Different brain stem and cortical regions exert their influence on different muscle groups and are predominantly used under different circumstances.

Two Groups of Pathways Originate in the Brain Stem

Ventromedial Pathways

This group of pathways descends in the ipsilateral ventral funiculi of the spinal cord and terminates predominantly on medial motor neurons (innervating axial and girdle muscles), on interneurons, and on the long propriospinal neurons in the ventromedial part of the intermediate zone (Figure 24–4A).

A characteristic feature of these pathways is the wide, *divergent distribution of their terminals.* Many axons terminate bilaterally in the spinal cord, as do those of interneurons in the area where they project. Individual axons of these systems also send collaterals to different segmental levels. About one-half of the axons that reach the lumbar cord also have collaterals in the cervical gray matter. The long propriospinal neurons controlled by this system also have many axons spreading widely up and down the cord.

The ventromedial system has three major components: (1) The *lateral and medial vestibulospinal tracts* originate in the lateral and medial vestibular nuclei and carry information for the reflex control of equilibrium from the vestibular labyrinth. (2) The *tectospinal tract* originates in the superior colliculus, a structure that is important in the control of eye movements directed toward visual targets. The tectospinal tract plays an important role in the coordination of eye and head movements. (3) The *reticulospinal tracts* originate in the reticular formation of the pontine and medullary tegmentum. The reticular formation is an extension into the brain stem of the spinal intermediate zone. All the components of the ventromedial pathways send collaterals to the reticular formation. Three additional brain stem nuclei also contribute to the ventromedial system: (1) the interstitial nucleus of Cajal, (2) the medial mesencephalic tegmentum, and (3) some

neurons in the locus ceruleus (a noradrenegic cell group).

Dorsolateral Pathways

The dorsolateral group of pathways descend in the lateral quadrants of the spinal cord and terminate in the lateral portion of the intermediate zone and among the dorsolateral groups of motor neurons innervating more distal muscles. In contrast to the ventromedial pathways, in which individual fibers send off large numbers of collaterals at different levels, the dorsolateral pathways tend to focus their terminations on a small number of spinal segments (Figure 24–4B).

The dorsolateral brain stem system is primarily composed of *rubrospinal fibers* that have their origin in the magnocellular portion of the red nucleus in the midbrain. Rubrospinal fibers cross the midline ventral to the red nucleus and descend in the ventrolateral quadrant of the medulla. The magnocellular portion of the red nucleus also gives rise to *rubrobulbar fibers*, which project both to the cranial nerve nuclei controlling facial muscles, and to nuclei with a sensory function, i.e., the sensory trigeminal nucleus and the dorsal column nuclei (the cuneate and gracile nuclei).

The cell populations that give rise to the ventromedial pathways and those that give rise to the dorsolateral pathways are involved in very different tasks. The ventromedial pathways ultimately act on the motor neurons controlling axial and proximal muscles, and thereby control the concerted activities of several muscle groups. In contrast, the dorsolateral pathways project to distal extremity muscles and act on a more restricted number of motor neurons, by virtue of both the reduced number of axon collaterals (as compared to the ventromedial systems) and the limited extent of the propriospinal connections that they control.

The Cerebral Cortex Controls the Two Brain Stem Pathways and the Spinal Networks

It is to the remarkable development of the cerebral cortex that we owe our extraordinarily varied repertoire of discrete voluntary movements. The messages from the cerebral cortex are conveyed to the motor neurons by two main routes: the *corticobulbar* and *corticospinal tracts.* These two fiber systems control the motor neurons in-

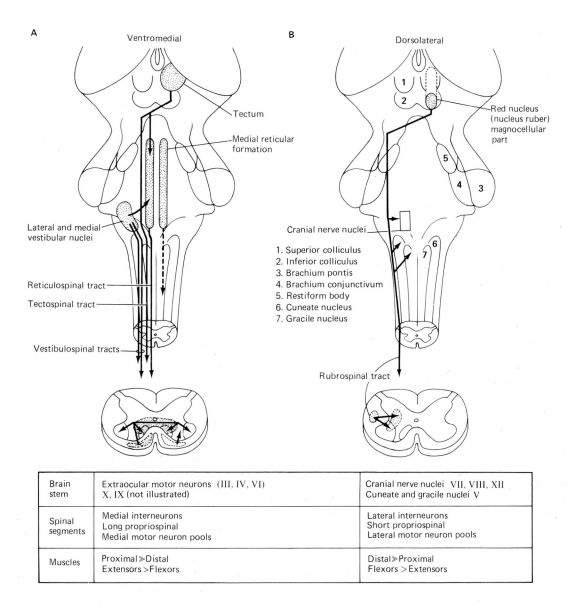

Brain stem	Extraocular motor neurons (III, IV, VI) X, IX (not illustrated)		Cranial nerve nuclei VII, VIII, XII Cuneate and gracile nuclei V
Spinal segments	Medial interneurons Long propriospinal Medial motor neuron pools		Lateral interneurons Short propriospinal Lateral motor neuron pools
Muscles	Proximal ≫ Distal Extensors > Flexors		Distal ≫ Proximal Flexors > Extensors

nervating cranial nerve nuclei and spinal segments, respectively. The two systems exert their actions directly on the motor neurons (or on interneurons closely related to them) as well as indirectly by their action on the reticulospinal and rubrospinal systems.

Strictly speaking, the *corticobulbar fibers* represent those cortical fibers terminating in the medulla oblongata. In practice, however, the term is often used to include those cortical efferents terminating either in cranial nerve nuclei or in areas giving rise to the descending brain stem pathways. The corticospinal fibers are all the fibers originating in the cortex and terminating in

24–4 Descending brain stem pathways.
A. Ventromedial systems. The main components are the reticulospinal, medial and lateral vestibulospinal, and tectospinal tracts which descend in the ventral funiculus. These terminate in the shaded portions of the spinal gray matter. **B.** Dorsolateral systems. The main pathway is the rubrospinal tract which originates in the caudal, magnocellular portion of the red nucleus. The rubrospinal tract descends in the contralateral dorsolateral funiculus terminating in the shaded area of the spinal gray matter. Target neurons and muscle groups controlled are indicated in box.

the spinal cord. In the medulla, the corticospinal fibers are grouped together to form the medullary pyramids. The term "pyramidal tract" is therefore often used synonymously with "corticospinal tract;" however, because many fibers leave the medullary pyramids to innervate brain stem nuclei, the terms "corticospinal" and "pyramidal" are not strictly synonymous.

Origin and Course of the Corticospinal and Corticobulbar Tracts

In man, approximately 30% of corticospinal and corticobulbar fibers originate from a strip of cortex where electrical stimulation evokes movements of different body parts. This area is the *precentral gyrus* of the frontal lobe (area 4 of Brodmann), also known as the *motor cortex*. Another 30% arise from area 6, a larger zone that lies in the frontal lobe anterior to area 4. The remaining 40% arise in the parietal lobe (especially in the somatic sensory cortex, i.e., areas 3, 2, and 1). The corticospinal and corticobulbar fibers course through the *posterior limb of the internal capsule* to the ventral portion of the midbrain, where they are collected in the middle two-thirds of the *cerebral peduncles.* In the pons, corticospinal fibers are no longer grouped together but rather form several small bundles of fibers interspersed among the pontine nuclei. Lower in the brain stem, in the ventral part of the medulla, corticospinal fibers again congregate to form the *medullary pyramids.* At the junction of the medulla and the spinal cord, the majority of the corticospinal fibers cross the midline to form the *pyramidal decussation.* The crossed fibers descend in the dorsolateral funiculi of the spinal cord, while the uncrossed fibers descend in the ventral columns. The columns form the *lateral* and *ventral corticospinal tracts.*

Terminations of the Corticospinal Tract

The lateral and ventral divisions of the corticospinal tract terminate in approximately the same regions of spinal gray matter as do the dorsolateral and ventromedial descending brain stem systems, respectively (Figure 24–5A and B). In humans the lateral corticospinal tract projects to sensory neurons in the dorsal horn (layers IV and V of Rexed), to interneurons in the intermediate zone, and to the motor neuron pools innervating distal limb muscles. The ventral corticospinal tract projects bilaterally to the motor neuron pools innervating axial and proximal muscles as well as to the adjoining portions of the intermediate zone. The fibers projecting to these three zones originate from different areas of the cerebral cortex (Figure 24–5B). The neurons projecting to the dorsal horn (via the lateral corticospinal tract) are located in the somatic sensory cortex of the postcentral gyrus. Those projecting contralaterally to the lateral parts of the intermediate zone and to the motor neurons innervating distal limb muscles are located in the motor cortex of the precentral gyrus, principally in regions controlling arm and leg muscles. The projections to the ventromedial parts of the spinal cord derive mostly from that part of the precentral gyrus where stimulation causes contraction of proximal and axial muscles and from area 6, the region of cortex anterior to the precentral gyrus. These regions of cortex also project in parallel to corresponding regions of the brain stem. Thus, the sensory cortex sends fibers to the dorsal column nuclei, while different areas of the precentral gyrus and area 6 influence the dorsolateral and ventromedial brain stem pathways.

Terminations of the Corticobulbar Tract

The corticobulbar fibers, which ultimately control muscles of the head and face, terminate in sensory and motor cranial nerve nuclei in the brain stem. In humans there are direct monosynaptic connections between corticobulbar fibers and motor neurons in the motor trigeminal, facial, and hypoglossal nuclei. The projections to the trigeminal motor nucleus are bilateral and approximately equal in size. The projection to the facial nucleus is also bilateral, although the cell groups innervating muscles of the lower face receive predominantly contralateral fibers. As a result, unilateral lesions that interrupt corticobulbar fibers on one side produce weakness of muscles of the contralateral lower part of the face. The projection to the hypoglossal nuclei is also asymmetrical, so that supramedullary lesions cause slight tongue deviation contralateral to the lesion.

Cortical Control of Motor Movement Is Achieved Only Late in Phylogeny

Phylogenetically, the corticospinal and corticobulbar pathways first appear in mammals. In the most primitive species, they distribute their

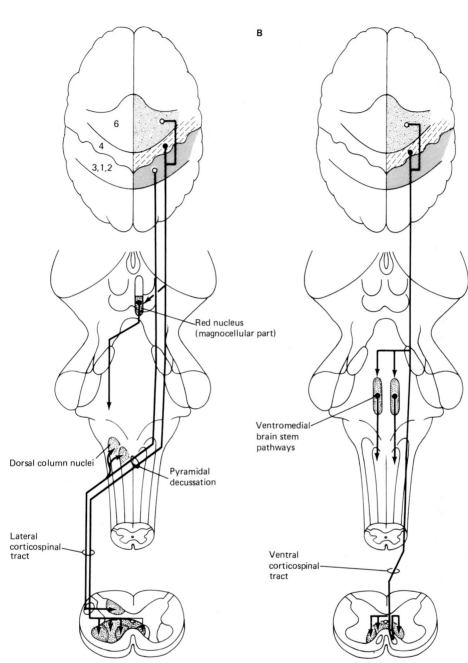

24–5 Descending cortical pathways. **A.** Crossed
pathways, originating from areas 4 and 6 of
Brodmann, cross at the pyramidal decussation, descend
in the dorsolateral funiculus and terminate in shaded
area of spinal gray. A few fibers cross the midline.
Collaterals reach rubrospinal neurons. The principal
area of termination of the corticospinal neurons in the

sensory cortex is the medial portion of the dorsal horn.
Collaterals project to dorsal column nuclei.
B. Uncrossed pathways. These take origin principally
in area 6 and in zones controlling neck and trunk in
area 4. Terminations are bilateral and collaterals
project to the ventromedial brain stem systems.

axons exclusively to sensory regions of the brain stem and spinal cord. In the hedgehog, a primitive mammal that has persisted essentially unchanged for millions of years, the corticospinal tracts are located in the dorsal columns and terminate exclusively in the dorsal horn. In this species the sensory and motor representations of the body surface overlap precisely on the cerebral cortex. With phylogenetic development, distinct sensory and motor representations of the body appear in the cortex and additional corticospinal terminations develop within the intermediate zone of the spinal cord. With still further development, there is a gradual increase in the number of corticospinal fibers distributed to more ventral regions of the spinal cord. Direct connections between corticospinal neurons and motor neurons appear first in lateral motor neuron cell groups (to distal limb muscles), then also in medial motor neuron cell groups. Thus, in the primate line, following transection of the pyramid, the number of degenerating terminals seen in the ventral horn increases progressively from prosimians (e.g., lemurs such as the bush baby) to monkeys (e.g., macaque), apes (e.g., chimpanzee and gorilla), and finally man. In the more primitive primates, degenerating terminals are seen only in the most dorsolateral cell groups innervating the most distal muscles, whereas in monkeys the entire lateral division of the motor neuron pool receives corticospinal input; in higher apes and man the medial motor neuron pools receive such terminations as well. In most carnivores (such as the cat) corticospinal fibers terminate exclusively in the dorsal horn and dorsolateral parts of the intermediate zone and do not make any direct connections with motor neurons.

Functional Considerations

The fact that the ventromedial and dorsolateral pathways end on different types of motor neurons and show different degrees of divergence has important functional implications. The dorsolateral brain stem and lateral corticospinal pathways control distal limb muscles. The presence of direct connections from the cortex to the motor neurons provides higher primates, including man, with the ability to control individual muscles independently from one another. This important capacity is known as *fractionation of movement*. It is completely and irretrievably lost following lesions of the pyramidal tract. Monkeys with interruption of pyramidal tracts are no longer able to grasp small objects between two fingers or to make isolated movements of the wrist or elbow. When attempting to grasp a small object, such an animal will use its hand as a shovel or, at best, it will contract all the digits at the same time around the object. These animals, however, show no impairment in their ability to maintain balance or to control axial and girdle muscles; they can walk and climb without difficulty. In contrast, lesions interrupting the ventromedial brain stem pathways produce profound disorders in righting and the animals become unable to sit or stand upright, to walk, and to climb.

The hierarchical superposition of several levels of control (i.e., corticospinal–brain stem–segmental interneurons–motor neurons) contributes to the marked recovery of motor functions following lesions of one or another system. Ablation of the precentral gyrus is followed immediately by a profound paralysis of the muscles controlled by that area. This paralysis, however, recovers to a remarkable extent. In different species, the extent and duration of the paralysis parallel the development of the direct corticospinal connections with motor neurons. It is briefer in monkey than man and still briefer in the cat, which lacks cortical motor neuronal connections altogether. Lesions of the corticospinal tract that spare the corticorubral projections allow the brain to control distal limb muscles through this pathway. In higher primates the rubrospinal pathway regresses somewhat relative to that of monkeys and other species, and the degree of functional recovery following cortical lesions is correspondingly smaller.

Inputs to the Motor Cortex
Corticocortical Connections

All regions of the cortex are ultimately capable of influencing the motor cortex through their *corticocortical* connections. These pathways take the form of white matter bundles that link the different regions of cortex with each other. The major cortical inputs to the precentral gyrus (area 4) arise from area 6, just anterior to it. This area in turn receives cortical projections from prefrontal areas (area 8) to which the occipital, parietal, and temporal lobes send important projections. These projections from other cortical areas relay the visual, somatic sensory, and auditory inputs that are used to guide movements. For example, connections from the visual cortex are critical for fine guidance of distal limb movements toward visual targets. In addition to this indirect projection to the motor cortex through area 6, there are direct, albeit weaker, projections from the primary somatic sensory areas (3, 1, and 2) as well as from the adjacent area 5 in the parietal lobe. The projections from the postcentral gyrus of the parietal cortex are organized in a strict somatotopic fashion: areas receiving sensory input from a given body part project to areas of the motor cortex controlling that same body part.

Finally, an additional source of corticocortical inputs comes from the corpus callosum, which relays information from one hemisphere to the other. Callosal fibers interconnect homologous areas of both the sensory and motor cortices. There is only one exception to this rule: the regions that receive information from, or project to the distal regions of the limbs do not receive callosal connections. These regions (the hand and foot areas of the sensory and motor cortices of the two hemispheres) are thus functionally disconnected from one another.

Subcortical Projections: Ventral Anterior and Ventral Lateral Nuclei of the Thalamus

The major input to area 6 and to the motor cortex comes from the two thalamic nuclei, the ventral anterior and the ventral lateral. In addition, the border zone between the ventral lateral and ventral posterior lateral nuclei is important in relaying peripheral somatic sensory information to the precentral gyrus. The bulk of the ventral anterior–ventral lateral complex relays information from two important subcortical integrating centers: the basal ganglia and the cerebellum. These two regions of the brain are exceedingly important clinically because of the motor disturbances that result from lesions within them. In both cases the symptoms are complex and the mechanisms giving rise to them are poorly understood. As we have seen, lesions affecting corticospinal and descending brain stem pathways

can be understood in rather simple terms: the lesions lead to a loss of facilitatory or inhibitory influences on segmental mechanisms. As a result there are (1) quantitative impairments in the performance of certain motor tasks (decrease in strength and speed of muscle contraction, loss of fractionation, etc.), and (2) impairment of muscle tone. When the cerebellum and basal ganglia are damaged the impairments reflect interference with the processing mechanisms leading to smoothly coordinated movements. The movements therefore become uncoordinated and clumsy, the spatial and temporal patterning of muscle contractions becomes abnormal, and involuntary movements appear. These phenomena will be discussed in Chapters 30 and 31.

Selected Readings and References

Evarts, E. V., Bizzi, E., Burke, R. E., DeLong, M., and Thach, Jr., W. T. 1971. Central control of movement. Neurosci. Res. Program Bull. 9:1–170.

Kuypers, H. G. J. M. 1973. The anatomical organization of the descending pathways and their contributions to motor control especially in primates. In J. E. Desmedt (ed.), New Developments in Electromyography and Clinical Neurophysiology, Vol. 3. Basel: Karger, pp. 38–68.

Lundberg, A. 1975. Control of spinal mechanisms from the brain. In D. B. Tower (ed.), The Nervous System, Vol. 1, The Basic Neurosciences. New York: Raven Press, pp. 253–265.

Lundberg, A. 1979. Integration in a propriospinal motor center controlling the forelimb in the cat. In H. Asanuma and V. J. Wilson (eds.), Integration in the Nervous System. Tokyo: Igaku-Shoin, pp. 47–64.

Other References

Eccles, J. C. 1964. The Physiology of Synapses. Berlin: Springer.

Sherrington, C. 1947. The Integrative Action of the Nervous System. 2nd ed. New Haven: Yale University Press.

Thomas J. Carew

Spinal Cord I: Muscles and Muscle Receptors

25

As pointed out in Chapter 24, the only way that the central nervous system can interact with the outside world is through its action on skeletal muscle. In this chapter we shall first discuss how skeletal muscles produce the forces necessary to move our limbs. Then we shall see how specialized receptors within skeletal muscles give rise to critical information concerning both the length of the muscle and the tension it is generating. Finally, we shall see that the central nervous system also has the capacity to control the inflow of information it is receiving from skeletal muscles by acting directly on the receptors located in those muscles.

Skeletal Muscle Types Are Functionally Specialized

Skeletal muscle fibers can be classified according to several criteria including color, mitochondrial content, vascularization, energy systems, and physiological properties (contraction and relaxation rates, degree and range of tension production, and fatigability). These various properties combine to produce two functionally important types of muscle: fast muscle and slow muscle (intermediate categories also exist that share some of the properties of each).

Fast muscles are pale in color, have few mitochondria, are poorly vascularized, and use glycolysis to generate energy (thus these fibers usually function under anaerobic conditions). These fibers are characterized by rapid contraction and relaxation (Figure 25–1), develop a wide range of tensions, and often fatigue quite rapidly. Thus these fibers are well suited for high-intensity short-duration muscular activity.

Slow muscles are red, have many mitochondria, are richly vascularized, and make use of oxidative metabolism. A high myoglobin content of these fibers specializes them for oxidative metabolism and gives them their red color. Slow muscles contract and relax slowly (Figure 25–1), develop tension over a narrow range, and are very resistant to fatigue. Thus these muscles are specialized for long-term contraction that is necessary in the maintenance of posture.

As mentioned above, there are intermediate classes of muscle fibers. These are red in color, have many mitochondria, and are richly vascularized. They are intermediate in contraction times, tension range, and fatigability. These fibers make use of both oxidative and glycolytic metabolism.

Motor Neurons Are Functionally Organized

As already discussed in Chapter 12, a *motor unit* is a functional entity composed of a single alpha motor neuron together with all the skeletal fibers it supplies.[1] Motor units can vary dramatically in size: in a small motor unit, a given motor neuron innervates only a few muscle fibers; in a large unit, a motor neuron can innervate as many as 1000 muscle fibers. There is an important functional consequence of motor unit size. The smaller the motor units, the more precisely controlled and finely graded will be the resulting movements. For example, muscles in the fingers and the extrinsic eye muscles have small motor units consisting of only a few fibers compared to limb muscles, such as the soleus or gastrocnemius, which have large units. This feature of motor organization is analogous to the principles of organization already described in the somatic sensory system (Chapter 17) and in the visual system (Chapter 21), where greater resolution within a particular sensory system is related to the size of

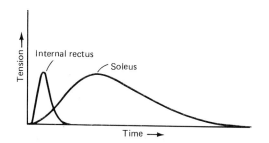

25–1 Twitch contractions of fast and slow muscles. For fast muscles such as extraocular muscles (e.g., the internal rectus), maximum twitch tension (resulting from a single brief electrical stimulus to the muscle) develops in about 7.5 msec, whereas in a slow muscle such as the soleus, maximum twitch tension develops only after about 100 msec. Notice also the difference in relaxation times. (Adapted from Henneman, 1980.)

the receptive fields. Small motor units provide a means of achieving fine control of movements or, by analogy to the sensory systems, they provide for greater motor sensitivity.

Just as muscle types differ in their ability to contract rapidly, so too do motor neurons differ in their ability to fire rapidly. Moreover, there is a close match between the functional properties of muscle types and motor neuron types: fast muscles are innervated by motor neurons that can fire at high frequencies and have fast conduction velocities, while slow muscles are innervated by motor neurons that fire at lower frequencies and have slower conduction velocities. The way in which this match of functional properties is brought about by the central nervous system will be discussed in Chapter 43.

The Nervous System Can Grade the Force of Muscle Contraction in Two Ways

Given the arrangement of motor units described above, how are graded forces generated by the nervous system? There are two principal answers to this problem: (1) increasingly larger numbers of motor units can be recruited to increase muscle tension *(recruitment)*; and (2) an individual motor neuron can fire faster to increase muscle tension *(rate coding)*.

Recruitment

Henneman and his colleagues have recently found that motor neurons are recruited by afferent input in an orderly fashion according to their

---

[1]The term "motor unit" should not be confused with the general term "unit," which is often used in neurophysiology to refer to a single neuron (as in "single unit recording"). The term "motor unit" refers not only to a single motor neuron, but also to the muscle fibers innervated by that motor neuron.

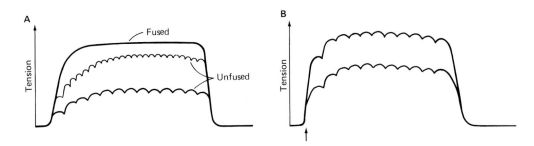

25–2 Effects of rate coding on muscle tension.
A. Examples of unfused and fused tetanus. Stimulation of a muscle fiber at progressively higher frequencies produces greater tension and the rate of increase in tension also increases. **B.** Effect of an initial doublet on tension produced by a train of stimuli. **Bottom trace:** Unfused tetanus is produced by a train of stimuli. **Top trace:** Much greater tension is produced when a single extra stimulus **(at arrow)** is added at the beginning of the stimulus train.

size. Neurons having the smallest fiber diameter (and therefore also the smallest cell bodies) have the lowest threshold for synaptic activation and thus are recruited by the weakest afferent input. Increases in the strength of the afferent input recruit progressively larger motor neurons. This is called the *size principle*.[2] The size principle also applies to human muscles during voluntary contraction. An important functional consequence of the size principle stems from the fact that large motor neurons usually innervate many muscle fibers (i.e., they constitute large motor units). Thus, as larger motor units are recruited, progressively greater *increments* of force are added.

Rate Coding

The second way the nervous system can command greater muscular force is through increasing the firing rate of motor neurons, or rate coding. When muscles are activated by successive action potentials whose interval is less than the muscle's twitch contraction time, the forces generated by each impulse will summate (this state of maintained contraction is called *tetanus*).

---

[2]The size of an excitatory postsynaptic potential depends upon the product of two factors: the synaptic current and the (passive) membrane resistance of the neuron. There is an inverse relationship between a neuron's surface area and its membrane resistance—the smaller the neuron, the larger its passive membrane resistance. Thus, a given synaptic current will produce a larger excitatory postsynaptic potential in a small neuron than in a large neuron.

Figure 25–2A illustrates the effect of spike frequency on the tension produced isometrically by a single fiber. At low and intermediate rates some relaxation can take place between impulses and the tension record shows ripples corresponding to the peaks of each twitch; this is called *unfused tetanus*. At very high frequencies a smooth tension record is observed; this is called *fused tetanus*. Most naturally occurring steady muscle contractions are produced by motor neurons firing at relatively low frequencies. The reason that our movements are not jerky is that several motor units are always activated asynchronously. Thus, when one motor unit is at the peak of its twitch, another may be relaxed.

The force developed by a motor unit also critically depends on its pattern of activity. R. E. Burke and his colleagues have shown that insertion of a single extra action potential at the onset of a relatively low-frequency stimulus train produces a remarkable "catchlike" enhancement of the tension output (Figure 25–2B). The tension produced by such a pair of spikes occurring close together (called a *doublet*) is much greater and develops much more rapidly than the sum of the tensions that would be produced by either spike alone. Moreover, the effect of the second impulse can last many seconds. Since the work of Gurfinkel in Russia, it is now recognized that this mechanism for increasing both the tension produced in a muscle and the rate at which that tension increases is critical in any rapid movement.

Muscles Have Specialized Receptors

Muscles and joints contain a variety of receptors. Some inform the central nervous system about the length and tension of the muscle. Others detect touch, pressure, and noxious stimuli. By far the most thoroughly understood of these receptor types are the stretch receptors in muscle: the muscle spindles and the Golgi tendon organs. As we shall see, although all of these receptors are sensitive to *stretch*, because of their anatomical

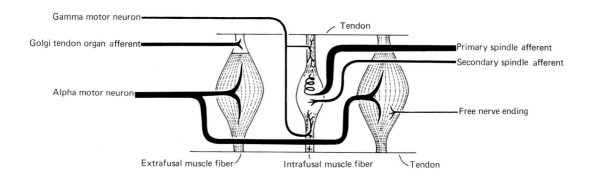

arrangement in the muscle (Figure 25–3) the information they convey to the central nervous system will either concern the *length* of the muscle (spindles) or the *tension* of the muscle (tendon organs).

25–3 Anatomical relationships of muscle receptors and their innervation. The muscle spindles (intrafusal fibers) are in **parallel** with the extrafusal fibers; the tendon organs are in **series**. The thicknesses of the afferent and efferent fibers represent their relative diameters. The intrafusal fibers do not actually attach to tendons; they attach directly to the extrafusal fiber, occupying only a small fraction of its length.

Muscle Spindles

The mammalian muscle spindle is a highly specialized receptor structure that is fusiform in shape and is distributed throughout the fleshy parts of skeletal muscle. Each spindle consists of an encapsulated group of fine, specialized muscle fibers and is expanded at its center in a fluid-filled capsule. Within this capsule the muscular elements are entwined by the terminal branches of the afferent fibers. These small muscle fibers within the spindle are called *intrafusal* fibers; they do not produce significant tension but regulate the excitability of the spindle afferents (as we shall see below). They are innervated by small motor cells of the ventral horn called *gamma motor neurons* (Figure 25–3). The large skeletal muscles that we have discussed previously (in the first section) are sometimes called *extrafusal fibers* to distinguish them from those in the muscle spindles. Extrafusal fibers are innervated by the large alpha motor neurons in the ventral horn.

Muscle spindles contain two types of intrafusal muscle fibers called *nuclear bag fibers* and *nuclear chain fibers* after the arrangement of nuclei found in their equatorial region (Figure 25–4). The bag fibers have clustered nuclei (two or three abreast), whereas the chain fibers have nuclei in single file. The bag fibers are also usually thicker and longer than chain fibers.

There are two types of afferent terminals in muscle spindles: primary and secondary. There are several differences between the primary and secondary endings. The most important difference is their relationship to the two types of intrafusal fibers. *Primary endings innervate every*

single intrafusal fiber within a spindle, however many there are, and irrespective of whether they are nuclear bag or nuclear chain fibers. *Secondary endings lie almost exclusively on nuclear chain fibers* (Figure 25–4). The primary endings have traditionally been called *annulospiral* and the secondary *flower spray*, but the detailed morphology of these different endings is probably not significant.

25–4 Nuclear bag and nuclear chain intrafusal fibers within a muscle spindle, each having its own efferent control. Group I (primary) afferents innervate both the nuclear bag and the nuclear chain fiber, whereas group II (secondary) afferents usually innervate only the nuclear chain fibers (however, they occasionally can innervate bag fibers, indicated by the thin branch). (Adapted from Matthews, 1964.)

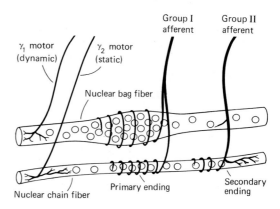

Golgi Tendon Organs

The Golgi tendon organ is a slender capsule approximately 1 mm long and 100 μm in diameter. Each receptor is in series with a discrete number of skeletal muscle fibers that enter the capsule through a tight-fitting, funnellike collar. The muscle fibers terminate in musculotendenous junctions after entering the capsule and give rise to collagen fiber bundles that become braided with one another and run the length of the capsule. The afferent fiber enters the capsule in the middle and branches many times, so that the axons of the afferent fiber become twisted within the braids of the collagen fiber bundles. When the skeletal muscle fibers contract (shorten) they cause the collagen bundles to straighten, which in turn compresses the axons of the afferent fibers, causing them to fire. Thus the braided arrangement of the collagen fiber bundles gives them a significant mechanical advantage in compressing the intertwined afferent axons, which makes those axons very sensitive to small changes in muscle tension.

Different Receptors Convey Information to the Central Nervous System Through Afferent Fibers of Different Sizes

The standard classification of muscle afferents was introduced by Lloyd and Chang 30 years ago. These investigators found that the myelinated afferent fibers from muscle fall into three main categories of diameters, which they numbered with Roman numerals (groups I, II, and III). As described in Chapter 15, Lloyd and Chang's classification system based on muscle nerves corresponds nicely to the classification of cutaneous afferents.

Subsequently, in 1954 Carlton Hunt studied the conduction velocity of fibers from different receptors. By inferring the fiber diameter from the conduction velocity,[3] he showed that the largest of the group I fibers (called Ia fibers) contain axons

---

³Years before, Hursh had shown that conduction velocity (in meters per second) is roughly six times the fiber diameter (expressed in micrometers). This conversion factor (conduction velocity = fiber diameter multiplied by 6) has subsequently been shown to be inexact for smaller diameter fibers, where the appropriate conversion factor has been estimated to be between 3 and 4. Thus a 3-μm fiber, which would have been estimated to conduct at 18 m/sec using Hursh's factor, actually conducts at approximately 9–12 m/sec.

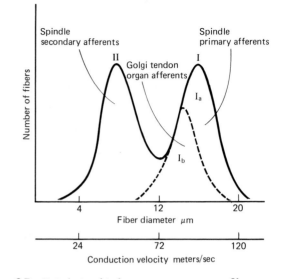

25–5 Relationship between receptor type, fiber diameter, and conduction velocity in muscle nerves. Note the bimodal distribution of afferents from muscle spindles (**solid line**) and the unimodal distribution of afferents from tendon organs (**broken line**). (Adapted from Hunt, 1954.)

that innervate the muscle spindles; the smaller diameter subpopulation of group I fibers (called Ib fibers) are from Golgi tendon organs. The Ia and Ib populations overlap considerably. The group II fibers contain smaller axons from muscle spindles. Thus, there are two types of afferents from muscle spindles: large primary afferents, and smaller secondary afferents. These relationships are summarized in Figure 25–5.

Much less is known about group III and the unmyelinated group IV (not shown in Figure 25–5), but these are probably fibers with free nerve endings. They are presumed to be responsible for sensations of muscle pressure and pain.

Muscle Stretch Receptors Convey Information About Muscle Length, Tension, and Velocity of Stretch

Our understanding of the basic difference between muscle spindles and Golgi tendon organs comes from a classic series of studies carried out by B. H. C. Matthews about 50 years ago. He found that, if one records from a muscle spindle afferent or a tendon organ afferent and *stretches* the muscle, the afferent from either the tendon organ or the spindle will *increase* its rate of discharge. On the other hand, if while still

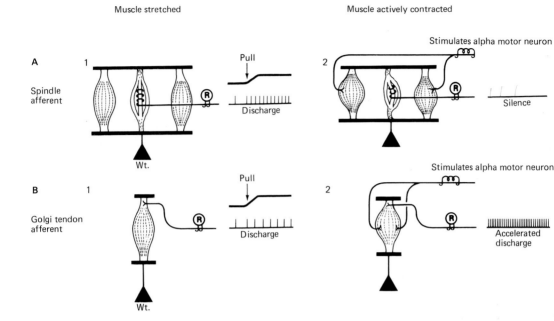

stretched the muscle is made to *contract actively* (for example by stimulation of the alpha motor neuron that supplies the muscle), *the tendon organ will further increase its discharge but the spindle discharge will decrease or cease altogether* (Figure 25–6). The reason for this difference in response lies in the location of the two types of receptors. The spindle organs are arranged in parallel with the extrafusal muscle fibers, while the Golgi tendon organs are arranged in series with the extrafusal fibers (Figure 25–3).

Passive stretching of the muscle will stretch and thereby activate both the tendon organ and the muscle spindle. (Stretching of the muscle spindle is called *loading* it.) Contraction further stretches the tendon organ (in fact, tendon organs are much more sensitive to muscle contraction than to passive stretch, as will be discussed in the next chapter). However, active contraction of the extrafusal muscles makes the intrafusal fibers go slack; it *unloads* the spindle (Figure 25–6A, 2) so that it is no longer stretched. Thus, during muscle contraction tendon organs increase their discharge and spindle organs decrease their discharge. These findings indicate that the tendon organs, because they are in series with the extrafusal muscles, are sensitive to *muscle tension*; whereas the spindle organs, which are parallel with the extrafusal fibers, are sensitive to *muscle length.*

When a muscle is stretched, the primary and secondary afferents in the muscle spindles re-

25–6 Afferent response from a muscle spindle (**A**) and a Golgi tendon organ (**B**). Both afferents discharge to stretch of the muscle (A*1*, B*1*), the Golgi tendon organ less than the spindle. However, when the muscle is made to contract actively by stimulation of its alpha motor neuron, the spindle is unloaded (A*2*) and therefore goes silent, whereas the tendon organ output is further increased (B*2*). (Adapted from Patton, 1965.)

spond quite differently. Both fiber types respond to static (steady-state) stretch, although secondary endings are a bit more sensitive, but the fibers respond differently to the dynamic phase of stretch (i.e., when the muscle is actually changing length). Primary endings are very sensitive to the dynamic phase of stretch while the secondary endings are not. *Thus the secondary endings are mainly sensitive to the length of the muscle, whereas the primary endings are sensitive both to the length of the muscle and to the velocity of stretching.*

The Central Nervous System Can Directly Control the Muscle Spindles

As discussed earlier, contraction of extrafusal muscle fibers is produced by large alpha motor neurons; intrafusal muscle fibers are controlled by smaller gamma motor neurons. Gamma motor neurons innervate the intrafusal muscle fibers at their polar regions, where the contractile elements of the fibers are located. The central (equatorial) region is almost devoid of contractile elements. Activation of a gamma efferent has the effect of contracting and shortening the intrafusal fiber at the ends, thereby stretching the equatorial region where the afferent endings are located.

Dynamic and Static Gamma Motor Neurons

There are two types of gamma motor neurons (Figure 25–4): one type innervates nuclear bag fibers *(gamma dynamic)*; the other type innervates nuclear chain fibers *(gamma static)*. Dynamic gamma fibers are often called γ_d, and static gamma fibers γ_s. The reason for the names dynamic and static is that these gamma motor neurons regulate the sensitivity of the spindle afferents to dynamic and static phases of stretch, respectively. This distinction can be best appreciated by examining an experiment carried out by Crowe and Matthews about 15 years ago (Figure 25–7). These investigators recorded from a single primary afferent fiber while stretching a muscle. The primary afferent response showed typical acceleration during the stretch (dynamic phase) and increased firing during the maintained stretch (static phase). They let the muscle relax and repeated the procedure, but this time they also activated a static gamma fiber before and during the stretch. This background gamma (static) activation enhanced the primary afferent response to static stretch. After letting the muscle relax they repeated the procedure a third time, this time stretching the muscle while stimulating a dynamic gamma fiber. This procedure enhanced the primary afferent response to the phasic (dynamic) phase of stretch. The reason the primary afferent response is influenced by both types of gamma fibers is that the Ia fiber innervates both the nuclear bag and the nuclear chain intrafusal fibers. As might be expected, because secondary (group II) afferents almost exclusively innervate nuclear chain fibers, these afferents are influenced almost exclusively by static gamma motor neurons.

Skeletofusimotor Innervation

Thus far we have considered how the central nervous system exerts relatively independent efferent control over (1) the intrafusal muscle fibers in the muscle spindles and (2) the extrafusal muscle fibers, by means of gamma and alpha

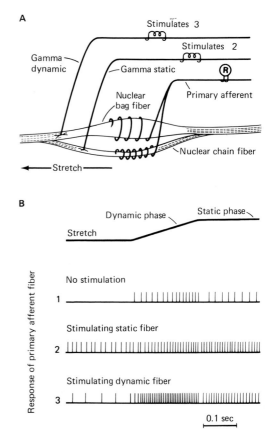

25–7 Crowe and Matthews' experiment demonstrating the difference between static and dynamic gamma motor neurons. **A.** Diagram of experimental procedure. **B.** Difference in the recorded primary afferent response when the stretch is superimposed on static or dynamic gamma activity. First, the extrafusal muscle is stretched and the primary afferent response is recorded *(1)*. Next, a static gamma motor fiber is stimulated prior to and during the stretch *(2)*. Then a dynamic gamma motor fiber is stimulated prior to and during the stretch *(3)*. (Adapted from Crowe and Matthews, 1964.)

motor neurons, respectively. However, in many animals (e.g., in amphibia) the central nervous system uses a simpler solution in which the same motor neuron innervates both the extrafusal fiber and the muscle spindle. This is called *skeletofusimotor* or *beta innervation*. Skeletofusimotor innervation has been found in animals as high on the evolutionary scale as carnivores, and it is likely that such innervation exists in man as well. The functional significance of beta innervation, compared with dual alpha and gamma systems, remains an intriguing question for future research.

Functional Role of the Gamma System

An important role of the gamma system is to allow the spindle to preserve its high sensitivity over a wide range of muscle lengths when the muscle is shortening during reflex and voluntary contractions. This function of the gamma system was first suggested by Hunt and Kuffler about 25 years ago. These investigators reasoned that during large active contractions of extrafusal muscles the spindles would become unloaded (Figure 25–6A, 2), thereby throwing them out of commission for signaling any further changes in muscle length. They suggested that one role of the gamma system (they did not distinguish between static and dynamic efferents) is to reload the spindle during active contractions, thereby keeping it responsive to further changes in length. Their experiments confirmed this suggestion, for they found that the characteristic pause in spindle discharge during a twitch contraction due to unloading of the spindle (Figure 25–8B) could be filled in by activation of a gamma efferent to the spindle during the contraction (Figure 25–8C). In other words, stimulation of the gamma motor neuron during the extrafusal con-

traction cinched up the spindle, preventing it from being unloaded during the contraction and thereby keeping it responsive to further changes in length.

To appreciate how the gamma system allows the spindle to preserve its high sensitivity over wide ranges of muscle length, we must consider how gamma motor neurons are controlled by descending influences. Gamma motor neurons for a particular muscle lie within the alpha motor neuron pool for the same muscle. Most descending systems that impinge upon alpha motor neurons (for example, those involved in postural adjustments or voluntary movements) will also activate the smaller gamma motor neurons. Thus alpha and gamma motor neurons are coactivated

25–8 A. Sustained tension elicits steady firing of Ia afferent. **B.** Characteristic pause in ongoing Ia discharge when the muscle is caused to contract by stimulation of its alpha motor neuron. The Ia fiber stops firing because the spindle is unloaded by the contraction. **C.** During a comparable contraction, a gamma motor neuron to the spindle is also stimulated, "filling in" the pause in Ia discharge by preventing unloading of the spindle during the contraction. (Adapted from Hunt and Kuffler, 1951.)

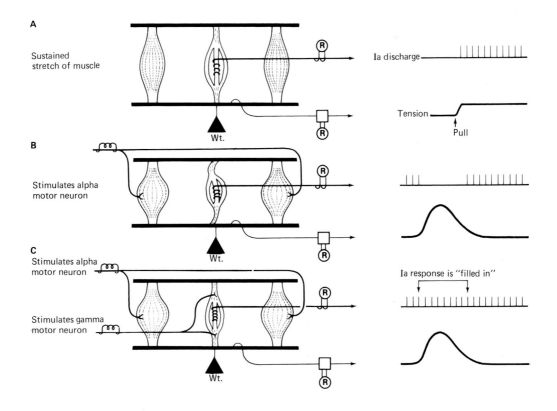

by descending systems. In the next chapter we shall return to the notion of coactivation. In addition, in our discussion of the central actions of the muscle spindles and their role in the stretch reflex, we shall also consider other possible roles of the gamma system such as compensation for variations in the mechanical properties of muscle or compensation for changes in load during voluntary movement.

Selected Readings and References

Harris, D. A., and Henneman, E. 1980. Feedback signals from muscle and their efferent control. In V. B. Mountcastle (ed.), Medical Physiology, 14th ed., Vol. 1. St. Louis: Mosby, pp. 703–717.

Henneman, E. 1980. Skeletal muscle. The servant of the nervous system. In V. B. Mountcastle (ed.), Medical Physiology, 14th ed, Vol. 1. St. Louis: Mosby, pp. 674–702.

Homma, S. (ed.) 1976. Understanding the stretch reflex. Prog. Brain Res. 44:1–507.

Matthews, P. B. C. 1972. Mammalian Muscle Receptors and Their Central Actions. Baltimore: Williams & Wilkins.

Stein, R. B. 1974. Peripheral control of movement. Physiol. Rev. 54:215–243.

Other References

Burke, R. E., Rudomin, P., and Zajac, III, F. E. 1976. The effect of activation history on tension production by individual muscle units. Brain Res. 109:515–529.

Crowe, A., and Matthews, P. B. C. 1964. The effects of stimulation of static and dynamic fusimotor fibres on the response to stretching of the primary endings of muscle spindles. J. Physiol. (Lond.) 174:109–131.

Gurfinkel, V. S., Surguladze, T. D., Mirskii, M. L., and Tarko, A. M. 1970. Work of human motor units during rhythmic movements. Biophysics 15:1131–1137.

Hunt, C. C. 1954. Relation of function to diameter in afferent fibers of muscle nerves. J. Gen. Physiol. 38:117–131.

Hunt, C. C., and Kuffler, S. W. 1951. Stretch receptor discharges during muscle contraction. J. Physiol. (Lond.) 113:298–315.

Hursh, J. B. 1939. Conduction velocity and diameter of nerve fibers. Am. J. Physiol. 127:131–139.

Lloyd, D. P. C., and Chang, H.-T. 1948. Afferent fibers in muscle nerves. J. Neurophysiol. 11:199–208.

Matthews, B. H. C. 1933. Nerve endings in mammalian muscle. J. Physiol. (Lond.) 78:1–53.

Matthews, P. B. C. 1964. Muscle spindles and their motor control. Physiol. Rev. 44:219–288.

Patton, H. D. 1965. Reflex regulation of movement and posture. In T. C. Ruch and H. D. Patton (eds.), Physiology and Biophysics. 19th ed. Philadelphia: Saunders, pp. 181–206.

Thomas J. Carew

Spinal Cord II:
Reflex Action

In the previous chapter we considered the peripheral machinery—muscles and receptors—involved in the production of movement. In this chapter we shall examine how this machinery is brought into action by the central nervous system to generate a wide variety of reflex acts. Reflexes are interesting for two reasons. First, they are among the simplest motor acts and have relatively elementary neuronal circuits. Moreover, descending influences from higher brain centers often use the same neuronal circuits to generate more complex behaviors. Therefore, achieving an understanding of the organizational principles of reflexes is an essential prerequisite for understanding more complex motor sequences. Second, reflexes are valuable clinical tools: they serve as a means of assessing the integrity of both afferent and motor connections as well as the general level of excitability of the spinal cord.

A fundamental principle of reflex organization is that information from particular receptors is conveyed by a particular system of afferent fibers to the spinal cord, where specific synaptic connections are made onto interneuronal circuits. These reflexes can be highly localized, such as stretch reflexes that involve the contraction of single muscles, or they can be quite widespread, such as flexion reflexes that involve the coordination of dozens of muscle groups to produce the withdrawal of an entire limb.

We shall begin our discussion of reflexes by considering some of the most elementary reflex responses—those of muscle origin. Reflexes of muscle origin have been the most extensively investigated because they are relatively simple and so much is known about the muscle receptors that mediate them. The muscle receptors we discussed in the previous chapter (primary and secondary muscle spindles and Golgi tendon organs) inform the central nervous system about the length and tension of the muscles. These reflexes are elegantly designed so that rapid corrections of motor output can be achieved automatically, at the level of the spinal cord, providing the higher centers of the brain with the necessary time to integrate other incoming information and make decisions about what would be the appropriate motor output.

Ia Afferents Contribute to the Stretch Reflex

Basic Features of the Stretch Reflex

At the turn of the century, Sir Charles Sherrington began his classic study of the reflex physiology of decerebrate cats. A prominent feature of these animals is that they show heightened reflexes and a dramatic increase in muscle tone in the extensor muscles of their limbs. Thus, decerebrate cats have been used extensively to study postural control (see Chapter 28). In examining the reflexes in the hind limb of a decerebrate cat, Sherrington and his colleague, E. G. T. Liddell, found that when they attempted to force the rigidly extended limb passively into a flexed position, the limb resisted the force by active muscular contraction. They called this the *stretch reflex* or *myotatic reflex* (*myotatic* from two Greek words meaning "extended muscle"). Liddell and Sherrington went on to publish a famous series of papers in 1924 and 1925 in which they examined the stretch reflex in the knee extensor (quadriceps) of the cat.

They distinguished between two components of the stretch reflex: (1) the *phasic component*, which is short lasting and relatively intense. This component is often called the knee jerk or tendon jerk because a brief reflex extension of the knee is produced by tapping the patellar tendon, thereby stretching the quadriceps; and (2) *the tonic component*, which is less intense but lasts longer and is thought to be important in the maintenance of

posture. Stretch reflexes are seen in both flexor and extensor muscles, but they are most highly developed in those muscles whose predominant action is to oppose gravity (these are called *physiological extensors*). The phasic component is triggered by movement of the limb (that is, the *change in muscle length*), whereas the tonic component is determined by the *steady stretch* of the muscles. Sometimes the phasic component predominates, so that the resistance offered by the limb to an imposed movement is great only while the limb is moving. Sherrington called this apparent decrease in resistance at the cessation of movement the *lengthening reaction* because the extensor muscle lengthens to assume the new flexed posture.

Sherrington discovered several important principles; perhaps the most important is the principle of *reciprocal innervation*. For example, with Liddell, he found that stretching the antagonist knee flexors (such as the biceps or the semitendinous muscle) inhibited the extensor stretch reflex. Thus, there is a reciprocal arrangement so that the final efferent output of the spinal cord provides for an integrated motor response.

Central Connections of the Ia Afferents

The synaptic connections made by the Ia afferents in the spinal cord were examined in detail in the pioneering studies of David P. C. Lloyd in the 1940s and beautifully accounted for the stretch reflex. Lloyd introduced the method of carefully grading electrical stimuli to nerves of muscle origin in order to activate fibers of a given diameter selectively, while recording the efferent (reflex) output of the spinal cord from the ventral roots. Remember that the threshold of a fiber to extracellular current is inversely related to its diameter.[1] Thus, with the weakest stimulus

---

[1] There can be some confusion relating the fact that large-diameter fibers have low thresholds, to the size principle (described in the previous chapter), which states that, given the same synaptic current, small neurons are recruited into activity before large neurons. Large axons have a lower threshold than small axons when stimulated with extracellular current because of their geometry. When current flows extracellularly it has two paths: (1) through the extracellular space, and (2) across the axon membranes. Cells with a large-diameter axon "see" more of the extracellular current than cells with a small-diameter axon. The lower input resistance of large neurons (compared to small ones), which raises their threshold to *synaptic* current, is more than offset by their increased axon diameter, which lowers their threshold to *extracellular* current.

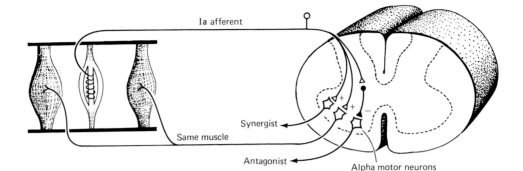

Ia afferent

Synergist

Same muscle

Antagonist

Alpha motor neurons

26−1 Basic reflex circuitry for the myotatic reflex. Ia afferents monosynaptically excite motor neurons to the same (homonymous) muscle from which they arise and motor neurons to synergist muscles. They also inhibit motor neurons to antagonist muscles through an inhibitory (**shaded**) interneuron.

strength, Lloyd could selectively activate the largest fibers (the Ia afferents) and examine the efferent volley, that is, the reflex action they produced. By increasing the stimulus further he could then activate the Ib afferents (of course the Ia fibers were still activated) and examine any new effects produced by the Ib fibers. By carefully measuring the latency of the efferent volley produced (1) by stretching of the gastrocnemius muscle and (2) by electrical stimulation of the dorsal root, Lloyd inferred the number of synaptic delays that exist in the reflex pathway. Using these techniques, Lloyd developed a coherent picture of the central connections of the Ia fibers in the spinal cord. A few years later, with the advent of intracellular recording techniques, Eccles and his colleagues confirmed and extended Lloyd's findings and the following picture emerged (Figure 26−1):

1. Ia fibers (from both extensor and flexor muscles) make direct monosynaptic excitatory connections with alpha motor neurons that innervate the same muscle from which the Ia fiber originated (these are called *homonymous muscles*). This type of excitation is called *autogenetic excitation;* the term simply means that an afferent from a particular muscle either excites or inhibits a motor neuron that produces a contraction of the same muscle. Thus the receptor can to some degree control the muscle in which it resides. The distribution of Ia afferent fibers to alpha motor neurons supplying homonymous muscles is quite extensive. Using an elegant technique called *spike-triggered averaging,* in which a computer is triggered by the impulse in a single Ia afferent to detect the excitatory postsynaptic potentials produced by that afferent in the alpha motor neurons, Mendell and Henneman recently estimated that a single Ia afferent (from cat medial gastrocnemius muscle) sends terminals to *all* of the motor neurons to that muscle—approximately 300 motor neurons!

2. Ia fibers also make direct monosynaptic excitatory connections with alpha motor neurons which innervate muscles that are synergistic (that is, they have the same action at the same joint) to the muscle from which the Ia fiber originated.

3. Ia fibers make direct excitatory connections with inhibitory interneurons; these in turn directly connect to and inhibit alpha motor neurons that control muscles that are antagonistic to those from which the Ia fiber originated. Thus the Ia fiber inhibits the antagonistic motor neuron disynaptically by means of an intercalated inhibitory interneuron. This class of interneuron, called the Ia inhibitory interneuron (*shaded* in Figure 26−1) has been extensively studied (see also Figure 26−2). Inhibition of antagonist motor neurons at the same time that homonymous and synergist neurons are excited is called *reciprocal inhibition.* This term implies that as motor neurons to homonymous and synergistic muscles that are appropriate to a particular action are excited, motor neurons to antagonistic muscles that are inappropriate to that action are inhibited.

Another important inhibitory spinal interneuron, the *Renshaw cell,* receives direct excitation from collateral branches of spinal motor neurons, and in turn inhibits many motor neurons including the one that gave rise to its input. This is called *recurrent inhibition* (Figure 26−2). Recurrent inhibition can have several functional consequences. Perhaps the most obvious one is that it tends to shorten the motor output from a particular collection of motor neurons

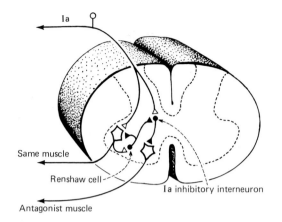

26–2 Elementary circuit underlying recurrent inhibition. The Renshaw cell, which is directly excited by collateral branches of spinal motor neurons, inhibits many motor neurons, including the one that gave rise to its input. It disinhibits antagonist motor neurons by inhibiting Ia inhibitory interneurons.

26–3 Role of Ia afferent fibers in the stretch reflex. **A.** Relationships among Ia afferents, spinal motor neurons, and somatic muscles. **B.** Passive stretch of the limb (**open arrow**) gives rise to an increased Ia fiber discharge (**solid arrow**). **C.** The Ia fiber discharge causes homonymous and synergist alpha motor neurons to fire (**solid arrows**), producing resistance to the stretch (**open arrow**). (Parts of this figure adapted from Merton, 1972.)

(called a *motor pool*). Recurrent inhibition may also highlight the output of motor neurons that are strongly activated, because those motor neurons will exert strong feedback inhibition (via the Renshaw cells) to other neighboring motor neurons, suppressing their output. The strongly activated motor neurons will themselves also receive recurrent inhibition, but because they are highly activated their output (though diminished) can still be expressed. The Renshaw cell was named after its discoverer, Birdsey Renshaw, by Eccles and his colleagues in 1954.

Among the many connections that the Renshaw cell makes, one of the most thoroughly studied is its direct connection to the Ia inhibitory interneurons. Studies of the distribution of Renshaw inhibition show that the Ia inhibitory interneurons receive their recurrent inhibition (via the Renshaw cells) from motor neurons to the same muscles that give rise to their Ia afferent input (Figure 26–2). Thus, alpha motor neurons and Ia inhibitory interneurons which receive the same Ia input seem to receive recurrent inhibition from the same set of Renshaw cells. One important functional consequence of this arrangement is that the Renshaw cell is in a position to limit the duration and magnitude of a Ia afferent–mediated reflex response, as Ia afferent

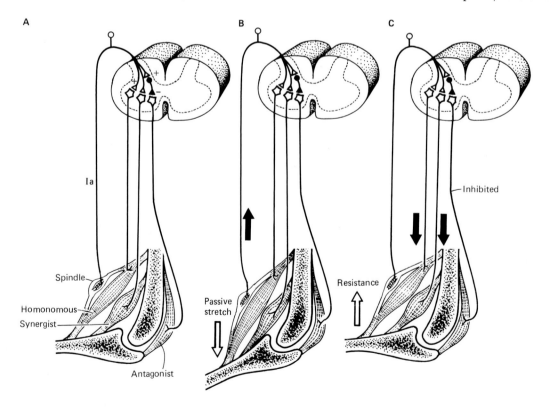

activation of a homonymous motor neuron will in turn produce Renshaw inhibition of that motor neuron and, at the same time, disinhibition of the antagonist motor neuron by inhibiting the Ia inhibitory interneuron.

If we now consider the central connections of the Ia fibers discussed above, along with the reflex actions described by Liddell and Sherrington, we can see how the Ia fibers contribute to the stretch reflex (Figure 26–3). In this example a stretch reflex of flexor muscles is illustrated. Passive extension of a partially flexed limb will stretch the flexor muscles, thereby stretching (loading) the muscle spindles of those muscles, which will give rise to a Ia fiber discharge from the spindles. The Ia fiber discharge will monosynaptically excite both the homonymous and synergistic (flexor) muscles and disynaptically inhibit antagonist (extensor) muscles.

Ib Afferents Contribute to the Inverse Myotatic Reflex

The reflex actions of the Ib afferent system are not as well understood as those of the Ia afferents. However, an appreciation of some of the functional properties of the Ib afferent system can be gained by examining the central connections of the Ib fibers. These connections were first studied by Laporte and Lloyd, who increased the strength of an electrical stimulus to a nerve of muscle origin just above that necessary to elicit the myotatic (Ia fiber–mediated) afferent response. They observed a reflex action that appeared to be opposite to the myotatic reflex, that is, the muscle of origin and its synergists were inhibited and the antagonists were excited. Thus Laporte and Lloyd called this the *inverse myotatic reflex*. The Ib fiber central connections are shown in Figure 26–4. Central connections of the Ib fibers have

three features: (1) all connections to motor neurons are made through interneurons; (2) Ib afferent effects are relatively infrequent in flexor muscles, whereas they are readily seen in extensors; and (3) the effects of Ib afferents are much more widespread in the spinal cord and somatic muscles compared to the restricted action of Ia afferents. The reflex actions of the Ib afferent system are not simply the opposite of those of the Ia afferent system, but are qualitatively different. Because the central connections of the Ib afferents are more widespread than those of the Ia afferents, and the Golgi tendon system measures *tension* whereas the spindle system measures *length*, many investigators believe that calling the reflex actions of the Ib system the inverse myotatic reflex may not be appropriate.

What is the function of this Ib afferent–mediated reflex? Because the Golgi tendon organs were known to have a high threshold when activated by passive stretch, it was originally believed that the primary function of the Ib afferent system was protective, i.e., that it prevented the muscle from producing excessive tension by inhibiting homonymous and synergist motor neurons and exciting antagonists. However, by stimulating single large motor fibers to the soleus muscle and recording the Ib fiber discharge, Houk and Henneman have recently found that the Golgi tendon organs are exquisitely sensitive to active muscle contraction. They have proposed that the Ib afferent system could act as a tension feedback system. Thus increases in muscle ten-

26–4 Central connections of the Ib afferent fibers.

All connections to motor neurons are through interneurons. In the relex mediated by the Ib afferent system, inhibitory interneurons **(shaded)** inhibit motor neurons to the muscle of origin and its synergists, and excitatory interneurons excite the antagonists.

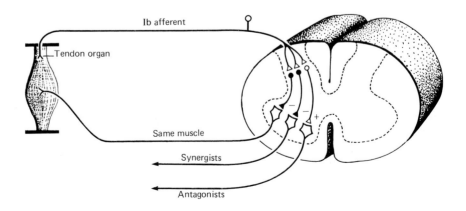

sion beyond a desired point would produce negative feedback from Golgi tendon organs that would inhibit the further development of tension. Decreases in muscle tension, occurring for example when a muscle begins to fatigue, would have the opposite effect: as the tendon organ is less activated there would be less inhibition onto homonymous and synergist motor cells and more tension would develop, compensating for the fatigue.

Recent findings by Lundberg and his colleagues have provided further insight into modes of action in Ib afferent reflex pathways. They found that interneurons in these pathways receive convergent short-latency excitation from low-threshold cutaneous afferents and from joint afferents. The functional implication of this convergence is quite interesting. For example, if a limb movement is initiated but suddenly meets a physical obstruction, low-threshold cutaneous and joint afferents would probably be activated by such an obstacle and their activity would facilitate Ib afferent inhibitory transmission, with the result that muscular tension in the limb would be reduced, preventing further force against the obstacle.

There is another interesting possible role for low-threshold joint afferent facilitation of Ib fiber transmission. If these afferents are activated at the end of a flexor or an extensor movement, their facilitation of Ib fiber inhibitory transmission might provide a mechanism to decrease force when a particular movement approaches the mechanical limit of the range over which the joint operates.

Group II Afferents Contribute to Stretch, Flexion, and Clasp-Knife Reflexes

The reflex actions of group II afferents have been the subject of lively controversy for many years because they evoke both direct (monosynaptic) and indirect (polysynaptic) actions in motor neurons. Moreover, different types of interneurons that mediate the polysynaptic actions appear to be switched on or off in different experimental preparations.

Direct Actions on Homonymous Motor Neurons: Stretch Reflex

In a series of ingenious experiments in 1969, P. B. C. Matthews at Oxford first suggested that spindle secondaries contribute significantly to the stretch reflex in decerebrate animals. Following this, experiments conducted in several laboratories using the spike-triggered averaging technique have shown conclusively that spindle secondaries produce monosynaptic excitation in homonymous motor neurons and have thus confirmed Matthews' suggestion.

Polysynaptic Pathways: Flexion and Clasp-Knife Reflexes

Eccles and Lundberg obtained intracellular recordings of different spinal motor neurons and found that electrical stimuli activating group II fibers in a variety of muscle nerves excite motor neurons to physiological flexors and inhibit those to physiological extensors. The postsynaptic potentials in the motor neurons produced by such stimulation occur with long latencies indicative of a polysynaptic pathway. These polysynaptic actions appear primarily in spinal preparations where, as we shall see, flexion reflexes can be elicited by stimulation of very different types of afferents. Thus the group II afferents have often been suggested to play a role in flexion reflexes, which will be discussed later in this chapter.

The effects of group II afferents are clinically relevant because in patients with spasticity they appear to give rise to the well-known *clasp-knife reflex*. In these patients, who otherwise show marked enhancement of stretch reflexes, there occurs a sudden melting away of muscle tone when a limb is passively moved. Experiments by Burke and his colleagues in Australia have shown that this melting away of the resistance offered by the muscles is strictly dependent upon the length of the muscle in question. Specifically, the greater the static length of the muscle, the less resistance is offered upon further stretch. Thus, a length-dependent inhibition of the stretch reflex is characteristic of the clasp-knife reflex. Because the spindle secondaries are the principal receptors capable of producing this length-dependent inhibition, and because it can be produced in experimental preparations where the inhibitory actions of the group II afferents are predominant, it seems most reasonable to conclude that the group II afferents contribute significantly to the clasp-knife phenomenon.

It had originally been thought that the inhibitory actions of Ib afferents from Golgi tendon organs might mediate the clasp-knife reflex, because it was believed that the tendon organs had high thresholds which might account for the abrupt inhibition of the stretch reflex characteristic of this reaction. However, as discussed previously, it is now known that the Golgi tendon organs are extremely sensitive to active muscular contraction and are active over most of the normal range of forces generated in muscles. Moreover, the inhibitory effects of the clasp-knife reflex far outlast the actual reduction of active muscle force, but tendon organ activity declines in parallel with the decline in muscle force. Thus, current thinking is that the Ib afferents may play some role, especially in initiating the clasp-knife reflex, but the inhibitory actions of the group II afferents are likely to be the principal cause of the length-dependent inhibition characteristic of this reflex.

Functional Significance of Reflexes of Muscle Origin

The Gamma Loop and the Length-Servo Hypothesis

The excitability of the stretch reflex depends critically upon tonic descending control from higher brain centers. The way in which higher centers influence the stretch reflex has thus received a great deal of experimental and theoretical attention. Descending control could produce a movement directly by acting on alpha motor neurons, or indirectly, by acting on gamma motor neurons. Direct activation of alpha motor neurons from higher centers will lead to contraction of somatic (extrafusal) muscles. Why, however, is there descending control onto gamma motor neurons? One attractive hypothesis is that activation of the somatic muscles can also be brought about indirectly by activation of gamma motor neurons from higher centers. This is called activation via the *gamma loop*. Activation of gamma motor neurons would stretch (load) the intrafusal mus-

cle spindles, giving rise to an increase in Ia fiber firing from the muscle, which in turn would activate the homonymous and synergist motor neurons, thereby producing a contraction of the extrafusal muscles (Figure 26–5).

Why would the nervous system follow such an indirect route to activate alpha motor neurons, since it is slower and less precise than direct activation? A creative suggestion for the role of the gamma loop was made by P. A. Merton, who recognized that spindle discharge can be modulated both by gamma motor neuron activity and by contraction of the extrafusal muscle. Merton proposed that the stretch reflex could be made to function as a *follow-up length-servo system* (Figure 26–6). When contraction of somatic muscles is produced by the gamma route, the extrafusal muscles contract to a given length (predetermined by the amount of gamma motor neuron discharge produced from higher centers; this discharge is called the *gamma bias*). If the extrafusal muscle shortens any further—for example, because of a sudden decrease in load—the spindles in the muscle become unloaded, with the result that the Ia fiber discharge from those spindles ceases, thereby removing their excitation to the alpha motor cells that bring about contraction of the extrafusal muscle (Figure 26–6C). The muscle then begins to relax until it lengthens to the point that the spindles are stretched (reloaded) and the muscle again contracts via the gamma loop. Thus the extrafusal muscle *follows au-*

26–5 Activation of alpha motor neurons via the gamma loop. The gamma motor neuron is activated by input from higher centers (1), producing shortening of the spindle (2), which gives rise to an increase in Ia fiber discharge (3), which in turn increases the alpha motor neuron output (4), thereby producing contraction of the extrafusal muscle (5).

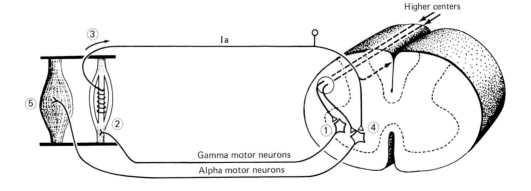

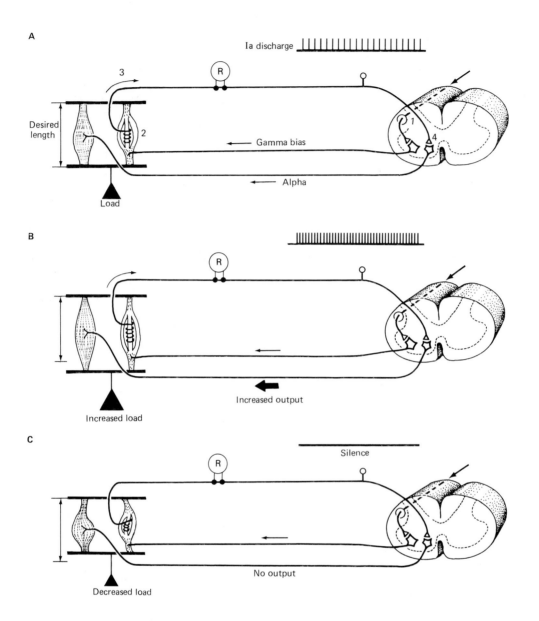

26-6 Length-servo hypothesis. **A.** Higher centers
activate alpha motor neurons via the gamma
loop (numbers as in Figure 26–5). The firing of the
gamma neurons (the gamma bias) increases the Ia fiber
discharge (recorded at **R**) enough to drive alpha motor
neurons, producing a reflex contraction of the muscle
to a given desired length. **B.** Increasing the load on the
muscle will increase Ia fiber discharge and thereby
increase alpha motor neuron output, counteracting the
increased load and returning the muscle to the desired
length. **C.** Decreasing the load unloads the spindle.
With no Ia fiber input the alpha motor neuron output
ceases and the muscle relaxes until the desired length
is achieved, at which point the spindle is reloaded.

tomatically the degree of contraction of the intrafusal fiber, which is determined by the gamma
bias. Merton suggested that this servo system
could provide for load compensation, as any
change in load (that is, the amount of stretch) on
the muscle could be counteracted by an increase
or decrease in Ia fiber discharge (Figure 26–6).
Thus, a central concept in any form of servo
hypothesis involving the gamma loop is the
notion of *misalignment between intended
muscle length and actual muscle length*, which
reduces to the difference between spindle length

and extrafusal fiber length. When there is no difference between spindle and extrafusal fiber lengths, there is no misalignment.

A direct test of Merton's hypothesis was recently carried out by Vallbo, who recorded from the Ia afferents from muscle spindles in his own wrist and finger flexor muscles (by means of fine wires inserted into his muscle nerves) during both rapid and slow voluntary movements. A critical prediction from Merton's hypothesis is that the Ia fiber discharge should *precede* contraction of the muscle because gamma motor cells are hypothesized to initiate the movement by contracting spindles, setting up a Ia discharge that then would activate alpha motor cells and produce measurable movement. In fact, Vallbo found that the Ia discharge *followed* electrical activity in the muscle (and the resultant muscle tension) after a short delay. This indicated that the movement was initiated by the direct alpha mode. However, the fact that the Ia afferents fired at all is important, for it showed that gamma motor neurons were also activated. Had the gamma motor neurons not been activated, the spindles would have been unloaded by the contraction and the Ia discharge would have ceased. Vallbo concluded that the alpha and gamma motor neurons are essentially coactivated. Coactivation of alpha and gamma motor neurons has subsequently also been observed in several other motor systems, including those involved in respiration, jaw contraction, human voluntary thumb movements, and (as we shall discuss in Chapter 28) locomotion. The work of Vallbo and others led to the proposition that the gamma loop might function in a *servo-assist mode*; that is, even though the gamma loop is not responsible for the initiation of a movement, it may still operate to assist in load compensation. However, today even this role is questioned. The basic problem is that, although the notion of load compensation by the gamma loop is admittedly attractive, the actual strength of the reflex connections within the spinal cord (this is called the *gain* of the reflex) is probably insufficient to play a significant role in load compensation.

Regulation of Stiffness Hypothesis

Another interesting possibility concerning the role of the stretch reflex has recently been advanced by Nichols and Houk, who suggested that the stretch reflex may compensate for variations in the mechanical properties of a muscle.

These investigators studied the purely mechanical properties of muscle by denervating the hind limbs of cats, thus eliminating the stretch reflex. They then caused the soleus muscles to contract by electrically stimulating their motor axons and, during the contraction, they either stretched or released the muscle by different amounts. They found that in response to large stretch the muscle force first increased but then suddenly gave way or yielded. However, in cats that were not denervated, so that the stretch reflex was active, the yielding of the muscle did not occur (Figure 26–7). Instead, during large stretch the muscle continued to generate increased force; that is, a more constant relationship between muscle tension and muscle length was maintained. Thus, Nichols and Houk proposed that the important variable that is regulated is the ratio of force (tension) change to length change—this is called muscle stiffness. The central idea is that the two reflexes we have discussed so far can act in combination to provide for a servo control of muscle stiffness rather than the Ia fiber–mediated reflex individually providing a length servo, and the Ib fiber–mediated reflex individually providing a tension servo.

Thus far we have considered the spinal connections of the Ia, Ib, and II afferents onto motor

26–7 "Yielding" (abrupt failure in muscular stiffness) in response to large stretch in the functionally isolated soleus muscle of the decerebrate cat is compensated for by the stretch reflex in the normal cat. (Adapted from Houk, 1979.)

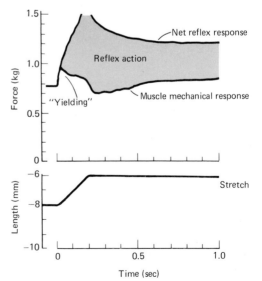

neurons. These afferents also activate a number of ascending fiber systems to inform higher brain structures, such as the cerebellum and cortex, about local affairs in the spinal cord and about the length, tension, and position of the muscles.

A general principle of spinal organization in the reflexes of muscle origin that we have discussed is that there is usually a relatively close match between the afferent input from a particular muscle or muscle group and the motor output (excitation or inhibition) to the same muscle group. This principle can be seen at much higher levels of motor organization as well, since it is known that some motor neurons in the cortex are activated by peripheral input from the specific target region (muscle groups) that those particular cortical motor neurons control (see Chapter 29).

Afferents from Cutaneous and Deep Receptors Mediate a Reflex Consisting of Ipsilateral Flexion and Contralateral Extension

Group III and IV afferents arise from receptors in muscle (deep receptors) and skin (cutaneous receptors). Both the myelinated group III and the unmyelinated group IV fibers carry information about painful stimuli (extreme pressure, heat, cold, etc.), and thus the reflexes that they produce serve as protective or escape responses. The predominant reflex pattern to which they give rise is ipsilateral flexion, usually accompanied by contralateral extension. This reflex response is mediated by polysynaptic connections in the spinal cord (Figure 26–8). The degree of flexion can vary from a flexor twitch, produced by relatively innocuous tactile stimulation, to a complete

withdrawal of the limb from a noxious stimulus. The crossed extensor part of the general reflex pattern makes sense, because it provides a way for an animal to maintain posture, with the extended leg bearing the weight of the body while the opposite limb is withdrawn from the noxious stimulus.

Because group II (discussed earlier) and group III muscle afferents can produce flexion responses, they are often lumped together with afferents from skin and joints and collectively called *flexor reflex afferents* (FRA). In common practice this has become a term (albeit an imprecise one) for almost any afferents that produce a flexion response.

The general picture described above has several important exceptions. For example, in a careful study of different classes of cutaneous afferents, Perl has shown that group II fibers can set in motion a bilateral flexion reflex. If group III fibers are also activated, however, the classical ipsilateral flexion and contralateral extension are seen. This is an important point, for it indicates that caution is necessary in interpreting many nerve stimulation studies, since one class of reflex actions can be hidden by another, more powerful reflex pattern.

Another important exception to the general scheme described above illustrates the point that many special reflex effects can be obtained from specific cutaneous regions. For example, in high spinal dogs light tactile pressure applied to the footpads of the forepaw produces marked reflex *extension* of the whole limb. This reflex is one of obvious utility when an animal is standing on the ground, for reflex tightening of the extensor muscles allows the animal to keep its leg straight au-

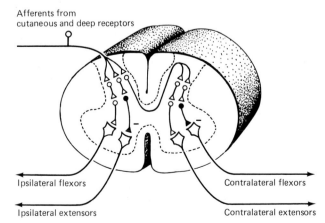

Afferents from
cutaneous and deep receptors

Ipsilateral flexors

Ipsilateral extensors

Contralateral flexors

Contralateral extensors

26–8 Basic circuitry for reflexes of cutaneous and deep receptor origin. The usual pattern is ipsilateral flexion and contralateral extension.

tomatically. However, another stimulus, such as a pinprick, to the same skin region of the footpad immediately produces a *flexion withdrawal* of the paw. Thus the quality of the stimulus as well as its location on the skin is an important determinant of the type of reflex action.

Reflex Activity Is Subject to Supraspinal and Intraspinal Influences

One striking feature of the afferent fiber systems we have considered is that their influence on motor neurons in the spinal cord is usually exerted via polysynaptic pathways. An important consequence of this convergence onto spinal interneurons is that there are multiple loci within the spinal cord where modulation of reflex responses can occur. A dramatic illustration of reflex modulation can be seen when all descending influence from supraspinal regions to spinal circuits is removed by cutting of the spinal cord. Immediately after this procedure, all reflex activity is lost (i.e., a condition of areflexia results); this condition is called *spinal shock*.

One might think that the loss of reflex activity after spinal transection is due to the trauma of the transection per se. However, Sherrington carried out a critical experiment that showed this is not so. He cut the spinal cord and waited for recovery from spinal shock. He then performed a second transection just below the previous one, and little or no spinal shock occurred, even though the surgical trauma of the second transection was comparable to that of the first. Sherrington concluded that the reflex depression is chiefly due to loss of facilitation from higher brain centers.

After some time, reflex activity begins gradually to return. In carnivores this may take only minutes to hours; in monkeys, days or weeks; and in man it can take several months or even longer. The reflexes that return become progressively more abnormal and exaggerated, developing into a condition of hyperreflexia. This is particularly true of flexion reflexes; these can become so exaggerated that cutaneous input will trigger a mass reflex involving generalized contraction of all flexor muscles. The hyperreflexia after spinal shock is not well understood. Many contributing factors have been suggested, including increased sensitivity of spinal interneurons and motor neurons to transmitter substances and removal of descending inhibitory influences from supraspinal centers onto reflex circuits. Another interesting suggestion, advanced by McCouch

and his colleagues, concerns the mechanism of late hyperreflexia in chronic spinal animals which occurs weeks or months after transection, when tendon reflexes have returned, and the flexor reflex becomes exaggerated. They suggest that the hyperreflexia is due at least in part to the sprouting of afferent pathways below the spinal transection. It is thought that terminals from supraspinal tracts degenerate, leaving postsynaptic vacancies on interneurons and motor neurons that are then filled by sprouting branches of the still intact afferent systems, and new connections are formed. Therefore, the recovery of reflex function actually reflects the establishment of new abnormal reflex actions rather than the restoration of normal reflex function. There is compelling evidence that in other regions of the central nervous system (especially in the red nucleus, the septal nucleus, and the hippocampus) sprouting occurs following a lesion and the newly sprouted connections can be functional.

Spinal shock reveals the importance of descending influences on spinal reflex circuits. However, there are also ascending influences exerted from lower spinal regions onto higher spinal regions. A fascinating example of this is the *Shiff-Sherrington reflex*. As mentioned earlier, a decerebrate animal shows exaggerated extensor reflexes of the limbs and neck *(decerebrate rigidity)*. If the spinal cord of a decerebrate animal is sectioned in the midthoracic region, below the level of spinal output to the forelimbs, the degree of extensor rigidity in the forelimbs increases dramatically. This is thought to occur because lower regions of the spinal cord exert inhibitory influences over higher regions that mediate extensor reflexes of the forelimbs.

The key principle that emerges from studies on the relative influence of supraspinal and intraspinal regions on spinal reflexes is that *the spinal cord contains within itself the basic neural machinery necessary to generate all reflex actions.* These local spinal circuits, however, are constantly modulated (both facilitated and inhibited) by descending pathways from higher brain regions as well as by other regions within the spinal cord itself.

Selected Readings and References

Henneman, E. 1980. Organization of the spinal cord and its reflexes. In V. B. Mountcastle (ed.), Medical Physiology, 14th ed., Vol. 1. St. Louis: Mosby, pp. 762–786.

Hunt, C. C., and Perl, E. R. 1960. Spinal reflex mechanisms concerned with skeletal muscle. Physiol. Rev. 40:538–579.

Lloyd, D. P. C. 1960. Spinal mechanisms involved in somatic activities. In H. W. Magoun (ed.), Handbook of Physiology, Section 1: Neurophysiology, Vol. 2. Washington, D.C.: American Physiological Society, pp. 929–949.

Lundberg, A. 1975. Control of spinal mechanisms from the brain. In D. B. Tower (ed.), The Nervous System, Vol. 1, The Basic Neurosciences. New York: Raven Press, pp. 253–265.

Matthews, P. B. C. 1972. Mammalian Muscle Receptors and Their Central Actions. Baltimore: Williams & Wilkins.

Other References

Burke, D., Knowles, L., Andrews, C., and Ashby, P. 1972. Spasticity, decerebrate rigidity and the clasp-knife phenomenon: An experimental study in the cat. Brain 95:31–48.

Chambers, W. W., Liu, C. N., and McCouch, G. P. 1973. Anatomical and physiological correlates of plasticity in the central nervous system. Brain, Behav. Evol. 8:5–26.

Eccles, J. C. 1964. The Physiology of Synapses. Berlin: Springer.

Eccles, J. C., Fatt, P., and Koketsu, K. 1954. Cholinergic and inhibitory synapses in a pathway from motor-axon collaterals to motoneurones. J. Physiol. (Lond.) 126:524–562.

Eccles, R. M., and Lundberg, A. 1959. Synaptic actions in motoneurones by afferents which may evoke the flexion reflex. Arch. Ital. Biol. 97:199–221.

Houk, J., and Henneman, E. 1967. Responses of Golgi tendon organs to active contractions of the soleus muscle of the cat. J. Neurophysiol. 30:466–481.

Houk, J. C. 1979. Motor control processes: New data concerning motoservo mechanisms and a tentative model for stimulus-response processing. In R. E. Talbott and D. R. Humphrey (eds.), Posture and Movement. New York: Raven Press, pp. 231–241.

Laporte, Y., and Lloyd, D. P. C. 1952. Nature and significance of the reflex connections established by large afferent fibers of muscular origin. Am. J. Physiol. 169:609–621.

Liddell, E. G. T., and Sherrington C. 1924. Reflexes in response to stretch (myotatic reflexes). Proc. R. Soc. Lond. B Biol. Sci. 96:212–242.

Liddell, E. G. T., and Sherrington, C. 1925. Further observations on myotatic reflexes. Proc. R. Soc. Lond. B Biol. Sci. 97:267–283.

Lloyd, D. P. C. 1943. Conduction and synaptic transmission of the reflex response to stretch in spinal cats. J. Neurophysiol. 6:317–326.

Mendell, L. M., and Henneman, E. 1971. Terminals of single Ia fibers: Location, density, and distribution within a pool of 300 homonymous motoneurons. J. Neurophysiol. 34:171–187.

Merton, P. A. 1953. Speculations on the servo-control of movement. In G. E. W. Wolstenholme (ed.), The Spinal Cord. London: Churchill Livingston, pp. 247–255.

Merton, P. A. 1972. How we control the contraction of our muscles. Sci. Am. 226(5):30–37.

Nichols, T. R., and Houk, J. C. 1973. Reflex compensation for variations in the mechanical properties of a muscle. Science (Wash., D.C.) 181:182–184.

Vallbo, Å. B. 1970. Discharge patterns in human muscle spindle afferents during isometric voluntary contractions. Acta Physiol. Scand. 80:552–566.

Vallbo, Å. B. 1971. Muscle spindle response at the onset of isometric voluntary contractions in man. Time difference between fusimotor and skeletomotor effects. J. Physiol. (Lond.) 218:405–431.

Lewis P. Rowland

Spinal Cord III: Clinical Syndromes

Knowledge of the anatomy and physiology of the spinal cord helps clinicians to recognize spinal cord disease (myelopathy), to localize the disease to a particular segment or region of the spinal cord, and often to identify the nature of the disorder. In this chapter we shall review the anatomy that is important in the examination of patients with neurological disorders of the spinal cord. We shall then consider the major diseases that affect the spinal cord.

The Clinically Important Anatomy Is Simple

The only descending tracts of clinical importance are the corticospinal tracts in the lateral columns of the spinal cord (Figure 27–1A). Other descending tracts such as the rubrospinal are also important in the control of posture and movement, but only the effects of lesions of the corticospinal tracts are evident clinically.

Three ascending tracts are important clinically:

1. The dorsal column–medial lemniscal system carries sensations of discriminatory touch, vibration, and joint position. The axons run ipsilateral to the roots of entry and cross to the other side above the spinal cord in the medulla after synapsing in the dorsal column nuclei (Figure 27–1B).

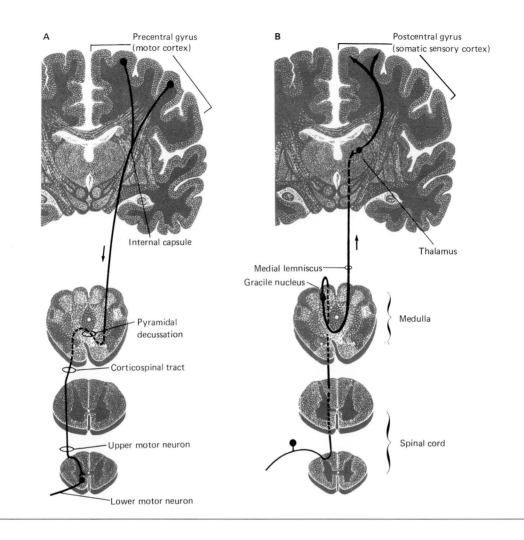

A

Precentral gyrus
(motor cortex)

Internal capsule

Pyramidal
decussation

Corticospinal tract

Upper motor neuron

Lower motor neuron

B

Postcentral gyrus
(somatic sensory cortex)

Thalamus

Medial lemniscus

Gracile nucleus

Medulla

Spinal cord

2. The lateral spinothalamic tracts convey sensations of pain, temperature, and crude touch from the other side of the body (Figure 27–1C).

3. The spinocerebellar tracts (Figure 27–1D) are involved in some hereditary ataxias but are not the source of symptoms in other spinal cord diseases.

Somatotopic Organization of the Spinothalamic Tracts Aids Diagnosis

The fibers in the corticospinal tracts, posterior columns, and spinothalamic tracts are somatotopically organized. This somatotopic organization is diagnostically important in two conditions, both of which affect the spinothalamic tracts: (1) lesions of the central parts of the cervical or thoracic cord and (2) surgical relief of pain.

Because the lowermost (sacral) fibers are pushed laterally by fibers entering from successively higher levels, the phenomenon called *sacral sparing* may occur with lesions of the central portion of the thoracic or cervical cord. As these lesions extend peripherally, they first compress the most medial fibers from lower segments but may not affect the most lateral sacral fibers. If this occurs, all cutaneous sensation may be abolished below the level of the lesion but the sacral segments (perineum, scrotum, and saddle area) are spared.

Neurosurgeons take advantage of the somatotopic organization of these tracts in the operation called *cordotomy*, sometimes performed to control intractable pain arising in the pelvis or

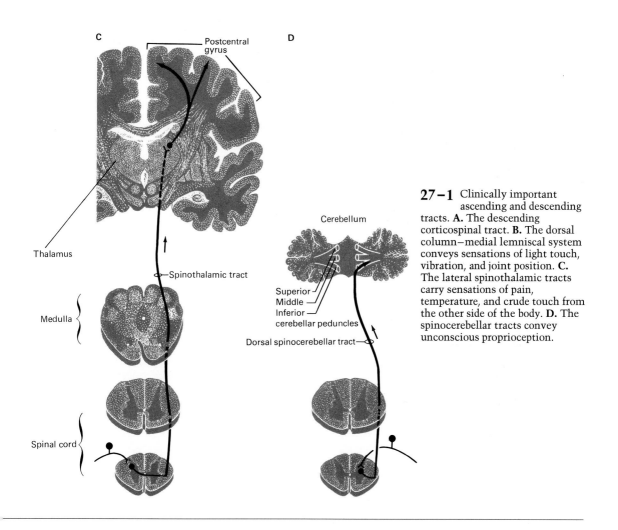

27–1 Clinically important ascending and descending tracts. **A.** The descending corticospinal tract. **B.** The dorsal column–medial lemniscal system conveys sensations of light touch, vibration, and joint position. **C.** The lateral spinothalamic tracts carry sensations of pain, temperature, and crude touch from the other side of the body. **D.** The spinocerebellar tracts convey unconscious proprioception.

legs. Because the spinal cord itself is insensitive to pain, it is possible to section the spinothalamic tracts selectively under local anesthesia. When the scalpel enters the outer aspect of the spinal cord and spinothalamic tract, the sacral fibers are encountered first. As the knife enters deeper levels, the level of sensory loss rises until the desired level is attained. Because the patient is awake and cooperative, the level of sensory loss can be ascertained repeatedly during the procedure.

Function Is Lost Below a Transverse Spinal Lesion

Lesions of the spinal cord give rise to motor or sensory symptoms that are often related to a particular sensory or motor segmental level of the spinal cord. Identification of the appropri-

ate level of the motor or sensory deficit is crucial to the recognition of focal intramedullary or compressive lesions which interrupt functions below the lesion. However, because segmental innervation of muscles of the trunk and thorax is difficult to identify, the level of motor dysfunction may not be evident. For instance, a lesion anywhere above L1 may cause upper motor neuron signs in the legs.

Motor Level

When motor roots are involved, or when motor neurons are affected focally, there may be evidence of a motor level. This evidence would include the typical lower motor neuron signs: weakness, wasting, fasciculation, and loss of tendon reflexes. The muscles and tendon reflexes

Table 27–1. Indicators of Motor Level Lesions

Root	Major muscles affected	Reflex loss
C3–5	Diaphragm	—
C5	Deltoid, biceps	Biceps
C7	Triceps, extensors of wrist and fingers	Triceps
C8	Interossei, abductor of the fifth finger	—
L2–4	Quadriceps	Knee jerk
L5	Long extensor of great toe, anterior tibial	—
S1	Plantar flexors, gastrocnemius	Ankle jerk

that serve as landmarks for locating motor level lesions are listed in Table 27–1.

Sensory Level

The characteristic pattern of sensory loss of a transverse spinal cord lesion is loss of cutaneous sensation below the level of the lesion, contralateral to the affected spinothalamic tract if the lesion is unilateral. The sensory level is often more evident than the motor level. However, spinal sensory loss has to be differentiated from the pattern of sensory loss caused by lesions of peripheral nerves or isolated nerve roots. In *multiple peripheral neuropathy,* there is a glove-and-stocking pattern, attributed to impaired axonal transport, so that the parts of the axons most severely affected are the ones most distant from the

Table 27–2. Indicators of Sensory Level Lesions

Root	Major sensory areas affected
C4	Clavicle
C8	Fifth finger
T4	Nipples
T10	Umbilicus
L1	Inguinal ligament
L3	Anterior surface of the thigh
L5	Great toe
S1	Lateral aspect of the foot
S3–5	Perineum

sensory neuron cell bodies in the dorsal root ganglia. In injuries of *single peripheral nerves,* the distribution of sensory loss is more restricted and can be recognized by reference to sensory charts that were originally plotted in traumatic injuries.

Nerve root or segmental sensory loss and spinal sensory levels can be identified by the typical dermatomes affected (Figure 27–2). The landmarks for the major sensory levels are listed in Table 27–2.

The spinal cord ends at the level of the body of the L2 vertebra. Below this level the spinal canal is occupied by the lower nerve roots (cauda equina).

In examining patients, students are sometimes perplexed by abnormalities that patients report but that do not seem to fit the disorder suspected. You should realize that sensory testing may be difficult in normal individuals and is especially difficult for anxious patients. Two general rules help: (1) If you find cutaneous sensory loss and the patient does not complain of paresthesias (tingling, pins and needles, lack of sensation, numbness), be wary of the reported sensory loss, which is probably an artifact of examination. (2) Conversely, if the patient does complain of paresthesias and you do not find any cutaneous sensory loss on examination, try again.

It Is Important to Distinguish Intra- from Extramedullary Disease

In practical terms, it is important to know whether the lesion arises within the spinal cord *(intramedullary or intra-axial),* or whether the spinal cord is being compressed by an external mass *(extramedullary or extra-axial).* The spinal cord is also vulnerable to trauma. Clinical characteristics may lead to a suspicion of spinal cord disease, but definitive diagnosis often depends upon radiographic contrast procedures, the most important of which is *myelography.* In this procedure a radiopaque material is introduced into the subarachnoid space to outline the spinal cord, nerve roots, and the bony margins of the canal, permitting assessment of compressive lesions or those that distort the cord from within. Selective catheterization of spinal blood vessels and injection of radiopaque dyes *(spinal angiography)* permits assessment of vascular lesions.

The application of these principles is best appreciated by the analysis of some typical spinal cord syndromes.

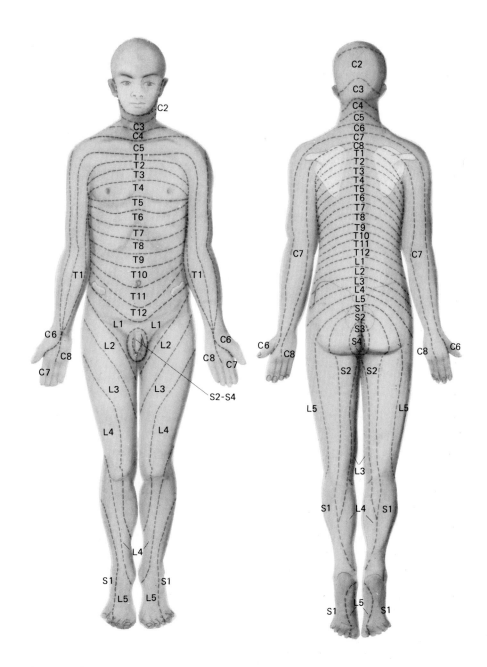

Lesions of the Spinal Cord Often Give Rise to Characteristic Syndromes
Complete Transection

27–2 Segmental arrangement of dermatomes. **S,** sacral; **L,** lumbar; **T,** thoracic; **C,** cervical.

The spinal cord may be completely severed acutely in fracture-dislocations of vertebrae or by knife or bullet wounds. Acute transection of the cord may also result from an inflammatory condition *(transverse myelitis)* or from compression due to a tumor, especially metastatic tumors.

In the latter conditions, symptoms evolve in days or weeks.

Immediately after a traumatic section of the cord, however, there is loss of all sensation and all voluntary movement below the lesion. Bladder and bowel control are also lost. If the lesion is above C3 respiration may be affected. Although upper motor neuron signs might be expected, tendon reflexes are usually absent—a condition of "spinal shock" that persists for several weeks. After a while, reflex activity returns at levels below the lesion. Hyperactive reflexes, clonus, and Babinski signs then appear. The legs become spastic; this condition is often preceded by intermittent hypertonia and flexor spasms that occur spontaneously or may be provoked by cutaneous stimuli. Later, there may be alternating flexor and extensor spasms, and the ultimately fixed posture may be either extension or flexion of the knees and hips. Bladder and bowel function may become automatic, emptying in response to moderate filling. Automatic bladder emptying may be retarded by severe distension of the bladder or infection in the acute stage, or by damage to lumbar or sacral cord segments.

Partial Transection

In partial transection of the spinal cord, some ascending or descending tracts may be spared. In slowly progressing lesions, as in compression by an extramedullary tumor, the same tracts may be affected but less severely, so that partial function is retained, but the specific motor and sensory signs can be recognized.

Hemisection (Brown-Séquard Syndrome)

As a consequence of spinal cord anatomy, hemisection of the right side of the cervical spinal cord (at C4, for example) would result in the following: (1) *ipsilateral (right) corticospinal signs,* with weakness of the right arm and leg, more active reflexes on that side, Hoffmann sign, Babinski sign, and possibly clonus; (2) *ipsilateral posterior column signs,* with loss of position sense and vibratory sensation; (3) *contralateral (left) loss of pain and temperature perception* to the level of C4 due to interruption of the right spinothalamic tract; and (4) *loss of autonomic function* resulting in the Horner syndrome (miosis, ptosis) on the same side.

Syringomyelia

Syringomyelia is a disease that leads to the formation of cysts within the spinal cord. The cause of the disease is unknown, but the lesion affects the central portion of the cord first and then spreads peripherally. Intramedullary tumors may

also cause the same syndrome. The clinical picture of syringomyelia is characterized by two unusual patterns of segmental dysfunction (involving cutaneous sensation and motor neurons) as well as interruption of ascending or descending tracts. Because the lesion starts centrally, the first fibers to be affected are those carrying pain and temperature sensations as they cross in the anterior commissure. This usually causes bilateral loss of sensation restricted to the segments involved and results in a "shawl" or "cuirass" pattern, affecting only a few cervical or thoracic segments and sparing sensation below. Sometimes the segmental sensory loss is unilateral. The lesion is chronic and the loss of sensation may lead to painless injuries of the digits or painless burns. Because touch perception is conveyed in posterior columns as well as corticospinal tracts, there may be dissociated sensory loss, sparing touch (as well as position and vibration). If motor neurons in the affected segment are affected, there are lower motor neuron signs (weakness, wasting, loss of reflexes) in the appropriate area. If the lesion extends laterally, the corticospinal tracts are affected and there may be upper motor neuron signs in the legs.

Subacute Combined Degeneration

Degeneration of the spinal cord that affects both the corticospinal tracts and the posterior columns (often called *combined degeneration*) is often the result of deficiency of vitamin B_{12}. This deficiency is most commonly due to loss of the gastric intrinsic factor, resulting in macrocytic anemia (pernicious anemia). As a consequence of combined degeneration, there is a gait disorder, with upper motor neuron signs and loss of position and vibratory perception in the legs. The loss of position sense may be so severe that the patient is uncertain of the location of his or her feet, resulting in unsteadiness of gait due to sensory loss rather than motor incoordination; this disorder is called *sensory ataxia.* Because the spinothalamic tracts are not involved primarily, loss of cutaneous sensation would not be expected but is actually almost universally present; this is attributed to the concomitant degeneration of peripheral nerves. The peripheral neuropathy may also attenuate the tendon reflexes, modifying or masking the expected upper motor neuron signs. Because this is a system degeneration rather than a focal cord lesion, there is no motor or sensory level.

Friedreich Ataxia

Friedreich ataxia is a genetic condition in which the distribution of spinal cord lesions is similar to that of combined system disease. In addition, spinocerebellar tracts are affected. As a result, the initial symptoms (in adolescence) are usually unsteadiness or ataxia in walking. Later there may be spastic weakness of the legs and loss of proprioception. The combination of lesions results in the incongruous appearance of Babinski signs although knee and ankle jerks are lost. Other cerebellar signs (nystagmus and tremor of the arms) may appear later. (The reason the tendon reflexes are lost is not clear, since there is no cutaneous sensory loss to imply peripheral neuropathy; perhaps the cerebellar influences on reflexes are important.)

Other Conditions

The two most common nontraumatic spinal cord disorders are probably amyotrophic lateral sclerosis (described in Chapter 14) and multiple sclerosis. Upper motor neuron signs and proprioceptive sensory loss are almost universally present in advanced cases of multiple sclerosis although there may be no signs of a level lesion; at autopsy these signs may be associated with many small lesions throughout the spinal cord. The combination of these signs with cerebellar signs (ataxia or tremor of the arms, nystagmus, dysarthria) or with a history of optic neuritis is almost diagnostic of multiple sclerosis. There is often a clinical episode of transverse myelitis, or there may merely be signs of a level lesion (in addition to signs of disorder elsewhere in the nervous system).

Selected Readings and References

DeJong, R. N. 1979. The Neurologic Examination. 4th ed. New York: Harper & Row.

Simpson, J. F., and Magee, K. R. 1973. Clinical Evaluation of the Nervous System. 2nd ed. Boston: Little, Brown.

Thomas J. Carew

Descending Control of Spinal Circuits

28

The motor neurons of the spinal cord are constantly bombarded by input from a variety of sources. The sources include muscle and cutaneous afferents through spinal interneurons, and several higher brain centers that act both directly on the spinal motor neurons and indirectly through interneurons. In this chapter we shall consider some of the forms of control that higher brain centers exert on segmental motor neurons and interneurons. Specifically, we shall discuss how descending control of spinal mechanisms is important in the maintenance of posture and in the control of locomotion. In the maintenance of posture, descending influences modulate motor output, which permits us to keep a set position in the face of changing external forces. In the control of locomotion, descending influences permit the expression of a rhythmic motor output by spinal circuits.

Neural Control of Posture
Decerebrate Rigidity Provides a Model System for Studying Posture

In a communication of the Royal Society in 1896 Sherrington described a condition of "long maintained muscular contraction" or exaggerated tonus of the limb extensors in cats that had undergone transection of the brain stem at the level of the midbrain.

Specifically, the transection was placed between the superior and inferior colliculi. He called this condition *decerebrate rigidity*. The animals typically had great stiffness in both fore and hind legs with abnormally high activity in extensor muscles, and this condition persisted indefinitely. Sherrington appreciated that this preparation might provide an experimental model for an important aspect of postural control, namely, the maintained tone in muscles that oppose gravity (usually extensor muscles) which is required for standing up straight. He therefore went on to study this preparation in detail.

Sherrington's most important finding concerning decerebrate rigidity was his discovery in 1898 that, after sectioning of the dorsal spinal roots to a particular limb, the limb "at once falls into flaccidity" while the other limbs remain rigid. Thus, cutting of the dorsal roots that carry afferent input from the limb selectively abolishes the rigidity in that limb. This indicated that the extensor rigidity is reflex in origin, requiring afferent input for its maintenance; thus he considered standing in the decerebrate preparation to be reflex in nature. It has subsequently become clear that several descending neural systems, especially the reticular, vestibular, and cerebellar, are critically involved in the tonic modulation underlying decerebrate rigidity. We shall therefore examine the role that each of these systems plays in controlling posture.

Reticulospinal Influences. A significant advance in our understanding of decerebrate rigidity came from the work of Magoun and his colleagues in the mid-1940s. They found that two different regions within the reticular formation of the brain stem had profound influence over the reflex activity of the spinal cord. Stimulation of a region in the medulla inhibited extensor reflex activity; they called this brain stem region the *medial reticular extensor inhibitory area*. Stimulation of another region, more rostral and lateral to the medullary region, facilitated extensor reflex activity; they called this region the *lateral reticular extensor facilitatory area*[1] (Figure 28–1). It is now known that the influence of both of these reticular areas is exerted onto both alpha and gamma motor neurons to extensor muscles. Thus the normal state of events, when both reticular systems are intact, is that there is a constant balance of descending facilitation and inhibition onto segmental alpha and gamma motor neurons.

How do these reticulospinal influences relate to decerebrate rigidity? The two reticular areas that exert their influence in the spinal cord receive excitatory input from various regions of the brain. In decerebrate rigidity the midbrain transection removes a major portion of excitatory input (mainly from cortex) to the inhibitory region Figure 28–1). Although some of the input to the facilitatory area is also removed, it still receives sufficient input, especially from ascending pathways, to exert its facilitatory influence in the cord. This facilitation, however, is now largely unopposed by the inhibitory region whose main excitatory input is missing, creating a severe imbalance favoring the facilitatory influence onto extensor motor neurons. Why is decerebrate rigidity reduced by cutting of the dorsal roots? The reason is that a large contribution of excitation to the extensor alpha motor neurons comes via the gamma loop. Consistent with this reasoning is the observation of Granit and his co-workers in Sweden that there is greatly increased gamma motor neuron activity in decerebrate animals. Here we can see the operation of the size principle. Because the gamma motor neurons are smaller than the alpha motor neurons, a given amount of increase in descending facilitatory input onto the alpha and gamma (extensor) motor neuron pool will activate the gammas more intensely. Because of the large contribution of gamma motor neurons in decerebrate rigidity Granit has called this form of rigidity *gamma rigidity*.

Vestibulospinal Influences. Although the imbalance in the reticulospinal system plays the major role in decerebrate rigidity, the vestibu-

---

[1]There can be some confusion about the anatomical basis for the functional regions of the reticular system described by Magoun and Rhines. There are two main reticulospinal tracts: (1) the *medullary*, which gives rise to the lateral reticulospinal tract, and (2) the *pontine*, which gives rise to the medial reticulospinal tract. The inhibitory area of Magoun and Rhines overlaps with the medullary (bulbar) region. Stimulation of this region, in addition to inhibiting extensors (as Magoun and Rhines showed) also excites flexors. Functionally this makes sense. The congruence of the facilitatory area with the pontine reticular area is much less clear, since the facilitatory area is lateral and rostral to the pontine region. When Magoun and Rhines called the inhibitory area *medial*, they meant this *with respect to the more rostral and lateral facilitatory area*. This bulbar region gives rise to the *lateral* reticulospinal tract. (For a clear and more thorough discussion of these points, see Brodal, *Neurological Anatomy*, New York, Oxford University Press, 1969, pp. 176–177, 222–223).

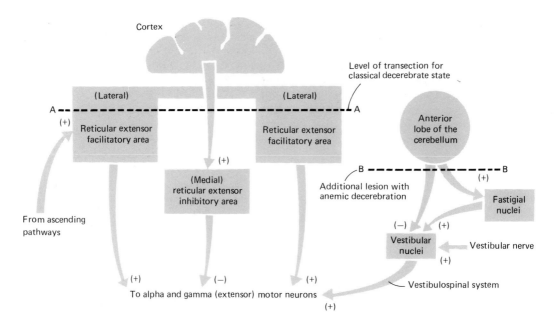

28–1 Major pathways involved in decerebrate and decerebellate rigidity. Mesencephalic transection (**A**) produces decerebrate rigidity; additional disruption of inhibition from the cerebellum onto Deiter's and fastigial nuclei (**B**) produces decerebellate rigidity.

lospinal system is also important. Unilateral destruction of the vestibular nuclei (especially the lateral or Deiter's nucleus) greatly reduces or even abolishes decerebrate rigidity on the side of the lesion. The reason for this is that Deiter's nucleus has powerful descending excitatory influence directly onto alpha and gamma (extensor) motor neurons. Without sufficient background excitation from Deiter's nucleus, the increased facilitation from reticulospinal neurons is not sufficient to maintain the rigidity.

Cerebellar Influences. If a decerebrate cat is also given a lesion of the anterior lobe of the cerebellum, extensor rigidity is increased; surprisingly, however, cutting of the dorsal roots in such a preparation no longer abolishes the rigidity. This was shown by Pollock and Davis, who were concerned about the surgical side effects of the midbrain transection used to produce decerebrate rigidity. They therefore devised a new kind of preparation to study rigidity which they thought was less traumatic. They produced an *anemic decerebration* by tying off both carotid arteries and

the basilar artery to interrupt the blood supply to, and therefore destroy, regions of the brain rostral to the mesencephalon. However, in this preparation the anterior cerebellum is also destroyed, and this proved to be the crucial difference from the decerebrate cat described by Sherrington. Sherrington actually had predicted this phenomenon 30 years previously when he found that electrical stimulation of the cerebellum abolishes decerebrate rigidity.

Why would ablation of the cerebellum increase rigidity and stimulation of the cerebellum decrease it? As we shall learn in Chapter 30, the Purkinje cells of the anterior lobe of the cerebellum produce direct inhibition of both Deiter's nucleus and the fastigial nucleus. As mentioned earlier, Deiter's nucleus in turn provides powerful excitation to alpha and gamma (extensor) motor neurons, and the fastigial nucleus provides powerful excitation to Deiter's nucleus. Thus, when the cerebellum is removed, Deiter's nucleus is relieved of the tonic cerebellar inhibition. Moreover, Deiter's nucleus now receives increased drive from the fastigial nucleus, which has also been relieved of cerebellar inhibition. These factors combine to allow the vestibulospinal pathway to overdrive extensor motor neurons (Figure 28–1). Cutting of the dorsal roots does not abolish this rigidity because alpha motor neurons now receive so much excitation *directly* from Deiter's nucleus that the contribution of excitation from the gamma loop is proportionately less important. Thus, even when the dorsal roots are cut, depriving the alpha motor neurons of gamma loop input, the alpha motor neurons still receive sufficient excitation from the vestibulospinal system to maintain the rigidity. Because of the preponderant role of direct excitation of alpha motor neurons from Deiter's nucleus in decerebellate rigidity, it is sometimes called *alpha rigidity*.

The main concept that has emerged from studying the decerebrate preparation is that there are static postural, stretch reflex mechanisms that help an animal maintain a set position in the face of changing external forces such as gravity. This interpretation is supported by the recent observation that animals that require significant flexor tone to maintain posture (such as sloths and opossums, which hang upside down from trees) show *flexor* rigidity after decerebration. Thus, it appears that decerebration does not just produce an exaggeration of extensor tone, but actually produces an exaggeration of postural tone, that is, increased tone in antigravity muscles. However, a word of caution is necessary. The extensor rigidity exhibited by a decerebrate animal is at best, as Sherrington put it, a "caricature of normal standing"—an extreme form which allows one to study some of the key factors in postural control. For example, when normal animals stand, they exhibit a distribution of muscle tone (with some coactivation of flexors and extensors), they show righting reflexes if placed on their side, they can adjust to changes in the slope of the ground by adjusting the weight distribution on their limbs, and so forth. Decerebrate animals show severe impairment in most of these abilities.

It is useful to distinguish between the decerebrate state described above and the decorticate state which is sometimes observed clinically and which can be produced in animals by transecting above, and thus sparing, diencephalic and mesencephalic structures. In animals the effects of decortication on posture are much less severe than those of decerebration: placing and hopping reactions are impaired, but decorticate animals show relatively normal tonic (postural) reflex activity. In humans, the decorticate state is characterized by flexor rigidity in the upper limbs. The reason is not known, although some speculate that in the upper limbs of humans, flexor muscles are antigravity muscles. When one examines the range and degree of postural impairment that accompany progressively greater amounts of de-

cerebration, from decorticate, to high decerebrate (mesencephalic), to low decerebrate (bulbospinal), and, finally, to spinal preparations, the general principle that emerges is the more decerebration, the greater is the impairment of tonic descending modulation.

A final point that can cause some confusion concerns the notion of *physiological extensors* often encountered in a clinical context. A muscle (or muscle group) is often considered to be a physiological *extensor* if that muscle's normal action is to oppose gravity, even though that muscle's anatomical action is *flexion*. An example will help to clarify this point. When standing upright, if we flex our toes against the ground this action opposes gravity. Thus this is considered physiological extension even though it is accomplished by an anatomical flexion. The important point is that physiological extension is a functional concept relating a muscle's action to the opposition of gravity.

Decerebrate Rigidity and the Clinical Syndromes of Spasticity and Rigidity. It is important to distinguish between experimentally produced hypertonus, such as decerebrate or decerebellate rigidity, and clinically observed motor impairment, such as spasticity and rigidity. Spasticity is a hypertonic, hyperreflexive state characterized by increased resistance to passive movement. It has three distinguishing characteristics: (1) It is unidirectional. This term is used because the resistance is usually much greater in antigravity muscles. Therefore, extending the arm meets with more resistance than flexing it because of increased tone in the biceps. The biceps of the arm are another example of physiological extensors, as flexing the elbow normally opposes gravity. (2) The resistance of the spastic muscle to passive extension largely depends upon the velocity of the movement: in mild spasticity little resistance is offered to slow extensions, whereas increased resistance is clearly present with rapid extension. (3) Finally, spastic patients show a hyperactive tendon jerk.

Rigidity is one of the major signs of parkinsonism. In contrast to spasticity, rigidity has the following characteristics: (1) The increased resistance to passive movement is bidirectional; that is, the resistance is seen more or less equally in flexors and extensors. (2) Rigidity is relatively independent of the velocity of movement. (3) Finally, parkinsonian patients do not show a hyperactive tendon jerk.

Considering our earlier discussion of decerebrate rigidity, some confusion can arise from the term *rigidity* used to describe *decerebrate rigidity*, as this form of experimentally produced hypertonus has the features of clinically observed *spasticity:* the resistance to passive movement is greater in extensors, it is velocity dependent, and it shows hyperactive tendon jerks. Thus, the experimental condition called decerebrate rigidity is actually a good animal model of clinically observed spasticity.

A final important observation is that the clasp-knife reflex, which is commonly seen in spastic patients (as discussed in Chapter 26), is absent in decerebrate cats. However, following a lesion of a specific region of the pontine reticular formation, the clasp-knife reflex appears. Thus, the pontine region of the mesencephalon tonically inhibits the clasp-knife reflex in decerebrate cats (presumably by inhibiting the inhibitory actions of the group II afferents in the spinal cord). This then is a clear example of a reflex pathway that is normally closed in the decerebrate state, but is opened by removing a descending inhibitory influence from a higher brain center. As we shall see in the following sections, opening and closing of reflex pathways also occurs in the normal control of posture and locomotion.

Descending Influences and Reflex Mechanisms Interact in Controlling Human Posture

Descending systems regulate posture not only by providing a tonic excitatory bias to extensor motor systems, but also by opening and closing spinal reflex circuits. An elegant series of recent studies by Nashner illustrates this point. Nashner investigated the stabilizing influences of long-latency stretch reflexes of the ankle joint of human subjects. *Long-latency reflexes* are thought to involve supraspinal as well as spinal circuits, and thus have considerably longer latencies (120 msec) than purely spinal reflexes such as the myotatic stretch reflex, which has a latency of 45–50 msec. Using a servo-controlled movable platform, he could produce body sway in two different ways: (1) by sliding the platform backward, which would cause the subject to sway forward (Figure 28–2A); or (2) by tilting the platform upward, which would cause the subject to sway backward (Figure 28–2B). Notice that in both cases ankle extensors (e.g., the gastrocnemius

muscles) would be stretched by the movement, triggering a stretch reflex that would extend the ankle joints. However, the consequences of ankle extension are quite different for the two movements. In the first case (induced forward swaying, Figure 28–2A), ankle extension *opposes* sway, whereas in the second case (direct ankle rotation, Figure 28–2B), ankle extension *increases* sway. Thus, in one instance the stretch reflex would be appropriate and in the other it would be inappropriate in maintaining normal posture. During these experiments, Nashner measured (1) the electrical activity of the medial portion of the gastrocnemius muscles, (2) the amount of ankle torque (torsional force exerted on the platform by the ankle musculature), and (3) the amount of body sway (see traces on the right-hand side of Figure 28–2).

Nashner found that with repeated trials, when the stretch reflex served to stabilize posture, the reflex became progressively more facilitated (Figure 28–2A), whereas when the reflex served to destabilize posture, it adapted and became progressively weaker. Thus, the same stretch reflex was enhanced when triggered in one context and suppressed when triggered in another context. Nashner used the term *postural set* to describe this context-specific tonic modulation of the stretch reflex. These results illustrate an essential point: *descending influences* (in this case postural set) *can gate reflex loops, that is, they can open or close them.* We shall see in later sections that gating of reflexes occurs in other types of motor output as well.

Neural Control of Locomotion

We have seen that tonic descending influences from a variety of higher centers can modulate the output of spinal circuits to maintain posture. Descending control is also involved in locomotion. Here a *tonic* descending message is translated into a *rhythmic or periodic locomotor output.* The way this is achieved by the central nervous system has been a subject of fascination to scientists for more than 100 years. Sherrington observed that alternating movements of the hind limbs of cats and dogs could be performed after their spinal cords had been severed. With his colleague F. W. Mott, Sherrington also found that cutting of the dorsal roots from a fore and a hind limb of a monkey had disastrous effects on the monkey's motor ability; the monkey would not use the limb at all during normal walking. These

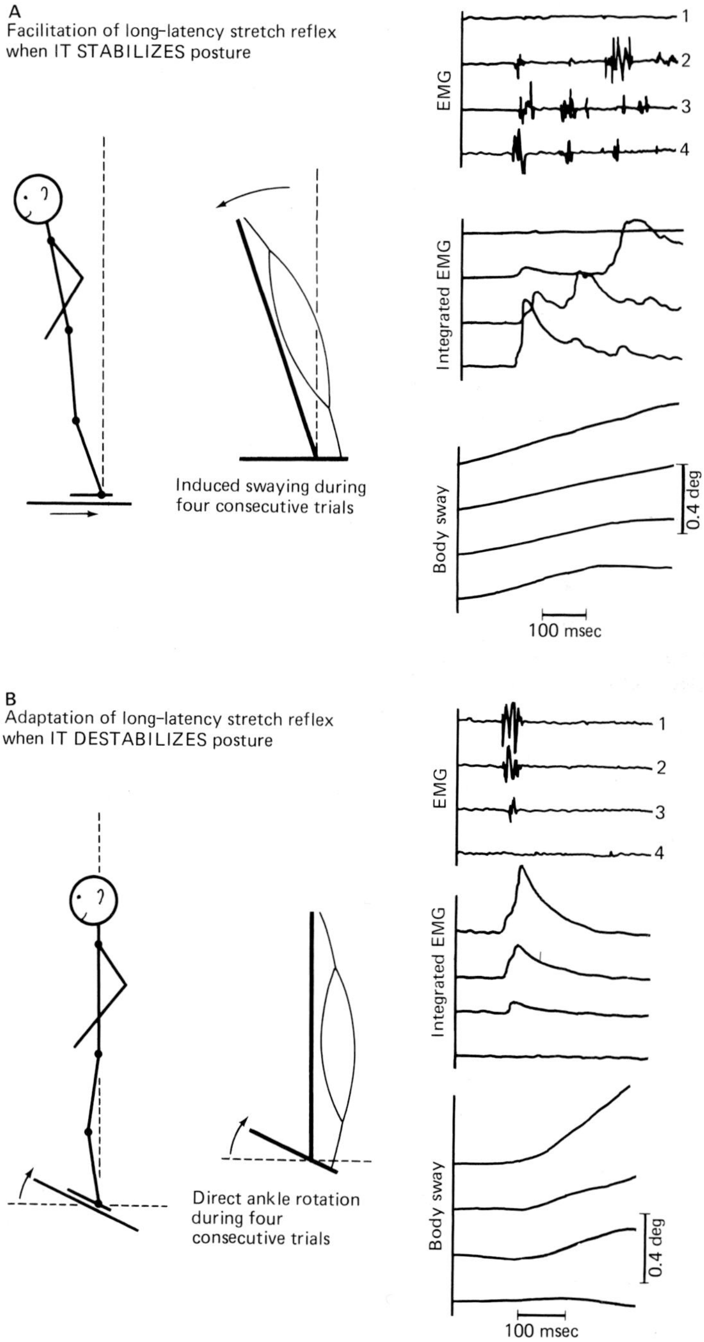

A
Facilitation of long-latency stretch reflex
when IT STABILIZES posture

Induced swaying during
four consecutive trials

28–2 Study of the facilitation and adaptation of the long-latency stretch reflex of the human ankle. **A.** Sway induced by unexpected backward movement of a platform triggers a long-latency stretch reflex that facilitates with repeated trials, because the reflex serves to stabilize posture. Notice reduction in body sway (**lower right-hand panel**) with four repeated trials as electromyogram (**EMG**) activity increases, i.e., as reflex facilitates. (**Numbers** opposite EMG traces refer to consecutive trials.) **B.** Direct ankle rotation triggers a long-latency reflex that diminishes (adapts) with repeated trials because the reflex serves to destabilize posture. (Adapted from Nashner, 1976.)

B
Adaptation of long-latency stretch reflex
when IT DESTABILIZES posture

Direct ankle rotation
during four
consecutive trials

observations suggested that peripheral (afferent) feedback is required for normal movement. They thus advanced the notion that locomotion might be accomplished by a set of "chain reflexes" in which the sensory input resulting from a given part of a step cycle would trigger the next part of the cycle by reflex action, giving rise to further afferent input which would trigger the next part, and so forth. In 1911 this idea was shown to be incorrect by T. Graham Brown, who found that sectioning of the spinal cord triggered rhythmic walking movements that persisted for a minute or so following the transection, even in animals whose dorsal roots had been previously severed bilaterally. Thus, *walking movements are not reflex in origin; they are generated by neurons located exclusively in the spinal cord.* Brown proposed, that, although afferent input was not essential for the fundamental motor pattern, it is probably important "in grading the individual component movements to the temporary exigencies of the environment." After more than 70 years this viewpoint is still believed to be essentially correct.

28–3 Spinal and supraspinal control of locomotion.
  A. Spinal cord and lower brain stem of the cat isolated from cerebral hemispheres by transection at point **A'–A.** Locomotion can be produced in this preparation by electrical stimulation of the mesencephalic locomotor region **(filled circle).** Transection of the spinal cord at point **B'–B** isolates the hind limb segments of the cord. The hind limbs are still able to walk on a treadmill after recovery from surgery. **B.** Locomotion of a cat transected at **B'–B** (as in part A) on a treadmill. Reciprocal bursts of electrical activity can be recorded from flexors during the swing phase and from extensors during the stance phase of walking (Adapted from Pearson, 1976.)

The next major advance in the study of locomotion was long in coming. In the mid-1960s, a group of Russian scientists, M. L. Shik, F. V. Severin, and G. N. Orlovsky, found that in decerebrate cats tonic electrical stimulation of the remaining brain stem caused animals to walk normally when placed on a treadmill (walking was unrelated to the pattern of electrical stimulation). Furthermore, the gait of the animal depended on the strength of the stimulation and the treadmill speed. Weak stimulation produced walking, whereas progressively stronger stimulation produced trotting and finally galloping. The region of the brain stem that produces walking is a rather circumscribed area of the mesencephalon which Orlovsky and co-workers called the *mesencephalic locomotor region (MLR)* (Figure 28–3). This preparation has proved to be very useful for studying the neural mechanisms of locomotion, since stimulation and recording from nerve cells can be accomplished while the animal is moving in place, and locomotion can be produced at will by appropriate stimulation of the mesencephalic locomotor region. In the past 15 years our understanding of locomotion has in-

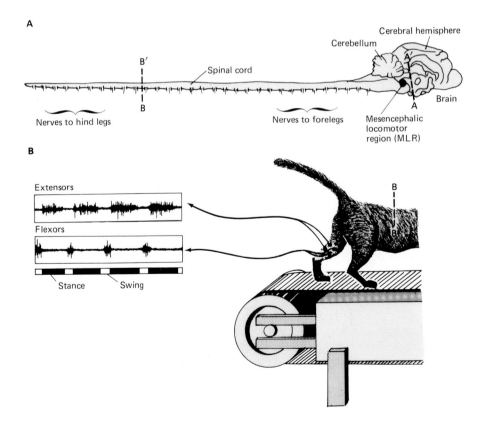

creased dramatically. In the rest of the chapter we shall consider some of the findings that have emerged.

Locomotion Is Controlled by a Central Program

The basic rhythmic pattern of neural activity underlying locomotion is generated by neurons intrinsic to the central nervous system. Thus there is a central program for locomotion. A *central program* is the expression of a neural circuit that produces a particular pattern of motor output which does not require afferent feedback for its essential pattern or maintenance. Thus, the demonstration of a central program for a behavior requires showing that a given behavioral output (such as the alternating contraction of flexors and extensors during walking) can be generated in the absence of peripheral (afferent) feedback. In this chapter we shall consider central programs that produce rhythmic or cyclic behaviors such as locomotion. However, central programs are also involved in many other types of motor acts, including voluntary movements (see Chapter 29) and complex sequences of innate behavior (see Chapter 46).

Grillner and his co-workers in Sweden (as well as the Russian group mentioned previously) have provided evidence that locomotion is produced by a central program. The experiments have been carried out in two ways: (1) locomotion has been examined in animals with dorsal roots to their limbs cut; and (2) alternating efferent output from ventral root filaments to flexors and extensors has been examined in cats paralyzed with curare (this has been called *fictive* locomotion, i.e., imitative locomotion). Both of these procedures eliminate afferent feedback to the spinal cord, the former by eliminating the afferent pathway, the latter by preventing movements which would in turn produce afferent feedback, and in both cases normal locomotor output is observed. Furthermore, by recording electrical activity in several leg muscles simultaneously, Grillner and Zangger have recently shown that the central program does not just produce alternate flexor and extensor activation, but a much more delicate pattern that correctly times the contraction of appropriate muscles at just the right moment for normal walking. Thus, there is very compelling evidence supporting Graham Brown's original observations that there is a central program for locomotion. Other terms often used synonymously with

central programs for locomotion are *pattern generators* or *neural oscillators.* These are essentially equivalent terms that are used to indicate a centrally located set of neurons that produce a rhythmic output without the necessity for afferent feedback.

Grillner and his colleagues have shown that cats with only the spinal cord connected to the limbs can be made to walk on a treadmill with a speed determined by that of the treadmill. Similar observations have been made on chronic spinal cats (transected at 1–2 weeks of age). Thus, *the central program is located in the spinal cord.* Furthermore, it has been shown that there are individual pattern generators for each limb. For example, in animals with spinal transections that isolate the hind limb segment (Figure 28–3B), normal treadmill walking of the hind legs can be produced either by electrical stimulation of the dorsal roots or by intravenous injection of L-DOPA (see below), and this walking does not require afferent feedback. Moreover, if one hind limb is prevented from walking, the other limb goes right on walking normally. By recording muscle activity in the restrained leg it can be shown that the central program to that limb is frozen in midcycle, while the other limb's program continues to cycle rhythmically. Thus, the pattern generator for each limb does not require activity in the other generators. However, when all limbs are active, as in normal walking, the pattern generators from the limbs are definitely coupled to one another. Finally, it has been shown that walking in high spinal cats is accomplished by coactivation of alpha and gamma (both dynamic and static) motor neurons. This has been determined by showing that spindle discharge increases during the contraction (shortening) of various limb muscles. It is evidence for coactivation because if gamma motor neurons were not coactive with alpha motor neurons, shortening of the muscle would unload the spindles, thereby reducing their discharge.

The Central Program Is Modulated by Descending Influences

Considerable experimental attention has been devoted to examining the descending control from supraspinal brain structures on spinal circuits. Neurons giving rise to the rubrospinal tract, the vestibulospinal tract (especially from Deiter's nucleus), and the reticulospinal tracts are rhythmically active in phase with locomotor movements. However, most attention has focused on noradrenergic neurons located in the locus ceruleus and the lower brain stem that send their axons to the lumbosacral region of the spinal cord. These neurons are believed to mediate, at least in part, the actions of the mesencephalic locomotor region first described by the Russian group. Grillner has carried out extensive experiments that support this notion. He found that many of the effects of stimulating the mesencephalic locomotor region can be mimicked by intravenous injection of the adrenergic precursor L-DOPA in the spinal cat. It is believed that L-DOPA is taken up into the spinal cord and acts to release norepiphrene from the terminals of noradrenergic fibers from the locus ceruleus. Thus, Grillner and Shik have suggested that the mesencephalic reticular formation gives rise to a command fiber system for locomotion. (The notion of command fibers will be discussed in detail in Chapter 46.) Other descending systems are also clearly important since chemical lesioning of the noradrenergic system does not abolish locomotion.

Ascending Information from the Spinal Cord Is Sent to Higher Brain Centers During Locomotion

Arshavsky and his colleagues in the Russian group have studied the activity of neurons in the ventral and dorsal spinocerebellar tracts during locomotion. These tracts carry input to the cerebellum from muscle spindles, tendon organs, and joint afferents. The dorsal spinocerebellar tract neurons (in Clarke's column) receive specific synaptic input from the muscle afferents and are therefore easily influenced from the periphery, whereas the ventral spinocerebellar tract neurons are more difficult to influence as they receive weaker and more diffuse peripheral input. Both dorsal and ventral spinocerebellar tract neurons are phasically active during locomotion. After deafferentation, the dorsal neurons are no longer phasically activated during locomotion, indicating that their modulation is from the periphery. However, Arshavsky and co-workers found that after deafferentation the ventral cells still show phasic modulation during locomotion, in perfect phase with the step cycle. This indicates that these neurons are involved in transmitting a copy of the central program for locomotion to the cerebellum. Thus, the dorsal and ventral spinocerebellar tracts transmit different information to the

cerebellum: the dorsal tract informs it about the *activity of muscles*, whereas the ventral tract informs it about the *active processes within the spinal cord* (in this case the pattern generation for locomotion).

Afferent Information Plays an Important Role in Locomotion

Although a central program exists for locomotion, afferent input is also critical in normal walking. Two roles of afferent information during locomotion have been elucidated by Grillner and his colleagues H. Forssberg and S. Rossignol. The first is in *switching the motor program from one phase to another*. During locomotion there are two phases in a step cycle: the *swing phase* (when the foot is off the ground and swinging forward) and the *stance phase* (when the foot is planted and the leg is moving backward relative to the body). The swing phase is mediated by flexors, the stance phase by extensors. Forssberg and co-workers have shown that preventing the extension of one hind leg of a spinal cat will inhibit the swing phase of that leg, and the limb will display maintained extensor muscle activity. When the limb is slowly extended, at a certain critical point the extensor activity will suddenly cease and a prompt flexion occurs. Thus, the afferent feedback during a critical part of the stance phase allows the central motor program to switch to the swing phase. Preventing the occurrence of the afferent input can, in a sense, arrest the central program in mid-cycle.

Another major action of afferent information during walking is to *open and close reflex pathways in different parts of a step cycle*. A typical reflex pattern exhibited by cats is a tactile placing reaction. Thus, if the top of a cat's foot is touched, the foot will rapidly be placed in a more rostral position by a prompt flexion and subsequent extension of the limb. A weak electrical stimulus to the top of the foot will produce exactly the same reflex. Forssberg and colleagues examined this reflex in spinal cats during locomotion on a treadmill. They found that electrical stimulation of the top of the foot during the swing (flexion) phase enhanced flexion of the limb and that identical stimulation during the stance (extension) phase enhanced *extension*. Thus, the effect of the stimulus is channeled (through interneurons) to flexors during the flexion phase of walking and to extensors during the extensor phase; in other words, a *reflex reversal* occurs. This is an elegant example of the basic phenomenon of gating in the spinal cord that was described in Chapter 24 and was discussed earlier in this chapter, both for the clasp-knife reflex in decerebrate and spinal cats, and in another form in Nashner's studies of stretch reflexes in human posture. This channeling of afferent input is important because a particular reflex may only be appropriate at certain times. For example, it would be adaptive for a tactile stimulus to the top of the foot to elicit flexion during the swing phase of locomotion because the reflex action is appropriate for stepping over something; but if the same flexion reflex was produced during the stance phase (when the animal's weight is being supported by the limb), it would not be adaptive because the animal would collapse. Thus, it appears that a major role of afferent input during locomotion is to both modulate the expression of the central program and channel reflex activity in order to compensate for a constantly changing terrain.

Quite recently the Russian group has investigated another form of modulation from higher brain centers—the scratch reflex in the cat. They have shown that this behavior shares many features with locomotion: (1) it is centrally programmed; (2) the pattern generator is located in the spinal cord (primarily in the fourth and fifth lumbar segments); (3) the reflex is modulated by afferent input (if the hind limb is moved out of the scratch position by extension of the hip, scratching will immediately stop); and (4) the ventral spinocerebellar tract (and, in addition, the spino-reticulocerebellar pathway) sends a copy of the central program to higher centers. Another very interesting finding of the Russian group is that locomotion and scratching might make use of at least some of the same spinal neurons, which can operate in different regimes depending upon the source of the tonic descending input. Thus, there may be an economy of spinal circuitry that can produce very different types of limb movements depending upon two factors: (1) the supraspinal centers that activate the circuitry, and (2) the type of afferent feedback that modulates the circuitry.

Our understanding of the neural mechanisms involved in locomotion has come almost exclusively from experiments on animals. An important question to consider is the relevance of these experiments to humans. The information we are acquiring from animal studies is likely to be of great importance in understanding the neural control of human locomotion. It is already

clear from a large amount of experimental work that diverse animals, both vertebrate and invertebrate, who locomote by such different means as swimming, flying, or walking, use the same general neural principles for locomotion. It appears that evolution may have found an optimal solution to accomplish locomotion: a central program as the basic motor framework, with afferent input providing reflex adjustment of the program to compensate for a changing environment. How could man pass up such an elegant solution?

Selected Readings and References

Granit, R. 1955. Receptors and Sensory Perception. New Haven: Yale University Press.

Grillner, S. 1975. Locomotion in vertebrates: Central mechanisms and reflex interaction. Physiol. Rev. 55:247–304.

Henneman, E. 1980. Motor functions of the brain stem and basal ganglia. In V. B. Mountcastle (ed.), Medical Physiology, 14th ed., Vol. 1. St. Louis: Mosby, pp. 787–812.

Pearson, K. 1976. The control of walking. Sci. Am. 235(6):72–86.

Other References

Arshavsky, Yu. I., Berkinblit, M. B., Gel'fand, I. M., Orlovskii, G. N., and Fukson, O. I. 1972. Activity of the neurones of the ventral spinocerebellar tract during locomotion. Biophysics 17:926–935.

Arshavsky, Yu. I., Berkinblit, M. B. Fukson, O. I., Gel'fand, I. M., and Orlovsky, G. N. 1972 Recordings of neurones of the dorsal spinocerebellar tract during evoked locomotion. Brain Res. 43:272–275.

Brown, T. G. 1911. The intrinsic factors in the act of progression in the mammal. Proc. R. Soc. Lond. B Biol. Sci. 84:308–319.

Forssberg, H., Grillner, S., and Rossignol. S. 1975. Phase dependent reflex reversal during walking in chronic spinal cats. Brain Res. 85:103–107.

Grillner, S. 1973. Locomotion in the spinal cat. In R. B. Stein, K. G. Pearson, R. S. Smith, and J. B. Redford (eds.), Control of Posture and Locomotion. New York: Plenum, pp. 515–535.

Grillner, S., and Shik, M. L. 1973. On the descending control of the lumbosacral spinal cord from the "mesencephalic locomotor region." Acta Physiol. Scand. 87:320–333.

Grillner, S., and Zangger, P. 1975. How detailed is the central pattern generation for locomotion? Brain Res. 88:367–371.

Lindsley, D. B., Schreiner, L. H., and Magoun, H. W. 1949. An electromyographic study of spasticity. J. Neurophysiol. 12:197–205.

Magoun, H. W. 1963. Reticulo-spinal influences and postural regulation. In H. W. Magoun, The Waking Brain. 2nd ed. Springfield, Ill.: Thomas, pp. 23–28.

Magoun, H. W., and Rhines, R. 1946. An inhibitory mechanism in the bulbar reticular formation. J. Neurophysiol. 9:165–171.

Mott, F. W., and Sherrington, C. S. 1895. Experiments upon the influence of sensory nerves upon movement and nutrition of the limbs. Preliminary communication. Proc. R. Soc. Lond. 57:481–488.

Nashner, L. M. 1976. Adapting reflexes controlling the human posture. Exp. Brain Res. 26:59–72.

Pollock, L. J., and Davis, L. 1930. The reflex activities of a decerebrate animal. J. Comp. Neurol. 50:377–411.

Pollock, L. J., and Davis, L. 1931. Studies in decerebration. VI. The effect of deafferentation upon decerebrate rigidity. Am. J. Physiol. 98:47–49.

Sherrington, C. S. 1898. Decerebrate rigidity, and reflex coordination of movements. J. Physiol. (Lond.) 22:319–332.

Shik, M. L., Severin, F. V., and Orlovskii, G. N. 1966. Control of walking and running by means of electrical stimulation of the mid-brain. Biophysics 11:756–765.

Claude Ghez

Cortical Control
of Voluntary Movement

The motor cortex and the magnocellular division of the red nucleus are the main supraspinal output centers. These two centers can independently control individual distal muscles of the extremities. These systems are especially important for fine voluntary movements, and lesions of them severely impair the strength and dexterity of movement. The motor cortex and the red nucleus are considered together because the motor cortex projects somatotopically to the red nucleus, and the corticospinal and rubrospinal pathways overlap in their field of action on spinal motor neurons and interneurons. In humans, however, the rubrospinal tract is small and its importance is controversial; we shall therefore focus primarily on the motor cortex and on the corticospinal tract.

The Motor Cortex Is
Somatotopically Organized

In 1870 Fritsch and Hitzig discovered that electrical stimulation of the cortical surface in dogs produced contraction of muscle groups on the opposite side of the body. This discovery was a major historical landmark in our understanding of how the brain controls movement. It showed that mechanisms controlling movements of different parts of the body are localized in different contralateral parts of the brain, which illustrated an important aspect of cortical function. Subsequently, Ferrier, and later Sherrington, demonstrated detailed maps of the cortex in primates showing particular points where stimulation evoked very discrete movements of the limbs and the face. At this time it was already known that the pyramidal tract had its origin in the motor cortex.

The areas where electrical stimuli produced muscle contractions were thought to represent centers responsible for controlling particular movements (a notion derived from phrenology, a doctrine considered in Chapter 1). Although this theoretical notion is not entirely accurate, the observation that a specific topographic relationship exists between a given cortical region and the muscle groups causing movements around specific joints provided a useful framework for clinicians. It was then possible to understand why weakness of the face, arm, or leg was observed with lesions in different parts of the contralateral side of the brain. In addition, clinicians were struck by the similarity between the movements evoked by electrical stimuli to the cortex and those occurring in focal epileptic seizures. The observations made in primates at the turn of the century by Ferrier and by Sherrington were later extended by Woolsey and his collaborators in a variety of other species and by Penfield in humans during the 1950s (Figure 29–1). Penfield stimulated the surface of the motor cortex of patients subjected to craniotomy for extirpation of tumors and found that body representation is arranged in an orderly fashion within the precentral gyrus: the head is represented close to the Rolandic fissure with the arm, trunk, and legs above it. There is, however, a disproportionately large representation of certain muscle groups, particularly those of the lower half of the face and the hands. Within the regions controlling limb muscles, stimulation was most prone to elicit flexor rather than extensor movements. A second, smaller somatotopically organized area, the "supplementary motor cortex" (M-II), was subsequently found in area 6 and over the medial side of the hemisphere in both monkey and man (Figure 29–1A).

Sensory Input to a Cortical Region Is Specifically Related to the Target of Its Output

In 1967 Hiroshi Asanuma introduced techniques for stimulating the depths of the motor cortex with microelectrodes. With this method current

29–1 Somatotopic representation in the motor cortex. **A.** Body representation in motor cortex (**M-I, M-II**) and sensory cortex (**S-I, S-II**) of the monkey. (Adapted from Woolsey, 1958.) **B.** Body representation in motor cortex of man. (Adapted from Penfield and Rasmussen, 1950.)

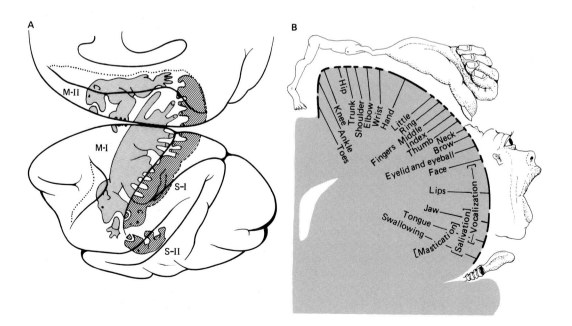

spread is greatly reduced and motor effects can be elicited with 100 times less current than needed in earlier studies. Moreover, it is possible to record the activity of single neurons whose target muscle can be inferred from the effects of stimulation within the same small regions of cortex.

Microstimulation and single unit recording rapidly led to two new observations. First, stimuli applied to the depths of the motor cortex produce contractions of individual, flexor or extensor muscles as well as restricted groups of muscles. In contrast, stimuli applied to the surface of the cortex almost invariably result in the contraction of several muscles or groups of muscles. The representation detected by microstimulation has finer grain in monkeys than in cats, and is finest in regions of the cortex controlling finger muscles. The points where stimuli elicit contractions of a given muscle with the lowest current densities are grouped in arrays oriented perpendicularly to the cortical surface—an arrangement reminiscent of the columns in the somatic sensory and the visual cortices. These columnar arrays in the motor cortex are called *cortical efferent zones.*

Asanuma next addressed the following question: What natural stimuli activate these cortical efferent zones? He found that a specific relationship exists between the target muscle and the peripheral areas (the receptive field) that excite the neurons within the efferent zone. The neurons receive input from either the muscles or the skin. Neurons within an efferent zone controlling a particular muscle receive peripheral input from either that muscle (proprioceptive inputs) or from a region of skin specifically related to the function of that muscle. For example, neurons within efferent zones controlling flexor muscles of the digits are activated by stretching of the same muscles or by cutaneous stimuli applied to the ventral surface of the digits and palm (Figure 29–2).

These topographic relationships indicate that the motor cortex may function as a positive feedback system that provides servo assistance when the moving limb segment encounters an unexpected obstacle. Obstacles are most likely contacted by the leading edge of the limb segment thus activating cutaneous receptors projecting to the efferent zone controlling the agonist muscle. Moreover, if the movement is appreciably slowed, misalignment will occur between the length of the muscle and its spindles (which are also shortening because of coactivation of the

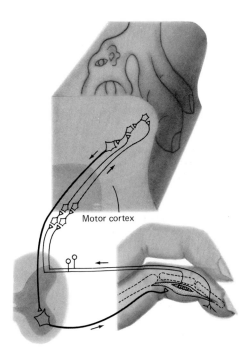

29–2 Input–output organization of the cortical efferent zone controlling the flexor muscle of a digit. Stretching of the muscle activates neurons in its efferent zone. (Adapted from Asanuma, 1973.)

alpha and gamma motor neurons), as we discussed in Chapters 25 and 26. This misalignment will also boost the output from the efferent zone.

The same organizational principle applies in the red nucleus, where a clear-cut somatotopic organization also exists: dorsal regions of the nucleus control individual muscles of the forelimb, and ventral regions control individual muscles of the hindlimbs. Neurons of the red nucleus also receive peripheral input from skin and muscle receptors in the body part controlled by that area. This leads us to a key principle: *the topographic relationships between input and output that hold for the stretch reflex also hold for the efferent zones of the red nucleus and the motor cortex.*

Cortical Motor (Pyramidal Tract) Cells Have Different Functional Properties

Initially it was thought that only the giant pyramidal neurons of the motor cortex, first described by Betz in 1874, gave rise to the pyramidal tract. It is now clear that this is not so. In humans the pyramidal tract carries about 1,000,000 axons, yet there are only 30,000 giant pyramidal (Betz) cells; over 500,000 axons come from smaller pyramidal cells in the motor cortex, and the other axons come from neurons lying outside the motor cortex. In humans, about 60% of the axons of the pyramidal tract come from the neurons of the motor cortex (called area 4 by Brodmann); the bulk of the remaining axons come from cells in area 6, the supplementary motor cortex that lies in front of area 4, and from the somatic sensory cortex (areas 3, 2, and 1) of the parietal lobe. In the macaque monkey, however, only about a third of pyramidal axons arise from neurons in the precentral gyrus. Neurons giving rise to pyramidal tract fibers are located in lamina V of the cortex.

Recently, the properties of individual neurons that make up the pyramidal tract have been studied with physiological methods. Axons from the thalamus and other areas terminate in superficial layers of the motor cortex and synapse on the distal dendrites of the pyramidal tract neurons and on interneurons. The interneurons, in turn, send impulses in a cascading fashion to other interneurons radially down the cortical columns to the pyramidal tract neurons. Because the pyramidal tract axons have different diameters they conduct at various velocities that range from 7 m/sec for the axons of small cells to 70 m/sec for the axons of large cells. Neurons at the extremes of this spectrum have different properties and connections. Thus, the rapidly conducting (giant) pyramidal tract neurons of Betz tend to fire with transient high frequencies and then to adapt more rapidly than do the small, more slowly conducting pyramidal tract cells.

Corticospinal Neurons Project to Motor Neurons and Interneurons and to Higher Brain Centers

Individual pyramidal tract neurons send off many collaterals before reaching the spinal cord. The collaterals end on other pyramidal cells as well as on cells of the red nucleus. Typically, the large pyramidal tract neurons send recurrent collaterals that inhibit (by means of an intercalated inhibitory interneuron) the small pyramidal tract neurons as well as cells of the red nucleus. Collaterals of small pyramidal tract neurons excite neurons of the red nucleus. Collaterals of the pyramidal tract neurons also project to the striatum, thalamus, and brain stem. In the brain stem collaterals end on reticulospinal neurons that project to the spinal cord, on brain stem

neurons that project to the cerebellum, and on cells of the sensory relay nuclei of the dorsal columns. These several sets of connections are thought to provide the control mechanisms of the brain and the sensory systems with an update of the commands distributed to the musculature. This kind of neural update has been called an *efferent copy* or *corollary discharge*. Its function is to keep the relevant portions of the brain informed of commands that motor centers are sending to the spinal cord.

How the corticospinal tract influences motor neurons was first investigated in the 1940s by D. P. C. Lloyd at Rockefeller University. In cats in which the brain stem, except for the medullary pyramid, had been transected, Lloyd stimulated the pyramidal tract rostral to the section. He used the monosynaptic reflex recorded in the ventral root following a stimulus applied to the dorsal root (see Chapter 26) as a test system for examining changes in excitability of motor neurons. Lloyd found that the time between the arrival of a descending pyramidal tract volley within the spinal cord segment and the first sign of facilitation of motor neurons allowed for at least two synaptic delays. Moreover, single volleys were ineffective, and facilitation by two or more pyramidal volleys was required. Lloyd therefore concluded that in the cat the corticospinal action on motor neurons has to be mediated through an interneuron.

A number of later studies have characterized the spinal interneurons that mediate the actions of the corticospinal and other descending tracts. Thus far only a small number of interneurons have been identified unequivocally. Some of these also mediate spinal reflexes, whereas others are propriospinal neurons that do not appear to mediate any simple reflexes. For example, in the cat, the earliest responses evoked in forelimb motor neurons by activity in the corticospinal and rubrospinal tracts are mediated by a group of propriospinal neurons located in the third and fourth cervical segments that project down the cord a few segments to the appropriate motor neuron pools. These propriospinal neurons integrate descending commands with ongoing sensory events.

In primates, and especially in man, corticospinal neurons excite alpha and gamma motor neurons directly in addition to influencing segmental interneurons. A characteristic feature of the connections between the corticospinal tract and the motor neurons is that with successive stimuli they undergo progressive facilitation.

Lesions of the Corticospinal System Cause Characteristic Symptoms

We have previously seen that pyramidal tract lesions produce a severe loss of fractionation of movement—that is, the ability to make independent movements with individual muscle groups. This results from the specificity of the cortico–motor neuronal connections established by many pyramidal axons. In addition, there is a loss of strength in voluntary muscle contraction. This loss is pronounced right after the lesion, but diminishes with time. There is also pronounced slowing of the rate of voluntary muscle contraction. This slowing is thought to result from loss of inputs from the fast, large pyramidal tract neurons to the motor neurons.

These defects impair the ability of the cortex to control motor output directly on a moment-to-moment basis. There are also symptoms that result from the withdrawal of tonic descending activity that maintains the excitability of motor neurons and interneurons in the spinal cord. We shall examine two of these symptoms: hypotonia and the Babinski sign.

Hypotonia

Pure lesions of the pyramidal tract in the medulla result in decreased muscle tone. This loss of tone is best observed by passively moving a limb segment about a joint and noting the decreased resistance offered by the muscles. Since the normal resistance derives in part from the stretch reflex that keeps the muscle slightly stiff, Sid Gilman, now at the University of Michigan, has reasoned that a decreased fusimotor tone might account for the flaccid state. To test this idea Gilman measured the activity of the muscle spindle. He found that in monkeys with pyramidal tract lesions, progressive increases in muscle length produced less discharge in spindle afferents than in normal monkeys (Figure 29–3).

The Extensor Plantar Response or Babinski Sign

The extensor plantar response is probably the single most important sign in clinical neurology and its presence is the signature of an *upper motor neuron lesion*, i.e., a lesion of the pyramidal pathway. The sign was discovered in 1896 by Joseph Babinski, a Polish neurologist in charge of a ward of syphilitic patients at the Pitie Hospital in Paris. A form of this disease (meningovascular

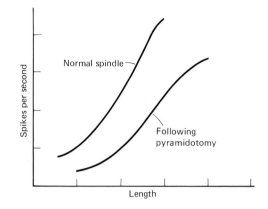

29–3 Response of muscle spindle primary to stretch before and after pyramidotomy. (Adapted from Gilman, 1973.)

syphilis) produces vascular lesions of the brain which often affect the corticospinal tract. Babinski noted that stroking the lateral aspect of the foot with a sharp object elicited a different "reflex" response in patients with corticospinal disease than it did in patients without this disorder. Normally, this stimulus produces flexion of all the toes, including the large one. In affected patients, however, there is a reflex extension of the big toe which may be accompanied by fanning of the others. (This extensor response of the big toe should be referred to as an *extensor plantar response* rather than a *Babinski sign* because several other pathological reflexes have also been described by Babinski.)

In 1932 Fulton and Keller, in a series of classic studies, showed that the extensor plantar response occurs only in anthropoid apes and man. In 1940 Sara Tower found that in addition to occurring with damage of the motor cortex, the extensor plantar response follows lesion of the medullary pyramids. More recently, William Landau and others have demonstrated that the extensor plantar response is an enhanced flexion reflex and is part of a larger family of withdrawal responses to noxious stimuli released by pyramidal lesions. (Extensors of the big toes represent physiological flexors, as they do not oppose the action of gravity.)

The appearance under pathological conditions of a reflex response that is normally absent illustrates clearly that central lesions can result in both loss of specific functions and release of functions otherwise kept in check by the system damaged by disease. Enhanced tendon reflexes typically occur when the lesion includes the cortical fibers that control other descending pathways in addition to the pyramidal tract. For example, lesions in the upper brain stem or in the internal capsule lead to enhancement of most stretch reflexes; this situation is comparable to that seen with decerebrate rigidity (see Chapter 28)—a state of spasticity. Cortical projections are therefore thought to tonically inhibit pathways that descend from the brain stem.

Upper and Lower Motor Neuron Lesions

Only neurons innervating muscles can accurately be called "motor neurons." Nonetheless, the concept of upper and lower motor neurons continues to be valuable clinically in diagnosing neurological disorders resulting in muscular weakness. In this situation the clinician must first decide whether the underlying disease affects the motor neuron and/or its axon (lower motor neuron lesion) or whether the disease interferes with descending commands (upper motor neuron lesion). It must be emphasized that many lesions can interfere with the normal balance of tonic inputs to the motor neurons and give rise to some features of the upper motor neuron lesion syndrome.

Lower motor neuron lesions often affect single muscles and are often associated with fasciculation (twitches of single fibers) and atrophy (loss of muscle volume). In addition, the affected muscles always show decreased tone, and tendon reflexes are reduced or absent (for further discussion see Chapter 27). In contrast, upper motor neuron lesions affect groups of muscles, atrophy is rare, muscle tone is often increased (spasticity), as are tendon reflexes, and the plantar response is extensor.

Single Neurons Code for the Intended Force of Voluntary Movements

To obtain a better idea of how voluntary movement is generated, it is necessary to know how the activity of individual neurons in the motor cortex and red nucleus relates to natural movements. In particular, we need to know how the pattern of cellular activity is reflected in voluntary movement. Do neurons of the motor cortex code for the extent and direction of movement or do they code for the force required to produce the movement?

To examine this question, Edward Evarts developed a technique for recording the patterns of discharge of identified pyramidal tract neurons in

an awake monkey while the monkey alternately flexed and extended its wrist (Figure 29–4A). The monkey was trained to grasp a handle and to move it first in one direction, then in the other. Movements of the arm and forearm were prevented by a rigid cuff. By means of a simple system of pulleys, Evarts was able to change the load that the monkey had to overcome to flex or to extend the wrist. Evarts noted that neurons recorded in the wrist area of the motor cortex changed their activity in relation to the direction of the wrist movement, some increasing their activity with flexion, others with extension. The firing of the neurons invariably preceded the onset of muscle contraction (Figure 29–4B).

Evarts next attempted to determine whether the displacement of the limb or the force exerted by the muscles was the major variable coded in the discharge frequency of the neurons. He reasoned that if neurons did code an intended change in position, without regard to force, then the discharge of the neurons should not be affected by the changes in load. To decide this question, he placed a weight on one or another side of the pulley system. Figure 29–4C shows typical findings in a pyramidal tract neuron that increased its activity with flexion of the wrist. When the weight opposes extension and aids flexion, the neuron no longer fires during that phase of movement. In this case movement is accomplished by relaxation of the antagonist muscles. Thus, Evarts found that pyramidal tract neuron output codes for intended force and not intended displacement.

To obtain a more precise understanding of the relationship between the patterns of neuronal discharge and the actual motor output, it is important to study the relationship between neuronal activity and the force exerted by the limb under isometric conditions when the muscle is not changing length. When muscle contraction displaces a limb, the agonist muscle shortens and this decreased length results in a decrease in muscle tension. Therefore, to maintain a desired force, the required neuronal drive becomes progressively greater the more the displacement that takes place. Because length–tension properties vary in a highly nonlinear fashion, it is difficult to establish the relationship between neural activity and force when the length of the muscle changes. To overcome this problem Smith, Hepp-Reymond, and Wyss in Zurich studied the activity of cortical neurons in monkeys trained to apply different levels of force to a strain gauge

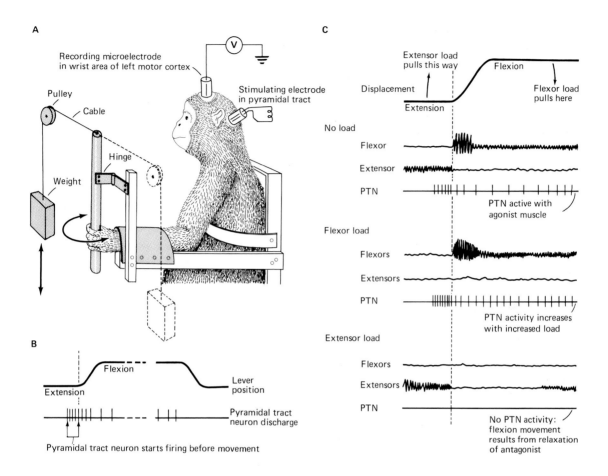

A

Recording microelectrode
in wrist area of left motor cortex

V

Stimulating electrode
in pyramidal tract

Pulley

Cable

Hinge

Weight

B

Flexion

Extension

Lever
position

Pyramidal tract
neuron discharge

Pyramidal tract neuron starts firing before movement

C

Extensor load
pulls this way

Flexion

Displacement

Flexor load
pulls here

Extension

No load

Flexor

Extensor

PTN

PTN active with
agonist muscle

Flexor load

Flexors

Extensors

PTN

PTN activity increases
with increased load

Extensor load

Flexors

Extensors

PTN

No PTN activity:
flexion movement
results from relaxation
of antagonist

pressed between the thumb and index finger. They distinguished three groups of neurons based on their patterns of activity (Figure 29–5A). One group, the *dynamic neurons,* changed their firing frequency just as the animal increased the level of force it was applying. The firing in these neurons then decreased even when a high steady force was being maintained. The second group, the *static neurons,* maintained a high level of activity during the entire interval when higher force was being exerted. The third group, the *mixed neurons,* showed intermediate properties.

The neurons within the magnocellular portion of the red nucleus have similar characteristics: the activity of a given neuron corresponds to the contraction of individual muscle groups. The firing rate of cells increases before the onset of movement or before a change in force exerted isometrically. Furthermore, the patterns of discharge of rubral neurons fall into the same three general classes as those of the motor cortex. However, whereas neurons in the motor cortex

29–4 Experiment demonstrating that activity of motor cortical neurons reflects the direction of force exerted. **A.** Setup for recording discharge of specific pyramidal tract neurons while awake monkey alternately flexes and extends its wrist. **B.** Pyramidal tract neuron starts firing before movement (**arrows**). **C.** Records of a pyramidal tract neuron (**PTN**) that increases its activity with flexion of the wrist. Flexor and extensor electromyograms and pyramidal tract neuron discharge records are shown under different load conditions. Absence of neuron activity with extensor load indicates that the neuron output codes for force rather than displacement.

are principally of the tonic and mixed types, most neurons in the red nucleus have phasic properties and static neurons are uncommon (Figure 29–5B).

Thus, three features characterize the cells in the motor cortex and the red nucleus:

1. These neurons change their activity in advance of the motor output.

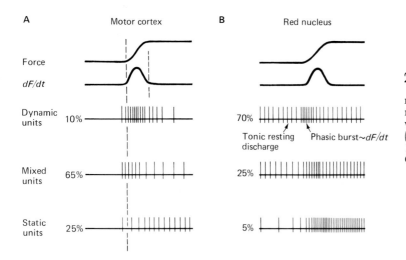

29–5 Patterns of activity of dynamic, static, and mixed neurons in the motor cortex (**A**) and red nucleus (**B**) of cats during voluntary isometric contraction. (Adapted from Ghez and Vicario, 1978a, and Vicario, Martin, and Ghez, unpublished.)

2. The increase in activity in these neurons depends on the direction of force exerted. Thus, individual cells in both systems can control the contraction of both flexor and extensor muscles.

3. The change in firing frequency of the neurons is related to the magnitude of the force exerted or to dF/dt, the first derivative of force.

To understand the functional significance of the phasic properties of neurons in the two major descending systems we need to recall that mus-

29–6 Rapid adjustments in isometric force. Records of a subject who tried to match the force applied on a lever to a target force. The initial burst of action potentials in the triceps muscle overcomes the inherent sluggishness of muscle responses. (Adapted from Ghez and Vicario, 1978b.)

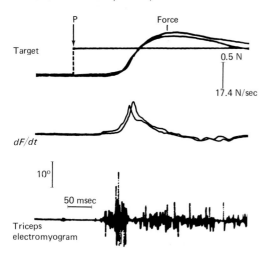

cles respond sluggishly to a low-frequency train of nerve impulses (see Chapter 25, Figure 25–2). When a muscle nerve is suddenly stimulated at a regular rate, tension in the muscle develops slowly. If higher stimulus frequencies are applied to the nerve, higher tension develops at a greater rate of change. The neuronal systems controlling the muscles are constrained by the fact that maximal tension is an inverse function of the time to reach that tension. Thus, it can take a relatively long time to develop low levels of force. However, we often need to make quick movements of small amplitudes. Kinematic studies of voluntary muscle contraction show that large forces do not require more time to reach their peaks than small ones. The slow response of muscles is overcome by a phasic command at the beginning of movement, typically associated with action potential doublets in individual muscle fibers. This can be seen by examining the electromyographic records of the agonist muscles when a subject rapidly adjusts the force he applies to a rigid surface. Figure 29–6 shows the records of a subject who tried to match the force applied on a lever to a target level using a visual cue. At the point marked P the target level of force was suddenly increased and the subject rapidly increased his force to the new level. To accomplish this increase the subject generated an initial burst of action potentials, recorded on the electromyogram of the agonist (triceps) muscle. This initial phasic command at the beginning of movement is designed to overcome the inherent sluggishness of muscles. This phasic command is thought to be produced by the dynamic neurons of the two descending motor systems.

The neurons controlling the force necessary for movement represent only a subpopulation of pyramidal tract neurons; other neurons have more complex properties and functions and these have not yet been fully characterized.

Intended Movement Requires a Preparatory Set

In voluntary movements pyramidal tract and rubrospinal neurons start firing 20–50 msec before any sign of muscle contractions, but other groups of neurons fire earlier. The activity of neurons in the basal ganglia and the deep cerebellar nuclei precedes the activity of neurons in the motor cortex and red nucleus. During many voluntary movements activation of the basal ganglia and deep cerebellar nuclei represents the end result of complex processes that start hundreds of milliseconds earlier. Kornhuber and his collaborators in Germany have shown that changes in the potentials recorded from the human scalp over the motor cortex begin about 800 msec before a voluntary finger movement (Figure 29–7). Although the mechanisms producing these potentials remain controversial, their occurrence underscores the fact that activity in the nervous system begins long before movement is actually performed. During this period the central nervous system is thought to set up a program which specifies how its neurons will respond to a stimulus.

Evarts and Tanji have investigated this program by recording the discharges of pyramidal tract neurons in monkeys that were trained to perform one of two different responses according to a preceding signal when a sudden perturbation was delivered to a handle that they were holding (Figure 29–8). The instruction to either push or pull the handle was given by illuminating one of two lamps in front of the animal. The signal to move was a sudden jerk either toward or away from the animal, produced by a motor attached to the handle itself. Pyramidal tract neurons were recorded in the motor cortex and the direction of limb movement with which the unit increased its activity was also determined.

Two interesting observations emerged from these experiments. First, the instruction itself elicited different changes in activity in the neuron according to the direction of movement called for. The effect also differed according to the muscle groups whose contraction was associated with activity in that cell. For example, a pyramidal tract neuron that was phasically active when the animal flexed its arm showed tonic increases in activity after the instruction to pull

29–7 Human premotor potentials. Potentials recorded from the human scalp over the motor cortex beginning about 800 msec before a voluntary finger movement (Adapted from Deecke et al., 1969.)

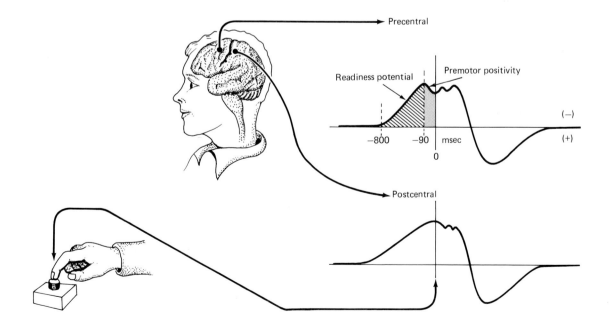

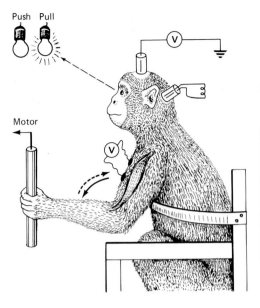

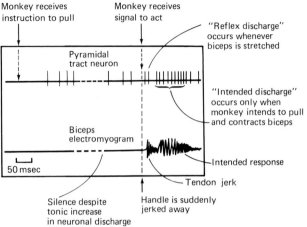

29–8 The activity of cortical neurons reflects the occurrence of a voluntary set preparing the nervous system to respond to a certain stimulus in a previously learned manner. In this experiment the sudden movement of the lever is the signal telling the monkey to go ahead with a previous instruction (i.e., to pull). This also pulls the biceps, evokes a tendon jerk, and excites the pyramidal tract neuron at short latency.

(i.e., to contract the flexor muscle) was given. This change in neural activity was, however, not associated with any change in muscle activity. Second, the perturbation delivered to the handle, constituting the signal to move, elicited two distinct bursts of discharge in the same neurons. The first burst, termed the *reflex discharge*, occurred whenever the biceps was stretched by sudden movement of the handle. This burst of activity is merely the result of the stimulus applied to the receptive field of the neuron, a reflection of the positive feedback system described by Asanuma. The later burst (appearing at a latency of about 50 msec), termed the *intended discharge*, was contingent on the instruction. The intended discharge occurred when the animal was instructed to pull (i.e., contract biceps); the discharge did not occur when the animal was to push. This intended discharge actually produces the intended response to the stimulus. The fact that its occurrence is dependent on context suggests that the sensory input can be gated through the pyramidal tract neurons by neuronal events set in motion by the instruction. The instruction is thought to put the nervous system in a specific state or *voluntary set.*

It is thought that the relationships between stimulus and response that are appropriate to a given context or instruction are established during an initial stage of learning. The learned relationship determines which muscle groups should contract and how much contraction should occur relative to the locus and intensity of stimulation. Once learned, the instruction signal puts the nervous system into the appropriate set, which in turn operates on a neural gate and enables sensory inflow to be channeled to the proper muscles. One of the principal reasons for invoking a gating mechanism is that the interval between the handle jerk and the intended discharge of the cortical neurons is very brief. Recent experiments suggest that similar mechanisms operate in the quickest responses we make to any stimulus be it visual, cutaneous, or auditory. Although we know neither where nor how this gating process takes place, it is a good bet that the principle of its operation is similar to that involved in the gating of interneurons described in Chapter 24.

We have previously seen how certain postural responses could be gated on or off according to the postural set. Similar mechanisms therefore permit us to maintain posture (in the case of Nashner's experiments) and to generate quick movements (in the case of experiments of Evarts and Tanji) in the face of predictable disturbances. These mechanisms are of great importance in the context of the overall hierarchical organization of the motor systems and provide a simple and fast process for converting stimuli to effective responses.

Selected Readings and References

Asanuma, H. 1973. Cerebral cortical control of movement. Physiologist 16:143–166.

Evarts, E. V. 1967. Representation of movements and muscles by pyramidal tract neurons of the precentral motor cortex. In M. D. Yahr and D. P. Purpura (eds.), Neurophysiological Basis of Normal and Abnormal Motor Activities. Hewlett, New York: Raven Press, pp. 215–253.

Phillips, C. G., and Porter, R. 1977. Corticospinal Neurones: Their Role in Movement. London: Academic.

Tanji, J., and Evarts, E. V. 1976. Anticipatory activity of motor cortex neurons in relation to direction of an intended movement. J. Neurophysiol. 39:1062–1068.

Other References

Babinski, J. 1896. Sur le réflexe cutané plantaire dans certaines affections organiques du système nerveux central. C. R. Soc. Biol. (Paris) 48:207–208.

Betz, V. 1874. Anatomischer Nachweis zweier Gehirncentrabl. Med. Wiss. 12:578–580; 595–599.

Deecke, L. Scheid, P., and Kornhuber, H. H. 1969. Distribution of readiness potential, pre-motion positivity, and motor potential of the human cerebral cortex preceding voluntary finger movements. Exp. Brain Res. 7:158–168.

Evarts, E. V. 1968. Relation of pyramidal tract activity to force exerted during voluntary movement. J. Neurophysiol. 31:14–27.

Evarts, E. V., and Tanji, J. 1976. Reflex and intended responses in motor cortex pyramidal tract neurons of monkey. J. Neurophysiol. 39:1069–1080.

Ferrier, D. 1875. Experiments on the brain of monkeys. —No. I. Proc. R. Soc. Lond. 23:409–430.

Fritsch, G., and Hitzig, E. 1870. Ueber die elektrische Erregbarkeit des Grosshirns. Arch. Anat. Physiol. Wiss. Med., pp. 300–332.

Fulton, J. F., and Keller, A. D. 1932. The Sign of Babinski. A Study of the Evolution of Cortical Dominance in Primates. Springfield, Ill.: Thomas.

Ghez, C., and Vicario, D. 1978a. Discharge of red nucleus neurons during voluntary muscle contraction: Activity patterns and correlations with isometric force. J. Physiol. (Paris) 74:283–285.

Ghez, C., and Vicario, D. 1978b. The control of rapid limb movement in the cat. II. Scaling of isometric force adjustments. Exp. Brain Res. 33:191–202.

Gilman, S. 1973. Significance of muscle receptor control systems in the pathophysiology of experimental postural abnormalities. In J. E. Desmedt (ed.), New Developments in Electromyography and Clinical Neurophysiology, Vol. 3. Basel: Karger, pp. 175–193.

Landau, W. M., and Clare, M. H. 1959. The plantar reflex in man, with special reference to some conditions where the extensor response is unexpectedly absent. Brain 82:321–355.

Leyton, A. S. F., and Sherrington, C. S. 1917. Observations on the excitable cortex of the chimpanzee, orang-utan, and gorilla. Q. J. Exp. Physiol. 11:135–222.

Lloyd, D. P. C. 1941. The spinal mechanism of the pyramidal system in cats. J. Neurophysiol. 4:525–546.

Penfield, W., and Rasmussen, T. 1950. The Cerebral Cortex of Man. New York: Macmillan.

Smith, A. M., Hepp-Reymond, M.-C., and Wyss, U.R. 1975. Relation of activity in precentral cortical neurons to force and rate of force change during isometric contractions of finger muscles. Exp. Brain Res. 23:315–332.

Tower, S. S. 1940. Pyramidal lesion in the monkey. Brain 63:36–90.

Woolsey, C. N. 1958. Organization of somatic sensory and motor areas of the cerebral cortex. In H. F. Harlow and C. N. Woolsey (eds.), Biological and Biochemical Bases of Behavior. Madison: University of Wisconsin Press, pp. 63–81.

Claude Ghez and Stanley Fahn

The Cerebellum

30

The cerebellum is a remarkable organ. Although it contains complete motor and sensory representations of the body, lesions of this structure produce neither muscle weakness nor disorders of perception; however, the cerebellum controls the timing and the pattern of muscles activated during movement. In addition, the cerebellum modulates spinal cord and brain stem mechanisms involved in postural control. Hence, lesions of the cerebellum produce disturbances in the coordination of limb and eye movements as well as disorders of muscle tone and posture. In this chapter we shall consider the function of the cerebellum in the context of its anatomy.

Regional Anatomy of the Cerebellum

The cerebellum is a convoluted bilaterally symmetrical structure located in the posterior fossa of the cranium. It is composed of an outer mantle of gray matter, the cerebellar cortex, internal white matter, and three pairs of deep cerebellar nuclei arranged on either side of the midline. The deep nuclei are the *fastigial, interposed* (globose and emboliform), and the *dentate* nuclei. These three nuclei mediate the bulk of the output of the cerebellum.

The cerebellum receives afferent information from the periphery via spinocerebellar tracts as well as from the brain stem and from the cerebral cortex. The output of the cerebellum (via the deep nuclei) is directed primarily to motor regions of the brain stem and cerebral cortex. The input and output connections course through three pairs of tracts on either side, called *cerebellar peduncles,* which connect the cerebellum to the brain stem. These peduncles are (1) the inferior cerebellar peduncle (or *restiform body*), (2) the middle cerebellar peduncle (or *brachium pontis*), and (3) the superior cerebellar peduncle (or *brachium conjunctivum*).

Rostrocaudal Divisions: Fissures, Lobes, and Lobules

A striking feature of the cerebellar surface is the presence of numerous parallel convolutions or *folia* running in a transverse direction (Figure 30–1). Five fissures separate groups of folia from one another. Two of the five fissures, the *primary fissure* and the *posterolateral fissure,* are deeper than the rest and divide the cerebellum into three major lobes—the anterior, posterior, and flocculonodular lobes. In front of the primary fissure

lies the anterior lobe; behind it lies the posterior lobe. The posterior lobe is separated from the flocculonodular lobe by the posterolateral fissure. Additional fissures divide the lobes into smaller groups of folia, known as *lobules,* whose names are given in Figure 30–1A and B.

Mediolateral Divisions: Vermis and Hemispheres

The cerebellum is also subdivided mediolaterally into a midline longitudinal strip, known as the *vermis,* and cerebellar *hemispheres* on either side (Figure 30–2A). The latter are composed of intermediate and lateral parts. These subdivisions of the cerebellar cortex project, in mediolateral sequence, to the various deep nuclei: the vermis to the fastigial nucleus, the intermediate part of the hemispheres to the interposed nucleus, and the lateral part to the dentate nucleus. The flocculonodular lobe projects to both fastigial and vestibular nuclei.

The different mediolateral divisions of the cerebellum are quite independent from each other. Thus, in contrast to the cerebral cortex, the cerebellar cortex has no commissural fiber systems allowing one region of the cerebellum to communicate with another.

Different Parts of the Cerebellum Have Different Phylogenetic Origins and Functions

Phylogenetically, the flocculonodular lobe represents the oldest portion of the cerebellum and is therefore called the *archicerebellum* (Figure 30–2B). This part of the cerebellum developed in relation to the vestibular apparatus, a functional relationship it has maintained in all the vertebrates. Through its connections with the vestibular nuclei the flocculonodular lobe is involved in the control of posture (via the vestibulospinal contribution to the medial descending brain stem pathway), the control of eye movements, and certain autonomic responses (e.g., motion sickness, which is prevented with lesions of the flocculonodular lobe).

The *paleocerebellum* (Figure 30–2B) arises later in phylogeny and consists of the anterior lobe and posterior parts of the vermis (pyramis and uvula). Both the anterior and posterior lobes of the cerebellum have complete sensory and motor maps of the body surface that overlap each other precisely. In both areas the most medial

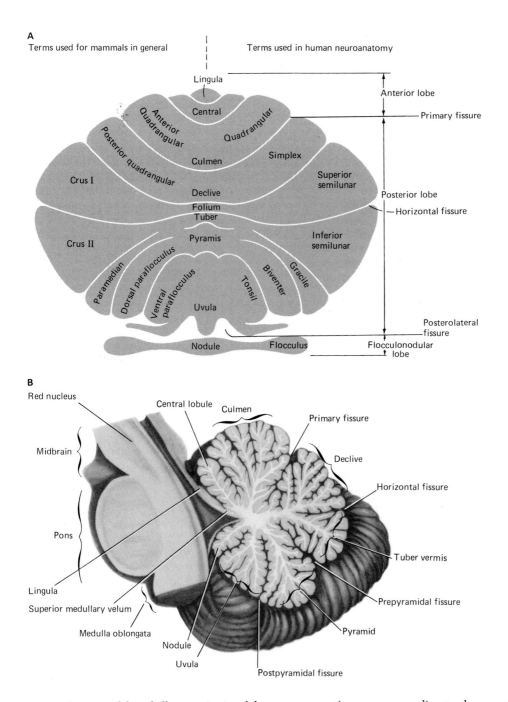

A

Terms used for mammals in general

Terms used in human neuroanatomy

Lingula

Central

Anterior Quadrangular

Quadrangular

Posterior quadrangular

Culmen

Simplex

Crus I

Declive

Folium

Tuber

Superior semilunar

Crus II

Pyramis

Inferior semilunar

Paramedian

Dorsal paraflocculus

Ventral paraflocculus

Tonsil

Biventer

Gracile

Uvula

Nodule

Flocculus

Anterior lobe

Primary fissure

Posterior lobe

Horizontal fissure

Posterolateral fissure

Flocculonodular lobe

B

Red nucleus

Central lobule

Culmen

Primary fissure

Midbrain

Declive

Pons

Horizontal fissure

Lingula

Tuber vermis

Superior medullary velum

Prepyramidal fissure

Medulla oblongata

Pyramid

Nodule

Uvula

Postpyramidal fissure

30–1 Rostrocaudal cerebellar organization: lobes, lobules, and fissures. **A.** Cerebellar surface represented in a schematic view where the lobes have been unfolded **B.** Sagittal section.

portions, corresponding to the vermis, receive information from axial regions of the body and project to medial descending systems. The intermediate part of the hemisphere receives information from the more distal portions of the limbs and controls them through the lateral descending pathways. The *neocerebellum,* the latest portion to develop, consists of the lateral parts of the

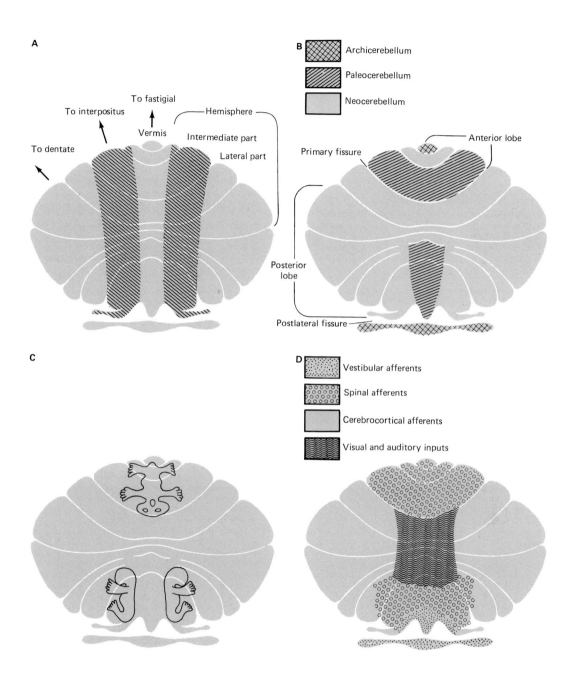

30–2 Organization of the cerebellum.
A. Mediolateral organization. **B.** Phylogenetic subdivisions. **C.** Somatotopic relations. **D.** Distribution of afferents.

cerebellum and the central portion of the vermis (Figure 30–2B). In higher primates and man we see the greatest development of the lateral parts of the cerebellar hemispheres and the associated dentate nuclei. The lateral parts of the hemisphere receive input from the association areas of the cortex but do not receive peripheral input directly. These regions of the neocerebellum are thought to play a role in the planning rather than in the execution of movement.

Organization of the Cerebellar Cortex

The Cortex Is Divided into Distinct Molecular, Purkinje, and Granular Layers

The cortex of the cerebellum has a uniform and regular structure consisting of five types of cells: stellate, basket, Purkinje, Golgi, and granule. These cells are arranged in three distinct layers.

The outer layer, the *molecular layer,* is composed of axons of the granule cells (which lie in a deeper layer) oriented longitudinally in the direction of the folium and known as the parallel fibers, and two types of interneurons—the stellate cells and the basket cells. This layer also contains the dendrites of certain neurons whose cell bodies are in deeper layers.

30–3 Synaptic organization of the cerebellar cortex. Purkinje cells are excited directly by climbing fibers and indirectly (via parallel fibers from the granule cells) by the mossy fibers. Stellate and basket cells, which are excited by parallel fibers, act as inhibitory interneurons. The Golgi cells act on the granule cells with feedback inhibition (when excited by parallel fibers) and feedforward inhibition (when excited by climbing and mossy fiber collaterals). The output of the Purkinje cell is inhibitory upon the cells of the intracerebellar and vestibular nuclei.

The next layer, the *Purkinje layer,* consists of a single layer of Purkinje cells. These cells provide the only output of the cerebellar cortex. The Purkinje cells are large (50 μm in diameter) and have flask-shaped cell bodies and an elaborate dendritic tree extending out in a single plane within the molecular layer in a fanlike fashion. The planes formed by the dendritic arborizations are transverse to the long axis of the folium and are perpendicular to the parallel fibers (Figure 30–3).

The innermost, *granular layer* is composed of densely packed Golgi neurons and granule cells. This layer contains an enormous number of neurons (about 100 billion), which exceeds the total number in the remaining parts of the brain. Under the light microscope small clear spaces can be seen within the granular layer; these are the *cerebellar glomeruli.* With the electron microscope they are seen to be composed of bulbous expansions along mossy fibers, forming rosette figures surrounded by dendrites of granule cells and axons of Golgi neurons. The entire complex is surrounded by a glial sheath. The glomeruli are the principal sites where mossy fibers make their synaptic terminations.

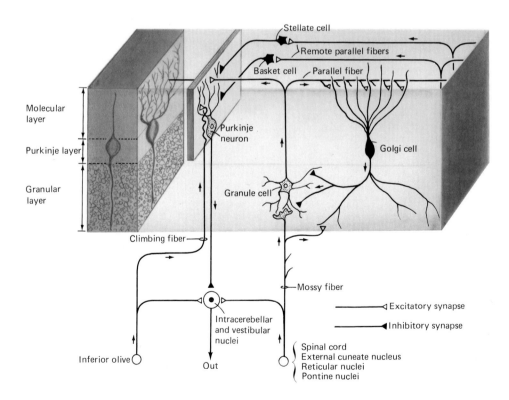

Input Reaches the Cortex via Two Excitatory Fiber Systems: Mossy and Climbing Fibers

Details of intrinsic cellular connections are better understood in the cerebellum than in other sites in the central nervous system. The cerebellum has a surprisingly simple synaptic organization: there are only two inputs (each of which is excitatory) and only one output (which is inhibitory).

Input reaches the cortex through two excitatory fiber systems (Figure 30–3): the *climbing fibers* (the axons of neurons in the contralateral inferior olive) and the *mossy fibers* (the axons of neurons whose cell bodies lie in the spinal cord and brain stem). Both afferent systems also connect with the neurons of the deep cerebellar nuclei, and provide them with background excitation. Each Purkinje neuron receives only one climbing fiber, although each single climbing fiber may diverge to about 10 Purkinje neurons. The climbing fiber wraps around the Purkinje neuron and makes numerous synaptic contacts on smooth portions of somatic and dendritic membrane and on small spines of the dendrites. The climbing fibers also make contact with granule, Golgi, and basket cells in the cortex. A single spike in a climbing fiber causes the Purkinje neurons to fire a burst of impulses. Elegant experiments by Rodolfo Llinás and his co-workers at New York University have shown that the late depolarizations that can be recorded intracellularly from Purkinje cells (and are also seen in extracellular recordings) are the result of dendritic calcium spikes which spread electrotonically to the soma.

All other sources of cerebellar input give rise to mossy fibers that do not terminate on Purkinje cells directly, but on the dendrites of granule cells (at the glomeruli). The granule cells in turn send their axons upward into the molecular layer, where they bifurcate and give rise to the parallel fibers. Each parallel fiber extends about 2 mm and intersects the perpendicularly oriented planes formed by the dendrites of many Purkinje neurons, making one or at most a few synapses with each Purkinje neuron that it passes. The synapses are formed between en passant varicosities of the parallel fiber and long spines on the distal dendrites of the Purkinje neuron. The spines protrude into the presynaptic varicosity of the parallel fibers.

Each parallel fiber excites a longitudinal array of about 50 Purkinje neurons. Conversely, each Purkinje neuron receives input from approximately 200,000 parallel fibers. Thus, in contrast to the small degree of convergence and divergence in connections between climbing fibers and Purkinje cells, there is enormous divergence and convergence in the mossy fiber paths and the derived parallel fiber system.

Whereas the granule cells are excitatory, the other interneurons in the cerebellar cortex (stellate cells, basket cells, and Golgi neurons) are inhibitory. The stellate and basket cells (which receive excitatory input from the parallel fibers) establish inhibitory synaptic contacts with the Purkinje neurons in the molecular layer (Figure 30–3); the stellate cells synapse at the level of the distal dendrites and the basket cells at the proximal dendrites and soma. In order to understand how these various inhibitory influences affect the spatial patterning of Purkinje cell output, it is important to consider the spatial arrangement of the projections of the different interneurons (Figure 30–4). Within each folium, the axons of the stellate and basket cells are oriented at right angles to the longitudinally oriented parallel fibers, and also at right angles to the vertically oriented dendritic branches of the Purkinje neurons (Figures 30–3 and 30–4). The stellate and basket cells, which receive input from narrow beams of parallel fibers, distribute their terminals to the Purkinje neurons on either side for about 1 mm. A localized mossy fiber input typically activates a small cluster of granule cells, giving rise to action potentials in just such a beam of parallel fibers. These in turn excite an array of "on-beam" Purkinje neurons, and, through their input to the stellate and basket cells, inhibit the surrounding "off-beam" Purkinje neurons. These inhibitory interneurons serve the function of spatially focusing the cerebellar cortical output (Figure 30–4).

The Golgi cells also receive their principal input from the parallel fibers in the molecular layer (where they have an elaborate dendritic tree) but distribute their terminals back to the granule cells (Figure 30–3). This is an example of feedback inhibition which cuts off the input after a brief delay. The Golgi neurons also receive direct input from mossy and climbing fiber collaterals (Figure 30–3). This feedforward inhibition of the granule cells reaches them sooner than signals that follow the parallel fiber–Golgi cell path. Thus, the net result of a localized mossy fiber input is the brief firing of a sharply defined population of Purkinje neurons.

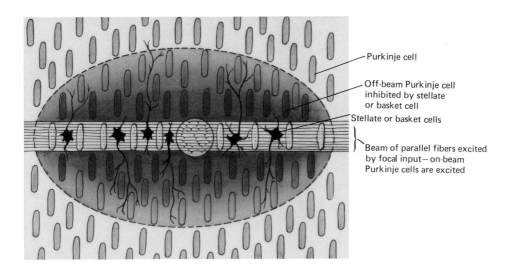

Purkinje cell

Off-beam Purkinje cell
inhibited by stellate
or basket cell

Stellate or basket cells

Beam of parallel fibers excited
by focal input—on-beam
Purkinje cells are excited

30–4 Excitation of beam of parallel fibers by focal
mossy fiber input. Schematic view of surface
of cerebellar folium. (Adapted from Eccles et al., 1967.)

In an important series of studies, Masao Ito in
Japan established that the Purkinje neurons make
only inhibitory connections. This inhibition is
exerted upon cells of the deep nuclei and cells of
the vestibular nuclei, whose spontaneous activity
is probably maintained by the excitatory collaterals of mossy and climbing fibers. Through its inhibitory action the cerebellar cortex is thought to
sculpt the output of the deep nuclei, chiseling
away unwanted background discharges.

Some of the neurotransmitters associated with
the five intrinsic neurons of the cerebellar cortex
are known. The inhibitory Purkinje, basket, stellate, and Golgi cells use gamma-aminobutyric
acid (GABA) as their neurotransmitter. The excitatory granule cell most likely releases glutamate. The neurotransmitters in the climbing and
mossy fibers are unknown. Because these fibers
come from a large number of different nuclei in
the central nervous system, a variety of transmitter substances is possible. The neurotransmitters
of neurons with cell bodies in the deep cerebellar
nuclei are also unknown. Norepinephrine-
containing fibers from the locus ceruleus also
terminate in the cerebellar cortex.

Afferent Connections of the Cerebellum

The cerebellum receives information from all
sensory receptors as well as from the cerebral cortex and brain stem nuclei. These inputs keep the
cerebellum informed of sensory events in the
periphery and of all commands originating in
motor and association areas of the brain. The
bulk of the information from both the periphery
and higher brain centers reaches the cerebellum
via the mossy fiber system. The climbing fibers
originate exclusively within the inferior olive and
will be discussed separately.

Sensory Input Is Conveyed via Direct
and Indirect Pathways

Afferent input from all body parts and all receptors reaches the cerebellar surface to form two
complete somatotopic maps. One is located in
the anterior lobe, the other is in the posterior
lobe. The two representations are inverted relative to one another (Figure 30–2C). The neck and
trunk are represented at the midline, and the extremities within the intermediate parts. Information from the head regions as well as acoustic and
visual inputs reach the face area of the cerebellar
cortex. Information from spinal levels is conveyed to the cerebellum by a multiplicity of
pathways both direct and indirect which terminate in the vermis and intermediate part of the
hemisphere (Figure 30–2D). The *direct pathways*
convey input directly to the cerebellar cortex
from spinal neurons and consist of the *dorsal* and
ventral spinocerebellar pathways, which relay
different types of input from the lower extremities. The *cuneocerebellar* and *rostral spinocerebellar pathways* convey equivalent information from the upper extremities. *Indirect pathways* have synaptic relays in either the inferior
olive (spino-olivocerebellar pathways) or in the
lateral reticular nucleus (spinoreticulocerebellar

pathways). Sensory fibers from the vestibular nerve and nuclei reach the flocculonodular lobe as well as the uvula via the inferior cerebellar peduncle.

The dorsal spinocerebellar tract originates from neurons in the column of Clarke (which lies between the levels of T1 and L2 and receives input from the leg). The cuneocerebellar tract originates in the external cuneate nucleus and projects to the ipsilateral vermis and intermediate zone via the inferior cerebellar peduncle. Dorsal spinocerebellar tract and cuneocerebellar tract fibers lie in the dorsolateral quadrants of the spinal cord while fibers to the external cuneate nucleus (from which the cuneocerebellar tract originates) lie in the dorsal columns. Both groups of fibers convey proprioceptive and cutaneous information from small peripheral regions to small discrete areas of the cerebellum via the inferior cerebellar peduncle.

The ventral and rostral spinocerebellar tracts cross in the spinal cord and reach bilateral regions of the anterior and posterior lobes via the superior cerebellar peduncle. Some of the information conveyed through these pathways arises from proprioceptive and skin afferents from wide regions of the body. The remainder comes from a group of spinal neurons called the *spinal border cells,* which derive their input from collaterals of descending fibers and from interneurons mediating the descending effects from supraspinal pathways. These interneurons are of considerable interest because they provide the cerebellum with information about the nature of the final command just before it is transmitted to the motor neuron, as we discussed in relation to locomotion (Chapter 28). Within the cerebellar cortex the areas of termination of ventral spinocerebellar tract fibers are widespread and bilateral.

Cerebral Input Is Conveyed via the Corticopontocerebellar Tract

The cerebellum also receives descending input from supraspinal centers. The bulk of this input derives from the cerebral cortex as the *corticopontocerebellar* pathway. This pathway projects to the pontine nuclei from collaterals of pyramidal tract axons as well as from corticobulbar fibers originating in most regions of the cortex. The pontine nuclei in turn send their axons primarily to the contralateral hemispheres (but also bilaterally to the parts of the vermis) via the middle cerebellar peduncle. The latter projection assumes progressively greater size and importance

with evolutionary development. In addition to the corticopontocerebellar system, fibers from the red nucleus, tectum, and other regions of the brain stem also project to the cerebellum, directly or indirectly (via the lateral reticular nuclei or the inferior olive).

Climbing Fiber Input

Neurons of the inferior olive, which give rise to the climbing fibers, project to all parts of the contralateral cerebellar cortex in a precise topographic fashion via the inferior cerebellar peduncle and end as climbing fibers. Spinal afferents coursing in all quadrants of the spinal cord (including the dorsal columns) reach the principal olive and the dorsal and medial accessory olives. These olivary neurons also receive descending input from midbrain and telencephalic structures. Physiological recordings show that most olivary neurons receiving peripheral input are strongly influenced by descending volleys from the cortex and other structures. Recent anatomical and physiological observations have shown that the olivary fibers project to narrow sagittal strips of about 1 mm width extending throughout the cerebellar cortex. Recent findings suggest that each strip receives information from a different peripheral location. It has been suggested that each sagittal zone represents a specific functional unit with appropriate efferent connections.

Cerebellar Input Systems Can Be Classified as Peripheral, Descending, or Convergent

From a conceptual standpoint these various input systems fall into three classes. One class of input systems faithfully reflects the activation of *peripheral receptors.* Vestibulocerebellar pathways and certain spinocerebellar pathways (e.g., the dorsal spinocerebellar tract) belong to this class. A second class of inputs includes *collaterals of descending pathways.* These tell the cerebellum of the central commands that initiate and control movement. Thus the motor cortex can influence cerebellar activity through collaterals of pyramidal tract axons. Finally, a third more complex and heterogenous class arises from spinal and brain stem neurons that receive their input from *converging descending and peripheral sources* (e.g., the ventral spinocerebellar tract and olivocerebellar pathways). The latter systems allows the cerebellum to monitor both the activity of peripheral receptors and that of certain brain stem systems.

Efferent Projections of the Cerebellum

Purkinje Cells Project to Deep Cerebellar Nuclei

As emphasized earlier, the Purkinje neurons represent the sole output of the cerebellar cortex, and their axons terminate on the deep cerebellar nuclei as well as on the vestibular nuclei. Through these nuclei the cerebellum is capable of exerting descending influences on the spinal cord, as well as ascending influences on the cerebral cortex. The output can be separated into three components: The first originates in the vermis and flocculonodular lobes and acts upon the fastigial and vestibular nuclei. The second, which originates in the intermediate parts of the cerebellar hemispheres, projects to the interposed nuclei. The third originates in the lateral parts and projects to the dentate nuclei. A knowledge of the patterns of cerebellar efferent connections is essential to an understanding of the nature and laterality of the deficits arising from clinical lesions. A simplified diagram of the major connections is presented in Figure 30–5.

Fastigial and Vestibular Projections Control Proximal Muscles

Fibers from the anterior and posterior vermis project to the ipsilateral lateral and descending vestibular nuclei in a somatotopic fashion. Upper and lower extremity regions of the cerebellum project to corresponding regions of the lateral vestibular nucleus, influencing the respective limbs. Since the lateral vestibular nucleus exerts an excitatory action on proximal and limb extensor motor neurons, interruption of cerebellar inhibition dramatically enhances extensor rigidity in the decerebrate preparation.

The cerebellar cortex also influences the lateral vestibular (Deiter's) nucleus through its projection to the fastigial nucleus. The two somatotopic areas of the anterior and posterior vermis project, respectively, to the rostral and caudal portions of the fastigial nucleus. These in turn converge on somatotopic areas of the lateral vestibular nucleus. The rostral portion does so directly, via the inferior cerebellar peduncle, and the latter indirectly, via crossing fibers, the so-called hook bundle of Russell or uncinate fasciculus. Because all deep cerebellar nuclei have an excitatory influence upon their target neurons it should not be surprising that lesions of the caudal part of the fastigial nucleus produce hypotonia of limb muscles in the decerebrate preparation.

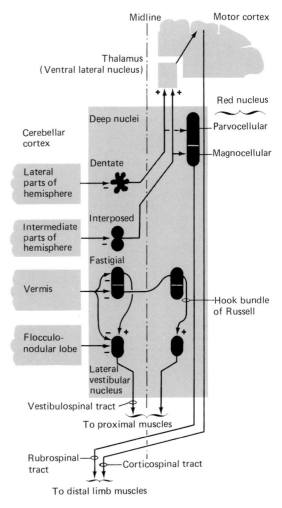

30–5 Major cerebellar output connections.

Fastigial fibers also project to the medial reticular formation and a small contingent of fastigial fibers ascends to the medial parts of the ventrolateral nucleus of the thalamus, which projects to cortical regions controlling proximal muscles.

Interposed (Globose and Emboliform) Nuclei Control Limb Muscles

The interposed nuclei project primarily to the contralateral red nucleus in the midbrain via the superior cerebellar peduncle. This pathway is also somatotopically organized and terminates in the magnocellular part of the red nucleus. This portion gives rise to the rubrospinal tract, which crosses the midline and controls the muscles of both upper and lower extremities, as does the corticospinal tract. Interposed neurons also send ascending fibers to the ventral lateral nucleus of the thalamus, which is a major input to the motor cortex.

Dentate Nucleus

This nucleus, which receives its input from the lateral parts of the cerebellar hemispheres, also sends its fibers through the superior cerebellar peduncle, crossing the midline as did the efferents from the interposed nuclei. Axons of dentate neurons then terminate primarily in the ventral lateral and ventral anterior nuclei of the thalamus, which project to the motor cortex. Since both the motor cortex and the red nuclei send crossed fibers down to the spinal cord, and since the superior cerebellar peduncle is crossed in the midbrain (a double crossing), *symptoms resulting from lesions of the cerebellar hemispheres are ipsilateral to the side of the lesion.*

The dentate nucleus also projects to the parvocellular portion of the red nucleus, which in turn sends axons to the ipsilateral olive via the central tegmental tract. The precise function of this massive feedback loop is a major mystery in cerebellar physiology. Lesions of this pathway give rise to a remarkable disorder known as *palatal myoclonus* in which patients show a continuous tremor of facial and pharyngeal muscle which persists even during sleep.

In summary, the mediolateral organization of afferent input topography is reflected in the output patterns of the different regions of the cerebellum. Midline vermal regions receive information from the neck and trunk and exert control over axial and girdle muscles via vestibular and

reticular connections. More laterally, the paravermal regions influence more distal limb muscles through rubral and cortical connections.

Different Parts of the Cerebellum Are Involved in the Planning, Initiation, and Control of Movement

The cerebellum is intimately involved in the regulation of muscle tone and in the initiation and coordination of voluntary movements. Some of the disturbances in muscle tone that follow lesions of one or another part of the cerebellum can be deduced from the connections just described, but it is still somewhat unclear how the cerebellum is involved in the coordination of movements. It is thought that the intent to perform a movement involves first the activation of motor association areas of the cerebral cortex (Figure 30–6). These areas are believed to act in cooperation with the lateral portions of the cerebellar hemispheres and the dentate nuclei during the early phases in the planning of movement that ultimately lead to a command to move. In fact these areas of neocerebellum receive their input from the frontal association areas of the cortex and send their output to the motor cortex via the thalamus. The motor cortex itself is conceived as a primary executive sending final commands to the appropriate muscle group. The intermediate parts of the cerebellar hemispheres are kept in-

30–6 Hypothetical flow diagram of information transfer in the initiation of voluntary movement. The thalamic relay for basal ganglia, cerebellar, and somatic sensory input is omitted for simplicity. (Adapted from Allen and Tsukahara, 1974.)

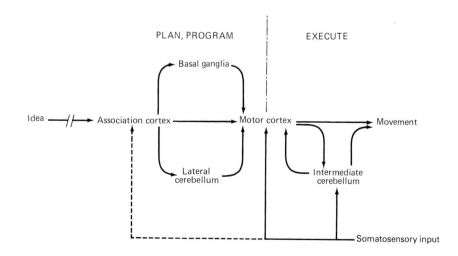

formed of the cortical command by collaterals of pyramidal tract fibers so that the evolving movement can be shaped, or sculptured, by the inhibitory action of Purkinje neurons on nuclear cells. These nuclear cells, in turn, by acting on the red nucleus and back on the motor cortex, may modify the evolving movement.

The notion that the neocerebellum is involved principally in the planning and initiation of movement while the intermediate parts of the cerebellar hemisphere are concerned with moment-to-moment control has received support from recent experiments in primates. W. T. Thach examined the patterns of activity of Purkinje neurons and of interposed and dentate neurons in awake monkeys performing one of several tasks involving flexion and extension of the wrist. In a series of experiments, he found that Purkinje neurons and dentate and interposed neurons fired in close temporal association with specific phases of movement (i.e., flexion or extension) and reflected the pattern of motor activity. (A somatotopic relationship exists between the parts of the body performing a movement and the location of cells whose activity is altered.) Characteristically, the changes in activity of dentate neurons occurred before changes could be seen in interposed neurons, although both preceded movement of the limb. In addition, through the study of a more complex task involving a sequence of movements, Thach also showed that many neurons in the dentate nuclei (which we have seen are related to the lateral portions of the cerebellar hemispheres) often exhibit a more complex pattern of activity than those of interposed neurons. Activity in these neurons seemed to reflect most precisely the direction of the next intended movement rather than the pattern of muscle contraction prevailing at the time. These observations support the idea that planning and initiation of movement occur in the lateral portions of the cerebellum. Further support has come from other recent experiments involving reversible lesions of the dentate nuclei. Vernon Brooks and his collaborators in Canada developed a technique for cooling the dentate nuclei of monkeys while they were performing a learned task, which consisted of making a prompt movement of the limb after a signal (light). The behavior was drastically changed when the dentate nucleus ipsilateral to the moving limb was functionally inactivated by cooling. First, the latency of the animal's response to the light (reaction time) was markedly prolonged. This was accompanied by a corresponding delay in the activity of neurons in the

motor cortex associated with the movements. Second, the movements became slower, more tentative, and inaccurate.

Is the cerebellum capable of storing information or learning new motor programs? Two observations are especially intriguing in this regard. The first was made by clinicians long ago. They observed that patients with lesions of the frontal cortex of the cerebral hemispheres initially show severe disturbances in complex motor tasks. With time, these disorders disappear, but they reappear dramatically following injury to the lateral cerebellum. Because similar disturbances do not normally follow cerebellar lesions alone, it is thought that the cerebellum is involved in compensating for disorders or in learning new motor routines. A second more recent line of evidence comes from the elegant work of A. Gonshor and G. Melvill Jones in Canada and David Robinson at Johns Hopkins. These authors studied the vestibulo-ocular reflex, which maintains the eyes on a fixed target if the head is rotated. In this reflex, motion of the head in a given direction (sensed by the vestibular labyrinth; see Chapter 35) produces eye movements in the opposite direction. When a subject wears prismatic lenses which reverse the left and right visual fields, the direction of the vestibulo-ocular reflex becomes reversed over a period of time. This change is prevented by lesions of the cerebellum.

When one considers cerebellar function, it is instructive to recall a fascinating comment made by a patient of Gordon Holmes who had a lesion of his right cerebellar hemisphere. "The movements of my left hand are done subconsciously, but I have to think out each movement of my right arm. I come to a dead stop in turning and have to think before I start again." Eccles has proposed that the cerebellum spares us this mental task. As a result, a general command may be given by higher brain centers and the specific details of the execution of movement are carried out automatically.

Diseases of the Cerebellum Affect Synergy and Muscle Tone

Disorders of the cerebellum result in a series of distinctive symptoms and signs which were beautifully described by Gordon Holmes in the early part of this century. The symptoms often help localize a disease process to specific portions of the cerebellum. One of the functions of the cerebellum disturbed by disease is *synergy*, the coordinated contractions of agonist and antagonist muscles to produce a smooth, well-controlled movement. Normally the cerebellum provides this control. *Asynergia* is the lack of synergy manifested in a combination of abnormally coordinated movements, including inaccurate range and direction *(dysmetria)*, amplitude, and force. Instead of smooth movement, there is *decomposition of movement,* in which the various components of the performance of an act are not executed in a smooth sequence. *Hypermetria* is an excessive extent of movement, as when a limb overshoots the desired point; and *hypometria* is a deficient extent of movement so that the limb stops before reaching the goal. *Past-pointing* is a feature of dysmetria. *Dysdiadochokinesia* is the irregular pattern of movement seen when a patient is performing rapid alternating movements, such as patting his thighs with alternating palms up followed by palms down (back of the hand) in a rapidly alternating pattern. The clinician commonly uses the term *limb ataxia* as equivalent to asynergia. *Ataxia* of gait is characterized by a wide stance and unsteady walking with a tendency to fall. The "drunken sailor's" gait is a characteristic ataxic gait.

Muscle tone is the degree of resistance to passive manipulation of the limbs. *Normal tone* can be defined as a slight constant tension of healthy muscles, so that when the limbs are handled or moved passively, they offer a modest resistance to displacement. *Hypotonia* is a cerebellar sign denoting diminished resistance to passive movement. *Lack of check* is the inability of a rapidly moving limb to stop rapidly and sharply; the limb overshoots and then may rebound excessively. *Tremor* is an oscillatory movement about a joint due to alternating contractions of agonists and antagonists. The characteristic tremor seen in cerebellar disease occurs with movement of a limb and is most marked at the end of the movement; this is known as *terminal tremor* and more commonly as *intention tremor.* Intention tremor commonly follows lesions in the superior cerebellar peduncle. *Titubation* is a truncal tremor and may be present when the patient is standing or sitting.

Disorders in the articulation of speech *(dysarthria)* are also seen in cerebellar disease. Symbols of speech are normal (i.e., there is no aphasia), but the mechanical aspects of speech are impaired. Speech is slurred and somewhat slow with prolonged syllables. This has been referred to as *scanning speech,* for there is a sing-song quality to it. *Nystagmus,* or see-saw rhythmical movements of the eyes, is a sign of vestibular dysfunc-

tion and may be present with a lesion involving the flocculonodular lobe.

A few principles relate to the localization of cerebellar disorders. (1) Lesions in the cerebellum produce disturbances in the ipsilateral limbs. (2) Because of the somatotopic organization of the cerebellum, lesions in the lateral part of the cerebellum produce limb asynergia, whereas lesions in the vermis produce disorders of the trunk (titubation, gait ataxia). (3) Symptoms from static lesions of the cerebellum tend to improve gradually with time.

Gait ataxia is the most common symptom in patients with cerebellar disease. Abnormal gait may appear with a lesion in any one of the major subdivisions of the cerebellum, especially the flocculonodular lobe, vermis, or anterior lobe.

Disease of the Archicerebellum (Flocculonodular Lobe) Causes Disturbances of Equilibrium

Because of the cerebellar connections with the vestibular system, disease in the flocculonodular lobe causes prominent disturbances of equilibrium, including ataxic gait and *wide-based station* (swaying with a tendency to fall to either side, forward, or backward). Nystagmus is also seen. The most common lesion involving the archicerebellum is a medulloblastoma, a tumor usually occuring in childhood.

Midline Disease of the Paleocerebellum (Anterior Lobe) Often Causes Disorders of Stance and Gait

A common disease involving the anterior lobes (vermis and leg areas) is a restricted form of cerebellar cortical degeneration occurring in alcoholic patients. The cardinal features resulting from disease in this part of the cerebellum are involvement of the legs and gait, with relative sparing of the arms. The heel–shin test (sliding the heel of one foot slowly down the shin of the opposite leg) is abnormal (asynergic). Gait is wide-based and ataxic.

Disease of the Neocerebellum Causes Disorders of Speech and Coordinated Movement

Lesions in the lateral parts of the posterior lobe result in asynergia of the ipsilateral limbs. Abnormalities of the finger-to-nose and heel–shin tests, with dysmetria, dysdiadochokinesia, lack of check, and hypotonia may all be present. Lesions in the vermis result in truncal swaying, titubation, and gait ataxia. Bilateral lesions are common in degenerative diseases of the cerebellum. Dysarthric speech may be present with bilateral involvement.

Selected Readings and References

Adams, R. D., and Victor, M. 1977. Principles of Neurology. New York: McGraw-Hill, pp. 52–59.

Eccles, J. C., Ito, M., and Szentágothai, J. 1967. The Cerebellum as a Neuronal Machine. New York: Springer.

Pompeiano, O. 1967. Functional organization of the cerebellar projections to the spinal cord. Prog. Brain Res. 25:282–321.

Thach, W. T., Jr. 1980. The cerebellum. In V. B. Mountcastle (ed.), Medical Physiology, 14th ed., Vol. 1. St. Louis: Mosby, pp. 837–858.

Other References

Allen, G. I., and Tsukahara, N. 1974. Cerebrocerebellar communication systems. Physiol. Rev. 54:957–1006.

Brooks, V. B. 1979. Control of intended movements by the lateral and intermediate cerebellum. In H. Asanuma and V. J. Wilson (eds.), Integration in the Nervous System. Tokyo: Igaku-Shoin, pp. 321–357.

Gonshor, A., and Melvill Jones, G. 1976. Short-term adaptive changes in the human vestibulo-ocular reflex arc. J. Physiol. (Lond.) 256:361–379.

Holmes, G. 1922. Clinical symptoms of cerebellar disease and their interpretation. Lancet 1:1177–1182; 1:1231–1237; 2:59–65; 2:111–115.

Llinás, R., and Sugimori, M. 1980. Electrophysiological properties of in vitro Purkinje cell somata in mammalian cerebellar slices. J. Physiol. (Lond.) 305:171–195.

Llinás, R., and Sugimori, M. 1980. Electrophysiological properties of in vitro Purkinje cell somata in mammalian cerebellar slices. J. Physiol. (Lond.) 305:197–213.

Meyer-Lohmann, J., Hore, J., and Brooks, V. B. 1977. Cerebellar participation in generation of prompt arm movements. J. Neurophysiol. 40:1038–1050.

Robinson, D. A. 1976. Adaptive gain control of vestibulo-ocular reflex by the cerebellum. J. Neurophysiol. 39:954–969.

Thach, W. T. 1978. Correlation of neural discharge with pattern and force of muscular activity, joint position, and direction of intended next movement in motor cortex and cerebellum. J. Neurophysiol. 41:654–676.

Lucien Côté

Basal Ganglia, the Extrapyramidal Motor System, and Diseases of Transmitter Metabolism

31

Three large subcortical nuclear groups—the caudate nucleus, the putamen, and the pallidum—are collectively called the *basal ganglia*. In turn, the basal ganglia and several associated subthalamic and midbrain structures are referred to as the *extrapyramidal system*. These nuclei participate in the control of movements along with the cerebellum, the corticospinal system, and other descending motor systems. Although part of the motor system, the basal ganglia do not project directly to the spinal cord. The insight that they have something to do with movement came from several astute clinicians who discovered that certain motor disturbances are invariably associated with lesions in the basal ganglia. These motor disturbances consist of (1) reduction in the speed of movement without paralysis (bradykinesia), (2) change in tone, and (3) abnormal, involuntary movements, including tremors.

Lesions of the basal ganglia are found in a variety of motor disorders, including Parkinson's disease, Huntington's disease, Wilson's disease, and Sydenham's chorea. Several of these diseases involve deficiencies in chemical transmitters. Parkinson's disease was the first disease of the central nervous system in which a defect in transmitter metabolism was shown to play a causal pathophysiological role. The study of diseased basal ganglia has provided important basic and clinical information about motor function; it has also, as we shall see later, provided paradigms for studying the relationship of transmitters to disorders of mood and of thought.

Anatomy of the Basal Ganglia

The caudate nucleus and putamen are composed of identical cell types, are fused anteriorly, and develop from telencephalic structures. Phylogenetically, these are the most recent nuclei of the basal ganglia and have been termed collectively the *neostriatum*. The pallidum (or globus pallidus) derives from the diencephalon, has different cytoarchitectural features, and is sometimes referred to as the *paleostriatum*. The pallidum has two divisions, the internal and the external, which are continuous caudally with the substantia nigra. Together the putamen and pallidum form a lens-shaped cellular aggregate which is called *lenticular nucleus*. The caudate nucleus lies medial to the internal capsule; the putamen and pallidum lie laterally (Figure 31–1).

Some authors group the amygdaloid nucleus

together with the basal ganglia. The amygdaloid is the oldest of these subcortical nuclei and is also called the *archistriatum*.[1] It has olfactory input and belongs functionally with the limbic system. We shall not consider it further here.

Two other structures are linked to the basal ganglia anatomically and functionally—the subthalamic nucleus and the substantia nigra. The subthalamic nucleus (of Luys) lies in the basal portion of the diencephalon, at the junction with the mesencephalon (Figure 31–1). The substantia nigra is the largest nuclear mass of the mesencephalon. It has two zones: (1) a ventral "pale" or "gray" zone (pars reticulata) that resembles the pallidum cytologically; and (2) a dorsal compact and darkly pigmented zone whose neurons contain neuromelanin in lysosomal granules. This pigment appears to be a polymerized form of dopamine metabolites. The dorsal zone contains a characteristic group of neurons that use dopamine as their neurotransmitter. Most axons from

---

[1]Convention has it that the term *striatum* is typically reserved for the *neostriatum*. The term *corpus striatum* is variously used to include the neostriatum and paleostriatum, and sometimes includes the archistriatum and claustrum (whose functional attribution is unknown). The term *basal ganglia* is also not without ambiguity and may, in the older literature, include all structures that constitute the corpus striatum, as well as the thalamus! The student is encouraged to refer to specific components.

31–1 Basal ganglia and their relationship to the substantia nigra, the subthalamic nuclei, and the red nucleus.

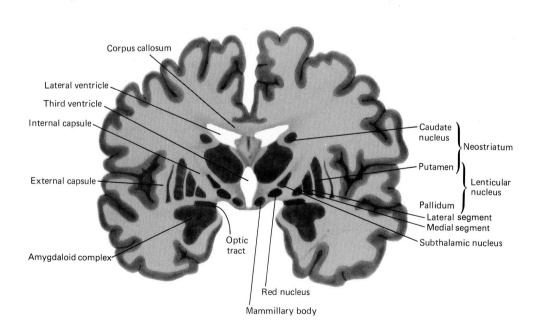

these cells project to the neostriatum and constitute the *nigrostriatal pathway.*

Basal Ganglia Receive Input from the Cortex, Thalamus, and Substantia Nigra, and Project Mainly to the Thalamus

The major afferent systems of the basal ganglia terminate in the caudate and putamen (neostriatum); the pallidum gives rise to its major efferent systems (Figure 31–2).

Afferent Connections

The neostriatum receives afferent input from three major sources. First, it receives input from the cerebral cortex in its entirety, including the motor cortex as well as sensory and association

31–2 Major afferents **(white arrows)** and efferent **(hatched arrows)** connections (Adapted from DeLong, 1974.)

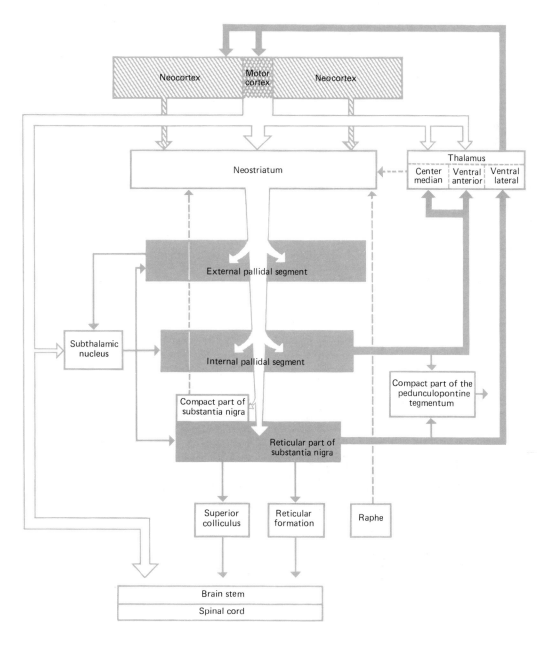

cortices. This corticostriatal pathway is topographically organized. Different parts of the cortex project to different parts of the neostriatum. A second afferent system arises from the intralaminar nuclei of the thalamus (via the internal capsule). The third, from the substantia nigra (also via the internal capsule), includes the dopaminergic pathway that was considered briefly above. There is also serotonergic input from the raphe nucleus.

Intranuclear Connections

Within the basal ganglia, fibers from both the caudate nucleus and the putamen project to both segments of the pallidum. These striatopallidal projections are topographically organized so that each part of the neostriatum projects to one circumscribed part of the pallidum. Because the corticostriatal pathway is topographically organized and the striatopallidal pathways are organized similarly, specific parts of the cortex act on different parts of the pallidum via the neostriatum.

Efferent Connections

The internal portion of the pallidum (pars interna) gives rise to the major efferents from the basal ganglia and these project to the thalamus (to the ventral lateral, ventral anterior, and intralaminar thalamic nuclei), and to the midbrain (especially to the substantia nigra).

The projections to the thalamus are conveyed by two fiber bundles, the ansa lenticularis and the lenticular fasciculus; these two bundles later fuse and reach the thalamus in the thalamic fasciculus. The thalamic nuclei that receive projections from the basal ganglia also receive projections from the cerebellum. The ventral anterior and ventral lateral nuclei of the thalamus in turn project to the prefrontal cortex and the precentral gyrus. This projection is by far the most important outflow of the basal ganglia. Through it the basal ganglia can influence the corticospinal and corticobulbar systems. This anatomical organization implies a key functional principle: the major way the basal ganglia and the other components of the extrapyramidal motor system can influence motor behavior is through the pyramidal system. The basal ganglia also have descending projections to the substantia nigra. These striatonigral pathways influence both portions of the substantia nigra and use GABA as their transmitter.

In summary, the basal ganglia receive massive input from the cortex and thalamus, and they project massively back to the thalamus (Figure 31–3). The basal ganglia do *not* project to nuclei that would allow them to have a direct effect on the motor activity of the spinal cord. From the anatomical organization alone it would seem that the basal ganglia are positioned for coordinating the activity of the cerebral cortex and thalamus. The ventral lateral and ventral anterior nuclei of the thalamus are important as links in the system of ascending fibers from the basal ganglia and the cerebellum to the motor cortex. These thalamic nuclei serve as integrating and funneling relay stations for information going to the motor cortex from the cerebellum and the basal ganglia.

The Basal Ganglia Are Important in the Initiation of Movement

It was once thought that there are three independent motor systems concerned with posture and movement: (1) the pyramidal (corticospinal) motor system, concerned with skilled, volitional movements; (2) the extrapyramidal system (the basal ganglia and associated subthalamic and midbrain structures), concerned with the postural adjustments that form the background for the execution of voluntary activity; and (3) the cerebellum, concerned with the coordination of movement. Anatomical and functional studies have now shown that the three systems are not independent of each other but are extensively interconnected at many levels, most importantly at the level of the thalamus. Thus, the three systems are best thought of as components of a single motor system.

Physiological evidence that the basal ganglia play an important role in the initiation and control of movement has recently been obtained in a series of studies by Mahlon DeLong. He recorded the activity of single neurons in different regions of the basal ganglia of awake monkeys while they performed a variety of voluntary movements. Many neurons were found that change their activity during movement of a specific body part. These neurons are typically clustered together, forming a somatotopic representation of the body. Thus, in the two segments of the pallidum, neurons whose activity relates to movements of the arms are found ventral to those whose activity relates to leg movements. Neurons related to movements were found in both the ventromedial part of the internal segment of

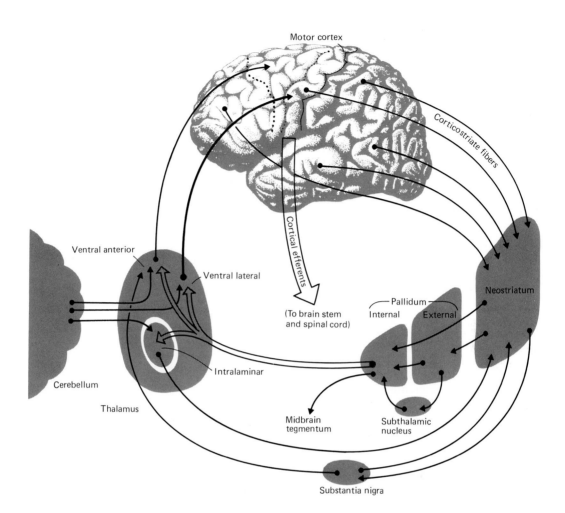

31–3 Critical role of the thalamic nuclei in mediating the connections of the basal ganglia to the motor cortex. (Adapted from DeLong, 1974.)

the pallidum and the lateral part of the reticular part of the substantia nigra. Characteristically, the changes in activity of some neurons took place before the movement of the body part and before the neurons of the motor cortex and cerebellum fired, a sequence suggesting that they might play a role in the initiation of movement itself.

Diseases of the Basal Ganglia Cause Characteristic Symptoms

Diseases of the basal ganglia and related subthalamic structures are characterized by disorders of muscle tone, postural reflexes, and involuntary movements (dyskinesia). The abnormal movements include the following: (1) *tremors* (regular, involuntary, oscillatory movements of a body part); (2) *athetosis* (slow, writhing movements of the fingers and hands, and sometimes of the toes

and feet, which can also involve the proximal part of the limb); (3) *chorea* (rapid, flick-like movements of the limbs and facial muscles that may resemble normal restlessness or fidgeting); and (4) *ballism* (violent, flailing movements involving proximal more than distal parts of the limb).

All motor disorders can be categorized into two classes of deficits: (1) primary functional deficits (negative symptoms), which are directly attributable to the loss of specific neurons by disease; and (2) secondary deficits (positive symptoms), which are due to the emergence of an abnormal pattern of action in otherwise normal neurons when part of their controlling input (usually their inhibitory input) is destroyed by disease (these are called *release phenomena*).

The abnormal movements that occur in basal ganglia disease are thought to fall into the second category. The pathological movements result from overactivity in neurons of the pallidum secondary to removal of inhibitory influences. Localized surgical lesions of the pallidum or of thalamic ventral anterior and ventral lateral nuclei designed to remove this excessive neuronal activity have alleviated some of the symptoms of the various forms of movement disorders. Some of the major movement disorders are summarized in Tables 31–1 and 31–2.

Parkinson's Disease

In 1817 James Parkinson, an English physician working in London, described the motor disorder that now bears his name: "involuntary tremulous motion, with lessened muscular power, in parts not in action and even when supported; with a propensity to bend the trunk forwards, and to pass from a walking to a running pace, the senses and intellects being uninjured."

Parkinson's disease (paralysis agitans), one of the best characterized diseases of the basal ganglia, is accompanied by (1) a rhythmical tremor at rest, (2) a unique kind of rigidity, and (3) a slowness in the initiation of movement as well as in the execution of movement (bradykinesia). This slowness is often evident in the way the patient gets up from a bed or chair and in the shuffling gait. The presumptive site of the lesion in Parkinson's disease is the dopaminergic projection from the substantia nigra to the striatum.

The tremor and rigidity of parkinsonism have been attributed to a loss of an inhibitory influence within the basal ganglia, leading to release of inhibition and an abnormal outflow from the internal portion of the pallidum to the ventral anterior and ventral lateral nuclei of the thalamus, and finally to the motor cortex. As in other movement disorders, surgical interruption of the outflow from the basal ganglia either in the pallidum or in the ventral lateral nucleus of the thalamus decreases the abnormal (disinhibited) neural activity and thus alleviates the tremor and rigidity. Unfortunately, the restricted voluntary movements (bradykinesia) do not improve, perhaps because they are primary deficit symptoms (see discussion above). Although surgical intervention is at times remarkably successful in alleviating tremor and rigidity, many patients do not improve significantly in their daily activities because bradykinesia and impaired postural reflexes are so disabling, and these remain unchanged. Moreover, tremor and rigidity often recur within a period of 1–3 years after surgery. Because of the success of drug therapy (see below), stereotactic surgery for parkinsonism is now rarely performed.

If many of the symptoms in parkinsonism are due to disinhibition, where are the diseased inhibitory neurons? What is the inhibitory transmitter? When viewed in this manner, parkinsonism becomes a disease whose pathogenesis can be examined in cell biological terms. A series of major breakthroughs in our understanding of the extrapyramidal motor system began in the late 1950s. Avid Carlsson, and, independently, two other Swedish pharmacologists, Bertler and Rosengren, observed that dopamine constitutes about one-half of the catecholamine in the brain, 80% of which is localized in the basal ganglia (an area that makes up less than 0.5% of the total weight of the brain). Soon thereafter, Hornykiewicz, studying human brains obtained at postmor-

Disease	Abnormal movements	Muscle tone	Primary anatomical locus
Parkinson's disease	Tremor	Rigidity	Substantia nigra
Damage to basal ganglia with birth trauma	Athetosis	Spasticity, paresis	Putamen, pallidum
Huntington's disease	Chorea	Hypotonus	Cortex, striatum
Hemiballismus	Ballism	Marked hypotonus	Subthalamic nucleus

tem examination, found that some brains had low amounts of dopamine, norepinephrine, and serotonin. In reviewing the medical histories of these patients, Hornykiewicz and colleagues discovered that all of the patients with low brain levels of biogenic amines had had Parkinson's disease at the time of death. Hornykiewicz next observed that, of the three amines, dopamine was most drastically reduced. Parkinson's disease therefore became the first documented example of a disease of the brain consistently correlated with a deficiency in a specific neurotransmitter. This discovery provided the impetus for a thorough search for neurotransmitter changes in other disorders of the brain, including depression, schizophrenia, and dementia.

Parkinsonian patients also show loss of nerve cells and depigmentation in the pigmented nuclei of the brain stem, the substantia nigra, and the locus ceruleus. The severity of changes in the substantia nigra parallels the reduction of dopamine in the neostriatum. Because the compact part of the substantia nigra contains almost all of the dopaminergic nerve cell bodies in the brain, these observations suggested that the nigrostriatal dopaminergic pathway is involved in Parkinson's disease. Subsequently, iontophoretic application of dopamine onto neurons of the basal ganglia showed that dopamine acts as an inhibitory transmitter. Although the evidence is not complete, it is thought that destruction of the dopaminergic neurons in the substantia nigra (by an as yet unspecified mechanism) leads to degeneration of the nigrostriatal fibers. The resulting reduction in the release of the inhibitory transmitter dopamine could lead to disinhibition and abnormal discharge of the cells in the neostriatum and in the pallidum that receive the nigral input (Figure 31–4). Thus, in addition to being correlated with a dopamine deficiency, the chief symptoms of Parkinson's disease seem to result from the loss of dopamine in the nigrostriatal neurons.

With these ideas in mind, Birkmayer and Hornykiewicz reasoned that parkinsonian patients might improve if the amount of dopamine in the brain could be restored to normal. Therefore they gave intravenous 3,4-dihydroxyphenylalanine (L-DOPA) to patients with parkinsonism. This amino acid is a precursor of dopamine. Unlike dopamine, L-DOPA crosses the blood-brain barrier (which normally excludes many substances). These investigators observed a remarkable, albeit brief, remission in their patients'

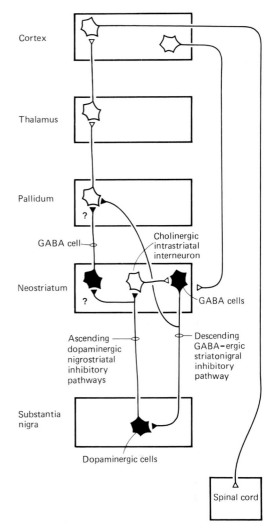

31–4 Interaction of neurons using GABA, acetylcholine, and dopamine in the neostriatum and substantia nigra. (**Shaded** neurons are inhibitory; **white** neurons are excitory.)

symptoms and thus provided a dramatic new approach to the treatment of Parkinson's disease.

L-DOPA therapy for Parkinson's disease is now widely used. Because L-DOPA is metabolized rapidly in most organs, a relatively large oral dose (4–5 g/day) is required. Less than 0.1% of the L-DOPA dose administered orally reaches the brain. A recent advance in L-DOPA therapy is to block the decarboxylation and transamination of L-DOPA (its degradative pathways with an inhibitor that does not cross the blood–brain barrier—L-(-)-α-hydrazine, 3, 4-dihydroxy-α-methylhydrocinnamic acid (carbidopa). About 80%

Table 31–2. Extrapyramidal Motor System Disorders

Disorder	Pathophysiology	Chemical changes	Clinical manifestations	Treatment
Parkinson's disease	Degeneration of the nigrostriatal pathway, raphe nuclei, locus ceruleus, and motor nucleus of vagus	Reduction in dopamine, serotonin, and norepinephrine	Slowly progressive disease; third most common neurological disease (affects 500,000 Americans); about 15% of patients have a first degree relative with the disease; mean age of onset is 58 years; findings are tremor at rest (3–6 beats/sec), cogwheel rigidity, bradykinesia, and postural reflex impairment	L-DOPA with or without peripheral DOPA decarboxylase inhibitor Anticholinergic agents: trihexyphenidyl (Artane) or benztropine (Cogentin), and others
Athetosis	Uncertain, but usually damage found in putamen and pallidum		Often seen with brain injury at birth (cerebral palsy); can be seen temporarily when too much L-DOPA is given to a Parkinson patient	Occasionally stereotactic cryosurgery used; no specific drug
Huntington's disease	Degeneration of intrastriatal cholinergic neurons and GABA-ergic neurons projecting to the substantia nigra	Reduction in choline acetyltransferase and glutamic acid decarboxylase activities and GABA	Progressive disease with associated dementia and death within 10–15 years; incidence about 10,000 cases in the United States; autosomal dominant; onset at any age, but usually in adulthood; findings are chorea, decreased tone (may occur), and dementia	No specific therapy; dopamine antagonists useful to control chorea. i.e., phenothiazines, butyrophenones; so far, GABA agonists not effective
Sydenham's chorea	Little data; in a few cases arteritis was seen in the basal ganglia, etc.	No data	Acute, self-limiting disease associated with rheumatic fever (50% of the time); usually seen between ages 5–15; prognosis good	Supportive dopamine antagonists

(continued)

Table 31–2 *(continued)*

Disorder	Pathophysiology	Chemical changes	Clinical manifestations	Treatment
Ballism	Damage to one subthalamic nucleus, often due to acute vascular accident	No data	Most severe form of involuntary movement disorder known; tends to clear up slowly.	Neuroleptics (butyrophenones)
Tardive dyskinesia	Alteration in dopaminergic receptors causing hypersensitivity to dopamine and its agonists	Cerebrospinal fluid homovanillic acid (acid metabolite of dopamine) levels are normal	Iatrogenic disorder due to long-term treatment with phenothiazines or butyrophenones; abnormal involuntary movements especially of the face and tongue; usually temporary but can be permanent	Stop offending drug Reserpine

less L-DOPA is needed to achieve optimum therapeutic benefits when it is administered together with carbidopa.

Although L-DOPA therapy has been hailed as the most significant breakthrough made in the treatment of Parkinson's disease, it is not the panacea hoped for originally. The long-term effects of L-DOPA on the brain could not be predicted when it was first introduced. At that time, cautious optimism was expressed that L-DOPA might not only ameliorate the symptoms of Parkinson's disease, but also arrest the disease and might even revert some of the degenerative changes seen in the substantia nigra. Experience gained in the past few years with L-DOPA therapy, however, indicates that these goals are not fulfilled. L-DOPA does not alter the course of the disease; it only controls some of the symptoms for a few years.

It is still unclear how L-DOPA ameliorates the symptoms of parkinsonism. Dopamine is normally synthesized in the nerve endings of dopamine cells in the striatum originating in the substantia nigra, taken up in vesicles, and released in the synaptic cleft when the cell fires. In parkinsonism, as many as 90% of the dopaminergic neurons have degenerated or are in the process of doing so. What then is the fate of L-DOPA in Parkinson's disease patients? Presumably the L-DOPA is taken up and converted to dopamine by

the remaining dopaminergic nerve cells. The few remaining healthy and the partially degenerated dopamine neurons may be able to compensate by carrying out the entire function of the nigrostriatal system once the rate-limiting enzyme for the synthesis of dopamine (tyrosine hydroxylase) is bypassed with the large amounts of L-DOPA. Another possibility is that DOPA decarboxylase, which is not specific to dopaminergic neurons and which is abundant and ubiquitous in the brain, can synthesize dopamine from the orally administered L-DOPA in nondopaminergic cells, for example, in serotonergic neurons, in other neurons, and perhaps even in glial cells. This pharmacologically induced dopamine might then be released or secreted in large enough amounts to act on appropriate target cells.

Huntington's Disease and the Dopaminergic–Cholinergic–GABA-ergic Loop

In 1872 George Huntington described a group of patients from certain families in East Hampton, New York, that he, his father, and his grandfather had observed over several generations of practice. The disease is characterized by three features: (1) heritability, (2) chorea, and (3) dementia. Later, the familial tendency of this disorder was documented further when it was shown that practically all patients with this disease on the east coast of the United States could be traced to a few ancestors who immigrated to the United States in 1630 from Bures, a small town in Suffolk, England. In one family, which could be traced through 12 generations (over 300 years), the disease was expressed in each generation. The usual age of onset is in the fourth or fifth decade. There is no way of knowing whether a genetically marked individual will get the disease until symptoms appear; when they do, the disease progresses ruthlessly until death.

Huntington's disease has recently been shown to involve cholinergic and GABA-ergic neurons in the neostriatum (Figure 31–4). Normally, a balance is maintained among the activities of three biochemically distinct but functionally interrelated systems: (1) the nigrostriatal dopaminergic system; (2) the intrastriatal cholinergic neurons; and (3) the GABA-ergic system, which projects from the striatum to the substantia nigra (Figure 31–4).

As we have seen, in Parkinson's disease reduction of the dopaminergic system causes an imbalance in the output of the pallidum to the thalamus, leading to tremor, rigidity, and bradykinesia. In Huntington's disease, on the other hand, there is profound destruction of small intrastriatal cholinergic neurons and of striatonigral GABA-ergic neurons. The dopaminergic cells in the substantia nigra then become disinhibited because their GABA-mediated inhibition is missing, and in turn they produce excessive inhibition of neurons with pallidal output to the thalamus. This is thought to produce the choreic movements of Huntington's disease. In line with the pathological changes, there is marked decrease in choline acetyltransferase, the enzyme required for the formation of acetylcholine, and in GABA and its biosynthetic enzyme, glutamic acid decarboxylase, in the neostriatum. These findings are consistent with the clinical observation that if a patient with Huntington's disease is given L-DOPA, the choreic movements are markedly worsened. Similarly, a patient with parkinsonism given too much L-DOPA develops involuntary movements such as chorea, athetosis, and dystonia. Thus, an imbalance anywhere in the dopaminergic–cholinergic–GABA-ergic loop can cause involuntary movements. This is a fundamental lesson in the pharmacology of the brain. As defects in one transmitter have widespread consequences that are both direct and indirect, so may therapeutic intervention have serious sec-

ondary consequences. Sometimes they are as serious as the disease itself!

Tardive Dyskinesia

Tardive dyskinesia is another clinical disorder that involves the extrapyramidal motor system and is manifested by involuntary movements, especially of the face and tongue. It is a medically induced disorder caused by long-term treatment with antipsychotic agents—the phenothiazines (e.g., chlorpromazine, perphenazine) and the butyrophenones (e.g., haloperidol)—that decrease the function of dopaminergic cells. It is not understood how these drugs affect the dopaminergic system, but they appear to block dopaminergic cells. In the long run this blockage leads to the receptors becoming hypersensitive to dopamine. The balance between the dopaminergic, intrastriatal cholinergic, and GABA-ergic systems is altered; consequently involuntary movements appear.

An Overall View

The diseases of the basal ganglia, particularly Parkinson's disease, stand historically with myasthenia gravis as diseases that made the medical community realize that specific components of chemical synapses are likely to be loci for disease. For each disease, rational treatment demands a good understanding of the various steps involved in synaptic transmission. Conversely, these diseases have proved to be a powerful motivational stimulus for expanding our insight into neuronal and brain function.

Selected Readings and References

Curzon, G. 1977 The biochemistry of the basal ganglia and Parkinson's disease. Postgrad. Med. J. 53:719–725.

DeLong, M. R. 1974. Motor functions of the basal ganglia: Single-unit activity during movement. In F. O. Schmitt, and F. G. Worden (eds.), The Neurosciences: Third Study Program. Cambridge, Mass.: MIT Press, pp. 319–325.

Marks, J. 1977. Physiology of abnormal movements. Postgrad. Med. J. 53:713–718.

Other References

Bertler, Å., and Rosengren, E. 1959. Occurrence and distribution of dopamine in brain and other tissues. Experientia 15:10–11.i40

Birkmayer, W., and Hornykiewicz, O. (eds.). 1976. Advances in Parkinsonism, Fifth International Symposium on Parkinson's Disease, Vienna. Basle: Roche.

Carlsson, A. 1959. The occurrence, distribution and physiological role of catecholamines in the nervous system. Pharmacol. Rev. 11:490–493.

Cotzias, G. C., Van Woert, M. H., and Schiffer, L. M. 1967. Aromatic amino acids and modification of Parkinsonism. N. Engl. J. Med. 276:374–379.

Evarts, E. V. 1976. Neurophysiological mechanisms in Parkinson's disease. In W. Birkmayer, and O. Hornykiewicz (eds.), Advances in Parkinsonism, Fifth International Symposium on Parkinson's Disease, Vienna. Basle: Roche, pp. 37–54.

Hornykiewicz, O. 1966. Metabolism of brain dopamine in human Parkinsonism: Neurochemical and clinical aspects. In E. Costa, L. J. Côté, and M. D. Yahr (eds.), Biochemistry and Pharmacology of the Basal Ganglia. Hewlett, New York: Raven Press, pp. 171–185.

Lee, T., Seeman, P., Rajput, A., Farley, I. J., and Hornykiewicz, O. 1978. Receptor basis for dopaminergic supersensitivity in Parkinson's disease. Nature (Lond.) 273:59–61.

Ungerstedt, U., Ljungberg, T., Hoffer, B., and Siggins, G. 1975. Dopaminergic supersensitivity in the striatum. In D. Calne, T. N. Chase, and A. Barbeau (eds.), Advances in Neurology, Vol. 9: Dopaminergic Mechanisms. New York: Raven Press, 57–65.

The Brain Stem and Reticular Core: Integration of Sensory and Motor Systems

V

The brain stem is the region of the central nervous system interposed between the spinal cord and the diencephalon. It is composed of many nuclei; long tracts, both motor and sensory; and the various components of the reticular formation, all compressed into a relatively small volume. Its clinical significance is far out of proportion to its volume, however. Damage there often has profound effects not only on motor and sensory processes but also on consciousness.

As most of the cranial nerves arise from the brain stem, it is convenient to discuss the organization of the cranial nerves here. Although they differ anatomically from spinal nerves, described in earlier chapters, the general principles underlying the organization of the cranial nerves are those already encountered in the chapters on spinal nerves. As the head is more complicated than the trunk and limbs, so are the nerves innervating the head. Moreover, many of the cranial nerves are concerned with special senses, such as vision, audition, vibratory sense, and taste.

The brain stem also contains neurons that govern several key reflex behaviors, in particular those involving eye movements. Two chapters in this section (Chapters 34 and 35) discuss this subject, as it serves as a good example of several neural systems regulating a single, albeit complicated, set of motor behaviors.

Finally, we shall consider the clinical consequences of damage to the brain stem. The resulting neurological syndromes often consist of many
symptoms that seem unrelated. These complex
syndromes occur because the long ascending and
descending tracts course near the various nuclear
groups and a single vascular accident may affect
neurons that mediate completely different aspects of sensation or motor function. The organization of the brain stem is so well known that it
is possible to predict consequences of brain stem
damage. Conversely, the clinical symptoms can
indicate the precise location of the lesion within
the brain stem.

James P. Kelly

Cranial Nerve Nuclei, the Reticular Core, and Biogenic Amine-Containing Neurons

32

The brain stem is the part of the brain that lies between the spinal cord and the cerebral cortex. It is divided into three major regions: the medulla oblongata, the pons, and the midbrain. (Rigorously speaking, the diencephalon is also included, but we shall consider that structure separately.) The brain stem is the rostral continuation of the spinal cord and shares principles of organization with the cord. As in the spinal cord, there are somatic and visceral afferent and motor fibers in the brain stem. In addition, however, the brain stem is concerned with a variety of special senses, and these senses, mediated by the cranial nerves, introduce a complexity not found in the spinal cord. Furthermore, lying outside the major tracts and nuclei of the brain stem, are nerve cells that seem less discretely organized at first glance, yet have an important modulatory effect upon the brain stem as a whole, and upon the spinal cord and the cerebral cortex. These neurons are termed collectively the *reticular formation* because they

are usually enmeshed in a network, or "reticulum," of fine fibers. Originally it was thought that the reticular formation was rather diffusely organized, but as we shall see, recent studies with fluorescent histochemical methods have shown that the neurons of the reticular formation make rather precise connections with other parts of the brain, and functional groups of neurons can be identified in the reticular formation on the basis of their neurotransmitter biochemistry.

We shall discuss the anatomy of the brain stem in three stages. First, we shall consider the major landmarks that characterize each of the three regions of the brain stem. Second, we shall describe the cranial nerves and associated nuclei, and follow the peripheral course of certain nerves to illustrate principles governing their distribution. Third, we shall examine the reticular core along with the trajectory of the major brain stem tracts to provide a three-dimensional grasp of this important part of the brain.

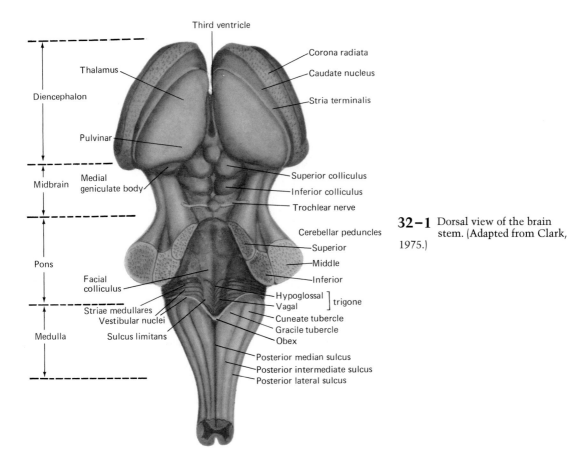

32–1 Dorsal view of the brain stem. (Adapted from Clark, 1975.)

Cranial Nerves Originate in the Brain Stem and Innervate the Head, Neck, and Special Sense Organs

The major features of the brain stem, evident in a dorsal view of the brain with the cerebral hemisphere and cerebellum removed, are shown in Figure 32–1. The dorsal surface of the midbrain is divided into four swellings—the superior and inferior colliculi; these are related, respectively, to the visual and auditory systems. Just behind the inferior colliculus, the fourth (trochlear) cranial nerve exits from the brain stem to innervate the superior oblique muscle of the eye. The dorsal surface of the pons is composed of the floor of the fourth ventricle medially and the three cerebellar peduncles more laterally. The caudal border of the fourth ventricle, termed the *obex* (Latin, barrier), is an important surgical landmark in the medulla. Lying lateral to the obex are the dorsal column nuclei and their associated tracts.

A ventral view of the brain stem (Figure 32–2) is more useful for displaying the origins of most cranial nerves. Note that the third (oculomotor)

nerve emerges at the caudal border of the midbrain and the sixth (abducens) nerve emerges at the caudal border of the pons. Both these nerves innervate extraocular muscles. The fifth nerve, which mediates sensation from facial skin, enters the pons laterally, midway between the fourth and sixth nerves. The twelfth (hypoglossal) nerve leaves the medulla just lateral to the medullary pyramids to innervate the intrinsic muscles of the tongue. The four purely motor nerves discussed thus far (nerves III, IV, VI, and XII) all exit from the brain stem relatively close to the midline. Ontogenetically and phylogenetically, these nerves belong to a common class (see below), and the motor neurons that give rise to them are always found adjacent to the midline of the brain stem.

A lateral view of the brain stem (Figure 32–3) is best for illustrating the origin of the seventh (facial) and eighth (vestibulocochlear) nerves at

32–2 Ventral view of the brain stem. (Adapted from Clark, 1975.)

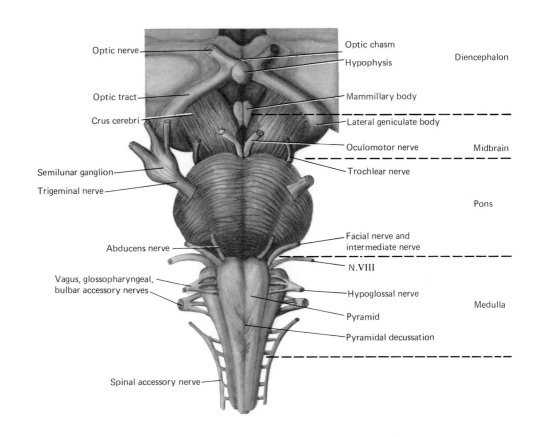

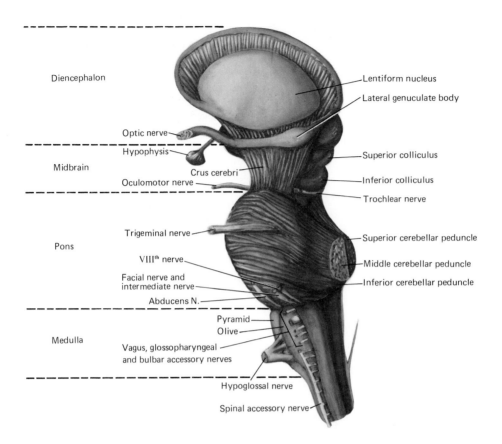

Diencephalon

Lentiform nucleus

Lateral genuculate body

Optic nerve

Hypophysis

Superior colliculus

Midbrain

Crus cerebri

Inferior colliculus

Oculomotor nerve

Trochlear nerve

Trigeminal nerve

Superior cerebellar peduncle

Pons

VIIIth nerve

Middle cerebellar peduncle

Facial nerve and intermediate nerve

Inferior cerebellar peduncle

Abducens N.

Pyramid

Olive

Medulla

Vagus, glossopharyngeal and bulbar accessory nerves

Hypoglossal nerve

Spinal accessory nerve

32–3 Lateral view of the brain stem. (Adapted from Clark, 1975.)

the pontomedullary junction. It is also evident in Figure 32–3 that the ninth (glossopharyngeal), tenth (vagus), and eleventh (accessory) nerves arise as a series of fine rootlets just dorsal to the inferior olive. Because these rootlets are packed so closely together, it is often difficult to determine the nerve to which an individual rootlet belongs. The functional classes of fibers found in these nerves will be considered in a subsequent section of this chapter.

The cranial nerves are concerned with two main functions: (1) the motor and general sensory innervation of the head and neck, and (2) the innervation of special sense organs. Clinically, these nerves are extremely significant, since disease states in the brain stem are often reflected in abnormal functions of one or more of them. Since the cranial nerves arise from different points in the nervous system, an examination of their function can often provide information about the exact site of a lesion in the brain. To understand better the organization of the cranial nerves, let us consider the phylogenetic and ontogenetic development of the spinal cord and the spinal nerves that arise from it. The principles governing the organization of the cranial nerves are quite similar to the principles governing the organization of the spinal nerves. However, the existence of special sense organs in the head and the complicated embryology of this region make the anatomy of the cranial nerves more intricate than the anatomy of spinal nerves.

Organization of Cranial Nerves Reflects Phylogenetic Development

The phylogeny of the cranial nerves provides insight into the anatomical organization of the head. Although in higher vertebrates the head seems to be a distinct structure, it actually developed by gradual modification of similar segments from the front end of a completely segmented organism. This phenomenon was described by J. Z. Young as follows[1]:

The fundamental segmentation of the head is not very easily apparent to superficial observation; the working out of its details is an excellent exercise in morphological understanding. Recognition of the segmental value of the various structures also makes them the more easily remembered. For instance, the nerves found in the head have been named and numbered for centuries by anatomists in an arbitrary series:

I. Olfactorious
II. Opticus
III. Oculomotorius
IV. Trochlearis (patheticus)
V. Trigeminus
VI. Abducens
VII. Facialis
VIII. Acusticus
IX. Glossopharyngeus
X. Vagus
XI. Accessorius
XII. Hypoglossus

Morphological study has shown that these nerves are not isolated structures, each developed independently, but that they represent a regular series of segmental dorsal and ventral roots of the head somites.

The idea of the essential similarity of structure of the head and trunk was early developed by Goethe, who tried to show the mammalian skull to be composed of a series of modified vertebrae. Unfortunately, this view cannot be maintained in detail and the theory was

brought to ridicule by T. H. Huxley and others. Ideas about the segmentation of the head were first correctly formulated by F. Balfour. In his studies of the development of elasmobranchs (1875) he showed that in the region of the head in front of the auditory capsule three myotomes, the pro-optic somites, can be recognized during development [Figure 32–4]. The auditory sac, pushing inwards and becoming surrounded by cartilage, then breaks the series of myotomes, so that several are missing in the adult, though the series is complete in the embryo.

If this analysis is correct we should be able to recognize that the nerves of the head belong to a series of dorsal and ventral roots, similar to that in the trunk, the ventral roots being those for the myotomes and the dorsal roots, running between the myotomes, carrying sensory fibres for the segment and motor-fibres for any non-myotomal musculature present. In the spinal region the dorsal and ventral roots join, but this is not the primitive condition (witness *Amphioxus* and the lampreys), and in the head region the earlier state of affairs

32–4 Segmentation of the head of a dogfish. **CR**, limit of neurocranium; **VR**, limit of visceral arch skeleton; **A**, auditory nerve; **AA¹**, preoccipital arch; **AA²**, occipital arch; **AB**, abducens nerve; **AC**, auditory capsule; **AH**, anterior head cavity; **C**, coelum; **F**, facial nerve; **GL**, glossopharyngeal nerve; **HA**, hyoid arch; **HM**, hypoglossal muscles; **HY**, hypoglossal nerve; **LA**, pila antotica; **M**, mouth; **M²**, **M⁶**, myomere 2, 6; **MA**, mandibular arch; **MB**, muscle bud; **NC**, nasal capsule; **OM**, oculomotor nerve; **PRF**, profundus nerve; **SCL**, sclerotome of segment 10; **SP¹**, **SP²**, ganglion of spinal nerve 1, 2; **T**, trochlear nerve; **TR**, trigeminal nerve; **V**, vagus nerve; **VGL**, vestigial ganglion of segment 7; **VC**, ventral coelom; **VRT**, ventral root of segment 6. (Adapted from Young, 1950.)

[1]Young, J. Z. The Life of Vertebrates, New York: Oxford University Press, 1950.

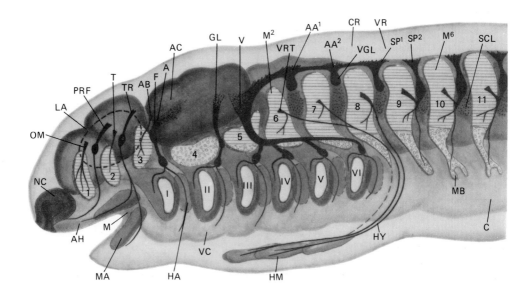

is retained, the dorsal and ventral roots remain separate. . . .

For example, the three pro-optic somites become completely taken up in the formation of the extrinsic muscles of the eye. There are six of these muscles, arranged similarly in all gnathostome vertebrates. The four recti roll the eye straight upwards, downwards, forwards or backwards, and the two obliques, lying farther forward, turn it, as their name suggests, upward or downward and forward. Of these muscles the superior, anterior, and inferior rectus and inferior oblique are all derived from the first myotome and are innervated by the oculomotor (third cranial) nerve. The superior oblique innervated by the trochlear nerve (fourth cranial), is the derivative of the second and the posterior rectus (external rectus of man), innervated by the abducens (sixth cranial), of the third somite. These three nerves are evidently the ventral roots of the three pro-optic somites. This arrangement is an extremely ancient and constant one. At some very early stage of vertebrate evolution all the myotomal musculature of the front part of the head became devoted to the movement of the eyes. This change occurred so long ago that it is not possible to reconstruct the stages by which the muscles originally forming part of the swimming series became attached to a cup-like outgrowth from the brain.

Most of the rest of the musculature of the head, including that of jaws and branchial arches, is derived from the somatopleure wall of the coelom and is therefore lateral plate or visceral musculature. This lateral plate muscle is indeed better developed in the head than in the trunk, where, as we have seen, all of the muscles, even of the more ventral parts of the body, are formed by downward tongues from the myotomes. The lateral plate origin of the jaw-muscles at once gives us the clue to the nature of some more of the cranial nerves, the fifth, seventh, ninth and tenth. These nerves all carry ganglia containing the cell bodies of sensory fibres and these are comparable to the spinal dorsal root ganglia. But the nerves also transmit motor fibres to the muscles of the jaws and branchial arches. They are in fact mixed roots, just as we have seen that the primitive dorsal roots should be, carrying the sensory fibres for the segment and motor-fibres for the non-myotomal muscles . . .

Cranial Nerves Contain Visceral and Somatic Afferent and Efferent Fibers

After the closure of the neural tube, the developing spinal cord is roughly cylindrical in outline, with a diamond-shaped central canal (Figure 32–5). The dorsal region of the cord is called the *alar plate*, while the ventral region is termed the *basal plate*. The cleft indicating the division between the alar and basal plates is termed the *sulcus limitans*. The division into alar and basal regions is significant because the sensory neurons

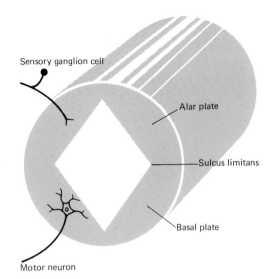

32–5 Organization of the primitive neural tube.

that receive input from the dorsal roots are derived from the alar plate, while motor neurons that send their axons out in the ventral roots are derived from proliferating cells in the neuroepithelium of the basal plate. There are two general classes of motor neurons in the spinal cord: *somatic efferent* neurons that innervate the skin and muscle of the trunk and limbs, and *visceral efferent* neurons that innervate the viscera of the body cavity. There are also two types of afferent neurons that have their cell bodies in the dorsal root ganglia. The types of afferent and efferent fibers in a spinal nerve are summarized in Table 32–1.

The pattern underlying the organization of the cranial nerve nuclei is similar to that underlying the organization of spinal nerves, in spite of considerable differences in phylogenetic history. Motor neurons that send their axons into the cranial nerves have their cell bodies in the brain stem. There are two broad types of motor neurons, *somatic efferent* and *visceral efferent*. The somatic

Table 32–1. Types of Fibers in Spinal Nerves

Fiber type	Structures innervated
Somatic efferent	Striated muscle
Visceral efferent	Smooth muscle, glands, blood vessels
Somatic afferent	Sensory receptors in skin, muscles, and joints
Visceral afferent	Viscera of the body cavity

efferent neurons look like the large motor neurons of the ventral horn in the spinal cord. The visceral efferent neurons of the brain stem are preganglionic parasympathetic neurons similar in appearance to those found in the intermediolateral cell column in the sacral region of the spinal cord. The afferent fibers in the cranial nerves have their cell bodies in sensory ganglia, analogous to the dorsal root ganglia, lying outside the brain stem. There are two broad types of afferent fibers in the cranial nerves: *somatic afferent* fibers that innervate skin and mucous membranes in the head and neck, and *visceral afferent* fibers that innervate internal organs.

Because of the presence of special sensory organs in the head, and the mixed embryological origin of muscle in the facial region, specialized types of fibers are found in the cranial nerves that do not exist in spinal nerves innervating the trunk. As a result, the two broad types of afferent and efferent neurons (somatic and visceral) in the cranial nerves may be further subdivided to include these specialized fiber types. There are *general somatic afferent* fibers innervating the skin of the face and the mucous membranes of the mouth as well as *special somatic afferent* fibers supplying the internal ear with sensory innervation. *General visceral afferent* fibers provide sensory innervation to internal organs such as the larynx and pharynx, while *special visceral afferents* mediate the sense of taste. These classes of afferent fibers and the cranial nerves that contain them are summarized in Table 32–2.

Classes of efferent fibers in the cranial nerves can be described in a similar manner. In the brain stem there are preganglionic general visceral efferent neurons that send their axons into some of the cranial nerves. These neurons are part of the parasympathetic nervous system. Their axons exit from the brain stem (as part of cranial nerves III, VII, IX, and X) and synapse upon neurons in the autonomic ganglia of the head. The postganglionic neurons in these ganglia innervate glands, blood vessels, and smooth muscle.

Sympathetic fibers may also join some of the cranial nerves during their course. These fibers have their cell bodies in the superior cervical ganglion, the most rostral part of the sympathetic chain. Postganglionic axons leave the superior cervical ganglion, run along with the internal carotid artery for part of their course, and then eventually join one of the cranial nerve branches to reach the appropriate end-organ. This issue will be discussed more extensively below and in Chapter 33.

Table 32–2. Classification of Afferent Fiber Types in Cranial Nerves

Fiber type	Structures innervated	Cranial nerves containing these fibers
General somatic afferent	Skin of the face and mucous membrane	V, VII, IX, X
Special somatic afferent	Sensory organs of the inner ear	VIII
General visceral afferent	Internal organs	IX, X
Special visceral afferent	Taste buds	VII, IX, X

Striated muscles in the head and neck are derived, during development, from two distinct sources, as described earlier. The extraocular muscles and the intrinsic muscles of the tongue are derived from myoblasts that migrate from the myotomes. These muscles are similar in their development to other striated muscles in the body and are innervated by somatic efferent neurons. The muscles controlling mastication, those controlling facial expression, and the striated muscles of the larynx and pharynx are derived from the primitive branchial arch system. These branchiometric muscles are innervated by *special visceral efferent* neurons. The organization of efferent neurons contributing to the cranial nerves is summarized in Table 32–3.

Table 32–3. Classification of Efferent Fiber Types in Cranial Nerves

Fiber type	Structures innervated	Cranial nerves containing these fibers
Somatic efferent	Muscles derived from the myotomes	III, IV, VI, XII
General visceral efferent	Glands, blood vessels, and smooth muscle	III, VII, IX, X
Special visceral efferent	Muscles derived from the branchial arches	V, VII, IX, X, XI

Cranial Nerve Nuclei Are Located in Distinct Regions of the Brain Stem

The system of classification used to describe the cranial nerve nuclei may seem awkward at first, but it is useful, since neurons belonging to particular functional classes are found consistently at certain locations within the brain stem. Each functional class of neurons forms a column that is oriented rostrocaudally in the brain stem. Each column is found in a relatively constant position, but it may be interrupted at points along its length. The general principles underlying the organization of these columns are illustrated in Figure 32–6, a diagrammatic cross section through the brain stem.

Neurons innervating the somatic muscles are found near the midline, immediately below the floor of the fourth ventricle (Figures 32–6 and 32–7). These neurons constitute the *somatic efferent column.* Therefore, neurons innervating muscles of the head derived from the myotomes are part of this column. Specifically, motor neurons innervating the extraocular muscles [via nerves III (oculomotor), IV (trochlear), and VI (abducens)] and motor neurons innervating the intrinsic muscles of the tongue [via nerve XII (hypoglossal)] are found in this position at different

rostrocaudal levels in the brain stem. Motor neurons innervating the muscles of branchiomeric origin are displaced ventrally and slightly laterally from the somatic efferent column (Figures 32–6 and 32–7). These branchiomeric motor neurons constitute the *special visceral efferent column.* Neurons innervating the various branchiomeric muscles are found at different rostrocaudal levels along this column. Neurons of the *general visceral efferent column* are found immediately lateral to the somatic efferent column (Figure 32–6). These are preganglionic parasympathetic neurons that send their axons into nerves III (oculomotor), VII (facial), IX (glossopharyngeal), and X (vagus).

Somatic Efferent Column

As noted above, this column of neurons is not continuous along its rostrocaudal extent. The somatic efferent column consists of the oculomotor nucleus (III), the trochlear nucleus (IV), the abducens nucleus (VI), and the hypoglossal nucleus (XII). Each of these nuclei is found in the same relative position, just below the floor of the fourth ventricle near the midline, but at a different rostrocaudal level. The locations of cranial nerve nuclei in the longitudinal axis of the brain stem are shown schematically in Figure 32–7 and in the series of transverse sections stained with the Weigert method presented in Figures 32–8 to 32–14; these sections are arranged in sequence

32–6 Organization of the cranial nerve nuclei shown in cross section of the brain stem.

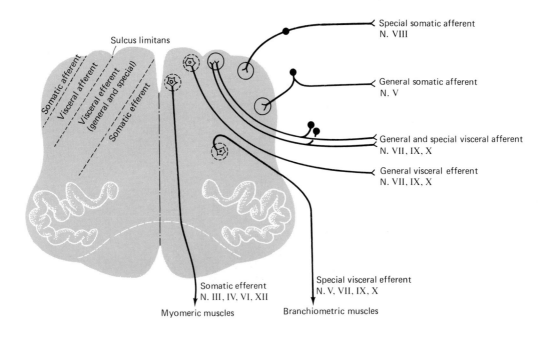

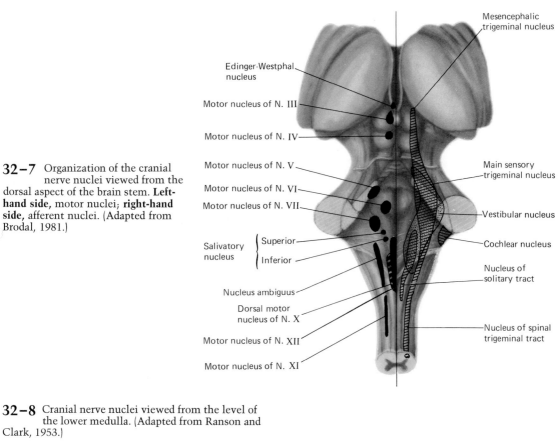

32–7 Organization of the cranial nerve nuclei viewed from the dorsal aspect of the brain stem. **Left-hand side**, motor nuclei; **right-hand side**, afferent nuclei. (Adapted from Brodal, 1981.)

Mesencephalic trigeminal nucleus

Edinger-Westphal nucleus

Motor nucleus of N. III

Motor nucleus of N. IV

Motor nucleus of N. V

Motor nucleus of N. VI

Motor nucleus of N. VII

Main sensory trigeminal nucleus

Vestibular nucleus

Cochlear nucleus

Salivatory nucleus { Superior / Inferior }

Nucleus of solitary tract

Nucleus ambiguus

Dorsal motor nucleus of N. X

Motor nucleus of N. XII

Motor nucleus of N. XI

Nucleus of spinal trigeminal tract

32–8 Cranial nerve nuclei viewed from the level of the lower medulla. (Adapted from Ranson and Clark, 1953.)

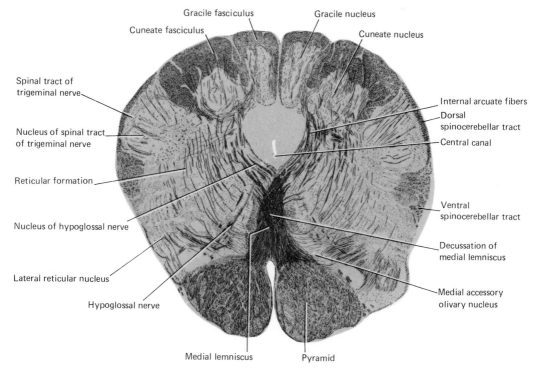

Gracile fasciculus

Gracile nucleus

Cuneate fasciculus

Cuneate nucleus

Spinal tract of trigeminal nerve

Internal arcuate fibers

Dorsal spinocerebellar tract

Nucleus of spinal tract of trigeminal nerve

Central canal

Reticular formation

Nucleus of hypoglossal nerve

Ventral spinocerebellar tract

Decussation of medial lemniscus

Lateral reticular nucleus

Medial accessory olivary nucleus

Hypoglossal nerve

Medial lemniscus

Pyramid

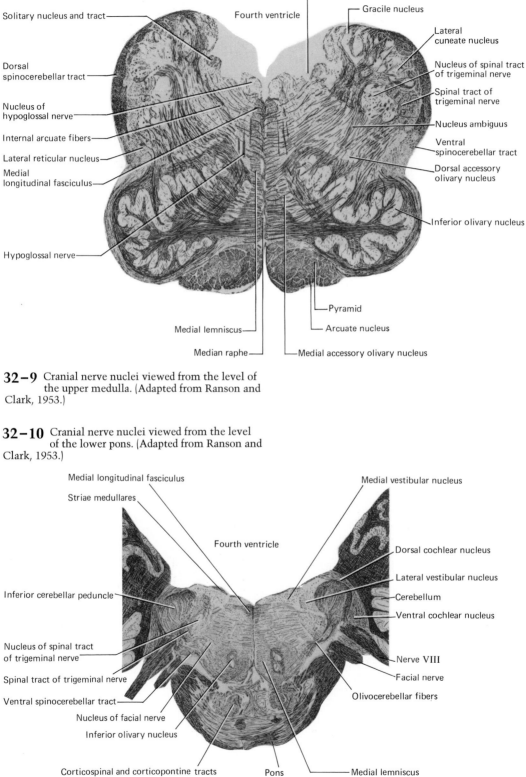

32–9 Cranial nerve nuclei viewed from the level of the upper medulla. (Adapted from Ranson and Clark, 1953.)

32–10 Cranial nerve nuclei viewed from the level of the lower pons. (Adapted from Ranson and Clark, 1953.)

Dorsal motor nucleus of vagus

Fourth ventricle

Gracile nucleus

Solitary nucleus and tract

Lateral cuneate nucleus

Nucleus of spinal tract of trigeminal nerve

Dorsal spinocerebellar tract

Spinal tract of trigeminal nerve

Nucleus of hypoglossal nerve

Nucleus ambiguus

Internal arcuate fibers

Ventral spinocerebellar tract

Lateral reticular nucleus

Dorsal accessory olivary nucleus

Medial longitudinal fasciculus

Inferior olivary nucleus

Hypoglossal nerve

Pyramid

Medial lemniscus

Arcuate nucleus

Median raphe

Medial accessory olivary nucleus

Medial longitudinal fasciculus

Medial vestibular nucleus

Striae medullares

Fourth ventricle

Dorsal cochlear nucleus

Inferior cerebellar peduncle

Lateral vestibular nucleus

Cerebellum

Ventral cochlear nucleus

Nucleus of spinal tract of trigeminal nerve

Nerve VIII

Spinal tract of trigeminal nerve

Facial nerve

Ventral spinocerebellar tract

Olivocerebellar fibers

Nucleus of facial nerve

Inferior olivary nucleus

Corticospinal and corticopontine tracts

Pons

Medial lemniscus

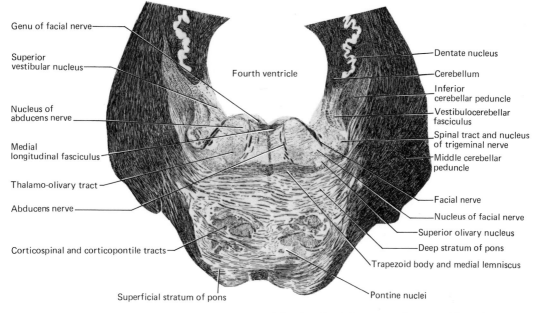

Genu of facial nerve

Superior vestibular nucleus

Nucleus of abducens nerve

Medial longitudinal fasciculus

Thalamo-olivary tract

Abducens nerve

Corticospinal and corticopontile tracts

Superficial stratum of pons

Fourth ventricle

Dentate nucleus

Cerebellum

Inferior cerebellar peduncle

Vestibulocerebellar fasciculus

Spinal tract and nucleus of trigeminal nerve

Middle cerebellar peduncle

Facial nerve

Nucleus of facial nerve

Superior olivary nucleus

Deep stratum of pons

Trapezoid body and medial lemniscus

Pontine nuclei

32–11 Cranial nerve nuclei viewed from the level of the midpons. (Adapted from Ranson and Clark, 1953.)

32–12 Cranial nerve nuclei viewed from the level of the upper pons. (Adapted from Ranson and Clark, 1953.)

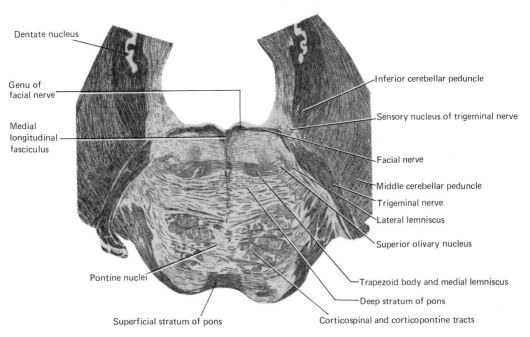

Dentate nucleus

Genu of facial nerve

Medial longitudinal fasciculus

Pontine nuclei

Superficial stratum of pons

Inferior cerebellar peduncle

Sensory nucleus of trigeminal nerve

Facial nerve

Middle cerebellar peduncle

Trigeminal nerve

Lateral lemniscus

Superior olivary nucleus

Trapezoid body and medial lemniscus

Deep stratum of pons

Corticospinal and corticopontine tracts

from the medulla to the midbrain. The third nerve nucleus lies in the rostral part of the midbrain (Figure 32–14) at the level of the superior colliculus. The fourth nerve nucleus lies more caudally in the midbrain, at the level of the inferior colliculus (Figure 32–13). The sixth nerve nucleus is in the pons (Figure 32–11), and the twelfth nerve nucleus is in the medulla (Figure 32–9).

Special Visceral Efferent Column

The motor neurons of the special visceral efferent column are also clustered in distinct nuclei that occupy the same relative position in the brain stem (Figure 32–6). They are displaced ventrally and laterally from the somatic efferent column. The motor nucleus of the fifth nerve lies in the pons (Figure 32–7). It is the most rostral component of the special visceral efferent column and contains the motor neurons that innervate the muscles of mastication. The motor nucleus of the seventh nerve (the facial nucleus) lies caudal to the motor nucleus of the fifth nerve in the pons (Figures 32–7 and 32–11) and contains motor neurons that innervate the muscles of facial expression. The special visceral efferent neurons contributing to nerves IX, X, and XI lie in the same relative position, but in the medulla. The branchiomeric motor neurons of nerves IX and X are clustered in a single group called the *nucleus ambiguus* (Figure 32–7) because it is penetrated by fibers running from the inferior olive to the cerebellum and is consequently difficult to identify in Nissl-stained sections. Neurons in the nucleus ambiguus (Figure 32–9) innervate striated muscles in the larynx and pharynx via nerves IX and X. The nucleus of the spinal accessory nerve (XI) is the most caudal member of this column. The motor neurons of this nucleus stretch into the cervical regions of the spinal cord; they innervate the sternocleidomastoid and trapezius muscles.

General Visceral Efferent Column

The general visceral efferent column, which lies immediately lateral to the somatic efferent column (Figure 32–6), is divided into four principal nuclei. The most rostral of these is the Edinger-Westphal nucleus (Figure 32–7). It lies adjacent to the third nerve motor nucleus and contains preganglionic parasympathetic neurons that send their axons out of the midbrain with the third nerve. These axons terminate in the ciliary ganglion. The postganglionic fibers innervate the pupillary constrictor and the ciliary muscle of the eye.

The superior and inferior salivatory nuclei are components of the general visceral efferent column in the rostral part of the medulla (Figure 32–7). The neurons of the superior salivatory nucleus send their axons into the root of the facial nerve (VII). Neurons in the inferior salivatory nucleus send their axons into the glossopharyngeal nerve (IX). The visceral efferent axons in both these nerves synapse on autonomic ganglia in the head; the postganglionic axons innervate salivary glands, mucous glands, and blood vessels. The inferior salivatory nucleus innervates, for example, the parotid gland via the otic ganglion. Some of the neurons in the superior salivatory nucleus innervate the sublingual and submandibular glands via the submandibular ganglion.

The last component of the general visceral efferent column is the dorsal motor nucleus of the vagus, which lies adjacent to the hypoglossal nucleus in the medulla (Figure 32–9). Neurons in the motor nucleus of the vagus give rise to preganglionic parasympathetic axons that run in the various branches of the vagus nerve to innervate the viscera of the body. Just lateral to the general visceral efferent column there is a slight indentation in the ventricular wall. This indentation is the *sulcus limitans*, the cleft that marks the division between sensory and motor regions of the developing neural tube. In the adult brain stem, this cleft marks the division between the afferent and efferent cell columns. The efferent neurons, described above, lie medial to the sulcus limitans. The afferent cell columns, to be described next, lie lateral to it.

Visceral Afferent Column

Neurons in the visceral afferent column (Figure 32–6) lie adjacent to the general visceral efferent column in the medulla and receive fibers conveying the sense of taste, fibers carrying input from the carotid body, and afferent fibers innervating the larynx and pharynx. This column of cells exists only in the medulla and is called the *solitary nucleus* (Figure 32–9). The neurons conveying sensory input to the solitary nucleus have their cell bodies in ganglia that lie outside the brain stem in association with cranial nerves VII (facial), IX (glossopharyngeal), and X (vagus). The centrally directed processes of the bipolar sensory neurons in these ganglia run into the brain stem and join the *solitary tract* (Figure 32–9), which

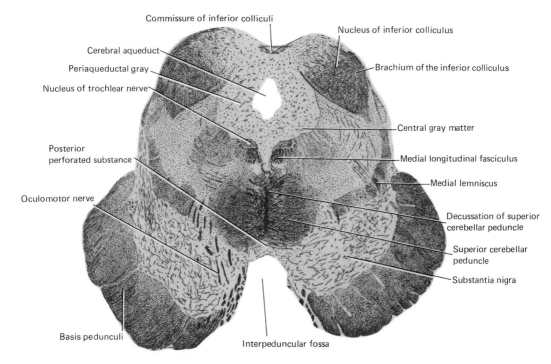

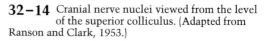

terminates in the solitary nucleus. The axons of many cells in the solitary nucleus run to the thalamus, where they synapse. Thalamic neurons, in turn, relay information about taste to the cerebral cortex.

32–13 Cranial nerve nuclei viewed from the level of the inferior colliculus. (Adapted from Ranson and Clark, 1953.)

Special Somatic Afferent Column

The somatic afferent columns (Figure 32–6) lie lateral to the visceral afferent column. The spe-

32–14 Cranial nerve nuclei viewed from the level of the superior colliculus. (Adapted from Ranson and Clark, 1953.)

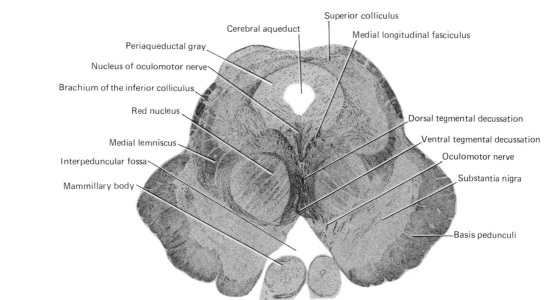

cial somatic afferent nuclei in the caudal part of the pons and the rostral part of the medulla receive the fibers of nerve VIII. The cochlear nucleus (Figures 32–7 and 32–10) receives the centrally directed branches of neurons in the spiral ganglion running in the cochlear division of the seventh nerve. The vestibular nucleus (Figures 32–7 and 32–10) receives input from the vestibular division of the eighth nerve; it is concerned with detecting the motion and position of the body in space. Both of these nuclei lie in the floor of the lateral recess of the fourth ventricle.

General Somatic Afferent Column

The general somatic afferent column is displaced ventrolaterally (Figure 32–6). It is composed of the three separate divisions of the sensory trigeminal nucleus, which are arranged in rostrocaudal sequence. The mesencephalic nucleus of nerve V (Figure 32–7) lies in the mesencephalon, the main sensory nucleus of nerve V lies in the pons, and the descending nucleus of nerve V runs the entire length of the medulla. The latter two nuclei receive sensory input from the muscles and skin of the face and mucous membranes of the mouth, mostly via nerve V. This sensory input is conveyed to the thalamus and then to the cerebral cortex. The organization of the trigeminal nuclei will be discussed in greater detail in Chapter 33.

Cranial Nerve Fiber Types Mix in the Periphery

The motor neurons of the cranial nerves and their associated sensory nuclei lie in distinct regions of the brain. In the periphery, however, there is considerable mixing of different fiber types. As an example of this phenomenon we shall examine the peripheral course of the facial nerve (VII).

The motor neurons of the facial nerve lie ventrolaterally in the pons (Figure 32–11). The axons of these cells run dorsomedially, curve sharply around the abducens nucleus (genu of the facial nerve; Figure 32–11), and then run ventrolaterally toward their point of exit at the lower borders of the pons. The facial nerve exits from the brain stem adjacent to the eighth nerve. The region immediately outside the brain stem, where both nerves are found, is termed the *cerebellopontine angle* (see Chapter 36 for the clinical significance of this region). As these two nerves run toward the internal auditory meatus, they are joined by

the small intermediate nerve. This nerve carries the sensory and the visceral efferent fibers (arising from the superior salivatory nucleus) associated with the facial nerve. After they leave the internal auditory meatus, the facial and intermediate nerves run in the facial canal (Figure 32–15). The facial canal at first runs directly laterally, but then takes a sharp bend posteriorly. The geniculate ganglion, containing the cell bodies of sensory fibers associated with the facial nerve, is found in the region of this bend. The facial canal then takes a second bend, directly ventrally, to reach the stylomastoid foramen, where the facial nerve exits from the cranium. Before it reaches the foramen, somatic motor axons leave the main trunk of the nerve to form the small stapedial nerve, which innervates the stapedius muscle (Figure 32–15). The stapedial muscle acts to dampen the motion of the ear ossicles in response to loud sounds. The remaining somatic motor fibers of the facial nerve leave through the stylomastoid foramen and branch widely in the periphery to innervate the muscles of facial expression (the frontalis, orbicularis oculi, orbicularis oris, and buccinator, for example).

The fibers of the intermediate nerve leave the facial nerve during its course through the facial canal. The greater superficial petrosal nerve leaves near the geniculate ganglion (Figure 32–15), and, oddly enough, runs back into the cranial cavity. This nerve passes just lateral to the internal carotid artery (Figure 32–15) and eventually exits from the cranium via the foramen lacerum. Here the nerve is joined by the deep petrosal nerve, which is composed of sympathetic axons arising from the sympathetic chain. These two nerves form the nerve of the pterygoid canal, which eventually reaches the sphenopalatine ganglion. The visceral efferent (parasympathetic) axons synapse here, and the postganglionic fibers course further in the periphery to innervate the lacrimal glands. These fibers actually reach the gland by joining a branch of the trigeminal nerve. The frequent association between autonomic axons and the branches of the trigeminal nerve will be considered in more detail in Chapter 33.

The chorda tympani leaves the facial nerve near the stylomastoid foramen (Figure 32–15). It runs through the tympanic cavity to join the lingual nerve, a branch of nerve V, which carries the preganglionic visceral efferent fibers of the chorda tympani to their termination in the sub-

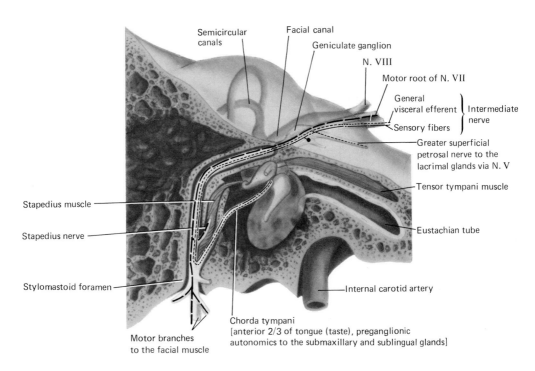

32–15 Peripheral course of the facial nerve.

maxillary ganglion. Postganglionic fibers from this ganglion innervate the submaxillary and sublingual glands.

The chorda tympani also contains sensory fibers mediating taste from the anterior two-thirds of the tongue. These fibers are distributed to the tongue via the lingual nerve and have their cell bodies in the geniculate ganglion. The centrally directed branches of these cells run in the intermediate nerve to reach the brain stem, where they synapse in the anterior one-third of the nucleus of the solitary tract.

If you understand the anatomy described above, you should now be able to explain why a lesion in the seventh nerve as it exits from the brain stem in association with the intermediate nerve would cause disturbances in the secretion of saliva and tears, a hyperacusis on the affected side, and a paralysis of the muscles of facial expression on the affected side accompanied by a severe diminution in taste sensation from the anterior two-thirds of the tongue.

Cranial Nerve Nuclei Are Modality Specific and Are Developmentally Distinctive

It is important to grasp several general themes that underlie the organization of the cranial nerve system. Most of the motor nuclei in the brain stem are associated with individual cranial

nerves; the oculomotor nerve has its own motor nucleus, for example, as do the trochlear nerve and the trigeminal nerve. These neurons are analogous to lower motor neurons in the spinal cord. They receive input from the motor area of the cerebral cortex and send their axons to muscles in the periphery. Afferent nuclei in the brain stem, on the other hand, often receive fibers from several cranial nerves. The solitary nucleus, for example, collects fibers carrying information about taste from the facial, glossopharyngeal, and vagus nerves. As we shall see in the next chapter, the descending nucleus of the trigeminal nerve also receives sensory input from several cranial nerves. The interesting point is that sensory information of a particular type, such as taste, is forwarded to a single nucleus irrespective of the cranial nerve pathway this information takes. This principle, considered before, appears again and again in discussions of sensory systems: *afferent fibers bearing similar modalities of input usually terminate within similar sites in the brain.*

The terminology used to describe the several classes of columns in the brain may seem difficult, and it is really not important in itself. It is just one means of describing the fact that neurons

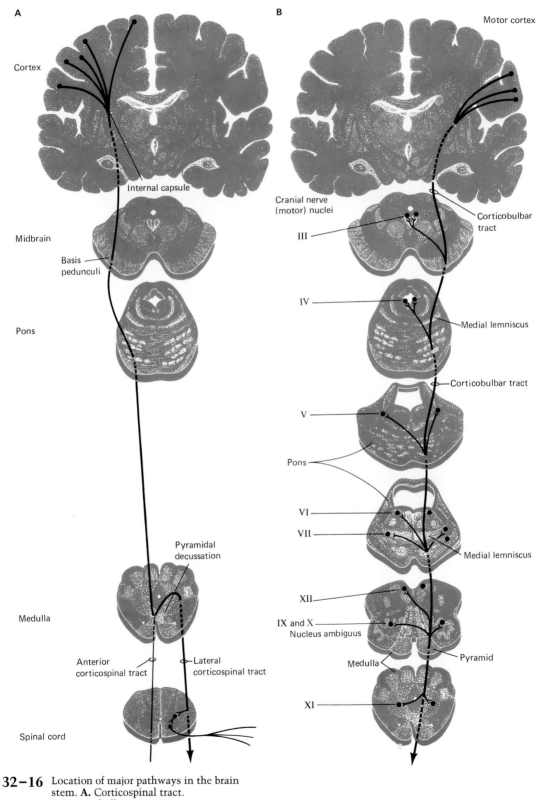

A

Cortex

Internal capsule

Midbrain

Basis
pedunculi

Pons

Pyramidal
decussation

Medulla

Anterior
corticospinal tract

Lateral
corticospinal tract

Spinal cord

B

Motor cortex

Cranial nerve
(motor) nuclei

Corticobulbar
tract

III

IV

Medial lemniscus

Corticobulbar tract

V

Pons

VI

VII

Medial lemniscus

XII

IX and X
Nucleus ambiguus

Pyramid

Medulla

XI

32–16 Location of major pathways in the brain
stem. **A.** Corticospinal tract.
B. Corticobulbar tract.

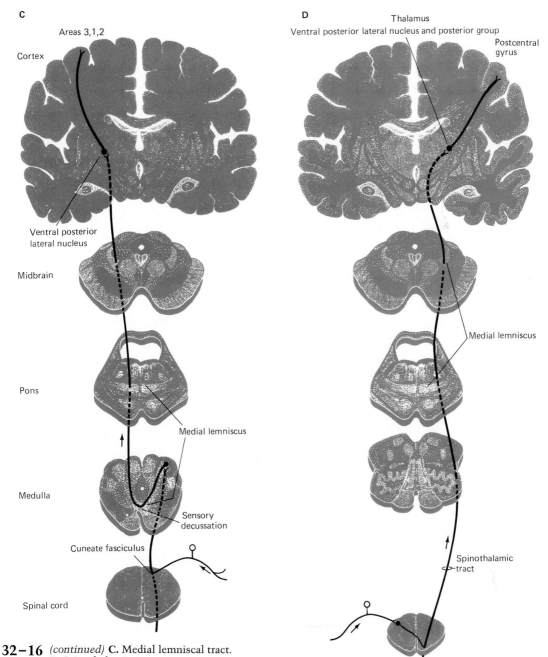

32–16 *(continued)* **C.** Medial lemniscal tract.
       D. Spinothalamic tract.

with different functional properties occupy consistently different positions in the brain stem. This positional distinction arises during development due to the proliferation and migration of cells from distinct parts of the neuroepithelium lining the neural tube. The eventual functional role of a neuron can therefore be correlated with the earliest events in its developmental history.

Specific Sensory and Motor Tracts Transverse the Brain Stem

The courses of four major tracts—the corticospinal, corticobulbar, medial lemniscal, and spinothalamic—through the brain stem are shown schematically in Figure 32–16. The corticospinal tract (Figure 32–16A) descends on the ventral aspect of the brain stem within the pyramids to the caudal border of the pons, where it decussates to form the lateral corticospinal tract. Because it is a circumscribed, relatively isolated bundle of fibers distinct from the spinal cord, few collaterals from it reach the reticular formation. Corticobulbar fibers (Figure 32–16B) also run in the pyramids, but peel off at various levels to reach the motor nuclei of the cranial nerves. The neurons that give rise to corticobulbar axons are upper motor neurons that have effects similar to those exerted by corticospinal axons upon spinal motor neurons. Medial lemniscal axons (Figure 32–16C) run initially near the midline after their origin in the dorsal column nuclei, but they fan out laterally before reaching the thalamus. The spinothalamic tract (Figure 32–16D) runs near the medial lemniscus after ascending from its origin in the spinal cord and gives off collaterals to the reticular formation. Outside of these tracts and a few others (e.g., the rubrospinal tract), the major cranial nerve nuclei, and nuclei related to cerebellar function (e.g., the inferior olive), the

rest of the brain stem is composed of reticular neurons and their processes.

It will become apparent in Chapter 36 that a knowledge of these tracts and of the cranial nerves is essential in clinical neurology. Vascular lesions often affect adjacent tracts and nuclei in the brain stem, and the symptoms that result from such lesions can be understood only if the regional anatomy is known in detail.

Reticular Neurons Form Widespread Networks

In addition to the cranial nerve nuclei and the specific ascending sensory pathways and descending motor tract, the brain stem contains the reticular formation. The reticular formation is composed of neurons that are outside of the major nuclear groups of the brain stem. In a sense, the reticular formation represents the rostral extension of the interneuronal network found in the spinal cord. In the brain stem, however, this network of neurons is much more extensive than in the cord. Some reticular neurons are actually found in circumscribed clusters (e.g., the locus ceruleus, see below) but others are not. One feature that nearly all reticular neurons have in common is the inordinately widespread network

32–17 Location of major reticular cell groups through a section of the medulla. (Adapted from De Armond, Fusco, and Dewey, 1976.)

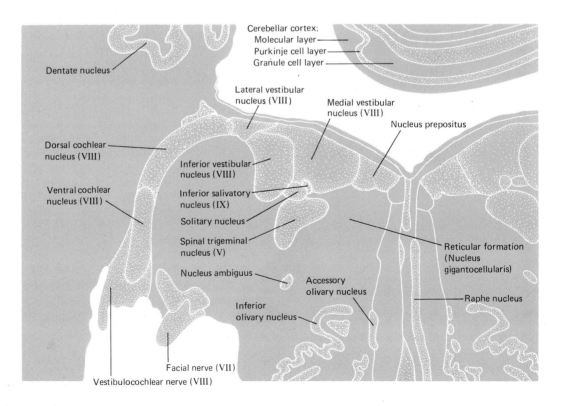

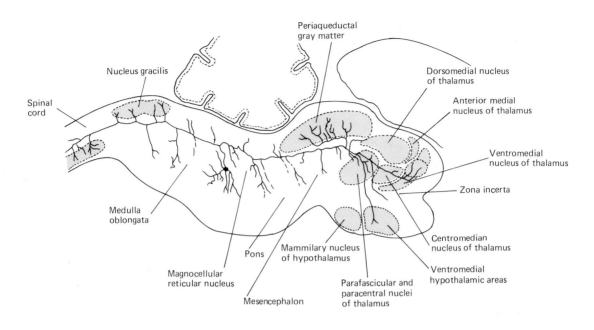

Periaqueductal gray matter

Nucleus gracilis

Spinal cord

Dorsomedial nucleus of thalamus

Anterior medial nucleus of thalamus

Ventromedial nucleus of thalamus

Zona incerta

Medulla oblongata

Centromedian nucleus of thalamus

Pons

Mammilary nucleus of hypothalamus

Magnocellular reticular nucleus

Ventromedial hypothalamic areas

Parafascicular and paracentral nuclei of thalamus

Mesencephalon

of connections that each establishes. The cells of the reticular formation connect with cells in the hypothalamus, the cerebral cortex, the cerebellum, and the spinal cord, so that it is not surprising that the influences exerted by reticular neurons are equally extensive. We shall first examine the general distribution of reticular neurons and then go on to consider their morphology and transmitter biochemistry. We shall end by considering some aspects of their function and their topological relationship to the major tracts of the brain stem.

The reticular formation is confined to the medulla, pons, and mesencephalon and is most conveniently divided along a medial to lateral axis. Lying in the midline are the *raphe nuclei*, so named because of their proximity to the midline seam or raphe. Adjacent to the raphe is the *large-celled region* of the reticular formation, and more laterally there is the *small-celled region*. Two examples of discrete nuclear groups that can be identified in these broad subdivisions of the reticular formation at the level of the upper medulla are the nucleus raphe magnus and the gigantocellular reticular nucleus (Figure 32–17). The *nucleus raphe magnus* is the source of axons that descend to the dorsal horn of the spinal cord and seem to play an important role in modulating input about painful stimuli to the dorsal horn (see Chapter 18). The *gigantocellular reticular nucleus* is the source of reticulospinal fibers that modulate the activity of spinal motor neurons (see Chapter 25).

32–18 Axonal plexus established by an individual gigantocellular neuron of the reticular formation of a 2-day-old rat. It emits an axon that bifurcates into an ascending and a descending branch. The latter gives off collaterals to the adjacent magnocellular reticular nucleus, the gracile nucleus, and the ventral horn in the spinal cord. The ascending branch gives off collaterals to the reticular formation and the periaqueductal gray and then appears to supply several thalamic nuclei—the parafascicular, paracentral, and others—the hypothalamus and the zona incerta. (Adapted from Scheibel and Scheibel, 1958.)

The unique feature of reticular neurons, irrespective of the nuclear group to which they belong, is the far-flung distribution of their axons, often in both rostral and caudal directions along the brain stem. An example of the axonal plexus established by a single gigantocellular reticular neuron is shown in Figure 32–18. The axon not only branches to reach the dorsal column nuclei and the spinal cord, but also ascends to terminate in the thalamus and hypothalamus. Neurons with this structural property are ideal for governing the level of activity of the nervous system as a whole.

Some Reticular Neurons Are Grouped According to Their Neurotransmitters

Studies of the brain using fluorescence histochemistry have shown that many reticular neurons contain monoamines and presumably use

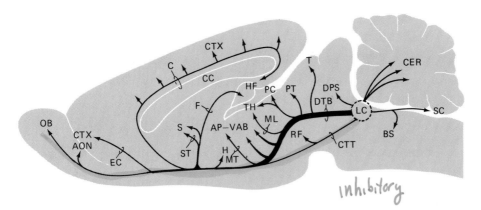

inhibitory

32–19 Connections established by the locus
ceruleus, viewed in the sagittal plane. **AON,**
anterior olfactory nucleus; **AP–VAB,** ansa
peduncularis–ventral amygdaloid bundle system; **BS,**
brain stem nuclei; **C,** cingulum; **CC,** corpus callosum;
CER, cerebellum; **CTT,** central tegmental tract; **CTX,**
cerebral neocortex; **DPS,** dorsal periventricular system;
DTB, dorsal catecholamine bundle; **EC,** external
capsule; **F,** fornix; **H,** hypothalamus; **HF,** hippocampal
formation; **LC,** locus ceruleus; **ML,** medial lemniscus;
MT, mamillothalamic tract: **OB,** olfactory bulb; **PC,**
posterior commissure; **PT,** pretectal area; **RF,** reticular
formation; **S,** septal area; **SC,** spinal cord; **ST,** stria
terminalis. **T,** tectum; **TH,** thalamus. (Adapted from
Cooper, Bloom, and Roth, 1978.)

these molecules as neurotransmitters. The three
most prominent groups of reticular neurons are
those that contain norepinephrine, dopamine, or
serotonin. It is possible, in sections of the brain
that have been treated with appropriate histochemical reagents, to identify the distinctive
fluorescence emitted by each of these biogenic
amines. The distribution of neurons containing
these monoamines can therefore be mapped
throughout the extent of the reticular formation.

Noradrenergic System

The locus ceruleus, which lies in the caudal midbrain and upper pons at the lateral margin of the
periaqueductal gray matter, is made up of noradrenergic neurons that have extensive axonal connections with the entire forebrain. At least five
noradrenergic tracts, chief among which is the
central tegmental tract, run rostrally from the locus ceruleus to the diencephalon and telencephalon (Figure 32–19). Fibers from this nucleus also

32–20 Connections of certain dopaminergic cell
groups in the brain stem.

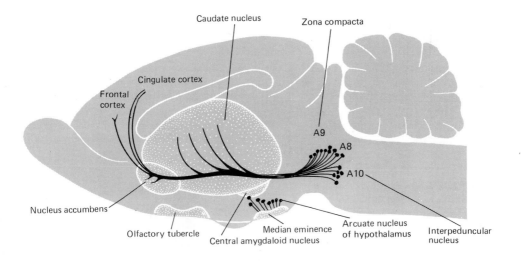

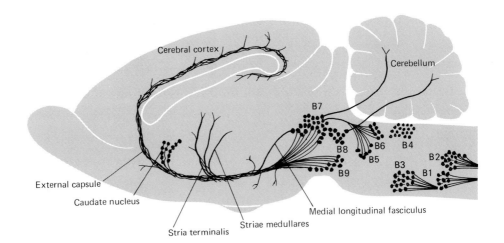

32–21 Distribution of the main serotonin-containing pathways in the rat central nervous system. (Adapted from Cooper, Bloom, and Roth, 1978.)

run through the superior cerebellar peduncle to reach the cerebellar cortex. Preliminary physiological studies have demonstrated that these axons have a net inhibitory effect in the regions where they terminate.

Dopaminergic System

The distribution of dopaminergic neurons in the brain stem was first mapped in 1964 by Dahlstrom and Fuxe, two pioneers in the study of monoaminergic neurons in the brain. They found that the dopaminergic system is extremely complex as the dopaminergic cell groups are small clusters found at several loci in the brain stem. They identified these clusters with the letter *A* (serotonin cell groups were identified with a *B*) followed by a number. The distribution of axons arising from several dopaminergic cell groups is shown in Figure 32–20. Many dopaminergic neurons are found in the ventral tegmentum of the midbrain and in the adjacent substantia nigra. The axons of these cells are directed toward the basal ganglia (see Chapter 31), the hypothalamus and the limbic system (see Chapters 37 and 38), and the neocortex.

Serotonergic System

The serotonergic neuron clusters, identified as groups B1–B9 by Dahlstrom and Fuxe, are often found along the raphe. The connections established by some of these cell groups are illustrated in Figure 32–21. The effect of the nucleus raphe magnus upon the dorsal horn of the spinal cord is probably mediated by serotonin. Electrical stimulation of this nucleus inhibits the cells that give

rise to the spinothalamic tract. The nucleus and the fibers arising from it contain serotonin, and serotonin released iontophoretically onto spinothalamic neurons inhibits them. Thus, reticular neurons can influence the processing of sensory information not only at higher centers via connections to the thalamus, but also at lower levels, even at the initial level of input to the spinal cord.

Reticular Core Function Reflects Neuronal Organization and Morphology

Because the reticular formation is composed of so many isolated cell clusters, it is difficult to study it physiologically, although significant advances are being made in examining reticular control of motor events and sensory processing in the spinal cord. Originally it was thought that the reticular core was a diffuse "activating" system that regulated general levels of activity in the brain. This view came from the experiments of Moruzzi and Magoun, who stimulated regions of the reticular core electrically and produced low-voltage, fast activity, reminiscent of the awake state, in the electroencephalograms of heavily anesthetized animals. Recent anatomical studies, however, have shown that the reticular core is not diffusely organized at all, but instead is composed of multiple cell groups that are specific in terms of their connections and neurotransmitter biochemistry. The "activation" of the brain for behavioral arousal and for controlling levels of awareness is evidently only one physiological role of the reticular core. Nevertheless, individual reticular neurons are designed structurally to influence distant parts of the brain. This is another clear example of the fact that the morphology of a neuron is closely tied to its biological function.

Selected Readings and References

Brodal, A. 1981. Neurological Anatomy. 3rd ed. New York: Oxford University Press, Chap. 7.

Cooper, J. R., Bloom, F. E., and Roth, R. H. 1978. The Biochemical Basis of Neuropharmacology. 3rd ed. New York: Oxford University Press, Chap. 7.

Dahlström, A., and Fuxe, K. 1964. Evidence for the existence of monoamine-containing neurons in the central nervous system. Acta Physiol. Scand. 62: Suppl. 232:1–55:

Young, J. Z. 1950. The Life of Vertebrates. Oxford: Clarendon Press, chap. 5.

Other References

Clark, R. G. 1975. Manter and Gatz's Essentials of Clinical Neuroanatomy and Neurophysiology. 5th ed. Philadelphia: Davis.

De Armond, S. J., Fusco, M. M., and Dewey, M. M. 1976. Structure of the Human Brain. 2nd ed. New York: Oxford University Press.

Moruzzi, G., and Magoun, H. W. 1949. Brain stem reticular formation and activation of the EEG. Electroencephalogr. Clin. Neurophysiol. 1:455–473.

Ranson, S. W., and Clark, S. L. 1953. The Anatomy of the Nervous System. 9th ed. Philadelphia: Saunders.

Scheibel, M. E., and Scheibel, A. B. 1958. Structural substrates for integrative patterns in the brain stem reticular core. In H. H. Jasper, L. D. Proctor, et al. (eds.), Reticular Formation of the Brain (Henry Ford Hosp. International Symposium). Boston: Little, Brown, pp. 31–55.

James P. Kelly

Trigeminal System

This chapter is concerned with the structure, connections, and functions of neurons associated with the fifth, or trigeminal, nerve. Probably the most important general principle that emerges from the study of the trigeminal system is that to a great extent different modalities of sensation, carried from the periphery to the central nervous system via a single nerve, are relayed to different sites in the brain. This anatomical principle is evident in the projection of the dorsal roots upon the spinal cord, but it is also essential to an understanding of the central trigeminal nuclei. As we shall see, pain and temperature input, proprioceptive input, and discriminative tactile input carried by the fifth nerve are relayed to distinct central sites. These several trigeminal nuclei, in turn, have characteristically different connections with other parts of the brain, so that a separation of afferent connections according to modality specificity is maintained at higher levels of the nervous system.

The Fifth Nerve Has Three Major Peripheral Branches

The trigeminal system provides sensory innervation to the face and the mucous membrane of the oral cavity, along with motor innervation to the muscles of mastication. The fifth cranial nerve is called *trigeminal* because it has three major peripheral branches—(1) the ophthalmic nerve, (2) the maxillary nerve, and (3) the mandibular nerve—which exit from the cranium through the superior orbital fissure, the foramen rotundum, and the foramen ovale, respectively. We shall first consider the sensory part of the nerve.

All Three Major Branches Contain Sensory Fibers

Sensory fibers, whose cell bodies lie in the semilunar ganglion, run in all three branches of the trigeminal nerve. The area of skin innervated by each branch of the nerve is shown in Figure 33–1. The overlap in the areas innervated by each branch of the trigeminal nerve is much smaller than the overlap in the spinal dermatomes of the trunk, but the overlap of the areas supplied by the fifth nerve with those supplied by the cervical dorsal roots is more extensive. In the perioral region there is bilateral overlap of innervation.

In the skin of the face, three physiological classes of receptors have been found: (1) mechanoreceptors, some sensitive to light touch and pressure, and others sensitive to pressure only; (2)

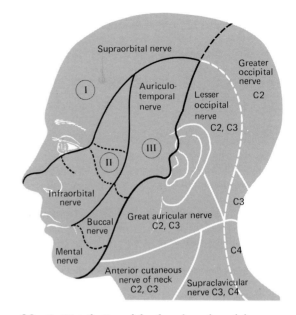

33–1 Distribution of the three branches of the trigeminal nerve. (Adapted from Brodal, 1981.)

thermoreceptors, sensitive to changes in skin temperature; and (3) nociceptors, sensitive to stimuli that damage the skin. In certain animals, most notably rodents, *mystacial vibrissae*, or whiskers, are found on the hairy skin of the face. These whiskers are used to explore the physical environment around the animal's head and, as we shall see later, they have a unique pattern of representation in the somatic sensory part of the central nervous system.

The peripheral receptive fields of trigeminal touch fibers vary considerably in size, but they are always smallest near the mouth. Nearly all these units are rapidly adapting. Slowly adapting touch units are very rare in facial hairy skin.

The trigeminal nerve provides sensory innervation to most of the oral mucosa, to the anterior two-thirds of the tongue, and to the dura mater of the anterior and middle cranial fossae. The sensory innervation of tooth pulp, as well as the surrounding gingiva and periodontal membrane, is also mediated by the trigeminal nerve.

Autonomic Fibers Run with Branches of the Fifth Nerve

In the periphery, autonomic fibers often join branches of the trigeminal nerve before they reach their final targets. As an example, let us examine the autonomic and general sensory inner-

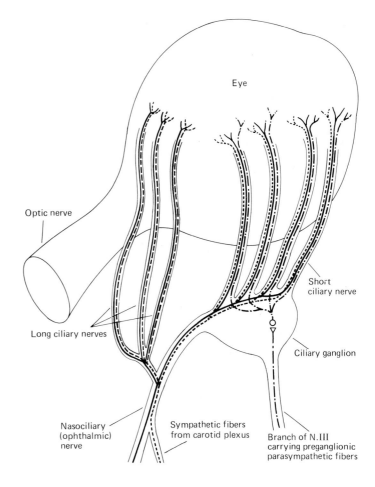

33–2 General sensory and autonomic innervation of the eye.

Eye

Optic nerve

Short ciliary nerve

Long ciliary nerves

Ciliary ganglion

Nasociliary (ophthalmic) nerve

Sympathetic fibers from carotid plexus

Branch of N.III carrying preganglionic parasympathetic fibers

vation of the eye (Figure 33–2). The *nasociliary nerve,* a branch of the ophthalmic division, innervates the sclera, the conjunctiva, and the cornea of the eye, and a portion of the nasal cavity. The several branches of the nasociliary nerve that innervate the eyeball are called *long ciliary nerves.* The ciliary ganglion is physically attached to one of the branches of the nasociliary nerve. The ciliary ganglion receives its input from a branch of the oculomotor nerve. Postganglionic axons leave the ganglion via the *short ciliary nerves* to reach the pupillary constrictor and the ciliary muscle of the eye. The sympathetic fibers innervating the pupillary dilator muscle have their cell bodies in the superior cervical ganglion. The axons of these cells course for a while in the internal carotid plexus, but eventually leave to join the nasociliary nerve. The sympathetic axons may reach their final target by running in either the long or short ciliary nerves. It is critical to remember that autonomic axons never leave the brain stem

with the root of the trigeminal nerve, but are commonly associated with branches of the nerve in the periphery. There may be some special developmental affinity between trigeminal and autonomic axons, or it may simply be that the wide peripheral spread of the trigeminal nerve makes it a convenient pathway for autonomic fibers to reach peripheral targets.

Fifth Nerve Fibers Ascend to the Main Sensory Nucleus and Descend to the Spinal Nucleus

The central branches of the bipolar cells in the semilunar ganglion enter the pontine region of the brain stem. It is important to note that the ratio of myelinated to unmyelinated fibers entering the brain stem in the trigeminal nerve root is about 1:1. In most spinal nerves, this ratio is nearly 1:4. Consequently, there are relatively few unmyelinated fibers in the fifth nerve. The ma-

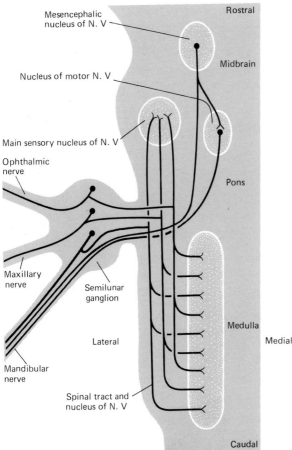

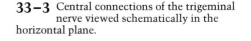

33–3 Central connections of the trigeminal nerve viewed schematically in the horizontal plane.

jority of entering nerve fibers, like dorsal root fibers, bifurcate into ascending and descending branches (Figure 33–3). The ascending branch terminates in the main sensory nucleus of the trigeminal nerve. The descending branch runs in the descending or spinal tract of the trigeminal nerve to terminate in the descending or spinal nucleus of the trigeminal nerve. A small number of fibers do not branch but go directly to either the main sensory nucleus or the spinal tract of nerve V. The analogy between the connections of the trigeminal fibers and the connections of dorsal root fibers is quite striking. The main sensory nucleus of nerve V corresponds to the dorsal column nuclei. The spinal tract and nucleus of nerve V correspond, respectively, to the tract of Lissauer and the substantia gelatinosa of the dorsal horn. In fact, the descending tract and nucleus of the trigeminal complex become continuous with their spinal analogues in the upper cervical region of the cord.

The Mesencephalic Nucleus of the Fifth Nerve Mediates Proprioception from the Face and Jaws

The mesencephalic nucleus (Figure 33–3) of the trigeminal nerve extends from the rostral end of the main sensory nucleus to the superior colliculus. It consists of a column of monopolar primary sensory neurons. This is the only instance in which primary sensory neurons lie within the adult vertebrate central nervous system. The peripheral branches of the mesencephalic neurons innervate stretch receptors in the jaw muscles and possibly provide some sensory innervation to the teeth and gums. A collateral branch from the mesencephalic nucleus goes directly to the motor nucleus of the trigeminal nerve (Figure 33–3), providing a monosynaptic reflex arc to the motor neurons similar to that provided by the Ia spindle afferents in the spinal cord. The trigeminal motor neurons send their axons into the mandibular nerve to supply the masseter, temporal, and pterygoid muscles. The motor nucleus of nerve V also innervates the anterior belly of the digastric muscle, the mylohyoid, and the tensor tympani.

The Spinal Tract and Nucleus of the Fifth Nerve Mediate Pain and Temperature Sensation

Let us now consider the anatomy of the sensory nuclei within the trigeminal complex in greater detail. Primary trigeminal fibers, descending in the spinal tract of nerve V, are arranged in somatotopic order. The location of this tract and its associated nucleus is shown in Figure 33–4, which is a drawing of a myelin stained section through the medulla.

Sensory fibers from the ophthalmic division of the nerve are found ventrolaterally in the tract, fibers from the mandibular division are found dorsomedially, and fibers from the maxillary division lie in between. Thus, there is an inverted representation of the ipsilateral face in the spinal tract of nerve V. Primary sensory fibers from other cranial nerves (VII, IX, and X) also enter the descending tract of nerve V. These fibers carry input from the concha of the auricle, the larynx, and the pharynx.

Most of the superficial fibers in the spinal tract of the fifth nerve are myelinated and tend to be larger (2–8 μm in diameter) than the fibers located at the internal aspect of the tract. The majority of the internal fibers are unmyelinated and are quite small (< 1 μm). If the trigeminal root is severed at its point of entry into the brain stem, the superficial fibers of the spinal tract degenerate but the deep fibers do not, indicating that the fine internal fibers are of local origin.

Near their point of termination, fibers in the descending tract turn abruptly inward and ramify in the underlying *spinal nucleus* of the fifth nerve. This nucleus is continuous with the main sensory nucleus of the fifth rostrally and descends caudally to the level of C2 in the spinal cord. The descending nucleus possesses three clear subdivisions along its rostro-caudal extent. The caudal part of the descending nucleus is called, logically enough, the *caudal nucleus.* (The appropriate, but cumbersome name is the *nucleus* of the *tractus spinalis V caudalis.*) It is

33–4 Location of the spinal tract and nucleus of the fifth nerve viewed from a cross section through the medulla. (Adapted from Ranson and Clark, 1953.)

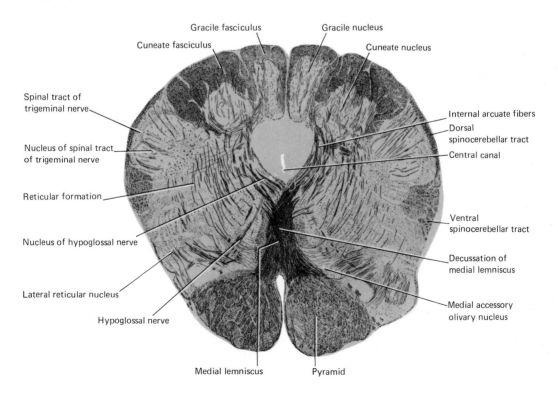

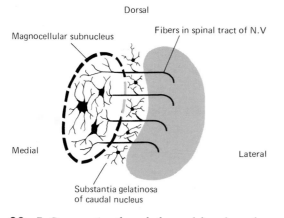

33-5   Cross section through the caudal nucleus of the fifth nerve.

organized just like the dorsal horn of the spinal cord (Figure 33-5). The external part of the nucleus caudalis underlying the spinal tract is called the *substantia gelatinosa* (because it is shot through with fibers). The internal part of the nucleus is composed of large cells and is called the *subnucleus magnocellularis*. The large cells are very similar to those seen in the deeper laminae of the dorsal horn in the spinal cord.

At a more rostral level, near the level of the obex, a change occurs in the structure of the descending nucleus. It becomes filled with scattered small cells and is called the *nucleus interpolaris*. More rostral still (just behind the main sensory nucleus) the cells of the descending nucleus become tightly packed; this segment of the descending nucleus of V is termed the *nucleus oralis*.

The subdivisions of the descending nucleus of V have different functional roles.

The Caudal Nucleus Mediates Facial Pain and Temperature Sensation

Interest in the caudal nucleus relates to its supposed role in the mediation of facial pain. *Trigeminal neuralgia* is a very distressing condition characterized by severe paroxysmal pain in the face, without any local affection of the skin or skull. The etiology of this condition is unknown. One treatment for this horrible ailment is to sever the nerve V root, thereby depriving the face of its sensory innervation. This operation alle-

viates the facial pain in some (but not all) patients, but it has several deleterious side effects. Cutting the fifth nerve interrupts the afferent limb of the blinking reflex by making the cornea anesthetic, so keratitis tends to develop.

The neurosurgeon Sjöqvist claimed that fine fibers of the trigeminal root, which presumably mediate facial pain, terminate selectively in the caudal nucleus. On the basis of this fiber pattern, he suggested that cutting the spinal tract of nerve V just before it enters the caudal nucleus might remove the pain fibers selectively, leaving the other aspects of facial sensation intact. The operation is technically possible because the descending tract and nucleus of nerve V bulge out of the lateral aspect of the medulla, forming the *tuberculum cinereum*, a structure that can be visualized directly. This operation, called the *medullary or trigeminal tractotomy of Sjöqvist*, is often successful in alleviating trigeminal neuralgia without totally eliminating facial sensation.

Because of the success of Sjöqvist's neurosurgical procedure in alleviating pain, in 1962 Wall and Taub suggested that the caudal nucleus would be a good site to study the properties of specific nociceptors. They examined the responses of cells in the caudal nucleus of anesthetized cats while mechanical stimuli were delivered to the face. Oddly enough, they could find no cells that were selectively responsive to stimuli that damaged tissue and would undoubtedly be painful in the awake animal. The success of the Sjöqvist procedure, therefore, seems paradoxical in the light of these physiological observations. Further experiments made in 1973 by Mosso and Kruger on the caudal nucleus of nerve V resolved this apparent paradox. They found that most cells in the magnocellular subnucleus (which is equivalent to the nucleus proprius of the dorsal horn) are sensitive to light mechanical stimuli delivered to the skin of the face, other cells are selectively responsive to vibratory stimuli, and still others respond to light touch of the cornea. In the substantia gelatinosa of the caudal nucleus (Figure 33-5), however, many cells respond only to heavy mechanical stimuli that would be painful in the awake cat. Specific nociceptors are most probably confined to this subdivision of the caudal nucleus, and since these cells are small and difficult to record from, they may have been missed by Wall and Taub. Specific thermoreceptors also appear to be confined to the substantia gelatinosa of the caudal nucleus.

The Interpolar Nucleus Mediates
Dental Pain

Recent evidence suggests that the interpolar nucleus, along with the caudal nucleus, plays an important role in mediating dental pain. The experiments that support this idea are important in a broad biological sense and they will be described here in detail.

It has been known for some time that section of the peripheral branches of the fifth nerve ganglion cells does not lead to complete degeneration of their central processes. In fact, this is true of all sensory ganglion cells associated with the cranial nerves, and dorsal root ganglion cells as well. However, Westrum and colleagues, in 1976, along with Gobel and Binck, in 1977, showed that very extensive degeneration of the central branches of the semilunar ganglion cells will occur if peripheral fifth nerve axons are cut and then prevented from regenerating back to their original sites of termination. They demonstrated this in experimental animals by removing the pulp from all the mandibular teeth on one side of the jaw. When the pulp is removed, the receptors connected with fifth nerve axons innervating the pulp are destroyed and the axons themselves are cut. Subsequent filling of the pulp chamber and root canal with dental cement prevents the pulp afferents from reaching receptors in their original terminal site. Deprived of their connections with the periphery, the trigeminal neurons innervating the pulp degenerate.

The degenerating central terminals of these neurons are found principally in the interpolar nucleus, which is undoubtedly an important locus involved in the mediation of pain from the tooth pulp. Electron microscopy or silver staining by the Nauta method can be used to demonstrate the distribution of degenerating terminals. It is remarkable that degenerating terminals are found in this nucleus on *both* sides of the brain, implying that the sensory representation of the pulp from an individual tooth is found on both sides of the brain stem. In addition, some degenerating terminals are also found in the substantia gelatinosa of the caudal nucleus. Finally, 30 days or so after pulp removal, transneuronal degeneration is found in the central sites where tooth pulp afferents terminate. When the pulp afferents degenerate, neurons receiving synapses from them are deprived of their normal input and undergo a transneuronal atrophy characterized by severe shrinkage of the cell body and dendrites. This is a clear-cut example of the fact that trophic interactions between axons and target organs are important biologically, and that blocking of these interactions may have a surprisingly widespread effect upon the neurons in a given pathway. This example has direct clinical relevance as well, since tooth pulp removal, accompanied by filling of the pulp chamber and root canal, is a routine practice used to halt the spread of carious infection.

The Oral Nucleus Mediates Sensation from the Oral Mucous Membranes

The oral nucleus, in a bizarre twist of nomenclature, appears to contain a portion of the representation of tactile sense from mucous membranes in the mouth.

The Main Sensory Nucleus Mediates Touch Sensation from the Face

Cells in the caudal nucleus send their rostrally directed axons to the other parts of the descending nucleus, as well as to the intralaminar nuclei and the posterior group of the thalamus on both sides of the brain. The intralaminar nuclei lie in the medullary lamina or fiber bundle that separates the major thalamic nuclei. The posterior group of nuclei is a poorly defined collection of cells lying just behind the ventral posterior nucleus of the thalamus. The terminal sites of the caudal nucleus are very similar to those of the spinothalamic tract, a pathway also implicated in the conduction of pain. As in the spinothalamic tract, the ascending efferents from the caudal nucleus also have collateral branches that terminate in the reticular formation of the brain stem.

From the ventral posterior medial nucleus of the thalamus, axons run to the face region in the primary somatic sensory cortex (S-I), which occupies most of the postcentral gyrus. Here there is a complete representation of the contralateral face and a bilateral representation of the perioral region (see Figure 33–7 below). The receptive fields of neurons in the face region of the somatic sensory cortex tend to be about two times larger than those seen at lower levels of the trigeminal system, and they have more pronounced inhibitory surrounds. The representation of the face lies in the ventrolateral part of the postcentral gyrus. The area of the cortex devoted to the mouth, peri-

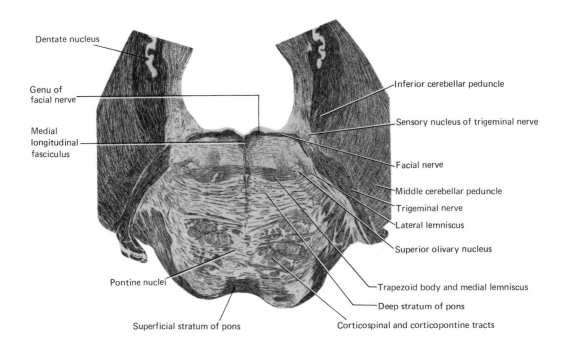

Dentate nucleus

Genu of
facial nerve

Medial
longitudinal
fasciculus

Pontine nuclei

Superficial stratum of pons

Inferior cerebellar peduncle

Sensory nucleus of trigeminal nerve

Facial nerve

Middle cerebellar peduncle

Trigeminal nerve

Lateral lemniscus

Superior olivary nucleus

Trapezoid body and medial lemniscus

Deep stratum of pons

Corticospinal and corticopontine tracts

33–6 Location of main sensory nucleus of nerve V in a myelin-stained section through the pons. (Adapted from Ranson and Clark, 1953.)

oral region, and tongue is disproportionately large with respect to the representation of other parts of the face. This reflects that fact that the peripheral innervation density is greatest in the region of the mouth.

Cells in the main sensory nucleus have receptive fields confined largely to the ipsilateral side of the face. Most of these have small receptive fields (ca. 5 mm in diameter) and respond to light mechanical stimuli. Tactile sensation from the teeth is represented in a distinct dorsomedial segment of the nucleus. The location of the main sensory nucleus is illustrated in a myelin stained section in Figure 33–6.

Ascending Axons from the Trigeminal Complex Reach the Thalamus

The majority of the cells in the main sensory nucleus of V, along with the cells in the nucleus oralis and the nucleus interpolaris, send their axons to the contralateral side of the brain where they join with the medial lemniscus and terminate in the *medial* part of the *ventro-posterior* nucleus of the thalamus (VPM). There is a small *ipsilat-*

eral projection to VPM from the main sensory nucleus of V; the tract carrying these fibers is the *dorsal trigeminal tract.* In the monkey and in humans, a curved cell-free band separates VPM (also called the *arcuate nucleus*) from VPL, the lateral part of the ventro-posterior nucleus devoted to the somatic sensory representation of the rest of the body. In VPM there is a somatotopic representation of the contralateral half of the face. The lower jaw is represented most ventrally and the mouth is represented closest to the midline. This is illustrated in Figure 33–7.

Ventral and posterior to the primary somatic sensory cortex is a second somatic sensory area (S-II). S-II is smaller than S-I, but it contains a complete representation of the entire body surface. The projection from the ventral posterior medial nucleus to the cortex terminates principally in S-I. S-II appears to receive a substantial part of its thalamic input from the sites where the spinothalamic tract and the caudal nucleus of descending nerve V terminate most heavily, the posterior group of nuclei in particular, but fibers from VPM also terminate in S-II. Some cells in the posterior group have branching axons that terminate in both S-I and S-II. The receptive fields of neurons in the posterior group are large and often include the face. Many cells in this part of the thalamus are *polysensory:* an individual neuron may respond both to stroking of the skin of the

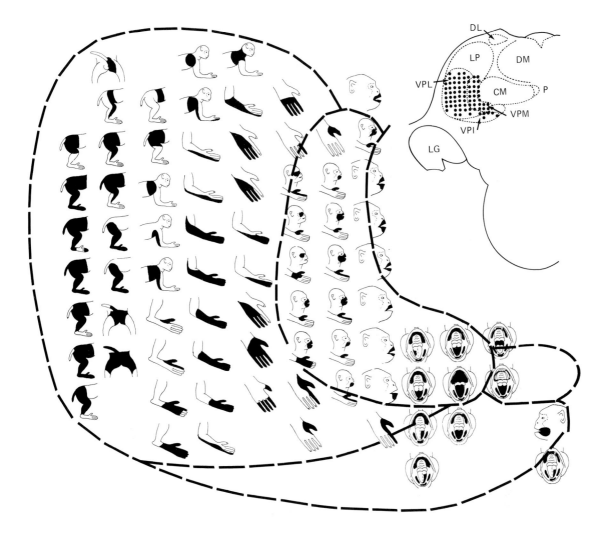

face and to auditory stimuli. Further work on the anatomy and physiology of the posterior group is required to define its functional role unequivocally.

Whiskers in Rodents Have a Unique Representation in the Cerebral Cortex

As Woolsey and Van der Loos showed in 1970, animals with mystacial vibrissae have a unique arrangement of cells in the portion of the somatic sensory cortex representing the face. The whiskers of the face in rodents, for example, are important tactile receptors. The pattern of the whiskers is extremely regular from animal to animal. At the base or follicle of an individual vibrissa there are specialized receptors that transduce the bending of the hairs into electrical

33–7 Somatotopic organization in the ventral posterior lateral and medial nuclei of the thalamus in the monkey determined by the evoked potential technique. The drawing of the thalamus was prepared from a frontal section of the brain in the plane of electrode penetrations; **dots** indicate positive points, and each figurine drawing is arranged accordingly. Tactile stimulation of the skin of the areas marked on the figurines evoked responses at the points indicated. With the exception of ipsilateral intraoral and perioral regions, all responses were obtained only from stimulation of the contralateral side of the body and head. **CM**, center median; **DL**, dorsolateral nucleus: **DM**, dorsomedial nucleus; **LG**, lateral geniculate body; **P**, parafascicular nucleus; **LP**, posterior lateral nucleus; **VPI, VPL, VPM**, ventral posterior intermedidate, lateral, and medial nuclei. (Adapted from Mountcastle and Henneman, 1952.)

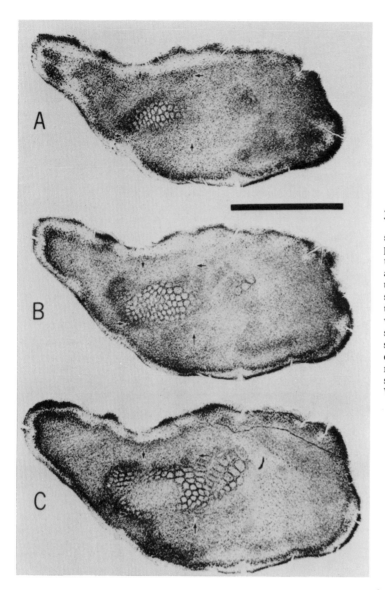

33-8 Organization of barrels in layer IV of the somatic sensory cortex of the mouse: photomicrographs of three serial tangential sections. Orientation: anterior, **left;** posterior, **right;** medial, **up;** lateral, **down. A** is the most superficial, **C** is the deepest of the three. **Arrows** point to some of the vessels which, appearing in subsequent sections, are commonly used to spatially relate serially cut sections to one another. Formalin fixation, methylene blue—C1, 50-μm-thick sections. **Bar,** 2mm. (Adapted from Woolsey and Van der Loos, 1970.)

activity in afferent fibers of the trigeminal nerve. Each whisker is innervated by a separate vibrissal nerve containing about 100 myelinated fibers. Recordings from these fibers have shown them to be highly sensitive to even the slightest movement of the whiskers. The fibers have their cell bodies in the semilunar ganglion and their central terminals in the main sensory nucleus and the oral nucleus of the descending trigeminal complex. These nuclei, as we have seen, project to the ventral posterior medial nucleus of the thalamus, which, in turn, projects to the primary somatic sensory cortex (S-I).

In layer IV of the somatic sensory cortex, where the fibers from the ventral posterior medial nucleus terminate, the neurons are arranged in discrete cytoarchitectural units termed *barrels* (Figure 33-8). This organization of the central representation of whisker stimuli is similar in principle to the organization described in Chapter 20 for the visual system and in Chapter 17 for the somatic sensory system. A single barrel contains about 2500 neurons arranged in a cylindrical aggregate about a hollow center. Each barrel is related to a particular whisker. The number of barrels is the same as the number of whiskers on the contralateral face, and the barrels are arranged in a regular pattern that mimics the topography of the whiskers. The barrel neurons are clustered in this manner to process tactile input derived from a single whisker. It is likely that physiological studies of the neurons in the cortical barrels will shed light on the way populations of cortical neurons process a unitary sample of peripheral input.

An Overall View

The functional role subserved by each of the central trigeminal nuclei is summarized in Table 33–1. The general principle underlying the organization of the trigeminal nerve is that the different modalities of sensation it mediates, and the motor output it generates, are processed by separate nuclei in the brain stem. The caudal nucleus of nerve V, for example, is concerned with pain and temperature sensation in the head, but not only from these regions innervated by the fifth nerve. Both the seventh and tenth nerves inner-

vate a small patch of skin in the conch of the ear, and the tenth nerve innervates the dura mater in the posterior cranial fossa. The cell bodies that give rise to the sensory axons lie in the geniculate and jugular ganglia associated with nerves VII and X. The central branches of the sensory neurons terminate in the spinal nucleus of nerve V, along with trigeminal fibers. Thus, even though sensory input from the head reaches the brain by radically different routes, this input is relayed to a single locus for further processing. As a result, the spinal nucleus of nerve V has a continuous map of the facial skin, oral mucosa, and dura mater, in spite of the fact that these regions are innervated by several cranial nerves.

Table 33–1. Functions of Trigeminal Nuclei

Nucleus	Function
Main sensory	Cutaneous sensation from skin of the face and from the oral mucosa; tactile sensation from the teeth
Spinal descending	
Oral	Cutaneous sensation from the oral mucosa
Interpolar	Sensation of pain from the tooth pulp
Caudal	Pain, temperature, and light touch from the skin of the face, and sensation of pain from the tooth pulp
Mesencephalic	Proprioception from the muscles of the face and the extraocular muscles; jaw reflex arc
Motor	Motor to muscles of mastication (masseter, temporalis, and pterygoid muscles), to the tensor tympani and tensor palati, and to the anterior belly of the diagastric muscle

Selected Readings and References

Brodal, A. 1981. Neurological Anatomy. 3rd ed. New York: Oxford University Press, pp. 508–532.

Gobel, S., and Binck, J. M. 1977. Degenerative changes in primary trigeminal axons and in neurons in nucleus caudalis following tooth pulp extirpations in the cat. Brain Res. 132:347–354.

Mosso, J. A., and Kruger, L. 1973. Receptor categories represented in spinal trigeminal nucleus caudalis. J. Neurophysiol. 36:472–488.

Sjöqvist, O. 1938. Studies on pain conduction in the trigeminal nerve. Acta Psychiatr. Neurol. Suppl. 17:1–139.

Wall, P. D., and Taub, A. 1962. Four aspects of trigeminal nucleus and a paradox. J. Neurophysiol. 25:110–126.

Woolsey, T. A., and Van der Loos, H. 1970. The structural organization of layer IV in the somatosensory region (S I) of mouse cerebral cortex. The description of a cortical field composed of discrete cytoarchitectonic units. Brain Res. 17:205–242.

Other References

Mountcastle, V. B., and Henneman, E. 1952. The representation of tactile sensibility in the thalamus of the monkey. J. Comp. Neurol. 97:409–439.

Ranson, S. W., and Clark, S. L. 1953. The Anatomy of the Nervous System. 9th ed. Philadelphia: Saunders.

Westrum, L. E., Canfield, R. C., and Black, R. G. 1976. Transganglionic degeneration in the spinal trigeminal nucleus following removal of tooth pulps in adult cats. Brain Res. 101:137–140.

Peter Gouras

Oculomotor System

34

Our eyes move so that we can locate, see, and track objects in visual space. The system that controls eye movement—the oculomotor system—is better understood than any other motor system in the mammalian brain. Because the eyeball is a constant load, the repertoire of eye movements produced by this motor system is fixed and predictable. There are five principal movements; these movements and the conditions that elicit them can be defined and analyzed quantitatively. We shall first examine the five types of eye movements and then consider how they are controlled by motor neurons and premotor cells in the brain.

Three Pairs of Muscles Move the Eyeball Along Three Axes

Each eye can be moved within the orbit in three directions: vertically, horizontally, and torsionally (clockwise and counterclockwise). These movements correspond to three imaginary axes, X, Y, and Z (Figure 34–1). Around the vertical (X) axis movement occurs in the medial and lateral direction, i.e., abduction and adduction, respectively. Around the horizontal (Y) axis movements are in the superior–inferior direction i.e., elevation and depression. Along the anterior–posterior (Z) axis the torsional movements are within the corneal plane. These rotatory movements are referred to

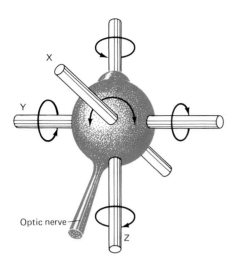

34–1 Principal axes of rotation, right eye. **X** is the vertical axis and also the center of motion. **Y** is the transverse axis and **Z** is the anterior–posterior axis.

as *intorsion* when the cornea moves along a circular arc in the nasal direction and *extorsion* when the cornea moves in the lateral direction. Eye movements are accomplished by three antagonistic pairs of muscles (Figure 34–2).

Although all extraocular muscles, to some degree, contribute to all eye movements by either contracting or relaxing, each movement involves only two muscles in any one plane. Thus, the lateral and medial recti are chiefly responsible for

moving the eyes along the horizontal plane. Both the inferior and superior recti and oblique muscles can move the eye along the vertical plane as well as twist the eye; their exact contribution to vertical or torsional movement depends upon the position of the eye in the orbit (Figure 34–3 and Table 34–1).

For most eye movements both eyes move together in the same direction; these movements are called *conjugate.* In convergence or divergence, however, the eyes move in opposite directions; these movements are called *disjunctive.* Muscles that are excited together in a movement (for example, the lateral and medial recti of opposite eyes in horizontal conjugate movements) are called a *yoked pair.* Muscles that work oppositely (for example, the lateral recti of both eyes in horizontal movements) are called an *antagonistic pair.* Note that antagonistic pairs for conjugate eye movements share the same nuclei on opposite sides of the brain stem (Figure 34–4); since eye movements involving pairs of antagonistic muscles are common, strong inhibitory interactions are important in governing the activity of their motor nuclei.

Eye muscles are among the fastest in the body. In contrast to other striated muscles, the extraocular muscles do not pull against gravity and

34–2 Origins and insertions of the extraocular muscles.

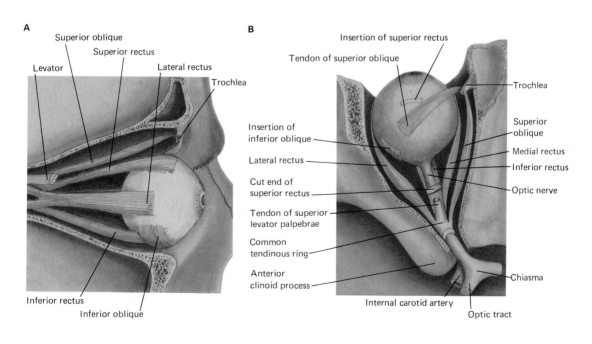

A

Levator
Superior oblique
Superior rectus
Lateral rectus
Trochlea
Inferior rectus
Inferior oblique

B

Tendon of superior oblique
Insertion of superior rectus
Trochlea
Insertion of inferior oblique
Lateral rectus
Cut end of superior rectus
Tendon of superior levator palpebrae
Common tendinous ring
Anterior clinoid process
Superior oblique
Medial rectus
Inferior rectus
Optic nerve
Chiasma
Internal carotid artery
Optic tract

Table 34-1. Innervation and Actions of the Extraocular Muscles

Nerve	Muscle	Main action	Subsidiary action
III	Superior rectus	Elevator, maximal on lateral gaze	Adduction, intorsion, raises upper lid
III	Inferior oblique	Elevator, maximal on medial gaze	Abduction, extorsion
III	Inferior rectus	Depressor, maximal on lateral gaze	Adduction, extorsion
IV	Superior oblique	Depressor, maximal on medial gaze	Abduction, intorsion
VI	Lateral rectus	Abductor	None
III	Medial rectus	Adductor	None

deal with the same mechanical load throughout life. The relatively few muscle spindles that do exist in extraocular muscles undoubtedly play a more general role in proprioception, possibly in muscle coordination or spatial orientation via the cerebellum. Most extraocular muscles (the medial, inferior, and superior rectus, and the inferior oblique) are innervated by the oculomotor nerve (III); the superior oblique is innervated by the trochlear nerve (IV), and the lateral rectus muscle is innervated by the abducens nerve (VI).

The positions in the brain stem of the motor neuron complexes that give rise to the three oculomotor nerves that move the eyeball are shown in Figure 34–4. The medial longitudinal fasciculus is an important tract that runs just beneath the floor of the ventricle near the midline. It carries neural signals coordinating these oculomotor nuclei with each other and with the vestibular system.

One of the major purposes of the oculomotor system is to keep images centered on the retinal region of greatest visual acuity. Although we can detect objects over a large visual angle (about 200°), we see them best within a relatively small arc in our visual field, the central 5°. This central area of high visual acuity corresponds to the fovea, a discrete retinal structure about 1 mm in diameter (Figure 34–5). To investigate objects in our visual environment optimally, images must be kept on the fovea for seconds or even minutes. If an object tends to wander off the fovea the motor system can correct this slippage by moving the head, body, or eyes.

Five Neural Control Systems Keep the Foveas on Target

The oculomotor system puts the foveas on target and keeps them there by means of five separate neural control systems, each sharing the same effector pathway—the motor neurons of the oculomotor nuclei in the brain stem. The five systems are (1) saccadic eye movement, (2) smooth pursuit movement, (3) optokinetic movement, (4) vestibulo-ocular reflex, and (5) vergence movement.

Saccadic Eye Movement System

The saccadic eye movement system is responsible for rapidly directing the foveas to a target of interest in visual space. This system generates a conjugate, rapid (ballistic) movement of the eyes that brings the fovea on a target of interest. These saccades are extremely rapid (up to 600°–700°/sec); there is a distinct advantage in making them

34–3 Paired action of extraocular muscles in looking up and to the right.

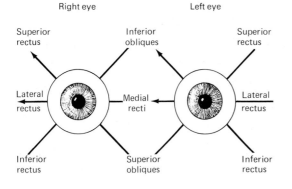

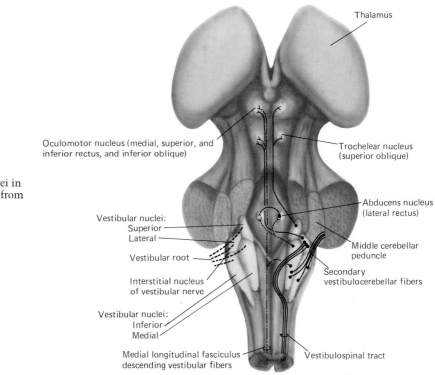

34-4 Location of the oculomotor nuclei in the brain stem. (Adapted from Carpenter, 1978.)

Thalamus

Oculomotor nucleus (medial, superior, and inferior rectus, and inferior oblique)

Trochelear nucleus (superior oblique)

Abducens nucleus (lateral rectus)

Vestibular nuclei:
Superior
Lateral

Vestibular root

Middle cerebellar peduncle

Secondary vestibulocerebellar fibers

Interstitial nucleus of vestibular nerve

Vestibular nuclei:
Inferior
Medial

Medial longitudinal fasciculus descending vestibular fibers

Vestibulospinal tract

34-5 Human fovea (approximately 1 mm in diameter). The oculomotor systems keep images centered on this area of high visual acuity.

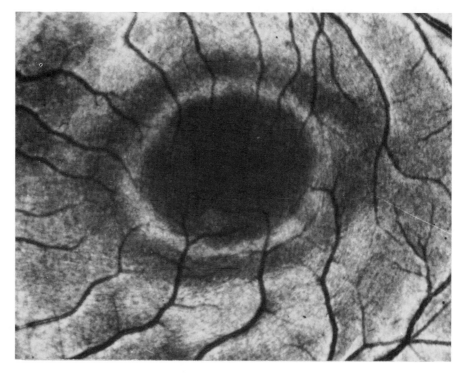

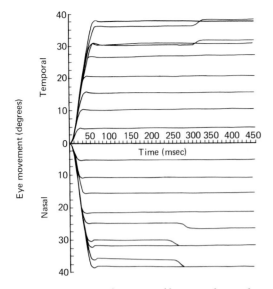

34−6 Superimposed tracings of horizontal saccadic eye movements in steps between 5° and 40° selected from one monkey as representative. All the responses to a target step were averaged with regard to magnitude, duration, and maximum velocity. The trajectory that best matched these averages and in addition possessed the appropriate overshoot and second saccade indicated by the majority of responses is plotted (Adapted from Fuchs, 1967.)

orbit must be known by the brain continuously in order to deliver appropriate commands for a saccade. The critical information that must be contained in any command is the direction and amplitude of the saccade. The direction is coded by the appropriate group of motor neurons excited and the amplitude by the duration (pulse-width control) of their discharge frequency.

Saccades are also under voluntary control and can be made in the dark or with closed eyes. Part of the command center appears to be located in the cerebral cortex, which sends signals to the brain stem that are thought to initiate each saccade, although this has not been proved experimentally. Saccades to the left are initiated in the right cerebral hemisphere and those to the right in the left hemisphere. It is possible to induce a conjugate eye movement by stimulating the frontal cortex.

Smooth Pursuit Movement System

The smooth pursuit eye movement system is concerned with keeping the fovea on a target once it has been located. The action of this system can be subdivided into several operations. If both eyes and the target are stationary, fixation (foveation) can be maintained by conscious effort, presumably by suppressing any additional saccades. During steady fixation on a target, there are, nevertheless, continuous, unconscious micromovements of the eyes, characterized as slow drifts and quick flicks (10−15 minutes of arc). The flicks are corrective movements that return the fovea to the target after a drift carries it too far away. The drifts, on the other hand, appear to be essential in order to continue seeing the target. Objects that are totally stabilized on the retinas, such as retinal blood vessels, disappear. We are able to continue seeing objects only if their edges are continuously moving on the retina. Take a thin flashlight and rub it gently along the scleral edge of your eye and see your retinal blood vessels appear, as the shadows they produce are made to move on your retina. Remember that cells in the visual cortex are best excited by *moving* contours of appropriate orientation.

If a target moves and the viewer remains stationary, the eyes pursue the target so that it remains continuously on the fovea. This smooth pursuit movement depends upon the brain calculating the direction and velocity of the target's motion on the retina. These operations appear to be carried out under the control of the occipital

quick because during rapid eye movement, vision becomes blurred. A saccadic eye movement is ballistic in the sense that once initiated it is extremely difficult to correct in flight. This was discovered by investigators who moved a target during that fraction of a second when the eyes were making a saccade to it; if this is done, the eyes always end up at the position where the target was at the beginning of the saccade. The ballistic nature of saccades can be interrupted only by combined head and eye movement via a vestibular input. Because saccades can be altered in flight they are not, however, truly ballistic and, as the model of Figure 34−12 implies, they may in fact be under continuous feedback control.

The rapidity with which a monkey can make horizontal saccades is shown in Figure 34−6. These movements are about twice as fast as those of man. The saccadic eye movement system depends upon the retina to sense where a target is in visual space; it also depends upon the initial position of the eyes in the orbit when the object is sighted. Both retinal position and eye position are taken into account before the command for a saccade is initiated. The position of the eye in the

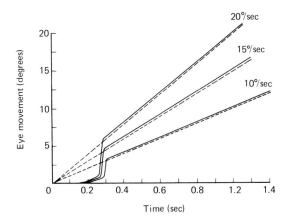

34–7 Smooth pursuit responses to 10°, 15°, and 20°/sec target ramps in the macaque monkey. (Adapted from Fuchs, 1967.)

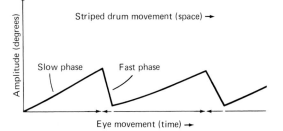

34–8 Optokinetic nystagmus induced by having a subject observe a rotating striped drum.

cortex, where perception of form occurs. In neurological diseases in which certain areas of the frontal cortex are destroyed, this fixation reflex can no longer be broken without blocking the visual input to the eyes. The smooth pursuit system can operate only with a target on the retina; it does not operate in darkness.

Smooth pursuit movements of a macaque monkey following a target moving at designated velocities are illustrated in Figure 34–7; note the quick saccade necessary to locate the target initially. The differences in properties of the smooth pursuit and saccadic eye movements are summarized in Table 34–2.

Optokinetic Movement System

When the head and body move through an object-filled space with the eyes open, a reflex compulsion to track these moving objects, especially large ones, is powerfully induced. Such oculomotor movements are well developed in birds as well as any moving animal with vision. This reflex can be induced by placing a subject within a rotating striped drum that completely surrounds him. The rotating drum will induce a rhythmic oscillatory movement of the eyes called *optokinetic nystagmus* (from the Greek *nystagmus*, for a nod that has a slow phase as the head drops, and a fast phase as the head snaps back to an erect position) (Figure 34–8). The eyes automatically begin to track one stripe on the drum, until it becomes impossible to do so without turning the head or body. Before this occurs, the eyes rapidly saccade opposite to the drum's direction of motion to allow fixation on a new stripe. This generates a rhythmic train of saw-tooth, conjugate eye movements, one slowly in the direction of drum movement, followed by one rapidly in the opposite direction. Eye movements in different directions can thereby be examined. If stripe size is varied, visual acuity can also be examined, especially in young children or uncooperative

Table 34–2. Comparison of the Properties of Saccadic and Smooth Pursuit Movements of the Eye

Property	Saccadic	Smooth pursuit
Visual acuity during movement	Poor	Excellent
Target required	No	Yes
Maximum velocity	700°/sec	50°/sec
Velocity under voluntary control	No	Yes, a function of target velocity
Stimulus to elicit a movement	Target displacement	Target velocity
	Rotation of body or head	Rotation of body or head
Latency	200 msec	130 msec
Barbiturate sensitivity	Least	Most
Type of response	Nonlinear	Linear
Control system	Discrete	Continuous

Source: Modified from A. F. Fuchs, J. Physiol. (Lond.), 1967, 191:609-631; and from A. F. Fuchs, *in* The Control of Eye Movements, Bach-y-Rita et al., eds, New York, Academic Press, 1971

adults. Similar nystagmoid movements occur when one looks out of the window of a moving train or bus (railroad nystagmus).

Vestibulo-Oculomotor Reflex System

The vestibular eye movement system is concerned with stabilizing the eye against sudden changes in head or body position. If the position of the body or head is altered, this reflex system keeps the eye looking in the same direction as it did prior to the imposed movement. The signal initiating this reflex arises not within the visual system, but in the membranous labyrinth of the inner ear, which detects movements of the head along the three axes of space (Figure 34–9).

Each of the three semicircular canals senses the acceleration of the head along a different axis and transmits these signals to neurons in the vestibular ganglion. Higher acceleration (i.e., greater head velocities) produces greater discharge rates along the nerves innervating any one canal. The change in head position is estimated by integration of velocity information coming from each canal, and a suitable correction signal is sent to the oculomotor nuclei to stabilize the eyes. These correction signals are phasic; they cease when head acceleration stops (i.e., when the head moves at a constant velocity).

34–9 Membranous labyrinth of the left inner ear. The vestibulo-oculomotor reflex is initiated here. (Adapted from Brödel, *in* Hardy, 1934.)

Rotation of the head in any direction, even in darkness, produces a vestibular-induced compensatory eye movement. Continued rotation on a turntable will also produce a reflex nystagmus called the *vestibulo-ocular reflex*. We shall consider this reflex in detail in Chapter 35. The fast phase is in the direction of rotation and the slow phase is in the opposite direction; this nystagmus ceases after about 20 sec of rotation at constant velocity; it commences transiently again at the cessation of rotation. The slow phase of this vestibular reflex functions to keep the eyes where they were before the rotation started; the fast return is undoubtedly a saccadic response to bring the object back into the range of the oculomotor system; the rhythmicity depends upon the feedback interactions in this control system. To test the integrity of the vestibulo-ocular reflex, clinicians often irrigate the external auditory meatus with hot or cold water. This produces a barrage of discharges over the ipsilateral eighth nerve, which ultimately drives the eyes contralaterally. When the eyes are driven too far eccentrically a reset saccade recenters them; the tonic drive of the eighth nerve causes them to move contralaterally again and the nystagmus is continued, thereby demonstrating the integrity of vestibular nerve function.

Vergence Movement System

The optokinetic, vestibulo-ocular, smooth pursuit, and saccadic systems generate conjugate eye movements. Whenever your eyes view an object

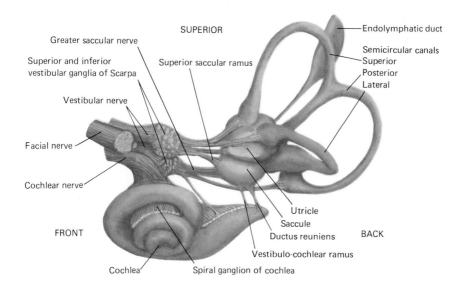

Greater saccular nerve

Superior and inferior vestibular ganglia of Scarpa

Vestibular nerve

Facial nerve

Cochlear nerve

FRONT

Cochlea

Spiral ganglion of cochlea

SUPERIOR

Superior saccular ramus

Utricle

Saccule

Ductus reuniens

Vestibulo-cochlear ramus

Endolymphatic duct

Semicircular canals
Superior
Posterior
Lateral

BACK

moving toward or away from you, each eye must move differently (disjunctively) in order to keep the image of this object precisely aligned on both foveas. If the object moves closer, the eyes must converge, if it moves away, they must diverge. This operation is performed by the vergence system. The stimuli for this reflex determine *stereopsis*, i.e., the fusion of a single image and a disparity signal producing a sensation of depth. The vergence system works in coordination with the pupil- and lens-controlling systems in the so-called accommodation reflex (see Appendix III). The control center for vergence appears to be located in the occipital cortex, especially the prestriate cortex, where stereopsis is mediated.

Misalignment

All five oculomotor control systems must move the eyes together precisely in order to maintain binocular vision. If the eyes are misaligned by muscle or nerve abnormalities, double vision *(diplopia)* occurs. Merely displacing the position of one eye relative to the other with one's finger is sufficient to cause diplopia. Inappropriate alignment of the eyes at rest is called *heterotropia*. As a result of heterotropia the contraction of one or several eye muscles is required to prevent diplopia, even for a distant target. After a while muscular effort often is no longer successful in aligning the two eyes so that the visual axes do not fix on the same point in space. This condition, called *strabismus* or squint, would result in diplopia were it not for the tendency to suppress the image from the weaker eye, the eye whose axis of vision was aligned by muscular effort. Unfortunately, suppression in turn leads to reduction in visual acuity in the squinting eye.

Oculomotor Neurons Have Distinctive Properties

All the motor neurons that drive eye muscles (those in cranial nerves III, IV, and VI) have similar properties. Their features can be illustrated by the example of a lateral rectus motor neuron that causes a lateral horizontal eye movement (Figure 34–10). This motor neuron discharges briskly before each muscle contraction (lateral abduction); the discharge then persists throughout the saccade. The duration of the burst is determined by the duration of the saccade. The larger the saccade, the longer the duration of the burst. In contrast, activity in the antagonist muscle, the me-

dial rectus, leads to inhibition of firing in the lateral rectus motor neuron.

Oculomotor neurons differ from spinal motor neurons in several ways: (1) Whereas spinal motor neurons tend to fire at 50–100 impulses/sec, oculomotor neurons fire at much higher rates of 400–600/sec. Firing at higher rates results from the intrinsic properties of the motor neurons and from the absence of recurrent inhibition, which is a prominent feature of the organization of spinal motor nuclei. (2) There are only a few muscle spindles in the eye muscles and no stretch reflexes. (3) Each motor neuron has its own threshold for steady firing. Therefore, an increase in muscle tension is achieved by the recruitment of motor neurons of different thresholds as well as by increases in the firing rate of each motor neuron.

34–10 A saccade to the left (indicated by a movement of the eye through angle, $\Theta°$) is associated with a burst of impulses (**D**) in the lateral rectus motor neuron that lasts the duration of the saccade no matter how long it is. Fixation in the new position is associated with steady firing at a slower rate that is proportional to the eccentricity of the fixation. Medial saccades do not cause a change in the firing pattern of the lateral rectus motor neuron. (Adapted from Fuchs and Luschei, 1970.)

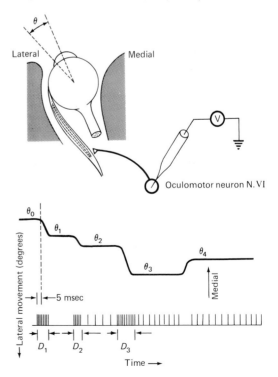

There Are Two Classes of Premotor Neurons

Two major regions impinge upon the motor neurons directly and indirectly and participate in the control of gaze: (1) the pontine gaze center of the reticular formation, and (2) the superior colliculus. The colliculus makes its influence felt through the pons. There are thought to be very few direct connections to motor neurons.

Pontine Gaze Center

There is clinical evidence that an area in the pontine reticular formation plays a role in eye movement. This is the only area in the brain besides the oculomotor nuclei where lesions cause conjugate paralysis of horizontal gaze. The eyes cannot move into the hemifield ipsilateral to the lesion but remain in the contralateral visual fields. Moreover, lesions cause an absence or slowing of saccades toward the side of the lesion when executed in the intact hemifield. Furthermore, stimulation of this area causes short-latency eye movement, and gross recordings in this area reveal large potentials that are generated 10–15 msec prior to a saccade.

Neurons in the pontine reticular formation seem to program eye movements. There are four types of neurons in the reticular formation of the pons that discharge in relationship to horizontal eye movements: burst cells, tonic cells, burst–tonic cells, and pause cells. We shall consider each of these in order to illustrate how a saccadic eye movement to an interesting target can arise (Figure 34–11).

Burst Cells. The burst cells exhibit a high frequency of neuronal activity for voluntary saccades. They are usually silent during fixation. The burst leads the saccade by 6–8 msec, and the number of spikes is proportional to the size of the saccade. Typically, these cells, which fire at a high frequency, discharge at the beginning of an eye movement and stop discharging after the eye reaches its new position. This group of neurons seems to create the burst of neural activity responsible for the saccade (Figure 34–10). The burst cells can be excited through vestibular, visual, and voluntary pathways to create voluntary saccades as well as the fast phases of vestibular and optokinetic nystagmus. Lesions in the pon-

34–11 Impulses of prototype neurons (pause, burst, burst–tonic, and tonic premotor cells in the pontine gaze center, and oculomotor neurons) in the oculomotor system and their changes in frequency which accompany an eye movement. The eye movement begins with a large saccade, then the eye remains stationary before returning part of the way to its initial position.

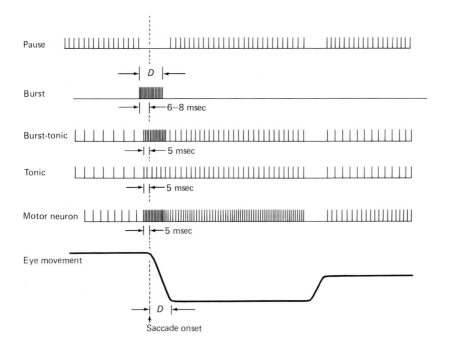

tine reticular formation that affect the burst cells selectively abolish the fast phase of vestibular nystagmus, suggesting that the locus for the different types of saccades resides in the reticular formation.

Tonic Cells. These cells have a steady firing rate with eye fixation, and the firing rate increases linearly with increasing lateral rotation of the eye. There is no change of activity with saccades. These premotor neurons are thought to be involved in initial slow pursuit and fixation movements, suggesting that the burst and the late steady-state firing of a motor neuron during a saccadic movement are produced by independent premotor cells.

Burst–Tonic Cells. These cells exhibit a burst of activity for lateral saccades and fire steadily during fixation. Thus burst–tonic cells increase their firing frequency with lateral eye rotation. These cells may be interneurons. They have been found in a variety of brain stem nuclei (the vestibular nucleus, the prepositus nucleus, and the interstitial nucleus of Cajal). In the vestibular nucleus, there are some neurons that discharge in close relation to head velocity, as well as eye movements, and are involved in the vestibulo-ocular reflex.

Pause Cells. In addition to the premotor neurons that discharge during different phases of eye (or head) movement, there are cells that fire at fairly constant rates but pause during rapid eye movements. These cells, located in the reticular formation and at the midline near the exit of the abducens nerve, seem to be involved in saccadic eye movements. They possibly disinhibit burst cells, and thereby allow the occurrence of specific saccades.

Interconnection of Cell Types. Figure 34–12 is a schematic diagram indicating how these various cells may be interconnected. Burst neurons and tonic neurons are thought to provide the input that produces the burst–tonic discharge of the motor neuron. At rest, pause neurons prevent the burst neuron from firing. The appearance of an interesting target can lead to a decision in the brain to look at the target. This is turn leads to a brief trigger stimulus that inhibits the pause neuron. This allows burst neurons to respond to the excitatory input from the target. The burst neurons now fire at a high rate, and the eye begins to

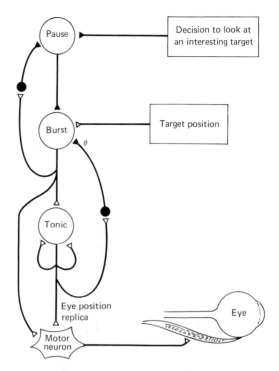

34–12 Schematic circuit showing how four classes of neurons (pause, burst, tonic, and motor neurons) can be synaptically connected to produce a saccade to a desired position in space. (Adapted from Robinson, 1981.)

move. A neural replica of the eye position (called a *corollary discharge*) is fed back and inhibits the burst neuron. When the eye is on target the burst neuron stops firing and the inhibitory connection from the burst neuron to the pause neuron is turned off, reactivating the pause neuron and ensuring that the burst neuron is deactivated.

Superior Colliculus

The superior colliculus is thought to relate visual input to oculomotor commands. The dorsal layer of the colliculus receives input from the entire visual field via direct retinal projections as well as from a cortical projection. The ventral layer of the colliculus in turn gives off fibers via the tectal spinal, tectal pontine, and tectal reticular tracts to the brain stem in the vicinity of the oculomotor neurons. In lower afoveate vertebrates (for example, the rabbit), many optic tract fibers go to the colliculus; in these animals, there are clear eye movements in response to moving stimuli. It is thought that in simple animals the colliculi play an important role in converting visual stimuli to oculomotor responses. The dorsal layer of the superior colliculus has cells that respond vigorously to movement in any direction. These cells are called *event detectors.*

Two Cortical Eye Fields Act on the Premotor Cells

Two regions in each hemisphere that have long been regarded as having special importance are the frontal and occipital eye fields. Together these eye fields are essential to the integrity of

34–13 Schematic representation of each neural center currently known to affect the common motor neuron output to the ocular muscles: the frontal cortex eye fields direct saccades; areas 17 and 18 of the occipital cortex direct fixation and smooth pursuit; area 19 directs vergence and stereopsis; the semicircular canals and the vestibular nucleus stabilize the eye in the head; and the cerebellum, superior colliculus, and pretectal nuclei coordinate those movements in ways we have yet to discover. (Adapted from Robinson, 1968).

pursuit and saccadic movements and the visual reflexes that depend on these basic movements. These two regions are functionally distinct, however, as can be shown by selective lesions.

Frontal Eye Fields

The frontal eye fields are located approximately opposite to the motor cortex and are situated in the region corresponding to Brodmann's area 8. These fields contribute to the initiation of voluntary gaze although they are not absolutely essential for initiation. Efferent projections leave this region, pass through the posterior limb of the internal capsule, and continue caudally in the central location within the cerebral peduncle. Arriving at the midbrain, the tract deviates away from the main bundle of peduncular fibers and passes a short distance to terminate in the general area of pontine gaze center interneurons. The frontal eye fields also project to the colliculus.

A lesion in the frontal eye fields produces a sustained, conjugate deviation of the eyes to the side of the lesion and an inability to move the

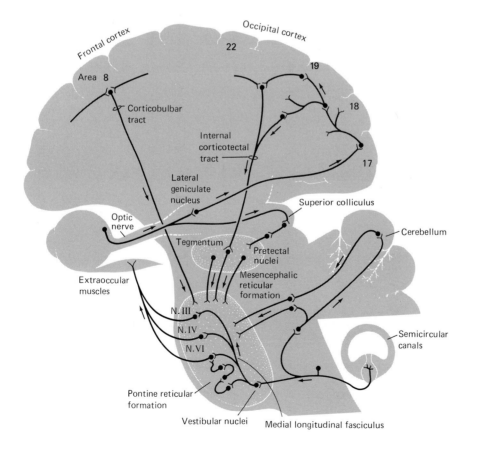

eyes voluntarily to the opposite direction (although rapid improvement usually occurs as a result of the compensatory effect of uncrossed fibers from the contralateral eye field). If there is bilateral destruction of frontal eye fields, the patient loses the ability to carry out lateral gaze voluntarily in either direction, as well as the ability to direct visual attention to an object introduced abruptly into the peripheral vision. The patient cannot initiate voluntary saccades and consequently is unable to initiate the visual fixation reflex. This deficit may only be transient; voluntary saccades appear to be permanently lost only when both the frontal eye fields and the superior colliculus are destroyed.

Occipital Eye Fields

Occipital eye fields are thought to be concerned with reflex activities. Ablation studies suggest that the occipital fields are involved in smooth pursuit tracking movements and in optokinetic nystagmus, including both the slow component (smooth pursuit movements) and the fast component (reflex saccade). The occipital eye fields also play some role in supporting the visual fixation reflex.

In disease states in which posterior cortical eye fields have been impaired and the frontal areas are still intact the patient may have little difficulty in voluntarily directing his gaze. Nevertheless, attempts to fixate on a target are undermined by severe instability and wandering of the eyes, with considerable deterioration of perception. Since the lesions also directly interfere with the visual pathway, there may be difficulties in assigning the causes of the visual and ocular impairments.

The Oculomotor System Has a Modular Organization

The oculomotor system is an example of the modular design of the brain. Specific groups of neurons perform specific operations: some compute head velocity, others compute eye velocity in space, others compute the differences between

the two, and still others relate these variables to retinal targets. Although each operation is performed by separate systems of cells, most modules influence and control the computations made by the others by means of synaptic interactions. Many modules also share computational circuits and all share the final common pathway of the system, the same oculomotor neuron pool. All the neural centers known to affect this pool are shown schematically in Figure 34–13. In addition to flexibility, modular design provides the neurologist with the opportunity to diagnose the precise point in the system that may have gone awry.

Selected Readings and References

Fuchs, A. F. 1967. Saccadic and smooth pursuit eye movements in the monkey. J. Physiol. (Lond.) 191:609–631.

Raphan, T., and Cohen, B. 1978. Brainstem mechanisms for rapid and slow eye movements. Annu. Rev. Physiol. 40:527–552.

Robinson, D. A. 1981. The use of control systems analysis in the neurophysiology of eye movements. Annu. Rev. Neurosci (in press).

Other References

Carpenter, M. B. 1978. Core Text of Neuroanatomy. 2nd ed. Baltimore: Williams & Wilkins.

Cogan, D. G. 1956. Neurology of the Ocular Muscles. 2nd ed. Springfield, Ill.: Thomas.

Fuchs, A. F. 1971. The saccadic system. In P. Bach-y-Rita, and C. C. Collins (eds.), The Control of Eye Movements. New York: Academic, pp. 343–362.

Fuchs, A. F., and Luschei, E. S. 1970. Firing patterns of abducens neurons of alert monkeys in relationship to horizontal eye movement. J. Neurophysiol. 33:382–392.

Hardy, M. 1934. Observations on the innervation of the macula sacculi in man. Anat. Rec. 59:403–418.

Robinson, D. A. 1968. Eye movement control in primates. Science (Wash., D.C.) 161:1219–1224.

Westheimer, G. 1954. Mechanism of saccadic eye movements. A.M.A. Arch. Ophthalmol. 52:710–724.

James P. Kelly

Vestibular System

35

The vestibular system detects the position and the motion of the body in space by integrating information from peripheral receptors located in the inner ear on either side of the head. Unlike taste, smell, vision, audition, and somethesis—the sensations we have considered earlier—the vestibular sense is not prominent in our consciousness. Although we are normally not aware of the vestibular dimension of our sensory experience, this experience is essential for the coordination of motor responses, eye movement, and posture. Moreover, malfunctioning of the vestibular system leads to dizziness and nausea—sensations that all too readily impinge upon our consciousness.

The inner ear, or labyrinth, is made up of two parts: the bony labyrinth and the membranous labyrinth. The *bony labyrinth* consists of a series of cavities in the petrous portion of the temporal bone. Inside the cavities, and designed to fit into them, is the *membranous labyrinth,* so called because it consists of tubes made up of fine membranes. The membranous labyrinth is separated from the bony labyrinth by a fluid called *perilymph.* Located in the membranous labyrinth are the peripheral receptors of the vestibular system—the vestibular hair cells.

The vestibular apparatus, in turn, is closely associated with the cochlea in the bony labyrinth. The vestibular portion of the membranous labyrinth is filled on the inside with fluid *(endolymph)* and communicates with the cochlea, the auditory portion of the labyrinth. On the outside, the perilymph that bathes the vestibular portion of the membranous labyrinth also is continuous with and bathes the outside of the cochlear duct, the auditory portion of the labyrinth.

The vestibular labyrinth consists of two sac-like swellings, the otolith organs—called the *utricle* and the *saccule*—and three directionally sensitive, more or less orthogonal, *semicircular ducts.* The sensory receptor cells in each of these structures respond to acceleration of the head, or to acceleration due to gravity. Different components of the end-organ respond to different aspects of force. The three semicircular ducts lie in different planes and therefore detect angular acceleration of the head in any direction in three-dimensional space. The otolith organs detect linear acceleration and are important for determining the position of the head under static conditions. Information from the peripheral receptors is relayed by the vestibular portion of the eighth nerve to the vestibular nuclei in the brain stem and to certain regions of the cerebellum. Different subdivisions of the vestibular nuclear complex are, in turn, connected with the motor nu-

clei of the extraocular muscles and with the spinal cord in a highly organized manner. The whole apparatus functions to keep the body balanced, to coordinate head and body movements, and most remarkably, to enable the eyes to remain fixed on a point in space even when the head is moving.

In this chapter we shall first consider the structure of the membranous labyrinth and the novel mechanisms of transduction used by the hair cells. We shall then consider the central connections of the vestibular system and its role in eye, head, and body coordination.

Organization of the Membranous Labyrinth

The organization of the membranous labyrinth is shown diagrammatically in Figure 35–1. The vestibular labyrinth is directly connected to the cochlear duct by the *ductus reuniens.* The saccule lies in the vestibule of the inner ear, and, like the cochlear duct, is directly affected by the fluid motion of the perilymph elicited by air-borne sounds. The other portions of the vestibular apparatus, the utricle and the semicircular ducts, are isolated from this fluid motion by the *mem-*

35–1 Organization of the membranous labyrinth. (Adapted from Iurato, 1967.)

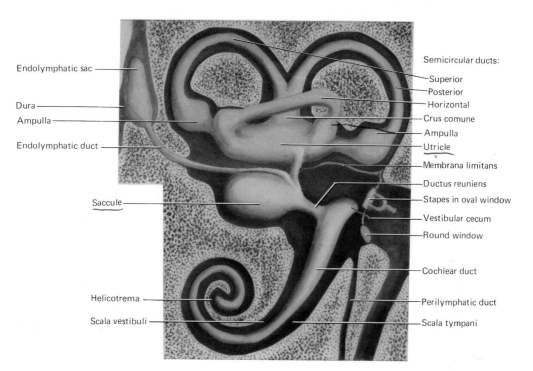

Endolymphatic sac

Dura

Ampulla

Endolymphatic duct

Saccule

Helicotrema

Scala vestibuli

Semicircular ducts:
Superior
Posterior
Horizontal
Crus comune
Ampulla
Utricle
Membrana limitans
Ductus reuniens
Stapes in oval window
Vestibular cecum
Round window
Cochlear duct
Perilymphatic duct
Scala tympani

brana *limitans,* and hence are unaffected by sound. The membranous semicircular ducts lie in the bony semicircular canals and are separated from them by narrow connective tissue spaces. There are three ducts on each side of the head: the anterior, posterior, and horizontal ducts. These ducts are paired with functional counterparts on the opposite side of the head so that at least one pair of ducts will be affected by any given angular acceleration.

Endolymph Fills the Vestibular Labyrinth and Perilymph Surrounds It

The membranous labyrinth is filled with a viscous fluid called endolymph. This extracellular fluid is peculiar because its ion composition is very similar to that of intracellular fluid: it has a high potassium concentration ($\approx$ 125 meq/liter) and a low sodium concentration ($\approx$ 40 meq/liter). These ion concentrations vary somewhat in different portions of the labyrinth, but they never approach the normal ion balance found in other extracellular fluids. The unusual ion concentration of endolymph may account, in part, for the fact that there is a net potential difference between the membranous labyrinth and the surrounding perilymph. The utricle is about 4 mV positive with respect to ground, while the cochlear duct is about 70 mV positive. The significance of these potentials is obscure at this time, but they may play some role in the transduction processes occurring in the hair cells.

Endolymph is probably produced by the stria vascularis of the cochlear duct, as noted in Chapter 23. It is drained into the venous sinuses of the dura mater by the endolymphatic duct. Perilymph is thought to be secreted by arterioles lying in the periosteum surrounding the labyrinth. It is drained into the subarachnoid space by the perilymphatic duct. If the normal production or drainage of either fluid is disturbed the function of the entire labyrinth is disrupted. The auditory disturbances caused by the overproduction of endolymph (Ménière's disease) were described in Chapter 23. Given the continuity between the cochlear duct and the vestibular labyrinth, it is not surprising that the vestibular system is also affected by the excessive production of endolymph. The dizziness (vertigo), nystagmus, and nausea associated with Ménière's disease are direct reflections of malfunction in the vestibular periphery caused by this fluid imbalance.

Specialized Regions of the Vestibular Labyrinth Contain Receptors

Both ends of each fluid-filled semicircular duct are continuous with the utricle (Figure 36–1), although one limb of the superior duct fuses with the posterior duct before joining the utricle. Each duct bears an enlargement called the *ampulla.* The epithelium of the duct in part of the ampulla is thickened and contains specialized receptor cells, the *vestibular hair cells;* the thickened zone containing the hair cells is termed the *ampullary crest* (see Figure 35–5). Peripherally directed processes of bipolar sensory neurons in the vestibular ganglion innervate the hair cells in the crest. The crest is covered with a gelatinous capsule called the *cupula,* which stretches from the crest to the roof of the ampulla. When the head undergoes angular acceleration, the viscous fluid in the semicircular ducts lags behind, due to inertia, and pushes on the cupula. As we shall see, this distortion of the cupula elicits a receptor potential in the hair cells of the crest and eventually alters the level of activity in the eighth-nerve fibers innervating them..

A portion of the floor of the utricle is thickened and contains hair cells along with the distal branches of vestibular ganglion cells. This zone, termed the *macula,* is the principal receptor region of the utricle. The macula is covered with a gelatinous substance in which crystals of calcium carbonate, called *statoconia,* are embedded. The macula of the utricle lies roughly in the horizontal plane when the head is held horizontally, so that the statoconia rest directly upon it. If the head is tilted or if it undergoes linear acceleration, the statoconia in the gelatinous mass will push the hairs of the receptor cells. A receptor-rich macula can also be found in the *saccule.* In contrast to the macula of the utricle, it is oriented vertically when the head is in its normal position. We shall not consider the saccule further at this time since preliminary evidence suggests that it may have an auditory function.

Nature and Function of Hair Cells
Hair Cells Are Polarized Structurally and Functionally

Vestibular hair cells, as mentioned above, are restricted to the ampullary crests of the semicircular ducts and the maculae of the saccule and utri-

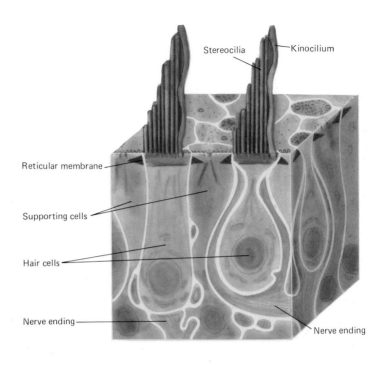

Stereocilia　Kinocilium

Reticular membrane

Supporting cells

Hair cells

Nerve ending

Nerve ending

35–2 Structure of the epithelium in the vestibular labyrinth showing hair cells with a typical arrangement of sterocilia and a kinocilium surrounded by supporting cells. (Adapted from Spoendlin, 1966.)

cle. Hair cells are separated from one another by supporting cells, to which they are joined at their apical surfaces by tight junctions (Figure 35–2). The free surface of each hair cell is thrown into a number of microvilli (40–69 per cell) called *stereocilia* and a single motile *kinocilium* (Figure 35–3A). In the semicircular ducts, these hairs project into the overlying cupula. The kinocilium is always found on one side of the hair bundle. This gives each hair cell a *morphological axis of polarization.* We can define the axis as running from the smallest stereocilium to the kinocilium. This structural arrangement is important because hair cells respond to bending of the apical hairs in a directional manner. Bending of the hair bundle toward the kinocilium leads to depolarization of the hair cell and an increase in the firing of afferent fibers in the eighth nerve, while bending away from the kinocilium leads to hyperpolarization of the hair cell and decreased firing in the vestibular fibers of the eighth nerve (Figure 35–3B).

The directional response of hair cells was most clearly demonstrated in a thoughtful series of experiments by Albert Hudspeth and David Corey (1977) of the California Institute of Technology. They removed the macula from the inner ear of a bullfrog, stripped it of the overlying statoconia,

and placed the preparation on the stage of a microscope. The hair bundle of an individual cell was then drawn into the tip of a small moveable capillary tube and the cell was impaled with a micropipette to make intracellular recordings of the response to movements of the hair bundle (Figure 35–4). The results of such experiments show that deflection of the hair bundle toward the kinocilium causes a conductance increase in the hair cell associated with depolarization, and that bending away from the kinocilium leads to a decrease in conductance and hyperpolarization of the hair cell. Corey and Hudspeth (1979) have also demonstrated that the receptor current is carried by K^+ in vivo, which seems reasonable since K^+ is relatively highly concentrated at the apical surface of the hair cells where the hair bundles are situated. As a result of this transduction mechanism at the apical surface, movements of the hair bundle are converted into potential changes in the hair cell itself.

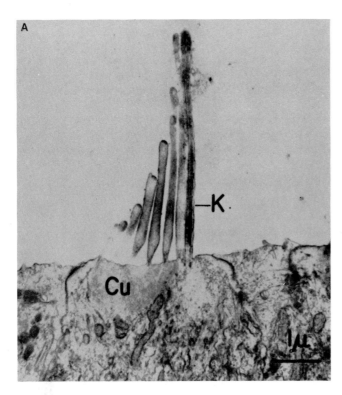

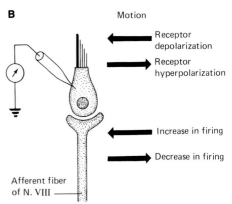

35-3 Apical hairs of the hair cell.
A. Transmission electron
micrograph of the hair cell apical surface
showing the stereocilia increasing in length
toward the kinocilium **(K).** The cuticle **(Cu)**
occupies the top of the sensory cell except
for an area around the basal body of the
kinocilium. Osmium tetroxide fixation,
uranyl acetate stain. ×11,000. (Adapted from
Flock, 1964.) **B.** Bending of apical hairs
affects the polarization of hair cells and firing
rate of eighth-nerve afferent fibers.

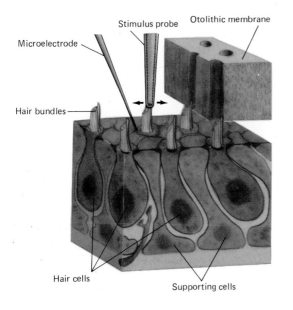

35-4 Experimental set-up for studying hair cell
responses. Hair cells and supporting cells
form an epithelial sheet supported by a layer of
connective tissue. The otolithic membrane, which
normally couples stimuli to the hair bundles of the
receptor cells, is shown partially dissected from the
site of experimentation. While the intracellular
potential is recorded through a glass microelectrode,
a hair cell is stimulated by a capillary stimulus probe
slipped over the tip of its hair bundle and moved
parallel to the epithelial surface **(arrows).** (Adapted
from Hudspeth and Corey, 1977.)

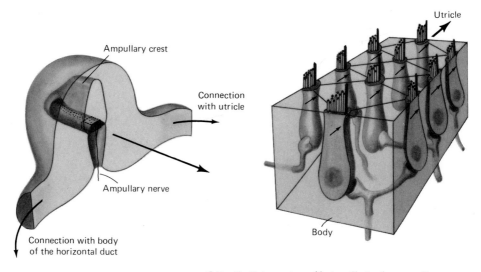

35–5 Orientation of hair cells in the ampullary crest of the horizontal duct.

Axes of Hair Cells Are Arranged in an Orderly Way

The hair cells in the ampullae of the semicircular ducts are arranged in an orderly pattern. In the horizontal ducts, the kinocilia all face toward the utricle (Figure 35–5), and therefore bending of the hairs in the direction toward the utricle is excitatory. The outcome of this morphological polarization can be demonstrated by extracellular single unit recordings from the afferent fibers

innervating the hair cells. The vestibular nerve fibers display a pronounced resting discharge at rates from 100 to 300 spikes/sec. If the sensory hairs are bent in one direction, this rate is increased, and if they are bent in the other, this rate is decreased (Figure 35–6). Therefore, the vestibular nerve fibers to each duct respond positively to rotation in one direction and, since there is a resting discharge, negatively to rotation in the opposite direction.

35–6 Directional selectivity of vestibular receptors to bending of the hairs. (Adapted from Flock, 1965.)

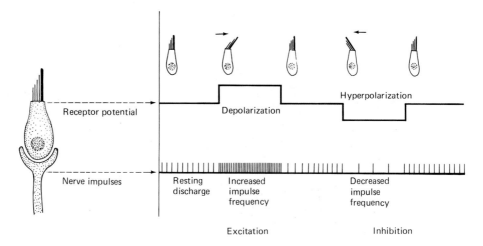

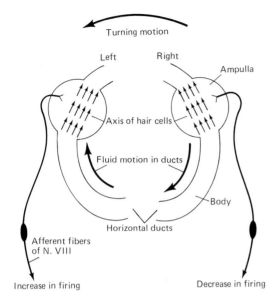

35–7 View of the horizontal ducts from above showing how paired canals work together to provide a bilateral indication of head movement.

35–8 Orientation of the anterior, horizontal, and posterior semicircular canals in the head.

Semicircular Ducts Work in Pairs

To examine the way that paired ducts on either side of the head work together, imagine that we are looking down on top of the two horizontal ducts (Figure 35–7). Remember that the horizontal ducts are connected to the utricle at either end (Figure 35–1). Furthermore, the morphological axis of polarization of each hair cell in both horizontal ampullae points toward the nearest juncture between the ducts and the utricle (the axes of the hair cells are indicated by *small arrows* in Figure 35–7). As the head turns to the left, the fluid in the ducts will lag behind the turning motion because of inertia. As a consequence, the fluid in the left duct will push the hair bundles in the direction of their axes of polarization, while the fluid in the right duct will push the hair bundles of the right ampulla against the axes. The hair cells of the left ampulla will therefore depolarize and excite the afferent fibers innervating them. The hair cells of the right ampulla will hyperpolarize, and afferent fibers innervating them will decrease their firing rate. The brain then receives two indications of this turning motion: an increase in the firing of eighth nerve fibers on one side, and a decrease on the other.

The horizontal ducts lie in the same plane on each side, so that it is natural that they work together to detect motion. The situation is not so

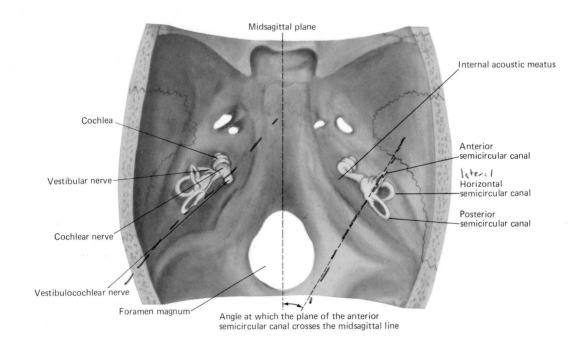

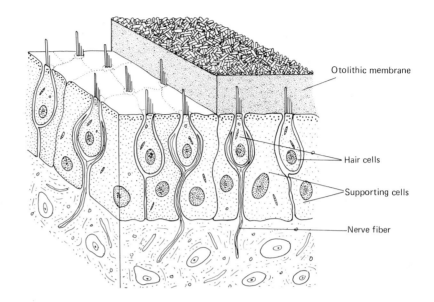

Otolithic membrane

Hair cells

Supporting cells

Nerve fiber

35−9 Structural organization of the utricular macula. (Adapted from Iurato, 1967.)

simple for the other ducts because of their orientation in the head (Figure 35−8). The anterior duct on one side lies approximately in the same plane as the posterior duct on the opposite side, so the anterior and posterior ducts of either side are functional pairs. Motion in the plane of these ducts will cause excitation of hair cells in one ampulla and inhibition in the other, and thus provide a bilateral indication of head movement.

Hair Cells in the Utricle Are Polarized Toward the Striola

Hair cells in the macula of the utricle are also arranged in an orderly pattern but they do not have their kinocilia facing in a single direction. The fact that the cells are not polarized in a uniform pattern in the utricular macula enables this structure to respond to tilt or to linear acceleration in any one of several directions. The hair cells of the utricle are in a specialized epithelium much like the crests of the ampullae. Their sensory hairs project into an overlying gelatinous matrix in which the otoliths are embedded (Figure 35−9). The macular hair cells are also polarized, since their kinocilia are located toward one side of the cells' apical surface.

The response of an individual macular hair cell to the gravitational force exerted by the statoconia is illustrated schematically in Figure 35−10. When the head is held in the horizontal plane, gravitational force is directed downward upon the hair bundle. When the head is tilted to

the left, the hair bundle of the cell is displaced along the axis of polarization, causing it to depolarize and excite its afferent fiber. A tilt to the right has the opposite effect. Therefore, the afferent fiber innervating an individual macular hair cell is either excited or inhibited by a given tilt of the head. The intriguing structural feature of the macula is that the axes of the hair cells all point toward a single curving landmark called the *striola*, as shown by the arrows in Figure 35−11. Tilt in any direction depolarizes some macular hair cells and hyperpolarizes others. This dual signal most probably aids in providing the brain with an accurate measure of head position.

35−10 Response of an individual macular hair cell to tilt of the head.

Gravitational force exerted by otoliths

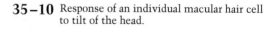

Vestibular hair cell

Tilt to the left (depolarization)

Tilt to the right (hyperpolarization)

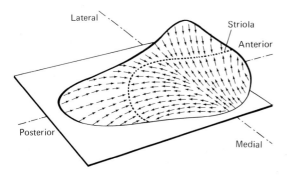

35-11 Distribution of hair cell axes in the macula of the utricle: surface view. (Adapted from Spoendlin, 1966.)

Central Connections of the Vestibular Labyrinth

The Labyrinth Has Dynamic and Static Functions

The vestibular labyrinth, therefore, has two relatively independent functions. The *dynamic* function, mediated by the semicircular ducts, enables us to detect motion of the head in space, and, as we shall see, is important for the reflex control of eye movements. The *static* function, mediated by the utricle, enables us to monitor the absolute position of the body in space and plays a pivotal role in the control of posture. We shall now consider the central connections established by ganglion cells innervating the ampullae of the ducts and the macula of the utricle. As might be expected, the central connections of these two sets of ganglion cells are different—a reflection of their distinctive physiological roles.

Vestibular Ganglion Processes Constitute Part of the Eighth Nerve

The afferent fibers of the vestibular system have their cell bodies in the vestibular ganglion (Scarpa's ganglion) lying near the internal auditory meatus. There are about 20,000 vestibular ganglion cells and each is bipolar; the peripheral process innervates the hair cells and the central process runs along with the cochlear fibers of the eighth nerve to terminate in the brain stem. Both the processes and the cell body are myelinated. The vestibular ganglion is divided into two portions: the *superior division* innervates the macula of the utricle and the cristae of the horizontal and anterior semicircular ducts, and the *inferior division* innervates the saccule and the crista of the

posterior duct. The centrally directed branches of cells in Scarpa's ganglion join with axons from Corti's ganglion in the cochlea to constitute the eighth cranial nerve. The nerve runs through the internal auditory meatus, along with the facial nerve. After exiting from the meatus, the eighth nerve runs through the cerebellopontine angle to reach the lateral aspect of the pons, where the axons enter the brain.

Each Nucleus of the Vestibular Nuclear Complex Has Distinctive Connections

The vestibular nuclear complex (Figure 35-12) occupies a substantial portion of the medulla beneath the floor of the fourth ventricle. Four distinct nuclei can be recognized in this complex: (1) the superior vestibular nucleus of Bechterew, (2) the lateral vestibular nucleus of Deiters, (3) the medial vestibular nucleus of Schwalbe, and (4) the inferior or descending vestibular nucleus of Roller. Each of the nuclei can be distinguished on the basis of its cytoarchitecture, but more importantly, each nucleus has a distinctive set of connections with the vestibular periphery and with

35-12 Location of vestibular nuclei in the brain stem: dorsal view.

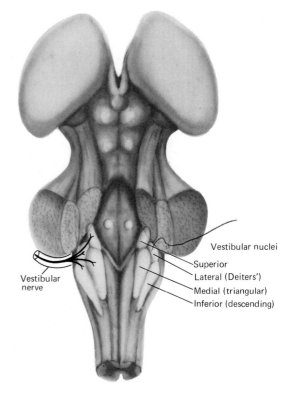

Vestibular nerve

Vestibular nuclei
Superior
Lateral (Deiters')
Medial (triangular)
Inferior (descending)

certain regions in the central nervous system, notably the spinal cord, the oculomotor nuclei (III, IV, and VI) of the brain stem, and the cerebellum.

Lateral Vestibular Nucleus. The lateral vestibular nucleus is roughly diamond shaped when viewed from the side. Only the rostroventral portion of the nucleus appears to receive primary vestibular fibers innervating the macula of the utricle. The dorsocaudal portion of the nucleus is dominated by input from the cerebellum and the spinal cord. Deiters' nucleus is easily recognized because it contains large cells, often 50–100 μm in diameter, along with smaller neurons. All of these cells send their axons into the vestibulospinal tract, which terminates in the ipsilateral anterior horn of the spinal cord from cervical to lumbar levels. This tract has a pronounced facilitatory effect on both alpha and gamma motor neurons to antigravity muscles.

The neurons in the rostroventral part of Deiters' nucleus respond selectively to tilting of the head. These neurons have a resting discharge which increases in response to tilt in one direction and decreases in response to tilt in the opposite direction. The magnitude of the response increases with increasing angle of tilt. A smaller number of rapidly adapting neurons respond whenever the angle of the body is changed. Both types of cells receive input from the macula of the utricle.

The neurons in Deiters' nucleus receive direct inhibitory input from the cerebellum. Electrical stimulation of Purkinje cell axons emanating from the vermis of the cerebellum produces monosynaptic inhibitory postsynaptic potentials in the large cells of Deiters' nucleus. As we have seen in Chapter 28, this finding is important for understanding decerebrate rigidity. This rigidity appears when the brain stem is transected above the level of the vestibular nuclei and is characterized by increased tone in the antigravity muscles. If the transection occurs caudal to the vestibular nuclei, the rigidity does not occur. Decerebrate rigidity is undoubtedly due to the unopposed excitatory effect of the lateral vestibulospinal tract upon motor neurons supplying the antigravity muscles. If the portion of the cerebellum connected to Deiters' nucleus is removed, this condition is greatly exacerbated, since the inhibitory effect of the Purkinje cell axons upon the giant cells is removed. Conversely, electrical stimulation of this part of the cerebellum alleviates the rigidity.

Medial and Superior Vestibular Nuclei. The medial and superior vestibular nuclei receive input principally from the cristae of the semicircular ducts. Cells in these nuclei send their axons into the *medial longitudinal fasciculus,* a tract running to rostral parts of the brain stem just beneath the midline of the fourth ventricle. The locations of these structures are indicated in Figure 35–13, a myelin-stained section through the

35–13 Relationship of medial longitudinal fasciculus to medial vestibular nucleus viewed through the lower pons.

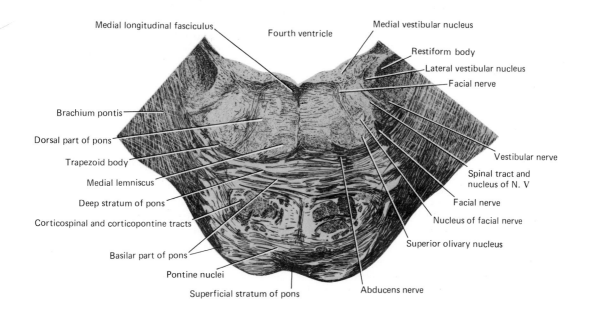

Medial longitudinal fasciculus · Fourth ventricle · Medial vestibular nucleus · Restiform body · Lateral vestibular nucleus · Facial nerve · Brachium pontis · Dorsal part of pons · Trapezoid body · Medial lemniscus · Deep stratum of pons · Corticospinal and corticopontine tracts · Basilar part of pons · Pontine nuclei · Superficial stratum of pons · Abducens nerve · Nucleus of facial nerve · Facial nerve · Spinal tract and nucleus of N. V · Vestibular nerve · Superior olivary nucleus

lower pons. The function of the medial and superior vestibular nuclei can be illustrated by examining the elementary vestibulo-ocular reflex arc.

To demonstrate this reflex, imagine that a person is being spun to the left about a vertical axis on a stool. When the acceleration to the left first begins, the eyes undergo a slow conjugate deviation to the right, in a direction opposite to the motion of the head. This tends to keep the eyes fixed on a single point in space. The eyes do not remain in this position; when they have reached the limit of their excursion, there is a rapid movement to the left, i.e., in the direction of the angular acceleration. These slow and fast movements are termed, respectively, the slow and fast phases of vestibular nystagmus. Note that the fast phase of nystagmus is in the direction of the angular acceleration. When the movement to the left is stopped abruptly it is equivalent to producing a rapid acceleration to the right due to the inertia of the fluid in the horizontal semicircular ducts. The eyes now undergo repeated slow movements to the left, accompanied by rapid return movements to the right until the vestibular stimulus subsides. This *postrotatory nystagmus* is used clinically to evaluate the functional state of the vestibular system.

A simplified circuit diagram for the initial phase of this vestibulo-ocular reflex is presented in Figure 35–14. As the head accelerates to the left, there is increased firing in the nerve fibers innervating the crista of the horizontal duct of the left side. This leads eventually, through several synaptic relays, to a contraction of the muscles that turn both eyes to the right. At the same time there is a diminution in the activity of nerve fibers innervating the crista of the right horizontal duct, and this causes a relaxation of antagonist muscles. These effects are achieved via specific sets of connections between the medial and superior vestibular nuclei and the motor nuclei of the extraocular muscles. For motion in planes other than the horizontal, the other ducts work together in pairs just as the horizontal ducts do. The anterior semicircular duct on one side is actually in the same plane as the posterior duct on the opposite side. So these ducts act together to analyze motion in or near the vertical plane.

This process can be examined experimentally by sealing a cannula in the left horizontal semicircular duct of an experimental animal and alternately pushing and pulling the endolymph while recording the tension in each of the extraocular muscles. When the endolymph is pushed, simu-

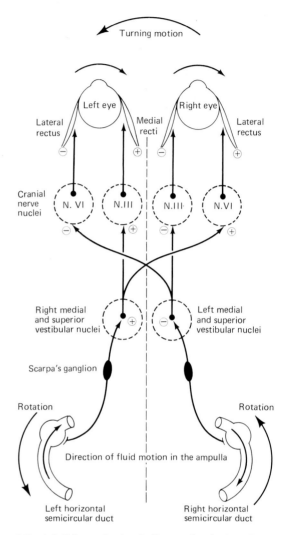

35–14 Schematic circuit diagram for the initial phase of the vestibulo-ocular reflex arc. Increase (+) or decrease (−) in rate of firing along a particular pathway is indicated.

lating a rotational movement to the left, the medial rectus of the left eye and the lateral rectus of the right eye contract, while the lateral rectus of the left eye and the medial rectus of the right eye show reduced tension.

Voluntary Control of Eye Movements. There is also, of course, voluntary control of eye movements. The most important regions of the cerebral cortex involved in voluntary ocular movements are the frontal eye fields, which are located in the frontal lobes. When the frontal eye fields are stimulated electrically on one side of

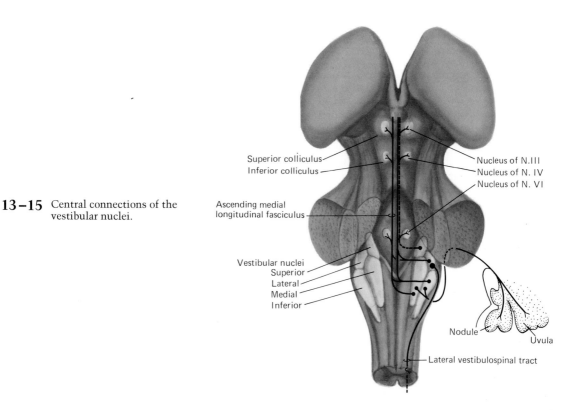

13-15 Central connections of the
vestibular nuclei.

Superior colliculus
Inferior colliculus

Nucleus of N.III
Nucleus of N. IV
Nucleus of N. VI

Ascending medial
longitudinal fasciculus

Vestibular nuclei
Superior
Lateral
Medial
Inferior

Nodule
Uvula

Lateral vestibulospinal tract

the brain, there is a conjugate deviation of the
eyes to the opposite side. Patients with lesions in
the frontal eye fields are unable to make voluntary eye movements to the side opposite the lesion, but other reflex movements of the eyes mediated by the vestibular system remain intact.

Descending Vestibular Nucleus. The descending vestibular nucleus appears to receive primary
vestibular fibers from the semicircular ducts and
from the utricle and saccule. It also receives
afferents from the vermis of the cerebellum and
from the fastigial nucleus. The majority of efferent fibers from the descending vestibular nucleus
run in the medial longitudinal fasciculus to higher centers in the brain stem. This nucleus, therefore, is structured to integrate input from the
peripheral vestibular apparatus and the cerebellum, and to affect the activity centers at higher
levels in the brain stem, perhaps the thalamus.

Some primary vestibular fibers terminate directly in the *flocculonodular lobe* of the cerebellum. These axons most probably terminate as
mossy fibers in the granular layer. They are important for the cerebellar control of posture.
Some neurons in the vestibular complex itself

(the medial and inferior nuclei) also send their axons to the cerebellum and are undoubtedly important for postural control. The central connections of the vestibular complex are summarized
in Figure 35-15.

An Overall View

The vestibular system is provided with a unique
peripheral receptor, the vestibular hair cell,
whose physiological properties determine many
aspects of vestibular function. Many peripheral
receptors, for example the Pacinian corpuscle, depolarize in response to an appropriate stimulus.
Others, for example vertebrate photoreceptors,
hyperpolarize. The vestibular hair cell, however,
may either depolarize or hyperpolarize depending
upon the direction of head movement or tilt. Furthermore, any motion of the head affects both
sides, so there must be extensive interaction in
the central nervous system between the inputs
arising from both labyrinths. The bidirectional
nature of the hair cell response, along with the
bilateral interaction of the labyrinth, is obviously
an advantage in providing multiple indications of
head movement and position.

An analysis of vestibular function shows rather clearly the important difference between *sensory* and *afferent* information reaching the brain. A large percentage of dorsal root fibers relay sensory information to the spinal cord. This information—about the size, intensity, or temperature of stimuli impinging upon the skin—is then relayed to higher centers in the brain and eventually reaches consciousness. Much of the input carried centrally via the vestibular division is purely *afferent* in nature; the input is used to mediate a variety of reflexes but much of it never reaches consciousness. Even though we may not always be aware of the functions of the vestibular system, its normal operation is essential for the performance of most motor behaviors.

Selected Readings and References

Brodal, A. 1981. Neurological Anatomy. 3rd ed. New York: Oxford University Press, pp. 470–495.

Corey, D. P., and Hudspeth, A. J. 1979. Ionic basis of the receptor potential in a vertebrate hair cell. Nature (Lond.) 281:675–677.

Flock, Å. 1964. Structure of the macula utriculi with special reference to directional interplay of sensory responses as revealed by morphological polarization. J. Cell Biol. 22:413–431.

Hudspeth, A. J., and Corey, D. P. 1977. Sensitivity, polarity, and conductance change in the response of vertebrate hair cells to controlled mechanical stimuli. Proc. Natl. Acad. Sci. U.S.A. 74:2407–2411.

Wilson, V. J., and Melvill Jones, G. 1979. Mammalian Vestibular Physiology. New York: Plenum.

Other References

Flock, Å. 1965. Transducing mechanisms in the lateral line canal organ receptors. Cold Spring Harbor Symp. Quant. Biol. 30:133–145.

Iurato, S. 1967. Submicroscopic Structure of the Inner Ear. Oxford: Pergamon.

Spoendlin, H. 1966. Ultrastructure of the vestibular sense organ. *In* R. J. Wolfson (ed.), The Vestibular System and Its Diseases. Philadelphia: University of Pennsylvania Press, pp. 39–68.

Wersäll, J., and Flock, Å. 1965. Functional anatomy of the vestibular and lateral line organs. In W. Neff (ed.), Contributions to Sensory Physiology. New York: Academic, pp. 39–61.

Lewis P. Rowland

Clinical Syndromes of the Brain Stem

36

Crowded into the small space for the brain stem are nuclei and nerve fibers for the cranial nerves, the long sensory tracts ascending from the spinal cord to the thalamus and cortex, and the motor pathways descending from the cortex and the subcortical nuclei to the brain stem and spinal cord. In addition, the reticular formation of the brain stem contains autonomic centers that control respiration, blood pressure, and gastrointestinal functions as well as centers for arousal and wakefulness. Finally, there is a narrow aqueduct for the circulation of the cerebrospinal fluid—the aqueduct of Sylvius—which is susceptible to occlusion. No region of the central nervous system is as densely packed with vital structures; it is not surprising that a small lesion in the brain stem can have disastrous results.

Accurate diagnosis of disorders of the brain stem requires detailed knowledge of the anatomy of the cranial nerves and of the ascending and descending tracts. Since nerves exit from the brain stem close to their origin, disturbances in the function of specific cranial nerves are useful for localizing a lesion to particular levels of the brain stem (Figure 36–1). Similarly, manifestations of disturbances of the long tracts can locate the lesion within a particular horizontal level to the medial or lateral segment of that level. Thus the combined information provided from disorders of tracts

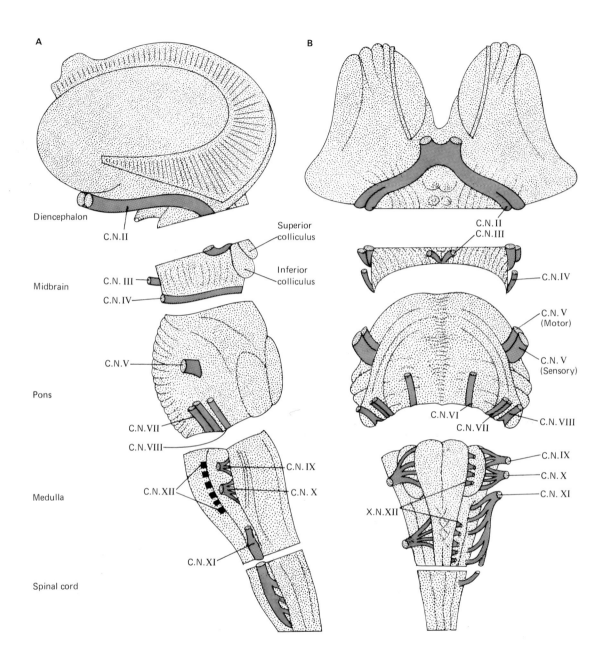

36-1 View of the brain stem showing the location of cranial nerves. **A.** Lateral view. **B.** Ventral view. (Adapted from Curtis, Jacobson, and Marcus, 1972.)

and cranial nerves can often pinpoint a lesion to a specific locus in the brain stem.

In this chapter the structures of the brain stem will be described from a clinical perspective. Rather than considering all possible abnormali-

ties, we shall concentrate on illustrative vascular lesions at four levels of the brain stem because they cause characteristic symptoms that can readily be inferred from the anatomy. Although we shall not consider them here, other conditions also affect the brain stem. For instance, lesions in the brain stem are common in multiple sclerosis and in brain tumors of the posterior fossa; other functions of the brain stem will be considered in Chapter 41.

Anatomical Considerations

To localize lesions within the brain stem, it is useful to delineate regions in the brain stem along two axes—a longitudinal one and a cross-sectional one. Along the longitudinal axis, areas of the brain stem that lie in the direction of the midbrain are called *upper, superior,* or *rostral;* areas in the direction of the spinal cord are called *lower, inferior,* or *caudal* (Figure 36–1). In cross section, the lowermost structures are called *ventral;* the upper structures are called *dorsal* or *segmental.*

In clinical practice it is critical to determine whether the site of a lesion is within or outside the brain stem proper. A lesion that directly affects the parenchyma, the tissue of the brain stem, is called *intra-axial, intramedullary,* or *parenchymal;* a lesion that is outside the brain stem—such as that affecting the peripheral course of a cranial nerve—is called *extra-axial.* Because of the anatomical arrangement, unilateral lesions within the brain stem tend to cause crossed syndromes, in which some signs are ipsilateral and others are contralateral to the lesion. Extra-axial lesions may affect only specific groups of cranial nerves, but extra-axial tumors may also compress the brain stem so that ascending and descending tracts are compromised, making it difficult to distinguish between intra- and

extra-axial lesions on clinical grounds. As an example of a common extra-axial lesion we shall consider the acoustic neuroma, a tumor that grows in the angle between the cerebellum and the pons.

Extra-Axial Lesions Are Illustrated by the Cerebellopontine Angle of the Tumors

Small extra-axial lesions affecting the brain stem often begin by causing isolated paralysis of individual cranial nerves. Neighboring parenchymal structures then become involved, indicating the location of the disorder. Isolated cranial nerve disorders, however, are more likely to be due to peripheral lesions, often brought about by compression of the nerves as they exit through the foramina of the skull. Intracranial tumors outside the brain stem may also begin this way. One such extramedullary tumor is the *acoustic neuroma,* which originates from Schwann cells of the sheath of the acoustic nerve within the acoustic canal. The tumor first compresses the cochlear nerve, giving rise to ringing in the ear

36–2 Syndrome of the cerebellopontine angle.
  A. Normal cerebellopontine angle.
B. Changes caused by an acoustic neuroma. (Adapted from Patten, 1977.)

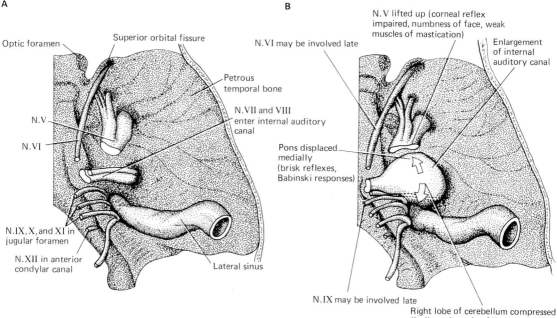

A

Optic foramen

Superior orbital fissure

N.V

N.VI

Petrous temporal bone

N.VII and VIII enter internal auditory canal

N.IX, X, and XI in jugular foramen

N.XII in anterior condylar canal

Lateral sinus

B

N.VI may be involved late

N. V lifted up (corneal reflex impaired, numbness of face, weak muscles of mastication)

Enlargement of internal auditory canal

Pons displaced medially (brisk reflexes, Babinski responses)

N.IX may be involved late

Right lobe of cerebellum compressed (ipsilateral ataxia of limbs, unsteady gait, falling to right side)

(tinnitus), loss of hearing, and ultimately deaf-ness. The distance from the internal auditory meatus to neighboring nerves and the brain stem is short (Figure 36–2). As the tumor grows into the angle between the cerebellum and the pons, the corneal reflex may be lost, signifying compression of afferent fibers of the trigeminal nerve. Later, other trigeminal motor and sensory functions may be lost. The next signs may in-volve the facial nerve (causing a lower motor neu-ron type of facial paralysis on the same side) or the ipsilateral cerebellar hemisphere (causing ip-silateral limb ataxia and intention tremor, or nys-tagmus). The brain stem ultimately becomes compressed, causing corticospinal tract signs or narrowing of the aqueduct to cause hydrocepha-lus and symptoms of increased intracranial pres-sure. With recent improvements in diagnostic technique, the tumor is usually detected clini-cally or by computerized tomography before it progresses to hydrocephalus. Because acoustic neuromas are benign accessible tumors, they can be removed surgically.

Intra-Axial Lesions Often Cause Gaze Palsies and Internuclear Ophthalmoplegia

Gaze Palsies

Many lesions of the brain stem cause abnormali-ties of gaze (conjugate movements of both eyes) or nystagmus (rhythmical oscillations of the eyes, with a fast component in one direction and a slow movement in the other direction). It is

36–3 Neural pathways subtending horizontal gaze and the effects of lesions. **A.** Pathways for horizontal gaze. 2–6: Lesions described in part B. **B.** Abnormalities of eye movements on attempted gaze to the right correspond to the numbered lesions in the horizontal gaze system shown in part A. 1, normal right gaze; 2, left cortical lesion (gaze to the right is impaired); 3; left medial longitudinal fasciculus lesion (impaired adduction of the left eye; nystagmus of abducting right eye); 4. left oculomotor nerve lesion (impaired adduction of left eye plus other manifestations of third nerve palsy, including the ptosis illustrated); 5, right abducens nerve lesion; 6, left vestibular nerve lesion (jerk nystagmus). (Adapted from Sears and Franklin, 1980.)

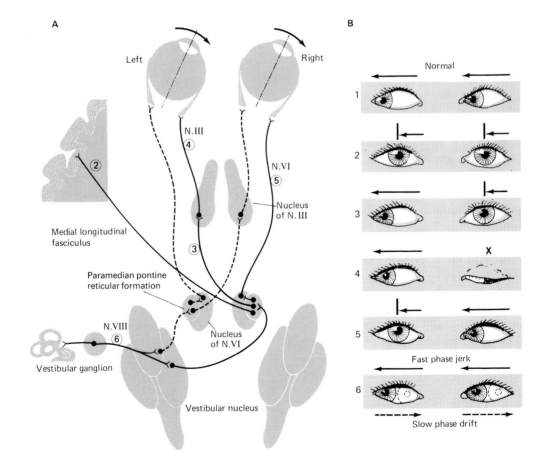

useful, therefore, to review the relationship between two of the centers controlling eye movements that were considered in Chapter 34—the cortical and pontine gaze centers (Figure 36–3).

As we have seen, discharging epileptic foci or electrical stimulation of frontal or occipital eye fields on one side causes both eyes to move conjugately to the opposite side (Figure 36–4A). Conversely, destructive lesions of the frontal area may result in impaired gaze toward the side opposite the lesion: after a lesion in the right frontal

lobe, for example, the patient cannot move the eyes conjugately to the left and they tend to drift to the right (Figure 36–4B). If a lesion in the right hemisphere also causes a left hemiplegia, the eyes would therefore seem to look *away* from the hemiplegia.

36–4 Disorders of gaze due to irritative lesion of frontal lobe or destructive lesions of either frontal lobe or pons. **+** = functioning gaze center; **P**, paretic limbs; ↑, Babinski sign. (Adapted from Patten, 1977.)

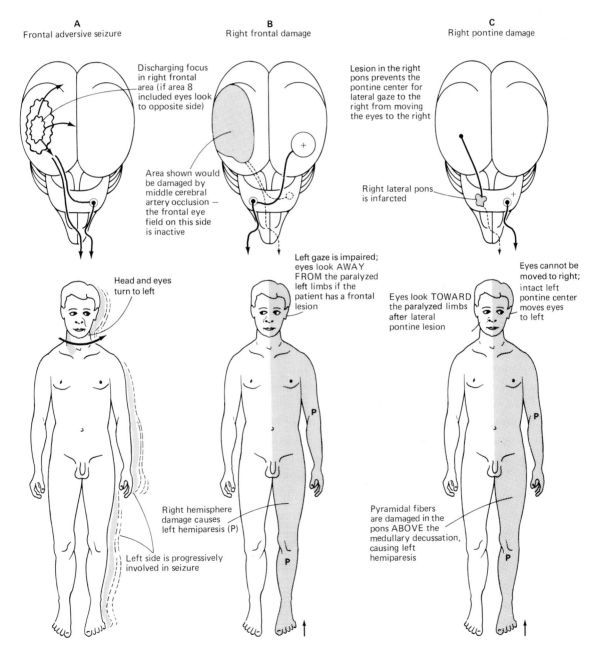

A
Frontal adversive seizure

Discharging focus in right frontal area (if area 8 included eyes look to opposite side)

Area shown would be damaged by middle cerebral artery occlusion — the frontal eye field on this side is inactive

Head and eyes turn to left

Left side is progressively involved in seizure

B
Right frontal damage

Left gaze is impaired; eyes look AWAY FROM the paralyzed left limbs if the patient has a frontal lesion

Right hemisphere damage causes left hemiparesis (P)

C
Right pontine damage

Lesion in the right pons prevents the pontine center for lateral gaze to the right from moving the eyes to the right

Right lateral pons is infarcted

Eyes look TOWARD the paralyzed limbs after lateral pontine lesion

Eyes cannot be moved to right; intact left pontine center moves eyes to left

Pyramidal fibers are damaged in the pons ABOVE the medullary decussation, causing left hemiparesis

The fibers descending from the cortical eye fields cross the midline to the contralateral pontine gaze center in the reticular formation, near the sixth nerve nucleus (Figure 36–3A). Lesions here impair gaze toward the side of the lesion. For instance, a destructive lesion on the right side of the pons impairs gaze to the right and the eyes tend to drift to the left. If corticospinal fibers are also involved, the right-sided lesion is above the decussation of the descending fibers; there would be a left hemiplegia, and the eyes look *toward* the left hemiplegia (Figure 36–4C).

Syndrome of the Median Longitudinal Fasciculus: Internuclear Ophthalmoplegia

Gaze to the right requires coordinated activity of the right lateral rectus muscle (sixth nerve) and the left medial rectus (third nerve). This integration depends upon functions of the pontine gaze center or *paramedian pontine reticular formation*. The paramedian pontine reticular formation sends fibers to the ipsilateral abducens nucleus and the contralateral oculomotor nucleus (Figure 36–3A). These fibers travel with vestibular and other fibers in the medial longitudinal fasciculus; a lesion here causes a characteristic combination of signs called *internuclear ophthalmoplegia* (Figure 36–3B, 3).

If the lesion is unilateral, there is impairment or paralysis of adduction of the eye on that side (Figure 36–3B, 3). By convention, lesions within the medial longitudinal fasciculus—as opposed to those in the paramedian pontine reticular formation—are named for the side of the affected medial rectus. The supranuclear nature of the impaired adduction on attempted gaze is demonstrated by preservation of medial rectus function in the reflex responses of convergence. (If rostral lesions involve the third nerve nucleus, convergence may also be lost.)

In internuclear ophthalmoplegia, there is often nystagmus of the abducting eye; the cause of the nystagmus is uncertain. Formerly attributed to an interruption of vestibular fibers, it is now regarded by some as evidence of persistent convergence; that is, the patient uses the only possible eye movement mechanism (convergence) remaining to cause the paretic medial rectus to adduct. Convergence, however, involves both eyes, causing the abducting eye to adduct momentarily. To resume its position, the abducting eye makes a quick movement to refixate on the laterally placed target, and this appears as nystagmus.

Vascular Lesions of the Brain Stem May Cause Characteristic Syndromes

The medulla is supplied by branches of the vertebral artery, including the posterior inferior cerebellar artery (Figure 36–5). The two vertebral arteries of each side join to form the *basilar artery*, which runs on the base of the pons and gives off three sets of branches: (1) *paramedian branches* supply midline structures of the pons; (2) *short circumferential branches* supply the lateral aspect of the pons and the middle and superior cerebellar peduncles; and (3) *long circumferential arteries*, the *inferior* and *superior cerebellar arteries*, also supply lateral portions of the brain stem and run around the pons to reach the cerebellar hemispheres. (The basilar artery terminates by dividing into the two posterior cerebral arteries, which are linked to the corresponding carotid arteries by the posterior communicating arteries to complete the posterior portion of the circle of Willis.)

Sometimes one branch is occluded individually to cause a restricted lesion in the brain stem (described below). Often, the vertebral or basilar artery itself is occluded, giving rise to a more extensive lesion, which may be unilateral or bilateral, that includes more than one of the characteristic syndromes due to occlusion of a single branch.

The longitudinal continuity of ascending and descending pathways places the different tracts in relatively constant medial or lateral positions that are maintained in cross sections at different levels. Because the locations of tracts and cranial nerve nuclei are fixed, specific combinations of signs are reliable indicators of the site of the lesion. Analysis of disorders of the brain stem is therefore greatly simplified by two principles: (1) Below the midbrain, manifestations referrable to long ascending and descending tracts indicate whether the lesion is medial or lateral (Table 36–1). (2) The specific cranial nerve signs delineate the actual level involved (Table 36–2). These signs, which indicate the location of the lesion in both the longitudinal and horizontal extent of the

36–5 Blood supply to the brain stem. **A.** Dorsal view. **B.** Three-dimensional view along the longitudinal axis of the brain stem. (Adapted from Patten, 1977.)

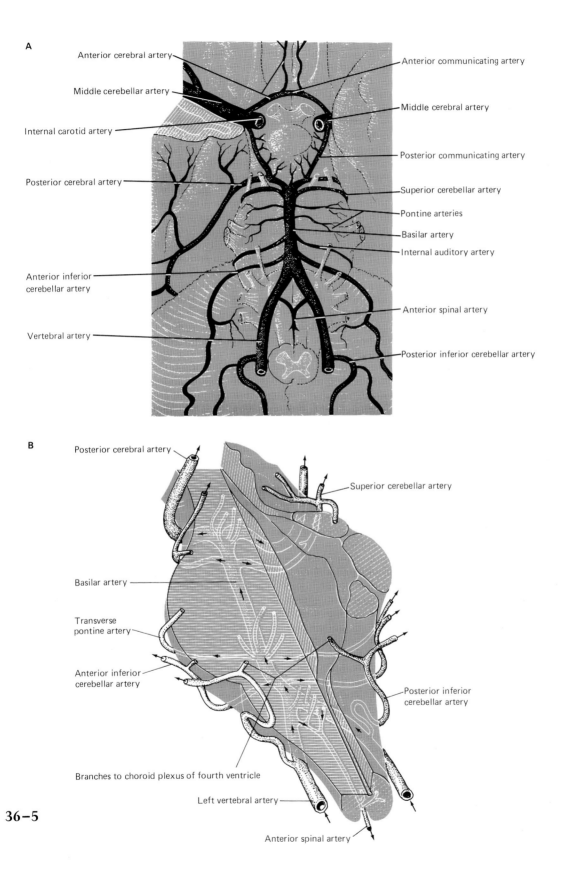

A

Anterior cerebral artery

Middle cerebellar artery

Internal carotid artery

Posterior cerebral artery

Anterior inferior
cerebellar artery

Vertebral artery

Anterior communicating artery

Middle cerebral artery

Posterior communicating artery

Superior cerebellar artery

Pontine arteries

Basilar artery

Internal auditory artery

Anterior spinal artery

Posterior inferior cerebellar artery

B

Posterior cerebral artery

Superior cerebellar artery

Basilar artery

Transverse
pontine artery

Anterior inferior
cerebellar artery

Posterior inferior
cerebellar artery

Branches to choroid plexus of fourth ventricle

Left vertebral artery

Anterior spinal artery

36–5

426

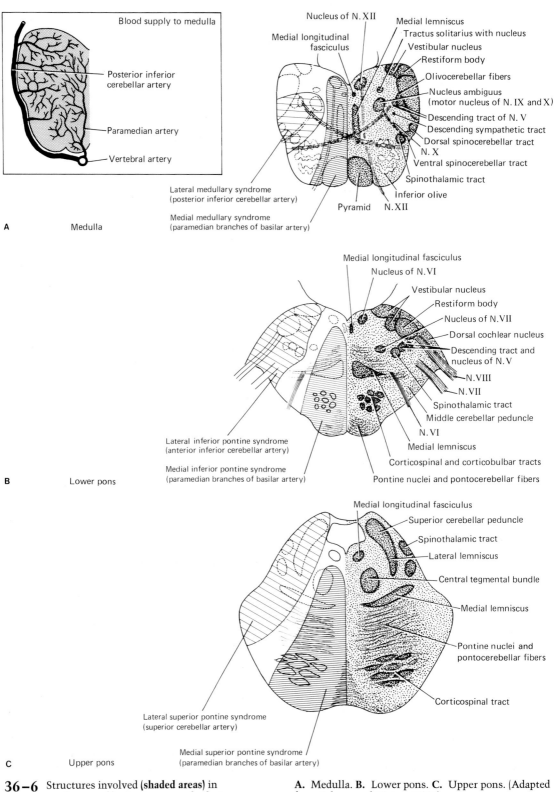

36–6 Structures involved (**shaded areas**) in syndromes of brain stem vascular lesions.

A. Medulla. **B.** Lower pons. **C.** Upper pons. (Adapted from Adams and Victor, 1977.)

Table 36–1. Features Common to Syndromes at Any Level of the Medulla or Pons

Syndromes	Structure involved	Signs
Medial	Corticospinal tract	Hemiparesis (contralateral)
	Medial lemniscus	Loss of position and vibration sense (contralateral)
	Cerebellar connections (pons)	Limb ataxia or nystagmus (ipsilateral)
Lateral	Cerebellar connections	Limb ataxia (ipsilateral)
	Sensory nucleus or descending sensory tract of trigeminal nerve	Loss of cutaneous sensation on face (ipsilateral)
	Descending autonomic fibers	Horner syndrome: miosis, ptosis, impaired sweating (ipsilateral)
	Spinothalamic tract	Loss of pain and temperature sensation (contralateral)
	Vestibular nuclei and connections	Nystagmus, nausea, vomiting
	Uncertain	Hiccup

brain stem, will make sense if you refer to the figures that accompany descriptions of the lesions.

Medial Syndromes of the Medulla and Pons

Medial lesions arise from occlusion of the paramedian branches of the basilar artery. A unilateral medial lesion in the pons or upper medulla will affect the corticospinal tract and medial lemniscus, with corresponding signs on the other side of the body (Table 36–1 and Figure 36–6), i.e., (1) contralateral hemiparesis and (2) contralateral loss of position and vibratory sensation. Cutaneous sensation, which is mediated by the spinothalamic tracts, is spared.

If the lesion is in the medulla, it will not affect the corticobulbar fibers to the facial nerve nucleus (which lies in the pons), so there will be no facial paralysis. Similarly, the connections to the cerebellum will be spared so that there may be no ipsilateral limb ataxia or nystagmus. Ataxia does occur, however, in medial pontine lesions because of damage to the crossing cerebellar connections of the middle cerebellar peduncle.

Because the different cranial nerves are characteristic of different levels of the brain, the special cranial nerve signs serve to identify the actual level of a medial lesion and allow one to distinguish between a medial syndrome of the medulla and a medial syndrome of the pons (Table 36–2 and Figure 36–6).

In the *medial syndrome of the medulla* (Figure 36–6A) the emerging fibers of the hypoglossal nerve (XII) are involved, causing ipsilateral weakness of that half of the tongue at first,

and wasting of that half of the tongue later. In the *medial syndrome of the pons* (Figure 36–6B) there may be paralysis of the lateral rectus muscle if the lesion is rostral and extends dorsally to affect the nucleus of the abducens nerve (VI) or the emerging fibers of the nerve; lesions involving the sixth nerve nucleus are likely to cause ipsilateral gaze palsy rather than isolated abducens palsy. There may also be nystagmus due to involvement of the medial longitudinal fasciculus or the vestibular or cerebellar connections.

Lateral Syndromes of the Medulla and Pons

Lateral lesions arise from occlusion of the posterior inferior cerebellar artery or the anterior inferior cerebellar artery. The resulting lesions involve different structures than do medial lesions Table 36–1) and Figure 36–6): the spinothalamic tract, descending autonomic fibers, the nucleus or descending sensory tract of the trigeminal nerve, vestibular nuclei, and cerebellar connections.

All lateral lesions involve a common set of six manifestations which may appear together or in different combinations (Table 36–1): (1) contralateral loss of pain and temperature sensation of the limbs and trunk due to damage of the spinothalamic tract; (2) ipsilateral Horner syndrome [miosis (small pupil with normal reaction to light), ptosis of the eyelid, and decreased sweating on the face] due to the interruption of descending autonomic fibers; (3) ipsilateral loss of cutaneous sensation on the face due to involvement of the

Table 36–2. Specific Syndromes Produced by Vascular Lesions of the Brain Stem

Syndrome	Artery affected	Structure involved	Specific manifestations
Medullary			
Medial	Paramedian branches	Emerging fibers of nerve XII	Ipsilateral hemiparalysis of tongue
Lateral	Posterior inferior cerebellar	Emerging fibers of nerves IX and X	Dysphagia, hoarseness, ipsilateral paralysis of vocal cord; ipsilateral loss of pharyngeal reflex
		Solitary nucleus and tract	Loss of taste on ipsilateral half of tongue
Inferior pontine			
Medial	Paramedian branches	Pontine gaze center, near nucleus of nerve VI	Paralysis of gaze to side of lesion
		Vestibular nucleus or connections, or medial longitudinal fasciculus	Gaze-evoked nystagmus
		Nucleus or emerging fibers of nerve VI	Paralysis of ipsilateral lateral rectus
Lateral	Anterior inferior cerebellar	Emerging fibers of nerve VII	Ipsilateral facial paralysis
		Pontine gaze center	Paralysis of gaze to side of lesion
		Nerve VIII or cochlear nucleus	Deafness, tinnitus
Superior pontine			
Medial	Paramedian branches	Medial longitudinal fasciculus	Internuclear ophthalmoplegia
		Uncertain	Palatal myoclonus

sensory trigeminal nucleus or descending tract; (4) nystagmus and nausea; (5) ataxia of the ipsilateral limbs due to interruption of cerebellar connections, the restiform body in the medulla, and the middle and superior peduncles in the pons; and (6) hiccup, for reasons not known. Lateral lesions do not, however, cause hemiparesis or loss of proprioception.

Vascular lesions can affect the brain stem at several levels to produce a variety of syndromes. The involvement of specific cranial nerves distinguishes the actual level of the syndrome.

The *lateral medullary syndrome* (Wallenberg) is caused by occlusion of the posterior inferior cerebellar artery or the vertebral artery (Figure 36–6A). This damages the dorsal portion of the lateral medulla (the lateral medullary tegmentum). In addition to the six common characteristics listed above, glossopharyngeal (IX) and vagal (X) cranial nerves may be involved, causing difficulty in swallowing (dysphagia), hoarseness of the voice due to paralysis of the ipsilateral vocal cord, and loss of the ipsilateral pharyngeal reflex (Table 36–2). There may also be loss of taste on the ipsilateral half of the tongue due to destruction of the solitary nucleus.

The *lateral syndrome of the lower pons* is due

to occlusion of the anterior inferior cerebellar artery (Figure 36–6B). It includes the six common lateral manifestations and three additional specific signs attributable to damage of the facial (VII) and auditory (VIII) nuclei (Table 36–2): (1) ipsilateral facial paralysis of the lower motor neuron type because the lesion involves either the facial nucleus or the emerging fibers of the seventh nerve; (2) deafness and tinnitus (ringing in the affected ear, a symptom of uncertain origin but characteristic of nerve deafness); and (3) ipsilateral gaze paralysis if the lesion extends medially to affect the pontine gaze center.

Lateral lesions of the midpons due to occlusion of a short circumferential artery cause a syndrome identical to that of the lower pons except that nerves VII and VIII are spared, and there is no abnormality of facial movement or hearing. Instead, trigeminal motor functions are implicated. In lateral lesions of the superior pons (Figure 36–6B), which are due to occlusion of the superior cerebellar artery, there are no specific cranial signs. In other words, facial paralysis and hearing loss imply a lateral lesion of the lower pons; trigeminal functions are impaired in the midpons; and none of these cranial nerves is affected in the upper pons.

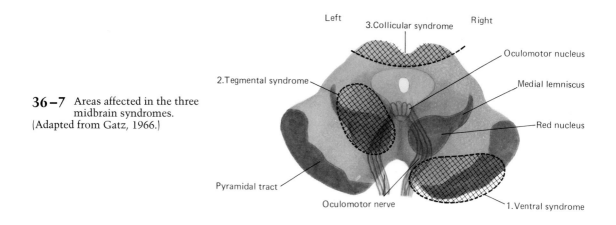

36-7 Areas affected in the three
midbrain syndromes.
(Adapted from Gatz, 1966.)

Midbrain Syndromes

The clinical anatomy of the mesencephalon is less complicated, but even in this small area, three separate syndromes are recognized (Figure 36-7). In the ventral syndrome a lesion of the cerebral peduncle causes (1) contralateral hemiparesis, including supranuclear facial paresis due to damage of the corticospinal and corticobulbar tracts, and (2) ipsilateral oculomotor nerve palsy due to damage of the emerging third nerve fibers.

In the *central or tegmental syndrome* there is again oculomotor nerve palsy (due to a lesion in either the nucleus or emerging fibers), but there is also a tremor or involuntary movement of the contralateral limbs, a condition called *hemichorea*, which is attributed to a lesion in the red nucleus. In addition, there is contralateral hemianesthesia that includes all primary forms of sensation, cutaneous sensation (spinothalamic), and proprioception (medial lemniscus). The corticospinal tract is spared if the lesion is limited, as in Figure 36-7.

The *dorsal or collicular syndrome* is usually due to an extra-axial lesion, most often a tumor of the pineal gland (pinealoma) that compresses the superior colliculi and pretectal structures, causing paralysis of upward gaze without affecting other eye movements.

Coma and the Locked-In Syndrome

Because brain stem mechanisms are so important in maintaining alertness, lesions in this area are likely to cause coma. It is therefore important to recognize brain stem signs in the examination of the comatose patient (Chapter 41) and in the eval-

uation of patients with mass lesions that are likely to cause brain stem signs due to downward tentorial herniation or compression of the medulla due to cerebellar herniation through the foramen magnum.

Bilateral lesions of the ventral pons, usually due to occlusion of the basilar artery, may interrupt the corticobulbar and corticospinal tracts on both sides. As a result, the patient is quadriplegic, unable to speak, and incapable of facial movement. This state may resemble coma, but the eyes are open and move, and the patient is fully conscious and able to communicate by movement of the eyelids or eyes although he or she is otherwise completely immobile or "locked in."

The variety of brain stem syndromes is therefore considerable, but analysis of these syndromes is of more than diagnostic importance; it tells us how the brain is organized and how it functions normally.

Selected Readings and References

Adams, R. D., and Victor, M. 1977. Principles of Neurology. New York: McGraw-Hill.

Ash, P. R., and Keltner, J. L. 1979. Neuro-ophthalmic signs in pontine lesions. Medicine (Baltimore) 58:304–320.

Bauer, G., Gerstenbrand, F., and Rumpl, E. 1979. Varieties of the locked-in syndrome. J. Neurol. 221: 77–91.

Britt, R. H., Herrick, M. K., and Hamilton, R. D. 1977. Traumatic locked-in syndrome. Ann. Neurol. 1:590–592.

Caplan, L. R. 1980. "Top of the basilar" syndrome. Neurology 30:72–79.

Glaser, J. R. 1978. Neuro-Ophthalmology. Hagerstown, Md.: Harper & Row.

Levin, B. E., and Margolis, G. 1977. Acute failure of automatic respirations secondary to a unilateral brainstem infarct. Ann. Neurol. 1:583–586.

Other References

Curtis, B. A., Jacobson, S., and Marcus, E. M. 1972. An Introduction to the Neurosciences. Philadelphia: Saunders.

Gatz, A. J. 1966. Manter's Essentials of Clinical Neuroanatomy and Neurophysiology. 3rd ed. Philadelphia: Davis.

Patten, J. 1977. Neurological Differential Diagnosis. London: Starke; New York: Springer.

Sears, E. S., and Franklin, G. M. 1980. Diseases of the cranial nerves. In R. N. Rosenberg (ed.), Neurology, Vol. 5 of The Science and Practice of Clinical Medicine. New York: Grune & Stratton, pp. 471–494.

Hypothalamus, Limbic System, and Cerebral Cortex: Homeostasis and Arousal

VI

A major function of the nervous system is to maintain homeostasis, the constancy of the internal environment. The regulatory processes that maintain the internal environment have intrigued some of the seminal physiologists of modern time: Claude Bernard, Walter B. Cannon, and Walter Hess. Although virtually the whole brain is involved in homeostatic functions, neurons controlling the internal environment are concentrated in the hypothalamus, a small area that comprises less than 1% of the total volume of the brain.

The hypothalamus and closely linked structures in the limbic system maintain homeostasis by regulating three interrelated functions: (1) endocrine secretion, (2) the autonomic nervous system, and (3) emotions and drives. By its control of the endocrine system and autonomic nervous system, the hypothalamus maintains homeostasis by acting *directly* on the internal environment. By means of its control over emotions and motivated behavior, the hypothalamus maintains homeostasis *indirectly* by acting through the external environment. Because it acts on the external environment through the regulation of emotional expression, the hypothalamus is also closely integrated with higher control systems located in the limbic system and in the neocortex.

In addition to regulating specific motivated behaviors, the hypothalamus and the cerebral cortex are involved in the maintenance of arousal—the general state of awareness that affects many behaviors simultaneously. The level of arousal varies from states of excitement on the one hand to drowsiness, sleep, and coma on the other. Because the electrical activity of the cortex provides an index of different levels of wakefulness, studies of arousal and sleep are leading to insights into the collective behavior of neurons. The electrical activity of the cortex also is important diagnostically for analyzing abnormalities of consciousness, particularly those due to epilepsy.

Irving Kupfermann

Hypothalamus and Limbic System I: Peptidergic Neurons, Homeostasis, and Emotional Behavior

37

In 1878 Claude Bernard, then professor at the Collège de France, first pointed out that human beings and other higher animals live in two environments:

a *milieu extérieur* in which the organism is situated, and a *milieu intérieur* in which the tissue element lives. The living organism does not really exist in the *milieu extérieur*—the atmosphere it breathes, salt or fresh water if that is its element—but in the liquid *milieu intérieur* formed by the circulatory organic liquid which surrounds and bathes all the tissue elements; this is the lymph and the plasma. . . . The *milieu intérieur* surrounding the organs, the tissue and their element never varies. . . . Here we have an organism which has enclosed itself in a kind of hot house. The peripheral changes of external conditions cannot reach it; it is not subject to them, but is free and independent. . . . All the vital mechanisms, however varied they may be, have only one object, that of preserving constant the conditions of life in the internal environment.

The vital mechanisms referred to by Bernard are centered in the hypothalamus and limbic system. Moreover, as Walter B. Cannon later pointed out, the mechanisms within the hypothalamus ensure not so much constancy but, rather, limited variability. The process by which this limited variability is achieved Cannon called *homeostasis*. The hypothalamus is so important because it is critically responsible for the homeostatic mechanisms that provide, to paraphrase Bernard, the necessary conditions for free and independent life.

The hypothalamus constitutes less than 1% of the total volume of the brain, yet it contains a large number of neuronal circuits concerned with vital functions. These circuits control the regulation of temperature, heart rate, blood pressure, blood osmolarity, and water and food intake. The hypothalamus and related structures in the limbic system are not the only structures in the brain involved in homeostasis. These structures, however, participate in the regulation of homeostasis by receiving information directly from the internal environment and by operating directly on the internal environment. This contrasts with other parts of the brain that regulate the internal environment largely indirectly through action on the external environment. These alternative means of regulating the internal environment often function in parallel. If a room is cold, one can maintain a constant body temperature by peripheral vasoconstriction, a primarily hypothalamic mechanism involving actions on the internal environment. In addition, one can utilize primarily thalamic and cortical mechanisms to operate on

the external environment, by, for example, closing the window or writing a note to the superintendent asking for more heat.

The hypothalamus exerts its influence on both the internal and external environments through three major systems: the endocrine system, the autonomic nervous system, and an ill-defined neural system concerned with motivation and drive. In this chapter we shall briefly examine the anatomy of the hypothalamus and limbic system and then consider how these structures regulate homeostasis, with an emphasis on endocrine and autonomic control. The next chapter will focus on the behavioral mechanisms of homeostatic regulation. In addition to homeostatic function, hypothalamic and limbic structures are important in the regulation of emotional behavior and sexual behavior. In this chapter we shall consider certain aspects of the neural control of emotions; Chapter 44 will deal with sexual behavior.

The Anatomy of the Limbic System and Hypothalamus Is Highly Complex

The hypothalamus is extensively interconnected with a ring of cortical structures that is part of the limbic system. This area is often referred to as the *visceral brain* because, in conjunction with the hypothalamus, it is concerned with the maintenance of basic autonomic and homeostatic function. An understanding of the anatomy of the hypothalamus can be facilitated by first considering the structure and interconnections of the components of the limbic system.

Higher Cortical Centers Communicate with the Hypothalamus via the Limbic System

The concept of the limbic system derives from the idea of a *limbic lobe*, a term introduced by Paul Broca to characterize the phylogenetically primitive cortical gyri that form a ring (Latin *limbus*, border) around the brain stem (Figure 37–1A). The limbic lobe includes the parahippocampal gyrus, the cingulate gyrus, and the subcallosal gyrus, which is the anterior and inferior continuation of the cingulate gyrus. It also includes the underlying cortex of the hippocampal formation, which is morphologically even more primitive. The hippocampal formation includes the hippocampus proper, the dentate gyrus, and the subiculum.

In 1937 James Papez, at Cornell University Medical School, suggested that the limbic lobe

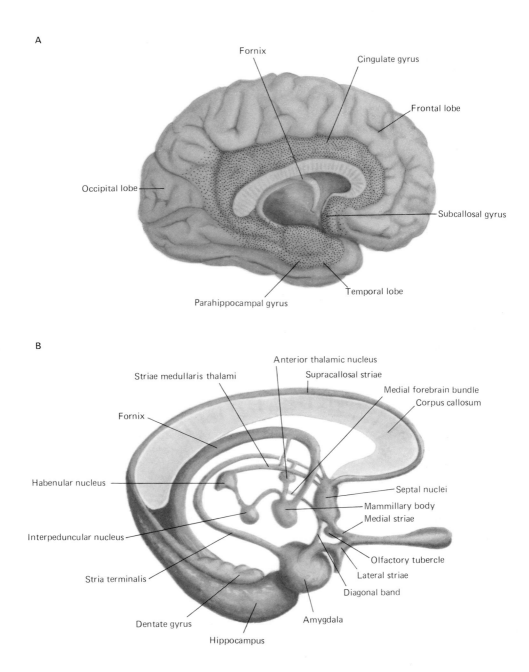

37−1 Limbic system structures. **A.** Medial view of the brain, showing the limbic lobe, which consists of primitive cortical tissue (indicated by dots) that encircles the upper brain stem. Also included in the limbic lobe are the underlying cortical structures (hippocampus and dentate gyrus). **B.** View of deep-lying interconnected structures that are included as part of the limbic system together with the structures of the limbic lobe.

formed a neural circuit that provided the anatomical substratum for emotions (Figure 37–2). He was influenced by experiments that suggested that the hypothalamus had a critical role in the expression of emotion. (We shall consider these findings later in the chapter.) Papez tried to answer the following question: How do higher cortical centers communicate with the hypothalamus? A cortical connection must exist, Papez argued, since emotions reach consciousness; likewise, thought (and other higher cognitive

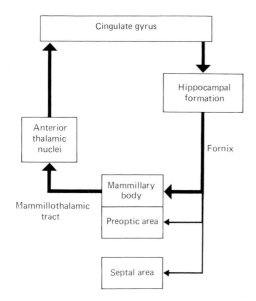

37–2 Modified version of neural circuit proposed by Papez **(thick arrows).** Known projections of the fornix to the septal area and hypothalamic regions (mammillary bodies and preoptic anterior hypothalamic area) are also indicated **(fine arrows).** The septal area of animals probably corresponds to a region near the anterior commissure of the human brain and is not related to the septum pellucidum.

functions) affects emotions. Papez therefore suggested that cortical influences were funneled to the hypothalamus via the cingulate gyrus to the hippocampal formation. The hippocampal formation processed this information and projected it, by way of the fornix, to the mammillary bodies of the hypothalamus (Figures 37–1 and 37–2). The hypothalamus in turn provided information to the cingulate gyrus by a pathway from the mammillary bodies to the anterior thalamic nuclei (via the mammillothalamic tract) and from the anterior thalamic nuclei to the cingulate gyrus (Figures 37–1 and 37–2).

In the same year that Papez outlined this circuit, Heinrich Klüver and Paul Bucy at the University of Chicago reported their extraordinary finding (which we shall also consider later) that bilateral destruction of the temporal lobe, a lobe which includes a number of limbic structures, produced dramatic changes in the emotional behavior of the monkey. The papers by Papez and by Klüver and Bucy provided the background for many of the subsequent theoretical and experimental approaches to the neurobiology of emotions.

The concept of the limbic system was ex-

panded subsequently to include other structures functionally and anatomically related to those outlined by Papez—regions of the hypothalamus, the septal area, the nucleus accumbens (a part of the caudate nucleus), and, finally, neocortical areas such as the orbitofrontal cortex. Also included in the limbic system is the amygdala, a subcortical structure located at the dorsomedial tip of the temporal lobe, and continuous with the uncus of the parahippocampal gyrus.

The *amygdala* is composed of numerous nuclei that are reciprocally connected to the hypothalamus, hippocampal formation, and thalamus. The amygdala gives rise to two major efferent projections. One projection, the *stria terminalis*, innervates the bed nucleus of the stria terminalis, the septal area, the nucleus accumbens, and the hypothalamus. The second efferent projection is the *ventral amygdalofugal pathway*; this pathway provides input to the hypothalamus, dorsomedial nucleus of the thalamus, and rostral cingulate gyrus. The amygdala in turn receives an important afferent input from the olfactory system and lesser inputs from other afferent systems. Despite extensive olfactory input, the amygdala is not essential for olfactory discrimination. Lesions and stimulation of the amygdala have produced effects similar to those found for the lateral or medial regions of the hypothalamus; these effects (as we shall see below and in the following chapter) include alterations of autonomic responses, emotional behavior, and feeding.

Modern anatomical studies have greatly expanded our knowledge of the connections of the limbic system and have demonstrated extensive and direct connections between the hippocampal formation and neocortical areas. The input connections of the hippocampus arise by way of the entorhinal cortex and the fornix. The entorhinal cortex receives input from areas of the association cortex and thereby provides a neocortical–limbic link. Some of the fibers from the entorhinal cortex on the way to the hippocampus (the *perforant path*) pass through the *subiculum*, a gray matter structure that is interposed between the primitive cortex of the hippocampus proper and the neocortical tissue of the temporal cortex. The subiculum receives a major output from the hippocampus and has extensive reciprocal connections with many areas of the brain, including several areas of the neocortex. It is of interest that the relative size of the subiculum increases in phylogeny and is greatest in humans. The subiculum is now known to be the origin of those fibers in the fornix that innervate the hypothalamus. The fornix also contains axons of hippocampal pyramidal cells that innervate non-hypothalamic structures.

The Structure of the Hypothalamus Reflects Its Diverse Functions

One of the prime functions of the hypothalamus, its control of the pituitary gland, can be inferred by its position dorsal to the pituitary, to which it

is attached by a stalk called the *infundibulum* (Figure 37–3). The posterior extent of the hypothalamus is delimited by the mammillary bodies. The anterior extent is delimited by the

37–3 Location and structure of the hypothalamus. **A.** Lateral view showing the relationship of the hypothalamus to the pituitary. **B.** Lateral view showing the positions of the main hypothalamic nuclear groups. (Adapted from Krieger and Hughes, 1980.)

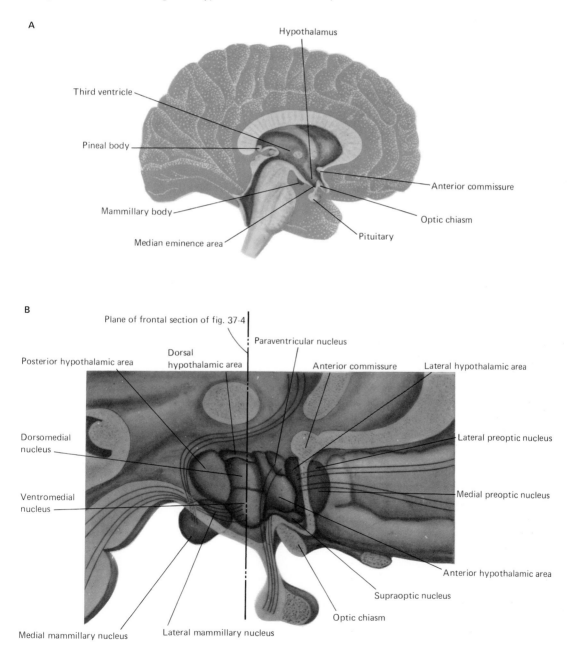

A

Hypothalamus

Third ventricle

Pineal body

Anterior commissure

Mammillary body

Optic chiasm

Median eminence area

Pituitary

B

Plane of frontal section of fig. 37-4

Paraventricular nucleus

Posterior hypothalamic area

Dorsal hypothalamic area

Anterior commissure

Lateral hypothalamic area

Dorsomedial nucleus

Lateral preoptic nucleus

Ventromedial nucleus

Medial preoptic nucleus

Anterior hypothalamic area

Supraoptic nucleus

Optic chiasm

Medial mammillary nucleus

Lateral mammillary nucleus

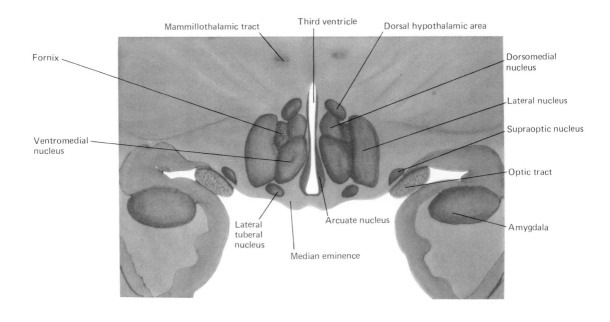

37–4 Frontal view of the hypothalamus (section along plane shown in Figure 37–3). (Adapted from Krieger and Hughes, 1980).

optic chiasm, preoptic area, and lamina terminalis.

The hypothalamus can be divided grossly into medial and lateral regions, separated by the descending columns of the fornix (Figure 37–4). The *medial region* contains most of the nuclear groups of the hypothalamus, including the well-delineated supraoptic and paraventricular nuclei, the ventromedial nucleus, and the suprachiasmatic nucleus. Immediately bordering the third ventricle, in a zone termed the *periventricular region,* is the periventricular nucleus and the arcuate nucleus. *The lateral region* of the hypothalamus contains some cell bodies but has extensive short-fiber, multisynaptic ascending and descending pathways. A major multifiber system in the lateral hypothalamus is the medial forebrain bundle. The medial basal region of the hypothalamus contains neurons that secrete peptide hormones that act as releasing factors (discussed later). In primates this region contains the characteristic tuberal nucleus as well as the arcuate nucleus and other nuclei found in lower animals.

Most fiber systems of the hypothalamus are bidirectional. One exception is the *hypothalamohypophysial tract,* which contains the axons of the paraventricular and supraoptic neurons, which terminate primarily in the posterior pituitary. The hypothalamus also receives one-way afferent connections directly from the retina. These fibers terminate primarily in the suprachiasmatic nucleus.

Projections to and from areas caudal to the hypothalamus are carried in the medial forebrain bundle, the mammillotegmental tract, and the dorsal longitudinal fasciculus. Fibers of the medial forebrain bundle pass through the lateral hypothalamus and continue rostrally to forebrain structures. Many aminergic neurons originating in the caudal brain stem course to neocortical regions via fibers in the medial forebrain bundle and its rostral continuation in the cingulum bundle. Other rostral structures are interconnected to the hypothalamus by means of the mammillothalamic tract, fornix, and stria terminalis (three tracts we have considered earlier in relation to the limbic system).

The Hypothalamus Contains Various Classes of Peptidergic Neuroendocrine Cells

A major principle to emerge from the study of the hypothalamus is that several cell groups in this region secrete peptides. Some peptides are released into the local or systemic circulation and serve as hormones acting on specific receptors located on distant cells. Others are released into a synaptic cleft and act in a manner analogous to transmitter substances. The actions of neuroactive peptides, no matter where they are released, tend to be enduring and to serve a so-called modulating function, controlling neuron excitability and synaptic effectiveness (see Chapter 10). These long-lasting actions are thought to be important for a variety of behavioral functions including the modulation of mood, motivational state, and learning.

Recent evidence indicates that many of the peptidergic neurons of the hypothalamus that project to other regions of the nervous system innervate, in particular, structures of the limbic system and structures related to the autonomic nervous system. For example, the paraventricular nucleus, in addition to its classical peptidergic projections to the posterior pituitary, sends oxytocin- or vasopressin-containing axons to the amygdala, locus ceruleus, parabrachial nucleus, vagosolitary complex of nuclei, and intermediolateral cell column of the spinal cord. In addition, neurons in the arcuate nucleus containing adrenocorticotropic hormone (ACTH), β-endorphin, and related peptides project to the thalamus, periaqueductal gray, limbic structures (nucleus accumbens, bed nucleus of the stria terminalis, and amygdala), and the major catecholamine-containing nuclei of the brain. The function of the extrahypothalamic peptidergic projections is largely unknown (see later section on the brain as a target organ of hormone action).

The Hypothalamus Controls Endocrine Function by Means of Peptidergic Neurons

One of the main functions of the hypothalamus is the control of the endocrine system. This is accomplished in two ways: (1) directly, by secretion of neuroendocrine products into the general circulation via the vasculature of the posterior pituitary (neural lobe or neurohypophysis), and (2) indirectly, by secretion of releasing hormones into the local portal plexus (within the median eminence), which drains into the blood vessels of the anterior pituitary (adenohypophysis).

The current understanding of the hypothalamus derives from the analysis of these two types of control by Ernest Scharrer at Western Reserve University, and by Geoffrey Harris at the Maudsley Hospital in London. Scharrer developed the concept of *neurosecretion*, the idea that certain neurons serve a dual role: as nerve cells that receive and transmit electrical information, and as

endocrine cells that release their secretory products into the blood stream (Figure 37–5). They function as "neuroendocrin transducers" to convert neural information into hormonal information. Harris recognized the importance of the blood supply that connects the pituitary to the hypothalamus (the pituitary–hypophysial–portal system) and showed that this vascular link carries hormonal information from the hypothalamus to the pituitary (Figure 37–6). These concepts form the basis of modern neuroendocrinology and of our current understanding of the hypothalamic control of endocrine activity.

The two types of endocrine control (direct and indirect) are mediated by two classes of peptidergic neuroendocrine cells. In both classes of neurons the various neurohormones or precursor peptides are synthesized in the cell bodies and packaged in neurosecretory vesicles that are transported rapidly down axons to axon terminals, where they are stored for secretion when the neuron is stimulated. The *magnocellular* (large) neuroendocrine neurons are located in the paraventricular and supraoptic nuclei, and release their secretion (the neurohypophysial hormones, oxytocin and vasopressin) into the general circulation by way of the posterior pituitary. The *parvicellular* (small) neurosecretory neurons are located in many different hypothalamic nuclei, particularly the medial basal portion of the hypothalamus, including the periventricular zone, the arcuate nucleus, and part of the ventromedial nucleus. The parvicellular neurons release their secretions into the portal vasculature to stimulate the anterior pituitary. The capillaries of the posterior pituitary and median eminence are highly fenestrated, facilitating the entry of the released magnocellular hormones into the general circulation (via the posterior pituitary) or of parvicellular hormones into the portal plexus (from the median eminence). Each of these two regions, composed of neurosecretory terminals and specialized capillaries, is called a *neurohemal organ*.

Magnocellular Neurons Release Oxytocin and Vasopressin

In 1950 Vincent DuVigneaud determined the amino acid structure of oxytocin and 4 years later he worked out that of vasopressin, thereby proving that the brain has peptides that can exert hormonal action. Vasopressin and oxytocin contain eight amino acids each (Table 37–1). As with most polypeptide hormones, both vasopressin

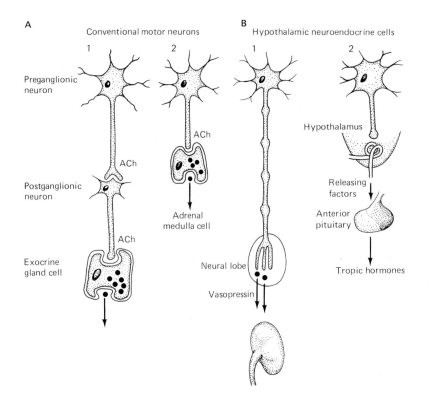

37–5 Comparison of the actions of conventional motor neurons and hypothalamic neuroendocrine cells. **A.** Conventional motor neurons. *1:* Exocrine glands are innervated by postganglionic neurons that stimulate secretion through direct action of acetylcholine (**ACh**) on membrane receptors. *2:* The adrenal medulla is innervated by preganglionic sympathetic neurons of the nervous system that end on cell receptors. **B.** Hypothalamic neuroendocrine cells. *1:* In the neurohypophysial system, the secretions (vasopressin or oxytocin) are formed in the cell body of the neuron, and transported by axoplasmic flow to the nerve terminals in the neural lobe of the pituitary. Activity of the neuron leads to the release of the hormone into the general circulation. *2:* In the adenohypophysial system, the secretions (hormone-releasing factors) are also formed in the cell body of the neuron and are transported by axoplasmic flow to nerve terminals in the median eminence (and in some species, the pituitary stalk). Activity of these neurons leads to secretion of the releasing factors into the hypophysial–portal circulation, and the release of hormones from the anterior pituitary. (Adapted from Reichlin, 1978.)

and oxytocin are cleaved from larger prohormones. The prohormones are synthesized in the cell bodies of the magnocellular neurons, and cleavage occurs within vesicles during transport along the axons of the neurons. Neurophysin is produced as a cleavage product in both vasopressin and oxytocin neurons; however, the neurophysin formed in one type of neuron differs somewhat from that produced in the other. Each neurophysin is released along with its hormone at terminals in the posterior pituitary.

Parvicellular Neurons Release Inhibiting and Releasing Hormones

The discovery of the structure of oxytocin and vasopressin and the work of Geoffrey Harris on the neural control of the anterior pituitary gland stimulated Roger Guillemin and Andrew Schally and their colleagues to isolate and characterize the structure of the hormones that regulate the anterior pituitary. After 12 years of intense work on several tons of hypothalamic fragments, the laboratories of Guillemin and Schally independently characterized the structure of thyrotropin-releasing hormone (TRH) (Figure 37–7). In

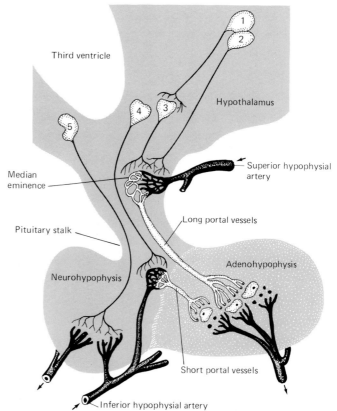

37–6 The functional elements of control of the pituitary by the hypothalamus. Peptidergic neurons that produce oxytocin or vasopressin *(5)* release their secretions into the general circulation via the posterior pituitary. Two general types of neurons are involved in anterior pituitary regulation. The peptidergic neurons *(3 and 4)* form the releasing hormones that enter the capillary plexus of the hypophysial–portal vessels. The second type of neuron is the link between the rest of the brain and the peptidergic neuron. These neurons, some of which are monoaminergic, are believed to end on the cell body of the peptidergic neuron in a conventional manner *(1)*, or to end on the axon terminal of the peptidergic neuron *(2)* by means of axo-axonic synapses. (Adapted from Reichlin, 1978; Gay, 1972.)

Third ventricle

Hypothalamus

Median eminence

Superior hypophysial artery

Long portal vessels

Pituitary stalk

Neurohypophysis

Adenohypophysis

Short portal vessels

Inferior hypophysial artery

1971 Schally characterized luteinizing hormone–releasing hormone, and in 1973 Guillemin characterized somatostatin (Figure 37–7).

It is now clear that most anterior pituitary hormones are controlled by peptide neurohormones or factors (a *factor* is a chemically uncharacterized hormone) synthesized by parvicellular neurons that release their product into the capillaries of the median eminence. The release of most of the hormones of the anterior pituitary is

regulated by both enhancing and inhibiting substances. For example, growth hormone is inhibited by somatostatin and stimulated by growth hormone–releasing factor (GHRF). There is evidence that at least one inhibiting hormone is not a peptide, i.e., dopamine, which inhibits the release of prolactin. In many instances, a single releasing hormone affects more than one pituitary hormone. All the hypothalamic releasing and inhibiting hormones are listed in Table 37–2 along

Table 37–1. Neurohypophysial Hormones

Name	Structure	Function
Vasopressin	$\overset{\displaystyle NH_2}{\underset{\rule{3em}{0pt}}{\underset{\text{S-S}}{\mid}}}$ Cys-Tyr-Phe-Glu-Arg-Cys-Pro-Arg-Gly-NH$_2$	Stimulates water resorption by the kidney
Oxytocin	NH$_2$ Cys-Tyr-Ile-Glu-Arg-Cys-Pro-Leu-Gly-NH$_2$ S-S	Stimulates uterine contraction and milk ejection

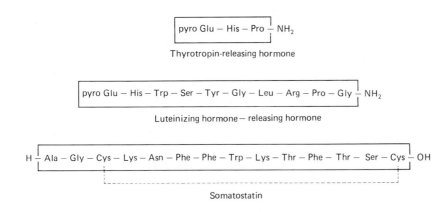

37–7 Structures of the known parvicellular hypothalamic hormones.

with their most common abbreviations and the anterior pituitary hormones they affect. The releasing hormones are not the only peptides of neurobiological interest found in neurons of the hypothalamus; the morphinelike peptides, β-endorphin and the enkephalins (see Chapter 18), are also found here, as are angiotensin II, substance P, neurotensin, and several other peptides.

Systematic electrical recordings from identified groups of neurons secreting releasing factors have not been made, but there is reason to believe that, as with magnocellular neurons, many of the parvicellular neurons discharge in bursts. This inference is based on the observation that hor-

monal secretion is typically pulsatile: blood concentrations of hormones show periodic surges throughout the day. This pattern is seen even for hormones, such as growth hormone, that regulate nonepisodic physiological functions. Episodic release may have evolved because the continuous exposure of a receptor in a cell membrane to its hormone often leads to inactivation of the receptor (down regulation). Down regulation occurs much more slowly in the case of periodic exposure.

Hypothalamic Neurons Participate in Four Classes of Reflexes

The hypothalamus has both neural and humoral outputs. Since humoral as well as neural factors affect hypothalamic function, the hypothalamus

Table 37–2. Hypothalamic Substances That Release or Inhibit the Release of Anterior Pituitary Hormones

Hypothalamic substance*	Anterior pituitary hormone
RELEASING	
Thyrotropin (TSH)-releasing hormone (TRH)	TSH, prolactin
Corticotropin-releasing factors (CRFs)	Adrenocorticotropin
Luteinizing hormone (LH)/follicle-stimulating hormone (FSH)–releasing hormone (LH/FSH-RH, LRH, or GnRH)	LH, FSH
Growth hormone (GH–releasing factor (GHRF or GRF)	GH
Prolactin-releasing factor (PRF)	Prolactin
Melanocyte-stimulating hormone (MSH)–releasing factor (MRF)	MSH
INHIBITING	
Prolactin release–inhibiting hormone (PIH; dopamine)	Prolactin
Growth hormone release–inhibiting hormone (GIH or GHRIH; somatostatin)	GH, TSH
Melanocyte-stimulating hormone release–inhibiting factor (MIF)	MSH

*Hypothalamic substances with known structures are termed *hormones*; chemically uncharacterized hormones are called *factors*.

also has both humoral and neural inputs. The hypothalamus can therefore participate in four classes of reflexes: (1) conventional reflexes involving neural input and neural output; (2) reflexes in which the input to the hypothalamus is neural and the output is humoral; (3) reflexes in which the input is humoral and the output is neural; and (4) reflexes in which both the input and output are humoral. In this and the next two sections we shall consider simple examples of these four types of reflexes, but any normal physiological function typically involves more than one of these hypothalamic reflex modes.

Milk Ejection and Uterine Contraction Are Regulated by a Neural Input and a Humoral Output

The paraventricular and supraoptic nuclei contain neurons that release oxytocin, which induces contraction of the myoepithelial cells of the mammary gland. Oxytocin also increases the amplitude of uterine smooth muscle contraction (only if the muscle is appropriately primed by estrogens). This action of the hormone facilitates expulsion of the baby during delivery. In 1964 Eric Kandel, then at Harvard Medical School, recorded intracellularly from oxytocin-releasing magnocellular neurons in the goldfish and found them to resemble conventional neurons in many respects. They have resting potentials, fire action potentials, and receive excitatory and inhibitory synaptic input. Electrical stimulation of the posterior pituitary results in antidromic action potentials in many of these neurons, demonstrating that they send axons to the posterior pituitary.

Cross and Green, in 1959, and Brooks and co-workers, in 1966, were the first to record from mammalian neurons in the supraoptic and paraventricular nuclei while animals were exposed to various sensory stimuli. In 1974 Lincoln and Wakerley succeeded in recording from identified neuroendocrine cells in the female rat while the rat was presented with a natural stimulus for oxytocin release—suckling of rat pups. Milk ejection was simultaneously measured by recording intramammary pressure. It was found that a continuous suckling stimulus produced periodic bursts of action potentials in many of the identified neuroendocrine cells. Approximately 13 sec after the burst, there was an increase in intramammary pressure, indicating the arrival of a pulse of oxytocin to the mammary glands (Figure 37–8). Thus, the oxytocin cells participate in a relatively simple reflex in which the afferent limb is neural and the efferent limb is humoral. As appears to be true for all the hypothalamic neurosecretory products, the release of oxytocin can be affected by higher brain structures. For example, in a lactating mother, the sight or sound of her child may trigger milk ejection. Presumably, excitatory cortical influences project to oxytocin-containing cells in the hypothalamus. Since anxiety and worry can inhibit the milk ejection reflex, inhibitory cortical influences may also affect these cells.

Urine Flow Is Regulated by a Humoral Input and a Humoral Output

The paraventricular and supraoptic nuclei also contain neurons that release the hormone arginine vasopressin (also called antidiuretic hormone, ADH). Vasopressin acts on the membrane permeability of the collecting ducts of the kidneys and convoluted tubules to increase their permeability to water, facilitating its recovery after filtration. This action results in a decrease of urinary volume and functions to conserve body water.

The neurons that release vasopressin exhibit spontaneous activity, consistent with the notion that there is a normal concentration of vasopressin in the blood that is decreased or increased according to physiological demand. Thus, in contrast to the neurons that release oxytocin, which tend to be triggered in an all-or-none fashion, vasopressin-releasing neurons show more graded responses. The functioning of the vasopressin system is therefore analogous to that of graded neural reflexes and the oxytocin system to that of fixed action pattern responses (to be considered in Chapter 46).

The firing of vasopressin-containing neurons and vasopressin secretion is enhanced by an increase in plasma osmolarity. Considerable evidence indicates that the afferent limb of the vasopressin response is mediated by osmotic (humoral) inputs directly to the hypothalamus. This hypothesis, first suggested by Verney in 1947, is strongly supported by the observation made by Sundsten and Sawyer in 1961 that animals can regulate vasopressin release even when the hypothalamus is disconnected from all structures except the pituitary. It has not been determined whether the vasopressin-producing cells respond directly to osmotic stimuli or whether the hypothalamus contains a separate group of

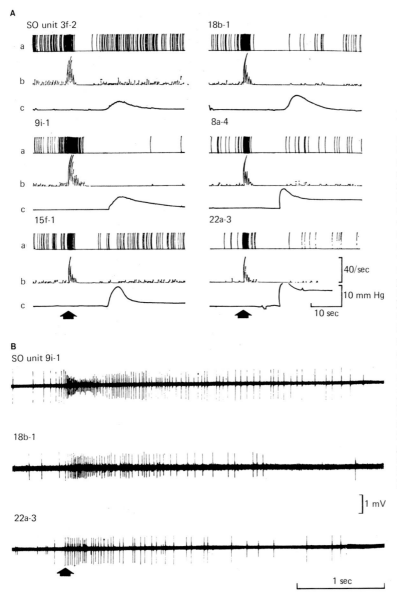

37–8 Recordings from oxytocin-releasing neuroendocrine cells in the female rat during suckling of pups illustrate the correlation of spike activity with milk ejection. **Arrows,** onset of neurosecretory response. **A.** Polygraph records of six responsive supraoptic neurons. Approximately 40 sec of spike activity, spanning one milk ejection, is shown for each unit. **Trace a,** unit activity in which each vertical deflection corresponds to a single action potential; **trace b,** an integration of the unit recording in which the height of the trace is proportional to frequency; **trace c,** recording of intramammary pressure. Note the difference in the background activity of the six units, the dramatic and stereotyped acceleration in spike activity about 13 sec before milk ejection, the peak rates of spike discharge (30–50 spikes/sec), the duration of the response, and the period of after-inhibition. **B.** Photographs on a greatly expanded time scale of the spike trains in three of the units illustrated in part A. (Adapted from Lincoln and Wakerley, 1974.)

osmoreceptive neurons, but there is some evidence for the second possibility. In 1976 Hatton found that there are neurons in the nucleus circularis (which is located between the supraoptic and paraventricular nuclei) that undergo morphological changes when the animal is dehydrated. Electrical stimulation of this region also produces a substantial release of vasopressin.

Other humorally mediated stimuli directly or indirectly affect vasopressin release. For example, anesthetic agents increase the release of vaso-

pressin, and ethanol decreases its release. The release of vasopressin is also controlled by neural inputs from blood volume receptors in blood vessels: decreased blood volume enhances vasopressin release, and increased blood volume inhibits vasopressin release. Afferent input probably also comes from temperature receptors in the skin: cold inhibits the release of vasopressin, while warmth enhances its release.

Some vasopressin-releasing cells send their axons to the external zone of the median eminence to terminate on the primary portal plexus, and in 1973 Zimmerman and colleagues at Columbia University showed that the portal blood contains high concentrations of vasopressin. These neurons function like parvicellular neuroendocrine cells and control the anterior pituitary. In fact, vasopressin may serve as one of the releasing factors for adrenocorticotropin. Stress, pain, and anxiety, which increase vasopressin release, also increase the release of adrenocorticotropin.

The Brain Itself Is a Target for Hormone Action

Feedback Loops Involve a Humoral Input and a Humoral Output

In every instance studied, the releasing hormones are found not only in the median eminence, but also in other regions of the brain, where their release presumably affects neural systems that control various behavioral functions. Releasing factors are particularly prominent in the limbic system. Neurons in limbic as well as hypothalamic structures also possess receptors that bind a variety of hormones. These receptors provide the substrate for *long feedback loops* in which the hormones of the target organ (product) can modulate their production by inhibitory effects on the brain (as well as on the anterior pituitary directly). There is also some evidence that pituitary hormones can have feedback effects *(short feedback loops)* on the brain in order to modulate their release. These effects are examples of reflexes in which both input and output are humoral.

Central Effects of Hormones on Behavior Involve a Humoral Input and a Neural Output

Because the individual neurons of various systems possess specific receptors, the action of circulating hormones can be quite precise and specific. Thus, a given hormone will activate or inhibit only a restricted population of neurons. Hormonal effects on these nerve cells (sometimes referred to as *modulatory effects*) are too slow to transmit complex information, but they are ideally suited to long-term regulation of excitability or synaptic effectiveness. These hormonal actions are thought to be involved in modifying mood and behavioral states, or in providing a trigger signal for the generation of a complex motor pattern in which the details are dependent upon conventional transmitter actions.

Releasing factors may modulate behavior by actions on the brain independent of their effects on the release of pituitary hormones. For example, Moss and McCann, and, independently, Pfaff, have found that subcutaneous injection of luteinizing hormone–releasing hormone into estrogen-treated female rats increases mating behavior as measured by the display of a stereotyped female sex behavior (lordosis). Similar effects are obtained after injection of luteinizing hormone–releasing hormone into the medial preoptic area and arcuate nucleus of the hypothalamus. The action of this releasing hormone does not appear to be mediated by an effect on the ovaries, since the effect is not abolished by hypophysectomy or ovariectomy as long as estrogen is provided. Similarly, in humans, systemic injection of thyrotropin-releasing hormone is sometimes followed by mood elevation, an effect that does not appear to be related to the degree of stimulation of the thyroid gland, as measured by the release of thyroxine. This finding suggests that the thyrotropin-releasing hormone may be acting directly on the central nervous system.

Hormones May Be Important For Learning

In lower animals, adrenocorticotropin (and melanocyte-stimulating hormone, which has peptide sequences in common with adrenocorticotropin) as well as vasopressin has been shown by deWied and others to facilitate the learning of tasks involving stress or aversive stimuli. These actions of adrenocorticotropin are not mediated by the adrenal glands, since it has been shown that the effects are still obtained in adrenalectomized animals. Furthermore, fragments of the adrenocorticotropin molecule with no corticotropic activity are also effective. The amino acid sequence of the fourth through seventh positions of adrenocorticotropin is sufficient to produce the behavioral effects on learning (Figure 37–9A). Similarly, analogues of vasopressin that have no antidiuretic properties are effective in facilitating memory (Figure 37–9B).

Evidence that hormones or peptides may regulate a variety of behavioral processes suggests an exciting new pharmacological approach to the effective treatment of behavioral disorders.

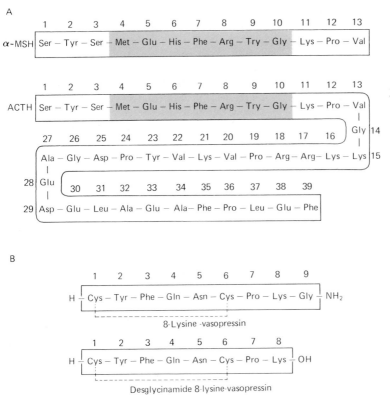

37–9 Fragments of certain peptide hormones affect memory retention although they lack the endocrine effects of the whole molecule. **A.** Amino acid sequences of complete α melanocyte-stimulating hormone (α-MSH) and adrenocorticotropic hormone (ACTH). **Shaded area,** peptide sequences 4–10 in α-MSH and in ACTH, which have been found to restore deficient learning behavior in hypophysectomized rats. **B.** Amino acid sequence of complete vasopressin molecule and the fragment desglycinamide-8-lysine vasopressin, which has been found to have a positive effect on memory retention.

The Hypothalamus Helps Regulate the Autonomic Nervous System

Although the hypothalamus has important hormonal inputs and outputs, it also mediates conventional reflexes involving simple neural inputs and outputs. The hypothalamus functions in this manner in its role as the so-called head ganglion of the autonomic nervous system. Much of what we know about the autonomic function of the hypothalamus stems from a long series of experiments started in the early 1930s by S. W. Ranson at Northwestern University and W. R. Hess in Switzerland. Ranson took advantage of the stereotaxic method developed by Horsley and Clarke in England, which permitted the precise and reproducible placement of electrodes in the deep structures of the brains of experimental animals by means of a triple-coordinate system that located each subcortical nucleus uniquely according to its position in the brain. (This technique was subsequently refined to allow neurosurgical approaches to lesions located below the cortex.) Previous attempts to stimulate the hypothalamus had utilized drastic surgical procedures to visualize the appropriate structures. Using the stereotaxic technique, Ranson systematically stimulated different regions of the hypothalamus and produced at various points in the hypothalamus almost every conceivable autonomic reaction, including alterations in heart rate, blood pressure, gastrointestinal motility, piloerection, and bladder contraction. The most prominent responses involved the sympathetic nervous system, and these effects tended to occur with stimulation of the lateral and posterior hypothalamus.

Most of Ranson's experiments were done on anesthetized animals. Hess extended Ranson's method by implanting electrodes and permanently fixing them to the skull of the animal. By attaching a long flexible cable to the implanted electrode he could observe the effects of brain stimulation in awake and completely unrestrained animals. In a brilliant series of investigations that ultimately earned him the Nobel Prize in 1949, Hess found that autonomic responses evoked by hypothalamic stimulation did not occur in isolation but in characteristic constellations that gave the appearance of being organized behaviors. For example, electrical stimulation of the lateral hypothalamus in cats elicited autonomic and somatic responses characteristic of anger: increased blood pressure, raising of the body hair, pupillary constriction, arching of the back, and raising of the tail. These observations indicated that the hypothalamus is not simply a motor nucleus for the autonomic nervous system: it is a coordinating center that integrates various inputs to ensure a well-organized, coherent, and appropriate set of autonomic and somatic responses.

The Hypothalamus Is Involved in Emotional Behavior

The evidence provided by Ranson, Hess, and others that stimulation of the hypothalamus produces autonomic, endocrine, and motor effects that resemble those seen during various types of emotional behaviors suggests that the hypothalamus integrates and coordinates the behavioral expression of emotional states. This idea is supported by lesion studies that indicate that different hypothalamic structures can be associated with a wide range of emotional states. Whereas stimulation of the lateral hypothalamus elicits anger, lesions of the lateral hypothalamus result in placidity. However, lesions of the medial hypothalamus result in animals that are highly excitable and are easily triggered into aggressive responses.

A similarly irritable animal is also produced by decortication. The responses seen in decorticated animals include lashing of the tail, vigorous arching of the back, jerking of the limbs, clawing, attempts to bite, and autonomic responses such as erection of the tail hairs, sweating (of the toe pads), micturition, defecation, and increased blood pressure. There is an increase in epinephrine and corticosteroid secretion into the blood. In 1925 Cannon and Britton termed this constellation of responses *sham rage* because it appeared to lack elements of conscious experience that are characteristic of naturally occurring rage. Sham rage reactions also differed from genuine rage in that the anger could occur spontaneously or could be triggered by very mild tactile and other stimuli. Even when elicited by strong stimuli, the sham rage response subsided very quickly when the stimulus was removed. Finally, the aggressive responses were undirected, and the animal sometimes bit itself. In 1928 Bard further analyzed sham rage by means of progressive transections down the neuraxis. He found that sham rage disappeared when the hypothalamus was included in the ablation (Figure 37–10). Nevertheless, a fragmented expression of emotional responses could still be obtained in animals in which the hypothalamus and all rostral forebrain structures had been removed. These responses (first described by Woodworth and Sherrington in 1904, who called them *pseudoaffective reflexes*), however, were much less coordinated than those seen with the hypothalamus left intact and required very strong stimuli to be elicited.

37–10 Brain transections used to study sham rage. Sagittal section of the cat brain. Transection of the forebrain at level **a** produces an animal that exhibits sham rage. Transection at the level of the hypothalamus (level **b**) also produces sham rage unless the posterior hypothalamus is included (level **c**), in which case only isolated elements of a rage response can be elicited.

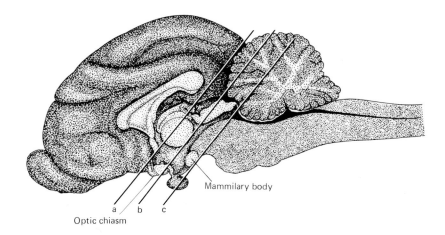

Mammilary body

Optic chiasm

a   b   c

Which forebrain structures account for the suppression of sham rage responses in normal animals? Bard and Mountcastle found that large portions of the neocortex could be removed without producing sham rage. Sham rage phenomena were seen when the lesion included structures of the limbic system (the cingulate cortex and amygdala).

In 1937, Klüver and Bucy reported that bilateral removal of the temporal lobe in the monkey—which included the amygdala and the hippocampal formation as well as the nonlimbic temporal cortex—produced a dramatic behavioral syndrome. The animals, formerly quite wild, became tame, showed a flattening of emotions, and exhibited remarkable oral tendencies (they put all manner of objects they encountered into their mouths). They also became hypersexual; i.e., they exhibited an enormous increase in sexual behavior, including mounting of inappropriate objects and species. Finally, the animals showed *hypermetamorphosis*—a compulsive tendency to take note of and react to every visual stimulus, while failing to recognize familiar objects. Some of the features of the Klüver-Bucy syndrome tend to be the opposite of those encountered in patients with temporal lobe epilepsy, who show decreased sexuality and heightened emotionality (see Chapter 1).

An attempt has been made to determine which structures account for the individual symptoms of the Klüver-Bucy syndrome. It appears that damage to the amygdala is particularly important in producing the oral tendencies, hypersexuality, and tameness; and damage to the visual association areas of the temporal cortex contributes to the visual deficits.

The current model of the neural basis of emotional behavior is not far from the ideas that Papez proposed more than 40 years ago. We think of the hypothalamus as functioning to integrate the motor and endocrine responses that produce appropriate emotional behavior. The forebrain suppresses emotional responses to trivial and inconsequential stimuli. Thus the forebrain connects the hypothalamus to the outer world in such a manner that appropriate autonomic and endocrine concomitants of emotions are expressed in response to external conditions. Forebrain structures also provide the neural mechanisms needed to effectively direct skeletomotor responses to external events, such that, for example, an object is appropriately approached or avoided. Finally,

the forebrain seems to be crucial for the conscious experience of emotions.

The interplay between the neural activity of the hypothalamus and the neural activity of higher centers results in an emotional experience to which we can attach words such as fear, anger, pleasure, and contentment. The behavior of patients in whom the prefrontal cortex (parts of which appear to be related to the limbic system) has been removed or who have lesions of the cingulate gyrus supports this concept. These patients are no longer bothered by chronic pain. They sometimes perceive pain and exhibit appropriate autonomic reactions, but the perception is no longer associated with a powerful emotional experience (see Chapters 18 and 48). Thus, noxious or pleasurable stimuli seem to have dual effects. These stimuli trigger a set of events that are integrated by the hypothalamus and result in an alteration of the internal state that prepares the organism for appropriate action (attack, flight, sexual experience, etc.). These autonomic reactions are relatively simple in execution and require no conscious control. However, in the execution of complex actions such as attack, the organism must interact with its external environment; forebrain mechanisms come into play in these interactions and modulate the behavioral repertoire much as proprioceptive sensory feedback from an uneven terrain modulates the central program for locomotion. Perhaps consciousness evolved as a result of the enormous complexity involved in dealing with the external environment. Compared to our internal environment, the external environment is far less predictable and provides a much richer variety of stimuli. Furthermore, in dealing with the external environment we often have the luxury of delaying our responses, thus permitting actions to be guided by images and plans.

Selected Readings and References

Brownstein, M. J., Russell, J. T., and Gainer, H. 1980. Synthesis, transport, and release of posterior pituitary hormones. Science (Wash., D.C.) 207:373–378.

Gellhorn, E. (ed.). 1968. Biological Foundations of Emotion: Research and Commentary. Glenview, Ill.: Scott, Foresman.

Guillemin, R. 1978. Control of adenohypophysial functions by peptides of the central nervous system. Harvey Lect. 71:71–131.

Hess, W. R. 1954. Diencephalon: Autonomic and Extra-pyramidal Functions. New York: Grune & Stratton.

Iversen, L. L. 1978. Neurobiology of peptides. Neurosci. Res. Program Bull. 16:209–370.

Meyerson, B. J. 1979. Hypothalamic hormones and be-haviour. Med. Biol. 57:69–83.

Mauk, M. D., Olson, G. A., Kastin, A. J., and Olson, R. D. 1980. Behavioral effects of LH-RH. Neurosci. Biobehav. Rev. 4:1–8.

Other References

Bard, P. 1928. A diencephalic mechanism for the expression of rage with special reference to the sympathetic nervous system. Am. J. Physiol. 84:490–515.

Bard, P., and Mountcastle, V. B. 1948. Some forebrain mechanisms involved in expression of rage with spe-cial reference to suppression of angry behavior. Res. Publ. Assoc. Res. Nerv. Ment. Dis. 27:362–404.

Bernard, C. 1878. Leçons sur les phénomènes de la vie communs aux animaux et aux végétaux. Paris: Baillière.

Brooks, C. McC., Ishikawa, T., Koizumi, K., and Lu, H-H. 1966. Activity of neurones in the paraventricular nucleus of the hypothalamus and its control. J. Physiol. (Lond.) 182:217–231.

Cannon, W. B., and Britton, S. W. 1925. Studies on the conditions of activity in endocrine glands. XV. Am. J. Physiol. 72:283–294.

Cross, B. A., and Green, J. D. 1959. Activity of single neurons in the hypothalamus: Effect of osmotic and other stimuli. J. Physiol. (Lond.) 148:554–569.

DeWied, D., and Gispen, W. H. 1977. Behavioral effects of peptides. In H. Gainer (ed.), Peptides in Neurobi-ology. New York: Plenum, pp. 397–448.

DuVigneaud, V. 1956. Hormones of the posterior pitu-itary gland: Oxytocin and vasopressin. Harvey Lect. 50:1–26.

Gay, V. L. 1972. The hypothalamus: Physiology and clinical use of releasing factors. Fertil. Steril. 23:50–63.

Harris, G. M. 1955. Neural Control of the Pituitary Gland. Monograph of The Physiology Society. Lon-don: E. Arnold.

Hatton, G. I. 1976. Nucleus circularis: Is it an osmore-ceptor in the brain? Brain Res. Bull. 1:123–131.

Kandel, E. R. 1964. Electrical properties of hypo-thalamic neuroendocrine cells. J. Gen. Physiol. 47:691–717.

Klüver, H. 1937. "Psychic blindness" and other symp-toms following bilateral temporal lobectomy in rhe-sus monkeys. Am. J. Physiol. 119:352–353.

Klüver, H., and Bucy, P. C. 1939. Preliminary analysis of functions of the temporal lobes in monkeys. Arch. Neurol. Psychiatry 42:979–1000.

Krieger, D. T., and Hughes, J. C. 1980. Neuroendocri-nology. Sunderland, Mass: Sinauer Associates.

Lincoln, D. W., and Wakerley, J. B. 1974. Electrophysi-ological evidence for the activation of supraoptic neurones during the release of oxytocin. J. Physiol. (Lond.) 242:533–554.

Moss, R. L., and McCann, S. M. 1973. Induction of mat-ing behavior in rats by luteinizing hormone-releas-ing factor. Science (Wash., D.C.) 181:177–179.

Papez, J. W. 1937. A proposed mechanism of emotion. Arch. Neurol. Psychiatry 38:725–743.

Pfaff, D. W. 1973. Luteinizing hormone-releasing factor potentiates lordosis behavior in hypophysectomized ovariectomized female rats. Science 182 (Wash., D.C.):1148–1149.

Ranson, S. W. 1934. The hypothalamus: Its significance for visceral innervation and emotional expression. Trans. College Physicians Phila. Ser. 4. 2:222–242.

Reichlin, S. 1978. Introduction. In S. Reichlin, R. J. Bal-dessarini, and J. B. Martin (eds.), The hypothalamus. Res. Publ. Assoc. Res. Nerv. Ment. Dis. 56:1–14.

Schally, A. V. 1978. Aspects of hypothalamic regulation of the pituitary gland. Its implication for the control of reproductive processes. Science (Wash., D.C.) 202:18–28.

Scharrer, E., and Scharrer, B. 1954. Hormones produced by neurosecretory cells. Recent Prog. Horm. Res. 10:182–232.

Sundsten, J. W., and Sawyer, C. H. 1961. Osmotic acti-vation of neurohypophysial hormone release in rab-bits with hypothalamic islands. Exp. Neurol. 4:548–561.

Verney, E. B. 1947. The antidiuretic hormone and the factors which determine its release. Proc. R. Soc. Lond. B. Biol. Sci. 135:25–106.

Zimmerman, E. A., Carmel, P. W., Husain, M. K., Ferin, M., Tannenbaum, M., Frantz, A. G., and Robinson, A. G. 1973. Vasopressin and neurophysin: High con-centrations in monkey hypophyseal portal blood. Science (Wash., D.C.) 182:925–927.

Irving Kupfermann

Hypothalamus and Limbic System II: Motivation

38

In Chapter 37 we described the role of the limbic system and the hypothalamus in the neuroendocrine and autonomic regulation of homeostasis. In this chapter we shall consider the control of homeostasis by the behavior of the organism. These behavioral responses typically occur in parallel to the autonomic and neuroendocrine responses. We shall first consider the concept of motivational state and how control systems analysis can be used in the study of drive and motivation. We shall then examine the application of control systems analysis, using as examples temperature regulation, feeding, and drinking. We shall next consider factors other than tissue deficits in the regulation of motivated behaviors. Finally, we shall discuss systems of the brain concerned with reward or reinforcement.

Motivational or Drive States Are Thought to Intervene Between Stimuli and Complex Responses

Psychologists refer to the internal conditions that control voluntary behavior as *motivational states*. Specific motivational states are referred to as *drive states*. Thus, behavioral regulation of body temperature is said to be due to a temperature-regulating drive. Other conditions that control behavior such as curiosity and sex are also spoken of as drives because these behaviors share certain features (e.g., arousal and satiation) with behaviors motivated by traditional drives. However, for the latter behaviors there do not appear to be any well-defined underlying physiological deprivation states such as are found for a drive such as thirst.

Drives or motivational states are hypothetical brain mechanisms that are thought to determine the intensity and direction of a variety of complex behaviors such as temperature regulation, feeding, thirst, and sex. Behavioral scientists posit these internal states because observable features of the external environment are not sufficient to predict all aspects of these behaviors. For simple reflexes, for example, the pupillary response, the properties of the stimulus appear to account in large part for the properties of the behavior. On the other hand, the features of highly complex activities (feeding, drinking, and reproductive behavior) are not precisely correlated with external stimulus conditions. For example, under some conditions (e.g., when a long time has passed since the last meal) a food stimulus might produce vigorous feeding responses in an animal; but at other times, the same stimulus might pro-

duce no behavior or even a rejection response. In this particular example, the motivational state of hunger is inferred to explain the loose correlation between stimulus and response.

Neurobiologists are now beginning to define the actual neural states that correspond to the hypothetical states inferred by psychologists. In some instances it has been possible to approach motivational states as examples of the interaction of external stimuli with internal stimuli. The problem of motivation thus can be reduced to that of a complex reflex under the excitatory and inhibitory control of multiple stimuli, some of them internal. This approach has worked well with temperature regulation. The relevant internal stimuli for hunger, thirst, and sexual behavior have been exceedingly difficult to manipulate or even to identify. Therefore, for these behaviors the concept of drive state remains useful for behavioral scientists. As more is learned about the actual physiology of hypothetical drive states, the need for invoking these states in order to explain behavior may disappear, to be replaced by more precise concepts derived from physiology and systems theory.

Motivational and Other Homeostatic Processes Can Be Analyzed in Terms of Control Systems

Temperature regulation as well as other homeostatic regulatory mechanisms can be conceptualized in terms of the types of control systems that regulate machines. While the existence of a specific physiological control system has never been proven, this approach has provided a convenient and precise language to describe concepts and experimental results. It permits us to organize our thinking about highly complex systems. Furthermore, the servomechanism analogy defines the nature of the problem of physiological control in terms of experimentally approachable elements that can be analyzed one by one.

As we shall see, analysis in terms of servocontrol systems has been most successfully applied to temperature regulation. Application to more complex regulatory behaviors such as feeding and thirst has been less successful, but this is probably still the best approach to the analysis of these poorly understood, multidetermined functions.

Control systems regulate a *controlled variable* (e.g., temperature) that is maintained within a certain range. One way of regulating the controlled variable is to measure it by means of a *feedback detector* and to compare it with a de-

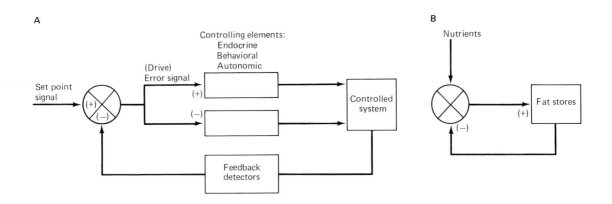

38–1 Servocontrol system for regulating body weight, temperature, etc. **A.** System using a set point to turn behavior on or off. When the feedback signal indicating the level of the controlled variable is below or above the set point, an error signal is generated, and this serves to turn on or to facilitate appropriate behaviors and physiological responses, and to turn off or to suppress incompatible responses. **B.** Servocontrol system without a set point, for control of fat stores. (Adapted from data of Di Girolamo and Rudman, 1968.)

sired value or *set point.* This is accomplished by an *integrator* or *error detector* that generates an *error signal* when the measurement of the controlled variable does not match the set point signal. The error signal then drives *controlling elements* that adjust the controlled system in the desired direction. In Figure 38–1, two sets of controlling elements are indicated, since all examples of physiological control seem to involve dual effects, inhibitory and excitatory, which function together to move the controlled system in a desired direction. The control system used to heat a home provides a good example of a familiar mechanical servomechanism that illustrates the above principles. The controlled variable is room temperature. The error detector is the home thermostat. The set point is the setting on the thermostat. Finally, the error signal is the output of the thermostat that turns the controlling element, the furnace system, on or off.

Temperature Is Regulated in Response to Peripheral and Central Input

Because temperature regulation requires integrated autonomic, endocrine, and skeletomotor responses, the anatomical connections of the hy-

pothalamus make it well suited for this task. Electrical stimulation of the hypothalamus indicates that it is organized anatomically in terms of dual mechanisms that control, respectively, increases and decreases in body temperature (Figure 38–2). Stimulation of the anterior hypothalamus in unanesthetized animals causes suppression of shivering and cutaneous vasodilation—responses that result in a drop in body temperature. Electrical stimulation of the posterior hypothalamus produces a set of opposite responses that function to generate or conserve heat. As with hypothalamically evoked fear responses (see Chapter 37), electrically induced temperature regulation also includes appropriate responses involving the skeletomotor system. For example, rostral hypothalamic stimulation produces panting, while posterior stimulation produces shivering.

The results of ablation experiments corroborate the critical role of the hypothalamus in regulating temperature. Lesions of the anterior hypothalamus result in chronic hyperthermia, and eliminate the major responses that normally dissipate excess heat. Lesions in the posterior hypothalamus have relatively little effect if the animal is maintained at room temperature (approximately 22°C). If, however, the animal is exposed to cold, it quickly becomes hypothermic due to a failure of the homeostatic mechanisms that generate and conserve heat.

The hypothalamus also controls endocrine responses to temperature challenges. Thus, in animal studies, it has been shown that long-term exposure to cold can enhance the release of thyroxine and thereby increase body heat by increasing tissue metabolism.

Temperature regulation nicely fits a model of a servocontrol system (or several systems) in which normal body temperature is the set point.

The integrator and many controlling elements appear to be located in the hypothalamus. The feedback detector appears to collect body temperature information from two main sources: peripheral temperature receptors located throughout the body (in the skin, spinal cord, and viscera) and central temperature receptors concentrated in the anterior hypothalamus. Note that, although both anterior and posterior hypothalamic areas are involved in temperature regulation, detectors of temperature, both low and high, are located only in the anterior hypothalamus. The hypothalamic receptors are probably hypothalamic neurons whose firing rate is highly dependent on local temperature, which in turn is determined primarily by the temperature of the blood.

The error signal of the temperature control system, in addition to driving appropriate autonomic, endocrine, and nonvoluntary skeletal responses, can also provide a signal to drive voluntary behavior that moves the controlled system in the direction that minimizes the error signal. For example, a rat can be taught to press a button to receive a puff of cool air in a hot environment. If the rat is placed in a room at normal temperature it will not press the cool-air button. If we now place a hollow probe into the anterior hypothalamus and locally warm this area by perfusing warm water through the probe, the rat will run to the cool-air button and press it. In the same rat we can demonstrate the summation of peripheral and central input to the hypothalamus by heating the environment and concurrently cooling or heating the hypothalamus (Figure

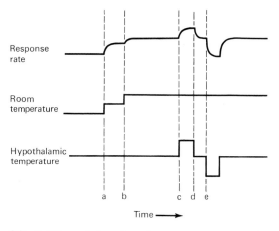

38–3 Effect of alteration of room temperature (points **a** and **b**) and of hypothalamic temperature (points **c**, **d**, and **e**) on the response rate of rats trained to respond for the reward of a brief burst of cool air. (Adapted from data of Corbit, 1973, and Satinoff, 1964.)

38–3). When both the environment and hypothalamus are heated, the rat presses faster than when either one is heated alone. Button pressing for cool air in a hot environment can be suppressed completely by directly cooling the hypothalamus. The control of body temperature is a clear example of the integrative function of the hypothalamus in autonomic, endocrine, and drive state control. Furthermore, we see how the hypothalamus operates directly on the internal environment or provides signals (derived from the internal environment) to control higher neural systems.

Feeding Behavior Is Regulated by a Variety of Signals

Feeding behavior also can be approached in terms of a control system in much the same fashion as temperature regulation, although at every level of analysis the understanding of feeding is less complete.

Set Point

One reason it appears that control theory can be applied to feeding behavior is that body weight seems to be controlled by some type of set point system. Humans often maintain body weight over a period of many years. Since even a small daily excess or deficit of caloric intake could result in a profound change of body weight over a

38–2 Sagittal section of human brain showing positions of hypothalamic regions concerned with heat conservation and heat dissipation.

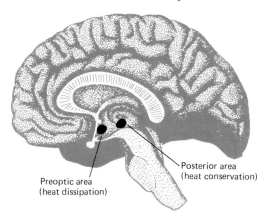

Posterior area
(heat conservation)

Preoptic area
(heat dissipation)

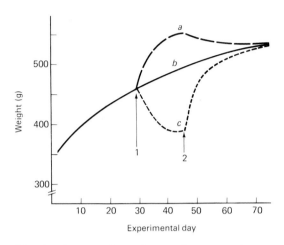

38–4 Schematized growth curve for a group of rats. At **arrow 1**, one-third of the animals were maintained on their normal diet (curve **b**), one-third were force-fed (**curve a**), and one-third were placed on a low-calorie diet (**curve c**). At **arrow 2**, all rats were placed on a normal diet. The force-fed animals lost weight and the starved animals gained weight until the mean weight of the two groups approached that of the normal growth curve (**b**). (Adapted from Keesey et al., 1976.)

period of years, in some way the body must provide feedback signals that control nutrient intake and metabolism. Control of nutrient intake can be clearly seen in animal studies in which body weight can be altered from the set point either by food deprivation or by force feeding. In both cases, animals adjust their subsequent food intake (either up or down) until they regain a body weight appropriate for their age (Figure 38–4). Animals are said to "defend" their body weight against perturbations.

Regulation of body weight, however, is different from regulation of body temperature. Whereas body temperature is remarkably similar from individual to individual, body weight has an equally remarkable dissimilarity from individual to individual. Furthermore, the *apparent* set point of an individual can vary as a function of stress, palatability of the food, exercise, and numerous other factors. One possible explanation for these observations is that the set point itself can change on the basis of different factors. Another possibility is that feeding behavior utilizes some control systems in which there are no formal, fixed set point mechanisms, but the systems function as if there were set points. Feedback systems of this type do exist in the body. In Figure

38–1B a negative feedback system for the regulation of fat stores in cells is shown. Apparently, the more fat stored in the cell, the less conversion there is of nutrients to fat. Thus, fat stores may directly or indirectly exert a negative feedback that is proportional to the level of fat. Because of this feedback mechanism, fat stores tend to be stable in the face of varying nutrient input. If, however, nutrient input is increased, the system will seek a new set point that is above the former value. In this system, the fat stores cannot increase the negative feedback signal (to meet the demands of higher nutrient input) unless the fat stores first increase somewhat. Automatic physiological feedback systems of this type may play an important role in regulating body weight.

Controlling Elements

Food intake has been thought to be under the control of two centers in the hypothalamus. In 1942, Hetherington and Ranson reported that destruction in the region of the ventromedial hypothalamic nuclei (See Chapter 37, Figure 37–4) and surrounding tissue produces hyperphagia, which results in severe obesity. In contrast, in 1951, Anand and Brobeck found that bilateral lesions of the lateral hypothalamus produce the opposite effect—a severe aphagia in which the animal dies unless force-fed and hydrated. Electrical stimulation of the hypothalamus produces the opposite effects. Lateral stimulation elicits feeding, whereas medial stimulation suppresses feeding. These observations suggested that the lateral hypothalamus contains a feeding center, and the medial hypothalamus a satiety center; however, this conceptually attractive conclusion is faulty. It is now clear that the brain is not organized into discrete centers that control specific functions. Individual functions are performed by neural circuits distributed among several structures in the brain. Attempts to define precisely the normal function of the lateral or medial centers have not provided clear results. Even a small lesion in the hypothalamus affects numerous systems and produces complex effects. The observed results of hypothalamic lesions on feeding are now thought to be due to a number of different factors, including effects on fibers of passage and the development of arousal, alteration of sensory information, alteration of set point, and alteration of hormonal balance. One or more of these effects may be seen in humans who have sustained damage to the hypothalamus due to vascular disease or a tumor.

Hypothalamic Lesions and Fibers of Passage. Lesions of the lateral hypothalamus have been found to damage dopamine-containing fibers coursing from the substantia nigra to the striatum. If these fibers are sectioned outside of the hypothalamus, animals exhibit a hypoarousal state and aphagia similar to that observed following lateral hypothalamic lesions. The hypothalamic aphagia, however, can be more profound and differs in detail.

The data suggesting that the effects of lateral hypothalamic lesions may be due to interruption of fibers of passage have led investigators to question whether the hypothalamus itself has *any* role in feeding behavior. Recent studies of the lateral hypothalamus have utilized local injection of kainic acid, a substance that produces a chemical lesion that primarily destroys cell bodies and does not severely damage fibers of passage. It was found that this type of lesion also produces aphagia and certain other aspects of a lateral hypothalamic syndrome.

Sensory–Motor Deficits. In some cases, lateral hypothalamic lesions may also sever fibers of the trigeminal system, and the resultant sensory loss can contribute to the aphagia. Sectioning of peripheral trigeminal input can also disturb feeding behavior. Sensory or motor deficits might contribute to the phenomenon of *sensory neglect* seen after lateral hypothalamic lesions. Sensory neglect is most easily seen following unilateral lesions of the lateral hypothalamus. Animals with these lesions show reduced responsiveness to visual, olfactory, and somatic sensory stimuli presented contralateral to the lesion. They also exhibit diminished responses to food presented contralaterally. It is not clear whether this phenomenon is due to disruption of sensory systems or to interference with motor systems directing responses contralateral to the lesion.

Altered sensory responses are also seen in hyperphagic animals with lesions in the region of the ventromedial nucleus. These animals show heightened responsiveness to the noxious or attractive properties of food and other stimuli (Figure 38–5). Thus, on a normal diet they will eat more than nonlesioned animals, but if the food is adulterated with a bitter substance they will eat less than normal animals. This effect is similar to

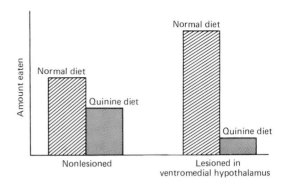

38–5 Amount of food eaten during a meal by rats with and without lesions of the ventromedial hypothalamus, placed on a normal diet or a diet adulterated with a bitter substance (quinine). Among rats with medial hypothalamic lesions, the animals fed the quinine diet decreased their food intake, whereas the rats fed the normal diet overate compared to controls.

that seen in nonlesioned animals that are made obese. Therefore, the altered sensory responsiveness to food seen in ventromedial hypothalamic lesioned animals probably is, at least in part, a consequence rather than a cause of the obesity. Schachter at Columbia has found that obese humans with no evidence of damage to the region of the ventromedial hypothalamus are also highly responsive to the taste properties of food. This finding supports the notion that hypothalamic damage is not the direct cause of this trait.

Alteration of Set Point. The results of several experiments have indicated that hypothalamic lesions may alter the set point for regulating body weight. In these experiments the animal's weight is changed by force feeding or starvation before the lesion. After a relatively small lateral hypothalamic lesion is made, the animals eventually resume eating, although ordinarily at a reduced level of intake.

An example of the results of this type of experiment is shown in Figure 38–6. If the weight of the animals is reduced before the lateral hypothalamic lesion, the animals eat and gain weight immediately after the lesion, instead of losing weight, as the control (nonprestarved) animals do. The prestarvation apparently brings their weight below the set point level determined by the lateral lesion. Analogous results are obtained after hypothalamic lesions that result in obesity.

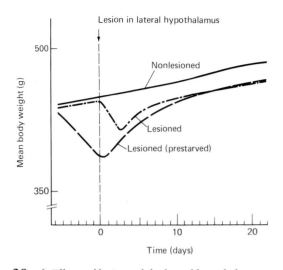

38–6 Effects of lesions of the lateral hypothalamus on feeding behavior and body weight. Three groups of rats were used. On day zero the animals of two of the groups received small lesions of the lateral hypothalamus. One of these groups and the control animals had been maintained on a normal diet; the other group was starved before the lesion and consequently lost body weight. Following the lesion, all animals were given free access to food. The lesioned animals that had not been prestarved initially decreased food intake and lost body weight. The food intake of the lesioned animals that were prestarved was not inhibited, and they rapidly gained weight. (Adapted from Keesey et al., 1976.)

Hormonal Effects. Feeding behavior is known to be affected by many hormones including sex steroids, glucagon, insulin, and growth hormone. Large lesions of the hypothalamus invariably affect many hormonal control systems. For example, lesions of the medial hypothalamus result in a greatly increased release of insulin when animals are exposed to food. This response may explain, at least in part, the hyperphagia and weight gain seen after medial lesions, since a large amount of insulin in the blood can elicit feeding responses and also promotes the conversion of nutrients into fat. Interestingly, animals with medial hypothalamic lesions show a relative increase in body fat even when their overeating is controlled by limiting their caloric intake to normal levels.

Nonhypothalamic Elements. Although the role of the hypothalamus in a variety of regulatory mechanisms has been emphasized in this chapter, it is important to realize that many other structures in the nervous system also contribute

to regulation. Indeed, a limited degree of homeostatic regulation continues to function even in the complete absence of the hypothalamus and structures rostral to it. For example, a rat with this type of lesion will feed if food is placed in its mouth and will reject food (satiate) after an appropriate amount of food has been ingested.

Signals Regulating Feeding

A great deal of research has been devoted to an analysis of the cues the organism uses to regulate feeding. These studies have shown that almost every conceivable regulatory mechanism that could be used *is* used under certain conditions. There are two main sets of regulatory cues for hunger: *short-term cues* regulate the size of individual meals, and *long-term cues* regulate overall body weight. Short-term cues consist primarily of chemical properties of the food acting in the mouth to stimulate feeding behavior and in the gastrointestinal system and liver to inhibit feeding. The short-term satiety signals apparently impinge on the hypothalamus via afferent autonomic pathways communicating primarily with lateral hypothalamic regions. The effectiveness of short-term cues is modulated by some long-term signal reflecting body weight (perhaps related to total fat stores). By this means, body weight is kept reasonably constant over a broad range of activity and diet.

Several humoral signals are suspected to be important for the regulation of feeding behavior. The hypothalamus has glucoreceptors that respond to blood glucose levels. This system, however, probably controls feeding *behavior* (in contrast to autonomic responses related to blood glucose) only in "emergency" states in which blood glucose levels fall drastically. More modest changes in blood glucose probably also activate the hypothalamic system and elicit autonomic and endocrine responses that facilitate gluconeogenesis. Other humoral signals that may suppress feeding include gut hormones that are released during a meal. The best evidence, although far from conclusive, is for a role of the peptide *cholycystokinin* (CCK) in satiety. Cholycystokinin is released from the duodenum and upper intestine when amino acids and fatty acids are present in the tract. The systemic injection of cholycystokinin can inhibit feeding behavior.

Cholycystokinin also appears to be one of the peptide neurotransmitters in neurons of the brain (see Chapter 10), and the injection of small quantities of it into the ventricles of animals also inhibits feeding. Therefore, the release of cholycystokinin in the brain may inhibit feeding independently of cholycystokinin released from the gut. This is an example of a hormone or neuromodulator that appears to have independent central and peripheral actions that are functionally related. Other examples include luteinizing hormone–releasing hormone (sexual behavior), adrenocorticotropic hormone (stress and avoidance behavior), and angiotensin (responses to hemorrhage; see the section on thirst). It is possible that separate peripheral and central peptide-containing cells may have derived evolutionarily from individual cells that performed multiple functions in more primitive forebearers (as appears to be the case in invertebrates, in which a single serotonergic neuron produces food arousal by both peripheral and central actions). It is also possible that certain similar actions of peripheral and central substances may be a reflection of the fact that peripherally acting hormones may have access to the brain. For example, Bergland and Page have provided evidence that substances released from the anterior pituitary may enter the brain by means of retrograde blood flow in pituitary portal blood vessels. Blood-borne hormones may find their way into the brain through regions where the blood–brain barrier is weak. Similar peripheral and central actions would help ensure that conflicting responses are not elicited.

Since a very large number of factors appear to regulate feeding, it is difficult to specify the conditions under which given factors operate and to assign quantitative estimates of the relative importance of the various factors. In many instances, elimination of one or more feedback signals does not simply result in a proportional alteration in food intake. It often appears as if the organism makes an overall judgment about nutrient needs based on multiple inputs. We tend to think of our exteroceptive sensory systems as being capable of more complex information processing than our interoceptive systems. Our exteroceptive systems are designed to provide highly accurate judgments about reality in the face of complex, incomplete, and even contradictory cues. For example, our visual system integrates the overall patterns of light and dark in order to make accurate judgments about the brightness of objects under highly variable lighting conditions. The brightness of an object is not determined simply by measuring the intensity of light reflected from the object; rather, the visual system estimates brightness by comparing the light intensity of an object with the intensity of the surround. Perhaps interoceptive systems are similarly flexible and clever and estimate nutrient need by assessing several mutually interdependent factors.

Thirst Is Regulated by Tissue Osmolality and Vascular Volume

The hypothalamus contains neural structures that can initiate drinking behavior. Unlike the ingestion of food, as long as a minimal amount of water is ingested, the precise amount taken in is relatively unimportant. Within broad limits, excess intake is readily disposed of. Nevertheless, a set point or ideal level of water intake appears to exist, since either too much or too little drinking results in an inefficient partitioning of the organism's limited time (which can be spent either on drinking behavior or on other necessary activities). A drinking bout that is too short has the result that the animal soon must interrupt other activities and initiate another bout of drinking in order to avoid underhydration. Drinking a large amount at one time results in unneeded time spent drinking, as well as urinating in order to eliminate the excess fluid. Under certain conditions, the freely selected level of water intake can be considerably above the minimal physiological requirement, although typically the urine output of animals, including man, is almost maximally concentrated.

Drinking is controlled by two main physiological variables: *tissue osmolality* and *vascular (fluid) volume*. These appear to be handled by separate but interrelated mechanisms. Drinking also can be controlled by dryness of the tongue, and by hyperthermia, detected at least in part by thermosensitive neurons in the anterior hypothalamus.

The feedback signals for water regulation derive from many sources. Osmotic stimuli can act directly on osmoreceptor (or sodium-level receptor) cells (probably neurons) in the hypothalamus. Osmotic or sodium stimuli acting on the tongue also can regulate drinking behavior.

The feedback signals for vascular volume are located in the low-pressure side of the circulation—the right atrium and adjacent walls of the great veins. Large volume changes may also affect arterial baroreceptors in the aortic arch and carotid sinus, and signals from these sources can initiate drinking. Low blood volume (as well as other conditions that decrease body sodium) also results in an increase of renin secreted from the kidney. The renin changes plasma angiotensinogen into angiotensin I, which is then hydrolyzed to the highly active octapeptide angiotensin II. *Angiotensin II* elicits three physiological mechanisms appropriate to a response to water loss: (1) vasoconstriction, (2) increased release of aldosterone, and (3) increased release of antidiuretic hormone. Angiotensin II may affect structures in the third ventricle that are outside of the blood–brain barrier that stimulate drinking behavior. The application of exceptionally low doses of angiotensin II to the subfornical organ (which protrudes into the third ventricle) can elicit drinking behavior. It should be noted, however, that the thresholds for eliciting the physiological effects of angiotensin II are considerably below those for eliciting drinking behavior.

The signals that terminate drinking are less well understood than the signals that initiate drinking. It is clear, however, that the termination signal is not always merely the absence of the initiating signal. This principle holds for many examples of physiological and behavioral regulation, including feeding. Thus, for example, drinking initiated by low vascular fluid volume (e.g., after severe hemorrhage) terminates well before the deficit is rectified. This is highly adaptive since it prevents water intoxication due to excessive dilution of extracellular fluids. It also prevents overhydration that could result because of a delay of absorption of fluid from the alimentary system.

Motivated Behaviors Can Be Regulated by Factors Other Than Tissue Deficit

In this chapter we have dealt with the role of tissue needs in signaling the nervous system to initiate appropriate behavioral and physiological responses to minimize or eliminate deficits. A thorough understanding of motivated behaviors, however, requires knowledge of a number of factors not related to tissue deficit. For example, sexual responses and curiosity appear not to be controlled by the lack of specific substances in the body. Even homeostatic responses such as drinking and feeding are regulated by innate and learned mechanisms that modulate the effects of the feedback signals that indicate tissue deficits. In humans in particular, learned habits and subjective feelings of pleasure can override interoceptive feedback signals. For example, people of-

ten choose to go hungry rather than eat food that they have learned to avoid. In addition to hedonic factors or pleasure, there are two factors that regulate motivated behaviors: the particular ecological requirements of the organism, and anticipatory mechanisms.

Ecological Constraints

The details of particular behavior patterns have been determined by evolutionary selection processes that shape responses such that they are appropriate for the ecology of the particular animal. One means of analyzing motivated behaviors in an ecological context is to do cost–benefit analyses similar to those done by economists. In feeding behavior, costs include the time and effort to search for and procure food. The benefit consists of nutrient intake that will ultimately support a given level of reproductive success. The spacing and duration of meals can be considered to reflect the operation of brain mechanisms that have evolved to maximize gain and minimize costs. According to this type of analysis, carnivores may eat very rapidly not because they have exceptionally powerful feedback signals indicating severe deprivation, but because they have evolved mechanisms that help ensure that their kill will not have to be shared with other animals. Ecological considerations need not preclude consideration of homeostatic mechanisms, since homeostatic mechanisms also have evolved to assist the organism in adapting to its particular environmental conditions.

Anticipatory Mechanisms

Homeostatic regulation often is anticipatory and can be initiated before any physiological deficit occurs. Clock mechanisms turn physiological and behavioral responses on and off before the occurrence of tissue deficit or need. One such common mechanism is a daily rhythm with a free-running period typically close to 24 hr, called a *circadian rhythm* (from the Latin *circa*, about, and *dies*, a day). In the presence of a repeated 24-hr signal, or *zeitgeber* (typically light–dark cycles) the circadian rhythm runs exactly 24 hr. Circadian rhythms are autogenous, and under constant dark the rhythms continue, although in periods of somewhat more or less than 24 hr. Circadian rhythms exist for virtually every homeostatic function of the body. Since many of the rhythms are coordinated, the hypothalamus

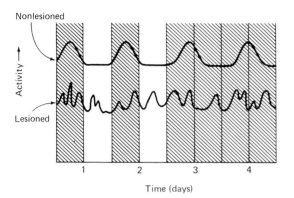

38–7 Effects of lesions of the suprachiasmatic
nucleus on daily activity rhythm of the rat.
Shaded areas, periods of darkness; **white areas,** periods
of light. Normal animals exhibit 24-hr rhythms during
periods of light and dark, and approximately 24-hr
rhythms in constant dark **(top trace).** Animals with
lesions of the suprachiasmatic nucleus completely lose
the 24-hr rhythm **(bottom trace).**

would seem to be the ideal location for a major
clock mechanism that would drive them, or at
least coordinate independent clock mechanisms
located throughout the brain. The results of lesions of the suprachiasmatic nucleus of lower animals support this suggestion (Figure 38–7). Animals with these lesions lose 24-hr rhythmicity of
corticosteroid release, feeding, drinking, locomotor activity, and several other responses.

Consistent with a role of the suprachiasmatic
nucleus in circadian rhythmicity is the finding of
Moore and Lenn that this nucleus receives direct
retinal projections. The presence of a circadian
mechanism in the suprachiasmatic nucleus provides a means of affecting many different systems
with a minimal amount of wiring, and it illustrates the advantage of clustering related functions into an anatomically discrete structure.

Hedonic Factors

In humans an unquestionable factor in the control of motivated behaviors is pleasure. Humans
will sometimes even subject themselves to deprivation in order to heighten the pleasure obtained
when the deprivation is relieved (e.g., skipping
lunch in order to enjoy dinner more), or to obtain
pleasure by satisfying some other need (e.g., diet-
ing to look attractive). Since pleasure is subjective, it is difficult to study in animals, but there
are reasons to believe that a similar variable may

control motivated animal behavior. For example,
in 1976 Sclafani found that rats given a very pal-
atable diet containing a variety of "supermarket"
foods (chocolate chip cookies, salami, etc.) eat
much more than when given a bland and compar-
ably nutritious diet of rat chow. The neural bases
of pleasure are poorly understood, but it seems
reasonable to hypothesize that these mechanisms
overlap or even coincide with brain mechanisms
(including those involving the hypothalamus)
that are concerned with reward and the reinforcement of learned behavior.

**Intracranial Self-Stimulation Can
Reinforce Behavior**

One of the most influential discoveries related to
mechanisms of drive was the finding of Olds and
Milner in 1954 that intracranial electrical stimulation of the hypothalamus and associated structures could act as a reward or reinforcement for
operant conditioning of animals (see Chapter 47
for the definition of operant conditioning). In
many respects, brain stimulation appeared to be
acting as an ordinary reinforcement such as food,
but there was one important difference. Ordinary
reinforcement is effective only if the animal is in
a particular drive state. For example, food rein-
forces only a hungry animal. Brain stimulation
seemed to work regardless of the drive state of
the animal. In 1963 these considerations led
Deutsch and Howarth to postulate that reinforcing brain stimulation does two things: (1) it
evokes a drive state, and (2) it activates systems
that are normally activated by a reinforcing stimulus. Support for this idea has come from subsequent observations that many of the points in the
brain that are effective in producing reward also
stimulate complex behavioral patterns such as
feeding and drinking. Brain stimulation at many
different sites in the brain has been found to be
reinforcing, but hypothalamic sites are particularly effective. Very effective sites are found along
the medial forebrain bundle and the structures it
innervates.

There have been many attempts to relate reinforcing brain stimulation to pathways utilizing
specific neurotransmitters—usually one or another biogenic amine. The available evidence indicates that pathways utilizing dopamine may be
involved in some way, although a complex behavioral phenomenon such as reinforcement is
exceedingly unlikely to involve only a single
transmitter.

An Overall View

It is important to realize that in addition to the hypothalamus many structures in the nervous system contribute to regulatory functions. Nevertheless, because of its intimate relationship with both the autonomic and the endocrine system, the hypothalamus appears to play a central role in the physiological and behavioral regulatory mechanisms that make life possible in higher organisms.

Selected Readings and References

Andersson, B. 1978. Regulation of water intake. Physiol. Rev. 58:582–603.

Bellisle, F. 1979. Human feeding behavior. Neurosci. Biobehav. Rev. 3:163–169.

Bligh, J. 1973. Temperature Regulation in Mammals and Other Vertebrates. Amsterdam: North-Holland.

Booth, D. A., Toates, F. M., and Platt, S. V. 1976. Control system for hunger and its implications in animals and man. In D. Novin, W. Wyrwicka, and G. A. Bray (eds.), Hunger: Basic Mechanisms and Clinical Implications. New York: Raven Press, pp. 127–143.

Friedman, M. I., and Stricker, E. M. 1976. The physiological psychology of hunger: A physiological perspective. Psychol. Rev. 83:409–431.

Rusak, B., and Zucker, I. 1979. Neural regulation of circadian rhythms. Physiol. Rev. 59:449–526.

Schoener, T. W. 1971. Theory of feeding strategies. Annu. Rev. Ecol. Syst. 2:369–404.

Other References

Anand, B. K., and Brobeck, J. R. 1951. Localization of a "feeding center" in the hypothalamus of the rat. Proc. Soc. Exp. Biol. Med. 77:323–324.

Bergland, R. M., and Page, R. B. 1979. Pituitary–brain vascular relations: A new paradigm. Science (Wash., D.C.) 204:18–24.

Corbit, J. D. 1973. Voluntary control of hypothalamic temperature. J. Comp. Physiol. Psychol. 83:394–411.

Deutsch, J. A., and Howarth, C. I. 1963. Some tests of a theory of intracranial self-stimulation. Psychol. Rev. 70:444–460.

DiGirolamo, M., and Rudman, D. 1968. Variations in glucose metabolism and sensitivity to insulin of the rat's adipose tissue, in relation to age and body weight. Endocrinology 82:1133–1141.

Hetherington, A. W., and Ranson, S. W. 1942. The spontaneous activity and food intake of rats with hypothalamic lesions. Am. J. Physiol. 136:609–617.

Keesey, R. E., Boyle, P. C., Kemnitz, J. W., and Mitchel; J. S. 1976. The role of the lateral hypothalamus in determining the body weight set point. In D. Novin, W. Wyrwicka, and G. A. Bray (eds.), Hunger: Basic Mechanisms and Clinical Implications. New York: Raven Press, pp. 243–255.

Moore, R. Y., and Lenn, N. J. 1972. A retinohypothalamic projection in the rat. J. Comp. Neurol. 146:1–14.

Olds, J., and Milner, P. 1954. Positive reinforcement produced by electrical stimulation of septal area and other regions of rat brain. J. Comp. Physiol. Psychol. 47:419–427.

Satinoff, E. 1964. Behavioral thermoregulation in response to local cooling of the rat brain. Am. J. Physiol. 206:1389–1394.

Schachter, S. 1971. Some extraordinary facts about obese humans and rats. Am. Psychol. 26:129–144.

Sclafani, A. 1976. Appetite and hunger in experimental obesity syndromes. In D. Novin, W. Wyrwicka, and G. Bray (eds.), Hunger: Basic Mechanisms and Clinical Implications. New York: Raven Press, pp. 281–295.

John H. Martin

Properties of Cortical Neurons, the EEG, and the Mechanisms of Epilepsy

39

From the perspective of comparative vertebrate biology, the human brain is characterized by a great expanse of cerebral cortex. One of the great challenges for neurobiology is to understand the functional organization of the cerebral cortex in relation to behavior. This challenge is central to understanding the role of the brain in higher functions.

As we have seen in previous chapters, differences in the function of the various regions of the cortex derive more from differences in the input–output organization than from differences in cellular properties or even intrinsic circuitry. In fact, studies of the intrinsic organization of the somatic sensory cortex by Vernon Mountcastle, and of the visual cortex by David Hubel and Torsten Wiesel, indicate that both regions share common features. The cells are oriented in vertical columns that run from the pial surface to the white matter. Moreover, cells in a column have similar properties that include receptive field position and effective stimulus features.

This work makes it clear that, even though different regions of the cerebral cortex have different cytoarchitectures and each region has its own morphological patterns, aspects of the intrinsic organization of the cortex are quite general. Moreover, aspects of the patterns of connections are general. For instance, the major input to

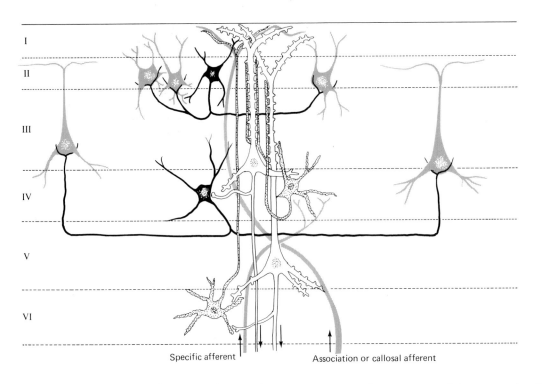

I

II

III

IV

V

VI

Specific afferent   Association or callosal afferent

39–1 Semidiagrammatic illustration of principal neuron types and their interconnections in the cerebral cortex. Note that the two large pyramidal cells in layers III and V receive multiple synaptic contacts from star-shaped interneuron (stellate cell) in layer IV. Basket cell inhibition is directed to the somata of pyramidal cells in layers II, III, and V. A fusiform cell is shown in layer VI. Major input to the cortex derives from specific thalamic nuclei (specific afferents) which is directed mostly to layer IV and association and callosal input (association and callosal afferents) which is in large part directed to more superficial layers. (Adapted from Szentágothai, 1969.)

primary sensory cortices comes from specific thalamic nuclei and is distributed predominantly to layer IV (Figure 39–1). Within any given column the neurons of layer IV function to distribute information locally, to other neurons located in the more superficial (or deeper) layers. Information from other cortical regions projects to neurons that lie superficial to layer IV. Output functions are served only by neurons in layers II, III, V, and VI. As a result it is attractive to think, as Mountcastle has suggested, that the column functions as the modular processing unit in the cortex.

In this chapter we shall elaborate further the features common to the organization of all areas of the cortex. We shall first consider the properties of individual cortical neurons and of glial cells and then examine three types of collective electrical activity of cortical neurons: (1) the electroencephalogram (EEG), (2) sensory evoked potentials, and (3) epileptiform activity.

The Cerebral Cortex Contains Three Types of Neurons and Three Types of Glial Cells

We have previously considered the layered structure of the cerebral cortex (see Chapter 16). Here we shall briefly review the three types of cortical neurons: pyramidal cells, stellate cells, and fusiform cells (Figure 39–1). Pyramidal cells are found in layers II and III as well as in layer V. Stellate cells are present in all layers but are most common in layer IV. The fusiform cells are observed primarily in layer VI.

Pyramidal cells, the most prominent of the three types of cells, are of particular interest for several reasons. First, the pyramidal cells represent the major efferent projections of the cerebral cortex. For example, the pyramidal cells of layer V of the motor cortex (the largest of which are called Betz cells after the Russian anatomist Vladimir Betz) project to the brain stem and spinal cord. The smaller pyramidal cells in layers II and III project to other cortical regions. Second, pyramidal cells have a very characteristic dendritic organization. The apical dendrites of pyramidal cells are invariably oriented perpendicular to the surface, often crossing several layers. This allows different input to impinge upon the dendritic tree at different points. In addition, the dendrites contain booster zones that amplify synaptic currents, thereby enabling distant synaptic sites to be effective (see below).

The stellate cells represent a collection of interneurons. For example, one type of stellate cell is the basket cell, an inhibitory interneuron whose axon projects horizontally throughout a local cortical region, forming synapses that envelop the soma of the postsynaptic cell (hence the name *basket*). This neuron is thought to mediate surround or pericolumnar inhibition, which enables cortical columns to function in relative isolation from neighboring columns. Stellate cells are also called granule cells because of their granule-like appearance in Nissl-stained sections. Fusiform cells are spindle shaped and are typically found in layer VI. Their axons often project out of the cortex.

As in other regions of the brain, in the cerebral cortex the ratio of glial cells to neurons is about 10 to 1. Of the major types of glia in the central nervous system (see Chapter 2), three are present in the cortex: astrocytes, oligodendrocytes, and microglia. Oligodendrocytes are smaller than the various astrocytes; they have a darker cytoplasm and nucleus, heavily condensed chromatin, and few neurofilaments. The oligodendrocytes form and maintain the myelin sheaths of the central nervous system. The function of astrocytes is less well understood. A number of functions have been attributed to them: they may (1) take up and store neurotransmitters [for example, glia have been shown to take up γ-aminobutyric acid (GABA); see Chapter 10], (2) serve as a spatial barrier to isolate neurons and to regulate ionic interactions, (3) provide a structural matrix of support for the central nervous system, (4) store and transfer metabolites from capillaries to neurons, and (5) provide substrate guidance during development.

Cortical Cells Have Special Properties Suited to Their Function

The pyramidal cell of the motor cortex is the only type of neocortical neuron that has been studied in detail because its large cell body is the easiest to impale with microelectrodes. In addition, many of these cells have an axon that projects out of the cortex along the pyramidal tract; this al-

lows electrophysiological identification of these cells by the recording of an antidromically conducted action potential in response to electrical stimulation of the long axon at subcortical levels. Interneurons have short axons and are therefore difficult to characterize. A recent technical advance in cellular physiological studies of cortical neurons is the development of the tissue slice preparation, which allows sections of neocortex or hippocampus to be studied in vitro. This preparation consists of a transverse slice of cortex that is removed from the animal and perfused and aerated in an experimental chamber. Isolated from the rest of the brain, the neurons can be visualized and there are no pulsations due to blood flow. Intracellular recordings can be obtained for several hours and cellular mechanisms can be studied effectively. Moreover, the microenvironment of the neurons can be manipulated.

Membrane Properties Permit High-Frequency Firing

Pyramidal cells have resting potentials of -50 to -70 mV and action potentials of 60 to 100 mV. These cells differ from spinal motor neurons in the configuration of their afterpotentials. Motor neurons display a prominent hyperpolarizing afterpotential that limits the firing frequency to a low and stable rate. This feature is presumably related to the mechanical properties of the muscle innervated. In contrast, neocortical pyramidal cells project onto other neurons and are not subject to the same temporal firing constraints as motor neurons. Such cells exhibit only a small afterhyperpolarization and can fire at frequencies greater than 100/sec. The hippocampal pyramidal cell represents an extreme example of a neuron that has no hyperpolarizing afterpotential and fires in brief high-frequency bursts. The time constant for neocortical pyramidal cells is typically longer than that for spinal motor neurons. The membrane properties of neocortical pyramidal cells therefore favor the development of temporal summation (see Chapter 7).

Dendritic Trigger Zones Boost Remote Input

Spinal motor neurons have a single trigger zone located at the initial segment of the axon. Cortical cells, however, have multiple trigger zones located in the dendritic tree in addition to the initial segment trigger zone. In 1961, Alden Spencer

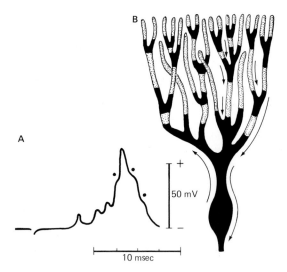

39–2 Dendritic spikes are produced by the dendritic trigger zones of cortical neurons. **A.** Sample intradendritic recording from a cerebellar Purkinje cell. Three all-or-none dendritic spikes precede the larger depolarization. **Dots** adjacent to the large depolarization correspond to inflection points and are presumably also dendritic spikes. **B.** Schematic representation of the probable set of events following orthodromic Purkinje cell activation of dendrites. Black areas on the dendrites correspond to sites capable of triggering dendritic spikes. In response to parallel fiber stimulation, active responses are initiated in the dendrites that summate, presumably at dendritic branch points **(downward arrows)**. When an impulse is initiated at an axonal locus, it is antidromically conducted only to proximal dendrites **(upward arrows)**. (Adapted from Llinás and Nicholson, 1971.)

and Eric Kandel, working at the NIH, recorded intracellularly from the somata of hippocampal pyramidal cells. They observed small unitary potentials ("fast prepotentials") and suggested that these are active dendritic responses observed remotely at the level of the soma. Subsequently, Rodolfo Llinás and his colleagues at New York University recorded intracellularly from the dendrites of the cerebellar Purkinje cells and found that these cells also have multiple trigger zones located in the dendrites. The intradendritic recordings revealed a complex action potential that has many notches on the rising and falling phases. These notches represent dendritic spikes; their variable shapes and sizes reflect different spatial relationships between the site of the recording microelectrode and the site of initiation of the dendritic spike (Figure 39–2). These spikes appear to be dependent upon Ca^{++} rather than Na^+ ions.

The dendritic trigger zones in cortical neurons seem to serve as booster zones for remote excitatory inputs, allowing them to influence the trigger zone in the axon, the final common trigger zone. In the spinal motor neuron the single-spike initiating zone summates synaptic inputs of various signs and magnitudes impinging on the soma and dendritic membranes. Inputs located farther out on the dendrites have comparatively less influence on the spike-generating mechanism than synapses near the soma. This situation would pose a serious problem, especially to the pyramidal cell, which possesses an apical dendrite 1 mm or more in length. The existence of multiple trigger zones allows synapses located on distal portions of the dendrites to exert an effect.

Powerful Inhibitory Synapses Are Located Close to the Soma

In 1959, Gray at University College, London, classified synapses in the cerebral cortex into two types (type I and type II) based on the morphological criteria considered in Chapter 9. Most type I synapses end on dendritic spines and are excitatory. Type II synapses end on the cell body or dendritic membrane and tend to be inhibitory. For example, in the cerebellum, the spine synapses on the Purkinje cell dendrites are type I and have been electrophysiologically identified as excitatory. The inhibitory basket cell synapses on the Purkinje cell body are type II.

In general, inhibitory synapses tend to be located closer to the cell body than do excitatory synapses. This location is important for information processing. For example, the basket cell synapses on the cell body of the neocortical pyrami-

39–3 Comparison of inhibitory postsynaptic potentials **(IPSPs)** recorded from a hippocampal pyramidal cell and a spinal motor neuron. (Adapted from Spencer and Kandel, 1968.)

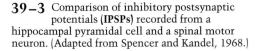
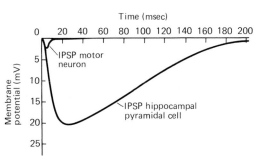

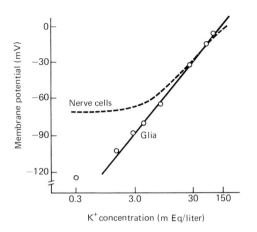

39–4 The relationship between membrane potential and external K$^+$ concentration (log scale) in nerve cells and glia. Note that the Nernst potential for K$^+$ predicts the glial membrane potential (**solid line**) over wide ranges of extracellular K$^+$ and poorly predicts the nerve cell membrane potential (**dashed line**). (Adapted from Orkand, 1977.)

dal cell and therefore can exert a final inhibitory veto on whether or not an impulse is generated at the initial segment (Figure 39–1).

Inhibitory synapses in cortical neurons are not only strategically located but also are very powerful. Cortical inhibitory actions are much larger and last 50 times longer than the inhibitory actions exerted on spinal motor neurons (Figure 39–3). Rather than simply inverting the synaptic sign in an excitatory pathway, large cortical inhibitory postsynaptic potentials can shape the spatial distribution of active cells in a population of neural elements by inhibitory "sculpturing."

Glial Cells Are Depolarized by Increases in Extracellular K$^+$

Intracellular recordings from glial cells by Stephen Kuffler and his colleagues have revealed that glial cells cannot develop action potentials.

Their membranes respond passively and they are believed not to have a role in signaling. However, the glial cell membrane is extremely sensitive to changes in extracellular K$^+$ concentrations because it is highly permeable to K$^+$. Slight increases in extracellular K$^+$ result in depolarization of the glial cell (Figure 39–4). Unlike nerve cells, the Nernst potential for K$^+$ accurately predicts the membrane potential of glial cells over very large values of extracellular K$^+$. During increases in neuronal activity, glial membranes become depolarized; this depolarization is apparently due to increased extracellular K$^+$ from firing neurons (Figure 39–5). Glial cells are thought to take up extracellular K$^+$ during intense neuronal activity and to buffer K$^+$ concentration in the extracellular space. Moreover, glia take up and store transmitters such as GABA. An elevation in intracellular K$^+$ concentration causes the release of stored GABA. Thus, glial cells may regulate extracellular neurotransmitter concentrations in relation to local neuronal firing and therefore may possess a subtle modulatory function.

The Collective Behavior of Neurons Can Be Studied Noninvasively in Humans by Using Macroelectrodes

Cortical function is dynamically related to interactions between large populations of neurons. A functional index of the behavior of neuronal ensembles can be achieved by constructing population responses from the individual cell responses probed with microelectrodes. In addition, the summated activity of large groups of neurons can be assessed with macroelectrodes by recording

39–5 Glial cell in visual cortex is depolarized by visual stimulus with preferred orientation of nearby neurons. Bars below intracellular recording indicate the orientation of visual stimuli, each of which is presented for period indicated by bracket. (Adapted from Kelly and Van Essen, 1974.)

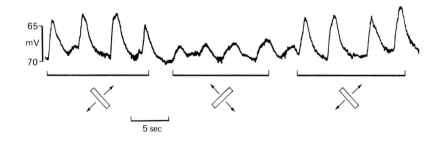

the electrical activity of large groups of neurons (and glia). This latter type of recording can be used in humans to assess cortical function. Recordings of electrical responses of neuronal ensembles may be taken directly from the exposed cortical surface at operation (electrocorticogram, (ECoG) or even from the surface of the scalp (EEG). These measurements of collective function are important for understanding epilepsy.

Macroelectrode recording of neuronal activity is similar to electrocardiography in that the electrical responses of neuronal ensembles can be recorded at sites that are distant from the source of the electrical activity. These recordings can be understood on the basis of a theory called *volume conduction,* which describes the flow of current through the extracellular space under various conditions of neural activity. To record the electrical activity of groups of neurons two electrodes are utilized: an *active electrode* is placed over the recording area, and an *indifferent electrode* is placed at some distance from this site. A variant of this technique, typically used in clinical EEG recordings, utilizes numerous active electrodes situated over different regions of the head. All recordings measure the potential difference between two electrodes: either between the active and indifferent electrodes or between two active electrodes.

All extracellular recordings are based on the fact that potential changes in neurons cause current to flow in the extracellular fluid. Although the resistance of this fluid is low, current flow across this extracellular resistance produces a potential change.

In previous chapters we focused on intracellularly recorded potentials; the extracellular resistance was neglected because it is so small compared to the very large resistance of the membrane. In order to understand extracellular potentials we must now focus on this small extracellular resistance. A constant current flowing across the transmembrane resistance will cause a much greater potential change across the membrane than will the same current flowing across the extracellular resistance. This is one reason intracellular potentials are very large (in the millivolt range) and extracellular potentials very small (in the microvolt range). As a first approximation it is possible to calculate the voltage difference between intracellularly and extracellularly recorded potentials using Ohm's law. An intracellularly recorded excitatory postsynaptic potential of 5 mV would be about 2.5 μV recorded just outside the cell:

$$\frac{V_{intracell}}{R_{membrane}} = \frac{V_{extracell}}{R_{extracell}} = \frac{5 \times 10^{-3}V}{1 \times 10^{9}\Omega} = \frac{V_{extracell}}{5 \times 10^{1}\Omega}$$

Therefore,

$$V_{extracell} = \frac{(5 \times 10^{-3})V}{(1 \times 10^{9})\Omega} (5 \times 10^{1})\Omega = 2.5 \ \mu V.$$

The flow of current in response to an excitatory postsynaptic potential at a site on the apical dendrite of a cortical pyramidal cell is shown in Figure 39–6. The excitatory postsynaptic potential is associated with an inward current at the subsynaptic membrane and an outward current along the large expanse of the extrasynaptic membrane. For simplicity, only one path of outward current is illustrated through the soma membrane. For the purposes of extracellular recording it is important to distinguish the sites of inward and outward current. The site of inward current is called the *sink* because this is where the current flows into the cell. The site of outward current is called the *source.* As illustrated in Figure 39–6, the sink is near the negative charge in the extracellular potential; the source is near the positive charge. This example can be taken one step further to consider the recorded

39–6 Current flow (**I**) in and around a cortical pyramidal cell. R_c, extracellular resistance; R_m, membrane resistance; R_a, axoplasmic resistance.

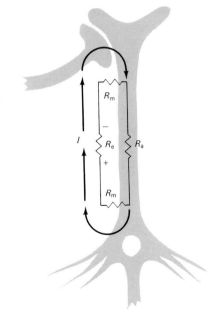

Table 39–1. Directions of Deflection in Recordings of Excitatory and Inhibitory Potentials

Postsynaptic potential	Intracellular Recording	Extracellular Surface Recording	
		Synapse in superficial layer	Synapse in deeper layer
Excitatory	Upward	Upward	Downward
Inhibitory	Downward	Downward	Upward

polarity of such responses. In this case the excitatory synapse is on a portion of the apical dendrite; thus the sink is located in the apical dendrite. The sink is therefore closer to a recording electrode located on the surface of the scalp than is the source, which is located in a deeper cortical layer. The convention adopted for the polarity of extracellular recording is that a negative potential is recorded as an upward deflection. Therefore, this excitatory potential is observed as an upward deflection on an EEG recording device. (In contrast, in intracellular recordings negative potentials are recorded as downward deflections.) The directions of deflection of recorded potentials in response to excitation and inhibition are summarized in Table 39–1.

Electroencephalograms Reflect Summated Postsynaptic Potentials in Cortical Neurons

An electroencephalogram (EEG) is a record of fluctuations of electrical activity in the brain recorded from the surface of the scalp. The recording electrodes are usually placed over the frontal, parietal, occipital, and temporal lobes according to a conventional scheme. In special circumstances, placement of nasopharyngeal or sphenoidal electrodes enhances the recording of activity from the medial temporal lobes. This is particularly important in patients suspected of having seizures originating in limbic structures. The EEG is used chiefly in the diagnosis of cerebral dysfunction (see the section on epilepsy below).

The frequencies of the potentials recorded from the surface of the scalp vary from 1 to 50 Hz (usually 1–30 Hz) and the amplitudes typically range from 20 to 100 μV. The amplitude of the EEG is attenuated by the skull and scalp. Although the frequency characteristics of the EEG potential are extremely complex and the amplitude may vary considerably even within a relatively short time interval, a few dominant fre-

quencies and amplitudes are typically observed. They are called *alpha* (8–13 Hz), *beta* (13–30 Hz), *delta* (0.5–4 Hz), and *theta* (4–7 Hz). In awake individuals either alpha or beta patterns of activity are seen (Figure 39–7).

Alpha rhythm (sometimes called *Berger rhythm* after Hans Berger, who was the first to identify it[1]) is generally associated with a state of relaxed wakefulness; it is recorded best over the parietal–occipital areas. *Beta waves* are normally seen over the frontal regions and more diffusely during intense mental activity. *Delta* and *theta activity* are associated with stages of sleep in the normal adult.

The EEG records the extracellular current flow associated with the activity of the individual

---

[1]Actually Caton was the first to identify the spontaneous electrical activity of the brain in 1875. Since Berger studied the EEG in disease states he is credited as the founder of electroencephalography.

39–7 An EEG recorded from the scalp surface at various points over the left and right hemispheres.

Left
Frontal

Beta

Temporal

Occipital

Right
Frontal

Temporal

Occipital

Alpha

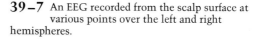
1 sec

cells underlying the electrode. While it might seem that the most obvious source for these extracellular potentials is the action potential–the largest signal generated by neurons—action potentials contribute little to gross surface potentials except possibly when there is synchronous activity in large groups of neurons. The bulk of the gross potentials recorded from the cortex results from extracellular current flow associated with summated postsynaptic potentials in synchronously activated vertically oriented pyramidal cells. The exact configuration of the gross potential is complexly related to the site and the sign of postsynaptic potentials. For example, extracellular current flow associated with excitatory postsynaptic potentials in deeper layers of the cortex is similar to current flow associated with inhibitory postsynaptic potentials in the more superficial layers (Table 39–1). Both of these conditions give rise to a surface positive potential. Knowledge of both extracellular current flow and anatomical pathways is essential for an understanding of the cellular basis of gross potentials.

Glial cells probably do not contribute to the EEG. Pyramidal cells are oriented parallel to one another and perpendicular to the surface of the cortex. Therefore, an extracellular potential is picked up with little attenuation due to geometrical factors because the sources and sinks are generated in response to a synaptic potential and are oriented perpendicular to the cortical surface. Since glial cells are not oriented in any particular fashion relative to one another or to the pyramidal cells, their contribution to the EEG is probably much less important than that of the pyramidal cells.

Stimulation of Sensory Pathways Is Recorded as Evoked Potentials

Another type of clinically interesting gross potential, the primary evoked potential, can be recorded from the cortex or scalp. This potential is due to a change in the ongoing electrical activity of neurons as a result of stimulation of the sensory organs or any part of a sensory pathway that leads from the periphery. Primary evoked responses are time-locked to the stimulus and are specific for the sensory system that evokes them. The evoked potential recorded from the scalp is not readily apparent in the background EEG, and special computerized averaging programs are necessary to display such potentials. For example, the primary evoked potential recorded over the somatic sensory cortex in response to an electrical stimulus or a tap to the skin has a short latency; its first phase is positive and is followed by a negative wave. The initial positive response is a result of excitation in the deeper cortical layers, arising from the ventral posterior lateral nucleus of the thalamus. The later negative response, with a longer latency, is a result of excitatory input to the superficial cortical layers. This *diphasic potential* may sometimes be observed to ride upon a positive wave of much longer duration. This wave probably reflects the longer duration inhibition at the level of the soma.

By using computer methods it has also become possible to record the contribution of noncortical structures to the evoked potential and thereby to learn something about the role of these regions in the processing of stimuli. For example, in the auditory system one can specify the contribution of

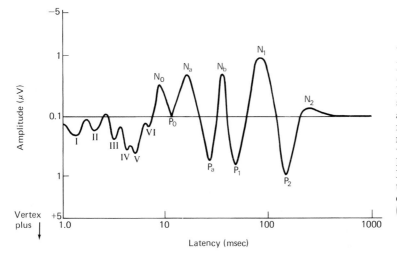

39–8 Auditory evoked potential components plotted on a logarithmic scale. Available evidence suggests that components **I** to **VI** are generated by the succession of structures in the auditory pathway from the auditory nerve to the medial geniculate nucleus. These potentials are called "far field potentials." Sources for later components (N_0–N_2– and P_0–P_2) probably include nonspecific thalamic nuclei, the auditory cortex, and association cortices. (Adapted from Picton et al., 1974.)

each relay in the auditory pathway to the recording from the scalp (Figure 39–8). This is possible because the tissue between a brain stem nucleus and the scalp electrode behaves as a volume conductor. Although the scalp electrode would better record local activity in the immediate environment of the electrode, with appropriate averaging unwanted signals are rejected and the stimulus-dependent activity of each relay becomes readily apparent in what is called the *far field potential*. In Figure 39–8 both far field potentials and cortical-evoked potentials are shown. The far field recording technique is proving to be important clinically in assessing subcortical sensory relay function. For example, in patients with demyelinating diseases (e.g., multiple sclerosis), destruction of the myelin sheath causes a decrease in conduction velocity; as a result the timing of the far field potentials is slower than normal.

Epilepsy Is Characterized by a Paroxysmal Depolarization Shift in Cortical Neurons

Epilepsy is one of the most common neurological diseases; about 1% of the world population suffers epileptic seizures. Epilepsy results when a large collection of neurons discharge in synchrony. Concomitant with this discharge, which can be recorded electrophysiologically, there are stereotyped paroxysmal alterations in behavior. Abnormal cellular discharge may be associated with a variety of causative factors including trauma, ischemia, tumors, infection, and metabolic derangements. In about half the patients, however, no specific etiology is found.

There are a number of classification schemes for epileptic seizures but the simplest reflects the extent of the brain affected.

Partial or *focal epilepsy* is a form that begins in a localized brain region. The clinical manifestations of partial seizures reflect the region of the brain involved. For example, an epileptogenic focus located in the precentral gyrus (motor cortex) results in involuntary twitching of the contralateral fingers and face. Commonly, there is sequential activation of different muscle groups as the abnormal electrical activity spreads from the focus to neighboring cortical tissue. Thus, the motor activity may involve first the fingers, followed by wrist, elbow, shoulder, and eventually the face and leg. Because a brilliant English neurologist, John Hughlings Jackson, first described the somatotopic organization of the motor cortex from observations made in patients with this type of seizure, these attacks are sometimes called Jacksonian motor seizures. The patient experiencing a Jacksonian seizure remains conscious provided that the abnormal activity remains restricted to one hemisphere. When the spread of epileptic activity includes the other hemisphere, consciousness is lost. Complex partial seizures *(psychomotor epilepsy)* are characterized by complicated psycho-illusory phenomena and semipurposeful complicated motor acts that result from the involvement of structures within the temporal lobe.

Generalized or *nonfocal epilepsy* from the outset involves large parts of the brain diffusely. Generalized seizures are subdivided into *petit mal* and *grand mal.* The characteristic symptom of petit mal epilepsy is transient absence (that is, transient loss of consciousness). Grand mal seizures are characterized by tonic–clonic movements. Some forms of generalized seizures are initially bilateral.

Focal epilepsy has been most widely studied because it is simpler than other forms, is easier to produce in experimental animals, and occurs frequently. An epileptic focus can be established in an experimental animal by applying a convulsant agent to the surface of the cortex. A common and effective method is the direct application of penicillin crystals. The events following penicillin-induced seizures in many respects resemble a naturally occurring epileptic focus.

The first characteristically abnormal electrical event after penicillin application is the intermittent appearance of high-voltage negative waves on the EEG (Figure 39–9). These are called *interictal spikes* because they resemble the spikes seen in the EEG between actual seizures in humans (Latin *ictus,* a stroke). As the interictal spikes become more frequent they become associated with a negative wave of slower time course. Collectively the fast (spikelike) and slow components are referred to as the *interictal EEG paroxysm.* The slow negative component may also be associated with low-voltage fast waves riding on the crest. When a full-blown seizure occurs it typically arises from these fast components.

The interictal EEG paroxysm provides a convenient and simple model for elucidating the electrophysiological mechanisms of epilepsy. Intracellular recording from neurons in an experimental epileptic focus show cellular discharges during the interictal spike that are driven by a large depolarization called the *paroxysmal depolarization shift* (PDS). The paroxysmal depolar-

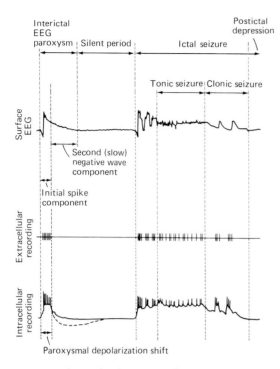

39–9 Relationship between surface recorded EEG discharges and intracellular and extracellular activity in a cortical epileptic focus. (Adapted from Ayala et al., 1973.)

Basic research in epilepsy provides a good example of the application of cellular techniques to the investigation of cortical disease. One of the goals of research in neurobiology is to use similar approaches for other neurological and psychiatric diseases. In subsequent chapters on sleep, instinctive behavior, psychoses, and learning, we shall see that a cellular approach is now beginning to be fruitful in the study of other human diseases.

Selected Readings and References

Ayala, G. F., Dichter, M., Gumnit, R. J., Matsumoto, H., and Spencer, W. A. 1973. Genesis of epileptic interictal spikes. New knowledge of cortical feedback systems suggests a neurophysiological explanation of brief paroxysms. Brain Res. 52:1–17.

Hubel, D. H., and Wiesel, T. N. 1977. Functional architecture of macaque monkey visual cortex. Proc. R. Soc. Lond. B Biol. Sci. 198:1–59.

Mountcastle, V. B. 1978. An organizing principle for cerebral function: The unit module and the distributed system. In G. M. Edelman and V. B. Mountcastle, The Mindful Brain. Cambridge, Mass.: MIT Press, pp. 7–50.

Orkand, R. K. 1977. Glial cells. In E. R. Kandel (ed.), Handbook of Physiology; Cellular Biology of Neurons, Vol. 1, Part II. Bethesda, Md.: American Physiological Society, pp. 855–875.

Prince, D. A. 1978. Neurophysiology of epilepsy. Annu. Rev. Neurosci. 1:395–415.

Schwartzkroin, P. A., and Wyler, A. R. 1980. Mechanisms underlying epileptiform burst discharge. Ann. Neurol. 7:95–107.

Spencer, W. A. 1977. The physiology of supraspinal neurons in mammals. In E. R. Kandel (ed.), Handbook of Physiology; Cellular Biology of Neurons, Vol. 1, Part II. Bethesda, Md.: American Physiological Society, pp. 969–1021.

Other References

Glaser, G. H. 1979. Convulsive disorders (epilepsy). In H. H. Merritt, A Textbook of Neurology. 6th ed. Philadelphia: Lea & Febiger, pp. 843–883.

Gray, E. G. 1959. Axo-somatic and axo-dendritic synapses of the cerebral cortex: An electron microscope study. J. Anat. 93:420–433.

Hamlyn, L. H. 1963. An electron microscope study of pyramidal neurons in the Ammon's Horn of the rabbit. J. Anat. 97:189–201.

Jewett, D. L., and Williston, J. S. 1971. Auditory-evoked far fields averaged from the scalp of humans. Brain 94:681–696.

Kelly, J. P., and Van Essen, D. C. 1974. Cell structure and function in the visual cortex of the cat. J. Physiol. (Lond.) 238:515–547.

ization shift is followed by a hyperpolarization. There are two hypotheses regarding the cellular mechanisms of the paroxysmal depolarization shift. According to one, the paroxysmal depolarization shift is a giant form of excitatory postsynaptic potential. Synchronous excitatory potentials summate to generate the observed large depolarization. The excitatory feedback circuits, ubiquitous in the cortex, are thought to provide the explosive and synchronous generators for depolarization shifts. Feedback inhibitory circuitry is thought to contribute to the hyperpolarization observed after a paroxysmal depolarization shift. It is easy to see how the normal balance between feedback excitation and inhibition could lead to epileptic activity when biased toward excitation. An alternative interpretation supported by the more recent cellular studies by Prince and by Llinás is that the paroxysmal depolarization shift results from active membrane processes intrinsic to a cell. According to this view, synaptic inputs serve only to trigger and synchronize this process across a population of cells. Dendritic spike-generating mechanisms involving Ca^{++} currents are thought to be important for this mechanism.

Kuffler, S. W. 1967. Neuroglial cells: Physiological properties and a potassium mediated effect of neuronal activity on the glial membrane potential. Proc. R. Soc. Lond. B Biol. Sci. 168:1–21.

Llinás, R., and Nicholson, C. 1971. Electrophysiological properties of dendrites and somata in alligator Purkinje cells. J. Neurophysiol. 34:532–551.

Picton, T. W., Hillyard, S. A., Krausz, H. I., and Galambos, R. 1974. Human auditory evoked potentials. I: Evaluation of components. Electroencephalogr. Clin. Neurophysiol. 36:179–190.

Spencer, W. A., and Kandel, E. R. 1961. Electrophysiology of hippocampal neurons. IV. Fast prepotentials. J. Neurophysiol. 24:272–285.

Spencer, W. A., and Kandel, E. R. 1968. Cellular and integrative properties of the hippocampal pyramidal cell and the comparative electrophysiology of cortical neurons. Internat. J. Neurol. 6:266–296.

Stockard, J. J., and Rossiter, V. S. 1977. Clinical and pathologic correlates of brain stem auditory response abnormalities. Neurology 27:316–325.

Szentágothai, J. 1969. Architecture of the cerebral cortex. In H. H. Jasper, A. A. Ward, Jr., and A. Pope (eds.), Basic Mechanisms of the Epilepsies. Boston: Little, Brown, pp. 13–28.

Dennis D. Kelly

Physiology of Sleep and Dreaming

40

. . . To die: to sleep;
No more; and by a sleep to say we end
The heart-ache and the thousand natural shocks
That flesh is heir to, 'tis a consummation
Devoutly to be wish'd. To die: to sleep;
To sleep: perchance to dream: ay, there's the rub;
For in that sleep of death what dreams may come . . .

(*Hamlet*, Act III, scene i)

Ideas about sleep and dreaming have always been critical to man's concepts of mind and consciousness. One line of thought has characterized sleep as an analogue of death during which mental function ceases, while another has held that sleep, like wakefulness, is a special form of mental activity. Almost eight centuries before Christ, Hesiod emphasized the overt behavioral quiet of the sleeper when he called "Sleep, the brother of death." However, there have been many throughout the history of thought who, like Shakespeare's Hamlet and Cervantes' Sancho Panza, have viewed sleep less as a suspension of life than as an opportunity to dream. Sigmund Freud, in *The Interpretation of Dreams* (1900), recognized that the mental activity that occurred during sleep represented for the scientist a unique avenue by which the unconscious motivations of the individual might be explored. To a significant extent the development in this century of modern research on the biology of sleep has also mirrored this historical dual focus upon the periodic interruption of waking consciousness and its replacement with an even more intense mental experience.

In a book published in 1913 that was to influence sleep research for several decades, Henri Piéron defined sleep as a state that is periodically necessary, with a rhythmicity relatively independent of external conditions, and characterized by complete interruptions of the brain's sensory and motor functions that link it to the environment. We now know that isolation from the environment is far from complete even in the deepest stages of sleep. Sensory impulses from the periphery can penetrate to cortical areas even during sleep, and, conversely, cortical motor commands reach alpha motor neurons in the spinal cord, although the output of the latter is actively inhibited. Nevertheless, the perspective offered by Piéron's definition remains important today, for we have yet to discover how or why the brain undergoes with extreme regularity such a profound change in its interactions with the environment and in its own functional organization.

Sleep Is a Rhythmic and Active Neural Process

As Piéron emphasized, sleep is a periodic, recurring process. There is a strict periodicity to the polyphasic sleep–wake cycle of the newborn and to the biphasic pattern of the child who naps in the afternoon, as well as to the monophasic, circadian cycle of the adult. The sleep–wake cycle is one of the endogenous rhythms of the body that become entrained to the day–night cycle. If a person is kept completely isolated from the external circadian changes of light and temperature, and also from social temporal cues and, in particular, from the knowledge of time, his sleep–wake rhythm will gradually drift from a strict 24-hr cycle to one of approximately 25 hr. This represents the length of the normal sleep–wake biorhythm for three-quarters of the adult population. In the remainder, the period between successive awakenings under isolated, free-running conditions stretches well beyond this norm. Figure 40–1 shows a striking example of a person whose free-running sleep–wake cycle lengthened to 33 hr. These data also help make the point that there probably is no single biological clock that triggers all of the body's circadian rhythms. For under free-running conditions such rhythms as body temperature, urine formation, and cortisol secretion may become desynchronized and change dramatically in their phase relationships with each other and with the sleep–wake cycle. Body temperature normally varies in a circadian pattern from a high in the late afternoon to a low in the early morning hours during sleep. Thus, under normal circadian conditions the sleep–wake and body temperature rhythms are linked. However, under free-running conditions, as in Figure 40–1, most vegetative functions such as body temperature cannot follow cycles longer than 25 hr. Therefore, when the sleep–wake cycle lengthens beyond this value, the two rhythms become desynchronized and free-run with different periodicities.

In addition to the circadian cycle of sleep and wakefulness, there are also fixed internal rhythms to sleep. It has been known since the late 19th century that the depth of human sleep varies systematically in five to seven orderly cycles each night. Had these intrinsic rhythms remained a central focus of sleep research, it is possible that a passive theory of sleep would not have so dominated thought, as it did, into the 1950s. This theory suggested that sleep was a pas-

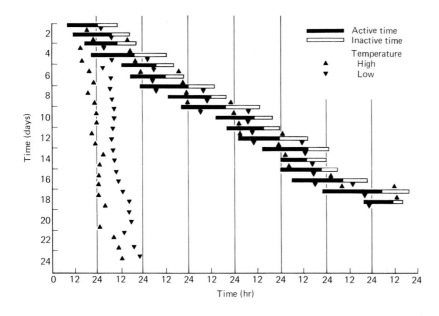

40–1 Desynchronization of two body rhythms in a free-running isolated subject. The free-running sleep-wake cycle lengthened to 33.2 hr, as evidenced by the drift to the right in the activity (**light line**)–rest (**dark line**) lines. The drift in the activity–rest plot is caused by the subject awakening (the beginning of the line) several hours later each day. Rectal temperature (plotted separately to the left) maintained a 24.8-hr rhythm. Thus, when superimposed upon the activity–rest plot, temperature shows more than one maximum or minimum per 33-hr cycle. (Adapted from Aschoff, 1969.)

sive state into which the brain lapsed when there was insufficient sensory stimulation to keep it awake. Sleep was viewed simply as the end of the waking state, and as a consequence of this perspective the central problem for neurophysiology was reduced to specifying those neural systems that maintained wakefulness—the primary, active state. Suppression of these arousal centers, brought about by the reduction of afferent impulses that maintained tonic arousal, was felt to be sufficient to erase wakefulness and thus induce sleep. However, in light of the extreme regularity of both the internal and circadian rhythms of sleep, it seemed unlikely to some researchers that such a temporal process could be explained in terms of gross fluctuations in the environmental barrage of sensory stimulation that was presumed to arouse the brain when present and to allow it to sleep when absent.

Compared to the simple notion of sleep as an

idling state somewhere near the low end of a continuum of vigilance (a theory to which we shall return in the next chapter in relation to the study of coma), the concept of sleep that emerged during the 1950s and 1960s was revolutionary. Sleep became recognized as an active process characterized by a cyclic succession of different psychophysiological phenomena. In the following sections we shall summarize the work that encouraged the view that sleep is an active function of the brain composed of at least two distinctive states. These stages of sleep are temporally programmed in a relatively predictable sequence each night, and they appear to be controlled by different, but linked, neurochemical systems.

The Stages of Sleep
Slow-Wave Sleep without Rapid Eye Movements

The EEG has through convention and convenience become the primary means of monitoring the stages of human sleep. As illustrated by Figure 40–2A, stages 1–4 of slow-wave sleep are characterized by progressively slower frequency and higher voltage activity and are correspondingly related to the depth of sleep. As a person initially cycles into sleep, the EEG progresses over a 30–45-min span through stages 1–4 of slow-wave sleep, and then the EEG retraces the same stages in reverse order over a similar time span (Figure 40–2B). During slow-wave sleep, the

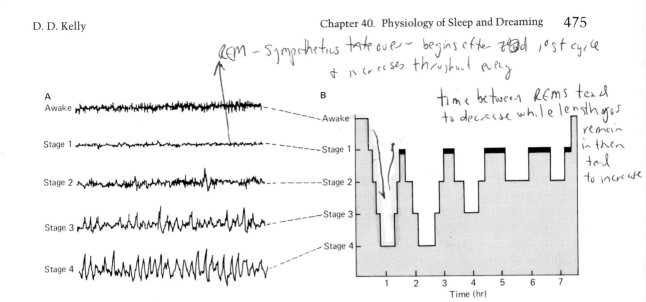

[Handwritten annotations: "REM - sympathetics take over - begins after 2nd 1st cycle & increases throughout every"; "time between REMs tend to decrease while length gos remain in then tend to increase"]

A. Awake / Stage 1 / Stage 2 / Stage 3 / Stage 4

B. Awake / Stage 1 / Stage 2 / Stage 3 / Stage 4

Time (hr)   1 2 3 4 5 6 7

muscles are relaxed, but somatic activity is not absent. In fact, normal sleepers make a major postural adjustment on the average of once every 20 min, and some sleepers every 5 min. Furthermore, during slow-wave sleep the autonomic indicators show a parasympathetic dominance. Heart rate and blood pressure decline; respiration declines and becomes more even; gastrointestinal motility is increased. The arousal threshold in slow-wave sleep varies inversely with EEG frequency, with stage 4 delta-wave sleep the most difficult to interrupt.

Sleep with Rapid Eye Movements

About 90 min after the onset of sleep, an abrupt change occurs in a number of tonic physiological measures. The EEG suddenly becomes desynchronized (low-voltage, fast activity, characteristic of stage 1) and brain temperature rises slightly. This active brain pattern seen in stage 1 (Figure 40–2A) is coupled with broad sympathetic activation. Heart rate and blood pressure increase; respiration becomes more rapid and irregular; and gastrointestinal movements cease. Head, neck, and general skeletal muscles are actively inhibited. Electromyographic measures become silent; there is a profound loss of muscle tonus except for eye and middle ear muscles.

Against the background of these *tonic*, or long-lasting physiological events characterizing this stage of sleep, a set of related and important *phasic* events occur. The first to be discovered among these events was rapid eye movements (REM), hence the name *REM sleep*. The middle ear muscles are also phasically active, and both rapid eye movement and middle ear muscle activity appear to be driven by phasic bursts of elec-

40–2 A. Electroencephalographic recordings during different stages of wakefulness and sleep. Each line represents 30 sec. The top recording of low voltage fast activity is that of an awake brain. The next four represent successively deeper stages of NREM slow-wave sleep. The stage 2 sample contains several characteristic bursts of waxing-and-waning waves (sleep spindles) of 1 to 2-sec duration. Stage 1 REM sleep can be distinguished from stage 1 NREM sleep only by additional electrooculographic and electromyographic criteria, the presence of which are indicated by the **dark bar** in the graph to the right. **B.** A typical night's pattern of sleep staging in a young adult. The time spent in stage REM sleep is represented by a **dark bar.** The first REM period is usually short, 5–10 min, but they tend to lengthen in successive cycles. Conversely, stages 3 and 4 dominate the NREM periods in the first third of the night, but are often completely absent during the later, early morning cycles. The amount of stage 2 NREM sleep increases progressively until it completely occupies the NREM periods toward the end of the night. Note that in this example, because the morning awakening interrupted the last REM period, the likelihood of a dream recall is good. If instead, the REM period had been completed and the sleeper had been awakened by an alarm from the next stage 2 NREM sleep, the chance of a dream recall would be greatly reduced.

trical activity that can be recorded in animals from the pons, oculomotor nuclei, lateral geniculate nuclei of the thalamus, and visual cortices. It is virtually certain that these monophasic sharp waves, referred to as pontine–geniculate–occipital (PGO) spikes, represent a primary triggering process for phasic ocular movements, since the first derivative of the electrooculogram ($\frac{dv}{dt}$ EOG) during rapid eye movement episodes in the cat reflects perfectly the PGO spike code.

During REM sleep the arousal threshold in animals is significantly increased. Thus by one criterion, external arousability, stage REM is the deepest stage of sleep. On the other hand, a human sleeper is also more likely to awaken spontaneously from REM sleep than from an equivalent period of any non-rapid eye movement (NREM) sleep stage; thus by another criterion, REM sleep is the lightest stage of sleep. Finally, if the sleeper is awakened and asked, "Were you dreaming?" a higher frequency of dream recall will be obtained during REM sleep (74–95% depending on the sleep laboratory) than during periods of non-REM sleep (0–51% according to Foulkes' 1962 study). The range in these values depends principally upon the working definition of dreaming adopted by different investigators, and hence in their method of questioning the subject. REM sleep has also been called *paradoxical sleep* (because of the presence of a waking EEG) or *D-sleep* (which refers to *d*reaming coupled with a *d*esynchronized EEG). In the latter terminology, non-REM sleep is referred to as *S-sleep* in reference to its characteristic *s*low-wave, *s*ynchronized, and *s*pindling EEG patterns.

Architecture of a Night's Sleep

During a typical night's sleep, as outlined in Figure 40–2B, the normal person will alternate between periods of REM and NREM sleep, with stage REM recurring at regular intervals five to seven times each night. A closer look at Figure 40–2B will also reveal that, following the first REM period, intervals between successive REM periods decrease throughout the night, while the length of each REM episode tends to increase. In all, REM sleep occupies approximately 20–25% of the sleep time of young adults. Stage 2 NREM sleep occupies about one-half of total sleep time, and stage 4 NREM sleep about 15%.

All sleep stages are epochal in character, with some 30 or more changes from stage to stage typical over a single 7-hr period. In addition to the cyclic occurrence of REM sleep, there is one other clear temporal characteristic that is noteworthy in human sleep: stage 4 NREM (deep) sleep appears primarily in the first half of the sleep period. Thus, the early morning hours with less stage 3 and 4 NREM sleep and with longer REM periods are characterized by more frequent awakenings even in the normal sleeper.

Stage 4 NREM and stage REM appear to be distinct periods. As we shall see in the next section, they also show markedly different developmental patterns within the lifespan of the individual. Stage 4 NREM sleep is highly responsive to the amount of prior wakefulness, while stage REM is much less so. Stage REM and stage 4 NREM are also differentially affected by certain drugs. A broad spectrum of psychoactive agents, particularly alcohol and the barbiturates, suppresses REM sleep, while stage 4 NREM sleep is somewhat less responsive to these drugs but responsive to other drugs. For instance, stage 4 NREM sleep is reduced by the benzodiazepines, Valium and Librium, to a much greater extent than REM sleep. We shall return to this important point in Chapter 41 when we consider the treatment of insomnia.

The Ontogeny of Sleep

Thus far we have considered only the nightly sleep patterning of the mature human brain. There are, however, some dramatic ontogenetic and phylogenetic patterns to the sleep process. As shown in Figure 40–3A, the daily sleep requirement of the human brain declines steadily throughout childhood and adolescence, levels off through the middle years, and then begins a further decline with the onset of old age. The most dramatic ontogenetic changes in the architecture of human sleep involve the amounts of stage REM (Figure 40–3B) and stage 4 NREM sleep (Figure 40–3C). The biological need for REM sleep apparently begins in utero. REM sleep fills approximately 80% of the total sleep time of 10-week premature infants, and 60–65% of the total sleep time of infants born 2–4 weeks prematurely. In full-term neonates REM sleep fills one-half of the normal 16-hr total daily sleep time. REM sleep declines sharply to 30–35% of sleep time by age 2 and stabilizes at about 25% by 10 years of age, after which it shows little change until the seventh or eighth decade. Thus, the absolute amount of REM sleep time per day shows a sharp decline from about 8 hr at birth to 1.5–1.75 hr by the onset of puberty. Stage 4 NREM sleep, on the other hand, shows an exponential decline throughout the developing and middle years. Stage 4 NREM sleep often disappears in persons over 60 years of age. This continuous decline in stage 4 NREM sleep in the elderly is correlated with an increase in the number of normal spontaneous awakenings and ultimately with a return to a biphasic circadian pattern of sleep (namely, a nap in the afternoon).

The striking pattern of the development of

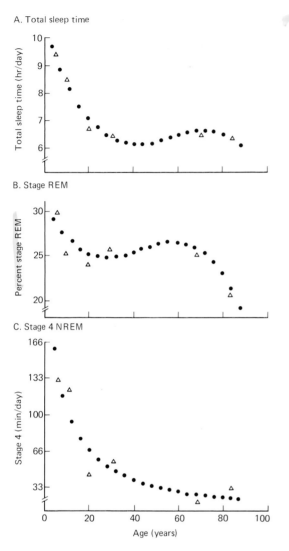

A. Total sleep time

B. Stage REM

C. Stage 4 NREM

40–3 Changes in sleep patterns with age. Δ, data points for the ages of 6, 10, 21, 30, 69, and 84 years; ●, best fitting theoretical curve by regression techniques. **A.** Sharp decline in sleep time during adolescence and further slight decrease with old age. (Adapted from Feinberg, 1969.) **B.** Percentage of sleep time spent in stage REM as a function of age. **C.** Minutes per day spent in stage 4 NREM sleep as a function of age.

REM sleep has prompted a number of theories that attempt to link the function of REM sleep to the maturational process. Because the ontogenetic pattern of REM sleep roughly parallels the maturation of corticofugal connections and the rate of cerebral myelinization, Howard Roffwarg and his colleagues have suggested that REM sleep may play a role in the developing nervous system analogous to that of physical exercise in the development of muscles. This early theory took into account the fact that REM sleep causes intense activation of neuronal circuits; indeed the consumption of oxygen by the brain is even greater during REM sleep than during either intense physical or mental exercise in the waking state. Thus, REM sleep was conceptualized as a potential source of internal stimulation necessary for proper maturation of the brain. However, this theory could not explain why dreaming continues after the brain has fully developed.

The Phylogeny of Sleep

A more recent and speculative theory of REM sleep has been proposed by Michel Jouvet of Lyon, France. It combines these ontogenetic observations with a phylogenetic perspective. EEG recordings in nonhuman primates show that their sleep stages are similar to those of humans. However, the sleep of rodents and smaller mammals and birds is characterized by only two distinct stages: slow-wave sleep, similar in appearance to human stage 4 NREM sleep; and activated sleep, equivalent to REM sleep in humans. These two sleep stages are seen in all mammals and birds. On the other hand, sleep associated with EEG desynchronization has not been clearly established in reptiles or amphibians, although EEG criteria may be relatively useless for establishing the homology of sleep patterns in species that possess virtually no neocortex. Because REM sleep is recognizable in mammals and birds but not in snakes or other reptiles, Jouvet suggested that it may be a later phylogenetic process related to homiothermy. As it is not found in cold-blooded animals, it is not necessary for life.

Jouvet has also discovered that bilateral destruction of the medial portion of the pontine nucleus locus ceruleus or of its descending pathway interrupts the strong motor inhibition of the REM state and allows one to observe the unparalyzed behavior of cats during REM sleep. By analogy with the human REM state, these animals appear to be acting out their dreams. The stereotyped behavior patterns most often exhibited when the other signs of REM sleep are present are those of predatory attack, rage, flight, grooming, exploration, and various other well-integrated, species-typical behavior patterns. These oneiric, or dream-related, movement patterns are strongly linked to PGO spikes.

Jouvet suggests that the stage REM "dreams" of lower mammals may represent a means of programming in advance species-typical behaviors, i.e., of practicing vital behavioral patterns before the specific environmental situation is encountered in the waking state. This is why, Jouvet argues, instinctive acts are nearly perfect the first time they are executed by individual members of the species: they have been practiced in dreams. Thus, by extension, dreams of all animals may be considered to be genetically preprogrammed. The control of instinctive behavioral sequences is added to the repertoire of the maturing brain during REM sleep when the necessary neuronal circuits are organized according to a genetic blueprint. In cold-blooded animals, Jouvet suggests this genetic readout may be completed in ovo before birth; hence, there is no need for the REM state. One additional and interesting observation drawn from the work of Sastre and Jouvet is that unparalyzed cats never display sexual behavior during REM episodes.

Despite the phylogenetic continuity of REM sleep across all mammals, Jouvet has not attempted to characterize the behavior patterns that developing human brains might practice during REM dreams. This theory remains very much a theory of REM sleep in nonhuman animals.

The Psychophysiology of Dream Content

The discovery by William Dement of the strong correlation between REM sleep and visual dreaming in humans has reversed many commonly held notions concerning dreams. While it was previously thought that dreaming was rare, modern physiological studies have proved that everyone dreams in regular REM cycles several times every night. It had been subjectively easy to think of dreams as infrequent because their memory traces are evanescent. The probability of dream recall falls to NREM levels within 8 min post REM sleep. As a result, we usually remember only morning dreams, which also turn out to be those with the oldest and most emotional psychological content.

Intensity Gradient of Dreams within a Night's Sleep

Successive REM periods during a single night's sleep are characterized by increasing physiologi-

cal intensity as measured by the frequency of phasic events (PGO spikes, rapid eye movements, middle ear muscle contractions, cardiorespiratory irregularities, muscular twitching, etc.). There is also a parallel increase through successive REM periods in the intensity of emotional tone and the activity of visual imagery in the content of the recalled dream. In this limited sense, eye movements appear to be related to dream imagery: eventful dreams are associated with more frequent rapid eye movements than inactive dreams. It is a matter of current dispute, however, whether any closer correspondence exists, as if the eye were scanning or looking at the dream. While some investigators find occasional correlations between specific eye movements and shifts of gaze in dream imagery, others find that eye movements are driven in a locked frequency pattern along with other phasic phenomena and therefore doubt that they are guided by subjective dream content.

Erection Cycles During Sleep

Another interesting physiological correlate of REM sleep that bears only a minimal relationship to dream content is penile erection. Erections slightly precede, then accompany, virtually every REM epoch in males. They are not caused by or correlated with overtly sensual dreaming, although there may be modulation of tumescence, as well as instances of ejaculation, at appropriate moments in a dream story. The ability to attain a normal erection during REM sleep has been used by some sex therapists to distinguish between physical and psychogenic causes of impotence in male patients.

Passage of Time in Dreams

Despite many popular anecdotes to the contrary, the passage of time in dreams is apparently not compressed. On the assumption that it would take more words to describe a long dream than a short one, Dement simply counted the number of words in dream reports and compared these to the length of REM episodes. The length of dream narratives showed a highly positive correlation with the duration of REM sleep. In another experiment in the same series, Dement awakened subjects either 5 or 15 min after the onset of REM sleep and asked them to select the correct interval on the basis of the apparent duration of whatever dream material they recalled. A correct choice was made in 83% of instances.

REM Versus NREM Mentation

Although dreaming is often discussed as synonymous with REM sleep, there is clear evidence that mental activity also occurs during NREM sleep. These reports are not just recalls of prior REM episodes, for they may be elicited during the very first NREM cycle of the evening. The probability of obtaining recall during NREM sleep depends greatly upon one's definition of what constitutes a dream. In general, as summarized in Table 40–1, NREM mentation is more poorly recalled, more similar to waking thought, less vivid and visual, more conceptual and plausible, under greater volitional control, less emotional, and more pleasant. An important exception to the latter is that most nightmares occur during stages 3 and 4 NREM sleep, a point to which we shall return in Chapter 41. The essential symptoms of true nightmares are respiratory oppression, paralysis, and anxiety. However, as is typical of NREM mental activity, such episodes are not accompanied by full dream narratives: rather, a single oppressive situation is recalled, such as being locked up in a tomb or having rocks piled on the chest.

Selective Deprivation of REM Sleep Results in a REM Rebound

REM Compensation Phenomenon

Because the onsets on REM periods are relatively unambiguous, it is possible to arouse sleeping subjects at the transition into REM sleep and thus to reduce REM sleep time drastically without curtailing NREM sleep. The first such experiments were performed on human subjects in 1960 by Dement, whose initial interest was in the consequences of REM deprivation for waking behavior. However, the most compelling finding was a dramatic shift in subsequent sleep patterns when deprivation procedures were removed. Curtailment of REM sleep for several nights was followed by a marked lengthening and increased frequency of REM periods, with more prolonged deprivation resulting in a larger and longer REM rebound.

Spike Deprivation Procedures

Similar deprivation studies in animals showed that as pressure for REM sleep increased as a function of prior REM deprivation, the phasic events accompanying REM sleep during recovery also became more frequent, thus revealing another mode of adjustment in which alterations

Table 40–1. Reported Characteristics of REM and NREM Mentation

Characteristic	Sleep stage		
	NREM 3 and 4	NREM 2 (ascending)	REM
Features present (percent positive responses)			
Dreaming content	51	51	82
Thinking content	19	23	5
Emotion felt by self	28	29	50
Visual	73	62	90
Physical movement of self	33	38	67
Only one other character	62	50	34
Shift in scene	28	38	63
Recall makes sense to dreamer in terms of recent experience†	69	75	48
Median judged duration of reported mental experience	5 (min)	5 (min)	5 (min)
Subject mean ratings of dream characteristics‡			
Anxiety	0.71	1.00	1.19
Violence–hostility	0.12	0.59	0.71
Distortion	1.12	0.41	1.68

Source: Adapted from Foulkes, D. The Psychology of Sleep, Scribner's, 1966.
†Question asked on postsleep questionnaire rather than during nocturnal interview.
‡Scale runs from 0 (low) to 5 (high).

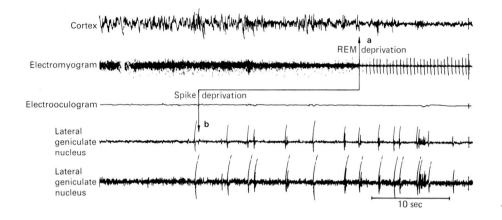

40–4 Comparison of spike deprivation and REM deprivation procedures. In REM deprivation procedures, the sleeping cat would be aroused at the exact onset of the REM period (**arrow a**), signaled by suppression of the electromyogram and activation of the EEG from the cortex. In spike deprivation procedures, the animal would have been aroused earlier (**arrow b**), immediately after the first POG spike seen in the two tracings taken from the lateral geniculate nucleus and before rapid eye movements appeared in the electrooculogram. (Adapted from Dement, 1965.)

in the intensity of REM sleep could contribute to the compensatory process. This suggested that the loss of phasic activity might be fundamental to the REM compensation phenomenon. To test this possibility, sleeping cats were deprived not only of REM sleep, but also of all PGO spike activity, even that small amount which normally occurs during NREM sleep. This procedure, called *spike deprivation*, is illustrated in Figure 40–4. Spike deprivation resulted in a substantially larger REM rebound during recovery. Conversely, when REM awakenings were carried out with exceeding gentleness, allowing the discharge of a large number of PGO spikes before NREM sleep was established, virtually no REM rebound occurred despite total suppression of the tonic events defining REM sleep (EEG activation, electromyogram suppression, penile erection, and brain temperature elevation). Despite the biological importance of REM sleep suggested by the compensation phenomenon, no studies have yet demonstrated a significant functional consequence of REM deprivation for the waking life of human subjects.

Several Neural Mechanisms May Be Responsible for the Sleep–Wake Cycle

In 1913 Henri Piéron suggested that physical or mental activity during the day probably produced some chemical that induced sleep and that during sleep the chemical was destroyed. Piéron siphoned cerebrospinal fluid from dogs kept awake for several days and injected this into the ventricular system of recipient dogs, who subsequently slept for 2–6 hr. This phenomenon was replicated in 1939 by Schnedorf and Ivy, but it was noted that hyperthermia usually followed injections of exogenous cerebrospinal fluid (a result of increased intracerebral pressure), and thus Piéron's notion of a central sleep-producing substance fell into disrepute.

Possible Sleep-Promoting Substances

In recent years improved biochemical techniques have led to the discovery and characterization of at least three potential sleep-promoting factors: one found in cerebral venous blood, another in cerebrospinal fluid, and a third in brain stem nervous tissue. In 1977 Schoenenberger and Monnier isolated a nonapeptide from the blood of rabbits in which the thalamus had been electrically stimulated to induce sleep. Because administration of this peptide (Trp-Ala-Gly-Gly-Asp-Ala-Ser-Gly-Glu) into the cerebral ventricles enhanced EEG delta waves typical of NREM sleep and reduced general locomotor activity, it has been named delta sleep–inducing peptide (DSIP). However, in most studies this peptide has proven to be a somewhat mild hypnotic and, like other peptides, its normal passage across the blood–brain barrier is difficult and slow.

In 1967 another peptide sleep-promoting substance (SPS) with a molecular weight of less than 500 was concentrated by means of selective filtration from the cerebrospinal fluid of sleep-deprived goats. This factor, which was purified by J. R. Pappenheimer's group, does not appear to be a neurotransmitter; it acts by increasing the duration of slow-wave sleep (but not REM sleep) and by decreasing locomotor activity in recipient subjects. However, the structure, source, site of action, and precise role of this cerebrospinal fluid factor in sleep are not known. A third factor extracted from the brain stem of sleep-deprived rats produces dose-dependent increases in both REM and NREM sleep when administered by any route; however, its precise structure is also as yet unknown.

Early Concept of the Reticular Activating System

Regardless of whether there may be cerebrospinal or systemic factors to guide the brain into periods of sleep, it is now certain that on a neural level the onset of sleep is an actively induced process. However, this fact has been widely accepted only in the past 20 years, largely through the efforts of Giuseppi Moruzzi. Previous research had suggested that sleep might be a passive function of the brain that occurred as a consequence of decreased sensory activation. This theory took root in the mid-1930s with the experiments of the Belgian neurophysiologist, Frederick Bremer.

Bremer was interested in whether the forebrain, when disconnected from the caudal brain stem and thus deprived of almost all sensory input, would continue to cycle between sleep and wakefulness. When Bremer completely transected the midbrain of a cat at a level between the superior and inferior colliculi (a *cerveau isolé preparation*), the isolated forebrain displayed a continuous EEG pattern of high-voltage slow-wave activity and permanently constricted pupils typical of sleep. If the transection was made instead between the caudal medulla and the spinal cord (an *encéphale isolé preparation*), the forebrain showed normal cycles of sleep and waking. Bremer reasoned that the isolated forebrain of the cerveau isolé preparation slept permanently because there was insufficient sensory input to arouse it. The bulbospinal transection of the encéphale isolé cat preserved the sensory input of the cranial nerves, particularly the fifth (trigeminal) and eighth (vestibulocochlear) nerves, and

this input in turn preserved normal sleep–wake cycling. To support this interpretation, Bremer showed that if the brain stem cranial sensory nerves were cut in an encéphale isolé preparation, a state of continuous forebrain sleep resulted similar to that with the cerveau isolé.

Bremer's assumption was that the stimulation that normally aroused the forebrain was carried rostralward via the specific sensory systems. However, in 1949 Giuseppi Moruzzi and Horace W. Magoun added a significant qualification to Bremer's theory by making partial lesions rather than complete brain stem transections at the midbrain level of the cat. They found that lateral tegmental lesions, which severed the classical ascending sensory pathways, did not significantly alter the balance between sleep and wakefulness. However, midline lesions that cut the rostral projections of the reticular formation resulted in a behavioral stupor and a permanently spindling EEG pattern that resembled sleep. They concluded that the ascending projections of a tonically active reticular formation (fed by collaterals from the specific sensory systems) activated the cortex and kept the forebrain awake, and that a reduction in this activity resulted in sleep. This passive view of sleep as a functional deafferentation regulated by an ascending reticular activating system was a dominant theme of sleep research for many years.

Evidence for a Sleep-Inducing Area in the Brain Stem

In the late 1950s workers in Moruzzi's laboratory were among the first to question the unitary view of the nonspecific reticular activating system. Batini found in 1958 that when brain stem transections were performed at the midpontine level, only a few millimeters caudal to the midbrain cuts of Bremer, cats remained permanently awake rather than permanently asleep. This suggested that the rostral reticular formation contained a population of neurons whose activity was required for wakefulness and, conversely, that the caudal brain stem contained neurons that were necessary for sleep. The latter fact was demonstrated in 1959 by another group of investigators working in Moruzzi's laboratory. Since the results of their experiment are particularly relevant to understanding the signs of coma following lower brain stem lesions, they will be more fully discussed in Chapter 41 (see Figure 41–5). In brief, they demonstrated that when injections of thiopental, a barbiturate anesthetic, were restricted to the rostral pons and cerebrum (by selectively tying off various cerebral arteries), awake cats were put to sleep, as might be expected. However, when only the caudal brain stem was anesthetized, the cat woke up if it had been sleeping, and synchronous EEG activity was replaced by desynchronous EEG activity. Thus, somewhere in the caudal brain stem was an area whose *activity* was needed to induce sleep.

Role of Serotonin

Later studies have suggested that this sleep-inducing area may be a collection of cells that lie in the midline of the medulla known as the *nuclei of the raphe* (meaning "crease" or "seam"). Jouvet found that destruction of 80–90% of the raphe nuclei produced complete insomnia in cats for 3–4 days. NREM sleep, but not REM sleep, gradually returned but never exceeded 2 hr/day. (Cats normally sleep 14.5 hr/day.) Smaller lesions resulted in more recovery, but REM sleep never reappeared until NREM sleep totaled at least 3.5 hr/day.

As we have seen in Chapter 32, the raphe nuclei are rich in cells that contain serotonin (5-hydroxytryptamine). The administration of 5-hydroxytryptamine directly into the cerebral ventricles or of 5-hydroxytryptophan, a precursor of serotonin, into the systemic circulation induces sleep. Raphe lesions depress cerebral levels of serotonin and the degree of serotonin depletion is directly correlated with the length of insomnia. Furthermore, a single dose of parachlorophenylalanine (PCPA), which inhibits the biosynthesis of serotonin, also suppresses sleep proportionately over the time course of its activity. Insomnia induced by an injection of parachlorophenylalanine can be quickly reversed by injecting 5-hydroxytryptophan.

There are several difficulties with the hypothesis that serotonin causes sleep. One is revealed when parachlorophenylalanine is administered chronically (Figure 40–5). After repeated daily injections of parachlorophenylalanine, insomnia eventually abates, with both REM and NREM sleep returning to approximately 70% of normal levels. This substantial recovery occurs even though serotonin levels continue to be depressed, which is a disappointment for the serotonin hypothesis. However, although sleep returns to cats chronically depleted of serotonin, the phasic events that normally occur in REM sleep appear

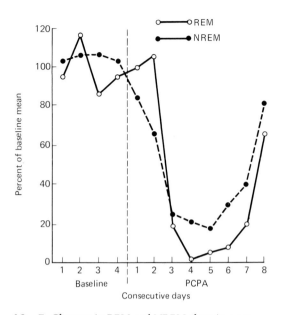

40–5 Changes in REM and NREM sleep in a cat that received parachlorophenylalanine (**PCPA**) for 8 consecutive days. Note that, following a drop in both types of sleep early during the course of drug treatment, by the eighth day sleep levels were returning toward normal baseline values. However, at the same time brain serotonin levels were approximately zero, suggesting that this neurotransmitter was not the crucial agent in the normal production of either REM or NREM sleep. (Adapted from Dement, 1965.)

to escape this background and to intrude into NREM sleep and even into waking behavior. Dement has described these sudden attacks as hallucinatory episodes in which the serotonin-depleted cats jump, snarl, and hiss at nonexistent stimuli. Therefore, serotonergic neurons may be involved in restricting PGO spikes and other phasic phenomena to REM sleep. As we shall see in Chapter 51, the same population of serotonergic neurons may be involved in the mood disturbances of depressed patients. It is perhaps not coincidental that depressive patients also suffer very serious disturbances of sleep.

Role of the Nucleus of the Solitary Tract

A secondary medullary system, located in the vicinity of the nucleus of the solitary tract, may also be involved in inducing sleep. Since activation of this area promotes sleep but damage does not result in insomnia, it may produce its effects upon sleep by modulating the arousal properties of the reticular formation (Chapter 32). Electrical stimulation of the nucleus of the solitary tract has a synchronizing effect upon forebrain EEG activity that long outlasts the stimulation. This portion of the medulla receives taste and visceral afferent input principally from the vagus nerve. Stimulation of afferent fibers in the vagus nerve also produces EEG synchrony, as does mild, low-frequency (3–8 Hz) stimulation of certain cutaneous nerves. Perhaps the calming effects of gently rocking a baby are mediated by this frequency-sensitive mechanism.

Distinct Regions of the Brain Stem May Trigger REM Sleep

In addition to the postulated involvement in NREM sleep of such brain stem populations as the raphe and the nucleus of the solitary tract, there is thought to be a special subset of anatomically and biochemically distinct regions that may trigger REM sleep. Most serotonergic neurons in the dorsal raphe nucleus in the midbrain periaqueductal gray matter fire at a maximal rate during waking and drastically reduce their firing rate during REM sleep. This pattern fits with the suggestion that they may normally suppress PGO waves. Some raphe neurons cease firing specifically during PGO spikes, while others remain silent throughout REM episodes. Jouvet suggested that these neurons inhibit more tonic REM events and their silence during REM sleep indicates a termination of this inhibition.

Noradrenergic Neurons

In the early 1960s Jouvet reported that large lesions of the pontine reticular formation (nucleus reticularis pontis oralis and nucleus reticularis pontis caudalis) abolished both electrophysiological and behavioral signs of REM sleep. Just caudal to this area, smaller lesions in the medial portions of the locus ceruleus abolished the descending muscular inhibition that normally accompanies REM sleep. The locus ceruleus is rich in noradrenergic cells, and most pharmacological manipulations that affect noradrenergic systems also affect REM sleep. However, a disappointing exception is that injections of α-methylparatyrosine, which suppresses the biosynthesis of norepinephrine and the activity of the locus ceruleus, do not abolish REM sleep in either cats or rats. It now appears evident that the locus ceru-

leus does not contain the executive mechanisms for REM sleep.

Cholinergic Neurons

It has also been suggested that cells of the nucleus of the gigantocellular tegmental field (the name now used to describe that area of the pons that encompasses both the nucleus reticularis oralis and nucleus reticularis caudalis) play a role in REM sleep. Cells in this region are among the largest in the brain; each divides and sends bifurcating axon processes throughout the telencephalon, diencephalon, midbrain, and hindbrain (Figure 40–6). In the rat brain, only 300 such giant cells (10% of the population of this region) can potentially affect 9 million cells of the brain stem reticular formation (90% of the population of this region); thus the architecture of these cholinergic cells suggests a broad, nonspecific role, and possibly an involvement in sleep. Direct pontine injections of carbachol, a cholinergic agonist, produce cortical desynchrony, rapid eye movements, and paralysis in cats. Similarly, systemic physostigmine, a cholinesterase inhibitor that increases cholinergic postsynaptic activity, induces REM sleep in NREM sleeping human subjects.

Allan Hobson and Robert McCarley at Harvard have described two populations of neurons in the pontine tegmentum that fire immediately before and during REM sleep. Reminiscent of serotonergic cells in the dorsal raphe, one population of cells that cluster in the gigantocellular tegmental field itself fires in a phasic manner throughout REM sleep and is consequently correlated with PGO spikes, rapid eye movements, and muscular twitches. A second population of tonic cells fires throughout REM sleep and is consequently correlated with cortical desynchrony and muscular paralysis. These cells are found in the nearby central tegmental field. In 1975 Hobson, McCarley, and P. W. Wyzinski also found a reciprocal arrangement between noradrenergic locus ceruleus neurons and the cholinergic cells of the gigantocellular field. Whereas gigantocellular neurons fired most rapidly during REM sleep, those in the locus ceruleus slowed down.

Hobson proposed that an intrinsic pattern of alternating activity between tegmental gigantocellular and locus ceruleus cells may account for the cyclicity of REM and NREM sleep, respectively. There are, however, several difficulties with this idea. The discharge of giant tegmental

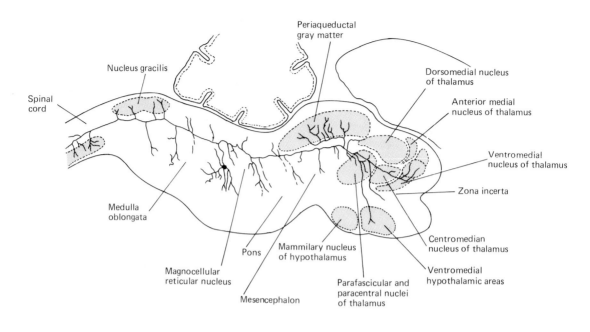

40–6 Saggital section of the brain of a 2-day-old rat showing the axonal branching of a single giant reticular cell. (Adapted from Scheibel and Scheibel, 1958.)

cells is most highly correlated with motor activity in waking, unrestrained cats, and thus appears not to be selective for REM sleep, but for motor activation per se. Another fact embarassing to the theory is the existence of giant tegmental cells in fish, reptiles, and amphibians, which do not display REM sleep.

A Perspective on Neurotransmitters and Sleep

In light of these recent discouraging findings regarding the monoaminergic and cholinergic models of the stages of sleep, it may now seem as if we actually know less about the neurophysiology of sleep than was presumed only 15 years ago when the biogenic amine hypothesis for sleep first emerged and before the experiments that challenged it were carried out. Since Piéron and before, each generation has examined its candidate for a hypnogenic substance. Recent fixation on the biogenic amines and on brain stem mechanisms has resulted in the comparative neglect of other transmitter systems and other brain areas such as the thalamus and other forebrain mechanisms. Sleep, like other functions of the brain,

probably makes use of more than one biochemical key in order to operate.

Selected Readings and References

Arkin, A. M., Antrobus, J. S., and Ellman, S. J. (eds.). 1978. The Mind in Sleep: Psychology and Psychophysiology. Hillsdale, N.J.: Lawrence Erlbaum Associates.

Cartwright, R. D. 1978. A Primer on Sleep and Dreaming. Reading, Mass.: Addison-Wesley.

Hartmann, E. L. 1973. The Functions of Sleep. New Haven: Yale University Press.

Jouvet, M. 1974. The role of monoaminergic neurons in the regulation and function of sleep. In O. Petre-Quadens and J. D. Schlag (eds.), Basic Sleep Mechanisms. New York: Academic, pp. 207–236.

Kales, A. (ed.). 1969. Sleep Physiology & Pathology. Philadelphia: Lippincott.

Other References

Aschoff, J. 1969. Desynchronization and resynchronization of human circadian rhythms. Aerosp. Med. 40:844–849.

Batini, C., Moruzzi, G., Palestini, M., Rossi, G. F., and Zanchetti, A. 1958. Persistent patterns of wakefulness in the pretrigeminal midpontine preparation. Science (Wash., D.C.) 128:30–32.

Bremer, F. 1936. Nouvelles recherches sur le mécanisme du sommeil. C. R. Séances Soc. Biol. Fil. 122:460–464.

Dement, W. C. 1965. An essay on dreams: The role of

physiology in understanding their nature. In New Directions in Psychology, Vol. 2. New York: Holt, Rinehart and Winston, pp. 135–257.

Feinberg, I. 1969. Effects of age on human sleep patterns. In A. Kales (ed.), Sleep Physiology & Pathology. Philadelphia: Lippincott, pp. 39–52.

Foulkes, D. 1966. The Psychology of Sleep. New York: Scribner's.

Foulkes, W. D. 1962. Dream reports from different stages of sleep. J. Abnorm. Soc. Psychol. 65:14–25.

Freud, S. 1953. The Interpretation of Dreams. Translated by J. Strachey. Vols. IV and V. London: Hogarth Press and The Institute of Psycho-Analysis.

Hobson, J. A. 1974. The cellular basis of sleep cycle control. Adv. Sleep Res. 1:217–250.

Hobson, J. A., McCarley, R. W., and Wyzinski, P. W. 1975. Sleep cycle oscillation: Reciprocal discharge by two brainstem neuronal groups. Science (Wash., D.C.) 189:55–58.

Monnier, M., Koller, Th., and Graber, S. 1963. Humoral influences of induced sleep and arousal upon electrical brain activity of animals with crossed circulation. Exp. Neurol. 8:264–277.

Moruzzi, G., and Magoun, H. W. 1949. Brain stem reticular formation and activation of the EEG. Electroencephalogr. Clin. Neurophysiol. 1:455–473.

Nagasaki, H., Kitahama, K., Valatx, J.-L., and Jouvet, M. 1980. Sleep-promoting effect of the sleep-promoting substance (SPS) and delta sleep–inducing peptide (DSIP) in the mouse. Brain Res. 192:276–280.

Pappenheimer, J. R., Miller, T. B., and Goodrich, C. A. 1967. Sleep-promoting effects of cerebrospinal fluid from sleep-deprived goats. Proc. Natl. Acad. Sci. U.S.A. 58:513–517.

Piéron, H. 1913. Le Problème Physiologique du Sommeil. Paris: Masson.

Roffwarg, H. P., Muzio, J. N., and Dement, W. C. 1966. Ontogenetic development of the human sleep–dream cycle. Science (Wash., D.C.) 152:604–619.

Sastre, J.-P., and Jouvet, M. 1979. Le comportement onirique du chat. Physiol. Behav. 22:979–989.

Scheibel, M. E., and Scheibel, A. B. 1958. Structural substrates for integrative patterns in the brain stem reticular core. In H. H. Jasper (ed.), Reticular Formation of the Brain. Boston: Little, Brown, pp. 31–55.

Schnedorf, J. G., and Ivy, A. C. 1939. An examination of the hypnotoxin theory of sleep. Am. J. Physiol. 125:491–505.

Schoenenberger, G. A., and Monnier, M. 1977. Characterization of a delta-electroencephalogram (-sleep) –inducing peptide. Proc. Natl. Acid. Sci. U.S.A. 74: 1282–1286.

Dennis D. Kelly

Disorders of Sleep and Consciousness

41

The inability to sleep, or to stay awake, is a hardship that can disrupt a life with extraordinary thoroughness. Sleep disorders can alter a person's mood and behavior to a degree often ignored by medical professionals. Thus a consideration of sleep disorders may not only enlighten our speculations about normal sleep, as outlined in the previous chapter, but it may also establish that sleep is not an isolated behavioral event; its quality may exert far-reaching effects upon the behavioral repertoire of the individual.

Although there are no compelling statistics on the actual number of people whose sleep is disturbed, it appears to be a widespread public health problem. Depending upon the criteria used to define a sleep problem, various quantitative surveys have placed the figure somewhere near one in five individuals. Among certain specialized populations, such as institutionalized mental patients, the figure can be astonishingly high. In a survey of 700 patients at St. Elizabeth's Hospital in Washington, D.C., 70% of those interviewed identified a sleep complaint as that which first prompted them to seek medical help. Whatever the actuarial data, it is the recorded experience of physicians that complaints about pain and about sleep are probably the two most common in medicine.

In this chapter we shall consider the most important sleep disorders within the context of the neural mechanisms of normal sleep outlined in the preceding chapter.

Insomnia Is a Symptom, Not a Unitary Disease

Insomnia is the chronic inability to obtain the necessary amount or quality of sleep to maintain adequate daytime behavior. Because of the emphasis upon the complaints and self-evaluation of the patient, this widely accepted definition of insomnia is, strictly speaking, independent of the actual number of hours the patient sleeps. As we shall see, insomnia is in reality many disorders, a number of which are still poorly understood.

Complaints of insomnia, like those of chronic pain, are so numerous that pharmaceutical houses report over $150 million in annual over-the-counter sales of nonprescription, mild hypnotic drugs. In addition to this excessive tendency in poor sleepers for self-medication, there is also a consistent tendency by the medical profession to overprescribe strong sleeping pills. The net result in this country is a serious problem of abuse of sleeping medications, which an expert panel of the National Academy of Sciences recently identified as a major public health hazard. To sketch the dimensions of the problem, in 1977 physicians in the United States wrote more than 25 million prescriptions for hypnotics despite evidence that the drugs then prescribed were largely ineffective and potentially dangerous. In that year over 8.5 million Americans took prescription sleeping pills at least once, and about one-quarter of these took the pills every night for 2 consecutive months or longer. As we shall see, there is little evidence that any currently available sleeping medication is effective for more than several days. Part of the reason for the consistent overtreatment of sleep complaints is that patients often exaggerate their insomnia.

Evidence is mounting that a patient's complaint of insomnia may not be sufficient grounds for a physician to conclude that there is something wrong with the physiology of an individual's sleep. Independent verification from a sleep partner is always advisable, particularly in the absence of encephalographic examination in a sleep laboratory. When tested in the laboratory, many self-professed insomniacs, particularly those without other pathology, have been found

to sleep, dream, and even snore, normally. When awakened, however, these sleepers may deny they have been asleep, particularly if aroused from REM sleep. In an early laboratory study, William Dement examined 127 self-professed "insomniacs" and observed a mean sleep onset time of 15 min and a mean sleep duration of 7 hr. He concluded that one cannot assume that "insomniacs" cannot sleep. One possibility is that such patients may dream they are awake.

Of those who actually cannot sleep, approximately 30–35% have a relatively simple organic explanation for the disturbance. The two most common are (1) disruptions of normal circadian rhythms, and (2) the inevitable consequences of aging. Normal circadian rhythms can be disrupted not only by travel ("jet lag") but also by other behavioral changes such as napping in the late afternoon on vacations, alterations in meal times, and so on. For reasons not well understood, the older one gets, the more difficult it seems to be to reset rapidly one's biological clock. Thus travel across time zones more seriously upsets the normal sleep patterns of the elderly. Even under stable conditions, most people over age 60 sleep no more than 5.5 hr/day. If they compare it to their prior habits, patients worry about this normal ontogenetic trend in their sleep pattern. As we saw in Chapter 40, the amount of stage 4 NREM sleep also declines with age. By the seventh decade it is virtually eliminated and, as a natural consequence, people spend proportionately more time in the lighter stages of NREM sleep, from which they awaken more often. Despite these normal explanations for their sleeping habits, persons 60 and older currently receive 39% of all sleeping pill prescriptions. Among nursing home patients, the prescription rate may run as high as 94% according to a report of the Institute of Medicine of the National Academy of Sciences.

Possibly the most common causes of insomnia are psychological disturbances. Anxiety tends to be correlated with difficulty in falling asleep, depression with early awakenings. In a study of patients with insomnia at the Hershey Medical Center in Pennsylvania, an emotional problem was the likely cause in 70%, with depression heading the list. However, most of these depressed patients had initially been treated with sleeping pills because their presenting complaint was lack of sleep, not depression.

Most of the hypnotic drugs used to treat in-

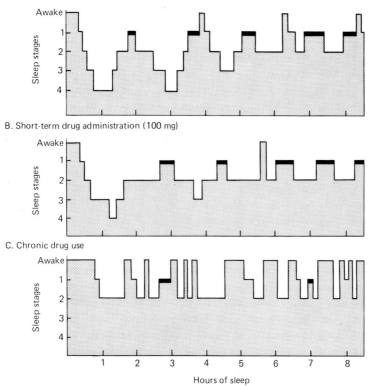

A. Untreated

B. Short-term drug administration (100 mg)

C. Chronic drug use

Hours of sleep

41–1 Effect of pentobarbital treatment on sleep staging in a young adult. **A.** Patient complained of early morning awakenings. **B.** Initially 100 mg pentobarbital lengthened the latency to the first REM period and decreased spontaneous awakenings. **C.** However, with chronic nightly use and an increased dose reflecting tolerance, it took the patient almost 1 hr to fall asleep and there were 12 awakenings during the night. Note also the suppression of both stage REM and stages 3 and 4 NREM sleep. REM sleep is represented by a **dark bar** during stage 1 sleep. (Adapted from Kales and Kales, 1973.)

somnia, although initially helpful, lose effectiveness within 2 weeks. Thus the repeated administration of barbiturates, such as pentobarbital or phenobarbital, gradually leads to an increase in the hepatic enzymes responsible for degrading these drugs. The result is that their pharmacological action is progressively diminished with prolonged use (Figure 41–1). Moreover, since enzymes in the liver tend to be relatively nonspe-

cific, a broad cross-tolerance to other hypnotics tends to develop at the same time. As we also noted in the preceding chapter, most hypnotics, especially barbiturates, severely suppress REM sleep, and drug withdrawal is associated with a profound REM rebound (Figure 41–2). Because of these properties, the administration of barbiturates beyond several days may actually aggravate insomnia. Unfortunately, most prescriptions for

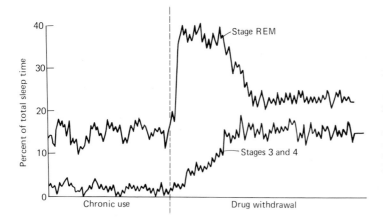

41–2 Abrupt withdrawal of hypnotic drugs causes a marked increase in previously suppressed REM sleep, which is coupled with an increase in both the frequency and intensity of dreaming. Stages 3 and 4 NREM sleep also recover to normal levels, but they do so gradually, displaying no overshoot or rebound phenomena. (Adapted from Kales and Kales, 1973.)

barbiturates are for 30 tablets or more, and more than one-half of these prescriptions are refilled.

For these reasons, there has been a notable shift away from the use of barbiturates as sleeping pills and toward the use of benzodiazepines. One of these, flurazepam, currently accounts for more than one-half of all prescriptions for hypnotics. Interest in flurazepam was sparked by two early reports based upon 10 patients that it remained effective for at least 28 consecutive nights. Like the barbiturates, the benzodiazepines are also addictive, but much less so. In other words, patients develop a tolerance for flurazepam more slowly than for pentobarbital. On the other hand, an active metabolite of flurazepam remains in the body far longer than barbiturate metabolites; in fact, for more than 24 hr. As a consequence, when the drug is used on consecutive nights there is a gradual increase in the amount of these breakdown substances in the blood levels. The amount of these breakdown substances in the blood after 7 nights of use is four to six times more than after the first night. As a result, the effects of this drug are felt increasingly during the day, with diminished alertness and hand–eye coordination. These symptoms in turn may impair driving ability or the operation of machinery and are aggravated by alcohol.

Nocturnal Enuresis Is Not Caused by Dreams

Like somnambulism, sleep terrors, and nightmares, nocturnal enuresis (bed-wetting) was once considered a dream-related disorder. As a result of recent laboratory studies made possible by the physiological discoveries outlined in the preceding chapter, these episodes have all been found to occur independently of typical periods of dream activity.

Bed-wetting is common in children and young adults. Its incidence has been estimated at 3–6% for the general population, 15% for "nervous" children, and 30% for institutionalized children. Among children, enuresis also shows a strong male preponderance. Idiopathic or essential enuresis (whose cause is not known) is correlated with decreased bladder capacity and is now widely believed, despite lack of experimental proof, to be related to a maturational lag in neurological control. Sometimes bed-wetting may be due to urinary tract anomalies, cystitis, diabetes mellitus, diabetes insipidus, or epilepsy.

In a typical enuretic episode, the sleeper awakes to find himself in soaked bedclothes, and can report little else. On the other hand, an observer can usually note a preceding period of agitated sleep, including gross body movements succeeded by several seconds of tranquility and apparent continuation of sleep, followed in turn by enuresis. Immediately after the incident, it is difficult to waken the sleeper, who is confused, disoriented even to the extent of denying that the bed is wet, and unable to recall any dreams.

Laboratory studies have confirmed that few enuretic episodes (3 of 22 in one study) are related to REM sleep. The initial trigger of the enuretic episode (the early body movements) is most often associated with EEG patterns of stage 4 NREM sleep, and this is followed by a rapidly rising limb of emerging NREM sleep. Micturition occurs in stages 4, 3, 2, or 1, depending upon the length of the period of calm intervening between the initial body movements and enuresis. The dreams often reported by patients to parallel enuresis are observed in the laboratory only if the subject is allowed to sleep into the next REM episode, during which the sensations arising from the wet bedclothes may be incorporated into the dream narrative.

A number of people have attempted to distinguish between primary and secondary forms of nocturnal enuresis. The distinction is based upon the consistency of the patient's prior history of enuresis (and thereby the presumed cause), and not upon the physiology of the episodes, which seem indistinguishable in the laboratory. Primary enuresis is defined by a consistent history of bedwetting from birth and is frequently interpreted as a CNS maturational lag, which expresses itself in no other symptoms. Secondary enuresis is diagnosed when bladder control during sleep has been achieved for several months or a year, and is then lost. One difficulty with the maturational hypothesis of primary enuresis is the extraordinary persistence of the symptom in otherwise normal young adults. For example, among 18–21-year-old military recruits, 1% were enuretic, and half of these revealed an uninterrupted developmental history of bed-wetting.

The drugs most commonly used to treat nocturnal enuresis are the tricyclic antidepressants, such as imipramine, and the benzodiazepines. Both of these drug classes reduce stage 4 NREM sleep, the stage of sleep from which enuretic episodes are apparently triggered.

Somnambulism Is an NREM Phenomenon

In the typical sleepwalking episode, the sleeper sits up quietly, gets out of bed, and walks about rather unsteadily at first, with his or her eyes open and with a blank facial expression. Soon the somnambulist's behavior becomes more coordinated and complex. He or she may avoid objects, dust tables, or go to the bathroom, occasionally mumbling or speaking incoherently. It is difficult to attract the sleepwalker's attention. There may be monosyllabic replies to questions. If left alone, the sleeper usually goes back to bed and upon awakening acknowledges little recollection of the night's activities or of dreaming. Until recently, somnambulism was almost universally interpreted as "acting out" dream activity.

In the laboratory, sleepwalking occurs almost always in stages 3 or 4 NREM sleep. In an early study, Dement observed 25 sleepwalkers for 5 nights each. During this time, he recorded 41 incidents, all initiated during the deepest stages of NREM sleep. Given the intense descending inhibition of spinal motor neurons and consequent paralysis during REM sleep, it would seem only reasonable that somnambulistic episodes should be unrelated to REM epochs.

Later studies have confirmed that sleepwalking occurs exclusively from NREM sleep, most frequently in the first third of the night when stages 3 and 4 predominate. In a remarkable study by Jacobson, Kales, Lehmann, and Zweizig, all-night EEG records revealed that high-voltage, slow-wave patterns often *commenced* as the sleeper began the nocturnal ramblings (Figure 40–3).

Enuresis and somnambulism, besides sharing a common origin in NREM sleep, also show similar family histories. One-third of the military recruits who had enuresis also had a personal history of sleepwalking, while another one-fourth said that someone in their family sleepwalked. As with enuresis, somnambulism is more common in children than adults, and its statistical decline with age parallels the normal decrease in the proportion of sleep time spent in stage 4 NREM.

41–3 Electrooculogram (EOG), electromyogram (EMG), and EEG records of a sleepwalking incident observed under laboratory conditions. A high-voltage, slow-wave EEG pattern commences as the sleepwalker sits up in bed, and NREM sleep patterns are maintained throughout the episode. (Adapted from Jacobson, Kales, Lehmann and Zweizig, 1965.)

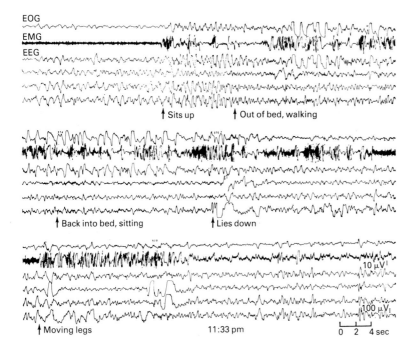

EOG
EMG
EEG

↑ Sits up   ↑ Out of bed, walking

↑ Back into bed, sitting   ↑ Lies down

↑ Moving legs   11:33 pm   0 2 4 sec

10 μV

100 μV

Night Terrors, Nightmares, and Terrifying Dreams Occur in Different Stages of Sleep

Upsetting dreams may occur during either REM or NREM sleep. Moreover, they possess, often to an exaggerated degree, the physiological and psychological characteristics of normal REM and NREM dreams as outlined in the preceding chapter. Bad dreams, during both REM and NREM, may occur either in children or, less frequently, in adults. Despite these simple paired distinctions, there is little consistency in the use of the terms night terror (pavor nocturnus), incubus, nightmare, and terrifying dream.

The sleep terror attack of children is perhaps the best characterized. Usually within 30 min of falling asleep the child abruptly sits up in bed, screams, and appears to be staring wide eyed at some imaginary object. His face is covered with perspiration and his breathing is very labored. In the same manner that sleepwalkers appear to be oblivious to external stimuli, consoling stimuli have no effect on the terrorized child. After the attack, which may last 1 or 2 min, dream recall is rare and usually fragmentary. The next morning, there is no recollection of the episode. This fragmented pattern of recall reminds one of NREM mentation. And so it was not surprising that, when Henri Gastaut observed night terror episodes in seven different children in his laboratory at Marseilles, all attacks occurred during a sudden arousal from stages 3 or 4 NREM sleep. There is recent evidence that night terrors may be suppressed by diazepam (Valium), and coincident with this is a measurable decline in the amount of stage 4 (delta-wave) NREM sleep.

A related NREM phenomenon is also seen in adults, although less frequently. The core symptoms of these NREM attacks in adults are respiratory oppression, partial paralysis, and anxiety— usually in that sequence. The anxiety is intense, with all the usual physiological signs: sweating, a fixed facial expression, dilated pupils, and difficulty in breathing. Well-structured dream activity is rare, consisting often not of a story, but of a poor recollection of a single oppressive situation, such as being locked up in a tomb or having rocks piled on the chest. Similar to the pavor nocturnus attack of the child, the subject usually has little memory of the attack the next morning. These patients also show greater than normal daytime anxiety. The name of these NREM attacks in the adult is *incubus,* which, given the root of this

Latin word (from *in* and *cubare*, signifying "to lie upon"), is an appropriate term to describe a phenomenon characterized by respiratory oppression. However, it also seems likely that a description of this same NREM phenomenon, characterized by extreme anxiety and oppressed breathing, may have been intended as the original meaning of the word *nightmare.* From the middle ages and before, many artists and writers believed that nightmares were caused by a nocturnal demon who pressed upon the sleeper's chest. The German word, *Nachtmar,* and the French word, *cauchemar,* both contain the ancient Teutonic root, *mar,* which means "devil." Cauchemar also derives from *caucher,* an ancient French verb meaning "to press," thus literally referring to a "pressing devil."

In contrast with the pavor nocturnus of children and the incubus of adults are the more common terrifying dreams that occur during regular REM periods in sleepers of all ages. As would be expected from the study of normal REM events, these contain complex imagery, have a story line, are vividly recalled, and are not accompanied by respiratory oppression, but rather by an exaggerated increase in all the phasic activity, PGO spikes and eye movements, that normally characterize stage REM. Unfortunately, these terrifying REM episodes are also sometimes referred to as nightmares. It would probably be clinically useful to distinguish high-anxiety dream phenomena into categories that can occur during either REM or NREM sleep. For instance, like other NREM sleep disturbances such as enuresis and somnambulism, the pavor nocturnus attacks of a child should decline as the patient matures and the deeper stages of NREM sleep come to account for proportionately less sleep time. In contrast, terrifying REM dreams would be expected to persist since, unlike stage 4 sleep, REM time does not change appreciably after childhood.

Sleep Apnea May Result in Hyposomnia or Hypersomnia

Another remarkable disturbance of sleep is characterized by the frequent, periodic cessation of respiration. Both the causes of sleep apnea and the presenting complaints of patients suffering from this disorder are extremely broad. Hence it is unlikely that sleep apnea represents a unitary disorder. In some cases of sleep apnea, the shift from wakefulness to sleep is assumed to be associated with a suppression of activity in the medullary respiratory center. This causes the diaphragm and the intercostal muscles to become immobile. In this phase of apnea, which lasts for 15–30 sec, blood oxygen levels fall and carbon dioxide levels rise, eventually stimulating the respiratory center and causing the respiratory muscles to begin functioning again. Often, however, the lungs do not fill with air because the throat has collapsed, perhaps a reflection of the relaxed state of most body muscles during NREM sleep. The extreme changes in the concentrations of oxygen and carbon dioxide in the blood that develop after 1 min or more without air arouse the sleeper. Muscle tone returns to the throat, and a few noisy, choking gasps refill the lungs. Arousal may last for only a few seconds until the blood gases return to normal. Then the person returns immediately to sleep and the cycle can be repeated—as many as 500 times during the night.

Some sleep apnea patients are apparently oblivious of their persistent nocturnal arousals and may actually complain of too much sleep. These patients were first described by Gastaut in Marseilles in 1965, who called their disorder hypersomnolent apnea syndrome. Later, Dement described another group of patients with a similarly disturbed sleep pattern who complained instead of insomnia. He believed that these patients do not habituate to the frequent nocturnal arousals or do not return to sleep immediately after the apnea. Approximately one-third of patients with sleep apnea complain of insomnia and two-thirds of hypersomnia.

Although some investigators have already proposed sleep apnea as a model for sudden infant death, or crib death syndrome, the mean age of sleep apnea patients recently in the nation's largest sleep clinic at Stanford University was 52 years, and the youngest patient was 38. Because relatively few physicians are aware of sleep apnea, the actual incidence of the disorder in the general population is still unknown. In almost all diagnosed cases of sleep apnea, a critical factor has been a report from a sleep partner that the subject snored loudly at night. Few drugs have been found effective in combating sleep apnea, although many are under investigation. In those cases not related to the central nervous system, in which the cause may be some form of upper airway obstruction, a tracheotomy has often successfully restored normal sleep.

A potentially useful perspective in this disorder may be offered by the finding that some otherwise healthy men frequently stop breathing for 10–54 sec during sleep. In one study of 30 men and 19 women, periods of sleep apnea occurred only in men (264 episodes), never in women, and were always accompanied by a drop in blood oxygen. For reasons not understood, the latter was most severe in men weighing over 200 lb. This mild form of sleep apnea often occurred in conjunction with snoring (which also occurs more frequently in men than women).

Narcolepsy: Irresistible Sleep Attacks Are Accompanied by Several REM-Related Symptoms

The principal symptom of narcolepsy is irresistible sleep attacks lasting 5–30 min during the day, which occasionally occur without warning and at behaviorally inappropriate moments. More often, the narcoleptic feels an overwhelming drowsiness preceding the attack and attempts to fight it off. If the patient naps, he or she awakes refreshed; 15 min is usually sufficient. One serious danger posed by narcolepsy is accidental death, and automobile accidents are a more frequent complication of narcolepsy than of epilepsy. In one study, 40% of the narcoleptic patients questioned admitted that they had fallen asleep while driving.

For many years this debilitating disorder was described mainly in textbooks of psychiatry and was interpreted within a psychological frame of reference as an unconscious escape from aversive situations. However, in the late 1950s, Yoss and Daly at the Mayo Clinic described a highly idiosyncratic set of symptoms that seemed to characterize narcoleptics from all walks of life and that cut across virtually all personality types. This made a psychogenic etiology for narcolepsy highly unlikely. Yoss and Daly discovered that, in addition to sleep attacks, the narcoleptic patient often exhibits an abrupt loss of muscle tone, a swoonlike reaction termed *cataplexy*, during which the patient may fall to the ground. Cataplexy usually occurs when the patient becomes emotionally excited, for instance during laughter or sexual excitement. Two other less frequent symptoms of narcolepsy are *sleep paralysis*, a brief inhibition of muscle tone during the transition from wakefulness to sleep and vice versa, and *hypnagogic hallucinations* (visual or auditory) at the beginning of sleep. The latter symp-

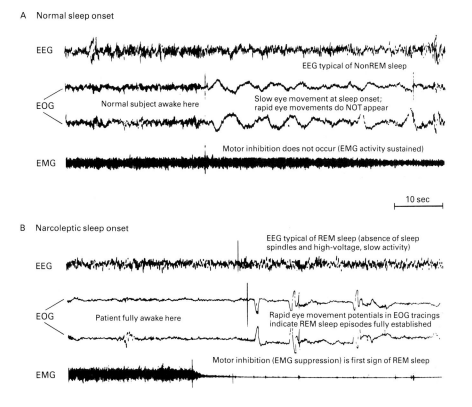

A   Normal sleep onset

EEG

EEG typical of NonREM sleep

EOG

Normal subject awake here

Slow eye movement at sleep onset;
rapid eye movements do NOT appear

Motor inhibition does not occur (EMG activity sustained)

EMG

10 sec

B   Narcoleptic sleep onset

EEG typical of REM sleep (absence of sleep
spindles and high-voltage, slow activity)

EEG

EOG

Patient fully awake here

Rapid eye movement potentials in EOG tracings
indicate REM sleep episodes fully established

Motor inhibition (EMG suppression) is first sign of REM sleep

EMG

toms occur in many normal people, but are exaggerated in narcoleptics. All four symptoms occur together in only 10% of diagnosed narcoleptic patients. In 70% of the cases, sleep attacks and cataplexy are not accompanied by sleep paralysis or hypnagogic hallucinations.

This quartet of symptoms has been interpreted physiologically as reflecting the intrusion of the normally inhibited properties of REM sleep into the waking state (sleep attacks and cataplexy) or into the transitions between wakefulness and sleep (sleep paralysis and hallucinations). In fact, narcoleptic patients can enter directly into REM sleep (Figure 41–4). As a result, *sleep-onset REM* is now considered a fifth defining symptom of narcolepsy. A sixth and newly discovered sign of narcolepsy is a *decreased voluntary sleep latency*. When tested every 2 hr throughout the day in a normal sleep setting, namely, while lying in bed, narcoleptics can usually fall asleep upon request within 2 min, whereas normal subjects take an average of 15 min to get to sleep.

In spite of the ability to fall asleep quickly and to enter the first REM period rapidly, narcoleptics

41–4 Narcoleptic patients can enter into REM sleep directly from the waking state. **A.** Sleep onset in the normal person is typified by a gradual change from a waking EEG dominated by alpha activity (10 Hz) to mixed lower frequency patterns coupled with the development of slow rolling eye movements in the electrooculogram (EOG) and little change in the electromyographic (EMG) recording of muscle tonus. **B.** In the narcoleptic, sleep onset is actually preceded by several seconds of markedly reduced EMG activity and then accompanied by conjugate (both traces) rapid eye movements. Sleep-onset REM usually lasts 10–20 min, after which, if the narcoleptic remains asleep, there will follow a typical progression through stages 1 to 4 of NREM sleep. (Adapted from Dement, Guilleminault and Zarcone, 1975).

generally show significantly less total REM time than normal and a disturbed sleep architecture. Because of this, one early hypothesis suggested that the irresistible sleep attacks during the daytime represented increased pressure to obtain REM sleep. Because the administration of stimulant drugs was commonly used to control the sleep attacks, this proposal was somewhat unsettling. These drugs suppress REM sleep, and thus it was feared that the treatment might contribute to the illness rather than its cure. However, it now seems that narcolepsy is probably more complex than might be explained by a simple REM deprivation state. Moreover, as outlined in the preceding chapter, the consequences of experimental REM deprivation are more or less restricted to subsequent sleep periods and intrude very little upon waking behavior.

The symptoms of narcolepsy respond differently to drugs that enhance transmission at central catecholaminergic synapses. The stimulants methylphenidate and d-amphetamine stimulate the release of newly synthesized transmitter at nerve terminals (and, to a lesser extent, attenuate reuptake) and aid in the control of sleep attacks, but have no effect upon the other symptoms of narcolepsy. The tricyclic antidepressant imipramine blocks reuptake of neurotransmitters by presynaptic terminals and prevents cataplexy, but has no effect on sleep attacks. Among other drugs that potentiate transmission at monoamine synapses, monoamine oxidase (MAO) inhibitors that prevent the enzymatic oxidation of the transmitter substance may improve all four primary narcoleptic symptoms.

There is a strong familial component to narcolepsy. It occasionally spans several successive generations. Onset is usually between the first and second decade. The American Narcolepsy Association estimates that 250,000 Americans suffer from this disease, most are undiagnosed and many are the object of disapproval for apparent laziness.

At present there are few promising leads as to the cause of narcolepsy. Since those drugs that are effective in narcolepsy are also known to inhibit REM sleep, some investigators prefer to characterize the symptoms of narcolepsy as a failure of the "reticular waking mechanism" to inhibit the REM sleep "system." This view assumes that wakefulness, and both REM and NREM sleep states, all involve independent neural units, and excitation of one actively inhibits the other two. Unfortunately, to be heuristic this genre of hypothesis depends in turn on our understanding of the cellular mechanisms controlling normal sleep, but this, as we have seen, has not yet been achieved. One promising development is that Dement recently discovered that a form of narcolepsy occurs naturally in dogs. The experimental advantage of a naturally occurring animal model of the disease may offer real hope

for a scientific understanding of the causes of narcolepsy in humans.

Loss of Consciousness: Coma Is Not Deep Sleep

At one time it was common in both the clinical and basic neural sciences to postulate a continuum of consciousness that ranged in graded levels of attention, alertness, relaxation, and drowsiness to sleep, stupor, and coma. It was generally believed that the level of excitation in the ascending reticular activating system determined the level of consciousness. Sensory impulses entering the reticular formation from the different modalities were assumed to merge and lose their specificity within this network of neurons. The reticular formation in turn acted as an energizer and exerted a broad facilitatory influence upon the rest of the nervous system. A reduction in the amount of impulses from the reticular formation would reduce the overall activity of the brain and consequently result in sleep.

However, with the discovery of the extraordinary amount of neural activity that characterizes sleep, the idea of a neurophysiological continuum from quiescence to excitation had to be abandoned. Moreover, activity of the reticular formation alone does not account for variations in levels of consciousness. As Alf Brodal, one of the major students of the anatomy of the reticular formation, has said, "It would be entirely misleading to consider the reticular formation the 'seat of consciousness.' "[1] Nevertheless, the brain stem reticular core plays a role in many clinical disorders of consciousness.

Transient Losses of Consciousness

Fainting, or syncope, most often results from a general reduction in cerebral blood flow, which compromises the ability of the brain to extract oxygen and needed nutrients. This involves a failure of the autoregulatory reflexes of the cerebral vessels (see Appendix IIB), which normally maintain a constant blood flow over a wide range of perfusion pressures. Autoregulation may fail if perfusion pressure falls below 60 mm Hg; too precipitious a fall can result from decreased cardiac

---

[1]A. Brodal, Neurological Anatomy, 3rd ed., New York: Oxford University Press, 1981, p. 442.

output or, more frequently, from decreased peripheral resistance, or both. One type of syncope, termed *vasovagal,* is reflexive in origin and is almost always related to pain, fear, or other emotional stress. In vasovagal syncope, stimulation of the autonomic nervous system usually precedes the drop in blood pressure and the patient is usually aware of "light-headedness" and impending fainting.

Coma

Sleep and coma differ behaviorally in terms of their arousal threshold, or relative reversibility. They can also be easily distinguished physiologically. Sleep is a highly active neurophysiological state during which cerebral oxygen uptake does not decline from normal waking levels. On the contrary, Seymour Kety found that cerebral oxygen uptake actually increases above normal during stage REM episodes. In contrast, oxygen uptake falls below the normal resting level in every studied example of coma. Thus, coma may be defined, by exclusion, as a nonsleep loss of consciousness which, unlike syncope, lasts for an extended period. Within the range of this definition, different clinical levels of unconsciousness, including lethargy, obtundation, stupor, and coma, have been distinguished clinically in terms of the degree of indifference exhibited by the patient to such common stimuli as talking, shouting, shaking, or noxious prodding. To a clinician, *stupor* is a state in which someone is responsive only to shaking, shouting, or noxious stimuli, whereas *coma* refers to total unresponsiveness.

Two general types of pathological processes may impair consciousness. One consists of a set of conditions that can cause widespread functional depression of the cerebral hemispheres; the other includes more specific conditions that depress or destroy critical brain stem areas. In 1972 Plum and Posner suggested that diseases causing stupor or coma must either affect the brain widely or encroach upon deep central structures. They classified these diseases into three categories: (1) sub- or infratentorial mass or destructive lesions (such as pontine hemorrhage) that directly damage the central core of the brain stem; (2) supratentorial mass lesions (such as may result from subdural hematomas) that indirectly compress deep diencephalic structures; and (3) metabolic disorders (such as hypoglycemia) that widely depress or interrupt brain functions.

Table 41–1. Final Diagnosis in 386 Patients with "Coma of Unknown Etiology"

Diagnosis	No.
Supratentorial mass lesions	
Epidural hematoma	2
Subdural hematoma	21
Intracerebral hematoma	33
Cerebral infarct	5
Brain tumor	5
Brain abscess	3
Total	69
Subtentorial lesions	
Brain stem infarct	37
Brain stem tumor	2
Brain stem hemorrhage	7
Cerebellar hemorrhage	4
Cerebellar abscess	2
Total	52
Metabolic and diffuse cerebral disorders	
Anoxia or ischemia	51
Concussion and postictal states	9
Infection (meningitis and encephalitis)	11
Subarachnoid hemorrhage	10
Exogenous toxins	99
Endogenous toxins and deficiencies	81
Total	261
Psychiatric disorders	4

Source: Adapted from Plum and Posner, 1972.

In Table 41–1, some of the clinical causes of coma in these three categories are listed along with their relative frequencies of occurrence.

When first confronted with a patient in coma, the physician usually asks, Where is the lesion and what is the cause? Another question that is often of diagnostic importance is, In what direction is the process evolving? In coma, the sequence of signs is likely to be as important in revealing the source as the full clinical picture at any given moment. The answers to these questions can often place the disease in one of the above categories and thus reduce the number of inferences required to specify the nature of the pathology. We shall next examine Plum and Posner's major categories.

Infratentorial Lesions. A pathological process that affects the brain stem reticular formation will probably never be restricted to the reticular formation alone. A tumor, vascular disorder, or infection is likely to involve other structures as well, with resulting signs and symptoms that involve cranial nerves, long ascending and descending pathways, and various nuclei. Tumors involving the mesencephalon and diencephalon may be followed by a loss of consciousness that lasts for months. The EEG in these patients may show synchronization, suggesting that this type of coma might actually involve normal sleep mechanisms. If these EEG signs are present, the clinical state of stupor might more appropriately be referred to as hypersomnia. This interesting, and often reversible, condition may also occur with tumors below the floor of the third ventricle. If the tumor is cystic and is emptied by aspiration, the stupor may promptly disappear. However, in other cases of tumors in the upper midbrain and diencephalon, decerebrate rigidity may be present in addition to loss of consciousness. This pattern may also be seen after occlusion of the basilar artery. Thus, in broad terms, these clinical and EEG patterns are compatible with the view that the upper brain stem and diencephalic regions are concerned with the general activation of the brain, or what is clinically called "crude consciousness."

The role of the lower brain stem in consciousness is less clear. Because the medulla and lower pons regulate respiration and cardiovascular functions, lesions of the lower brain stem are apt to be rapidly fatal. Unconsciousness in these cases is often accompanied by disturbances in breathing, lowering of blood pressure, and other brain stem signs (tetraplegia, Babinski signs due to corticospinal tract damage, pinpoint but reactive pupils following disruption of descending sympathetic pathways, and absence of ocular movements). Pontine hemorrhage results in these clinical signs before there are disorders of blood pressure and respiration.

On those rare occasions when patients with extensive lesions of the pons and medulla survive for long periods, the EEG may show a desynchronized pattern, as in the waking state (alpha coma). These clinical findings in humans corroborate the classic experiments in cats performed in 1959 by Magni, Moruzzi, Rossi, and Zanchetti. They were the first investigators to conclude that there must be some region in the caudal brain stem whose activity is necessary to put the brain to sleep. They tied off cerebral blood vessels so that the arterial supply to the medulla and lower pons was isolated from that of the upper pons, midbrain, and cerebrum (Figure 41–5). Injections of the barbiturate anesthetic, thiopental, into the

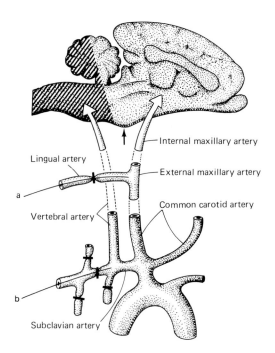

41–5 Procedure for establishing separate perfusion in a cat's brain of either medulla, caudal pons, and posterior cerebellum (**striped**) or rostral pons, midbrain, and upper cerebrum (**stippled**). **Black arrow** indicates level of clamping of the basilar artery which separated the vertebral–basilar arterial circuit (**b**) from the carotid (**a**). (Adapted from Magni, Moruzzi, Rossi, and Zanchetti, 1959.)

stippled rostral brain stem and forebrain anesthetized the cat, as might be expected. However, when only the striped caudal brain stem was anesthetized, the cat woke up if it had been sleeping. The animal's slow-wave, synchronous EEG was replaced by a desynchronized waking EEG. As described in the preceding chapter, the current consensus among sleep investigators is that the structures in the lower pons and medulla responsible for the active induction of NREM sleep are the midline nuclei of the raphe or the nucleus of the solitary tract, or both. The solitary nucleus is a pontine structure that receives both taste and visceral information, but it also, when stimulated with low-frequency current, causes a synchronizing of the cortical EEG.

In short, with regard to the general category of infratentorial lesions, both experimental and clinical observations of limited brain stem dysfunction are consistent with the notion that the subset of reticular neurons that have a tonic activating function upon the cerebrum is not distributed evenly throughout the whole brain stem, but only in the most rostral part.

Supratentorial Lesions. Supratentorial structural lesions (those occurring rostral to the tentorium cerebelli, the dural invagination that separates the posterior cerebrum from the cerebellum) usually cause coma in one of two ways. The first is by destroying a critical amount of cerebral cortex bilaterally; the second is by subjecting the brain stem and diencephalic structures that lie below the tentorium to compression or traction. If the lesion is unilateral, it may cause transtentorial downward herniation of either the medial temporal lobe *(uncal herniation)* or more medial diencephalic structures *(central herniation)*. As a result of the asymmetry of the lesion, there may be asymmetry of limb movements or tendon reflexes due to involvement of the corticospinal tract. There may also be decerebrate posturing (arms and legs extended) in response to noxious stimuli. This may be due to the compromised function of the rubrospinal and corticospinal systems, which normally exert a net facilitatory effect upon flexor muscles, and the consequent release of the vestibulospinal system, which facilitates extensor muscle groups. The pupillary response to light is decreased or absent. In uncal herniation, the most sensitive sign is that the ipsilateral pupil will be dilated because the third cranial nerve is compressed as it passes through the tentorium, leaving sympathetic influence on the pupil unopposed. In central herniation, one or both pupils tend to be in mid-position because the pressure on the midbrain disrupts both parasympathetic and sympathetic pupillary influences. With continuing, long-term compression of the brain stem, eye movements cease, including reflex responses to head rotation and to ice water applied to the tympanic membrane. (The normal response is a forced deviation of the eyes to the opposite side, away from the stimulus.) As brain stem compression moves caudally, a sequence of abnormal respiratory patterns ensues: Cheyne–Stokes breathing characterized by rhythmic waxing and waning of the depth of respiration, with regularly recurring periods of apnea; prolonged periods of hyperventilation; intermittent bouts of irregular or ataxic breathing; and, finally, apnea.

Cerebral infarctions, unless massive and accompanied by considerable brain swelling, do not often cause coma. In fact, the loss of extensive amounts of cerebral tissue (even hemispherectomy) may be sustained without impaired alertness. More important as a cause of coma is brain swelling. Therefore, cerebral hemorrhage is more likely than infarction to cause coma, and it is often accompanied by the typical signs of rostral–caudal transtentorial herniation outlined above. Other supratentorial lesions that commonly cause coma are subdural hematoma, cerebral tumor, and cerebral abscess.

Metabolic Coma. Prior to complete loss of consciousness, metabolically caused coma is usually preceded by gradual changes in mentation or cognition. However, in some conditions, such as hypoglycemia, the onset of coma may be abrupt. For obvious reasons, asymmetrical changes in tendon reflexes or other focal signs are less likely in metabolic states than with structural lesions. Common symptoms in metabolic comas are tremor, asterixis (rapid loss of postural tone, most easily demonstrated by asking the patient, if sufficiently awake, to extend the wrists), and myoclonus (sudden, nonrhythmic jerks of limbs). The respiratory changes in metabolic coma vary with the cause. For instance, opiate drug overdose causes respiratory depression, while hepatic coma is characterized by hyperventilation. As a rule (which is useful in diagnosis), ocular movements are only rarely affected in metabolic coma, unless the coma is quite severe. The pupillary reflex to light is also normally preserved until death, except in comas caused by anoxia or ischemia or by certain toxins, such as atropine.

The causes of metabolic coma are extremely varied and difficult to systematize. They include diffuse brain anoxia or ischemia, hypo- or hyperglycemia, thiamine deficiency, exogenous poisons (including ethanol, opiates, barbiturates, heavy metals, and aspirin), acid–base derangements, hyper- or hypocalcemia, pulmonary disease (carbon dioxide narcosis), uremia, liver failure, hypo- or hyperthermia, and meningitis.

The Determination of Cerebral Death Represents a Medical, Legal, and Social Decision

Despite improved resuscitative techniques, some comas are not reversible. The peculiar susceptibility of the brain to acute anoxia renders it particularly likely to suffer irreparable damage while resuscitative measures may be restoring vitality to less vulnerable organs. The resulting paradox is that of a dead brain in an otherwise living body—a condition beyond deep coma. Legally, physicians determine whether a patient is alive or dead. The development of equipment that artificially maintains respiration and other vital functions and the need of modern transplant surgery for access to viable organs have drawn broad ethical and legal attention to the desirability of agreeing on the medical criteria of cerebral death. In medical practice, the signs of brain death are irreversible coma and lack of spontaneous respiration. The specific criteria used to diagnose brain death differ in different hospitals. One set of criteria was suggested by a task force organized by the National Institute of Neurological and Communicative Diseases and Stroke (Table 41–2). Other sets of criteria were reviewed by Peter Black in 1978.

Because cerebral death usually results from a severe anoxic condition that affects the brain diffusely, the cardinal clinical symptoms (1–4 in Table 41–2) reflect a complete absence of centrally mediated behavioral responses and reflexes, including respiration. However, the criteria were drafted particularly to guard against the false terminal diagnosis of patients made comatose and apneic by reversible drug intoxication or by other lesions that can occasionally mimic cerebral death. One serious and common problem is that persons with self-induced metabolic coma have often taken several drugs, including alcohol, that together may have synergistic effects and may make the identification of drugs in the blood difficult; hence, the need for stringent laboratory testing of brain viability.

The most widely used indication of brain death is an isoelectric electroencephalogram, or electrocerebral silence. This hybrid term is operationally defined as an EEG record with no biological activity greater than 2μV between scalp or referential electrode pairs 10 cm or more apart with interelectrode resistances of 100–10,000 ohms (with needle electrodes, 100–100,000 ohms). While the EEG offers the most significant laboratory information concerning cerebral death, an isoelectric EEG does not indicate the location of the lesion. The percentage of patients with brain stem, or infratentorial, lesions showing electrocerebral silence is approximately the same (63%) as those with diffuse cerebral lesions (60%) or focal cortical lesions (62%).

In many European countries brain death is

Table 41–2. Criteria for Cerebral Death (Brain Death) Proposed by the Collaborative Study of Cerebral Death

Prerequisite
  All appropriate diagnostic and therapeutic procedures have been performed

Criteria (to be present for 30 min at least 6 hr after the onset of coma and apnea)
  1. Coma with cerebral unresponsivity (see definition 1)
  2. Apnea (see definition 2)
  3. Dilated pupils
  4. Absent cephalic reflexes (see definition 3)
  5. Electrocerebral silence (see definition 4)

Confirmatory test: Absence of cerebral blood flow

Definitions
  1. Cerebral unresponsivity: a state in which the patient does not respond purposively to externally applied stimuli, obeys no commands and does not utter sounds spontaneously or in response to a painful stimulus
  2. Apnea: the absence of spontaneous respiration, manifested by the need for controlled ventilation (that is, the patient makes no effort to override the respirator) for at least 15 min
  3. Cephalic reflexes: pupillary, corneal, oculoauditory, oculovestibular, oculocephalic, ciliospinal, snout, cough, pharyngeal, and swallowing
  4. Electrocerebral silence: an EEG with an absence of electrical potentials of cerebral origin over 2 μV from symmetrically placed electrode pairs over 10 cm apart and with interelectrode resistance between 100 and 10,000 ohms.

Source: Adapted from A Collaborative Study, 1977.

equated with total cerebral infarction, and the absence of cerebral blood flow is the principal legal sign. Unfortunately, angiography and most other techniques for determining cerebral blood flow are currently too invasive for routine use in patients hovering between life and death. However, in more chronic cases, the demonstration of intracranial circulatory arrest for 30 min should reasonably eliminate the possibility of cerebral viability even if blood flow can then be reestablished. Of 2650 patients surveyed who displayed coma, apnea, and an isoelectric EEG in the absence of drug intoxication and hypothermia, none survived. Thus, empirically, these criteria are conservative. However, judgments about life and death are always applied in a social context. In addition to satisfying the physician, it is perhaps equally important that criteria not offend society's notion of what constitutes reasonable assurance of death.

Selected Readings and References

Black, P. McL. 1978. Brain death (first of two parts). N. Engl. J. Med. 299:338–344.

Black, P. McL. 1978. Brain death (second of two parts). N. Engl. J. Med. 299:393–401.

Dement W., Guilleminault, C., and Zarcone, V. 1975. The pathologies of sleep: A case series approach. In D. B. Tower (ed.), The Nervous System, Vol. 2: The Clinical Neurosciences. New York: Raven Press, pp. 501–518.

Plum, F., and Posner, J. B. 1972. The Diagnosis of Stupor and Coma. 2nd ed. Philadelphia: Davis.

Solomon, F., White, C. C., Parron D. L., and Mendelson, W. B. 1979. Sleeping pills, insomnia, and medical practice (summary of report of the Institute of Medicine, National Academy of Sciences). N. Engl. J. Med. 300:803–808.

Other References

Brodal, A. 1981. Neurological Anatomy, 3rd ed. New York: Oxford University Press, chap. 6.

Broughton, R. J. 1968. Sleep disorders: Disorders of arousal. Science (Wash., D.C.) 159:1070–1078.

A Collaborative Study. 1977. An appraisal of the criteria of cerebral death. A summary statement. J.A.M.A. 237:982–986.

Gastaut, H., and Broughton, R. 1965. A clinical and polygraphic study of episodic phenomena during sleep. In J. Wortis (ed.), Recent Advances in Biological Psychiatry, vol. 7. New York: Plenum, pp. 197–221.

Jacobson, A., Kales, A. Lehmann, D., and Zweizig, J. R. 1965. Somnambulism: All-night electroencephalographic studies. Science (Wash., D.C.) 148:975–977.

Kales, A., and Kales, J. 1973. Recent advances in the diagnosis and treatment of sleep disorders. In G. Usdin (ed.), Sleep Research and Clinical Practice. New York: Brunner/Mazel, pp. 59–94.

Kety, S. S. 1960. Sleep and the energy metabolism of the brain. In G. E. W. Wolstenholme and M. O'Connor (eds.), The Nature of Sleep. Boston: Little, Brown, pp. 375–381.

Korein, J. (ed.). 1978. Brain death: Interrelated medical and social issues. Ann. N. Y. Acad. Sci. 315:1–454.

Magni, F., Moruzzi, G., Rossi, G. F., and Zanchetti, A. 1959. EEG arousal following inactivation of the lower brain stem by selective injection of barbiturate into the vertebral circulation. Arch. Ital. Biol. 97:33–46.

Williams, R. L., and Karacan, I. 1973. Clinical disorders of sleep. In G. Usdin (ed.), Sleep Research and Clinical Practice. New York: Brunner/Mazel, pp. 23–57.

Yoss, R. E., and Daly, D. D. 1960. Narcolepsy. Arch. Intern. Med. 106:168–171.

Development

VII

Our understanding of the adult nervous system and its control of behavior has been considerably enhanced by research into the development of the brain. Behavior is dependent on the precise and specific interconnections between nerve cells; developmental studies can elucidate how this pattern of connections is established and how it is maintained. The nervous system develops in a series of steps that are precisely timed, and the temporal sequence is characteristic of each neural structure. As a result, each neuron connects only with certain target cells and not with others. In addition, the connections are often formed at specific locations on the target cells.

It is now clear that the total genetic information available to an animal—perhaps 10^5 genes in mammalian cells—is simply not sufficient to specify the total number of neuronal interconnections—perhaps 10^{15}—that are made. The development of the nervous system therefore involves epigenetic processes in which specific portions of the genetic information contained within developing cells are sequentially activated and modulated.

Epigenetic influences arise either from within the embryo, or from the external environment. The internal environment includes surface interactions between cells and the diffusion of chemical substances over long distances or between neighboring cells. The external environment includes nutritive factors, appropriate sensory and social experiences, and learning. A variety of internal and external factors impinge upon a developing cell. The actions of several of these factors are thought to be critical for enabling a neuron to differentiate appropriately. Each signal is presumably not only chemically, but also temporally and possibly topographically specific. To be effective, the signal often has to act on the cell at a particular stage of development.

In this series of chapters we shall consider the development of the brain in a broad context. In addition to examining the early stages of development, we shall describe how internal factors, such as androgenic hormones, continue to determine structural aspects of the brain during early postpartum development. Finally, in the context of development, we shall also consider the aging of the brain.

Samuel Schacher

Determination and Differentiation in the Development of the Nervous System

The central question in developmental biology is: How does a single cell, the fertilized ovum, give rise to so many types of cells? A distinctive aspect of this question is: How do neurons develop and how do they interconnect specifically? In other tissues of the body the identity of the cells is expressed by the particular proteins that the cell makes and by the interaction of the cell with its neighbors. Beyond ensuring that a cell is located in the appropriate organ and belongs to a certain group of cells, the precise position of a cell is generally not particularly important. Often the cell is a member of a fairly homogeneous population of similar cells, all of which interface with each other in similar ways. A beta cell will secrete insulin no matter where in the pancreas it is located. For neurons, however, position within the organ is critical. The properties of each neuron in the brain are determined not only by the proteins it makes and the chemical transmitter that it releases, but also by its location and interconnections within the brain. Thus the function of a cholinergic neuron in the motor nucleus of the spinal cord will be very different from that of a cholinergic neuron in the retina or in the cortex of the temporal lobe. A cholinergic neuron in each of these positions will connect and interact with different groups of neurons, and these interactions, as we have seen, determine the functioning of a cell.

Thus the development of the nervous system can be viewed in terms of three critical issues: (1) How do nerve cells originate? (2) How do the cells differentiate their appropriate properties in the appropriate position within the nervous system? (3) How do neurons form correct connections with one another so as to generate appropriate behavior? In this chapter we shall consider the first two questions. In Chapter 43 we shall consider how appropriate synapses are formed to generate behavior.

The development of the nervous system occurs in two steps. The first, *determination*, ensures that a certain cell population will give rise to the nervous system (neurons and glia). The second stage, *differentiation*, ensures that cells that descend from that determined population form neurons which make highly specific interconnections with one another and with their targets. These two broad stages in turn can be subdivided into many sequential cellular processes controlled by precise spatial and temporal signals. The timing of these signals serves to restrict the options available to cells in achieving their final differentiated state. Because the development of any one cell or brain structure appears to be the result of a great number of essentially independent sequential and vectorial steps, the process often becomes irreversible at one point or another during its course.

Fundamental to modern biology is the view that the structure and function of a cell or an organ—and its activities or behavior—are genetically specified. One category of developmental signals that is responsible for the sequential cellular processes involved in differentiation consists of *intrinsic factors*, or mechanisms within the cell that turn its genes on and off. However, with the development of eukaryotic cells, the expression of the genetic blueprint, the *phenotype*, is always shaped to some degree by *extrinsic* or *epigenetic* factors arising in the cell's environment. In this chapter we shall describe how, during the stages of determination and differentiation, genetic and extrinsic signals interact in the development of the nervous system.

Determination Occurs by Means of an Interaction Between Mesoderm and a Special Region of Ectoderm

The cells of the nervous system originate from a specific sheet of cells in the *ectoderm*, the outer layer of the embryo (Figure 42–1). This sheet of cells, the *neural plate*, consists of about 125,000 cells. It folds into a long, hollow, tubelike structure, called the *neural tube*. From the rostral part of the neural tube three swellings emerge that are the precursor areas of the three major sections of the brain (Figure 42–2)—the forebrain, midbrain, and hindbrain (medulla and pons).

The transformation of these ectodermal cells into cells that ultimately will give rise to the nervous system (the so-called *neuroectoderm*) is determined by the end of the gastrula stage of

42–1 Genesis of the nervous system from the ectoderm of a human embryo during the third and fourth weeks after conception. **Left,** external view of the developing embryo; **right,** corresponding cross-sectional view at about the middle of the future spinal cord. **A.** The central nervous system develops from the neural plate, a flat sheet of ectodermal cells on the dorsal surface of the embryo. **B.** The plate folds to form the neural groove. **C.** The groove closes into a hollow structure called the neural tube. **D.** The head end of the central canal widens to form the ventricles, or cavities, of the brain. (Adapted from Cowan, 1979).

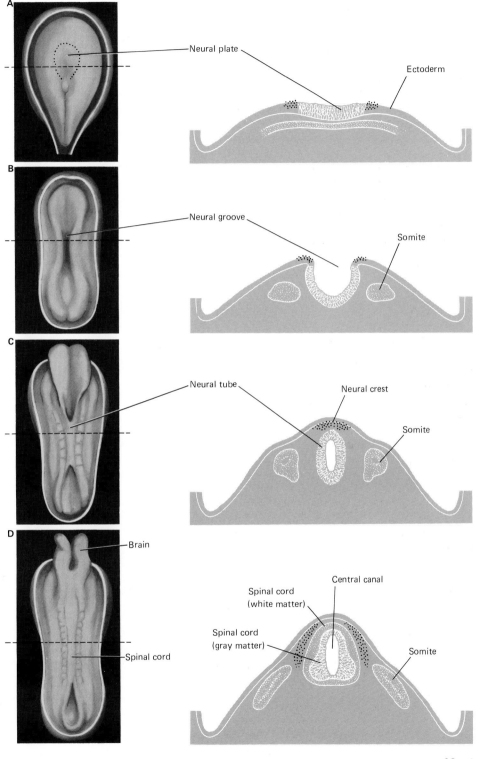

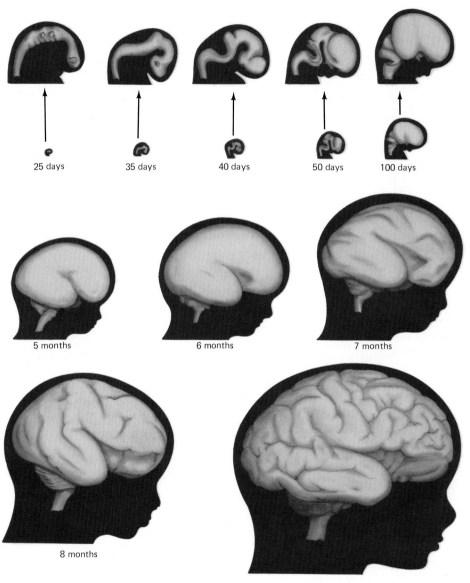

25 days   35 days   40 days   50 days   100 days

5 months   6 months   7 months

8 months

9 months

42–2 Embryonic and fetal stages in the development of the human brain viewed from the side. The first five embryonic stages are shown enlarged to an arbitrary common size to clarify their structural details. The drawings of the brain from 5 to 9 months are all reproduced at the same scale: approximately four-fifths life-size. The three main parts of the brain (the forebrain, midbrain, and hindbrain) originate as prominent swellings at the head end of the early neural tube. In human beings the cerebral hemispheres eventually overgrow the midbrain and the hindbrain and also partly obscure the cerebellum. The characteristic convolutions and invaginations of the brain's surface do not begin to appear until about the middle of gestation. Assuming that the fully developed human brain contains on the order of 100 billion neurons and that virtually no new neurons are added after birth, one can calculate that neurons must be generated in the developing brain at an average rate of more than 250,000/min. (Adapted from Cowan, 1979.)

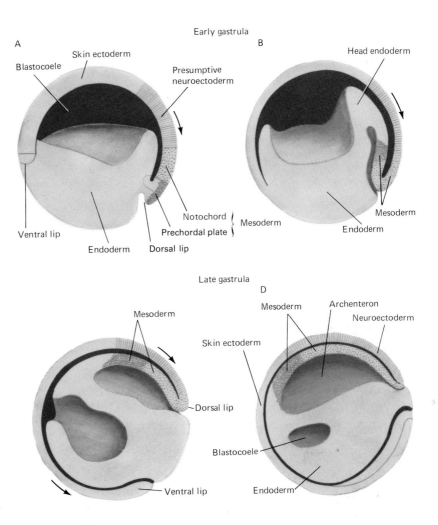

42-3 Gastrulation: inward cellular invagination and formation of the mesodermal layer in amphibians. **A.** In early gastrula, mesoderm cells lie on the surface of the embryo and begin to migrate toward the dorsal lip. **B.** Mesoderm cells migrate inward and underneath the ectoderm. C and **D.** Mesoderm cells continue to migrate beneath the neuroectoderm so that prechordal plate mesoderm lies underneath rostral neuroectoderm and notochord lies underneath caudal neuroectoderm. (Adapted from Saunders, 1970.)

embryogenesis (Figure 42–3). Determination implies a restriction in the capabilities of embryonic cells to differentiate into other tissues. For example, if prospective neuroectoderm is removed from an early gastrula stage embryo and transplanted to a different region in a host embryo, it will differentiate into skin, muscle, or gut depending on its new location in the host embryo. By the end of gastrulation, transplanted neuroectoderm can only become neural tissue.

Determination of the neuroectoderm occurs as a result of the process of *neural induction*. In the early part of this century, Hans Spemann and his colleagues in Germany, working on amphibian embryos, demonstrated that determination of neuroectoderm is induced by the underlying embryonic mesoderm that is formed during gastrulation. Spemann and Mangold transplanted presumptive mesoderm into the embryonic cavity (blastocoele) of an early gastrula host embryo (Figure 42–4A). As a result of cellular migrations that occur during gastrulation, the transplanted mesoderm came to be positioned underneath ectoderm that normally gave rise to trunk epidermis (Figure 42–4B). As development continued,

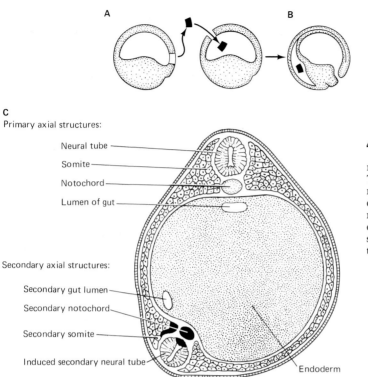

Primary axial structures:

Neural tube

Somite

Notochord

Lumen of gut

Secondary axial structures:

Secondary gut lumen

Secondary notochord

Secondary somite

Induced secondary neural tube

Endoderm

42–4 Spemann and Mangold's experiment demonstrating the role of mesoderm in neural induction. Transplantation of presumptive mesoderm into the embryonic cavity of an early gastrula host embryo resulted in the ectoderm of the trunk epidermis developing into a secondary set of axial structures, including neural tissue. (Adapted from Saunders, 1970.)

however, the ectoderm of the trunk epidermis was induced by the underlying mesoderm to develop into nervous tissue (Figure 42–4C).

The presence of underlying mesoderm is essential for the determination of neuroectoderm. In the early 1930s, Johannes Holtfreter, also working in Germany, developed techniques that prevented the normal inward invagination and migration of presumptive mesoderm during gastrulation. In the presence of hypertonic salt solutions, the presumptive mesoderm, instead of moving inward and beneath the ectoderm (Figure 42–3) moved away from the ectoderm. The resulting exogastrulated embryo developed

some normal mesodermal structures (somites and the notochord) but failed to develop a nervous system (Figure 42–5).

The investigations of Spemann and Holtfreter demonstrated the importance of mesoderm–ectoderm interactions in the determination of the nervous system. These findings led to the question: What is the nature of this interaction? The early work of Holtfreter, and the subsequent work of Saxen and Toivonen have indicated that neural induction is due to one or more chemical factors released from mesoderm. For example, cultured explants of neuroectoderm will differentiate into neural tissue if cultured together with

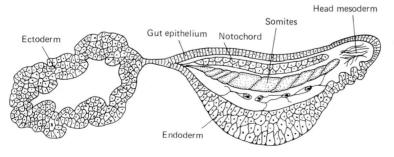

Head mesoderm

Somites

Ectoderm   Gut epithelium   Notochord

Endoderm

42–5 If the mesoderm is prevented from invaginating and instead moves away from the ectoderm, the exogastrulated embryo fails to develop a nervous system. (Adapted from Bodemer, 1968.)

embryonic mesoderm. Neural induction will still occur if filters with pore sizes ranging from 0.1 to 0.8 μm are placed between the neuroectoderm and mesoderm. These filters would block the passage of particles larger than ribosomes, polio viruses, and synaptic vesicles, but would permit the diffusion of most macromolecules between the tissues and prevent direct physical contact between the tissue layers. Experiments with intervening filters with smaller pores have indicated that the inducers may be peptides; induction is blocked if the intervening filter prevents the diffusion of molecules with molecular weights greater than 1000 daltons.

The Interaction between Mesoderm and Ectoderm Produces Regional Specificity: The Anterior–Posterior Axis

A second feature of the interaction between mesoderm and ectoderm is the development of *regional specificity* along the anterior–posterior axis. By the end of gastrulation, the major divisions of the nervous system (forebrain, midbrain, hindbrain, and spinal cord) are specified in the neuroectoderm.

The specification of the nervous system along the anterior–posterior axis of the embryo is thought to result from a gradient of inducing factors released by the mesoderm. Two aspects of the mesoderm–ectoderm interaction can contribute to the formation of gradients: (1) As gastrulation proceeds, the underlying mesoderm exerts its inductive effects first on posterior regions of

the neuroectoderm (the regions that will give rise to the spinal cord) and then moves progressively toward the anterior regions (which will give rise to the forebrain). Thus, the posterior neuroectoderm is influenced by underlying mesoderm for a longer period of time. (2) Posterior neuroectoderm comes in contact with a greater number of mesodermal cells (somite and notochord) than do the anterior regions.

In order to examine how quantitative differences in the interactions between ectoderm and mesoderm could lead to regional specificity in the neuroectoderm, Toivonen and Saxen cultured cells from disaggregated neuroectoderm of presumptive forebrain together with cells of trunk mesoderm in varying proportions. They found that the formation of specific neural structures was dependent on the ratio of mesoderm cells to neuroectoderm cells in the mixture. When few mesoderm cells were present compared to ectoderm cells, only anterior forebrain structures were formed (Figure 42–6, A–C). Increasing the number of mesoderm cells in relation to the ectoderm cells produced progressively more caudal structures (Figure 42–6, D–F). These experiments suggest that the different regions in the neuroectoderm can be specified as a result of dif-

42–6 Percentages of different neural and mesodermal structures that developed in reaggregates consisting of different ratios of presumptive neural (**black**), and mesodermal (**white**) cells cultivated in vitro. (Adapted from Toivonen and Saxen, 1968.)

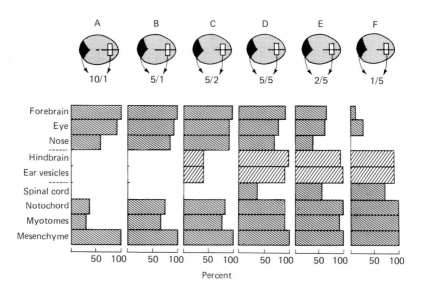

ferences in the extent of interactions between the mesoderm and the ectoderm.

Regional Specification Is Irreversible

Regional specification of the nervous system along the anterior–posterior axis of the embryo is irreversible. It occurs at the late gastrula stage, early in development, before the neural tube has formed and when most of the nervous system has not yet been generated. At that point, only a few neurons have begun to differentiate. If at this point specified neuroectoderm is transplanted into a host embryo in an inverted position so that specified forebrain neuroectoderm is placed in a posterior part of the host embryo, the nervous system will nevertheless develop as already programmed. The specified, transplanted forebrain structure continues to develop as forebrain even though it now is located in a posterior portion of the host embryo. Thus, the process of neural induction and regional specification determines the overall regional organization of the entire nervous system. As we shall see, however, local details of the regional specification can still be modulated by later signals that are critical for the differentiation of specific neuronal populations and their interconnections.

Differentiation Occurs in Three Phases

Once it has been determined that a region will become part of the nervous system, its cells begin to differentiate. Differentiation involves three important phases: (1) proliferation and generation of specific classes of neurons; (2) migration of cells to characteristic positions; and (3) maturation of cells with specific interconnections. We shall consider each of these phases in turn.

Proliferation Occurs in Specific Locations and at Specific Times

Cell Proliferation Occurs in Each Region of the Brain at a Particular Germinal Zone

The neural tube is formed after the invaginated folds of the neuroectoderm or neural plate fuse in the dorsal midline and separate from the surface ectoderm (Figures 42–1 and 42–7). Fusion of the neural tube takes place in the presumptive cervical region, and subsequently extends rostrally and caudally. Cell proliferation starts only after the neural tube has closed. Once it begins, the simple layer of epithelial cells that formed the neural plate is rapidly transformed into a thick layer of cells. Throughout the neural tube, cell proliferation takes place in characteristic areas called *germinal zones*. For most regions of the central nervous system, the germinal zone is located adjacent to the ventricular surface.

Actively dividing or *stem cells* undergo characteristic cellular changes during the course of the cell cycle (Figure 42–8). As a result, the cell nuclei come to lie at different levels of the epithelium. The nuclei migrate toward the ventricular surface and withdraw their processes before dividing. After cell division the daughter cells send out their processes and the nuclei return to the deeper part of the epithelium to replicate their DNA. After several divisions the neurons lose the ability to divide. The postmitotic cells then leave the germinal zone and migrate to their appropriate position, either as immature neurons (that never again divide) or as glial cell precursors (that can divide).

Certain Neurons Proliferate Again After Migration

With few exceptions, neurons that migrate are postmitotic and will never again divide. There are a few exceptions, however, and these are both interesting and important. In the forebrain, nerve cells leave the ventricular zone and migrate to a special region called the *subventricular zone*, which lies between the ventricular zone and the intermediate zone (see Figure 42–11). In the subventricular zone the neurons proliferate again to give rise to the small neurons and glial cells of the basal ganglia and related deep nuclear structures, as well as to some cells of the cerebral cortex. As we shall see later, cells that have migrated from the ventricular zone to the subventricular region of the hindbrain undergo still another migration to reach the pial surface of the cerebellum, where they form the external granular layer. The cells of this layer then proliferate to form the granule cells and the other interneurons of the cerebellum.

Different Types of Cells Are Generated at Different Times

Within any given structure of the nervous system, different cell types are generated during

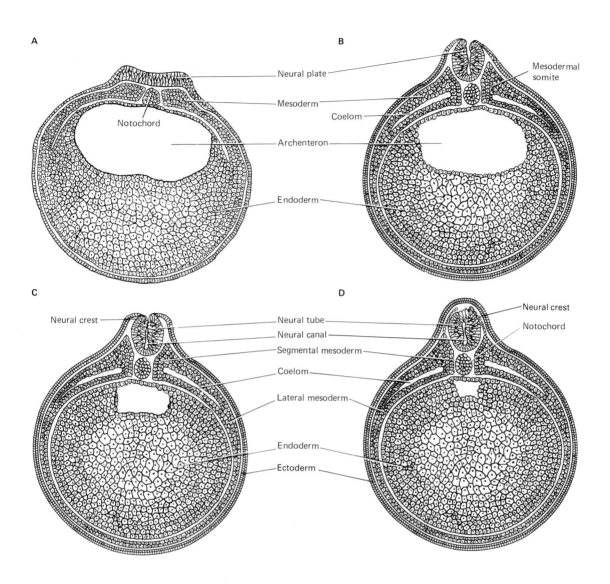

A

Neural plate

Mesoderm

Notochord

Archenteron

Endoderm

B

Mesodermal somite

Coelom

C

Neural crest

D

Neural crest

Notochord

Neural tube

Neural canal

Segmental mesoderm

Coelom

Lateral mesoderm

Endoderm

Ectoderm

specified periods of time. The analysis of a variety of different regions indicates several general rules:

1. Large cells develop first.
2. Motor cells develop before sensory cells.
3. Interneurons develop last.
4. Glial cells develop after neurons.

A given structure such as the cerebral cortex or the spinal cord has a variety of cell types. How these different cell types within a neuronal structure are generated is not yet known. Specific cell types may be determined early if they are direct descendants of stem cells that have been rigidly committed to a particular developmental program. For example, a group of stem cells may

42–7 Neurulation: formation of the neural tube and neural crest. **A** and **B.** The neural plate invaginates. **C** and **D.** The folds fuse and separate from the ectoderm. (Adapted from Saunders, 1970.)

become "determined" to be motor cells at an early stage in development and subsequently give rise only to precursor motor cells. Alternatively, a given stem cell may give rise to many types of cells that differentiate appropriately only later. The differentiation of the cells is then influenced by the time at which they are generated and the local environmental conditions into which they migrate (see below).

Phase of cell cycle

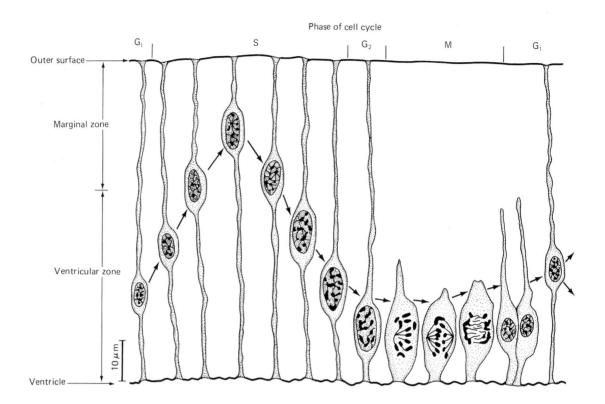

42–8 Nuclear movements during the cell cycle in the germinal zone. Actively dividing cells in the ventricular zone show characteristic movements of their nuclei which can be described in terms of four stages of the cell cycle: G, S, G_2, and M. During DNA synthesis (**S**) the nuclei are positioned in the marginal zone. The nuclei then migrate to the ventricular surface during G_2, retract their processes, and undergo mitosis (**M**). The daughter cells can either resume the mitotic cycle and enter the G_1 phase of the cell cycle or stop dividing and migrate away from the ventricular zone. (Adapted from Jacobson, 1978.)

Migration Affects Cell Differentiation

As examples of the development of neural organization we shall consider two neural components, the neural crest and the cerebellum.

Neural Crest Cells Are Influenced by Their Local Environment

During the closure of the neural tube, some cells at the margins of the neural plate separate dorsally from the neural tube to form the neural crest (Figures 42–1 and 42–7). Cells from the neural crest migrate to populate the entire embryo. The cranial part of the neural crest gives

rise both to neurons and to glial cells that form a variety of structures: the cranial ganglia (V, VII, VIII, IX, X), the autonomic ganglia of the digestive tract, the ciliary ganglion, Schwann cells, melanocytes, and pia-arachnoid meninges covering the diencephalon and telencephalon. The neural crest of the trunk gives rise to spinal sensory ganglia, sympathetic ganglia, the chromaffin cells of the adrenal medulla, and the ganglia of the postumbilical intestinal tract.

The diversity of its cell types and their wide distribution in the mature animal make the neural crest an interesting system for examining the effects of cell migration and local environment on neuronal development. Nicole LeDouarin and her colleagues in France have found that the local environment in which the migrating crest cells ultimately find themselves greatly influences the subsequent development of their specific biochemical properties. In order to carry out these pioneering experiments, LeDouarin developed a natural marking technique for determining the original source of neurons derived from neural crest cells. The technique is based on the histologically detectable differences in the structure of the nuclei between two species of birds, quail and chick. Because of these differ-

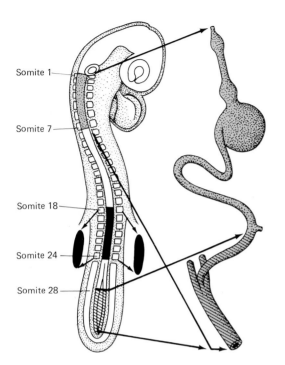

Somite 1

Somite 7

Somite 18

Somite 24

Somite 28

42–9 Distribution of neural crest cells that give rise to parasympathetic neurons of the digestive tract and adrenergic cells of the adrenal medulla. The parasympathetic neurons of the digestive tract are derived from neural crest cells in the anterior (Somite 1–Somite 7) and posterior (below Somite 28) portion of the neural tube. The sympathetic ganglia are derived from crest cells in region Somite 7–Somite 28. The adrenergic cells of the adrenal medulla are derived from crest cells in the region Somite 18–Somite 24. (Adapted from LeDouarin et al., 1975.)

ences, she could transplant "naturally marked" neural crest cells from one region of a donor species to another in the host species.

In the first group of experiments LeDouarin determined which regions of the neural crest give rise to the sympathetic and parasympathetic nervous systems (Figure 42–9). She transplanted specific quail neural tube regions (with the associated neural crest) to corresponding positions in the host chick embryos. She later examined the mosaic embryos for the location of quail cells and found that the parasympathetic ganglia are derived from crest cells that come from the anterior portion (somite levels S1–S7) and the posterior portion (below S28) of the neural tube. In contrast, the ganglia of the sympathetic nervous system are derived from the intermediate level neural crest cells (somite levels S7–S28).

LeDouarin then asked: Is the fate of a neural

crest cell that is destined to be either a sympathetic neuron (synthesizing norepinephrine) or a parasympathetic neuron (synthesizing acetylcholine) determined before or after migration to the appropriate sites? To answer this question, LeDouarin transplanted regions of quail neural tube (including the associated neural crest) to heterotypic regions of the chick embryo (Figure 42–10). For example, she took neural crest cells from somite region 18–24 (the sympathetic precursor region) in the quail and transplanted them to somite region 1–7 (a parasympathetic region) in the chick (Figure 42–10A). The transplanted quail cells migrated along routes typical of crest cells from somite region 1–7. These cells ended up in parasympathetic ganglia and functioned as parasympathetic neurons releasing acetylcholine as their transmitter. A similar reversal in transmitter biosynthesis was observed when presumptive parasympathetic crest cells from quail (anterior neural crest) were transplanted to somite region 16–26 (sympathetic and adrenal medulla) in chick embryos. The quail cells migrated to the adrenal medulla and differentiated adrenergic properties (Figure 42–10B). These experiments indicated that the route of migration for the different neuronal elements is determined by their position in the neural crest. Moreover, the final differentiated state of the neuron is *not* determined prior to migration; rather, it is strongly influenced by the interaction between the migrating cells and the environment along the migration route and at the final destination.

LeDouarin's work with embryos has been extended in an elegant series of experiments by Furshpan, Potter, Patterson, and their colleagues at the Harvard Medical School with immature sympathetic neurons in dissociated cell culture. These neurons normally maintain their adrenergic properties in culture and synthesize norepinephrine. However, if the neurons are cultured together with a variety of nonneural cells, they develop cholinergic properties: they contain choline acetyltransferase, synthesize acetylcholine, and make effective cholinergic synapses on appropriate targets. The neurons do not have to be in direct contact with the nonneural cells for these cholinergic properties to appear. The nonneural cells secrete a substance into the medium, and this diffusable factor, as yet uncharacterized, can itself cause sympathetic neurons to develop cholinergic properties. Thus, these experiments with neural crest cells indicate that the environment in which developing neurons find them-

A   B

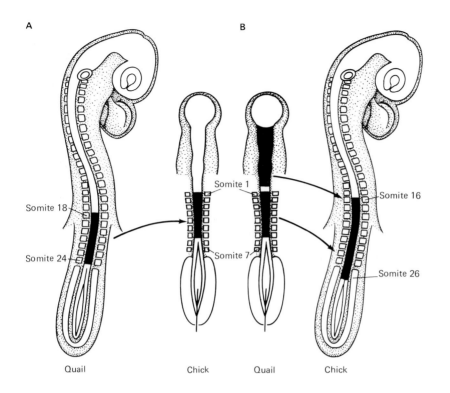

Somite 1

Somite 18

Somite 24

Somite 7

Somite 16

Somite 26

Quail   Chick   Quail   Chick

42–10 Heterotypic transplantation of quail neural tube and crest into chick embryos. **A.** Neural cells from region Somite 18–Somite 24, which normally migrate to the adrenal medulla and synthesize norepinephrine, are transplanted to region Somite 1–Somite 7, which gives rise to cells that migrate to form the parasympathetic ganglia of the digestive tract and synthesize acetylcholine. The transplanted cells migrate to the digestive tract and develop cholinergic properties. **B.** Crest cells that normally migrate to the digestive tract and synthesize acetylcholine are transplanted into a region in which cells typically migrate to the adrenal medulla (Somite 16–Somite 26) and synthesize norepinephrine. The transplanted cells migrate to the adrenal medulla and develop adrenergic properties. (Adapted from LeDouarin et al., 1975.)

selves can affect the expression of transmitter synthesizing capabilities. Apparently, an extrinsic chemical factor is critical in activating (or deactivating) genes controlling the synthesis of acetylcholine or norepinephrine.

Cell Interactions Aid Migration in the Cerebellar Cortex

The cerebellar cortex is a precisely interconnected and well characterized network consisting of five neuronal elements (see Chapter 30). Studies of the development of the cerebellar cortex have revealed two features that appear to be quite general and are shared with other parts of the nervous system. First, young (postmitotic) neurons leave their germinal zone and typically migrate past older cells to reach their final position (as occurs, for example, in the thickening of the wall of the brain; Figure 42–11). Second, the migration and final position of the neurons may be influenced by the intimate interaction between the migrating cells and a particular type of glial process, the radial glial fibers. These cellular processes are derived from glial cells, called *Bergmann astrocytes*, which span the entire length of the cerebellar cortex.

During the course of development, the cerebellar cortex consists of several histologically distinct zones (Figure 42–12). Initially there is a single germinal zone at the surface of the fourth ventricle (the *ventricular zone*). This zone gives rise to the Purkinje cells and the Golgi cells. These large neurons, the first to develop in the cerebellar cortex, migrate from the ventricular zone through the marginal *intermediate zones* to form the Purkinje cell layer. A second germinal zone, called the *external granule layer*, now forms at the pial surface. The cells of the external granule layer are initially derived from part of the germinal zone on the fourth ventricle called

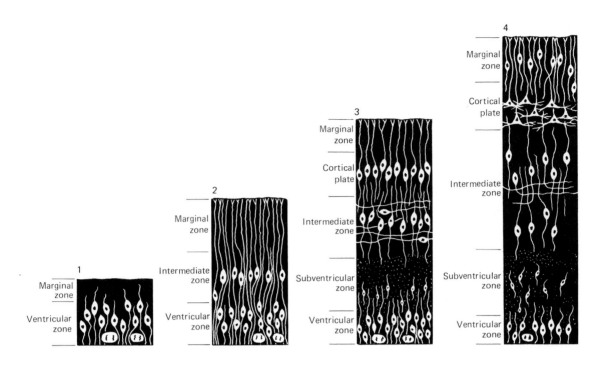

42–11 Progressive thickening of the wall of the developing brain. At the earliest stage *(1)* the wall consists only of a "pseudostratified" epithelium, in which the ventricular zone contains the cell bodies and the marginal zone contains only the extended outer cell processes. When some of the cells lose their capacity for synthesizing DNA and withdraw from the mitotic cycle *(2)*, they form a second layer, the intermediate zone. In the forebrain the cells that pass through this zone aggregate to form the cortical plate, the region in which the various layers of the cerebral cortex develop *(3)*. The cortical cell layers develop in an inverted fashion such that cells in deeper layers (i.e., layer VI) develop first. The cells in the superficial layers must migrate past older cells to reach their appropriate position. At the latest stage *(4)* the original ventricular zone remains as the ependymal lining of the cerebral ventricles, and the comparatively cell-free region between this lining and the cortex becomes the subcortical white matter, through which nerve fibers enter and leave the cortex. The subventricular zone is a second proliferative region in which many glial cells and some neurons in the forebrain are generated. (Adapted from Jacobson, 1978.)

the *rhombic lip.* These cells migrate along the pial surface of the cerebellum to form this second multicellular, layered germinal zone, where they begin to proliferate extensively.

The external granule layer generates the interneurons of the cerebellum, the basket cells and stellate cells of the molecular layer, and the granule cells of the granule layer. The birth of these neurons coincides with the stage when the Purkinje cell layer is nearly completed and the Purkinje cells have begun to spin out their primary dendritic processes. The neurogenesis of the molecular layer interneurons (basket and stellate cells) is completed first (at birth in primates), while the granule cells continue to be generated afterward (for periods of 6 months to 2 years after birth in primates).

The development of the granule, basket, and stellate cells illustrates the importance of cell interactions in neuronal differentiation. For example, in order to reach the final destination in the granule layer, the granule cells must migrate from the external granule layer across the molecular and Purkinje cell layers. This migration is shown in Figure 42–13. As the granule cell becomes bipolar, with its processes oriented parallel to the pial surface and perpendicular to the Purkinje cell dendrites, it extends a third process into the molecular layer. The granule cell body then moves along the extended process, leaving the bipolar processes behind to form the parallel

fibers. These parallel fibers become the axons of granule cells that make synaptic contacts with the dendritic spines of Purkinje cells. The direction of growth of the cytoplasmic process in the molecular layer and the movement of the cell body are guided through the intervening layers by radial glial fibers formed by the processes of Bergmann astrocytes (Figure 42–14). These glial cells,

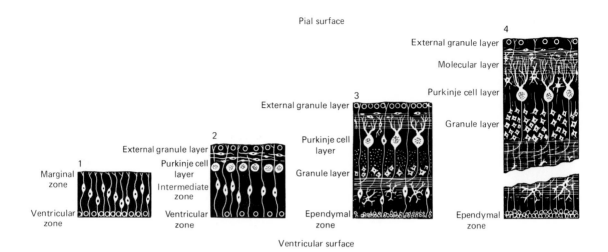

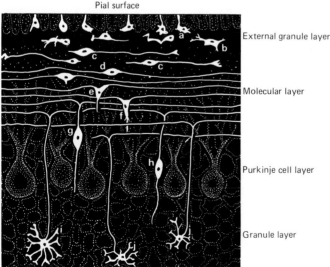

42–12 Development of the cerebellar cortex. At the earliest state *(1)*, the developing cerebellum has two zones, the ventricular zone and the marginal zone, which contain the cell bodies and processes, respectively, of actively dividing cells. As cells become postmitotic *(2)*, they migrate through the intermediate zone and form the Purkinje cell layer. At this time, cells migrating along the pial surface form a second germinal zone, the external granule layer. As development continues *(3 and 4)*, the Purkinje cells develop their dendritic processes, and cerebellar interneurons migrate from the external granular layer and differentiate their processes to form the molecular and granule layers. The germinal zone bordering the ventricle is now called the ependymal zone, which gives rise to ependymal cells lining the ventricle, the glial cells, and the neurons of the deep cerebellar nuclei. (Adapted from Jacobson, 1978.)

generated in the ventricular zone, have their cell bodies positioned just beneath the Purkinje cell layer. Before granule cell migration, the Bergmann astrocytes project radially oriented fibers to the pial surface. The migrating granule cells move along the fibers until they reach the granule layer.

Pasko Rakic has suggested that the interaction between migrating granule cells and radial glial fibers is essential for the survival and normal development of the granule cells. This idea is supported by observations made on an autosomal recessive mutation in mice known as *weaver*. Animals with this mutation show muscular weakness, unsteadiness of movement, and severe

42–13 Migration of cerebellar granule cells. As a granule cell becomes postmitotic (**a**) in the external granular layer, it begins to spin out bipolar processes (**b, c, d**) that are parallel to the pial surface and perpendicular to the Purkinje cell dendrites. The cell extends a third process (**e, f**) into the molecular layer, and the cell body moves along this growing process (**g, h**) through the molecular and Purkinje layers to reach its final position **i, j**) in the granule layer. (Adapted from Jacobson, 1978.)

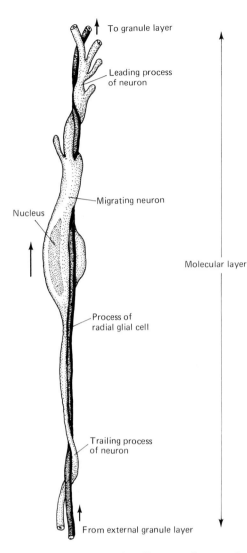

42–14 Migrating granule cell moves along a radial glial fiber to the granule layer. (Adapted from Rakic, 1971.)

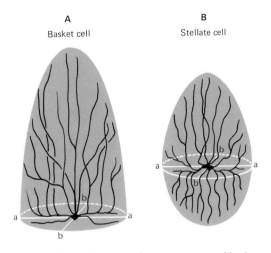

42–15 Three-dimensional reconstruction of basket and stellate cells. **A.** When the cell body of the basket cell becomes fixed in position close to Purkinje cell bodies by granule cell parallel fibers laid down perpendicular to the basket cell **(plane ab)**, its dendrites lengthen toward the pial surface, contacting large numbers of parallel fibers. **B.** Stellate cells become fixed within the molecular layer and grow dendrites in both directions perpendicular to the parallel fibers to contact older and new parallel fibers. (Adapted from Rakic, 1973.)

tremor. Examination of the cerebellum reveals extensive loss of granule cells. The lack of granule cells does not result from a diminution of cell proliferation in the external granule layer, but from an inability of granule cells, once generated, to migrate to their appropriate position. Electron microscopic analysis of homozygous and heterozygous weaver mice shows extensive degeneration of radial glial fibers prior to the onset of migration by the granule cell or extensive aberrant orientation of the glial fibers across the cerebellar cortex. These changes in the radial glial fibers are sufficient to explain the degeneration of granule cells at the junction of the external granule layer and the molecular layer and in the molecular layer itself. Areas in which radial glial fibers are present and properly oriented show little granule cell degeneration.

The interneurons of the molecular layer—the basket cells and stellate cells—arrive at their final position in a different manner. Interneurons of the molecular layer become postmitotic and remain as round cells at the junction of the molecular layer and the external granule layer. As more parallel fibers are formed by the granule cells, the postmitotic interneurons of the molecular layer begin to extend bipolar processes perpendicular to the parallel fibers. As additional parallel fibers are formed around the interneuron cell bodies and their bipolar processes, the interneurons become fixed in place. The bipolar processes now branch upward or downward to maximize the number of parallel fiber contacts. For example, the earliest interneurons generated, the basket cells (Figure 42–15A), come to be positioned close to the Purkinje cell bodies on a shallow bed of recently formed granule cell parallel fibers. As more parallel fibers are laid down externally and at right angles to the basket cells, their cell bodies are fixed in position. Now their dendrites lengthen enormously by growing externally toward the pial surface, making contacts with an increasing number of parallel fibers.

Interneurons that are generated later are fixed in position in the middle of the molecular layer and become stellate cells. These cells can grow dendrites internally to make contacts with older parallel fibers and externally to make contacts with new parallel fibers (Figure 42–15B). Thus, the manner in which basket and stellate cells develop suggests that they do not originate as separate types of neurons but as one type of cell whose mature position and phenotype are influenced by the time of generation and local interactions with granule cell parallel fibers.

Neuronal Maturation Consists of Four Discrete Steps

Important new information on neuronal maturation has been obtained from experiments with genetic mutants of invertebrates, whose nervous systems contain far smaller numbers of neurons and are therefore less complex than those in higher animals. Because of their short generation time, it is technically easier to obtain mutants and to raise large populations of isogenic strains. Consequently, these studies with simple invertebrates have been fruitful for assessing the extent to which the genetic program determines the structure of the nervous system and its behavior. Most information has come from studies on the fruit fly, *Drosophila*, by Seymour Benzer and his collaborators at the California Institute of Technology; on the nematode worm, *Caenorhabditis elegans*, by Sydney Brenner and his co-workers in Cambridge, England; and on the small crustacean, *Daphnia*, by Cyrus Levinthal and his collaborators at Columbia University.

These and other studies have shown that neuronal maturation consists of four stages: the outgrowth and elongation of axons, the elaboration of dendritic processes, the expression of appropriate biochemical properties (such as specific transmitters and membrane receptors), and the formation of synaptic connections between appropriate cells.

Axon Outgrowth and Elongation Are Subject to Intrinsic and Extrinsic Influences

For a neuron to make appropriate connections with distant target cells, it must send its axons in

the right direction. In general, the initial outgrowth of an axon is in the direction it must take to reach its final destination. This directional specificity may be determined intrinsically, or it may be influenced by certain trophic substances that attract the growing axon. As we shall see in Chapter 43, an example of a trophic substance that influences axon outgrowth is nerve growth factor.

Growing axons can be guided to their targets by an appropriately oriented substrate, such as radial glial fibers of Bergmann astrocytes of the cerebellum (described above), or by nerve fibers that have reached the target area previously. Thus, young neurons can send their axons along a fiber pathway that has been laid down by older cells. For example, in the developing visual system of the small crustacean *Daphnia*, certain photoreceptors send out "pioneering" fibers which serve as guides for the axons of other photoreceptors to interconnect with appropriate central neurons.

The growth of the axon and its ability to interact with the environment occur at a specialized structure at the tip of the growing axon, the *growth cone*, which was first described by Santiago Ramón y Cajal in fixed tissue, by R. G. Harrison in tissue culture, and by C. Speidel in the intact animal. The growth cone is a specialized expanded region of the axon that often has an undulating membrane which gives rise to numerous *filopodia*; these motile extensions of the growth cone can reach 20 μm in length. Growth cones contain a variety of cytoplasmic organelles, including mitochondria, microtubules, neurofilaments, and microfilaments (the contractile elements involved in intracellular motility), numerous vesicles, and smooth endoplasmic reticulum (sources of membranes for growth). In addition, the growth cone is capable of pinocytosing material from the extracellular environment which can be transported in a retrograde fashion to the cell body (see Chapter 11). The uptake of material and its transport to the cell body may allow the growing axon to inform the cell body of appropriate signals from the periphery for correct growth and synapse formation.

Genetic Factors and Synaptic Interactions Influence the Elaboration of Dendritic Processes

Two important factors are thought to contribute to the formation and elaboration of dendritic processes: intrinsically determined, presumably genetic, factors and appropriate synaptic interactions. Studies on the development of a variety of cells, including pyramidal cells in the cerebral cortex and Purkinje cells in the cerebellum (neurons with stereotypic dendritic patterns), indicate that the initial formation and orientation of the dendritic processes are determined by intrinsic factors, whereas the final shape and morphological specializations (i.e., dendritic spines) are dependent on the local interactions with afferent synaptic input. For example, the absence of specific afferent connections to Purkinje cells in the cerebellum will often produce changes in the normal shape and morphology of the dendrites of the Purkinje cells.

Specific Chemical Factors Influence Neuronal Differentiation

Little information is currently available concerning the control of the biochemical differentiation of neurons. However, two diffusible proteins have been shown to influence strongly the induction of specific biochemical pathways for transmitter biosynthesis. As mentioned above, nerve growth factor plays a critical role in the development of sympathetic neurons. One effect of nerve growth factor is to induce the synthesis of the enzymes tyrosine hydroxylase and dopamine β-hydroxylase in developing adrenergic cells. We have also briefly considered another diffusible factor recently discovered by Patterson and his colleagues. This factor is secreted by a variety of cells and induces the development of cholinergic properties in sympathetic neurons grown in tissue culture. The ability to induce cholinergic properties in these cells, however, is restricted to a very precise stage in their development.

Synapse Formation Is Directed by Neuronal Recognition and Other Processes

As we shall see in the next chapter, once the axon's growth cone has reached the general area of the target, it must select the appropriate cell, and in many instances the appropriate topographic position on the cell, to form a synapse. Obviously, some form of recognition, perhaps a specific surface interaction, signals the cell that appropriate contact has been made. Surface interactions have been shown to be crucial in the selective aggregation of specific cells in tissue culture when disaggregated cell types are mixed. As we shall see, similar mechanisms may be utilized by interacting neurons for the recognition and formation of appropriate synapses.

Neuronal recognition alone, however, is clearly not sufficient to account for the formation of specific connections. Neuronal specificity derives not from a single step of recognition but from a program of development that is the result of two large families of processes. First, there is the overall developmental sequence that includes various phases (induction, proliferation, cell migration, axonal outgrowth, dendrite elaboration, cell death, and neuronal recognition) that are patterned in space and time by the various controlling factors discussed above. Second, as we shall see in Chapters 43 and 52, these connections are finally stabilized by the appropriate environmental conditions in postembryonic life. Thus, the challenging task remains of determining how the brain is wired, and of delineating further the roles of the genes and of environmental clues in achieving this remarkable organization.

Selected Readings and References

Cowan, W. M. 1979. The development of the brain. Sci. Am. 241(3):112–133.

Jacobson, M. 1978. Developmental Neurobiology. 2nd ed. New York: Plenum.

LeDouarin, N. M., Renaud D., Teillet, M. A., and LeDouarin, G. H. 1975. Cholinergic differentiation of presumptive adrenergic neuroblasts in interspecific chimeras after heterotopic transplantations. Proc. Natl. Acad. Sci. U.S.A. 72:728–732.

Patterson, P. H. 1978. Environmental determination of autonomic neurotransmitter functions. Annu. Rev. Neurosci. 1:1–17.

Rakic, P. 1971. Neuron–glia relationship during granule cell migration in developing cerebellar cortex. A Golgi and electronmicroscopic study in *Macacus rhesus*. J. Comp. Neurol. 141:283–312.

Other References

Bodemer, C. W. 1968. Modern Embryology. New York: Holt, Rinehart and Winston.

Brenner, S. 1974. The genetics of *Caenorhabditis elegans*. Genetics 77:71–94.

Cajal, S. R. 1929. Etude sur la neurogenèse de quelques vertébrés. Trans. by L. Guth as Studies on Vertebrate Neurogenesis. Springfield, Ill.: Thomas, 1960.

Harrison, R. G. 1907. Observations on the living developing nerve fiber. Anat. Rec. 1:116–118.

Hotta, Y., and Benzer, S. 1976. Courtship in *Drosophila* mosaics: Sex-specific foci for sequential action patterns. Proc. Natl. Acad. Sci. U.S.A. 73:4154–4158.

Lopresti, V., Macagno, E. R., and Levinthal, C. 1973. Structure and development of neuronal connections in isogenic organisms: Cellular interactions in the development of the optic lamina of *Daphnia*. Proc. Natl. Acad. Sci. U.S.A. 70:433–437.

Quinn, W. G., and Gould, J. L. 1979. Nerves and genes. Nature (Lond.) 278:19–23.

Rakic, P. 1973. Kinetics of proliferation and latency between final cell division and onset of differentiation of cerebellar stellate and basket neurons. J. Comp. Neurol. 147:523–546.

Rakic, P., and Sidman, R. L. 1973. Weaver mutant mouse cerebellum: Defective neuronal migration secondary to abnormality of Bergmann glia. Proc. Natl. Acad. Sci. U.S.A. 70:240–244.

Saunders, J. W., Jr. 1970. Patterns and Principles of Animal Development. New York: Macmillan.

Spiedel, C. C. 1933. Studies of living nerves. II. Activities of ameboid growth cones, sheath cells, and myelin segments, as revealed by prolonged observation of individual nerve fibers in frog tadpoles. Am. J. Anat. 52:1–79.

Spemann, H. 1938. Embryonic Development and Induction. New Haven: Yale University Press.

Toivonen, S., and Saxen, L. 1968. Morphogenetic interaction of presumptive neural and mesodermal cells mixed in different ratios. Science (Wash., D.C.) 159:539–540.

Eric R. Kandel

Synapse Formation, Trophic Interactions Between Neurons, and the Development of Behavior

43

Behavior depends upon the formation of appropriate interconnections among neurons in the brain. In the previous chapter, we learned how neurons first become determined and how they migrate to their final position and begin to differentiate. In this chapter we shall focus on the subsequent stages of neuronal differentiation which we considered only briefly in the last chapter. We shall specifically focus on one of the critical questions in developmental neurobiology: How do neurons form appropriate synaptic connections? The formation of stable synaptic connections is not the result of a single event but a sequence of events that can be studied in terms of three questions, each of which can be analyzed independently:

1. How do neurons seek each other out (pathfinding)?
2. How, having found one another, do two neurons form a functioning connection (synapse formation)?
3. How, having formed a synapse, do two neurons influence each other's subsequent program of differentiation and survival by means of synaptic actions (transneuronal influence on differentiation)?

These questions turn on the problem of selectivity. How does a cell's axon know where to go and, once it gets there, to stop and form an appropriate connection? In particular, to what degree and by what means do cells in the nervous system make precise connections?

In analyzing the steps in synapse formation we shall also consider to what degree the functions of the nervous system and the expression of behavior are determined by developmentally programmed maturation on the one hand, and environmentally arranged learning on the other. We shall examine the extent to which neural connections result from invariant processes of regulation, growth, and differentiation and the extent to which they are formed as a result of experience and learning.

In the late 1920s and early 1930s psychologists believed that most of the connections between neurons in the brain are not inherently determined. These psychologists maintained that developmental forces leave the central nervous system an unorganized network capable only of random reactions. Out of this randomness, behavioral feedback from trial-and-error learning produces a coherent neural organization. According to this view, interconnections between cells are directed by the pattern of stimulation that the organism receives from its external environment. Alternatively, a number of modern biologists have maintained that the complexity of the brain demands a prescribed developmental program. These alternative possibilities have given rise to two views of development that, by analogy to constitutional law, may be called the loose and the strict constructionist view. According to the *loose constructionist view*, there is only a limited developmental program. A key role in the formation of synaptic connections is played by learning. According to the *strict constructionist view* there is an extensive genetic and developmental program in synapse formation and a more limited role for learning.

While keeping these overall issues in mind, we shall first narrow our focus and begin our examination of synapse formation by considering the simplest example—the synapses between a motor neuron and a muscle. In this well-studied and easily accessible synapse one can see clearly the type of influences a neuron can exert on its target. Motor neurons exert at least two types of influence on muscle, and muscle fibers can influence the neurons that innervate them. Let us consider each interaction in turn.

Motor Neurons and Muscle Influence Each Other's Development

Neurons Can Influence the Speed of Muscle Contraction

Adult cats (and other mammals) have two types of muscles that can be distinguished by their speed of contraction: fast (pale) and slow (red). Fast muscles depend on glycolytic metabolism, whereas slow muscles, rich in myoglobin, depend on aerobic respiration. Fast muscles are involved in phasic contractions; slow muscles are involved in postural adjustment. The relationship of motor neurons to muscle has been studied by John C. Eccles and his colleagues, who found that motor neurons and muscles have matching properties. Motor neurons that innervate fast muscles have a rapid conduction velocity and a brief hyperpolarizing afterpotential and can therefore fire rapidly at 30–60 impulses/sec. Motor neurons that innervate slow muscles conduct slowly and have a larger afterpotential. These motor neurons fire more slowly at 10–20 impulses/sec.

Newborn kittens have only slow muscles. The differentiation of muscle into fast or slow occurs over a period of weeks after birth. How does this differentiation occur? Do the motor neurons determine the properties of the muscle, or does the muscle determine the properties of the motor neurons? To examine this question Arthur J. Buller and Eccles switched nerves and muscles surgically and found that the neurons, independent of the muscles they innervated, retained their properties. In contrast, the muscles changed their contractile properties when their innervation was changed. A fast muscle was converted to a slow muscle as a result of being innervated by a slow motor neuron, and slow muscles converted to fast muscles (Figure 43–1). This transformation is quite remarkable for two reasons. First, as this experiment illustrates, the differentiation into fast or slow muscle is not an all-or-none process that occurs only once in the developmental history of the organism; the process of differentiation is maintained continuously throughout life. A change in innervation at any time will lead to the redifferentiation of the muscle. Second, the fast and slow muscles differ in their myosin light chains. The initial differentiation and any subsequent redifferentiation involve the initial expression and subsequent alteration in specific gene products. Thus, the phenotype or

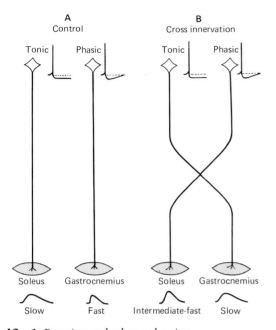

43–1 Experimental scheme showing cross-innervation of motor axons to slow and fast muscles. **A.** Control. **B.** Cross-anastomosed preparations. The unique characteristics of the two species of motor neurons do not change after cross-innervation. However, fast muscles are completely transformed to slow muscles and slow muscles are changed into an intermediate form.

the type of myosin synthesized by the muscle is controlled by the nervous system!

What is responsible for this step in redifferentiation? Is there a chemical influence that flows from the nerve to the muscle—perhaps something released in conjunction with the neurotransmitter? Or is the signal simply the pattern or speed of contraction that the neuron imposes on the muscle? Terje Lømo and his colleagues have found that at least part of the differentiation of muscle is determined by the pattern of activity, i.e., the frequency of contraction. Thus, in this simple instance motor innervation is critical for the differentiation of fast and slow muscles because it determines the rate at which the muscle will contract.

Neurons Can Influence the Chemosensitivity of the Muscle Membrane

The acetylcholine receptors of vertebrate skeletal muscles normally are largely restricted to the re-

gion of the end-plates (the site where the motor nerve synapses on the muscle). Here the density exceeds 20,000 receptor molecules/μm². In contrast, a few micrometers away the density of receptors falls to extremely low levels, less than 50/μm². Julius Axelsson and Stephen Thesleff in Sweden have found that if the nerve is cut and allowed to degenerate, acetylcholine receptors soon appear in extrajunctional regions. Receptors are no longer restricted to the end-plate, but are found in almost homogeneous distribution all over the muscle fiber, although the density of receptors in the extrasynaptic region never quite reaches the density of the denervated end-plate (Figure 43–2). This diffuse distribution of new receptors does not simply represent the unmasking of receptors that are already present in the membrane in occult form, but the synthesis of new receptors and their insertion into the membrane.

Three other observations are related to the appearance of new receptors. (1) If one reinnervates the muscle, receptors disappear from the extrajunctional regions. The distribution of the receptor again becomes restricted to the region of the end-plate. (2) Embryonic muscle is diffusely sensitive to acetylcholine. Once it becomes innervated, however, its sensitivity to acetylcholine becomes restricted to the end-plate region. (3) A muscle fiber innervated by one nerve fiber can no longer be innervated by another. Thus, once synapse formation has occurred, restriction of chemosensitivity may be one of the several mechanisms that prevent other nerve axons from forming synapses on the muscle.

What restricts the distribution of acetylcholine receptors with innervation and leads to their spread with denervation? One early notion was that the transmitter substance (acetylcholine) or some other (trophic) substance flows from nerve to muscle and is responsible for restricting the ACh receptors. When the nerve is cut, the substance stops flowing and new receptors are inserted into the extrajunctional membrane. Although this view was generally accepted and very influential, Lømo and Jean Rosenthal have shown it to be only partly correct. The appearance of receptors in the extrajunctional region after denervation is mostly due to *disuse,* the lack of contraction (use) of the muscle normally produced by activity in the nerve. Similarly, use of the muscle accounts in large part for the decrease in the receptor density in the extrajunctional region of innervated muscle.

A

ACh pipette

Intracellular electrode
for potential recording

End-plate
region

|←—100 μm—→|

Muscle fiber

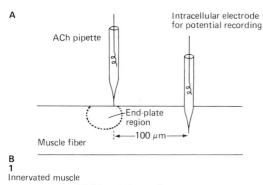

B
1
Innervated muscle

Visible end-plate region

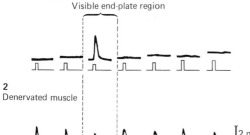

2
Denervated muscle

[2 mV

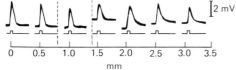

0   0.5   1.0   1.5   2.0   2.5   3.0   3.5
mm

43–2 Changes in the distribution of acetylcholine
(**ACh**) receptors following denervation. **A.**
Iontophoretic technique for mapping the distribution
of the receptor by applying a small amount of
acetylcholine by means of an extracellular electrode
(pipette) at various points along the muscle.
Intracellular recordings show depolarizing ACh
responses when acetylcholine is applied to a region of
the muscle membrane containing receptors. **B.** *1.* In
innervated muscle, the receptors are largely restricted
to the end-plate. *2.* Following denervation, receptors
are also found in the extrasynaptic membrane of the
muscle fiber. (Adapted from Axelsson and Thesleff,
1959.)

Use does not account for all of the restriction.
For example, if the muscle is disused (by applying
a cuff of tetrodotoxin to the nerve), the spread of
ACh receptors (as assayed by the binding of α-
bungarotoxin, a substance that binds specifically
with the acetylcholine receptor; see Chapter 10)
is not as great as when the nerve is cut. Furthermore, simulation of the electrical activity of the
normal innervation cannot completely restrict
the acetylcholine receptors to the end-plate zone
of denervated muscle. Part of the restriction of
the receptors seems to require the passage of
some (as yet unspecified) substance from nerve to
muscle. There are precedents for thinking so.

Gerald Fischbach and his colleagues at Harvard
have found that during the development of synapses in tissue culture cholinergic axons rapidly
induce high-density clusters of acetylcholine receptors at the site of transmitter release in skeletal muscle. This clustering of receptors is also
thought to be due to the release of one or more
unidentified substances released by the motor
axon. Fischbach has isolated an active factor from
brain and spinal cord that is present in cholinergic neurons. This material appears to be a peptide
that increases the number of receptor clusters by
40-fold.

We have thus far considered the influence of
neurons on the muscles they innervate, but the
influence at these synapses flows both ways.

Muscles Influence the Outgrowth of Motor Neurons

The study of the retrograde influence of muscle
on nerve cells began with a classic series of experiments by Ross Harrison (who also developed
the technique of tissue culture) and by Victor
Hamburger in chick embryos (Figure 43–3). By
removing a limb bud (or by adding extra limb
buds), Harrison and Hamburger artificially restricted (or enlarged) the target field of innervation to which the outgrowing nerves were exposed. In a typical experiment, a chick embryo
(which normally has a limb bud on the left and
right side) is surgically deprived of one bud on the
third day of incubation, about 24 hr before the
outgrowing axons from the motor neurons reach
the limb. As a result, a scar forms. As the axons
of the motor neuron grow out they at first look
quite normal. However, when the outgrowing
axons encounter the scar rather than the muscle,
they are thought to send a signal back to the
motor neurons causing them to shrivel up and
die. There is massive degeneration of the motor
cells destined to innervate the amputated limb
(Figure 43–3A).

During normal development an excess of motor neurons is generated during the period of motor cell proliferation. Many (about 50%) of these
potential motor neurons die after neuromuscular
synapses are established because they do not
form functional contacts, so that the population
of motor cells is reduced to the number found in
the normal adult. Ablation of the limb bud accen-
tuates the normally occurring cell death, with the
result that all the motor neurons that would be
innervating the limb die. If, on the contrary, a

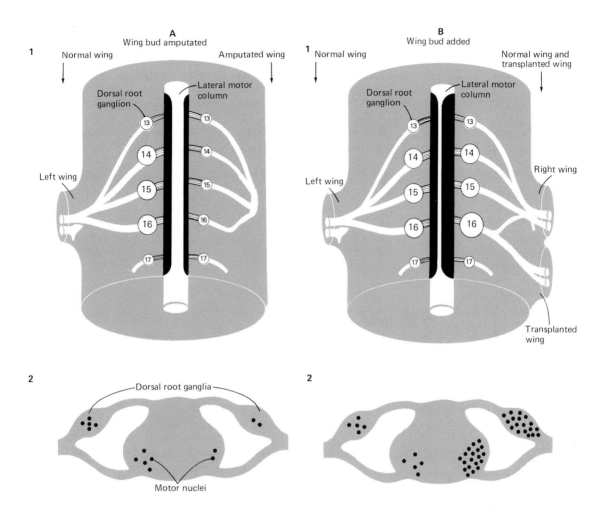

43–3 Hamburger's experiments showing the effects of amputated wing bud (**A**) and enlarged wing bud target area (**B**) on the size of the motor column and dorsal root ganglia in various spinal segments. *1.* Longitudinal view of the spinal cord showing the lateral motor columns and the dorsal root ganglia. *2.* Cross-sectional view at one level.

second limb bud is added to one side, there is a great increase in the size and number of motor neurons (Figure 43–3B). The existence of a greater field of innervation leads to the ultimate survival of more cells than ordinary because of a reduction in preprogrammed cell death. (In amphibians, supernumerary limbs actually lead to the de novo outgrowth of more nerve cells.)

Thus, targets in the periphery have a profound impact on the survival of the motor neurons. The regulation of the number of presynaptic neurons by the size of the target suggests that innervating neurons compete for some aspect of the target. Perhaps during this critical stage of development some chemical material synthesized by the muscle—and present in only a limited amount—is required by the neuron for its continued growth. It seems that unless neurons grow out and form successful synapses on the muscle they act as if deprived of an essential nutrient and die. (Perhaps

they are simply deprived of a signal to their own metabolic machinery or of the opportunity for activity.) According to this view, for a motor neuron to survive it must compete with other outgrowing neurons for a restricted nutrient that can be obtained only by making successful contacts with its target muscle cell.

The number of surviving neurons is not the only parameter regulated in a population of cells by the target. The actual number of synaptic contacts is also regulated. As is true of neurons, more synapses are initially formed than survive. For example, several motor axons synapse on each embryonic muscle fiber. After a few weeks, however, surplus synapses are eliminated by local retraction of terminal branches. Dale Purves has shown, for sympathetic innervation, that the elimination of a quantitatively incorrect number of synapses helps to ensure that the connections that are retained are qualitatively correct.

Nerve Growth Factor Is an Example of a Trophic Signal

What trophic signal might the postsynaptic cell be emitting to encourage the survival of the newly differentiated motor cells? This is one of the great questions in developmental neurobiology. The only available clue comes from the studies of Rita Levi-Montalcini and her colleagues on developing sympathetic neurons. In 1951 Levi-Montalcini and Hamburger discovered that implantation of a mouse sarcoma into a 3-day chick embryo resulted in a five- to sixfold increase in the number of cells of sympathetic ganglia that innervated the sarcoma. They showed this increased growth to be due to a diffusible substance that they called *nerve growth factor* (NGF). There is now evidence that many normal cells in the body store, secrete, and perhaps synthesize nerve growth factor. (The submaxillary salivary gland of some vertebrates is a particularly good storage depot). Although the mode of action of nerve growth factor in the nervous system is not fully known, NGF is thought to be a trophic substance critical for the development and maintenance of sympathetic neurons. Thus, treatment of newborn animals with antibody to nerve growth factor causes sympathetic ganglia to atrophy. (This procedure is therefore called an *immunosympathectomy*.) In contrast, administration of nerve growth factor stimulates the outgrowth of processes from sympathetic neurons, and its presence enhances and often is essential for the survival of embryonic sympathetic neurons. Moreover, Levi-Montalcini, Leslie Iversen, Hans Thoenen, and their colleagues have found that nerve growth factor is taken up by the terminals of sympathetic neurons by pinocytosis and carried by fast retrograde axonal transport to the cell body (see Chapter 11).

Nerve growth factor, a protein with three subunits, has been isolated and purified. It has a molecular weight of 130,000. The β subunit alone is responsible for the biological activity. It is a dimer with a molecular weight of 25,000, and

the basic monometric unit is a polypeptide chain made up of 118 amino acids. The fact that the amino acid sequence is remarkably similar to that of proinsulin suggests that both polypeptides may have evolved from a common precursor molecule and their mechanisms of action may be similar in some respects.

The growth of motor neurons to muscles does not require nerve growth factor. Most developmental neurobiologists, however, think that nerve growth factor is only one of many growth factors that are likely to be discovered in the near future.

Regenerating Connections Provide Evidence of Specificity in the Central Nervous System

The experiments we have considered thus far have been concerned with the final steps in the formation of a synapse. These final steps are regulated in several ways: some are regulated by the presence of molecular signals or nutrients from target cells; others require only that the presynaptic neuron activate the postsynaptic cell. We shall now consider the questions: What controls the early steps in synapse formation? Are these controls more specific? How precise are the steps whereby one cell finds and contacts another? The best documentation for the specificity of synapse formation comes from a series of experiments by Roger Sperry, now at the California Institute of Technology, on the visual system.

Sperry was intrigued with the question: How is the visual system put together? How do nerve fibers know how to grow to their appropriate place, and how precise are the interconnections that they form? Sperry worked with lower vertebrates (frogs, salamanders, and goldfish) because of their remarkable capacity for regeneration. He found that when he cut the optic nerve of a newt, a lizard, or a goldfish the nerve would regenerate completely, leading to full restoration of vision. Even though a scar formed in the optic nerve following section, regenerating fibers found their way through the scar, came out successfully on the other side, and made the synaptic contacts necessary for normal vision.

Using the optic nerve of goldfish, Sperry next carried out another series of experiments on connection specificity. In order to understand these experiments, we first have to appreciate some of the experimental advantages of the goldfish visual system (Figure 43–4). In the goldfish the op-

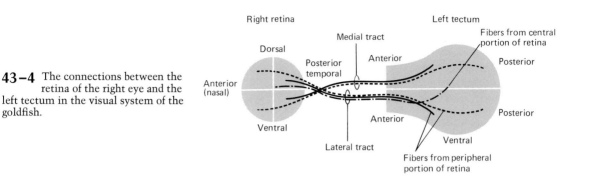

43–4 The connections between the retina of the right eye and the left tectum in the visual system of the goldfish.

tic nerve fibers cross completely in the optic chiasm. All the optic nerve fibers from the right eye cross to the left, and most connect to the left optic tectum, a structure that is analogous to the mammalian superior colliculus. On leaving the retina the fibers split into two tracts: the medial and the lateral optic tracts. Fibers from the dorsal retina run in the lateral tract to the ventral part of the tectum, while fibers from the ventral retina run in the medial tract to the dorsal tectum. Fibers from the anterior retina join one or the other tract to the tectum and then leave that tract to end up in the posterior tectum, whereas fibers from the posterior retina leave the tracts early to end up in the anterior part of the tectum. Finally, after the fibers have run their course in the superficial parallel layers of the tectum, they exit from this layer by dipping down into an underlying plexiform layer. Fibers arising from the outer periphery of the retina exit from parallel layers soon after entering the tectum and abruptly enter the plexiform layer whereas those from more central points along a given retinal radius delay their entrance into the plexiform layer until they reach correspondingly more central zones of the tectum (Figure 43–4).

Thus the normal pathways of optic nerve fibers are complicated, and regenerating optic nerve axons are confronted with several consecutive points of decision comparable to a type of multiple-Y maze. To return to the tectum by its own original pathway, a given regenerating axon must make a number of correct decisions. (1) It must correctly select the medial or the lateral tract. (2) It must make a series of selections along the circumference of the tectum and decide whether to turn radially into the parallel layer of the tectum or continue to push ahead tangentially in the main tract. (3) When it enters the parallel layer of the tectum the fiber must again, as it advances from the periphery to the center, se-

lect whether to grow on further centrally within the parallel layer or to dip downward into the plexiform layer. (4) Finally, after entering the plexiform layer the different types of retinal fibers must select the proper neuron to synapse upon. This selection must be made not only with reference to tectal topography and directionality in vision, but also with respect to other features of vision, such as color and feature detection properties.

Sperry took advantage of this multiple decision point arrangement in an elegant experiment in which he combined bilateral optic nerve section with the removal of large portions of retina on one side. By removing nerve cell bodies from the retina, he ensured that there would be no outgrowth from that part of the retina. Then he looked at what happened to axons regenerating from the remaining part of the retina. By this means he could determine (1) to what degree chemical specificity is important, as opposed to mechanical guidance or other factors, and (2) to what degree specific connections are important in contrast to random ones.

Sperry destroyed the dorsal part of the retina and asked: How specific is preference for tract? He found that despite the fact that fibers coming from the ventral part of the retina have a choice of tracts, they choose only the appropriate medial tract and enter the dorsal tectum (Figure 43–5A, 1). No fibers entered the lateral tract, and the ventral tectum was left empty. Similarly, when he destroyed the ventral part of the retina and cut the optic nerve, the axons from the dorsal retina chose the lateral tract and went to the ventral tectum (Figure 43–5A, 2).

In a second set of experiments Sperry tested the preference of regenerating fibers for the point of entrance into the tectum along its circumference. When the anterior (nasal) part of the retina was excised, the severed fibers from the posterior

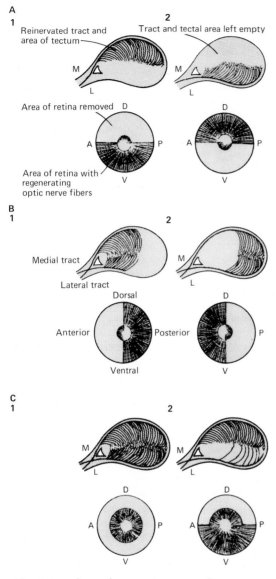

43–5 Specificity of outgrowing connections between the retina and the tectum of the goldfish. **A.** Preference of regenerating nerve fibers for appropriate division of optic tract and site in tectum: regenerating fiber patterns obtained after complete nerve section and ablation of dorsal *(1)* or ventral *(2)* hemiretina. **B.** Preference of regenerating nerve fibers for appropriate point of entrance into the tectum along its circumference: regenerating fiber patterns obtained after removal of anterior (nasal) *(1)* or posterior (temporal) *(2)* hemiretina **C.** Preference of regenerating nerve fibers for appropriate point of entrance into the plexiform layer: regenerating fiber patterns obtained after removal of the complete peripheral retina *(1)* and after removal of only the dorsal part of the peripheral retina *(2)*. (Adapted from Attardi and Sperry, 1963.)

(temporal) retina split into two groups: one group entered the medial tract and the other, the lateral tract. Axons from both tracts entered and reinnervated the anterior regions of the tectum and did not extend into the posterior region (Figure 43–5B, *1*). When the posterior (temporal) half of the retina was removed, the regenerating fibers from both ventral and dorsal quadrants of the anterior (nasal) retina split into two groups: one group entered the medial tract and the other, the lateral tract. Within both tracts, most of the fibers were found to remain in the tract until they approached the posterior region of the tectum, where they dipped into the tectum to enter the plexiform layer (Figure 43–5B, *2*).

In a third set of experiments, Sperry tested whether, after their entry into the parallel layer of the cortex, regenerating axons would show any preference for the point of entrance into the underlying plexiform layer. When the peripheral retina was removed, the outgrowing fibers from the central retina entered the tectum through both the medial and lateral tracts, but once having entered the tectum the fibers from each tract did not descend into the plexiform layer until after they had reached the central zone (Figure 43–5C, *1* and *2*). The fibers from the central retina bypassed the entire margin of the optic lobe, although the outgrowing optic nerve fibers had multiple opportunities to make contacts among the dense populations of neurons, and possibly glia and capillaries, in the optic tectum. Of these many opportunities, the fibers refused all but the appropriate ones. Incorrect zones in the tectum were consistently bypassed and left empty. When the fibers reached the appropriate part of the optic tectum they met neurons whose location and chemical properties were apparently right for the formation of synaptic junctions. Then and only then were the synapses formed. This pattern is not unique to regenerating connections. A similar specificity has been found during the initial outgrowth from the eye to the tectum in chick embryo by Max Cowan and James Kelly.

The remarkable specificity encountered in these regeneration experiments suggested to Sperry that the development of synaptic connections involves three sequential events:

1. Positional specificity. According to Sperry, the acquisition of positional information by cells within both the eye and the tectum could be accomplished by coding both populations of cells along two axes, so that each cell is marked in relation to its neighboring cells. For example, in the eye the cells could be marked according to anteroposterior (nasotemporal) and dorsoventral axes. As a result of these topographic labels, retinal ganglion cells would acquire differential affinities, possibly of a cytochemical nature, for intercellular recognition according to their location in the retina. The neurons in the optic tectum undergo parallel differentiation and acquire matching or complementary affinities according to their position in the tectum.

2. *Pathfinding of target.* The outgrowing axons of the ganglion cells are postulated to be guided to appropriate zones in the tectum by a series of chemical and mechanical clues.

3. *Selective formation of synapses on the basis of complementary chemoaffinities.* Retinal neurons are presumed to form synaptic connections preferentially with selected tectal neurons having matching or complementary cytochemical affinities. The incoming axon recognizes specific cues for appropriate synapse formation. Sperry has suggested that the synapse is formed not only on an appropriate cell, but at a specific topographic portion of the cell's surface. It is not known how this is accomplished, but perhaps specific glycoproteins or glycolipids in the extracellular region of the synapse, such as the basement membrane of the nerve–muscle synapse, may provide a cue. Following the formation of the nerve–muscle synapse, the basement membrane is actually specialized in the region of contact. Some basement membrane *fuzz* is always present in the cleft space separating pre- and postsynaptic elements, even after the establishment of initial contact, and may have a recognition role even in central synapses.

None of the ideas about specific mechanisms underlying these three developmental sequences postulated by Sperry has yet been tested in a compelling manner, but a number of experiments have provided some support for aspects of these hypotheses.

Some Affinity Based on Position Seems to Exist Between Pre- and Postsynaptic Elements at Certain Synapses

One way to find out whether neurons have acquired positional specificity is to displace a group of neurons from their normal position, allow them to form connections, and then determine whether the connections are appropriate to the original or to the new position. It is assumed that neurons become specified according to their relative position in different parts of the nervous system at particular times in their developmental cycle. If the neurons had acquired their specificity before they were displaced, they would form connections appropriate to their original position. In examining this problem Sperry specifically addressed the broad question we posed at the beginning of this chapter: To what degree are connections between neurons determined by built-in developmental specificities, and to what degree are they due to patterns of impulses or to experience?

In amphibians it is possible to cut the optic nerve and rotate the eyeball on its optic axis by 180°. The eye will then heal in the new position. When Sperry tested the visual responses of frogs whose eyes had been rotated he found that the responses were inverted by 180°. Thus, for objects lying in the upper anterior (now temporal) visual field, the animal reached in the direction of its lower posterior (now nasal) field (Figure 43–6). These maladaptive responses persist indefinitely without correction. These findings indicate that optic nerve fibers remain connected to their initially appropriate tectal cell despite the persistent behavioral inappropriateness. This inability to reeducate the visual system suggests that the neural connections in this system are laid down in an invariant manner without regard for the adaptiveness of the functional effect. Moreover, as predicted by Sperry, the tectum is also topographically polarized. Myong Yoon, one of Sperry's students, recently rotated a piece of tectum at 180° and found that it retained its original topographic polarity.

Further evidence for positional specificity has been presented by Marcus Jacobson, then at Johns Hopkins University. He demonstrated that the two retinal gradients develop independently (Figure 43–7). Jacobson rotated the eye cups of larval amphibian embryos at very early stages—before the optic nerve grows out, and therefore considerably before the connections between eye and brain develop. He found that a rotation made prior to stage 29 (a specific early developmental stage) results in the eye cup forming a normal projection. Thus, retinal position has not been specified before this stage. Rotation 10 hr later, at stage 30, leads to a normal dorsoventral retinal axis, but inversion of the anteroposterior retinal axis. Thus, the position of the anteroposterior axis has become specified by this stage. Rotation at stage 31, 5–10 hr later still, leads to total inversion, indicating that both axes have been spec-

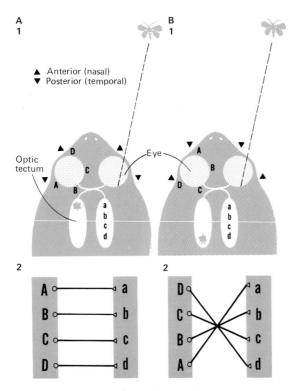

43–6 Eye rotation shows that visual connections in the frog are not determined by experience. Eyes and optic tecta viewed from above (1) and in schematic representation (2). **A.** Normal eyes. The projections of a fly and of four retinal points (**A, B, C, D**) are indicated on the tectum (**a, b, c, d**). **B.** Rotated eyes. Neural connections remain the same after the eyes are rotated 180° so that the posterior (temporal) retina (▼) now lies anterior and the anterior (nasal) retina (▲) is posterior. (Adapted from Lund, 1978.)

all the connections. Most likely, the cells are marked by quantitative differences. For example, one can conceive of a cell surface label that would work as follows: two morphogenetic gradients operating at right angles impose coordinates on the retina. Two gradients in the tectum similarly mark each tectal cell. Each gradient represents the distribution of a particular cell surface molecule, perhaps a glycoprotein, that is produced at one end of an axis of cells and removed at the other end. The substance is freely diffusible in the extracellular space between the cells, and a certain fixed proportion of the molecules is taken up by each cell so that the cells closest to the site of production take up the most molecules and those farthest away take up the least. Once taken up by the cell, the substance alters the surface properties of the cell in a characteristic way.

An alternative to a cell surface label (an alternative that at the moment is less attractive but not excluded) is for each cell to occupy a specific position in the retina simply as a result of the temporal sequence determined by its birthdate, time of migration, etc. The axons of the cells are then ordered in the optic nerve according to the position of the cell body in the retina, and the axons in turn impose this order on the tectum. This idea is favored by R. M. Gaze in England and by several other investigators. Jonathan Horton, Martha Greenwood, and David Hubel have recently examined this possibility in the mammalian optic nerve and found evidence against it.

ified. These results indicate that before stage 29 the retinal cells are not specified. After stage 30 there is a rapid specification of the two retinal axes within 24 hr. Stages 29–30 therefore are a *critical period in development* after which retinal specification becomes irreversible. *Critical periods are a common feature of the development of the nervous system.* As we have seen before and shall see again later, critical periods have been found in the development of other parts of the nervous system and even in the types of behaviors they control (for sexual differentiation, see Chapter 44; for social and perceptual skills, see Chapter 52).

It seems improbable that each cell in the retina would have a unique marker protein that distinguishes it qualitatively from every other cell because, as we have seen, there are not enough genes to code for all the retinal cells, much less

43–7 Jacobson's model, according to which a neuron in the retina receives positional information from two gradients in two all-or-none developmental steps. By observing projections from eye cups (of larval amphibian embryos) that had been rotated during various developmental stages, Jacobson determined that the anteroposterior retinal axis, but not the dorsoventral, is specified at stage 30; the dorsoventral retinal axis is specified at stage 31.

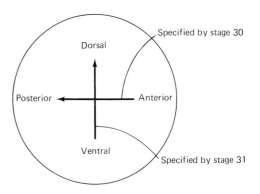

Horton et al. found that axons in the optic nerve that come from neighboring cells in the retina become scattered throughout the nerve, indicating that there is no retinotopic order at all among the axons. Nevertheless, whatever the details of the mechanisms prove to be (and it is likely that more than one is involved), *the problem of neuronal specificity clearly does not reduce itself to a single recognition event, but to a program of separate events, each played out at a specific time.* It is therefore likely that specific affinity and positional clues are both operative but to different degrees at different stages.

Pathfinding May Be Guided by Chemical Signals

The mechanisms whereby axons go to one region rather than another are poorly understood. It seems likely, however, that axons follow different clues in different parts of the nervous system. Axons readily follow a variety of physical clues that are provided by the nonneural substrate along which they migrate. Under some circumstances axons receive clues from neighboring axons. None of these mechanisms, however, quite explains how axons find their way over great distances. A remarkable experiment that has thrown some light on this vexing problem was recently carried out in young rats by Levi-Montalcini. She injected nerve growth factor into the brain and found that axons of sympathetic neurons, which normally do not invade the central nervous system, grew into the brain in great abundance toward the source of the nerve growth factor, presumably following chemical tracts created by the diffusion of nerve growth factor from its site of injection. Nerve growth factor will also stimulate the outgrowth of the processes of sympathetic neurons in tissue culture. These findings suggest that outgrowing fibers can sense and respond to chemical signals and gradients and that nerve growth factor and other chemotactic signals might act over considerable distances to lead outgrowing nerve fibers to their appropriate targets.

Synapses Form Selectively

If synapse formation—the actual wiring of connections—is preprogrammed and specific (except for some fine tuning), one should be able to demonstrate that critical aspects of the basic wiring are present at birth and are not dependent on subsequent learning. Hubel and Torsten Wiesel addressed this problem in both the cat and the monkey and found that in the retina, the lateral geniculate nucleus, and area 17 of the visual cortex, the types of response properties found in the adult are largely present in newborn animals. Thus, although some fine details of the interactions between neuron and muscle and between neuron and neuron are regulated by experiential factors, the recognition of one cell by another seems to be quite specific and appears to require pre-existing information on the part of both the pre- and postsynaptic cell. The exact mechanisms, however, are not known. One attractive idea is that each outgrowing nerve fiber finds its way by means of a series of clues and by trial and error. Gap junctions form, or some other means of exchanging information between the two cells develops, to allow the exchange of clues between the pre- and postsynaptic cell. Once a chemical synapse is established, the biochemical and electrical properties of the postsynaptic element (and probably of the presynaptic element as well) can be further modulated by use and by trophic interaction so as to make the connection work optimally.

The main findings emerging from studies of the development of the brain and of behavior therefore support a relatively strict constructionist view, according to which the major connections of the nervous system are established primarily under genetic and developmental control and the initial establishment of the connection occurs in the absence of learning. However, as we shall see in Part VIII, learning is important for subsequent fine tuning and maintenance, and for regulating the strength of the connections.

Selected Readings and References

Attardi, D. G., and Sperry, R. W. 1963. Preferential selection of central pathways by regenerating optic fibers. Exp. Neurol. 7:46–64.

Cowan, W. M. 1979. The development of the brain. Sci. Am. 241(3):112–133.

Edds, M. V., Jr. 1967. Neuronal specificity in neurogenesis. In G. C. Quarton, T. Melnechuk, and F. O. Schmitt (eds.), The Neurosciences: A Study Program. New York: Rockefeller University Press pp. 230–240.

Jacobson, M. 1978. Developmental Neurobiology. 2nd ed. New York: Plenum.

Levi-Montalcini, R. 1975. NGF: An uncharted route. In F. G. Worden, J. P. Swazey, and G. Adelman (eds.), The Neurosciences: Paths of Discovery. Cambridge, Mass.: MIT Press, pp. 245–265.

Lømo, T., and Westgaard, R. H. 1976. Control of ACh sensitivity in rat muscle fibers. Cold Spring Harbor Symp. Quant. Biol. 50:263–274.

Lund, R. D. 1978. Development and Plasticity of the Brain. New York: Oxford University Press.

Purves, D., and Lichtman, J. W. 1978. Formation and maintenance of synaptic connections in autonomic ganglia. Physiol. Rev. 58:821–862.

Stent, G. S. (ed.). 1977. Function and Formation of Neural Systems. Berlin: Dahlem Konferenzen.

Weeds, A. G., Trentham, D. R., Kean, C. J. C., and Buller, A. J. 1974. Myosin from cross-reinnervated cat muscles. Nature (Lond.) 247:135–139.

Other References

Axelsson, J., and Thesleff, S. 1959. A study of supersensitivity in denervated mammalian skeletal muscle. J. Physiol. (Lond.) 147:178–193.

Buller, A. J., Eccles, J. C., and Eccles, R. M. 1960. Interactions between motoneurones and muscles in respect of the characteristic speeds of their responses. J. Physiol. (Lond.) 150:417–439.

Gaze, R. M., Keating, M. J., and Chung, S. H. 1974. The evolution of the retinotectal map during development in Xenopus. Proc. R. Soc. Lond. B Biol. Sci. 185:301–330.

Hamburger, V. 1934. The effects of wing bud extirpation on the development of the central nervous system in chick embryos. J. Exp. Zool. 68:449–494.

Hamburger, V. 1977. The developmental history of the motor neuron. The F. O. Schmitt Lecture in Neuroscience. Neurosci. Res. Program Bull. 15 Suppl.: 1–37.

Harrison, R. G. 1935. On the origin and development of the nervous system studied by the methods of experimental embryology. Proc. R. Soc. Lond. B Biol. Sci. 118:155–196.

Hendry, I. A., Stöckel, K., Thoenen, H., and Iversen, L. L. 1974. The retrograde axonal transport of nerve growth factor. Brain Res. 68:103–121.

Horton, J. C., Greenwood, M. M., and Hubel, D. H. 1979. Non-retinotopic arrangement of fibres in cat optic nerve. Nature (Lond.) 282:720–722.

Jacobson, M. 1968. Development of neuronal specificity in retinal ganglion cells of Xenopus. Dev. Biol. 17:202–218.

Jessell, T. M., Siegel, R. E., and Fischbach, G. D. 1979. Induction of acetylcholine receptors on cultured skeletal muscle by a factor extracted from brain and spinal cord. Proc. Natl. Acad. Sci. U.S.A. 76:5397–5401.

Kelly, J. P., and Cowan, W. M. 1972. Studies on the development of the chick optic tectum. III. Effects of early eye removal. Brain Res. 42:263–288.

Levi-Montalcini, R. 1952. Effects of mouse tumor transplantation on the nervous system. Ann. N.Y. Acad. Sci. 55:330–343.

Lømo, T., and Rosenthal, J. 1972. Control of ACh sensitivity by muscle activity in the rat. J. Physiol. (Lond.) 221:493–513.

Lømo, T., Westgaard, R. H., and Dahl, H. A. 1974. Contractile properties of muscle: Control by pattern of muscle activity in the rat. Proc. R. Soc. Lond. B Biol. Sci. 187:99–103.

Sperry, R. W. 1951. Mechanisms of neural maturation. In S. S. Stevens (ed.), Handbook of Experimental Psychology. New York: Wiley, pp. 236–280.

Thoenen, H., Otten, U., and Schwab, M. 1979. Orthograde and retrograde signals for the regulation of neuronal gene expression: The peripheral sympathetic nervous system as a model. In F. O. Schmitt and F. G. Worden (eds.), The Neurosciences: Fourth Study Program. Cambridge, Mass.: MIT Press, pp. 911–928.

Yoon, M. G. 1976. Topographic polarity of the optic tectum studied by reimplantation of the tectal tissue in adult goldfish. Cold Spring Harbor Symp. Quant. Biol. 50:503–519.

Dennis D. Kelly

Sexual Differentiation
of the Nervous System

44

Most behavioral and perceptual functions of the nervous system, such as the regulation of food intake or body temperature, are performed and organized within an individual. However, the process by which the species is maintained demands the coordinated contributions of two of its members. There are also strong ontogenetic restrictions upon reproductive behavior. The demands of conceiving and nurturing a new member of the species are such that the responsibility is withheld from the very young and the very old, being reserved for an intermediate age when the organism has reached maturity but has not yet lost strength and vigor. We might expect, therefore, that when we examine the brain for an explanation of these dimorphic, but interdependent, reproductive behaviors, we will find a sexually differentiated neuronal organization that is open to a wide range of developmental influences. An implication of extreme importance is that sex-linked neural differentiation might also extend to some nonreproductive behaviors.

In this chapter we shall consider the recent experimental evidence that suggests that there are morphological and functional differences in the nervous systems of males and females. Sexual differentiation is another example of the developmental plasticity of the brain in which the genetic make-up (nature) of the organism provides the range of potential for the individual but the environment (nurture) is required to shape the final outcome. Similar developmental strategies will be encountered in the emergence of other behaviors in the infant nervous system. Characteristic of such developmental plasticity is the existence of a *critical time period* during which specific interactions between the growing brain and its environment (internal as well as external) mold future behavioral capacities. Critical periods reflect the sequential nature of the growth process; at each stage of development a choice between alternatives is made. Once a time-dependent critical choice is made, subsequent steps make it difficult to reverse the process.

Reproductive Behaviors Are Sexually Dimorphic

Before we examine the nervous system, it will be useful to outline the different reproductive patterns that will be used later as behavioral markers of male–female neural differentiation. Vertebrate mating behavior is richly varied across species. However, ethologists have described a fundamental pattern of copulatory behaviors that shows strong sexual dimorphism and that is common to a broad range of warm-blooded animals. (The term *dimorphism* refers to the existence of two distinct forms within a species; *sexual dimorphism* refers to different forms of behaviors shown by males and females.) According to this pattern, basic heterosexual mating involves three states:

1. The orientation and courtship of two partners, generally involving both the identification of an appropriate mate and some signal of readiness
2. Certain clear-cut, gender-specific postural adjustments by which the female exposes her genitals and the male attains intromission (the insertion of the penis in the vagina)
3. Mutual genital reflexes that lead to insemination.

It is useful to remember this behavioral pattern, for it applies to a wide range of species, has been found to correspond to different levels of neural integration, and serves to make explicit the sexually dimorphic patterns of reproductive behavior whose neural basis we shall examine in subsequent sections.

The mating patterns of ring doves can serve as a specific example. The male dove bows and coos; the partners interlock beaks and strut around cooing and charging. Abruptly, the female assumes a posture whose purpose seems to be to make her oviduct accessible to the male. She spreads her wings, extends her tail and flexes her legs. The male dove mounts from the rear, performs a minor balancing act with his wings and feet, and, as an aid in attaining intromission, clasps the feathers on the back of his partner's neck with his beak. It is in this phase of the general vertebrate pattern that the dimorphic behaviors of males and females show extraordinary cross-species homologies. The males of a variety of mammals, such as rats, guinea pigs, rabbits, cats, and monkeys, perform with remarkable similarity, mounting the female from the rear, clasping the back of the neck in their mouths and, after gaining intromission, thrusting with the pelvis. At the same time, female behavior is also highly organized, but more species specific. The female rat, for instance, crouches tensely and interrupts these pauses with darting movements to various areas of the cage. When mounted or touched from the rear, she exhibits a lordotic elevation of the rump. The female cat is more active. She brays, occasionally swipes at the male, assumes an estral crouch, flexes the forelimbs, arches the back in a concave lordotic posture, throws the tail to one side (exposing her genitalia), and, while mounting occurs, treads with her hind limbs. Female monkeys and chimpanzees bend slightly forward at the hips, presenting their genitalia, while the male mounts from the rear. Thus, on at least one descriptive level, the copulatory behaviors of vertebrates exhibit more consistent patterning within the sexes across species than between males and females of the same species. It is primarily for this reason that neurobiologists have used mounting and lordosis as the behavioral markers for neural differentiation, rather than other dimorphic behaviors of less consistent cross-species occurrence.

One difficulty encountered by an experimental focus upon reproductive behaviors is that in the limited behavioral repertoires of lower animal forms, apparently gender-specific courtship behaviors often serve other purposes. Consequently, both male and female copulatory patterns may be exhibited by the opposite sex in environmental circumstances that have little to do with reproduction. For instance, the female sexual posture is used by both sexes as a submissive or turn-off gesture during intraspecific encounters for dominance.

Gonadal Hormones Influence the Sexual Differentiation of the Brain

The mature gonads of males and females produce different profiles of steroid sex hormones. Is it possible that testicular hormones produce male behavior equally well in adult males and females and that ovarian hormones produce female behavior equally well in adult males and females? If so, the sex-related patterns of behavior we have outlined above could be explained solely by the type of hormones that are present in the body. This is the theory of *hormone specificity*. An alternative view of behavioral sex differences for which there is good evidence is that during a specific perinatal critical period certain target tissues in the brain develop a specific sensitivity to the hormones appropriate to one sex or the other. This is the theory of *host specificity*. We shall also see that, in addition to producing selective sensitivity to hormones, events during the same critical period effect in the brain a gender-specific, organizational blueprint, which in adulthood will result in appropriate sexual behaviors being emitted in response to hormonal stimulation.

In the adult, the primary influence of circulating steroid sex hormones is to activate sexual responses. For example, as shown in Figure 44–1, administration of estrogen will increase sexual receptivity in female rats in an orderly, dose-dependent manner. However, in the developing organism (particularly the fetus), there is evidence that the most important action of the same hormones is to influence the differentiation of specific body tissues in males and females, including parts of the brain. Both male and female genotypes are thought to be compatible with either brain sex phenotype; determination of the latter is influenced by exposure to steroid hormones during a critical period of growth early in life.

Let us begin with a review of clinical and veterinary evidence which suggests that the brain of a developing fetus is essentially undifferentiated and bipotential and that, despite its genetic make-up, it is potentially compatible with either sexual orientation. For example, when male and female twin cattle are born, the female is invariably nonreproductive. She does not cycle and is

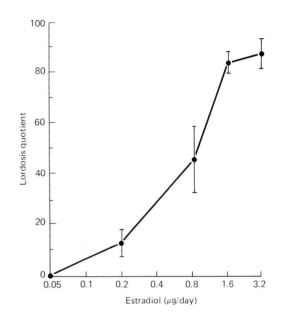

44–1 Sexual receptivity induced in female ovariectomized rats after eight daily subcutaneous injections of estrogen (estradiol benzoate). Note that the higher the dose of estrogen, the greater is the receptivity as measured by the lordosis quotient (the number of lordotic responses of the subject divided by the number of mounts multiplied by 100). (Data from Bermant and Davidson, 1974.)

infertile. Since this freemartin effect does not occur when both twins are female, it has long been suspected by dairy farmers, if not medical researchers, that the presence of a male fetus in the womb may affect the normal development of a female twin.

Spontaneously occurring hormonal deficiencies during early human development have produced two syndromes that are even more informative. The first, a condition known as *Turner's syndrome,* is an anhormonal state in which gonadal tissue does not form. It characteristically results in the phenotypic female who, because of the lack of gonads, fails to show the pubertal changes associated with the gonadal activity of adolescence. Patients with Turner's syndrome are usually not regarded by their families as unfeminine at any time during their preadolescent development. Many cases are discovered only when these children fail to manifest the female signs of puberty at the normal time. If treated with ovarian hormones during the period of adolescence, they respond as normal females. Moreover, to the extent that the literature permits such a statement, the sexual preference and libido of such individuals closely parallel those of the heterosexual female. The important point, however, is that individuals suffering from Turner's syndrome are not genetic females (XX); but neither are they genetic males (XY). The evidence available from karyotypes indicates that the majority possess only one chromosome, which, in the human, is invariably an X chromosome, since having only a Y chromosome is lethal.

Another genetic anomaly involves individuals incapable of responding to androgens. Hence, this condition is called the *androgen insensitivity syndrome.* Although there is disagreement among investigators, the genetic disorder in this instance is not generally considered to be a defect of the sex chromosomes, but rather of the autosomes, or nonsex chromosomes. Even when this autosomal factor is present, individual cases may go undetected in genetic females, in whom physiological responses to androgens are relatively less important. Accordingly, the syndrome has been primarily associated with genetic males. This asymmetry of detection gave rise to an unfortunate misnomer for the condition, for it used to be known clinically as *testicular feminization.* However, the testes of these individuals are not feminizing, nor do they secrete hormones that in their types or pattern resemble the hormones of the ovary. Nevertheless, as the old term implies, genetic males possessing the abnormal genes are indistinguishable from phenotype females in their external appearance as well as in their psychosexual orientation and libidinal interests. Apparently, this genetic disorder prevents or blocks responsiveness to androgens throughout development, early as well as late. It may also be assumed that the gonadal secretions during early development are essentially similar to those in normal genetic males, since there is a normal appearing testicular morphology and an absence of the Müllerian duct derivatives.

The implication that may be drawn from these clinical states is that the female form and its psychosexual orientation can develop in the absence of hormonal influences from the gonads. Moreover, the pattern of female development is not restricted to a female genotype. Individuals who are genetically male can and do develop under special circumstances along lines as feminine as those characteristic of normal females. In order to integrate these clinical phenomena with experimental findings concerning sexual differentiation of the organism in utero, it will be necessary to consider the hormonal environment in which fetuses of both sexes develop.

Perinatal Hormones Affect the Sexual Differentiation of the Developing Organism

In considering the development of gender identity, it is useful to distinguish between homotypical and heterotypical steroid sex hormones. *Homotypical hormones* are those of a given sex administered to the same sex, whereas *heterotypical hormones* are those of one sex given to the other sex. These terms may also be applied to gender-specific behaviors: *homotypical behavior patterns* are those appropriate to the reference gender and *heterotypical behavior patterns* are those appropriate to the opposite sex.

Fetal Exposure to Heterotypical Hormones Causes Hermaphroditism in Genetic Females

Normally, during pregnancy the fetuses of both sexes are exposed to the high levels of circulating estrogens in the maternal blood. Naturally, estrogen is homotypical for female fetuses and heterotypical for male fetuses. One question that arises is, What would happen if this normal relationship were reversed in an experimental animal, bringing female fetuses under heterotypical hormone influences? There are two consequences. If high doses of testosterone are injected into the mother, female offspring are born as hermaphrodites. Their external genitalia are indistinguishable from those of normal males. However, internal female tissues are also present in the abdomen. Thus, exposure to an unusual amount of male hormone during the fetal period markedly distorts organ development in the female, partially reversing the differentiation of the peripheral sex apparatus. The second and more intriguing effect is that the adult sexual behavior of hermaphroditic females is also altered. When subsequently treated with estrogen and progesterone, genotypic female guinea pigs show some elements of homotypical sexual behaviors—lordosis, for example—but their capacity for this behavior is greatly reduced as compared with normal control females. On the other hand, these animals display much more mounting behavior than a normal female. When later treated with testosterone as adults, they display a degree of heterotypical mounting comparable to that of normal males, and the female pattern of lordosis is suppressed.

In these early experiments by Phoenix and others, the behavioral results were complicated by the development in the hermaphrodite of a penis, but much subsequent work has shown that this peripheral change alone cannot account for the alterations in behavior. From these results, it appears that testosterone administered to the genetic female during fetal development affects not only the differentiation of external genitalia, but also the differentiation of neural tissues mediating later patterns of sexual behavior. On the other hand, the administration of testosterone does not have similar effects upon the later sexual behavior of male fetuses.

Steroid Hormones Influence Perinatal Development Only During "Critical Periods"

The clinical and experimental evidence considered thus far indicates that the developing nervous system of either gender may be bipotential. A female pattern of anatomical and behavioral organization can emerge in either an anhormonal or maternal-dominated prenatal environment, but the emergence of a male pattern requires the active influence of androgens. If androgens are needed for the development of normal male fetuses, an important question is: Where in the maternal uterine environment do androgens come from? Most experiments on this question have been carried out on the rat, which has a 21-day gestation period. These studies show that the male testes begin to synthesize androgens as early as the 13th day of fetal development (8 days prior to birth). Moreover, biochemical assays demonstrate that this secretion of androgens continues in newborn rats until the 10th day after birth.

The possibility that the androgens produced by the immature gonads of the developing male rat are responsible for further masculinization can be checked simply by removing the testes. Castration on the day of birth deprives the male rat of testicular androgens only for little more than one-half of the period that these hormones are normally present. Despite this relatively crude approximation to the anhormonal syndromes described earlier, these animal experiments have demonstrated that neonatal castration has profound effects upon the sexual de-

velopment of genotypic male rats. Rats deprived of their testes at either 1 or 5 days of age develop behavioral characteristics normally present only in genotypic females. When injected with estrogen and progesterone as adults, they display lordotic behavior when mounted by normal males. In contrast, males castrated at 10 days of age or later show little or no tendency to display lordosis under comparable conditions.

There is additional evidence that the effects of perinatal male hormones upon subsequent sexual behavior are a result of their influence upon the developing central nervous system rather than the peripheral sexual apparatus. It has been known for over a century that if the ovaries from one animal are transplanted into the abdomen of another, they become highly vascularized, but not innervated. If the recipient is a male, the ovaries, though they will survive, will not cycle, due to the tonic, nonsurging gonadotropic secretions in the male. Gonadotropin refers to the secretion of both of the trophic hormones, luteinizing hormone (LH) and follicle stimulating hormone (FSH).

In 1962 Barraclough and Gorski demonstrated that the female cyclic pattern of gonadotropin secretion by the pituitary does not depend directly on the genetic sex of the animal, but depends instead on the absence of androgen during the perinatal period. As we saw, this critical period in the rat is probably the first week after birth. Under normal circumstances, the cyclic pattern of gonadotropin secretion develops in the female but is prevented from developing in the male by his own secretion of androgens. A recent experiment by Raisman illustrates this point (Table 44-1). Treatment of the normal genetic female rat with a single dose of androgen on the 4th day of postnatal life permanently abolishes the ability to ovulate in the adult. Conversely, castration of the male within 1 day of birth results in an adult which, if transplanted with ovaries, can exhibit cyclic ovulation and behavioral estrus. The same manipulations carried out after the critical period are ineffective. Thus, androgen treatment of the female on the 16th day of life (after the critical period) or castration of the male on the 7th day of life (after the testes have had 1 full postnatal week to secrete androgens) does not affect the normal development and expression of the adult function proper to the genetic sex of the animal.

While the critical period for the androgenization of the rat brain appears to involve the first postnatal week, the evidence for critical periods

Table 44–1. Adult Gonadotropic Secretion Patterns in Rats Subjected to Neonatal Endocrine Manipulation[a]

Genetic sex	Age (days) 0 5 10 15 20 Critical				Adult LH Secretion Pattern
Female	—		—		Cyclic
	1.25 mg TP Day 4		—		Non-cyclic
	—		1.25 mg TP Day 16		Cyclic
Male	—	—			Non-cyclic
	Castrate Day 1	—			Cyclic
	—	Castrate Day 7			Non-cyclic

Source: Adapted from Raisman, 1974.

[a]Genetic females were either untreated (top row) or given a single dose of testosterone propionate (TP) either during the critical period (middle row) or after it (bottom row). Males were either intact or else castrated on either the 1st or the 7th day of life.

in other species is less precise. In the guinea pig, which has a 68-day gestation period, the critical period for masculinization appears to stretch between days 30 and 40 in utero. In rhesus monkeys, with a 168-day gestation period, the brief androgenizing burst of testicular activity occurs entirely in utero, probably during the middle stages of gestation, although its exact span is disputed. In the human it is estimated that the critical period may occur during the third or fourth month of gestation. Exactly what determines the timing of the critical period is unknown, although it appears to be related to the degree of maturity of the young at birth and is probably related to the stages of neural differentiation. Both the rhesus monkey and guinea pig are born relatively well developed compared to the rat.

It is also important to note that this critical period in neural development—which roughly corresponds to the period when the gonads of the normal male are active—is in fact a period of sensitivity to a broad spectrum of steroids, many of which are not normally present. Experimental masculinization of the brain may result from exposure to such functionally diverse compounds as testosterone, androstenedione, estradiol, diethylstilbesterol (DES), and even dichlorodiphenyl-trichlorethane (DDT). Paradoxically, it appears that the principal active hormone that determines the natural male brain pattern in newborn rats is estradiol, one of the estrogens. Even though the hormone that reaches the brain is testosterone, it is converted to estradiol by enzymes in the nerve cells that are the targets of sexual differentiation. In this light, it is not surprising that in experiments in vivo estradiol has been found to be eight times more effective than testosterone in androgenization. The normal fetuses of both sexes are probably protected from high maternal estrogen by an estrogen-binding protein called α-fetoprotein. This protein is manufactured by the fetal liver and is found in blood and cerebrospinal fluid. Testosterone is not so bound and thus gains unhindered access during the critical period to steroid-concentrating neurons, where it can be converted to estradiol. Thus, from a neurochemical point of view, it is probably imprecise to look upon feminization of the brain as a passive emergence of an anhormonal state. We shall find additional reason later for viewing the normal differentiation of a female brain as an active morphological process.

Another important property of the critical period for sexual differentiation is that it does not represent a simple binary choice between complete androgenization and feminization. Intermediate degrees of each are possible. Recent studies with rodents, which produce litters containing many pups, have shown that female fetuses that develop between male fetuses have significantly higher concentrations of testosterone in both their blood and amniotic fluid than do females that develop between other female fetuses. Vom Saal and Bronson have demonstrated that these two types of females also differ during later life in many sexually related characteristics including activity levels, aggressiveness, and acceptability as mating partners to males. Thus, normal individual variations in sex-linked behavioral characteristics of adult female mice can be traced to differential exposure to testosterone during prenatal development due to intrauterine proximity to male fetuses.

Sexually Differentiated Brains Have Different Physiological Properties

Does a brain that mediates male behaviors differ from one that mediates female behaviors? What are the properties of a masculinized brain? We have already mentioned in other contexts some

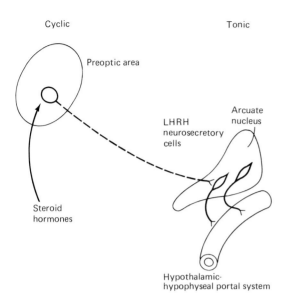

44-2 Two populations of cells in the hypothalamus may be responsible for the cyclic release of luteinizing hormone by the anterior pituitary in the normal female. Estrogen stimulates preoptic cells that activate arcuate nucleus cells, which in turn increase their secretion of luteinizing hormone–releasing hormone (**LHRH**). In the androgenized brain, preoptic cells are not susceptible to such hormonal stimulation and when stimulated electrically do not exert similar influences upon arcuate neurosecretory cells.

of the properties of brains that become sexually differentiated during the critical period. We shall now make these explicit, summarize them, and add to the list.

First, as illustrated in the experiment by Raisman, an androgenized rat brain exhibits a tonic secretory pattern of luteinizing hormone, whereas the pattern of the female brain is cyclic. One hypothesis of the cellular basis for this difference in male and female brains involves neurons in the preoptic area of the hypothalamus. In normal females the estrogen secreted by growing ovarian follicles stimulates these preoptic cells, which in turn may activate cells of the arcuate nucleus. The arcuate cells increase their secretion of a neurohormone (luteinizing hormone–releasing hormone, LHRH), which prompts a surge in the production of luteinizing hormone by the anterior pituitary (Figure 44-2). LHRH is a decapeptide that regulates the release of both luteinizing hormone and follicle stimulating hormone (FSH), and thus it is also known as gonadotropin releasing hormone GnRH). Hence it is the receptivity of the preoptic cells in the normal female hypothalamus, and also their synaptic connections

with arcuate cells, that impose a cyclic pattern upon luteinizing hormone release. In an androgenized brain, not only are these preoptic cells refractory to such hormonal activation, but even their direct electrical stimulation fails to alter luteinizing hormone release by the pituitary.

Second, receptor molecules for steroid sex hormones develop within cells located in similar brain regions of both sexes; however, the fine distribution and steroid-concentrating properties of these cells differ slightly in androgenized and nonandrogenized brains. Steroid-binding cells are found in the hypothalamus (particularly in the preoptic area), amygdala, midbrain, and spinal cord (where their distribution differs most markedly between the sexes). There are also a few steroid-binding cells in the frontal cortex and, for reasons that will become clear later, it is interesting that these cortical sites disappear as the rat matures into adolescence.

Unlike receptors for neurotransmitter substances (see Chapter 10), steroid receptors are not components of the neuron's external membrane. By using radioactively labeled gonadal steroids, these receptors have been found in the cytoplasm; upon binding with the steroid, they migrate to the nucleus of the neuron. This experimental technique is illustrated in Figure 44-3, and the regional distribution of neurons that take up the labeled hormones is shown in Figure 44-4. The hormones are accumulated and retained by means of specific intracellular receptor proteins that apparently reside in the cytoplasm of the sexually differentiated target cell. The hormone–protein complex is able to enter the nucleus and interact with the genes, thereby triggering the target cell to carry out its functional response to the hormone. Therefore, exposure to hormones early in development could conceivably alter the ability of the nuclei of certain cells to respond to hormones later in life, although this has not been conclusively shown.

Although both males and females possess similar profiles of steroid sensitive cells (that is, both estrogen and testosterone receptors exist in the brains of both sexes), Whalen and Massicci have found clear sex differences in the degree of binding and retention of estrogen by the nuclei of cells in the hypothalamus. After injections of radioactive estrogen, the nuclei of hypothalamic cells isolated from normal female rats retain more estrogen, and for a longer time after injection, than do the nuclei of male hypothalamic cells.

Third, the mature animal with an androgen-

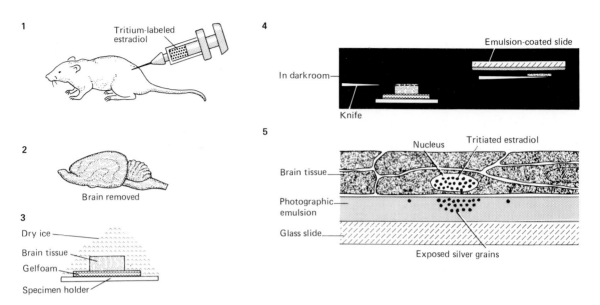

44–3 Autoradiographic method for identifying the location of steroid target neurons in ovariectomized rats. Two hours after radioactively labeled estradiol is injected *(1)* the rat's brain is removed *(2)* and frozen *(3)*. In a darkroom, frozen sections of the brain are placed against a photographic emulsion and stored for several months *(4)*. Electrons from the decaying tritium atoms expose silver atoms in the emulsion *(5)*. The densest accumulation of tritiated estradiol molecules is found in the nuclei of cells whose distribution in the brain is shown in Figure 44–4. (Adapted from McEwen, 1976.)

44–4 Regional distribution of estradiol-sensitive neurons in the brain of an albino rat: sagittal section just adjacent to the midline. Within the hypothalamus the greatest concentration of receptor sites (**dots**) is in the preoptic–suprachiasmatic area and the arcuate–ventromedial area. (These are the areas responsible for controlling the release of luteinizing hormone by the pituitary; see Figure 44–2.) In more lateral sections (not shown) the amygdala and orbital frontal cortex also appear as targets. (Adapted from McEwen, 1976.)

ized brain will exhibit male mounting behavior when exposed to androgens. This will occur whether the hormones are administered systemically or implanted directly into the anterior hypothalamus. Adult males that had been castrated during the critical period cannot be behaviorally activated by androgens. This behavioral demasculinization can be prevented in castrates by replacing androgens within the same critical period. A quite dramatic example of such remasculinization in rats is presented in Figure 44–5, *broken line.* Male rats were castrated at birth and then administered androgens at different times during the next 2 weeks. When the androgens were replaced within 2 days of birth, these castrated males exhibited appropriate male-like responses in the presence of testosterone in adulthood. However, as the interval between castration and replacement increased, the remascu-

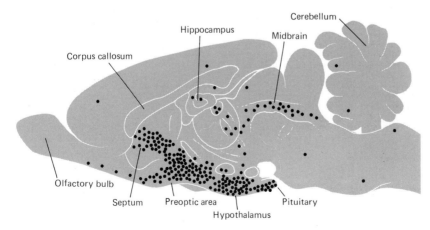

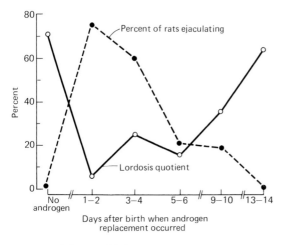

44–5 Adult sexual behavior of six groups of neonatally castrated rats given testosterone replacement therapy at different ages. (Adapted from Beach, Noble, and Orndoff, 1969.)

linizing effect of early androgen replacement therapy declined.

A fourth and separate property of masculinized brains is that they are relatively insensitive to estrogens. In normal males there is an active suppression of the lordotic response, which in adult feminine brains may be elicited by estrogen. The display of adult lordotic behavior following priming with estrogen is not genetic. It is either established or inhibited by the perinatal hormonal environment. This has been demonstrated in male rats in the same castration–replacement paradigm described above. Female sexual behavior was measured in terms of a lordosis quotient (percent of mounts by a stud male that elicited lordosis in the castrated test animals; Figure 44–5, *solid line*). Early androgen replacement during the critical period effectively suppressed adult heterotypical behavioral responses to estrogen.

Although the critical periods for activating male ejaculatory behavior and suppressing lordotic behavior appear to be roughly comparable in Figure 44–5, Whalen and Edwards have provided strong evidence to suggest that the suppression in masculinized brains of heterotypical, female behavior patterns *(defeminization)* is a separate process from the active organization of homotypical male behavior patterns *(masculinization)*. If neonatal male rats are castrated and replacement therapy during the critical period consists only of injections of androstenedione, these animals will display a blend of male behavior and incomplete suppression of female behavior as adults. In addition to having different sensitivities to hormones, the two independent processes—masculinization and defeminization—probably occur at slightly different times in the developmental sequence.

Fifth, events during the critical period appear to result in strong sex differences in the behavioral repertoires of prepubertal juveniles. These gender-specific behavior patterns extend beyond reproductive behaviors. They are not dependent upon either sensitivity to, or activation by, steroid hormones, as these differences manifest themselves during the relatively anhormonal, prepubertal period. Masculinized rhesus monkeys show an increase in rough-and-tumble play, an increase in aggressive encounters, and a decrease in maternal imitative behaviors. There are also consistent differences in the proportion of play time spent by androgenized and nonandrogenized individuals with members of the same brain sex. Thus, besides their effects upon subsequent hormonal sensitivities, perinatal hormones appear to exert some permanent organizational effects upon the nervous system which may have an effect upon nonmating or nonsexual adult behavior.

Sexual Differentiation Is Reflected in Neural Morphology

Is there a morphological basis for the androgen-dependent process in the developing central nervous system that apparently underlies the gender-specific patterns of neuronal organization? Several investigators have described morphological sex differences in neuronal nuclear size (particularly in the preoptic area and ventromedial hypothalamus), in the size of neuronal processes and synaptic terminals in the arcuate nucleus, and in the density of dendritic fields of neurons in the preoptic area. The fourth, and most salient, morphological difference was found by Gorski, Gordon, Shryne, and Southam to be the presence in the male of a large cell group in the preoptic hypothalamic area. This sexually dimorphic nucleus is visible to the naked eye and is markedly reduced in the female.

At the ultrastructural level, Raisman and Field have described a sexually distinct synaptic organization of nonamygdaloid afferents to the preoptic area of the hypothalamus. They suggest that the relative apportionment of synapses upon dendritic spines versus shafts might represent very different patterns of connections in the two sexes and thereby serve as a mechanism of sexual differentiation.

Steroid sensitivity appears to be regionally specific within the hypothalamus. Toran-Allerand performed important experiments with hypothalamic slices from newborn mouse brains maintained in culture. One-half of the slice was exposed to an androgenizing compound, testosterone and/or estradiol; the other served as a control. She discovered that not all neurons in the hypothalamus are androgen sensitive. The most sensitive neurons are located in the anterior preoptic and infundibular–premammillary regions. If the meninges of the explant are removed and the cells are exposed to an androgenizing agent, there is a marked increase in the outgrowth of neurites (new axons and dendrites). Compare the control hypothalamic explant shown in Figure 44–6A with the steroid-exposed slice in Figure 44–6B.

The steroid-stimulated growth of these neu-

44–6 Photomicrographs of mirror slices of hypothalamic explants from the same newborn mouse demonstrate steroid sensitivity in this region. **A.** Control culture showing silver-impregnated neurites coursing outward in hairlike wisps from the margin of the explant. **B.** The neuritic growth of the homologue exhibits an extraordinarily dense plexus formation and extends almost three times as far as in the control. This growth was stimulated by the addition of estradiol (100 ng/ml) to the fluid bathing the culture. (From Toran-Allerand, 1978.)

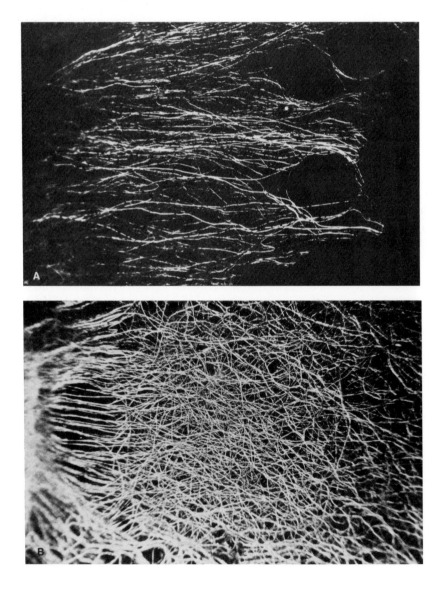

rites is dose dependent, in that low concentrations of steroid result in a relatively sparse radiation of processes. The morphological response of target cells to masculinizing agents also includes extensive arborization (branching) of the new processes. Despite the dramatic nature of the hormone-stimulated growth, the phenomenon involves only small groups of neurons; not all cells in a given nucleus appear to be steroid sensitive. Thus, these in vitro effects appear to be highly specific morphologically. Furthermore, when the culture is pretreated with antibodies to estradiol, which bind and inactivate estradiol (the androgenizing agent), there is no hormone-dependent outgrowth of neurites. In autoradiographic studies, Toran-Allerand has found that estradiol-concentrating neurons occur only in cultures that are steroid responsive.

The principal implication of these developmental in vitro studies is that the different neuronal organization imposed upon the brains of males and females by sex steroids may result from alterations in the growth rate of axons and dendrites of select steroid-sensitive cells. During the critical period, steroid sex hormones might bias the rate of axonal differentiation in different regional populations and ultimately, thereby, neural circuitry. Since the amount of postsynaptic space is limited and constant, sexual differentiation of neural connections could occur as a result of changes in the balance of competition for postsynaptic sites between axonal populations of different origins. For example, if the partition of postsynaptic space between dendritic spines and shafts is determined competitively in time, the rate of growth of incoming neurites from different nuclear groups could determine the synaptic organization of the hypothalamus in the two sexes. In the context of this competitive morphological theory, the emergence of a female pattern of neural organization would not represent a primordial property of nervous tissue or the passive emergence of an intrinsic state; rather, both male and female patterns of neuronal organization may require equally active morphological mechanisms.

A Wide Range of Behaviors Is Influenced by Sex Differences in CNS Organization

Thus far we have focused primarily upon the dimorphic reproductive behaviors of males and females as the primary behavioral markers of brain sex. We shall now explore the broader implications of this research in the context of two questions: First, what other types of behavior might be influenced by sex differences in the cellular organization of the brain? Second, to what extent might sexually differentiated neural organization, and its consequent behavioral biases, be influenced by environmental events within the life span of the individual?

Several lines of recent, converging evidence suggest that the repertoire of behaviors that are influenced by the perinatal hormonal environment may extend well beyond the domain of reproductive behaviors. For example, Goldman has demonstrated in rhesus monkeys that a clear-cut sexual dimorphism exists in the developmental processes that underlie certain frontal lobe cognitive functions. In both infant and adult male monkeys, lesions of the orbital prefrontal cortex result in impaired performance on a wide variety of tests involving spatial discrimination. In contrast, identical lesions in infant females do not induce similar deficits until the animal has reached the age of 15–18 months. Thus the effects of orbital prefrontal lesions are age dependent, and the age at which this part of the cortex becomes involved in spatial learning differs markedly between the sexes. The earlier participation of the masculine frontal cortex in object-reversal learning may also be related to the subsequent superiority of male monkeys in these tasks as adults. Prenatal exposure of developing female monkey fetuses to androgens both erased this sex difference in the performance levels of adults and produced in infancy a malelike susceptibility to the disruptive effects of cooling the surface of the orbital prefrontal cortex. This demonstrates that the frontal cerebral cortex of the monkey is sexually dimorphic in its rate of development—a fact that may be related to the previously mentioned existence of steroid-sensitive neurons in the frontal cortex of rats. These receptor sites, demonstrable only in infancy, have been reported by McEwen to disappear by puberty.

If differences exist in the rate of cortical maturation in nonhuman primates, it is plausible that similar sex differences might occur in the brains of humans, particularly because the development of localized higher cortical functions extends over a long preadolescent period. In Chapter 48 the specialization of cognitive functions in the left and right hemispheres of the mature human brain will be described. Relevant to the present context. Witelson has recently found significant sex differences in the rate of maturation of the apportionment of these cognitive functions between the two hemispheres.

The behavioral test procedure used to assess the relative participation of the two hemispheres in spatial processing involved tactual perception. Children were required to palpate simultaneously, out of view, two different meaningless shapes for 10 sec, each one with the index and middle fingers of one hand. The children then tried to identify the two shapes they felt from a visual display that contained six shapes. In adults, tactile shape discrimination depends mainly on the right hemisphere, and to make the test as dependent as possible on the right hemisphere, Witelson designed her stimuli to be meaningless shapes, not readily labeled. Regardless of their level of proficiency, which largely overlapped that of girls, boys performed in a manner consistent with right hemisphere specialization (i.e., left hand identification was superior to right) as early as the age of 6 years. Girls showed evidence of bilateral representation (no clear hand superiority) until the age of 13 years, suggesting that boys develop a greater hemispheric specialization at an earlier age and, therefore, that over an extended period of development a sex difference may exist in the hemispheric allocation of cognitive functions.

Witelson has also pointed out that sexual dimorphism in the neural organization underlying cognition may have educational implications. For instance, reading is considered to involve both spatial and linguistic processing. The brains of boys and girls may be differentially organized for the cognitive processes involved in reading at a time in development when they are learning to read. Different approaches in teaching reading, such as the look–see and phonetic methods—which stress different cognitive strategies and, by inference, depend on different neural structures in two different sexes—may not work equally well in girls and boys.

If the right hemisphere in girls is not specialized for a particular cognitive function, then it may retain greater plasticity for a longer period than that of males. Clinical impressions are consistent with this idea. Language functions appear to transfer more readily to the right hemisphere in females than in males following damage to the left hemisphere in childhood. The extended plasticity of the young female brain also suggests that females may have a lower incidence of developmental disorders associated with possible left hemisphere dysfunction, for which greater plas-

ticity of the right hemisphere might be advantageous. Males display a higher incidence of developmental dyslexia, developmental aphasia, and infantile autism. All of these syndromes have language deficits as a dominant symptom. However, it is possible that these observations may not be related. Furthermore, in humans sex differences in the susceptibility of developing brains to early damage has not yet been related to hormonal events during the prenatal critical period.

Nevertheless, there is, as we have seen, clear evidence for sexual differentiation of cortical functions and for differential susceptibility to early brain damage in nonhuman primates. Thus, although we are still at an early stage in our understanding of potential sex differences in human neural organization, the extent of gender-typical behavioral biases that may be related to perinatal events appears to be quite broad and not limited to reproductive responses.

Human Sexuality and Learning

It is often tempting to view any intrinsic biological control mechanism, such as the perinatal differentiation of the nervous system discussed above, as representing a fixed, relatively permanent constraint upon behavior. In reality, however, there are very few fixed action patterns in the human repertoire. Although strongly biased by neural organization, most brain-regulated behaviors remain flexible and open to modification within the life span of the individual, often to an extraordinary degree. For example, despite our inheritance of a finely tuned regulatory system for food consumption and body weight, there are certain nonpathological life experiences that can override the homeostat for body weight and produce obesity in otherwise normal individuals. A person may develop a passionate interest in fine food and wines, may get a job as a restaurant critic, and so on. The brain is also outfitted with intrinsic circuits for modulating aggressive and other emotional behaviors; nevertheless, without apparent neuropathology, individuals can become pacifists or terrorists for ideological reasons. In a similar vein, there is ample social evidence that the neural organization of reproductive behaviors, while *biased* by hormonal events during a critical prenatal period, certainly does not exert an immutable influence over adult sexual behavior or even over an individual's psychosexual orientation. Within the life span of the individual, religious, social, or economic motives can prompt biologically similar persons to become celibates, swingers, prostitutes, or rapists.

While the research outlined in this chapter may alert us to the idea that perinatal hormones may influence sexuality in adulthood, it would be a mistake to ignore this environmental perspective and to assume that the sexual identity of the adult may be permanently cast in the synaptic organization of the diencephalon. A single dramatic example may suffice to remind us of the overriding role of life experiences in molding human sexuality. This case history, reported by Money and Ehrhardt, involves a set of monozygotic male twins who, besides sharing an identical genetic constitution, were presumably exposed to the same hormonal environment in utero. During a circumcision procedure at the age of 7 months, the penis of one of the boys was accidentally removed by means of the electrocautery. Following discussions with the parents, the child was 4 months later reassigned as a girl and surgical reconstruction of the genitalia was begun. The subsequent experience of the family with their new daughter was later summarized by the mother:

The mother stated that her daughter by four and a half years of age was much neater than her brother, and in contrast with him, disliked to be dirty: "She likes for me to wipe her face. She doesn't like to be dirty, and yet my son is quite different. I can't wash his face for anything. . . . She seems to be daintier. Maybe it's because I encourage it. . . . One thing that really amazes me is that she is so feminine. I've never seen a little girl so neat and tidy as she can be when she wants to be. . . . She is very proud of herself, when she puts on a new dress, or I set her hair. She just loves to have her hair set. She just loves it."[1]

Even allowing for a mother's natural bias, the behavioral flexibility shown by an individual adjusting to a new sexual role, in this case as in many others, is extremely impressive. This and other testimony implies that, although perinatal factors may bias human adult sexuality, extraordinary life experiences can still exert a commanding influence.

---

[1]Money, J. and Ehrhardt, A. A., Man and Woman, Boy and Girl, Baltimore: Johns Hopkins University Press, 1972, p. 119.

Selected Readings and References

Bermant, G., and Davidson, J. M. 1974. Biological Bases of Sexual Behavior. New York: Harper & Row.

Goy, R. W., and Goldfoot, D. A. 1973. Hormonal influences on sexually dimorphic behavior. In R. O. Greep and E. B. Astwood (eds.), Handbook of Physiology; Section 7: Endocrinology, Vol. 2. Washington, D.C.: American Physiological Society, pp. 169–186.

Goy, R. W., and Goldfoot, D. A. 1975. Neuroendocrinology: Animal models and problems of human sexuality. Arch. Sex. Behav. 4:405–420.

McEwen. B. S. 1976. Interactions between hormones and nerve tissue. Sci. Am. 235(1):48–58.

Toran-Allerand, C. D. 1978. Gonadal hormones and brain development: Cellular aspects of sexual differentiation. Am. Zool. 18:553–565.

Other References

Barraclough, C. A., and Gorski, R. A. 1962. Studies on mating behaviour in the androgen-sterilized female rat in relation to the hypothalamic regulation of sexual behaviour. J. Endocrinol. 25:175–182.

Beach, F. A., Noble, R. G., and Orndoff, R. K. 1969. Effects of perinatal androgen treatment on responses of male rats to gonadal hormones in adulthood. J. Comp. Physiol. Psychol. 68:490–497.

Goldman, P. S., Crawford, H. T., Stokes, L. P., Galkin, T. W., and Rosvold, H. E. 1974. Sex-dependent behavioral effects of cerebral cortical lesions in the developing rhesus monkey. Science (Wash., D.C.) 186:540–542.

Gorski, R. A., Gordon, J. H., Shryne, J. E., and Southam, A. M. 1978. Evidence for a morphological sex difference within the medial preoptic area of the rat brain. Brain Res. 148:333–346.

Money, J., and Ehrhardt, A. A. 1972. Man and Woman, Boy and Girl. Baltimore: Johns Hopkins University Press.

Phoenix, C. H., Goy, R. W., Gerall, A. A., and Young, W. C. 1959. Organizing action of prenatally administered testosterone propionate on the tissues mediating mating behavior in the female guinea pig. Endocrinology 65:369–382.

Raisman, G. 1974. Evidence for a sex difference on the neuropil of the rat preoptic area and its importance for the study of sexually dimorphic functions. Res. Publ. Assoc. Res. Nerv. Ment. Dis. 52:42–49.

Raisman, G., and Field, P. M. 1971. Sexual dimorphism in the preoptic area of the rat. Science (Wash., D.C.) 173:731–733.

Toran-Allerand, C. D. 1976. Sex steroids and the development of the newborn mouse hypothalamus and preoptic area in vitro: Implications for sexual differentiation. Brain Res. 106:407–412.

vom Saal, F. S., and Bronson, F. H. 1980. Sexual characteristics of adult female mice are correlated with their blood testosterone levels during prenatal development. Science (Wash., D.C.) 208:597–599.

Whalen, R. E., and Edwards, D. A. 1967. Hormonal determinants of the development of masculine and feminine behavior in male and female rats. Anat. Rec. 157:173–180.

Whalen, R. E., and Massicci, J. 1975. Subcellular analysis of the accumulation of estrogen by the brain of male and female rats. Brain Res. 89:255–264.

Witelson, S. F. 1976. Sex and the single hemisphere: Specialization of the right hemisphere for spatial processing. Science (Wash., D.C.) 193:425–427.

Lucien Côté

Aging of the Brain and Dementia

Age robs us of all things, even the mind

(Virgil, *Eclogues* IX, line 51)

45

Virgil's observation is as true today as it was when he wrote it over 2000 years ago. The human life span has not increased significantly, but the average human life expectancy has increased markedly, especially since the turn of this century. This increase is largely due to medical advances such as the reduction in infant mortality, vaccination, and the availability of antibiotics, diuretics, and other drugs. In 1900 the average life expectancy was about 25 years less than in 1980, when a man's life expectancy was approximately 71 years and a woman's 78 (Figure 45–1). Moreover, life expectancy continues to increase. During the decade between 1968 and 1979 it has risen at a rate of 1 month per year for all persons over 50. In particular, there has been a significant decrease in both heart disease and stroke. However, as we shall see, this increase in life expectancy has unmasked a new epidemic: *dementia*, a deterioration of mental function that accompanies aging in certain susceptible individuals.

Most gerontologists (scientists interested in the problems of aging—biological, psychological, and social) agree that lengthening the life span of humans has dubious merit if the quality of life is not preserved. The ultimate goal of research on aging is not only to lengthen the human life span, but also to maintain and enhance the quality of life in the aged.

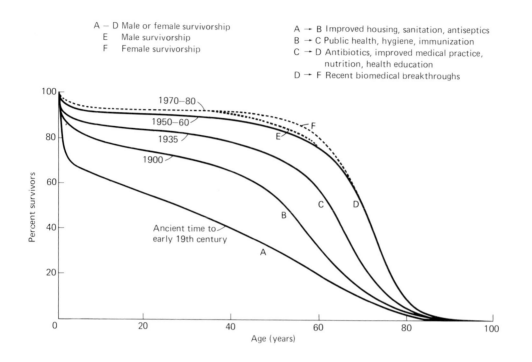

A – D Male or female survivorship
   E   Male survivorship
   F   Female survivorship

A → B Improved housing, sanitation, antiseptics
B → C Public health, hygiene, immunization
C → D Antibiotics, improved medical practice, nutrition, health education
D → F Recent biomedical breakthroughs

45–1 Human survivorship trends from ancient times to the present. These idealized curves illustrate the rapid approach to the limiting rectangular curve that has occurred during the past 150 years. **Inset:** major factors responsible for these transitions. Note that life expectancy for males has changed only slightly since 1950 in the 50+ age group. However, female survivorship has improved significantly during this period, at least in part because of better treatment of reproductive system malignancies. (Adapted from Strehler, 1975.)

In this chapter we shall examine what is known of the molecular mechanisms of aging, focusing in particular on the aging brain and on some illnesses characteristic of age that produce severe memory loss and intellectual deterioration.

Several Hypotheses Have Been Proposed for the Molecular Mechanisms of Aging

Several lines of evidence suggest that aging occurs as the result of changes in informational macromolecules. At least three hypotheses have been advanced that relate aging to changes in the nucleic acids. Zh. A. Medvedev has proposed a redundant message theory, according to which there is an accumulation with age of mutations and chromosome anomalies. As these errors accumulate in functioning genes, reserve (redundant) sequences, containing the same information on DNA molecules, take over until the redundancy is exhausted, and senescence follows. On the other hand, B. L. Strehler has suggested that aging is part of a larger developmental sequence. Just as certain genes program phases of embryonic development, specific genes exist that actually program the aging processes in the organism. Strehler proposed that the changes of old age result from the normal reading out of a genetic program that begins at conception and ends in senility. A third hypothesis, supported by many researchers on aging, maintains that the genetic apparatus does not contain a program for senescent changes per se, but that errors in duplication of DNA increase with age because of random damage and insults that occur with time (wear and tear, radiation effects, and so on). When a significant number of errors accumulate, abnormal RNA and protein molecules are formed and these cannot function normally. The burden of errors results in senescence.

Hypotheses other than those involving genetic material have also been advanced. A particularly intriguing idea, based upon the work of Leonard Hayflick, is that cells possess a biological clock that dictates the life span. Hayflick has found that normal human fibroblasts grown in culture divide regularly until they cover the entire surface of the culture flask. If the cells are transferred in equal numbers to two flasks containing fresh medium they will divide until they again become confluent. Each transfer is called a *passage* or a *doubling*. Normal cultured human fibroblasts can double only a limited number of times (about 50 times) over a period of 7–9 months. Starting at around the 35th passage they gradually slow down their rate of division and eventually stop dividing and die. Fibroblasts from older human donors double significantly less than those obtained from human embryos. Thus the number of cell doublings is roughly related to the age of the cell donors.

The longevity of the species from which fibroblasts are obtained also is a factor in dictating the number of possible passages. Fibroblasts from mouse embryos (whose expected life span is 3 years) divide about 15 times before they die; fibroblasts from humans (with a life span of 70–80 years) divide about 50 times; and those from Galapagos tortoises (with a life span of 175 years) divide about 90 times. Thus the number of passages is roughly related to the longevity of the species.

If nuclei from young fibroblasts are interchanged with those of old fibroblasts (a transfer technique made possible by using cytochalasin B and centrifugation), the newly formed hybrid cells double according to the age of the nuclei and not of the cytoplasm. Thus the biological clock seems to be located in the nucleus of the fibroblast. These and other studies indicate that at least some aspects of aging are intrinsic or genetic.

The Human Brain Decreases in Weight During Aging

No matter what the fundamental processes that underlie senescence, the consequences of aging in the human brain can be devastating when they impair normal mental functions. Recent statistics indicate that about 11% of Americans over 65 years of age show mild to moderate mental impairment, and 4.4% (900,000 Americans) in this group are seriously demented. About 70% of these patients show pathological findings consistent with Alzheimer's type of dementia, as discussed below. Once dementia develops, life expectancy is less than 5 years. An estimated 120,000 patients die each year of severe dementia, and thus dementia is the fourth most common cause of death in humans (after cancer, heart disease, and stroke). Given more effective modes of treatment for cancer and heart disease in the future, the average life span of man is expected to

increase significantly. This achievement will be of dubious value since the incidence of dementia rapidly increases with every added year of life. Approximately 25% of individuals above age 80 show significant dementia.

The morphological changes seen in presenile and senile dementia *(Alzheimer's disease)* are also found to some degree among the nondemented aged, but in dementia the number of lesions is much greater and they have a different distribution. By age 80 the brain normally has decreased in weight by less than 15%; but in demented patients the decrease may be much greater. In addition, the gyri are thin and the sulci prominent. In some patients, however, the functional deficit is even greater than these atrophic changes would indicate, suggesting that much of the tissue without gross lesions is also abnormal.

Four Characteristic Cellular Changes of Aging Occur with Increased Frequency in Dementia

There are many types of microscopic changes in the brains of aged humans. Four of these are particularly prominent and important: the accumulation of lipofuscin granules, granulovacuolar organelles, neuritic plaques, and neurofibrillary tangles.

Lipofuscin granules are pigmented subcellular organelles that autofluoresce green, yellow, or brown (Figure 45–2). With age these granules accumulate in the cytoplasm of neurons. They are thought to be large end-stage lysosomes that accumulate recycled membrane and other cellular detritus that cannot be further catabolized by the neuron. There is no evidence that the accumulation of these large granules impairs the function of the neurons. The rate of accumulation with age seems to be characteristic for certain cell groups. For example, neurons of the olivary and dentate nuclei of the human brain contain lipofuscin granules in the first decade of life. By age 60 the granules occupy most of the cell body of these neurons. On the other hand, the cells of the pallidum contain little lipofuscin until late in life. There is no explanation for these differences between cell types.

Granulovacuolar organelles accumulate in the cytoplasm and dendrites of degenerating nerve cells of the hippocampus and adjacent cortex (Figure 45–3). Each vacuole has a limiting membrane with a small dense granule in its center. These organelles are much more numerous in

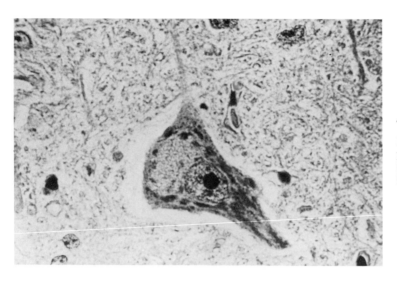

45-2 Spinal cord motor cell with a large aggregate of lipofuscin occupying a major portion of the cell body (hematoxylin and eosin stain). (From Duffy, 1974.)

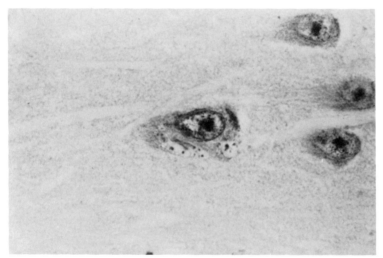

45-3 Granulovacuolar organelles in the cytoplasm of a neuron. Each organelle consists of a small vacuole with a central argyrophilic granule. (From Duffy, 1974.)

brains of demented patients (Alzheimer's disease) than in age-matched, nondemented people.

Neuritic (senile) plaques are most dense in the hippocampus but they are also found in parts of the neocortex (Figure 45-4). Plaques are seen in brains of nondemented old people but are much more common in Alzheimer's disease. These extracellular plaques, which are about 5–100 μm in diameter, are best visualized with reduced silver stains. They are composed of a central core of amyloid, surrounded by masses of neural processes undergoing various degrees of degenerative change. Glial cells form their outer margins. The precursors of these plaques are small groups of

enlarged neurites containing clusters of mitochondria and lysosomes.

Neurofibrillary tangles (Alzheimer's bodies; Figure 45-5) are one of the most common histological features in the brains of patients with Alzheimer's disease (but they can also be present in Down's syndrome, postencephalitic parkinsonism, and amyotrophic lateral sclerosis–Parkinson dementia). A few neurofibrillary tangles are commonly found in nondemented, aged individuals. These organelles are composed of large bundles of twisted tubules measuring about 20 nm in diameter at their widest, and constricted at about 80-nm intervals to a width of about 10 nm. Each

45−4 A senile plaque
consisting of masses of
granular and filamentous
argyrophilic material, with an
amorphous core. Amyloid-like
material is present in the core of
the plaque (Bielschowsky silver
stain). (From Duffy, 1974.)

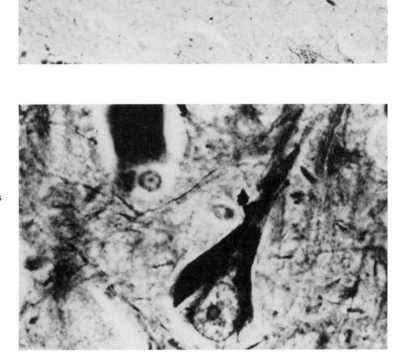

45−5 Neurofibrillary
degeneration in nerve cells
of the cerebral cortex. Large
bundles of abnormal twisted
tubules with marked affinity for
silver, giving the jet black
appearance seen with the
Bielschowsky silver stain.
(From Duffy, 1974.)

twisted tubule is made up of a pair of helical 10-nm filaments. These lesions are found uniquely in human brain; so far they have not been found in other species unless they are induced experimentally by the injection of aluminum into the brain.

Arnold Scheibel and others have found profound changes in the somatodendritic apparatus leading to loss of dendrites with age, especially in demented individuals (Figures 45−6 and 45−7). Initially, swelling and distortion of the somatodendritic silhouette is seen, followed by progressive loss of dendrites. These changes may be closely related to the increased choking of the cytoplasmic space with abnormal tubular material. Loss of dendrites would severely diminish synaptic interactions and decrease the capacity for neurons to process information. These changes are thought by some to be better indices of neural aging than all other histological findings described thus far (Figure 45−8).

Vascular changes were once believed to be a primary cause of the degenerative changes of the aging brain. Lesions of blood vessels characteristic of arteriosclerosis do play a significant role in a relatively small number of patients with dementia. Recent studies by B. E. Tomlinson and his colleagues indicate that vascular disease with

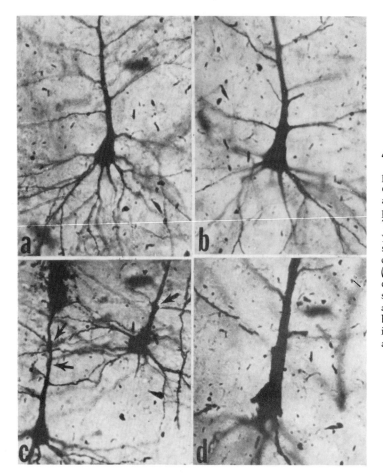

45–6 Very early senescent changes in pyramidal cells of the prefrontal cortex. **a** and **b**: Pyramidal cells from the third and fifth layers in an 83-year-old patient. Both are presumably within normal limits. **c**: Third-layer pyramidal cell from a 96-year-old patient showing early swelling of cell bodies and lumpiness developing in dendrite shafts **(arrows)**. **d**: Third-layer pyramidal cell from an 83-year-old man showing swelling, especially of apical shaft, and a loss of most basilar dendrites. Golgi impregnation. ×220. (From Sheibel and Scheibel, 1975.)

multiple cerebral infarcts is responsible only for about 15% of the cases of dementia, whereas at least 50% of the demented patients have changes consistent with Alzheimer's disease. Another 20% of demented patients show both vascular disease and Alzheimer's disease. The popular notion that hardening of the arteries is a common cause of dementia is therefore not true.

Characteristic Biochemical Changes Take Place in the Brain with Aging

It is important to ask whether Alzheimer's disease is only an accelerated process of aging or a pathological process quite distinct from normal aging. Similarly, is Parkinson's disease, which occurs in the middle and later years of life, an accelerated aging process in a discrete area of the brain, the basal ganglia?

These questions are best approached biochemically, but a major impediment to research on ag-

ing in man has been the difficulty of obtaining human brain tissue for analysis. Animal studies are not completely satisfactory for this purpose because there are many species differences in the aging process of the brain. For example, mice show relatively little change in brain weight, water content, and DNA concentration with increasing age. In contrast, man and other primates show significant loss in brain weight and increase in DNA with senescence. Studies on primates, such as rhesus monkeys, are difficult because of their long life span. Studies of time-dependent biochemical changes associated with aging in humans are therefore best carried out in human brain.

By age 80, there is a 30% reduction in total brain protein. Concomitantly, there is a progressive increase in total DNA, presumably caused by proliferation of glial cells (gliosis) with only a slight increase in water content. Lipid constituents (neural fats, cerebrosides, and phospha-

45-7 Progressive senile changes in
cortical spindle cells. **a:**
Fourth layer spindle cell from superior
temporal gyrus, 89-year-old man. Cell
appears normal. **b:** Spindle cell
showing irregular swelling of cell
body and apical process with partial
loss of deep process. **c** and **d:** Lower
fourth layer spindle cell from superior
temporal gyrus of a 96-year-old man
showing irregular swelling of soma
and apical process and partial loss of
horizontal branches. Golgi
impregnation; a, b, and c ×220; d ×440.
(From Scheibel and Scheibel, 1975.)

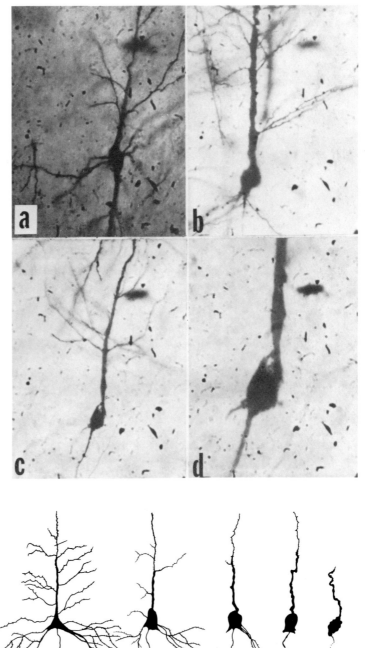

45-8 Progression of senile
changes in cortical
pyramidal cells. **a:** Golgi
impregnation. **b:** Bielschowsky
stain. (Adapted from Scheibel and
Scheibel, 1975.)

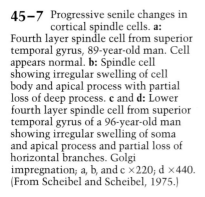

tides) show a minimal decrease with age. Thus, the pattern of chemical changes in the human brain with senescence appears to be characteristic for each major class of molecules.

Most interesting are the changes in neurotransmitter systems (enzymes, receptors, transmitters, and their metabolites). The synthesis and degradation of acetylcholine, dopamine, norepinephrine, serotonin, and other neurotransmitters are carried out by enzymes (see Chapter 10). Therefore, alterations in these enzymes with age could explain some of the characteristics of senescence: altered sleep pattern, mood, appetite, neuroendocrine functions, motor activity, and memory. We have already seen that there is impaired neurotransmitter function in some degenerative disorders of the nervous system. In Parkinson's disease (Chapter 31) there is a profound reduction in the amount of dopamine in a discrete system of the brain (extrapyramidal motor system) leading to severe motor impairment. In Huntington's disease, the levels of glutamic acid decarboxylase activity, γ-aminobutyric acid (GABA), and choline acetyltransferase activity are sharply reduced. With age, there also is a drastic reduction in the enzymes involved in the synthesis of dopamine and norepinephrine. Similar, but less severe changes occur in the activities of glutamic acid decarboxylase and choline acetyltransferase.

In Alzheimer's disease the most dramatic changes occur in cholinergic neurons. Choline acetyltransferase and acetylcholinesterase activities are reduced by 80–90% in the hippocampus, amygdaloid complex, and adjacent temporal and parietal cortex. These changes are also seen in the basal ganglia, cerebellum, thalamus, and brain stem, but to a lesser degree. On the other hand, the concentration of muscarinic receptors is not altered significantly in any region examined.

Dementia Is Prominent in the Clinical Syndromes of Aging

The word *dementia* denotes a progressive decline in mental function, including acquired intellectual skills. It can be caused by many abnormal processes and therefore usually lacks diagnostic specificity. Some of the potentially treatable causes of dementia are infections of the brain and the meninges, nutritional diseases (vitamin deficiency), endocrine and metabolic diseases, intracranial mass lesions, chronically increased intra-

cranial pressure, normal pressure hydrocephalus, and cerebrovascular diseases. As a group, about 15% of cases of dementia are treatable.

It is generally agreed now that the most common forms of dementia—presenile and senile dementia (Alzheimer's disease)—constitute the same disease entity. Except for the age of onset, they are indistinguishable both pathologically and clinically. The disease is usually insidious in onset, and often becomes obvious to the family after a minor stressful period to the patient. The early manifestations include forgetfulness, untidiness, transient confusion, periods of restlessness and lethargy, and errors in judgment. Recent memory impairment, often associated with no loss, or even an enhancement of remote memory, is seen. There is a loss of interest in current events and eventually patients are restricted to a wheelchair or bed. Death often occurs due to complications such as pneumonia, urinary tract infection, or heart failure.

Dementia is sometimes seen in several members of the same family, suggesting that heredity plays a role, but the method of transmission is probably multifactorial. One form of dementia is thought to be of viral origin. *Jakob-Creutzfeldt disease* is a relatively rare subacute spongiform encephalopathy seen in adults that is characterized clinically by dementia, myoclonic jerks, and often ataxia. The disease is transmissible to chimpanzees and humans and is thought to be due to a slow virus. Recently D. C. Gajdusek and his colleagues have demonstrated a transmissible agent in one or two alleged cases of Alzheimer's disease with dominant autosomal inheritance. This observation raises the possibility that Alzheimer's disease may be linked to a transmissible agent. A breakthrough in understanding the cause and treatment of Alzheimer's disease is necessary if we are to resolve a growing medical crisis.

An Overall View

Although one of the eternal interests of mankind, the process of aging is not yet understood. Clinical and pathological findings, fragmentary ideas about mechanisms, and uncertain hypotheses largely constitute the scientific information now at hand. Modern gerontologists believe that the aging process, like other mechanisms in neurobiology, will become clearer when approached with the insights and techniques of cell biology and biochemistry.

Selected Readings and References

Hayflick, L. 1975. Current theories of biological aging. Fed. Proc. 34:9–13.

Roth, M. 1978. Diagnosis of senile and related forms of dementia. In R. Katzman, R. D. Terry, and K. L. Bick (eds.), Aging, Vol. 7: Alzheimer's Disease: Senile Dementia and Related Disorders. New York: Raven Press, pp. 71–85.

Samorajski, T., and Ordy, J. M. 1972. Neurochemistry of aging. In C. M. Gaitz (ed.), Advances in Behavioral Biology, Vol. 3: Aging and the Brain. New York: Plenum, pp. 41–61.

Tomlinson, B. E., and Henderson, G. 1976. Some quantitative cerebral findings in normal and demented old people. In R. D. Terry and S. Gershon (eds.), Aging, Vol. 3: Neurobiology of Aging. New York: Raven Press, pp. 183–204.

Wiśniewski, H. M., and Terry, R. D. 1973. Morphology of the aging brain, human and animal. Prog. Brain Res. 40:167–186.

Other References

Boyd, W. D., Graham-White, J., Blackwood, G., Glen, I., and McQueen, J. 1977. Clinical effects of choline in Alzheimer senile dementia. Lancet Vol. II, No. 8040, p. 711.

Côté, L. J., and Kremzner, L. T. 1975. Age-dependent changes in the activities of enzymes related to the formation and degradation of neurotransmitters in human brain; correlation with the levels of polyamines. In VIIth International Congress of Neuropathology, Budapest, Hungary. Amsterdam: Excerpta Medica, pp. 433–441.

Dastur, D. K., Lane, M. H., Hansen, D. B., Kety, S. S., Butler, R. N., Perlin, S., and Sokoloff, L. 1963. Effects of aging on cerebral circulation and metabolism in man. In J. E. Birren et al. (eds.), Human Aging: A Biological and Behavioral Study. Public Health Service Publ. No. 986. Washington, D.C.: U.S. Government Printing Office, pp. 57–76.

Davies, P., and Maloney, A. J. F. 1976. Selective loss of central cholinergic neurons in Alzheimer's disease. Lancet Vol. II, No. 8000, p. 1403.

Duffy, P. (ed.). 1974. Neuropathology: An Illustrated Course. Philadelphia: F. A. Davis.

Etienne, P., Gauthier, S., Johnson, G., et al. 1978. Clinical effects of choline in Alzheimer's disease. Lancet Vol. I, No. 8062, pp. 508–509.

Gajdusek, D. C. 1978. Slow infections with unconventional viruses. Harvey Lect. 72:283–353.

Gibbs, C. J., Jr., Gajdusek, D. C., Asher, D. M., Alpers, M. P., Beck, E., Daniel, P. M., and Matthews, W. B. 1968. Creutzfeldt-Jakob disease (spongiform encephalopathy): Transmission to the chimpanzee. Science (Wash., D.C.) 161:388–389.

Hayflick, L. 1980. The cell biology of human aging. Sci. Am. 242(1):58–65.

Marsden, C. D., and Harrison, M. J. G. 1972. Outcome of investigation of patients with presenile dementia. Br. Med. J. 2:249–252.

McGeer, E., and McGeer, P. L. 1976. Neurotransmitter metabolism in the aging brain. In R. D. Terry and S. Gershon (eds.), Aging, Vol. 3: Neurobiology of Aging. New York: Raven Press, pp. 389–403.

Medvedev, Zh. A. 1972. Repetition of molecular–genetic information as a possible factor in evolutionary changes of life span. Exp. Gerontol. 7:227–238.

Scheibel, M. E., and Scheibel, A. B. 1975. Structural changes in the aging brain. In H. Brody, D. Harman, and J. M. Ordy (eds.), Aging, Vol. 1: Clinical, Morphologic, and Neurochemical Aspects in the Aging Central Nervous System. New York: Raven Press, pp. 11–37.

Signoret, J. L., Whiteley, A., and Lhermitte, F. 1978. Influence of choline on amnesia in early Alzheimer's disease. Lancet Vol. II. No. 8094, p. 837.

Strehler, B. L. 1975. Implications of aging research for society. Fed. Proc. 34:5–8.

Strehler, B., Hirsch, G., Gusseck, D., Johnson, R., and Bick, M. 1971. Codon-restriction theory of aging and development. J. Theor. Biol. 33:429–474.

Walford R. L. 1974. Immunologic theory of aging: Current status. Fed. Proc. 33:2020–2027.

White, P., Goodhardt, M. J., Keet, J. P., Hiley, C. R., Carrasco, L. H., Williams, I. E. I., and Bowen, D. M. 1977. Neocortical cholinergic neurons in elderly people. Lancet Vol. I, No. 8013, pp. 668–671.

Behavior

VIII

One of the main functions of the nervous system is to generate behavior. As we have seen in the section on development, the neuronal controls of behavior emerge gradually as the brain develops. At first the development of the brain is largely under the control of genetic and developmental programs. External environmental influences begin to exert their effects in utero, but they become of prime importance only after birth. During an early, critical period, depriving an animal of a normal social, physical, or hormonal environment can have profound consequences for the subsequent maturation of the brain and therefore of behavior. Consequently, a knowledge of the innate (genetic and developmental) as well as the environmental determinants is needed to understand fully any behavior. This knowledge is also essential for developing rational therapeutic principles for the treatment of mental disorders.

In considering the interaction of innate and environmental factors in the control of behavior, we shall focus in particular on two higher functions: language and learning. Study of the capability for language and for learning provides some of the best information available about the organization, logical operations, and limitations of the human mental processes and the representation of their various functions in the human brain. We shall review the evidence, based in part on clinical observations, that different cortical regions often work together to control specific higher functions. In particular, we shall consider studies in humans and certain lower animals that show that the left and right hemispheres are not simple functional mirror images but have their own specialized capacities.

We shall also see how the modern disciplines of neurophysiology, anatomy, biochemistry, and psychology have converged and, together with astute clinical observation, have provided fresh support for the idea first proposed by the Hippocratic physician over two millenia ago that the appropriate study of the mental processes begins with the study of the brain.

Irving Kupfermann

Innate Determinants of Behavior

46

All behavior is the result of the interaction of two factors: inborn factors, either genetic or developmental, and environmental factors. The relative importance of these two determinants varies, but even the most rigid, genetically determined behavior can be modified by the environment, and the most plastic behavior, such as language, is influenced by innate factors. Because inborn factors provide the substrate upon which environmental factors act, we shall consider the innate determinants of behavior before considering the process of learning in the next chapter.

In this chapter we shall first discuss the historical and recent thinking about the innate aspects of behavior—thinking that has revolved around the concept of instinct. Next, we shall consider possible neural mechanisms underlying certain types of innate behaviors in animals. Finally, we shall examine the question of whether humans have innate behavior.

Instinct Has Been Defined in Various Ways

A good starting point for considering the innate determinants of behavior is the concept of *instinct*. This concept has a long and controversial history. Antecedents to the notion of instinct can be traced to the beginning of written history. The ancient Greek philosophers and the later Christian theologians sought to exalt humans and to set them apart from lower animals by arguing that the behavior of humans was guided by reason, whereas the behavior of lower animals was the result of *natural instincts*, a term that came to be applied to complex, unreflexive, and unlearned behaviors.

These early explanations of human and animal behavior were not based on systematic observations or experiments. Modern scientific usage of the term *instinct* dates to the latter part of the 19th century and the influential writings of Charles Darwin. Darwin's work on the evolution of species indicated that there were no sharp discontinuities between the evolution of man and of lower animals. Darwin therefore suggested that the behavior of lower animals must be guided not only by instinct but also by primitive forms of the same reasoning processes that guide human behavior. More importantly, Darwin argued that since man evolved from lower animals, man's behavior also must be guided by instincts. These notions were soon amplified by psychologists who saw in the concept of instinct a way to explain much of human behavior on the basis of a few underlying principles. For example, Sigmund Freud suggested that all normal and abnormal human behavior is powerfully shaped by two fundamental instincts: a life (or sexual) instinct, and a death (or aggressive) instinct. These instincts provide a form of mental force that energize various behaviors. In contrast, in an influential book entitled *An Introduction to Social Psychology* published in 1908, William McDougall postulated that humans have up to a dozen instincts: flight, repulsion, curiosity, pugnacity, self-abasement, self-assertion, parenting, reproduction, desire for food, gregariousness, acquisition, and construction.

These systematic theories about human instincts were soon challenged by John Broadus Watson and other members of the school of behaviorism. Behaviorists rejected the idea that the best way to understand behavior is through the study of the mind—the inner forces that determine behavior. Behaviorists argued that the only aspects of behavior that can be studied are observable indices, not inner forces. The behaviorists pointed out that the notion of instinct was being used in two different ways—one referred to observable acts, the other to unobservable strivings. Freud, McDougall, and other psychologists used the term *instinct* to refer to *unlearned inner strivings and propensities that guide behavior.* Viewed in this way, instincts are unobservable motivational variables—that is, intervening variables that are invoked to aid in the explanation of behavior (see Chapter 38). In contrast, many biologists used the term *instinct* to refer to *stereotyped observable sequences of motor movements that are unlearned.* Behaviorists rejected the view of instincts as inner strivings because it was a mentalistic concept. They argued that the true science of behavior must deal only with observable responses and should not deal with inferred unobservable phenomena such as thoughts, propensities, ideas, images, or inner strivings. The behaviorists argued that this view of instinct as an explanation of behavior, in addition to being mentalistic, merely renamed phenomena and explained nothing. Thus, the aggressiveness of man was supposedly explained by an aggressive instinct; generosity was due to an instinct of altruism, and so forth.

Although some behaviorists admitted that stereotyped unlearned motor patterns might exist in lower animals, most behaviorists also had difficulty with the notion of instinctive behavior as *completely* unlearned acts. They pointed out that one can never prove that a given behavior is completely free of learning. Even if one carefully observes an organism and controls its environment, there may be unsuspected sources of environmental stimuli that allow the animal to learn. The more radical behaviorists felt that all behavior could be explained on the basis of simple reflexes and principles of learning. Under the pervasive influence of behavioristic philosophy, most American experimental psychologists abandoned the consideration of innate determinants of behavior and focused almost exclusively on the study of learning. In many instances, processes that were formerly called *instincts* were renamed *drives* (e.g., hunger, sex, thirst, and curiosity) and were studied independently of considerations of whether they were innate or learned.

Ethologists Define Instincts as Inborn Motor Patterns

During the period 1920–1950, when American psychologists had abandoned considerations of instincts, European zoologists, such as Konrad Lorenz and Nikolaas Tinbergen, began a series of studies that laid the groundwork for what became known as *ethology*—the study of the naturalistic behavior of animals, with emphasis on inborn determinants. The ethologists advanced the study of instincts in two ways. First, they limited themselves to the biological definition of instinct as inborn stereotyped sequences of motor movement. Second, the ethologists carried out experiments. Although previous scientists had speculated about the role of instinct in behavior, the ethologists were the first to observe and experiment systematically on inborn behavior. These studies, carried out in a wide variety of species, led to a partial reconciliation of the older mentalistic concepts of instinct and the anti-instinct philosophy of the behaviorist movement.

While acknowledging some of the criticisms directed at the concept of instinct as unlearned behavior, ethologists pointed out that it was virtually impossible to explain certain behaviors of lower animals on the basis of learning alone. For example, a female bird that has been isolated from other birds since hatching is still able to build a perfect nest as an adult and can clean and care for its young. Such behavior cannot have been learned covertly while the animal was maturing. Moreover, ethologists emphasized the fact that instinctive behavior is not completely unaffected by the environment, as all behavior is the result of an interaction between the genes of the animal and its internal and external environments. However, just as physical structures can be inherited, so certain behaviors appear to be inherited, and a consideration of genetic factors in behavior is a useful approach toward clarification of the concept of instinct.

As the ethologists pointed out, asking whether a behavior is instinctive is virtually equivalent to asking whether the behavior is inherited. Seen from this standpoint, the problem of instinct reduces to the question: Is it possible to inherit behavior? This question is best considered in terms of the ontogeny of the brain, the organ that controls behavior.

Can Behavior Be Inherited?

Psychologists have traditionally considered behavior to be the result of the operation of the mind. At one time the mind was considered to be ethereal and it was difficult to envisage how aspects of the mind could be inherited. As we have seen in earlier chapters, most neural scientists believe that the mind represents a set of processes or functions. According to this view the mind is not a structural entity, but rather a set of functions carried out by the brain. Mind is what the brain does, just as walking is one of the things that legs do. It would be confusing to ask where the walk of the legs is, and whether the walk could be inherited. If mind and behavior are functions of the brain, it becomes easy to see how behavior can be affected by genetic factors, just as is the function of every other organ of the body.

Nevertheless, there has been great resistance to the notion that behavior, particularly human behavior, can be inherited. Part of the reason for this resistance has been a mistaken notion of what inheritance of behavior really means. Take, for example, the question: Is mental illness inherited? So posed, the question implies that a complex behavioral disorder is controlled entirely by a set of genes that were inherited. Clearly this cannot be so. The expression of inherited factors always depends upon an interaction of genetic and environmental factors. Thus, you can inherit genes that program you to grow tall, but if you are not raised with the appropriate diet you will be short. Although learning may or may not be important for the expression of a genetic factor, one or more nonspecific environmental factors (e.g., appropriate nutrition, light, etc.) will always be important. *Innate or inborn behaviors are responses that are not highly dependent upon specific learning experiences in which information is extracted from the environment.* However, there is no sharp distinction between learned and innate behaviors. There is instead a continuous gradation, from rigid responses that are almost independent of the animal's history, to responses that are exquisitely sensitive to environmental factors. What the ethologists call *instinctive behaviors is a special class of innate behaviors that consist of relatively complex sequences of responses.* Instinctive behaviors are now often termed *species-specific behaviors* because they characterize a given species, much as do morphological or physiological features. In the following sections we shall consider several examples of the influence of environment on the expression of genetic information related to behavior.

Sign Stimulus and Fixed Action Pattern Are Two Key Concepts in the Analysis of Species-Specific Behavior

In the course of investigating examples of rigid behavior patterns that seem to require a minimum of experience for their expression, Lorenz, Tinbergen, and other ethologists developed a theoretical orientation based, in part, on two useful

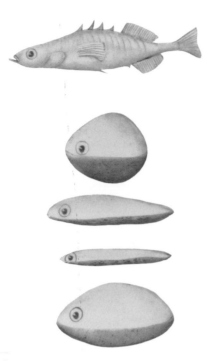

46–1 Models of the stickleback fish. The top model
is an accurate imitation but lacks a red belly.
The next four models have a red underside and are
more frequently attacked than the top model. (Adapted
from Tinbergen, 1951.)

concepts: sign stimulus and fixed action pattern.
Complex inborn behavior patterns in lower animals typically are released by specific stimulus
conditions; the specific effective stimulus is
termed a *sign stimulus* or *releaser*. Behavioral
analysis has shown that animals, given a complex
stimulus condition, often respond to certain very
specific features of a situation, not the total stimulus condition.

The role of sign stimuli is illustrated by a
beautiful, and now classic series of studies by
Tinbergen on the sexual behavior of stickleback
fish. During mating season the male stickleback
develops a bright red abdomen. The red abdomen
provokes fighting responses from other males,
but elicits approach responses from females. The
precise nature of the stimulus was studied by the
use of models. A model resembling a stickleback
in every detail except the red belly did not elicit a
response (Figure 46–1). On the other hand, a
model that had a red underside, but otherwise did
not resemble a stickleback, very effectively released fighting behavior in males and mating behavior in females. However, the cue was more

specific than the mere presence of red, since the
same model that elicited fighting was ineffective
when it was turned upside down. A similar analysis has revealed that the swollen abdomen of the
female serves as a different sign stimulus for the
male, and triggers mating behavior. The sign
stimuli eliciting mating or attack are effective in
animals that have been raised in total isolation
and are therefore said to operate through an innate releasing mechanism.

Species-specific behaviors typically begin with
a phase of *appetitive behavior*, which consists of
highly variable responses that serve to aid the organism in finding appropriate environmental
stimuli, or a goal object (e.g., mate, food, water,
or nesting material). Appetitive behavior is followed by a phase of *consummatory behavior*,
which consists of chains of relatively stereotyped
movements, termed *fixed action patterns*. Each
fixed action pattern is a *behavioral sequence* that
is triggered by an environmental cue (the sign
stimulus).

In a sense, a fixed action pattern is like a reflex, in that it is a behavioral response elicited by
a specific stimulus and its expression does not require previous learning. It differs from a simple
reflex in that it is preceded by a phase of appetitive behavior. Furthermore, whereas the features
of reflex responses (e.g., strength and duration)
are often closely related to the features of the
evoking stimulus, most of the features of fixed
action patterns are independent of the parameters
of the evoking stimulus. For reflexes, the nervous
system produces a relatively simple transformation of the sensory input. For fixed action patterns, however, the nervous system produces a
highly complex transformation of the input. By
and large, the duration, latency, and intensity of
fixed action patterns are only loosely related to
stimulus parameters (Figure 46–2). A related feature is that fixed action patterns typically consist of a complex response sequence, often stereotyped but not always rigidly so.

Finally, unlike reflex responses, a fixed action
pattern can sometimes occur in the total absence
of any observable eliciting stimuli. This so-called
vacuum activity, or *displacement behavior*, often occurs in situations in which the animal is
placed in conflict between two mutually exclu-
sive responses, such as attack and escape. Displacement activities include feeding, sleeping,
and very often body-cleaning movements such as
preening and scratching. Two neurophysiological
hypotheses have been proposed to explain dis-

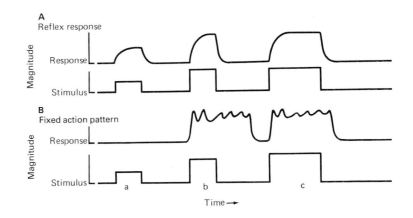

46–2 Hypothetical reflex and fixed action pattern elicited by stimuli differing in intensity and duration. **A.** A simple reflex, for example, pupillary constriction elicited by a light. **B.** A fixed action pattern, such as courtship behaviors in fish or birds, in response to an appropriate sign stimulus. For both the reflex and fixed action patterns, three responses to three types of stimuli are shown: **a,** a weak and brief stimulus; **b,** a strong and brief stimulus; and **c,** a still stronger and prolonged stimulus. Note that the simple reflex response reflects the nature of the stimulus, whereas the fixed action pattern is triggered by the stimulus but the nature of the response is not closely linked to the nature of the stimulus.

placement activity. One theory is based on a loose hydrodynamic analogy. According to this notion, displacement is the result of the "overflow" or "sparking over" of some type of hypothetical motivational energy. The motivational energy that would ordinarily flow into channels that energize one behavior therefore overflows into a new channel and energizes some other behavior. The second theory is based on the idea that behavior is organized hierarchically, such that a dominant response inhibits all subordinate responses. During conflict, when two behaviors are elicited in equal strength, the two behaviors inhibit one another. The inhibitory effects of each behavior on subordinate behaviors are thus eliminated and subordinate responses are disinhibited. Background weak stimuli, such as mild skin irritation can now effectively elicit responses that previously had been inhibited by more dominant responses. Behavioral evidence favors the disinhibition theory of displacement activity, but final judgment must await further understanding of the relevant neurophysiological mechanisms.

Fixed Action Patterns Are Generated by Central Programs

What is the neural basis for complex fixed action patterns? Are the properties imposed by the central nervous system, with the stimulus acting primarily to release the pattern? Or are these merely complex chains of reflexes, with the guiding stimuli provided by the animal's proprioceptive input? The latter notion was championed by the great British neurophysiologist Charles Sherrington. According to this idea, each reflex in a chain of responses produces proprioceptive or other

sensory input that elicits the next reflex response. In order to approach this issue experimentally, it is necessary to eliminate all sources of peripheral sensory input that could provide the cues needed for the chain of reflexes. Such experiments have now been done elegantly in several invertebrates in which it is possible to remove the nervous system from the animal and thereby completely isolate it from any possible sensory feedback. Experiments of this type have been done on flying, walking, swimming, and feeding responses in insects, crustaceans, and molluscs. In each instance, the isolated nervous system still generates the same sequence of motor output shown by the intact animal. Sensory input typically modifies the strength or frequency of the central program, but the essential pattern does not require timing cues from sensory feedback.

Evidence for the existence of central motor programs has also been obtained in vertebrates. The data indicating a central program for locomotion in the cat were outlined in Chapter 28. Many other responses, some quite complex, also

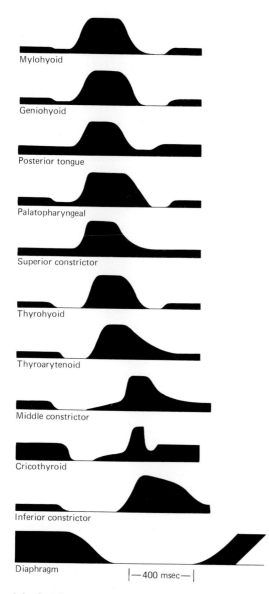

Mylohyoid

Geniohyoid

Posterior tongue

Palatopharyngeal

Superior constrictor

Thyrohyoid

Thyroarytenoid

Middle constrictor

Cricothyroid

Inferior constrictor

Diaphragm |—400 msec—|

46–3 Schematic summary of electromyographic
activity in deglutition in the dog. The height
of the line for each muscle indicates the intensity of
the action observed, ranging from complete inactivity
to the maximum occurring in deglutition. (Adapted
from Doty and Bosma, 1956.)

appear to involve built-in motor programs in vertebrates. These include swallowing, biting,
grooming, orgasm, coughing, yawning, vomiting,
and startle. Swallowing provides a well-studied
example. This response is triggered by stimulation of the pharynx. Once triggered, the behavior
involves a complex sequential activation of at
least 10 different muscles (Figure 46–3). Superfi-

cially, at least, the swallowing response appears
to be a fixed action pattern. Robert Doty and
James Bosma examined the reflex control of swallowing by looking at the pattern of muscle contraction (elicited by the electrical stimulation of
pharyngeal nerves) before and after anesthetiza-
tion of the pharynx or removal of various muscles
either surgically or by application of a local anesthetic. Nothing that was done to alter or eliminate sources of peripheral feedback produced a
significant change in the motor sequence of swallowing. However, different arousal levels, as well
as pharyngeal stimulation, can produce some alterations in the strength and duration of the motor output. Thus, in swallowing, as in locomotion, the details of the pattern can be modified
somewhat by external sensory feedback but the
basic pattern is internally generated.

What is the neural basis underlying the triggering of fixed action patterns? In 1938 C. A. G.
Wiersma, at the California Institute of Technology, reported the exciting discovery that in crayfish, a complete, complex motor output can be
triggered by the stimulation of individual neurons, which he later called *command neurons.*
The firing of one such neuron could elicit a complex defensive response involving dozens of different muscles. Command neurons have divergent synaptic outputs that excite or inhibit a
population of follower neurons that are interconnected in ways that generate specific patterns of
motor output. In mammals there is no evidence
for unique neurons that can function as command neurons do in invertebrates. Nevertheless,
it is attractive to speculate that the function of
command neurons in mammals may be performed by a group of cells—a command
system—that work together to provide the trigger for preprogrammed motor acts. Recent evidence indicates that even in invertebrates, in
many cases, complete complex motor acts are not
triggered by single command neurons; rather,
parts of the complete act are triggered by individual cells. Furthermore, just as the generation of a
perception depends upon a number of feature detectors operating in parallel, the generation of a
highly complex motor act may involve the operation of a number of command systems, each of
which is responsible for some limited aspect of
the movement.

Certain command systems appear to be driven
by neural mechanisms that are tuned to specific
features of sensory input. Ethologists refer to this
type of mechanism as the *innate releasing mechanism.* The nature of innate releasing mecha-

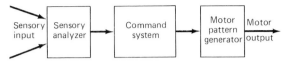

46–4 Simplified model of neural organization underlying fixed action patterns.

nisms is largely unknown. We do know, however, that individual neurons of the sensory systems of vertebrates can respond to highly specific features of sensory input (see Chapter 21), and it is reasonable to assume that neurons of this type are important elements of innate releasing mechanisms. A highly simplified model of the possible neural basis of fixed action patterns is shown in Figure 46–4. Feature detection neurons, as part of a sensory system or an innate releasing mechanism, are excited by specific sensory input and provide excitation to command neurons or command systems. The command system, in turn, provides a trigger for a central motor program that generates a stereotyped behavioral sequence.

Higher Mammals and Humans Also Seem To Have Certain Innate Behavior Patterns

The bulk of research on innate behavior has been done on nonmammalian species, but considerable evidence indicates that mammals, including primates, also exhibit innate behaviors. A particularly elegant example of research on monkeys is provided by a study by Gene Sackett at the University of Wisconsin. Sackett tried to determine whether the behavioral responses toward a specific visual stimulus were innate. He raised individual monkeys in complete isolation from their mothers and other monkeys. When these animals were given an opportunity to view various types of photographs, they greatly preferred to view images of other infant monkeys over nonmonkey images. Until they were 10 weeks old, they preferred pictures of monkey over nonmonkey objects even if the monkey image showed threatening gestures. As they matured, however, they abruptly decreased their preference for monkeys with threatening gestures. They began to be disturbed by photographs of threatening monkeys but not by other types of images. Sackett's experiments clearly demonstrate that primates have innate releasing mechanisms.

What is the role of innate factors in determining human behavior? Unfortunately, as a result of the inherent and ethical limitations on the study of humans, no definitive conclusions are yet possible. The primary determinants of complex human activities such as warfare, marriage, and religion are clearly the result of learning and culture. The degree to which these activities may be influenced by innate factors is unknown. Although learning plays an enormous role in human behavior and humans do not have any clear-cut highly complex chains of inborn behaviors such as those seen in lower animals, the comparative data we shall consider here and the studies on the hormonal determinants of gender identity considered earlier (Chapter 44) indicate that there may also be innate determinants of human behavior. Four types of data support this conclusion: (1) the evidence for genetic factors influencing human behavior; (2) the universality of certain human behavior patterns; (3) the existence of motor patterns that resemble fixed action patterns; and (4) the existence of relatively complex motor patterns in the absence of any obvious specific learning experiences.

Certain Behavioral Traits Have a Hereditary Component

Some of the best evidence for a hereditary factor in behavior is in the areas of severe mental illness, in particular, schizophrenia. For many years neurobiologists felt that it was difficult to conceive of schizophrenia, with its extreme disorder of thought and perception, as entirely due to a faulty environment acting on an individual who is essentially normal genetically. As outlined in Chapter 50, the study of identical twins and of adopted individuals has now demonstrated conclusively that there is an important genetic component to this behavioral disorder. For example, a number of investigators have examined the probability (concordance) of one twin being schizophrenic when the other is known to be schizophrenic. Various studies have found that the concordance rate in monozygotic twins (who have identical genes) is about 60%, whereas in dizygotic twins (who share half their genes) the concordance rate is about 10%. The incidence of schizophrenia in the general population is less than 1%. The high concordance rate in monozygotic twins is consistent with the view that there is a genetic component to schizophrenia.

Although the evidence from twin studies indicates that there is a genetic factor in schizophrenia, the same evidence proves that nongenetic factors are also important. A concordance rate in monozygotic twins of 60% means that in 40% of the cases only one twin has schizophrenia. Because the genes of identical twins presumably are the same, something else must be different. There is evidence that, when one twin has schizophrenia and the other does not, the second twin frequently exhibits schizoid characteristics *(schizotypal syndrome)*—that is, mild schizophrenia-like symptoms such as excessive shyness, withdrawal, and suspiciousness—that are found in normal individuals. Thus, the inherited trait may be a schizoid tendency that appears as schizophrenia under the appropriate environmental stresses.

Another area of human behavior in which there is evidence for genetic factors is intelligence. Although it is not completely clear exactly what is measured by intelligence tests, there is wide agreement (but not complete unanimity) that, whatever they do measure, scores on intelligence tests are partly a function of inherited factors. This area of research has generated a great deal of controversy, particularly around the issue of whether or not any sex differences or differences among racial, national, or ethnic groups are due to genetic factors. Of course, the fact that intelligence may be affected by genetic factors *in no way* provides support for the notion that any group differences are due to genetic factors. There are no existing studies that unequivocally support that hypothesis. Furthermore, the nature of the problem is such that it may well prove to be extremely difficult to obtain any firm conclusions on this issue.

Many Human Behaviors Are Universal

A large number of behaviors are found in all humans regardless of differences in their environmental or cultural backgrounds. There are common reflex behaviors that we all share, such as the deep tendon reflexes, the eye blink response, and startle reflexes. In addition, we have common basic drives and needs, such as hunger, thirst, and sex. Equally important and widespread are human needs not related to simple tissue deficits. For example, to varying degrees, people of all cultures have a need for social contact and for variety of sensory experience.

One of the best examples of a complex set of human behaviors that is universal is emotional expression, first systematically studied by Darwin. Facial expressions of anger, fear, disgust, and joy are recognized to a high degree even between individuals of cultures that have had no contact.

Thus, the recognition of certain emotional expressions probably has a strong innate component. Furthermore, the facial motor patterns themselves tend to be surprisingly similar across cultures.

Humans also exhibit behavior patterns that appear to be analogous to the displacement activities of animals (discussed above). For example, during conflict situations or in periods of stress, people often show grooming behavior such as scratching, and handling and stroking of their hair.

Fixed Action Patterns

Although humans do not possess clearly delineated chains of complex behavior characteristic of the innate behavior patterns of lower animals, they do have simpler behaviors that bear resemblance to the fixed action patterns of lower animals. Many emotional expressions, such as the startle response and smiling, involve a stereotyped sequence of movements. Smiling in human infants appears to be under the control of a specific sign stimulus. The eliciting stimulus has been studied by the use of models, much in the way that colored wax models have been used to study mating behavior in fish. Although young infants smile in response to a human face, studies with models indicate that the response is not to the face as a whole, but rather to certain specific features (Figure 46–5). Contrasting elements (eyes, in the case of a real face) appear to be of particular importance. As the child matures, however, other elements of the face assume increasing importance. Even in adults, eyes appear to function in some ways as a sign stimulus. A striking example is the brow flash response, studied by Irenäus Eibl-Eibesfeldt in widely different cultures. This stereotyped response, which many of us are unaware that we use, consists of a rapid raising and dropping of the eyebrows. In widely different cultures, it occurs as part of a greeting response between familiar individuals.

Certain Complex Patterns Require Little or No Learning

Although there are numerous examples of widespread behavior patterns in humans that are unlikely to be entirely learned, in many instances the precise role of learning is difficult to assess. In animal studies, the role of learning can be studied by raising animals in highly restricted environments. In humans these types of experi-

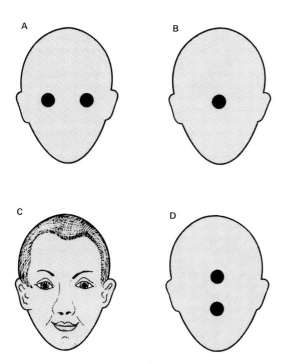

46–5 Types of patterns utilized to study the sign stimuli eliciting smiling in young babies. In babies of about 6 weeks of age, patterns **A** and **D** were more effective than **C** and **B**. Thus, the critical features appear to be multiple spots of high contrast. As the babies matured, the dot patterns became progressively less effective in eliciting a smile, while the face image became more effective. (Adapted from Ahrens, 1954.)

ments are not possible, but we can gain insight from examples of "natural" experiments. Thus, for example, babies who are blind at birth have a very limited opportunity to learn facial expressions. Nevertheless these children exhibit certain more or less normal looking responses. For these blind babies, smiling in response to a sound can even involve convergence of the eyes toward the source of sound. Chapter 52 contains some further examples of abilities and disabilities in humans with limited environmental experiences.

The Brain Sets Limits on the Structure of Language

The ability to communicate by means of highly complex language sets humans apart from other animals. Languages differ greatly from culture to culture, and one might therefore conclude that language is not affected by innate determinants; however, this is clearly not so. The nature of lan-

guage is limited and shaped by the nature of our sensory–motor apparatus. For example, languages do not utilize frequencies of sound that we cannot hear or produce. More importantly, Noam Chomsky at the Massachusetts Institute of Technology and many other linguists account for the fact that widely different languages have common underlying principles of grammar by proposing that the actual structure of languages is determined by conceptual constraints imposed by the structure of the brain.

It is difficult to experiment on humans to clarify the interaction of environmental factors and biological constraints in the development of language. However, several animal models of language now exist. Although there is some question about whether or not animal communication is a true form of language, nonhuman primates can be taught a form of limited communication utilizing sign language. Birds have a natural song language, although this clearly is not language in the human sense. Bird song, however, is a highly complex auditory output that serves a primitive communicative function. Studies of bird song by M. Konishi, P. Marler, W. H. Thorpe, and others provide a fascinating and instructive example of the interaction of innate factors with the environment. Early investigators posed the question as to whether a bird learns its song from other birds or whether it is inborn. Studies soon revealed that the question had no simple answer; furthermore, there are great differences between birds. In some birds, such as chickens, normal sound production occurred even when animals were raised in isolation and never heard another bird. In songbirds, such as a chaffinch or white crowned sparrow, the song is distorted if the animal is raised in isolation.

A remarkable discovery made by Masakazu Konishi in 1965 was that if the birds were deafened at birth, their adult song was even more distorted than if they were raised in isolation (Figure 46–6). This suggests that to perfect their song these birds must hear themselves sing. They must therefore have a built-in auditory model or template against which the song they produce is compared. This template is present even if the bird never hears another bird, since under these conditions its song is not random, but resembles, although imperfectly, the normal song. When given a chance to hear a song, the bird produces a much more normal song. Variations in the song heard as a young bird result in similar variations in the adult song, but only within certain narrow limits. Most songbirds will not learn to imitate

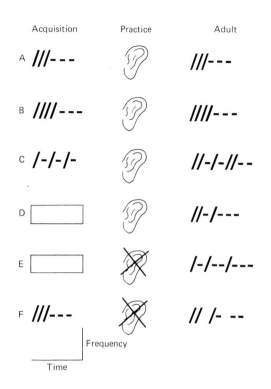

| Acquisition | Practice | Adult |

A ///- - -

B ////- - -

C /-/-/-

D ☐

E ☐

F ///- - -

Frequency

Time

46-6 Acquisition of bird song in birds such as the chaffinch. Each column of traces under **Acquisition** and **Adult** represents a schematized sound spectrogram of the nature of the song the bird was exposed to (acquisition period) or the nature of the

song the bird sang as an adult. The abscissa indicates time, the ordinate frequency. (For example, the song illustrated in part A consists of three brief notes of ascending frequency, followed by three brief notes of constant frequency.) Songs are acquired during initial exposure in the first few months of life (acquisition period). During the "practice" period parts of the acquired song are sung, but the full song does not appear until the bird is an adult. The figure shows 6 types of experiments in which birds were exposed to different song patterns or no song (**rectangle**) during the acquisition phase. The role of auditory feedback during the practice phase was studied by deafening the birds in some experiments (**crossed out ear**). **A** and **B.** The normal adult sings a song that is similar to the one heard during the early acquisition phase. **C.** However, there are constraints on exactly what can be learned. When exposed to an "unusual" song (i.e., very different from what is commonly heard in the wild), the adult song does not bear a close resemblance to that originally heard. **D.** Birds that do not hear any song during the acquisition phase nevertheless develop a song that is somewhat similar to the normal pattern (shown in A and B). **E.** However, if the birds cannot hear themselves during the practice period, the song is highly abnormal. **F.** If birds hear a normal pattern during acquisition but cannot hear themselves during practice, then their song is close to normal. Experiment D suggests that, even if not exposed to an appropriate song during acquisition, the bird can in effect, teach himself the appropriate song if he has feedback telling him how he sounds. Thus the bird has a built-in template that "tells" him how the song should sound. As shown in experiments A, B, and C, the built-in template can be modified, within limits, by experience.

songs that deviate too far from their "normal" song—the song commonly encountered in the wild.

These observations illustrate the fact that *biological constraints* set limits on the degree and nature of the effects the environment can produce. In recent years there has been a growing appreciation of the fact that the operation of biological constraints not only applies to the learning of bird song, but also functions importantly for all learning, including complex human learning.

Selected Readings and References

Eibl-Eibesfeldt, I. 1970. Ethology, The Biology of Behavior. New York: Holt, Rinehart and Winston.

Fieve, R. R., Rosenthal, D., and Brill, H. (eds.). 1975. Genetic Research in Psychiatry. Baltimore: Johns Hopkins University Press.

Hirsch, J. (ed.). 1967. Behavior–Genetic Analysis. New York: McGraw-Hill.

Manning, A. 1972. An Introduction to Animal Behavior. 2nd ed. Reading, Mass.: Addison-Wesley.

Kupfermann, I., and Weiss, K. R. 1978. The command neuron concept. Behav. Brain Sci. 1:3–39.

Other References

Ahrens, R. 1954. Beitrag zur Entwicklung des Physiognomie-und Mimikerkennens. Z. Exp. Angew. Psychol. 2:412–454, 599–633.

Chomsky, N. 1957. Syntactic Structures. The Hague: Mouton.

Darwin, C. 1872. The Expression of the Emotions in Man and Animals. London: Murray.

Doty, R. W., and Bosma, J. F. 1956. An electromyographic analysis of reflex deglutition. J. Neurophysiol. 19:44–60.

Freud, S. 1940. An Outline of Psychoanalysis. Trans. by J. Strachey. New York: Norton, 1949.

Kety, S. S., Rosenthal, D., Wender, P. H., and Schulsinger, F. 1968. The types and prevalence of mental illness in the biological and adoptive families of adopted schizophrenics. In D. Rosenthal and S. S. Kety (eds.), The Transmission of Schizophrenia. Oxford: Pergamon, pp. 345–362.

Konishi, M. 1965. The role of auditory feedback in the control of vocalization in the white-crowned sparrow. Z. Tierpsychol. 22:770–783.

Lorenz, K. Z. 1950. The comparative method in studying innate behaviour patterns. Symp. Soc. Exp. Biol. 4:221–268.

Marler, P., and Hamilton, W. J. III. 1966. Mechanisms of Animal Behavior. New York: Wiley.

McDougall, W. 1908. An Introduction to Social Psychology. London: Morrison & Gibb. Reprinted London: Methuen, 1960, and New York: Barnes & Noble, 1960.

Sackett, G. P. 1966. Monkeys reared in isolation with pictures as visual input: Evidence for an innate releasing mechanism. Science (Wash., D.C.) 154: 1468–1473.

Sherrington, C. 1947. The Integrative Action of the Nervous System. 2nd ed. New Haven: Yale University Press.

Thorpe, W. H. 1956. Learning and Instinct in Animals. Cambridge, Mass.: Harvard University Press.

Tinbergen, N. 1951. The Study of Instinct. Oxford: Clarendon Press.

Watson, J. B. 1930. Behaviorism. Rev. ed. New York: Norton.

Wiersma, C. A. G. 1938. Function of the giant fibers of the central nervous system of the crayfish. Proc. Soc. Exp. Biol. Med. 38:661–662.

Irving Kupfermann

Learning

47

The Most Elementary Forms of Learning Are Nonassociative

The Two Main Forms of Associative Learning Are Operant and Classical Conditioning

Classical Conditioning Involves Associating a Conditional and an Unconditional Stimulus

Operant Conditioning Involves Associating a Response with a Stimulus

Other Types of Learning Also Are Governed by Principles of Operant and Classical Conditioning

Biological Constraints Help Determine the Efficacy of Reinforcers

The Neural Basis of Learning and Memory Can Be Summarized in Four Principles

Memory Has Stages

Long-Term Memory Is Represented by Physical Changes in the Brain

Memory Traces Are Widely Distributed

The Hippocampus and the Temporal Lobes Are Particularly Important for Human Memory

Selected Readings and References

Other References

In the previous chapter, we considered behavior as the outcome of an interaction between inborn and environmental factors. The environmental factor most important in shaping behavior in humans is learning. Consequently, the study of learning is central to the understanding of both normal and abnormal behavior. Learning is thought to contribute to the genesis of certain mental and somatic diseases. Conversely, the principles of learning obtained from laboratory studies are used in the treatment of patients with these diseases. Finally, behavioral techniques based on learning are now used widely in neurobiological and clinical research to assess the effects of brain lesions and drugs.

In order to understand the neuronal basis of learning it is first necessary to understand learning as a behavioral process. There is a large literature on behavioral studies of learning, but, fortunately, much of this literature can be reduced to a few basic principles. We shall introduce these principles and then examine the neural basis of learning and memory.

In its most general sense, *learning* is a process whereby animals and humans modify their behavior as a result of experience. In contrast, *memory* is the process whereby the learned information is stored and read out.

There are two general types of learning: associative and nonassociative. All forms of *associative learning* involve the formation of an association between a stimulus and a response, or between two stimuli. *Nonassociative learning* is a somewhat simpler form of learning that does not involve the obvious formation of an association between a stimulus and a response.

The Most Elementary Forms of Learning Are Nonassociative

The most ubiquitous forms of learning are nonassociative and include habituation and sensitization. *Habituation*, first systematically studied by the Russian biologist Ivan Pavlov, is the decrease in a behavioral reflex response to a stimulus when the stimulus is repeated and has no noxious effects. An example of habituation is the failure of a person to show a startle response to a loud noise that has been regularly presented. Another type of nonassociative learning is *pseudoconditioning* or *sensitization*. In this type there is an increased reflex response to a stimulus that follows an intense or noxious stimulus. For example, a small withdrawal response produced by a weak noxious tactile stimulus can be considerably enhanced if it occurs after an intense and painful pinch. Sensitization occurs whether or not the intense stimulus is presented close in time to the weaker stimulus; no association between the two stimuli is needed. There are many types of more complex learning in which there is no obvious associational element but in which hidden forms of association may be present. These include sensory learning, in which a continuous record of sensory experience is formed, and imitation learning, which includes aspects of the acquisition of language.

The Two Main Forms of Associative Learning Are Operant and Classical Conditioning

There are numerous types of associative learning, but only two have been extensively utilized clinically: classical and operant conditioning. Classical conditioning was introduced into behavioral science by Pavlov at the turn of the century when he recognized that learning frequently consists of the acquisition of responsiveness to a stimulus that originally was ineffective.

Classical Conditioning Involves Associating a Conditional and an Unconditional Stimulus

The essence of *classical conditioning* is the pairing (or association) of a *conditional stimulus* (also called conditioned stimulus or CS), such as a light, with an *unconditional stimulus* (also called unconditioned stimulus, UCS, or reinforcement), such as a shock to a leg or food on the tongue. The stimulus to be conditioned originally produces no response or small responses unrelated to the response eventually learned. On the other hand, the unconditional stimulus reliably produces an overt response, the *unconditioned response.* When the conditional stimulus is repeatedly followed by the unconditional stimulus, the conditional stimulus comes to elicit responses *(conditioned responses)* that resemble the unconditioned responses. It is as if the conditional stimulus becomes an anticipatory signal for the occurrence of the unconditional stimulus, and the animal responds as if anticipating the occurrence of the unconditional stimulus. Thus classical conditioning can be thought of as a process in which the animal learns that one stimulus predicts the occurrence of another. For example, if a light is followed by the presentation of meat, the animal will, after a number of pairing trials, treat the light as if it were meat, and the light itself will produce salivation. Actually, the conditioned response is not precisely identical to the unconditioned response, but the similarities of the two responses are great enough that it is useful to think of conditioning as a process whereby the subject learns to react to the conditional stimulus as if it were a substitute for the unconditional stimulus. Depending upon whether the unconditional stimulus is rewarding (food, water) or punitive (shock, acid), classical conditioning is further subdivided into *appetitive conditioning*, in which the unconditional stimulus is rewarding, and *defensive conditioning*, in which the unconditional stimulus is noxious or punitive.

The discovery of classical conditioning represented for Pavlov not only a means of studying learning, but also a means of approaching the objective study of the mind—the inner workings of the brain. He appreciated the fact that if one can train animals to make differential responses to stimuli, one has a means of communicating with the animal. For example, one way of asking a dog whether it can see colors is to determine if lights of different colors can be used as discriminative stimuli for classical conditioning. During *discriminative training*, one stimulus (CS$^+$) is presented in association with reinforcement on some trials. On other trials, another stimulus (CS$^-$) is presented but is never followed by reinforcement. If the CS$^+$ and CS$^-$ are similar in certain respects, the animal will initially exhibit generalization, that is, it will show conditioned responses to both the reinforced and nonreinforced stimuli. If the animal can discriminate between the stimuli, then after continued training it will show conditioned responses primarily or exclusively to the CS$^+$ and not to the CS$^-$. By appropriately manipulating the hue and intensity of visual stimuli one can determine whether the animal is responding to color rather than to differences in brightness. By this means we can determine quite precisely the perceptual capabilities of an animal.

An important principle of conditioning is that the conditioned response decreases in intensity or probability of occurrence if, after a conditioned response has been established, the conditional stimulus is repeatedly presented without the unconditional stimulus. This process is known as *extinction*, a form of forgetting. Thus, a light that has been paired with a food unconditional stimulus will gradually cease to evoke salivation if the light is repeatedly shown in the absence of food. Extinction is just as important as conditioning itself, since continuing to respond to cues that no longer have significance is nonadaptive. The available evidence indicates that extinction is due to an active inhibitory process that suppresses the conditioned response.

The process of extinction may underlie the therapeutic changes resulting from a clinical technique known as *systematic desensitization* (although other interpretations of this method have been offered). Systematic desensitization was introduced into psychiatry by Joseph Wolpe, a South African physician who used it to decrease neurotic anxiety or phobias that are evoked by certain definable environmental situations, for example, fear of heights, crowds, or public speaking. The patient is first taught a technique of muscular relaxation. Then, over a period of days, the patient is told to imagine a series of progressively more severe anxiety-provoking situations, while using relaxation to inhibit any anxiety that might be elicited. At the end of the series, the strongest potentially anxiety-provoking situations can be brought to mind without concomi-

tant anxiety. This desensitization, induced in the therapeutic situation, often generalizes to real-life situations that the patient subsequently encounters.

Operant Conditioning Involves Associating a Response with a Stimulus

A second major paradigm of associational learning, introduced by Edward Thorndike of Columbia University, is *operant conditioning* (sometimes called *instrumental conditioning*, or *trial-and-error learning*). A typical laboratory example of operant conditioning can be illustrated by placing a hungry rat in a test chamber with a lever protruding from one wall. Because of previous learning as well as innate response tendencies and random activity, the rat will occasionally press the lever. If when the rat presses the lever it promptly receives food, its subsequent rate of lever pressing will increase above the spontaneous rate. Intuitively one can describe the animal as having learned that a certain response (lever pressing) among the many it has emitted (e.g., grooming, rearing, and walking) is rewarded with food. Armed with this information, whenever the rat is hungry and finds itself in the same chamber, it is likely to make the appropriate responses.

If we think of classical conditioning as the formation of an association between two stimuli (the conditional stimulus and the unconditional stimulus), operant conditioning consists of the formation of an association between a response and a stimulus. Unlike classical conditioning, which is restricted to specific reflex responses that are evoked by specific, identifiable stimuli, operant conditioning involves behaviors (called *operants*) that apparently occur spontaneously, or with no recognizable eliciting stimuli. Thus, operant behaviors are said to be emitted rather than elicited, and when such behaviors produce favorable changes in the environment (that is, when they either are rewarded, or result in the removal of noxious stimuli) they tend to increase in probability of occurrence (that is, the animal repeats them). This process is known technically as *reinforcement;* this term refers to the more general observation that those behaviors that are rewarded tend to be repeated at the expense of behaviors that are not, while behaviors followed by aversive, though not necessarily painful consequences *(punishment)* are generally not repeated. Experimental psychologists agree that this simple notion probably reflects an important principle (the *law of effect*) that governs much voluntary behavior.

Superficially, operant and classical conditioning appear to be dissimilar, involving completely different arrangements of stimuli and responses. However, the laws that govern operant conditioning and those that govern classical conditioning are remarkably similar, suggesting that the two forms of learning may be manifestations of a common underlying neural mechanism. For example, in operant conditioning, as in classical conditioning, timing is critical: typically, the reinforcer must follow the operant response closely. If the reinforcer in operant conditioning is delayed, only weak conditioning occurs. Similarly, in classical conditioning, there is generally poor learning when there is a long delay between the conditional stimulus and the unconditional stimulus.

Operant conditioning exhibits stimulus discrimination, as does classical conditioning. If reinforcement is presented in the presence of one stimulus (called S^+) but not in the presence of another (S^-), the animal gradually stops responding in the presence of the nonreinforced stimulus. In addition, operantly conditioned responses exhibit extinction just as do classically conditioned responses. If reinforcement is not given when the animal responds, the probability of a response decreases and the animal eventually ceases to respond.

A major principle to emerge from studies of the extinction of operant responses is that the rate of extinction is slowed when subjects have been maintained on a schedule of *partial reinforcement* rather than on a continuous reinforcement schedule. A partial reinforcement schedule is one in which the animal is not reinforced for every response but only for certain responses, as determined by some pattern or schedule. For example, on a *fixed ratio schedule*, the rat in the test chamber, or a worker in a factory, is rewarded only after a specific number of responses have been emitted. Reinforcing this type of piecemeal work can produce very high rates of responding. Gambling behavior provides a nice example of how occasional reinforcement (in this case, on a *variable ratio schedule*) can powerfully maintain behavior in some people, even when there are very long periods of nonreinforced responses. On an *interval schedule* the subject is reinforced only after a certain time has elapsed since the prior reinforcement. A weekly salary can be thought of as a form of interval schedule. One

reasonable interpretation of why extinction is delayed after exposure to partial reinforcement is that the organism learns that even a long absence of reinforcement for any given response does not mean that later responses will not be reinforced.

Operant conditioning is not limited to the skeletomotor system. Neal Miller and others have shown that autonomically mediated responses such as changes in blood pressure and heart rate also can be modified by appropriate reinforcers. On the basis of these findings, operant conditioning techniques have been used in an attempt to modify high blood pressure, cardiac arrythmias, and other pathological conditions involving the autonomic nervous system.

Principles of operant conditioning have sometimes also been applied to the management of psychiatric disorders. One important therapeutic application is the management of severely disturbed institutionalized patients with behavioral problems, such as the shouting of obscenities, messiness, poor hygienic habits, etc. The positive, constructive behavior whose frequency should be increased is first precisely defined. Then an effective reinforcement is found (compliments, privileges, money, or food). Finally, nurses and orderlies are trained to provide reinforcements when the desired behavior is emitted by the patient. In some cases it has proved convenient to use tokens as reinforcers. The tokens are accumulated by the patients and can then be used to obtain privileges or desired objects. In other instances simple praise or attention can serve as an effective reinforcement if it is used consistently after the desired behavior and is not inadvertently given when undesirable behavior occurs.

Other Types of Learning Also Are Governed by Principles of Operant and Classical Conditioning

In addition to classical and operant conditioning there are other more complex types of learning. Although these higher forms of learning differ in detail from the simpler types we have considered, there is reason to believe that the broad principles of learning apply to many types of learning. At the same time, however, knowledge of the details of the specific learning tasks and of the capabilities of the individuals involved can make the difference between successful and unsuccessful application of learning principles to specific species of animals or to individual clinical cases. For example, not all reinforcers are equally effective with all responses. This principle is dramatically illustrated in studies of *food aversion,* also called *bait shyness,* as it apparently is the means by which animal pests such as rats and mice learn to avoid poisoned bait foods. If a distinctive taste stimulus, such as vanilla, is followed by nausea produced by a poison, an animal will develop a powerful aversion to that specific taste very quickly. Unlike most other forms of conditioning, food aversion develops even when the unconditional stimulus (poison) occurs with a long delay (up to hours) after the conditional stimulus (specific taste).

The food aversion paradigm has been applied in the treatment of chronic alcoholism. The patient is given alcoholic beverages to smell and taste, followed by a powerful emetic such as apomorphine. The pairing of alcohol and nausea rapidly results in aversion to the taste of alcohol. Food aversion learning has several other important implications in medicine. First of all, it may be a means by which people with an undiagnosed disease (e.g., Addison's disease) unintentionally become conditioned to avoid diets that are deficient in critical nutrients (e.g., salt) and which produce a chronic state of malaise. In addition, recent evidence indicates that the malaise associated with certain forms of cancer may induce food aversion conditioning to items in the ordinary diet of the patient. This in part, might account for depressed appetite in cancer patients. Furthermore, the nausea that follows chemotherapy for cancer can produce aversion to foods that were tasted before the treatment.

Biological Constraints Help Determine the Efficacy of Reinforcers

For most species, including man, food aversion conditioning is restricted to *taste stimuli* associated with subsequent *illness.* Food aversion develops poorly, or not all, if the salient taste is followed by a painful stimulus. Conversely, if a visual stimulus, instead of a taste stimulus, is paired with the nausea, an animal also does not develop aversion to that visual stimulus. Pairing of a shape with a painful stimulus, however, does result in that stimulus rapidly acquiring aversive or fear-producing properties but not nausea. Thus, the choice of an appropriate reinforcer is dependent upon the nature of the response to be learned; the choice is limited by and sometimes determined by biological constraints on learning. Evolutionary pressures have predisposed the brains of different species of animals to learn the association between certain stimuli (or between a certain stimulus and a response) much more readily than between other stimuli. Within a given species, genetic and experiential factors also can modify the effectiveness of a reinforcer. Thus, the results obtained with a particular class of reinforcer may vary enormously from species to species and from individual to individual within a species, particularly in humans.

The Neural Basis of Learning and Memory Can Be Summarized in Four Principles

Although the literature on the neurobiology of learning is extensive, much of what is known can be summarized in just four principles: (1) memory has stages and is continually changing; (2) long-term memory is represented by physical changes in the brain; (3) memory traces are widely distributed throughout the nervous system; and (4) the hippocampus and temporal lobes appear to have unique functions in the human memory process. We shall consider information obtained by gross techniques, such as ablation, electrical stimulation, and drugs. Studies of cellular mechanisms of learning will be considered in Chapter 52.

Memory Has Stages

Probably the oldest observation in the biology of memory was made by an anonymous observer many thousands of years ago who noted that he had selective amnesia for recent events after being knocked unconscious. This phenomenon was subsequently thoroughly documented in studies on animals, utilizing a variety of traumatic agents including electroconvulsive shock, physical trauma to the brain, and drugs that depress neuronal activity or inhibit protein synthesis in the brain. Clinical studies also indicate that brain trauma can produce a retrograde amnesia (forgetting of previously learned associations) that is particularly prominent for recent events— typically within a few days of the trauma. Thus, recently acquired memories are readily disrupted, whereas older memories are quite resistant to disturbance. Once something has been learned, the span of time during which memory is labile varies—from several seconds to several years— depending upon the nature of the task, the strength of the learning, and the species of animal.

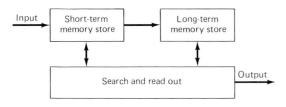

47–1 Model of memory storage system.

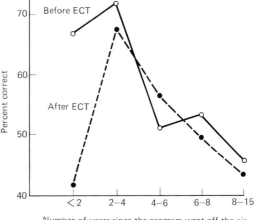

Number of years since the program went off the air

47–2 Data showing that recent memories are more susceptible to disruption than older memories. Patients were tested on their ability to recognize correctly the name of television programs that were on the air for one year between 1957 and 1972. Testing was done before and after the patients received electroconvulsive shock therapy (ECT) for treatment of depression. After the shock, the patients showed a significant (but transitory) loss of memory for recent programs (1 or 2 years old) but not for old programs. (Adapted from Squire et al., 1975.)

The studies of memory disruption have contributed to a commonly used model of the memory storage system (Figure 47–1). Input to the brain is processed into a short-term memory store. This information is later transformed by some process into a more permanent long-term store. To complete the model, a system has been added that functions to search the memory store and to read out the information as demanded by specific tasks. In this model, interference with the retention of previous experience can occur either by partially destroying the contents of a memory store or by disrupting the search and read-out mechanism. In traumatic amnesia at least part of the disruption must be due to a disturbance of the search and read-out mechanism. This conclusion stems from the observation that, after trauma, some memory for once forgotten events gradually returns. If the stored memory had been completely destroyed, there would be no way for the memory to be recovered.

Observation of patients undergoing a series of shocks for the treatment of depression have confirmed and extended experiments originally made on lower animals. Larry Squire and his associates at the University of California Veterans Hospital employed a memory test that could reliably quantify the degree of memory for relatively recent events (1–2 years old), old events (3–9 years old), and very old events (9–16 years old). They required subjects to identify various television programs that were broadcast for a single year between 1957 and 1972. The patients were initially tested and then tested again (with a different set of television programs) after the electroconvulsive shock therapy. The results of this experiment are shown in Figure 47–2. Both before shock therapy and after shock therapy, correct memory of the programs steadily decreased with the time since the memory was first formed. This is a reflection of the all too familiar process of forgetting. After the shock therapy, the patients showed a significant but transitory memory loss

for programs that had gone off the air 1 or 2 years previously, but not for the older programs.

One interpretation of observations such as these is that the read-out of relatively recent memories is easily disrupted until they have been converted into a long-term memory form. Once converted, they are relatively stable, but with time there is a gradual loss of the stored information or a diminished capacity to retrieve the information even without external trauma. Thus the memory process, at least as assessed by susceptibility to disruption, is *always undergoing continual change with time.*

Several experiments on the effects of drugs on learning support the idea that the memory process is time-dependent and is subject to modification when the memory is first formed. James McGaugh and associates at the University of California at Irvine have shown that subconvulsant doses of excitant drugs such as strychnine can improve the retention of learning even when the drug is administered after the training trials. If the drug is given to the animal soon after training it facilitates retention that is tested the next day. If, however, the drug is given several hours after training, it has no effect.

Long-Term Memory Is Represented by Physical Changes in the Brain

How is information stored? Short-term memory could be mediated by a variety of short-term neural plastic events that we considered in Chapter 8, such as posttetanic potentiation or presynaptic inhibition. One type of very brief short-term memory (iconic memory) for visual events is probably due to brief visual retinal afterimages after exposure to visual stimuli. Thus, if a person is allowed to view briefly a matrix of many letters and numbers, he can accurately recall specific elements of the matrix; but, unlike most forms of learning, accuracy of recall diminishes extremely rapidly, typically in less than 1 sec. The time before accuracy diminishes can be extended by increasing the brightness of the visual stimulus, and the time course for the decline of accuracy parallels the decay of the visual afterimages. Visual afterimages are due, at least in part, to photochemical processes in the retina. Thus, one very simple form of short-term learning appears to be encoded by a transient physical change in the peripheral receptors.

Another possible mechanism for encoding short-term memory is that the information is stored in the form of ongoing neural activity that is maintained by excitatory feedback connections between neurons (Figure 47–3). This type of activity could reverberate within the closed loop of neurons and might maintain activity for some period of time. The mechanism is interesting because it does not involve any long-duration physical changes in nerve cells. The memory for the event is maintained by the ongoing neuronal activity. There are few experiments to support this notion, and it seems unlikely that this will prove to be a common mechanism for memory.

47–3 A reverberating circuit might be used to encode short-term memory. Brief excitatory input can produce long-lasting neural activity because of the circulation of spikes among neurons that excite one another.

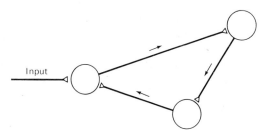

An intriguing and central problem in the study of the neural basis of learning is the nature of long-term changes—those changes that can be maintained for 10 or more years. Two possibilities exist. First, but not likely, is the possibility that reverberating circuits like those postulated to underlie short-term memory may persist and represent long-term memory as well. The second possiblity is that long-term memory is related to some permanent functional or structural change in the brain. A simple experiment can distinguish between these alternatives. If all neuronal activity is temporarily stopped, memories represented by the dynamic mechanism (reverberating circuits) should be permanently abolished. Neuronal activity can be silenced by the use of deep anesthesia, anoxia, or cooling of the brain. When this is done, short-term or recent memories are disrupted, but older memories are not. Thus, at least for older memories, it is safe to conclude that they are not mediated by reverberatory activity but, more likely, involve a physical change in the brain. Because of the enduring nature of memory, it seems reasonable to postulate that in some way the changes must be reflected in long-term alterations of the connections between neurons. We shall consider this question again in Chapter 52.

Memory Traces are Widely Distributed

Whatever the nature of the memory traces, it seems clear that they are not localized to any one brain structure. Pavlov, the father of physiological studies of learning, believed that the learning process was limited to the neocortex. The American psychologist Karl Lashley, at Harvard, spent most of his scientific career making lesions in the cortex to define precisely where the representation of learning (the *engram*) was located. He never succeeded. Lashley and others found that although cortical lesions can seriously disrupt learning, animals can relearn certain tasks even when completely decorticated. Furthermore, as first shown by P. S. Shurrager and E. Culler in 1940, classical conditioning of certain simple reflexes can be mediated by the spinal cord even after it has been completely isolated surgically from the brain. Thus, all parts of the nervous system appear to have the types of plastic properties needed for memory storage. We know that even for a simple learning task many channels of information are used, and that there is ample opportunity for the storage of redundant information throughout the brain.

Although simple redundancy may explain in part why a given limited lesion does not eliminate specific learning, a more important factor may reside in the very nature of the learning process. Two now outdated notions of learning provided the theoretical background of early efforts to locate the engram. One notion was that learning consists of the strengthening of simple connections between sensory and motor areas of the brain. A lesion of the appropriate sensory or motor area or of the connection between the two should eliminate the learning. A second notion of learning was that it consists of the laying down of a series of traces that provide a faithful record of sensory experience. Surgical removal of the trace should obliterate specific memories. Behavioral studies have shown that learning involves neither the simple formation of stimulus–response bonds, nor a faithful reproduction of sensory experience; rather, *it appears that learning consists of the accumulation of bits and pieces of information, which the brain can then utilize to reconstruct the past and thereby guide behavior appropriately.*

The following experiment illustrates the limitations of a simple stimulus–response interpretation of learning. A subject lays his hand, palm down, on an electrical grill; a light (conditional stimulus) is turned on and he is immediately shocked on a finger. His finger will withdraw (unconditioned response), and after several light–shock conditioning trials, he will withdraw his finger when the light alone is presented. He has been conditioned; but what exactly has been conditioned? It looks as if the light is triggering a specific pattern of muscle activity that results in withdrawal. However, what if he now places his hand on the grill upside down, and the light is presented? If a specific pattern of muscle activity is conditioned, the light should produce a response that moves the finger *into* the grill. On the other hand, if he has acquired the information that light means grill shock, he may make a variety of responses appropriate to that information. In fact, when this experiment was done, the subject moved his finger away from the grill; i.e., he made an adaptive response, even though it involved motor movements antagonistic to the ones originally made. Therefore, the original learning did not consist of the rote learning of a specific response to a specific stimulus, but rather learning consisted of the acquisition of information that the brain could use to solve problems.

Many experiments indicate that the accumu-

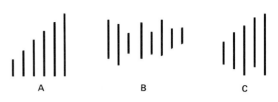

47–4 Role of conceptual ability in memory read-out. **A.** Original pattern of sticks presented to young children. **B.** Typical drawing of children asked to show what they had just seen. **C.** Drawing showing improved memory when children were tested 6 months later. (Adapted from Piaget and Inhelder, 1969.)

lation of knowledge about past events is an active process. First of all, what goes into the memory store is a representation of information that has been distorted as a result of processing by our perceptual apparatus. Optical illusions illustrate that we do not remember an objective version of reality, but rather a highly modified version that is altered on the basis of past experience and principles of perceptual analysis. Once the information is stored, what comes out of the memory store—what we recall—also involves a reconstruction rather than a faithful reproduction of the internal store.

An excellent example of how learning and memory need not be a simple read-out or copy of experience is provided by the work of Piaget and Inhelder, who studied memory in a group of preschool-age children. The children were presented with a series of sticks graded in size (Figure 47–4A). The investigators then asked the children to describe what they saw or to draw what they remembered. Some of the children drew sticks, but the sticks were not ordered in size (Figure 47–4B). In fact, the children had not yet developed the conceptual capacity to arrange objects according to size. Six months later, the same children were again asked to recall what had been presented. Astonishingly, some of the children reproduced the sticks more accurately and ordered them according to size (Figure 47–4C). Had memory storage improved? Probably not. What had happened is that the children had matured to the point where they now had mastered the concept of ordering, and thus could utilize this conceptual framework in recalling information that they had previously stored. Here again we see the brain utilizing numerous bits and pieces of stored information to provide a coherent and meaningful memory of a past event. As with finger conditioning, learning about the sticks was not due to the simple formation of a bond between a stimulus and a response.

A final example illustrating the nature of memory is provided by studies that analyzed the content of the memories of previously learned stories. The recalled versions were shorter, more coherent, and had substitutions not present in the original. The subjects were unaware of where they were substituting and often the substituted part of the story was felt to be the most certain. The subjects were not confabulating; they were merely recalling in a way that made sense out of the original material. Recall of past experience may involve a reconstruction process in which past experiences are utilized as clues to help the brain reconstruct, in the present, a past event of significance. The brain uses inferences, shrewd guesses, and suppositions to generate a consistent and coherent picture.

These examples of the nature of learning make it clear why the naive attempt to remove the engram surgically, failed. While the physical changes representing learning are likely to be localized to specific neurons, the complex nature of learning ensures that these neurons are widely distributed in the nervous system. Therefore, even after extensive lesions, some trace often remains. Furthermore, the brain has the capacity to take the remaining limited information, work it over, and reconstruct a relatively good reproduction of the original.

The Hippocampus and the Temporal Lobes Are Particularly Important for Human Memory

Despite the diffuse representation of memory in the central nervous system, certain lesions produce greater effects on memory than do others. In humans, lesions of the temporal lobes and closely associated structures produce the most dramatic effects on learning. Damage to the temporal lobes does not destroy specific prior memories, but rather interferes with the acquisition of new ones. Thus, these structures are not registers or banks for memory storage, but are somehow involved in the process in which memories are placed into storage or are removed and read out from storage. A clue that the temporal lobes are important for memory came from the observations of the neurosurgeon Wilder Penfield at the Montreal Neurological Institute. In the course of temporal lobe surgery for the control of epilepsy, Penfield electrically stimulated the exposed tem-

poral lobes in fully conscious patients. The patients reported vividly experiencing past events. For example, stimulation of one point on the temporal lobe caused a patient to hear a specific melody that she felt she had heard in the past. Repeated stimulation of the same point evoked successive experiences of hearing that same melody.

Additional evidence for a role of the temporal lobes in memory has come from the study of a few epileptic patients who underwent bilateral removal of the hippocampus and associated structures in the temporal lobes. Brenda Milner at the Montreal Neurological Institute found that these patients exhibited a profound and irreversible deficit of recent memory. They virtually lost the capacity to form new long-term memories, but previously acquired long-term memories remained intact. For example, they remembered their names and how to talk. Short-term memory was also unaffected; but the transition from short-term to long-term memory was virtually absent for most types of learning. If the patient was told to remember the number 7, he could repeat the number immediately upon being asked. If, however, the patient was distracted, even briefly, he had no recollection of the number. The extent of the deficit is indicated by the observation that one patient failed to recognize individuals even after years of contact. Curiously, despite the deficits in verbal memory, these patients could learn motor tasks.

An amnestic syndrome similar to that seen in patients with bilateral removal of the temporal lobe structures can also be seen in patients suffering from Korsakoff's psychosis. This disease, which results from chronic alcoholism and its nutritional deficiency, is characterized by confusion and severe deficit of recent memory. Careful study of the precise nature of the deficit in amnestic subjects has revealed that at least part of the problem may arise from an inability of these patients to suppress interfering memories of previously learned material. Elizabeth Warrington and Lawrence Weiskrantz at Cambridge University in England have found that these individuals show remarkably better memory if the task is structured so as to minimize interference from older learning. One way to accomplish this is to use prompts or partial cues during the tests for recall. Thus, these patients, and perhaps patients with temporal lobe lesions, may not have a primary deficit in memory storage, but rather in memory retrieval. Efforts to simulate this memory deficit in animals by producing hippocampal lesions have been disappointing. The most promising analogous deficit is that produced in primates by a combined lesion of the hippocampus and amygdala.

Electrophysiological studies of the hippocampus (and several other brain regions) during the acquisition and retention of learned tasks have revealed correlations between performance and the activity of single cells. For example, Theodore Berger and Richard Thompson at the University of California at Irvine have found a remarkably high correlation between unit activity of hippocampal pyramidal cells and a classically conditioned eye-blink response in the rabbit. It is not known whether these correlations represent plastic changes occurring at the site of the recording electrodes or reflect altered neural activity at distant sites presynaptic to the recorded cells.

A major task confronting workers interested in the neurobiology of learning is to determine whether, and in what way, reported alterations in the brain are causally related to behavioral changes. A second task is to determine the mechanisms underlying the relevant plastic changes. To this end, a number of simplified vertebrate and invertebrate animal preparations are being investigated and some of the information deriving from these studies is reviewed in Chapter 52.

Selected Readings and References

Hilgard, E. R., and Bower, G. H. 1975. Theories of Learning. 4th ed. Englewood Cliffs N.J.: Prentice-Hall.

Kanfer, F. H., and Phillips, J. S. 1970. Learning Foundations of Behavior Therapy. New York: Wiley.

Lashley, K. S. 1950. In search of the engram. Symp. Soc. Exp. Biol. 4:454–482.

Yates, A. J. 1970. Behavior Therapy. New York: Wiley.

Other References

Berger, T. W., and Thompson, R. F. 1978. Identification of pyramidal cells as the critical elements in hippocampal neuronal plasticity during learning. Proc. Natl. Acad. Sci. U.S.A. 75:1572–1576.

McGaugh, J. L., and Herz, M. J. 1972. Memory Consolidation. San Francisco: Albion.

Miller, N. E. 1969. Learning of visceral and glandular responses. Science (Wash., D.C.) 163:434–445.

Milner, B. 1966. Amnesia following operation on the temporal lobes. In C. W. M. Whitty, and O. L. Zangwill (eds.), Amnesia. London: Butterworths, pp. 109–133.

Pavlov, I. P. 1927. Conditioned Reflexes: An Investigation of the Physiological Activity of the Cerebral Cortex. London: Oxford University Press.

Penfield, W. 1958. Functional localization in temporal and deep Sylvian areas. Res. Publ. Assoc. Res. Nerv. Ment. Dis. 36:210–226.

Piaget, J., and Inhelder, B. 1969. The Psychology of the Child. New York: Basic Books.

Shurrager, P. S., and Culler, E. 1940. Conditioning in the spinal dog. J. Exp. Psychol. 26:133–159.

Squire, L. R., Slater, P. C., and Chace, P. M. 1975. Retrograde amnesia: Temporal gradient in very long term memory following electroconvulsive therapy. Science (Wash., D.C.) 187:77–79.

Thorndike, E. L. 1911. Animal Intelligence. New York: Macmillan.

Warrington, E. K., and Weiskrantz, L. 1970. Amnesic syndrome: Consolidation or retrieval? Nature (Lond.) 228:628–630.

Wolpe, J. 1958. Psychotherapy by Reciprocal Inhibition. Stanford: Stanford University Press.

Irving Kupfermann

Localization of Higher Functions

48

More than a century ago two German physiologists, Franz Joseph Gall and his student, Johan Kasper Spurzheim, developed a new approach to mental function that they named *cranioscopy*; it was later renamed *phrenology*. Gall, Spurzheim, and subsequent phrenologists sought to localize specific mental functions on the basis of the size and position of specific bumps on the head. The size of the bumps were thought to reflect the development of underlying brain regions. This early attempt at cerebral localization was considered scandalous by many, not because it derived from a primitive scientific idea, but because cerebral localization implied a mechanistic view of the mind.

Phrenology failed in its aims. However, as we have seen in Chapter 1 the studies of aphasia by Paul Broca, Karl Wernicke, and other clinical neurologists supported the idea that specific higher functions are associated with specific cortical regions. For many years, these observations were ignored by both clinical and experimental neurologists in favor of the idea that the brain, and particularly the cerebral cortex, acted as a whole. In the 20th century this view was expounded most forcefully by Karl Lashley, who felt that various parts of the brain were equipotential in function, and that for many functions, virtually any part of the brain could substitute for any other part. Nevertheless, even the proponents of this antilocalization view had to admit that specific sensory and motor functions could be associated with well-defined anatomical loci. Subsequent evidence, to be considered in this chapter, indicates that even highly complex brain functions can be associated with specific brain areas. Localization does not imply, however, that any specific function is exclusively mediated by only one region of the brain. Most functions require the integrated action of neurons located in different regions of the brain. Localization of function simply means that certain regions of the brain appear to be more concerned with one set of functions than with others.

The regions of the brain we shall consider in this chapter are located in the frontal, temporal, and parietal lobes, and are termed the *association areas of the cortex*. These areas of cortex were also sometimes called *silent areas*, since they produce little or no obvious motor or sensory effects when electrically stimulated. The association cortices increase in relative size throughout phylogeny and reach their greatest extent in the

48–1 Drawing approximately to scale of the cerebral hemispheres of four mammals. Note both the increase in size and relative increase in amount of association cortex. (Adapted from Thompson, 1975.)

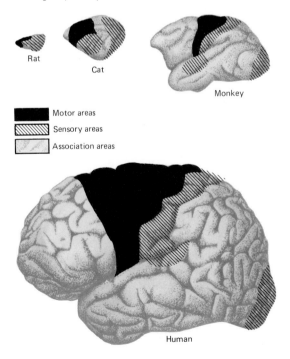

Rat

Cat

Monkey

■ Motor areas
▨ Sensory areas
▨ Association areas

Human

human brain (Figure 48–1). The association areas of the cortex were initially believed to be links between the various sensory cortices on the one hand, and between the sensory and the motor cortex on the other. As a result, the association areas were thought to be the anatomical substrate for thought and perception—higher functions that were believed to be generated by the association of different sensory events or of sensory with motor events.

Much of our knowledge concerning the localization of higher functions in the association cortex has been obtained from the study of patients who have had sustained damage to the cortex due to trauma, cerebrovascular disease, tumors, or brain surgery. Particularly instructive are the results from patients who have had tissue removed in the treatment of a variety of behavioral and neurological disorders. These patients have a relatively well-defined surgical lesion. In some instances clinical evidence has been amplified by experiments in animal studies, in which it is possible to make localized lesions and to obtain detailed electrophysiological information. In this chapter we shall consider the function of the association areas in the two cortical hemispheres. We shall give particular attention to the recent discovery that, although the human brain superficially appears to be symmetrical, it is actually not. The left and right hemispheres each have their own special talents and weaknesses.

The Prefrontal Cortex Is Thought to Be Involved in Certain Learning Tasks and in Emotional Behavior

The most extensively studied association region is the prefrontal cortex, which assumes prodigious proportions in lower primates and humans (Figure 48–2). This region is located on the lateral, medial, and inferior frontal surfaces, anterior to the agranular motor and premotor areas. Functional studies on monkeys have defined five prefrontal regions (Figure 48–3). All of these areas have afferent input from the dorsomedial nucleus of the thalamus. The anterior cingulate gyrus is often also included in the prefrontal area, even though it is innervated not by the dorsomedial but by the anterior thalamic nuclei.

Studies on monkeys suggest that various regions of the prefrontal cortex are concerned with different functions. In the 1930s Carlyle Jacobsen, working in the laboratory of John Fulton at Yale University, demonstrated that bilateral re-

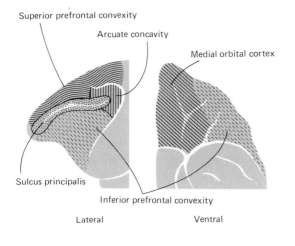

48–2 Proportion of the brain taken up by the prefrontal cortex (**shaded area**) in five species (brains not to scale). (Adapted from Warren and Akert, 1964.)

48–3 Various subregions of the prefrontal cortex in the rhesus monkey. (Adapted from Rosenkilde, 1979.)

Superior prefrontal convexity

Arcuate concavity

Medial orbital cortex

Sulcus principalis

Inferior prefrontal convexity

Lateral   Ventral

moval of the prefrontal cortex in primates results in a severe deficit in the ability to perform a task that involves delayed spatial response. In this task, a hungry monkey is shown a piece of food and, while the animal watches, the food is placed under one of two containers. After a delay of 5 sec or longer, the animal is permitted to select one of the containers. Normal animals quickly learn to select the container covering the food, whereas animals with prefrontal damage do very poorly on this task. The lesioned animals can perform well only if no delay is interposed after the experimenter covers the food. Jacobsen therefore concluded that the prefrontal region might be involved in short-term memory. This idea was supported by the finding that animals with prefrontal lesions also do poorly on a delayed spatial alternation task in which the animals must alternate right and left choices between two containers, with a delay interposed between each choice.

Subsequently it was shown that a relatively small lesion around the sulcus principalis is sufficient to produce the deficit in spatial delayed response and alternation in nonhuman primates. In fact, the deficit is specific to these tasks and is evident only if the task involves both a delay and a spatial aspect. Animals with a lesion in the sulcus principalis have no deficit on discrimination problems involving no delay or on tasks in which predelay spatial cues are not important. For example, in the apparatus illustrated in Figure 48–4, the animal could perform well on a delayed matching to sample problem in which it is shown one of several different objects and after a delay has to select that object from among several objects that are presented.

Jacobsen also found that prefrontal lesions result in an alteration of the emotional responsiveness of animals. Operated chimpanzees no longer exhibit signs of rage and anger when they fail to receive rewards in the testing situation. Subsequent research has suggested that this alteration in emotional response is not due to damage of the sulcus principalis but rather may be related to the medial orbital cortex. Damage limited to the medial orbital cortex decreases the normal aggressiveness and other emotional responsiveness of primates. Furthermore, electrical stimulation of the orbital cortex produces many autonomic responses (increases in arterial blood pressure, dilation of the pupils, salivation, and inhibition of pyloric peristalsis), suggesting that this area may be involved in a generalized arousal reaction. This interpretation is supported by the observa-

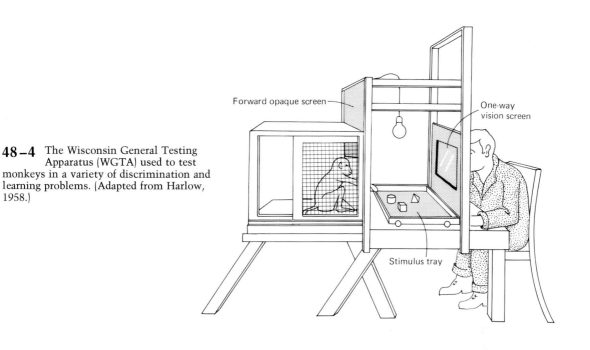

48–4 The Wisconsin General Testing Apparatus (WGTA) used to test monkeys in a variety of discrimination and learning problems. (Adapted from Harlow, 1958.)

Forward opaque screen

One-way vision screen

Stimulus tray

tion that orbital stimulation induces a generalized desynchronization (arousal response) of the cortical electroencephalogram (see Chapter 39) and an increase in plasma cortisol.

Jacobsen reported his observations of the calming effect of cortical lesions in chimpanzees at the second International Neurology Congress in London in 1935. This report inspired Egas Moniz, a Portuguese neuropsychiatrist, to suggest that destruction of the prefrontal connections in humans might serve as a treatment for severe mental illness. Moniz collaborated with a neurosurgeon, Almeida Lima, and the first prefrontal lesions were done in Lisbon only a few months after Jacobsen's report. These early attempts were soon followed by an extensive application of various procedures that involved either ablation of prefrontal areas or interruption of the fiber tracts that connect the prefrontal lobes with the thalamus or other areas of cortex. These tracts include (1) the *cingulum,* a multifiber bundle in the white matter of the cingulate gyrus that connects the frontal and parietal lobes with the parahippocampal gyrus and adjacent temporal cortex, and (2) the *thalamocortical projections* from the dorsomedial thalamic nucleus.

The early results of prefrontal lobotomy appeared favorable. Many patients seemed to show a reduction in anxiety. The later, more controlled studies failed to confirm this finding. Further-

more, prefrontal lobotomy was associated with a high incidence of complications, including the development of epilepsy and abnormal personality changes such as a lack of inhibition on the one hand and a lack of initiative and drive on the other. However, intellectual capability as measured on conventional tests of intelligence was little affected by these operations even though large lesions were often made. This came as a surprise since it was believed that the huge frontal lobes in humans must in some way be related to higher mental function, such as abstract thought and reasoning.

After several well-controlled evaluative studies failed to show benefits from psychosurgery, the use of this operation went into decline in the 1950s. In recent years there has been a resurgence of interest in modified forms of psychosurgery based on attempts to make highly localized lesions that might reduce anxiety without producing unfavorable side effects. Several studies suggest that a small lesion limited to the cingulum produces favorable results. Despite the high percentage of the patients who show improvement, it is not yet possible to conclude that the improvement is due to the surgery rather than to a placebo effect or to spontaneous recovery. In drug studies it is often possible to use the patient as his own control by administering the drug and then withdrawing it; but the effects of brain surgery are irreversible. These studies therefore require a matched sample of untreated control patients, and this requirement is rarely fulfilled.

As pointed out in Chapter 37, lesions in this region of the cortex also appear to reduce the suffering associated with chronic, intractable pain. Thus, the association areas of the frontal lobes seem to be involved in the production of anxiety. In this role, frontal areas of the brain may contribute to the capacity of animals to weigh the consequences of possible future actions and to plan accordingly.

The Association Areas of the Temporal Lobe May Be Concerned with Memory Functions

In addition to limbic structures, the primary auditory projection area (Brodmann's area 41), and the regions associated with language (in the human brain, the posterior region of area 22), the temporal lobe contains large areas of association cortex. The superior temporal association regions are related to the auditory system, whereas the middle and inferior temporal areas are related to visual function.

Lesions of the inferior temporal region in monkeys result in deficits in the rate of learning of visual tasks. The deficits, which are not due to blindness, are most dramatic when the visual task is complex. For example, inferotemporal lesions interfere with the ability of an animal to improve performance progressively (learning set) when a long series of related visual problems is presented. In addition to interfering with the acquisition of a learned visual task, inferotemporal lesions interfere with the retention or memory of visual tasks. Lesions of the superior temporal cortex of animals result in deficits in the learning of auditory patterns without producing deafness.

As mentioned in Chapter 47, major insights into the functions of the human temporal lobes have come from the work of the neurosurgeon Wilder Penfield. Penfield stimulated various points on the temporal lobe electrically in awake patients prior to the removal of diseased epileptic tissue. As expected, stimulation of the primary auditory areas produced crude auditory sensations. In contrast, stimulation of the superior temporal gyrus produced alterations in the perception of sounds, including auditory illusions and hallucinations. The hallucinations had a rather startling feature. The patients reported that the experience was re-

markably real, almost as if they were re-experiencing a past event. The evocation of complex experiential phenomena after stimulation of the temporal lobes occurs only in patients with epilepsy in the temporal lobe; however, such experiences are relatively specific to the temporal lobe and are not reported following stimulation of other cortical areas.

Many of the patients studied by Penfield, and others, subsequently had a temporal lobe removed for the treatment of epilepsy. The lesion did not include Wernicke's speech area but did typically include portions of the hippocampus. The capacities of these patients have been thoroughly studied by Brenda Milner and her associates. As discussed in Chapter 47, in the few instances in which both the left and the right temporal lobes were removed, patients had a profound and irreversible impairment of the capacity to form long-term memories. After unilateral removal of the temporal lobe, Milner found that there was also some interference with memory. Compared to the bilateral lesions, the unilateral lesion produced only a mild deficit. Furthermore, the degree of impairment depended on the side of the brain that had the lesion and on the type of material to be memorized. Patients with removal of the temporal lobes on the left side had difficulty in remembering verbal material such as a list of nouns, whereas patients with a right-sided removal had normal verbal memory but had difficulty in remembering patterns of sensory input. When presented with a series of pictures of human faces, some of which were repeated, patients with the right temporal lobe removed had difficulty remembering whether they had previously seen a given face. The degree of memory deficit was dependent on the nature of the visual material to be memorized. When given a task involving geometric figures, patients with temporal right lobe removal did not have this difficulty, but given a task involving irregular patterns of line drawings, they did experience difficulty. One possible explanation for these findings is that geometrical patterns can easily be expressed and then stored in a verbal fashion (square, triangle, etc.), whereas faces and irregular patterns cannot be readily encoded verbally. This general pattern of left hemisphere lesions producing deficits in the processing of verbal material, and right hemisphere lesions producing deficits in the processing of sensory pattern information has been repeatedly encountered in studies of brain-damaged patients.

The Association Areas of the Parietal Lobe Are Involved in Spatiomanipulative Tasks and Processing of Verbal Information

The parietal association cortex includes all of the parietal lobes except the postcentral gyrus, the primary sensory area for somatic sensory function. Animal studies of the posterior parietal cortex have revealed that lesions in this area produce subtle deficits in learning tasks involving somesthesis. In addition, there are deficits in certain complex nonsomesthetic tasks involving the selection of different objects placed before the animal.

Studies of single cells in the parietal cortex of monkeys by Vernon Mountcastle and associates and by David Robinson, Michael Goldberg, and Gregory Stanton have revealed that certain cells respond to visual stimuli or during visually guided movements. Unlike cells in the visual cortex, the intensity of the response to a series of identical stimuli is remarkably variable. In particular, the activity of the cell is enhanced when the animal attends to the stimulus. These results are consistent with the notion that the parietal cortex is involved in processes associated with attention to the spatial aspects of sensory input and perhaps with the manipulation of objects in space.

Patients with damage to the parietal lobes often show striking deficits, including abnormalities in body image and in perception of spatial relations. In addition, damage to the dominant (usually left) parietal lobe tends to produce *aphasia* (disorder of language, see Chapter 49), and *agnosia* (an inability to perceive objects through a particular normally functioning sensory channel). An example of a particularly striking agnosia after damage to the parietal cortex is *astereognosia* (an inability to recognize the form of objects by touch in the absence of any major somatic sensory deficits).[1]

Lesions of the nondominant parietal lobe are not complicated by disturbances of language. A striking feature of patients with right parietal lobe damage is their lack of appreciation of the spatial aspects of all sensory input from the left side of the body as well as of external space. Although somatic sensations are relatively intact, the patients sometimes completely ignore half of the body (neglect syndrome) and may fail to dress, undress, and wash the affected side. The patients may deny that the arm or leg belongs to them when the limb is passively brought into their field of vision. The patients may also deny the existence of associated hemiplegia and may attempt to leave the hospital prematurely since they feel there is nothing wrong with them. Disturbance of the appreciation of external space takes the form of neglect of visual stimuli on that side of the body. These patients sometimes also exhibit a severe disturbance in their ability to copy drawn figures (constructional apraxia or dyspraxia). In some instances this deficit may be so severe that the patient may draw a figure in which one-half of the body is completely left out.

Patients with a neglect syndrome due to an inferior right parietal lesion can show a deficit in the nonsyntactic processing of language. Kenneth Heilman and his associates have found that patients with lesions in the inferior right parietal lobe fail to appreciate those aspects of a verbal message (e.g., emotional tone) that are conveyed by the tone, loudness, and timing of the words as opposed to the actual sense of the words. The patients also have difficulty in modulating the sound of their verbal output and convey poorly the nonsyntactic aspects of language. These clinical observations suggest that the right homologue of Wernicke's area may also have a subtle language function dealing with certain nonsyntactic aspects of language.

The Sodium Amytal Test Directly Reveals Lateralized Functions

Several techniques have been developed to study hemispheric lateralization in patients without brain damage. One procedure of great clinical importance is the *sodium amytal test*. This method was developed to determine which hemisphere is dominant for speech functions, so as to avoid neurosurgical procedures that might destroy language ability in a patient. Although speech functions appear to be lateralized to the left hemisphere in most people, this is not universally

---

[1] An important clinical syndrome associated with damage to the inferior regions of the parietal cortex is known as *Gerstmann's syndrome*. Patients with Gerstmann's syndrome are characterized by (1) left–right confusion (for example, an inability to determine whether a particular part of the body of the examiner is left or right), (2) finger agnosia (difficulty in naming fingers when a specific finger is touched, despite the absence of major deficits of finger sensations), (3) dysgraphia (a deficit in writing, in the absence of motor or sensory deficits of the upper extremities), and (4) dyscalculia (a deficit in the ability to carry out mathematical calculations). Not all the symptoms are seen in every patient.

Table 48–1. Linguistic Dominance
and Handedness

Handedness	Dominant hemisphere (%)		
	Left	Right	Both
Left handed	64	20	16
Right handed	90	10	0
Ambidextrous	60	10	30

Data from Branch et al., 1964.

true. In this test, the patient is instructed to count aloud, and sodium amytal, a fast-acting barbiturate, is injected into the left or right internal carotid artery. The drug is preferentially carried to the hemisphere on the same side as it is injected and produces a brief period of dysfunction of that hemisphere. When the hemisphere dominant for speech is affected, the patient stops counting and does not respond to the command to continue.

One of the first problems explored with this technique was the relationship between handedness and speech lateralization (Table 48–1). Do left-handed individuals have left hemisphere speech, as do right-handed people, or do they have right hemisphere speech? The sodium amytal test has revealed that almost all right-handed people have left hemisphere speech. Surprisingly, the majority of left-handed people also have left hemisphere speech; but a significant number, about 20–40%, have right hemisphere speech. Furthermore, some left-handed people appear to have control of speech in both the right and left hemispheres. In these patients, neither right nor left injections of sodium amytal suppresses speech function. Thus, in a sizable proportion of left-handed people lateralization is weak or absent.

The sodium amytal test has yielded other unexpected results. Some investigators have reported that unilateral injection of the drug not only affects speech, but also mood. The nature of the effect on mood is related to the side of injection: left injections tend to produce a brief depressed mood, and right injections tend to produce euphoria. These effects were seen at doses smaller than those needed to block speech. The results suggest that functions related to mood or affect may also be lateralized to some degree in the human brain. This suggestion is consistent with the clinical observation that some patients with damage to the left hemisphere are excep-

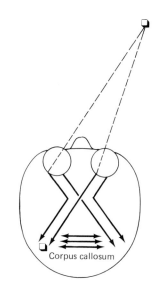

48–5 Superior view of the brain, showing crossed projections from the nasal retina and uncrossed projections from the temporal retina. An image in the right visual field stimulates the left temporal retina and right nasal retina; the information therefore projects to the left hemisphere. The information can secondarily reach the right hemisphere if the corpus callosum is intact. (Adapted from Sperry, 1968.)

tionally upset about their symptoms. In contrast, patients with damage to the right hemisphere sometimes exhibit a pathological lack of concern for their disability.

The findings obtained from several indirect, noninvasive methods correlate well with those from the sodium amytal test. One test uses brief (tachistoscopic) visual stimuli presented either to the right or left visual hemifield and involves either a visuospatial task (e.g., recognizing a face) or a verbal task (e.g., recognizing a word). Because of the nature of the visual pathways (Figure 48–5), the image of a visual stimulus that is restricted to one visual field is projected first to the opposite hemisphere. The information is then transmitted, presumably in a slightly degraded form, to the opposite hemisphere via the corpus callosum. On verbal tasks, right-handed subjects typically perform slightly better when the stimuli are presented to the right visual field, which is contralateral to their verbal hemisphere. In contrast, spatial tasks are performed better when stimuli are presented to the left visual field. Left-handed subjects show greater variability with regard to the visual field superior for the task. Similar results are obtained with the *dichotic auditory task*, in which lateralization is assessed by presenting different auditory stimuli to both ears simultaneously and determining which ear is better at recognizing the auditory inputs. For right handed subjects, the left ear tends to be better for certain nonverbal auditory tasks (e.g., recognition of music), whereas the right ear is better for verbal material. The results of this test suggest that the crossed auditory pathways functionally dominate the uncrossed pathways.

Split Brain Experiments Reveal Important Asymmetries

Perhaps the most dramatic experimental evidence for the localization of function to one rather than another hemisphere comes from research on patients who have had the corpus callosum and the anterior commissure—the major commissures interconnecting the two hemispheres—cut in an attempt to prevent the spread of epileptic activity from one side of the brain to the other. Studies of these patients show that each hemisphere is capable of functioning independently. Although the right hemisphere is mute and cannot communicate verbally about its experience, the mute hemisphere can do many of the things that the verbal hemisphere is capable of doing. Basic processes such as sensory analysis, memory, learning, and calculation can be performed by either hemisphere. The ability of the mute hemisphere is limited when the task involves complex reasoning or analysis, however.

It seems intuitively obvious that the corpus callosum and other commissures serve to integrate the functions of the two hemispheres. Nevertheless, when patients with sectioned anterior commissure and corpus callosum are observed in a casual manner it is difficult to tell that there is anything wrong with them. Indeed, early investigators failed to find any deficits. By 1940 Warren McCulloch concluded with irony that the only proven role of the corpus callosum was "to aid in the transmission of epileptic seizures from one to the other side of the body" (cited by Sperry in 1964). As recently as 1950 Lashley facetiously reiterated his feeling that the purpose of the corpus callosum "must be mainly mechanical. . ., to keep the hemispheres from sagging."

The functional role of the hemispheric commissures first became apparent in studies by Ronald Myers and Roger Sperry in so-called split-brain animals in which communication between the hemispheres was eliminated by sectioning of the corpus callosum. In addition, Myers and Sperry limited visual input to one hemisphere by cutting the optic chiasm and thereby destroying the crossed visual fibers. Unlike normal animals, when these animals were trained on complex visual discriminations using one eye, they behaved as if they were completely naive when tested with the untrained eye. In other words, the effects of the training experience were limited to the hemisphere receiving the visual input. In a classic series of studies, Sperry and Michael Gazzaniga subsequently examined the function of the corpus callosum in humans by carefully studying a group of patients commissurotomized for epilepsy. They confirmed earlier studies on animals and indeed found that under the appropriate experimental conditions a severe limitation in the ability of these patients to perform certain tasks could be demonstrated. The appropriate conditions consisted of tasks that forced one hemisphere to work independently of the other.

One reason that these patients do so well in real-life situations is that ordinarily both hemispheres obtain common information that allows integration of function even though direct interhemispheric communication is absent. For example, as the eyes scan the environment, each hemisphere receives a complete representation of the visual world. Since the optic chiasm is intact in these patients, portions of the same visual images are projected to each hemisphere.

Sperry and Gazzaniga, however, arranged the experimental situation so that cross cues were eliminated. One simple way to accomplish this is to use brief, tachistoscopic visual stimuli that are projected exclusively to either the right or left visual field. Such visual stimuli project only to the opposite hemisphere, for in the absence of callosal fibers the visual information is unable to gain access to the ipsilateral hemisphere (Figure 48–5). Using this technique, a simple experiment immediately reveals the deficit. When a subject was presented with an apple in the right visual field and questioned about what he saw, he said—not surprisingly—"apple." If, however, the apple was presented to the left visual field the patient would deny having seen anything, or if prompted to give an answer, would guess or confabulate. This is not because the right hemisphere is blind or is unable to remember a simple stimulus. The patient could readily identify the object if he could point to it or could pick it out

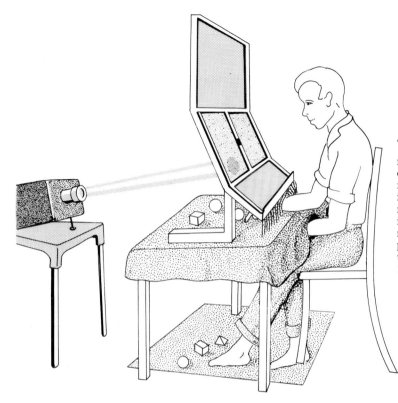

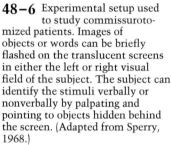

48–6 Experimental setup used to study commissurotomized patients. Images of objects or words can be briefly flashed on the translucent screens in either the left or right visual field of the subject. The subject can identify the stimuli verbally or nonverbally by palpating and pointing to objects hidden behind the screen. (Adapted from Sperry, 1968.)

from several others presented under a cover (Figure 48–6). In other words, when visual stimuli were limited to the right hemisphere, the patient could not say what he saw, but was perfectly able to identify the object by nonverbal means. This suggests that although the right hemisphere cannot talk, it indeed can perceive, learn, remember, and perform motor tasks.

Furthermore, the right hemisphere may be capable of primitive understanding of language. For example, many words projected to the right hemisphere can be read and understood. If the letters D-O-G are flashed to the left visual field, the patient will select a model of a dog with his left hand. More complicated verbal input to the right hemisphere, such as commands, are comprehended relatively poorly. The right hemisphere appears to be almost totally incapable of language output, but may be able to process linguistic inputs.

The right hemisphere is not merely a left hemisphere that lacks verbal capacity, however. In fact, on certain perceptual tasks, the right hemisphere outperforms the left hemisphere. For example, in a task involving fitting together pieces of colored wooden blocks to make a coher-

ent pattern, patients performed much better with the left hand than with the right. Thus, as indicated earlier, the nonspeech hemisphere is superior on spatial–perceptual problems. This is most evident when the tasks involve manipulation of the environment.

There is some indication that not only can the two hemispheres function independently, but in a commissurotomized patient, they also can interfere with each other's function. For example, in block design tasks performed with the nondominant hand (i.e., the hand ipsilateral to the verbal hemisphere), the dominant hand sometimes attempts to interfere with the solution, usually to the detriment of the successful solution of the problem. In addition, the dominant hemisphere sometimes directs verbal comments about the performance of the nondominant hemisphere, frequently exhibiting a false sense of confidence on problems in which it cannot know the solution, since the information was projected exclusively to the nondominant hemisphere. These observations have sometimes been interpreted to indicate that patients with split brains function with two independent minds, each with its own stream of consciousness. In these pa-

48–7 Type of chimeric figures used to test commissurotomized patients. (Adapted from Levy, Trevarthen, and Sperry, 1972.)

tients, either hemisphere is capable of directing behavior. Which hemisphere gains control seems to depend upon which hemisphere is best suited for the type of task to be performed. This is seen clearly in experiments with chimeric figures of faces with, for example, the right half of the face a male and the left half a female (Figure 48–7). Commissurotomized patients, when shown this chimeric figure with a fixation point directly in the middle, verbally report that the face is that of a male; but if asked to point to the face when shown a series of whole faces, they point to a female face. Presumably, either hemisphere is capable of pointing. Nevertheless, the more competent right hemisphere appears to control this task. When the task requires a verbal answer, of which the right hemisphere is incapable, the left hemisphere controls the task.

Each hemisphere has its own strengths as well as weaknesses with regard to a given task. Certain tasks are best performed in an analytic mode, in which the problem is broken down into logical elements, and this type of task is well suited to verbal encoding. On the other hand, other tasks may be best performed not by sequential analysis but by some type of simultaneous processing of the whole input. For example, we ordinarily recognize a familiar face not by determining that it has or does not have given features such as a mustache, glasses, and small nose, but rather by some process whereby all these elements are integrated into a single perception. The face simply looks familiar or not familiar. If we had to verbalize how we recognize a face, we would find it difficult and time consuming. In a greatly oversimplified but didactically useful way, we may think of our brains as consisting of a combination of a

left hemisphere that tends to be an intellectual, rational, verbal, and analytical thinker; and a right hemisphere that tends to be a perceiver and an emotional, nonverbal, and intuitive thinker. Each hemisphere is, in principle, capable of independent function, but normally, integration of function is maintained by means of extensive commissural connections.

Why Is Function Lateralized?

The question as to why lateralization of function exists in the human brain involves two major issues. First, how does lateralization develop within the life span of the individual? Second, what functional advantages, if any, does lateralization confer? We shall consider each of these questions in turn.

Hemispheric dominance develops gradually. In young individuals either hemisphere can develop into the verbal hemisphere. For example, young children who sustain acute brain damage to one of the hemispheres suffer only relatively slight deficits in their existing linguistic capacity, and these mild deficits are frequently almost fully reversed after a brief period of time. Even after complete removal of the left hemisphere, most young children can develop virtually normal speech and language capabilities. In adults, extensive damage to the dominant hemisphere results in severe deficits in speech functions, and recovery is slow or absent. Moreover, as mentioned in Chapter 44, there are differences in the rates at which this lateralization process develops in boys and girls, and hence there are sex differences in vulnerability to left hemisphere damage in preadolescents. Since speech becomes fixed in the left hemisphere at an earlier age in boys, they are more like to suffer more severe and enduring language disruptions after cortical injury in childhood.

In the developing individual, either hemisphere can attain full linguistic competence. Why then does the left hemisphere become dominant in the great majority of people? It is likely that, at least in part, dominance develops in the left hemisphere because of an inherent anatomical asymmetry in the human brain. As recently as 1968, it was widely believed that there was no gross asymmetry in the human brain. At that time, Norman Geschwind and Walter Levitsky, at the Harvard Medical School, published the results of an experiment of breathtaking simplicity. They studied the gross dimensions of 100 human brains, using nothing more than a camera and a

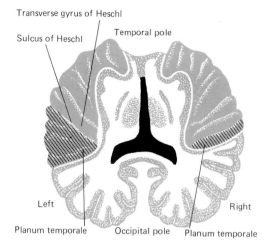

48–8 Coronal section through a human brain in the plane of the Sylvian fissure at the level of the planum temporale of the temporal lobe. The left planum is larger in the majority of human brains. (Adapted from Geschwind and Levitsky, 1968.)

ruler to make measurements of the *planum temporale*, a region on the upper surface of the temporal lobe that includes the classical speech area of Wernicke. The results were clear-cut (Figure 48–8). The left planum was larger in 65% of the brains; the right planum was larger in only 11% of the brains; and in 24% of the brains the left and right sides were approximately equal in size. Subsequent work with a variety of techniques, including computerized tomography, has confirmed these results and established that similar asymmetries are present even in the human fetus. These observations suggest that an inherent anatomical asymmetry may initially favor the left hemisphere for the development of language functions. Once one hemisphere begins to specialize it will excel at that function, which in turn prompts its further development.

What are the functional advantages of lateralization? Is lateralization merely a by-product of certain inherent asymmetries of the developing nervous system, or are there certain advantages to the development of restricted localization of neural circuits concerned with similar functions? In each neuron there is great regional differentiation between parts of the cell concerned with different functions. Groups of neurons are located together in nuclear groups, layers, or columns, and groups of columns of similar function, in turn, are arranged in cortical sheets. Lateralization may reflect the ultimate extension of a prin-

ciple that serves to organize neurons into progressively larger functional units because of an evolutionary adaptation that minimizes the amount of "wiring" and maximizes the speed of communication between neurons that are likely to work in concert.

Whatever factors promote lateralization of function, they are not limited to humans. Anatomical asymmetry of the brain has been demonstrated in a number of other animals, including the great apes, monkeys, cats, rats, and birds. In some instances asymmetry of function has been demonstrated in lower animals. This is best documented in certain of the species of birds that learn their song by listening to other birds (see Chapter 46). In studies of canaries, Fernando Nottebohm at Rockefeller University found that a lesion in the avian equivalent of the left cortex severely disrupts song production, whereas a right lesion has less effect (Figure 48–9). After a left lesion, there can be recovery of song, but there is no recovery if a right lesion is then made. This suggests that the right hemisphere can mediate singing when the left hemisphere is damaged. As in humans, there are interesting sex differences in this animal model of hemispheric dominance. Centers for vocal control are larger in certain species of male birds that learn to sing by reference to auditory information than in females that normally do not sing. Several of the song control areas in the left hemisphere contain neurons that bind testosterone, and in the canary it has been shown that the presence or absence of circulating testosterone modulates the amount of singing during the life span of the bird.

One means by which it was hoped to obtain insight into the possible advantages or disadvantages of lateralization of function was by studying the capacities of left-handed individuals, since a relatively high proportion of them appear to lack distinct lateralization. Nevertheless, careful studies of populations of normal individuals have not found any deficits in left-handed people. Curiously, a number of studies have indicated that in various clinical populations with behavioral problems there is a slightly greater incidence of individuals who are left handed or who exhibit incomplete lateralization. An above normal incidence of sinistrality has been reported among patients with problems such as epilepsy, cerebral palsy, stuttering, mental retardation, and dyslexia. One possible reason for increased sinistrality in certain clinical populations is that there may be a slightly increased incidence of brain

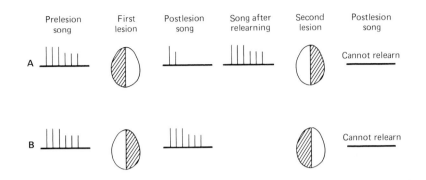

48–9 Effects of unilateral brain lesions on song in birds. **A.** A left lesion was made first, followed by a right lesion. **B.** A right lesion was made first, followed by a left lesion. When the first lesion was on the left side the song was disturbed (although it could be relearned); whereas when the first lesion was on the right side the song was not affected. In both cases the song was lost and could not be relearned after the second lesion.

damage in left-handed compared to right-handed individuals. When (and if) early brain damage produces a switch of handedness, it will result in a greater number of right to left switches than left to right, since there is a much greater incidence of right handedness. Of course, the overwhelming majority of left-handed individuals do not have brain damage. It is clear that although on theoretical grounds cerebral lateralization should provide for more efficient function, as of yet there are no conclusive data establishing this point.

An Overall View

The material presented in this chapter indicates that even the most complex functions of the brain have some topographic organization. This has great clinical importance and explains why certain syndromes are characteristic of disease in specific regions of the brain, including those syndromes concerned with higher functions. It is unlikely, however, that any complex behavior—especially highly complex functions such as thought, perception, and language—will ever be understood in relation to one region of the brain apart from an understanding of the relationship of that region to other regions. As recognized by Lashley and others, assigning functions to specific regions of the brain presents something of a philosophical problem, since no part of the nervous system functions in the same way alone as it does in concert with other parts. Furthermore, when a part of the brain is removed, the behavior of the organism is more a reflection of the capacities of the remaining brain than of the part of the brain that was removed. Nevertheless, approaching the nervous system by reducing its activities into anatomically discrete units has given us considerable clues about the contribution of individual parts to the functioning of the whole.

Selected Readings and References

Fulton, J. F. 1951. Frontal Lobotomy and Affective Behavior: A Neurophysiological Analysis. New York: Norton.

Hardyck, C., and Petrinovich, L. F. 1977. Left-handedness. Psychol. Bull. 84:385–404.

Milner, B. 1974. Hemispheric specialization: Scope and limits. In F. O. Schmitt and F. G. Worden (eds.), The Neurosciences: Third Study Program. Cambridge, Mass.: MIT Press, pp. 75–89.

Other References

Branch, C., Milner, B., and Rasmussen, T. 1964. Intracarotid sodium amytal for the lateralization of cerebral speech dominance. J. Neurosurg. 21:399–405.

Gazzaniga, M. S., and LeDoux, J. E. 1978. The Integrated Mind. New York: Plenum.

Geschwind, N., and Levitsky, W. 1968. Human brain: Left–right asymmetries in temporal speech region. Science (Wash., D.C.) 161:186–187.

Harlow, H. F. 1958. Behavioral contributions to interdisciplinary research. In H. F. Harlow and C. N. Woolsey (eds.), Biological and Biochemical Bases of Behavior. Madison: University of Wisconsin Press, pp. 3–23.

Jacobsen, C. F. 1935. Functions of frontal association area in primates. Arch. Neurol. Psychiatry 33:558–569.

Lashley, K. S. 1950. In search of the engram. Symp. Soc. Exp. Biol. 4:454–482.

Levy, J., Trevarthen, C., and Sperry, R. W. 1972. Perception of bilateral chimeric figures following hemispheric deconnexion. Brain 95:61–78.

Milner, B. 1968. Visual recognition and recall after right temporal-lobe excision in man. Neuropsychologia 6:191–209.

Moniz, E. 1936. Tentatives Opératoires dans le Traitement de Certaines Psychoses. Paris: Masson.

Mountcastle, V. B., Lynch, J. C., Georgopoulos, A., Sakata, H., and Acuna, C. 1975. Posterior parietal association cortex of the monkey: Command functions for operations within extrapersonal space. J. Neurophysiol. 38:871–908.

Myers, R. E. 1955. Interocular transfer of pattern discrimination in cats following section of crossed optic fibers. J. Comp. Physiol. Psychol. 48:470–473.

Nottebohm, F. 1979. Origins and mechanisms in the establishment of cerebral dominance. In M. S. Gazzaniga (ed.), Handbook of Behavioral Neurobiology, Vol. 2. New York: Plenum, pp. 295–344.

Penfield, W. 1958. Functional localization in temporal and deep Sylvian areas. Res. Publ. Assoc. Res. Nerv. Ment. Dis. 36:210–226.

Robinson, D. L., Goldberg, M. E., and Stanton, G. B. 1978. Parietal association cortex in the primate: Sensory mechanisms and behavioral modulations. J. Neurophysiol. 41:910–932.

Rosenkilde, C. E. 1979. Functional heterogeneity of the prefrontal cortex in the monkey: A review. Behav. Neural Biol. 25:301–345.

Sperry, R. W. 1964. The great cerebral commissure. Sci. Am. 210:42–52.

Sperry, R. W. 1968. Mental unity following surgical disconnection of the cerebral hemispheres. Harvey Lect. 62:293–323.

Thompson, R. F. 1975. Introduction to Physiological Psychology. New York: Harper & Row.

Tucker, D. M., Watson, R. T., and Heilman, K. M. 1977. Discrimination and evocation of affectively intoned speech in patients with right parietal disease. Neurology 27:947–950.

Warren, J. M., and Akert, K. (eds.). 1964. The Frontal Granular Cortex and Behavior. New York: McGraw-Hill.

Richard Mayeux

Disorders of Speech and Learned Movements: Aphasia and Apraxia

49

Important insights into the functioning of the human cerebral cortex have come from the clinical observation of the changes in behavior produced by certain diseases. Nowhere is localization of higher functions better demonstrated than in disturbances in language *(aphasia)* and in gestures *(apraxia).* In this chapter we shall illustrate how relatively simple neurological tests can provide accurate diagnoses of lesions in the cerebral cortex.

Aphasias Are Disturbances in Language Caused by Brain Damage

Aphasia is different from disorders of speech that result from weakness or incoordination of the muscles that control the vocal apparatus. These are referred to as *dysarthria* (difficulty in articulation) or *dysphonia* (difficulty in vocalization). Because the left hemisphere is dominant for language in the majority of people, aphasia typically is encountered following damage to that hemisphere.

There are several types of aphasia with distinct clinical characteristics. With a simple neurological examination, almost any alert, cooperative patient can be tested to determine the type of aphasic disorder. The examination of an aphasic patient should include an evaluation of the following: spontaneous speech or verbal output,

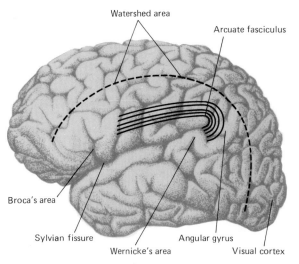

Watershed area

Arcuate fasciculus

Broca's area

Sylvian fissure

Wernicke's area

Angular gyrus

Visual cortex

49-1 Primary language areas of the brain. Broca's area is the motor-speech area adjacent to the motor cortex that controls the movements of articulation, facial expression, and phonation. Wernicke's area lies in the posterior superior temporal lobe and includes the auditory comprehension center. Wernicke's and Broca's areas are joined by a fiber tract called the arcuate fasciculus.

repetition of words or phrases, comprehension of language, naming of objects, reading ability and writing skill, and associated neurological signs.

We have previously considered the areas in the cerebral cortex concerned with language (Chapter 1). Referring to those anatomical structures (Figure 49-1 and Table 49-1) will aid the reader in distinguishing the various types of aphasia and in localizing the pathology.

Clinical Features

Verbal Output. One of the most striking features of aphasia is abnormal conversation and spontaneous speech. Verbal output is usually described as either nonfluent or fluent. *Nonfluent* speech is characterized by a decreased output to 50 words/min or less, increased effort when attempting to produce words, poor articulation, decreased phrase length (at times so sparse that each sentence may contain only one or two words, which are usually nouns *(telegraphic speech)*, and speech with poor rhythm *(unmelodic speech)*. Patients with nonfluent aphasia usually are damaged in the frontal lobe anterior to the Rolandic fissure (central gyrus). This condition is frequently called *anterior aphasia*. Examples of anterior aphasia in Table 49-1 are Broca aphasia and transcortical motor aphasia. Broca aphasia is the most common form of nonfluent aphasia; the lesion that produces this disturbance usually involves Broca's area (the motor-speech area; Figure 49-1).

The patient with a *fluent* aphasia has a normal output of words with little or no articulatory disturbance and speaks in sentences with normal phrase length. These patients, however, have *circumlocution* (roundabout, indirect phrasing characterized by lengthy meaningless locutions when a specific word is needed), and they substitute general and less precise words such as "thing" or "them" for names of specific objects. The verbal output of the fluent aphasic is therefore characterized by "empty speech" with long sentences that have few substantive words and contain little information. Patients with fluent aphasia may also use the wrong word or wrong sound within a word *(paraphasia)* or make up new words *(neologisms)*. Fluent aphasia usually results from lesions posterior to the Rolandic fissures and is usually called *posterior aphasia*. Examples of posterior aphasias noted in Table 49-1 are Wernicke, conduction, and transcortical sensory aphasias.

Repetition. The repetition of words or phrases is an important and often overlooked language function. A patient's ability to repeat words, numbers, and phrases upon command implies that the perisylvian language centers are still intact. These centers are Broca's area, Wernicke's area (auditory language comprehension center), and the arcuate fasciculus, which interconnects them (Figure 49-1). A lesion that interrupts the arcuate fasciculus anywhere between Broca's area and Wernicke's area produces a conduction aphasia and results in a repetition disturbance.

Table 49–1. Clinical Characteristics of Aphasias

Type	Verbal output	Repetition	Comprehension	Naming	Associated signs*	Lesion
Broca	Nonfluent	Impaired	Normal	Marginally impaired	RHP, apraxia of the left limbs and face	Left posterior inferior frontal
Wernicke	Fluent	Impaired	Impaired	Impaired	±RHH	Left posterior superior temporal
Conduction	Fluent	Impaired	Normal	Impaired (paraphasic)	±RHS, apraxia of all limbs and face	Left parietal
Global	Nonfluent	Impaired	Impaired	Impaired	RHP, RHS, RHH	Left frontal temporal parietal
Anomic	Fluent	Normal (anomic)	Normal	Impaired	None	Left posterior inferior temporal, or temporal–occipital region
Transcortical Motor	Nonfluent	Normal	Normal	Impaired	RHP	Left medial frontal or anterior border zone
Sensory	Fluent	Normal	Impaired	Impaired	±RHH	Left medial parietal or posterior border zone
Mixed (isolation)	Nonfluent	Normal	Impaired	Impaired	RHP, RHS	Left medial frontal parietal or complete border zone

*Abbreviations: RHP, right hemiparesis; RHH, right homonomous hemianopsia; RHS, right hemisensory defect.

Repetition disturbances can also occur with aphasias of the Broca, Wernicke, and global types.

Comprehension. Comprehension is usually tested by having the patient follow commands or answer questions. There are three main types of comprehension disturbance. A *receptive disturbance* is an inability to comprehend spoken language while comprehension of written language may be spared. This occasionally occurs in Wernicke aphasia. A *perceptive comprehension disturbance* results when the auditory language comprehension center is completely damaged, and is most characteristic of Wernicke and transcortical sensory aphasias. *Semantic comprehension disturbance* is characterized by an inability to understand specific words or the specific meaning of certain words. This can be seen in conduction aphasia and less frequently in patients with Broca aphasia.

Naming. Difficulty in naming or finding the right word is usually called *anomia*. Clinical observations suggest that the type of anomia varies with the anatomical localization of the lesion. *Word-production anomia* is seen in anterior (Broca) aphasia. The patient is unable to produce the correct word even though he appears to know the word he wants to use. *Word-selection anomia* occurs in patients with lesions at the posterior temporal occipital junction (anomic aphasia). This form of aphasia results only in an inability to name objects. *Semantic anomia* occurs with lesions in the area of the dominant angular gyrus of the parietal lobe (conduction aphasia) and results in a perceptual word-finding impairment.

Occasionally *modality-specific (tactile, visual, auditory)* or *category-specific anomias* can result from lesions in the parieto-occipital or occipital region. An example of this is *color anomia*, caused by left occipital lobe lesions. In color anomia the patient is unable to name colors correctly but maintains the ability to match colors and to name other objects.

Associated Reading and Writing Disturbances. Patients with aphasia generally write as they speak, fluently or nonfluently. *Agraphia*, loss of the ability to write, is a symptom that rarely occurs alone. Reading disturbances, or *alexia*, occur with almost every aphasia. Two varieties of alexia occur with specific neuroanatomical lesions that are not associated with other significant disorders of language. *Alexia without agraphia* or pure word blindness occurs with lesions in the left occipital area in the corresponding posterior genu of the corpus callosum. These lesions are usually produced by infarctions in the branches of the left posterior cerebral artery. These patients are unable to read at all and often have an associated color anomia. In addition, the patients are unable to derive meaning from spelled out words (i.e., D-O-G = dog), and in turn are unable to spell words correctly. *Alexia with agraphia* occurs with lesions in the supramarginal or angular gyrus (Figure 49–1). This lesion may be caused by a variety of disorders that include tumor and stroke. The patients generally have a very mild anomia. The major deficit is the loss of the ability to read and write; other language functions are relatively spared.

Associated Signs. Other neurological signs can also help to localize the area of disturbance in most aphasic patients. For example, patients with anterior aphasia almost always have a right hemiparesis that is usually worse in the arm and face than in the leg. On the other hand, patients with posterior aphasia usually have no fixed neurological sign; however, a few have a mild sensory loss or visual field disturbance (Table 49–1).

Clinical Syndromes

Broca aphasia (motor, expressive, or anterior aphasia) is associated with lesions that include the posterior portion of the inferior frontal gyrus of the left hemisphere (Figure 49–1). Language output is nonfluent and repetition is usually impaired. Auditory comprehension of language is

spared, but naming ability may be slightly to moderately impaired. A right hemiparesis is always present due to the proximity of the motor cortex and underlying internal capsule.

Wernicke aphasia (sensory, receptive, or posterior aphasia) is associated with lesions around the left posterior superior portion of the temporal lobe (Figure 49–1). Output is fluent and paraphasic, but comprehension is severely impaired. Repetition is also impaired due to severe comprehension disturbance, and naming is usually paraphasic. Other neurological signs may be absent, but a right visual field defect can be seen in some patients.

Conduction aphasia is usually correlated with a lesion involving the arcuate fasciculus in the supramarginal gyrus of the parietal lobe or, less frequently, the posterior superior aspect of the left temporal lobe (Figure 49–1). Verbal output is characteristically fluent with many paraphasic intrusions and word-finding pauses. Comprehension remains intact, but repetition is markedly impaired even for simple words. In most patients limb and facial apraxias occur (discussed in the next section).

Anomic aphasia, in which the only language impairment involves word finding, is found with lesions at the posterior aspect of the left inferior temporal lobe, near the temporal-occipital border. It may occasionally be accompanied by a right quadrantanopic visual field defect.

Global aphasia, or total aphasia, occurs with lesions that destroy the entire perisylvian region. Patients are unable to speak or comprehend language and cannot read, write, repeat, or name. A complete right hemiplegia and right hemisensory defect are usually present and accompanied by a right homonomous hemianopsia.

The *transcortical aphasias* are characterized by two common features, namely, preserved repetition and a lesion that is outside the perisylvian language centers. These aphasias are most often related to infarction at the junctions of the vascular territories of the middle, anterior, and posterior cerebral arteries which are known as the border zone or watershed area (Figure 49–1). *Transcortical motor aphasia* (TCM) is a nonfluent aphasia and resembles Broca aphasia with intact comprehension, while *transcortical sensory aphasia* (TCS) is a fluent aphasia with defective comprehension. In transcortical motor aphasia, the lesion is usually anterior to Broca's area in the frontal lobe, while transcortical sensory aphasia is produced by a lesion in the parietal–temporal–occipital junction. If the entire border zone (frontal–parietal–occipital) is involved, the patient may only be able to repeat words *(echolalia)* and manifest no other linguistic competence. This is usually referred to as an isolation of speech syndrome, but more appropriately it should be called a *mixed transcortical aphasia.*

Apraxia Is a Disorder in the Execution of Learned Movement

Apraxia, originally defined by the German neurologist Hugo Liepmann at the end of the 19th century, is a disorder in the execution of learned movement that cannot be explained by weakness, incoordination, sensory loss, poor verbal comprehension, or inattention to commands. The mechanism of this disorder can be understood by considering the anatomical pathways by which movements are normally carried out in response to verbal command. Wernicke's area (auditory language comprehension center) is located in the left posterior temporal lobe. When one is asked to carry out a movement with the right hand, the order is probably transmitted from Wernicke's area through the left parietal lobe in the arcuate fasciculus to the left premotor region (Figure 49–2). The premotor region, in turn, transmits the information to the precentral motor cortex, which gives rise to the pyramidal tract and contains fibers that activate nerve cells controlling muscle movement. A similar mechanism must occur when the subject is given a command to use the left hand, but the information must be transmitted across the corpus callosum to the premotor region in the right hemisphere and from there to the right precentral motor cortex. As illustrated in Figure 49–2, intrahemispheric callosal transmission may occur either between the anterior motor areas (from the left premotor to the right premotor cortex) or between the more posterior auditory comprehension areas (from Wernicke's area in the left posterior superior temporal region to the corresponding region in the right hemisphere); the existence of the latter pathway of callosal fibers has not been conclusively demonstrated, hence this pathway is indicated by a broken line in Figure 49–2.

Three types of apraxic syndromes are easily recognized; two of them are often associated with aphasia. In patients with conduction aphasia, there is usually no paralysis. The site of the le-

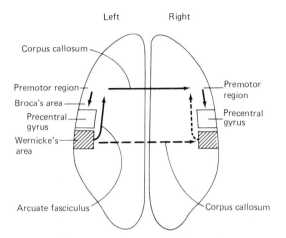

49–2 Human brain viewed from above showing probable intrahemispheric and transcallosal pathways for voluntary movement with the right or left limbs in response to a verbal command.

sion is in the left parietal lobe (in particular, the arcuate fasciculus). In a patient without sensory loss there is usually a limb apraxia. This occurs because the command that is heard and understood in Wernicke's area cannot be transmitted to the premotor area via the arcuate fasciculus. Therefore, the patient will fail to carry out verbal commands for movement with either hand, for example, to point to objects in the room.

Broca aphasia is usually associated with right hemiplegia. In addition, many of these patients fail to respond correctly to a command to use the nonparalyzed left arm even though they are able to comprehend the command. This apraxic disorder appears to result from the destruction of callosal fibers at their origin in cells in the left premotor region of the cerebral cortex. Loss of callosal fibers prevents impulses from the left premotor area from reaching the corresponding right premotor area. In addition, these patients may fail to carry out certain facial movements to such commands as "pretend to blow out a match." This symptom can be explained by the destruction of the left precentral facial area, which produces paralysis on the right side of the face; furthermore, impulses from the left premotor facial area cannot traverse the corpus callosum to the corresponding area in the right hemisphere. Facial apraxia commonly occurs in patients with Broca aphasia.

Finally, there is a rare type of apraxia that occurs with surgical destruction of the anterior two-thirds of the corpus callosum. In this particular lesion, the motor association cortices of both hemispheres remain intact but pathology prevents the transcallosal transmission of impulses between them. This results in an intriguing clinical situation in which the patient can carry out verbal commands perfectly well with his right hand, but not with his left, because the information cannot reach the premotor area of the right hemisphere.

An Overall View

Disorders of language and learned movement are common clinical problems. Much information about them can be gained by careful bedside neurological examination. In fact, our current understanding of language and motor behavior has developed from just this approach. In the future, sophisticated imaging techniques such as computerized tomography, in conjunction with careful clinical examination, should further our understanding of the anatomical and physiological bases of verbal behavior and skilled movement.

Selected Readings and References

Benson, D. F. 1979. Aphasia, Alexia, and Agraphia. New York: Churchill Livingstone.

Benson, D. F., and Geschwind, N. 1976. The aphasias and related disturbances. In A. B. Baker and L. H. Baker (eds.), Clinical Neurology, Vol. 1. New York: Harper & Row, chap. 8.

Other References

Benson, D. F. 1978. Neurological correlates of aphasia and apraxia. In W. B. Matthews and G. H. Glaser (eds.), Recent Advances in Clinical Neurology, Number 2. Edinburgh: Churchill Livingstone, pp. 163–175.

Benson, D. F., Sheremata, W. A., Bouchard, R., Segarra, J. M., Price, D., and Geschwind, N. 1973. Conduction aphasia. Arch. Neurol. 28:339–346.

Geschwind, N. 1967. The varieties of naming errors. Cortex 3:97–112.

Geschwind, N. 1971. Current concepts: Aphasia. N. Engl. J. Med. 284:654–656.

Geschwind, N. 1975. The apraxias: Neural mechanisms of disorders of learned movement. Am. Sci. 63:188–195.

Geschwind, N., and Fusillo, M. 1966. Color-naming defects in association with alexia. Arch. Neurol. 15:137–146.

Geschwind, N., Quadfasel, F. A., and Segarra, J. M. 1968. Isolation of the speech area. Neuropsychologia 6:327–340.

Heilman, K. M., and Scholes, R. J. 1976. The nature of comprehension errors in Broca's, conduction and Wernicke's aphasics. Cortex 12:258–265.

Liepmann, H. 1914. Bemerkungen zu v. Monakows Kapitel "Die Lokalisation der Apraxis." Monatsschr. Psychiatr. Neurol. 35:490–516.

Edward J. Sachar

Psychobiology of Schizophrenia

50

Some of the most exciting developments in modern psychiatry have come from the application of neurobiological approaches to the study of normal and abnormal mental processes. In this and the next chapter we shall consider recent progress in understanding the mechanisms underlying two of the most serious mental illnesses, schizophrenia and the affective psychoses. We shall be considering results obtained from genetic, pharmacological, and biochemical studies of patients with these disorders.

The Diagnosis of Mental Illnesses Must Meet Certain Criteria

Research on any illness requires the ability to make a reliable diagnosis of that illness. Diagnosis in psychiatry is generally more difficult than in the rest of medicine because for most mental disorders there as yet is no demonstrable specific brain pathology with which to confirm the clinical diagnosis. Furthermore, there are no satisfactory animal models for disorders such as schizophrenia and major depression. In addition, the symptoms of mental illness are expressed primarily in overt behavior, cognition, and subjective feelings, and these are considerably more difficult to quantify than pulse, temperature, and blood pressure. As a result, it is also more difficult to achieve good and reliable agreement between independent assessors of mental symptoms.

In order to establish a diagnostic category, three criteria should initially be met: (1) a group of symptoms must be identified that can be reliably assessed; (2) the group of symptoms must be shown to cluster together in certain patients, forming a syndrome; and (3) the group of symptoms must effectively distinguish these patients from others.

The proposed diagnostic category must then be validated against one or more independent measures. Five independent measures are commonly sought.

1. *Clinical course.* A diagnosis can be validated by showing that patients with this distinguishing symptom syndrome also follow a characteristic clinical course (for example, a progressive unremitting social deterioration, or recurrent cycles of recovery followed by relapse of the same type of syndrome).
2. *Natural history.* The syndrome may have a characteristic onset at a particular age or an association with a specific precipitant.
3. *Response to specific treatment.* The syndrome may respond relatively specifically to one class of drugs and not to another. This has recently proved to be an extremely important validator.
4. *Genetic profile.* Blood relatives or twins of the patients may prove to have a disproportionately higher incidence of the same disorder than the population at large.
5. *Biochemical or hormonal abnormalities.* The demonstration of a specific biological abnormality that is associated with the condition is also a powerful validator.

Schizophrenia Can Now Be More Accurately Diagnosed

Severe mental disturbances that involve profound misinterpretations of perception, accompanied by delusions, hallucinations, or disordered thinking, are called *psychotic illnesses.* The major psychotic illnesses are divided into two groups: the schizophrenic psychoses and the affective psychoses. Schizophrenia is the most crippling of the psychotic illnesses and primarily strikes teenagers and young adults.

Recent advances in the classification of mental disease have led to the development of rigorous criteria for the reliable diagnosis of schizophrenia, and for its separation from many other psychotic disorders that have some similar features. These advances are exemplified in the third and greatly revised edition of the *Diagnostic and Statistical Manual of Mental Disorders* (DSM-III), published in 1980 by the American Psychiatric Association.

These improved criteria for diagnosing schizophrenia have emerged only gradually from decades of research that began in the early part of the 20th century with the careful clinical observations of two great pioneers, Emil Kraepelin in Germany and Eugene Bleuler in Switzerland. On the basis of data gathered from hundreds of cases, Kraepelin and Bleuler identified certain psychotic symptom syndromes that were associated with characteristic long-term outcomes. Kraepelin identified an illness that he called *dementia praecox* because of its early age of onset, usually in adolescence, and his belief that the disease invariably followed a progressively deteriorating course. He was careful to separate the illness from manic depressive psychoses, which had different symptoms and followed a different course characterized by remissions and relapses. Bleuler dropped the term dementia praecox because he found that some cases had their onset in adulthood rather than in adolescence and because occasionally cases remitted. Bleuler also provided a more detailed analysis of the symptoms associated with the disease, and named it *schizophrenia* (splitting of the mind).

Much of the research that has followed that of Kraepelin and Bleuler has served to differentiate schizophrenia more clearly from many other psychotic disorders that have some similar features, by using the validating methods described above. A variety of other mental illnesses (manic depressive psychoses, brief reactive psychoses, paranoid states, and even organic brain syndromes and psychoses associated with drug intoxication) in the past have been sometimes called schizophrenia. These are now all excluded.

The current criteria include a psychotic episode with a minimum number of specific symptoms: (1) certain types of delusions (for example, of being persecuted, or of having one's feelings, thoughts, and actions controlled by an outside force); (2) certain types of hallucinations, especially auditory (e.g., hearing voices commenting on the patient's actions); and (3) a disorder of thought, consisting of incoherent speech and a loss of the normal association and sequence between ideas. Very frequently psychotic patients exhibit bizarre behavior such as unusual postures or rigidities.

Schizophrenia is characterized by one or more episodes of psychosis, with long intervening periods of social isolation, lack of motivation, flat affect, and eccentric behavior. The latter are referred to as residual symptoms and, because of their persistence, these symptoms in many ways are the most crippling part of the illness. To make a definitive diagnosis, at least 6 months of continuous illness are required. This period of illness includes the psychotic phase and a time during which there are either prodromal (warning) or residual nonpsychotic symptoms. Prodromal signs include social withdrawal, impairment in role-function, odd behavior and ideas, and impairment in personal hygiene. In making the diagnosis of schizophrenia it is important to exclude an affective disorder or an organic mental syndrome. The prognosis of schizophrenia is generally (but not always) poor, with frequent psychotic relapses and a progressive decrease in social functioning as the years go by.

There Is an Important Genetic Component to Schizophrenia

The incidence of schizophrenia in the general population is about 1%. Franz Kallmann at the New York State Psychiatric Institute found that the incidence of the disease was dramatically increased in the families of schizophrenics, but it is difficult to separate genetic from social factors in a closely knit family setting. A genetic basis for the disease cannot simply be inferred from the increased incidence in families of schizophrenics. As Seymour Kety, one of the major investigators of the genetics of mental illness, has observed, many things run in families and not all are nec-

essarily genetic—wealth runs in families, poverty runs in families and even the nutritional deficiency, pellagra, used to run in families. Nevertheless, the evidence for an important genetic contribution to the development of schizophrenia is now overwhelming. There is a tenfold increase in schizophrenia in the first-degree relatives of schizophrenics. Children with one schizophrenic parent have a 10% chance of developing schizophrenia whether they are raised with their biological parents or by foster parents who are normal. Concordance for schizophrenia is 40–60% in monozygotic (identical) twins, but only 13% in dizygotic (fraternal) twins—the same as for siblings. But there are many discordant monozygotic pairs of twins in which one has schizophrenia and the other does not, and this indicates that other factors besides genetic ones are important for the development of schizophrenia.

Some of the clearest evidence for a genetic component in schizophrenia has come from studies of adopted children in Denmark. From adoption records Kety, Paul Wender, and David Rosenthal reconstructed the complete cohort of children adopted soon after birth during a certain specified period of time. This large population contained some children who ultimately developed schizophrenia. Information was gathered from records and interviews about both the adoptive parents and the biological ones, and similar information was obtained from sets of parents of control groups of adoptees who had grown up to be mentally healthy. Kety, Wender, and Rosenthal found that, in contrast to the normal adoptees, the adoptees who grew up to become schizophrenic had a much greater incidence of schizophrenia in the biological families of origin but not in the adoptive families (Table 50–1).

Table 50–1. Diagnoses of Schizophrenia or Related Disease in Relatives of Schizophrenic Adoptees and in Relatives of Control Adoptees*

Psychiatric diagnoses	Biological relatives		Adoptive relatives	
	Schizophrenic	Control	Schizophrenic	Control
Chronic schizophrenia	2.9†	0	1.4	1.1
Latent schizophrenia	3.5	1.7	0	1.1
Schizophrenia, uncertain subtype	7.5†	1.7	1.4	3.3
Total	14.0†	3.4	2.7	5.5

Adapted from Kety, 1978.
*Expressed as a percentage of total biological and adoptive relatives.
†Statistically significant.

The adoptive studies also revealed a high incidence of a certain nonpsychotic syndrome in the biological families of the schizophrenic adoptees. This *schizotypal syndrome* (previously called *borderline schizophrenia*) resembles a mild form of schizophrenia and includes, among other traits, tangential rambling speech, eccentric beliefs, poor rapport, suspiciousness, magical thinking, and social isolation. It seems likely, then, that this nonpsychotic condition is genetically related to schizophrenia, being a milder form.

These genetic studies have revolutionized our thinking about schizophrenia. Many earlier observations suggested that schizophrenia is a disorder caused primarily by psychosocial and environmental factors, particularly by pathological parenting. It was, for example, noted that mothers of schizophrenic patients were often odd individuals with disturbed thinking and communication patterns. The investigators in these earlier studies probably were mistaking the signs of a hereditary disorder that affects both parent and child, for a *pathogenic* psychosocial interaction between parent and child.

Specific Drugs Are Effective in the Treatment of Schizophrenia

Until the 1950s there was no specific effective treatment for schizophrenia. The introduction of reserpine and, particularly, in 1954, of the phenothiazines (beginning with chlorpromazine), followed by butyrophenones (e.g., haloperidol) and then other chemical classes of antipsychotic drugs (thioxanthenes, indolones, etc.), dramatically improved the treatment of the psychotic phase of schizophrenia (Figure 50–1). Originally it was believed that these drugs were primarily tranquilizers, calming patients without unduly sedating them. These agents do have a fast effect, rapidly calming in hours the acutely agitated, excited, assaultive patient. However, by 1964, it was established that the drugs also have a delayed but very powerful therapeutic effect on the core symptoms of schizophrenia; over several weeks, they improve or abolish the delusions, hallucinations, and disordered thinking (Table 50–2). Moreover, these drugs have been shown to be capable of inducing full remissions of the psychosis in the great majority of patients having their first episode, whether the patients are agitated or apathetic, with great superiority over placebos. Finally, maintaining remitted patients on anti-

Table 50–2. Differential Response of Schizophrenic Symptoms to Phenothiazines

Symptoms of schizophrenia	Response
Primary	
Thought disorder	+++
Blunted affect	+++
Withdrawal	+++
Autistic behavior	+++
Accessory	
Hallucinations	++
Paranoid ideation	+
Grandiosity	+
Hostility, belligerence	0
Nonschizophrenic	
Anxiety, tension, agitation	0
Guilt, depression	0

Adapted from Klein and Davis, 1969.

psychotic medication reduces the rate of relapse by at least two-thirds. In contrast, a number of controlled studies have shown that psychotherapy is ineffective in treating the acute psychotic phase of schizophrenia. It is no better than a placebo for the acute psychosis, and psychotherapy in addition to antipsychotic drugs has no advantage over drugs alone.

In the long-term maintenance of schizophrenics, however, psychotherapy and drugs have some advantage over drugs alone. Although treatment with drugs appears to work on the psychotic symptoms, such as disordered thought and delusions, drugs do not compensate for the poor social skills and lack of social adjustment that develop during the course of the illness. Thus strong social support of schizophrenic patients is still a necessary adjunct to chemotherapy.

Antipsychotic Drugs Affect Dopaminergic Transmission

The genetic predisposition to schizophrenia and the effectiveness of the antipsychotic drugs suggest that schizophrenia may result from a biochemical defect in the brain, the nature of which may be inferred from the mode of action of these drugs. The first clue to the cellular action of these drugs came from an analysis of their major side effects. The drugs tend to produce an extrapyramidal syndrome that resembles parkinsonism (hence the term *neuroleptic*, meaning an agent that stimulates the nervous system). As in parkinsonism, the drug-induced extrapyramidal syn-

A
Phenothiazine derivatives

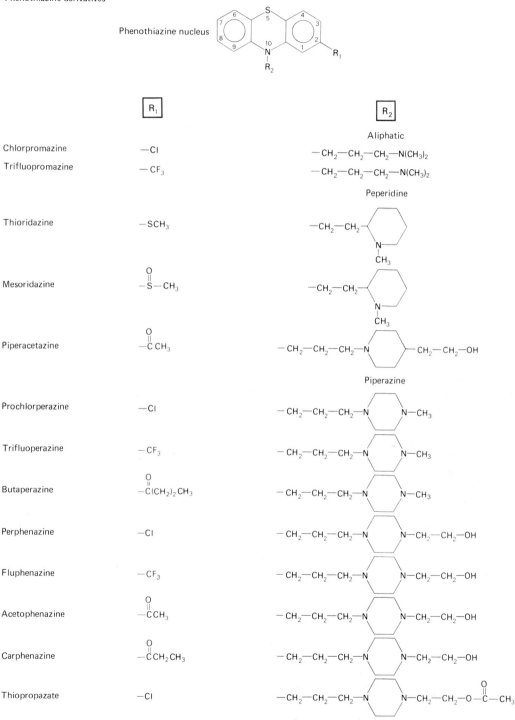

(continued)

50–1 Drugs used to treat schizophrenia. **A.** Structural relationships of phenothiazines. A circle drawn within the hexagonal ring indicates an aromatic (benzene-type) moiety.

B

1 Thioxanthene derivatives

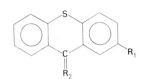

	R₁	R₂

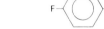

Chlorprothixene —Cl —CH—CH₂—CH₂—N(CH₃)₂

Thiothixene —SO₂N(CH₃)₂ —CH—CH₂—CH₂—N☐N—CH₃

2 Butyrophenones

Haloperidol

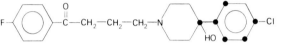

● Portion of molecule most often substituted

Droperidol

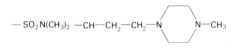

3 Diphenylbutylpiperidenes

Pimozide

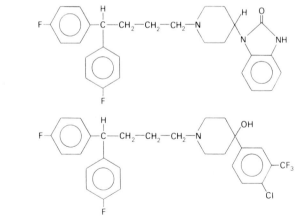

Penfluridol

50−1 Drugs used to treat schizophrenia *(continued)*
    B. Structural relationships of thioxanthene
derivatives, butyrophenones, and diphenylbutylpiperidines.
(Adapted from Kety et al., 1975.)

drome is reversed by anticholinergic agents. Because parkinsonism is thought to be due to a deficiency in dopaminergic transmission (see Chapter 31), this side effect suggested that antipsychotic drugs interfere with the action of dopaminergic neurons. Following an initial suggestion by the Swedish pharmacologist Avid Carlsson, a series of investigations has established that despite the differences in chemical structures (Figure 50–1), almost all the drugs that are effective antipsychotic agents interfere with dopaminergic transmission mostly by producing a blockade of dopamine receptors. Moreover, almost all drugs that block dopaminergic transmission have therapeutic effects in schizophrenia. Thus, while the effects on the central nervous system of each of the antischizophrenic drugs differ to some degree, interference with dopaminergic transmission appears to be an essential feature of the therapeutic effect of all the antipsychotic agents.

There are four key observations implicating blockade of dopaminergic transmission in the action of antipsychotic drugs:

1. Antischizophrenic agents bind to dopamine receptors in cell-free biochemical filter assays, displacing dopamine and other neuroleptics (see Chapter 10). Most persuasively, the milligram-for-milligram potency of the antipsychotic drugs in binding to dopamine receptors in filter assays closely approximates their relative therapeutic potency. Originally it was believed that these drugs exerted their action by specifically blocking equally all dopamine receptors. Recent evidence suggests, however, that there are at least two and perhaps several more types of dopamine receptors. One type (called D1) is linked to an adenylate cyclase; this receptor is located postsynaptically and has a low affinity for most types of antipsychotic drugs. A second type of receptor (called D2), also located postsynaptically, is not linked to this cyclase. This receptor has a high affinity for all antipsychotic drugs, and it is believed that a major action of these drugs is exerted through this receptor.

In addition to these postsynaptic receptors on other neurons there are inhibitory *autoreceptors* on dopaminergic neurons (this receptor type is not yet well characterized but seems not to be linked to a cyclase). These autoreceptors are located on the cell body and presynaptic terminals of the dopaminergic neuron and control both

the rate of firing and the release of dopamine from the dopaminergic neuron by the action potentials that invade the terminal (Figure 50–2; see also Chapter 8).

2. Antischizophrenic drugs cause an increase in the firing rate of the dopaminergic neurons and therefore increase the concentration of the breakdown product of dopamine (homovanillic acid) in the cerebrospinal fluid. This initially paradoxical finding has now been shown to be at least partially due to a blockade of inhibitory dopamine autoreceptors. Because of disinhibition resulting from blockade of the autoreceptor or through some other feedback effect, the dopaminergic neuron fires more frequently and releases more dopamine. This leads to an increase in the concentration of the dopamine metabolite, homovanillic acid, in various body fluids.

3. Dopaminergic drugs [such as L-dihydroxyphenylalanine (L-DOPA), amphetamine, and apomorphine] cause a characteristic behavioral syndrome in animals consisting of repetitive, stereotyped movements. Antischizophrenic drugs block this syndrome.

4. Antischizophrenic agents stimulate the secretion of prolactin by the pituitary; this secretion is normally tonically inhibited by release of dopamine from the medial basal hypothalamus. The relative potency of various agents in the chemical treatment of psychotics is proportional to their ability to stimulate secretion of prolactin.

The antischizophrenic drugs do not act solely on dopaminergic transmission. Some antipsychotic agents affect various other transmitter systems. For example, chlorpromazine has some blocking action on norepinephrine and serotonin receptors, and all phenothiazines cause a secondary increase in the synthesis of monoamine transmitters. However, these effects do not correlate with clinical potency and may be responsible instead for some of the side effects of the drugs.

A Dopamine Hypothesis of Schizophrenia Has Been Proposed

Two types of findings have led to the development of the hypothesis that schizophrenia results from an excess of dopaminergic transmission. First, there is the action of antipsychotic drugs on dopamine receptors described above. Second, dopamine agonists (Figure 50–3) and other drugs

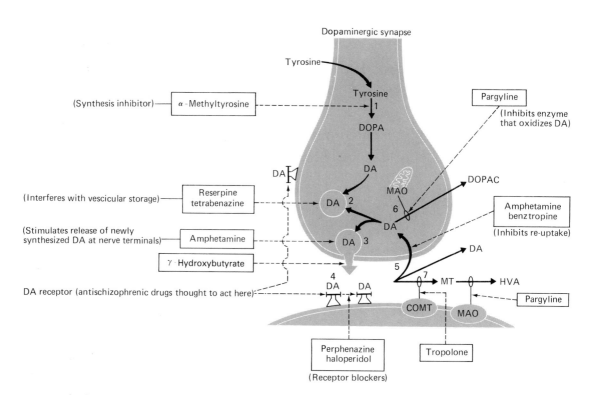

50–2 The dopaminergic synapse, showing key steps in the synthesis and degradation as well as the sites of action of various psychoactive substances. (Adapted from Cooper, Bloom, and Roth, 1978.)

Step 1. Enzymatic synthesis: (a) Tyrosine hydroxylase reaction blocked by the competitive inhibitor, α-methyltyrosine and other tyrosine hydroxylase inhibitors.

Step 2. Storage: Reserpine and tetrabenazine interfere with the uptake–storage mechanism of the amine granules. The depletion of dopamine produced by reserpine is long-lasting and the storage granules appear to be irreversibly damaged. Tetrabenazine also interferes with the uptake–storage mechanism of the granules except that the effects of this drug do not appear to be irreversible.

Step 3. Release: γ-hydroxybutyrate effectively blocks the release of dopamine by blocking impulse flow in dopaminergic neurons. Amphetamine administered in high doses releases dopamine but most of the releasing ability of amphetamine appears to be related to its ability to effectively block dopamine re-uptake.

Step 4. Receptor interaction: Apomorphine is an effective dopamine-receptor stimulating drug, with both pre- and postsynaptic sites of action. Perphenazine and haloperidol are effective dopamine-receptor blocking drugs.

Step 5. Re-uptake: Dopamine has its action terminated by being taken up into the presynaptic terminal. Amphetamine, as well as the anticholinergic drug benztropine, is a potent inhibitor of this re-uptake mechanism.

Step 6. Monoamine oxidase (MAO): Dopamine present in a free state within the presynaptic terminal can be degraded by the enzyme MAO, which appears to be located in the outer membrane of the mitochondria. Dihydroxyphenylacetic acid (DOPAC) is a product of the action of MAO and aldehyde oxidase on dopamine. Pargyline is an effective inhibitor of MAO. Some MAO is also present outside the dopaminergic neuron.

Step 7. Catechol-O-methyl transferase (COMT): Dopamine can be inactivated by the enzyme COMT, which is believed to be localized outside the presynaptic neuron. Tropolone is an inhibitor of COMT.

that enhance the action of dopamine (cocaine, amphetamine, and L-DOPA) can induce psychotic syndromes resembling paranoid schizophrenia.

The molecular alterations in dopaminergic

transmission that occur in schizophrenia are not known. There are four possibilities: (1) too much dopamine is released by the dopaminergic neurons; (2) dopaminergic receptors are hypersensitive to the normal amount of dopamine released;

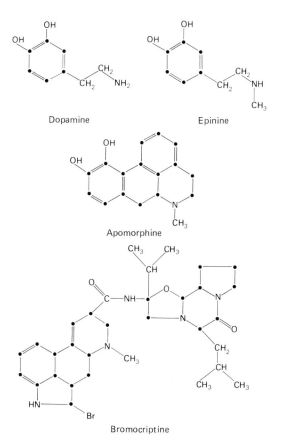

50–3 Chemical structures of dopamine agonists.

(3) an antagonistic neurotransmitter system is underactive; and (4) there is malfunction of a feedback pathway (neuronal or hormonal) that controls a component of the dopamine system.

These possibilities are listed not because there is evidence that any one of them plays a determining role in the pathophysiology of the disease, but to indicate that a variety of cellular mechanisms might alter synaptic transmission and that we need to be cautious about simplifying hypotheses. At the moment, there is no direct biochemical evidence for excessive dopaminergic activity in schizophrenics, although a disturbance in a small brain region would be hard to demonstrate. Recent postmortem studies have, however, shown an increase in the binding capacity of dopamine receptors in membranes from schizophrenic brains, but this may be secondary to long-term treatment with antipsychotic agents that block dopamine receptors.

The Neuropathology of Schizophrenia Might Be Localized in the Mesolimbic Dopaminergic System

The possibility that dopaminergic transmission is disturbed in schizophrenia raises further questions. There are many components to the dopamine system in the brain. Which component is critical for schizophrenia? The vague suggestion that a disorder in dopaminergic transmission is involved in schizophrenia is analogous to knowing that a disorder of cholinergic transmission is critical for myasthenia gravis without knowing that the defect is located at the synapse between motor neurons and voluntary muscle. Imagine how much time might have been lost looking for disturbances in functions among the millions of widely distributed cholinergic neurons in the brain had we not been aware, early on, that the defect in myasthenia gravis resides in a specific and peripherally situated (and easily accessible) locus. Thus, in schizophrenia (as in depressive disorders, which will be considered in Chapter 51) the challenge is to move from an initial set of pharmacological clues to more precise anatomical localization.

Formaldehyde-induced histofluorescence microscopy (see Chapter 10) has been very helpful in this regard. It has revealed that there are three principal (and several minor) dopaminergic systems in the brain (Figure 50–4).

1. *The nigrostriatal system.* There are dopaminergic cell bodies in the substantia nigra with axons that project primarily to the putamen and the caudate nucleus. As was pointed out in Chapter 31, partial degeneration of this system contributes importantly to the pathogenesis of Parkinson's disease.
2. *The mesocortical system.* Dopaminergic cell bodies are located in the ventral tegmental area of Tsai, medial and superior to the substantia nigra. The axons of these cells project to the limbic system—specifically to the mesial components, the nucleus accumbens, the olfactory tubercle, the nuclei of the stria terminalis, and parts of the amygdala—and to the lateral septal nuclei, the mesial frontal, anterior cingulate, and entorhinal cortex.
3. *The tuberoinfundibular system.* Dopaminergic cell bodies in the arcuate nucleus of the median eminence project their axons to the pituitary stalk. This system is important for aspects of neuroendocrine regulation.

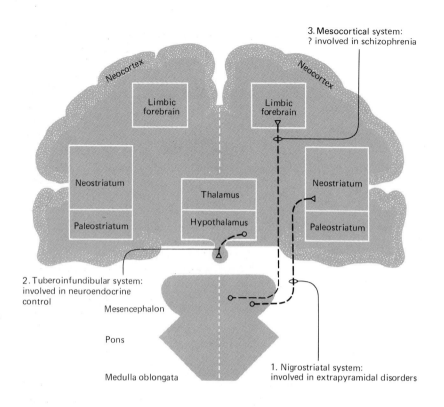

3. **Mesocortical system:**
? involved in schizophrenia

Neocortex

Neocortex

Limbic forebrain

Limbic forebrain

Neostriatum

Neostriatum

Thalamus

Paleostriatum

Hypothalamus

Paleostriatum

2. **Tuberoinfundibular system:**
involved in neuroendocrine control

Mesencephalon

Pons

Medulla oblongata

1. **Nigrostriatal system:**
involved in extrapyramidal disorders

50–4   Three central dopaminergic tracts and their presumed function.

The role of the limbic system in emotions and in memory (see Chapters 38 and 47) and the superficial similarity between schizophrenia and certain types of psychomotor epilepsy have made it attractive to speculate that a dysfunction in the mesolimbic dopaminergic system may be involved in the etiology of schizophrenia.

Among the projections of the mesolimbic dopaminergic system, the projection to the nucleus accumbens is receiving the most interest. Janice Stevens of the University of Oregon has suggested that the nucleus accumbens and its related structures serve as *gates* or *filters* for information concerned with affect (or state of feeling) and with certain types of memory projections from the hippocampus to other parts of the brain (hypothalamus and frontal cortex) and that this dopaminergic projection modulates the flow of neural activity through this filter network. The nucleus accumbens is the most prominent of the limbic nuclei and is located between the anterior pole of the caudate nucleus, the olfactory tubercle, and

the septum. This nucleus (as well as the other targets of the mesolimbic dopaminergic projection) receives massive converging input from the hippocampus (and the amygdala) and projects in turn to the septum, hypothalamus, and frontal lobes—areas that might well be involved in schizophrenia.

There Are Important Weaknesses in the Dopamine Hypothesis

There are, however, important problems with the dopamine hypothesis for schizophrenia both from a conceptual and a clinical point of view. From the conceptual point of view, it is difficult to extrapolate from the mechanisms of action of a therapeutic agent to the causal mechanisms of the disease, since pharmacological manipulation may produce changes that compensate for the disease without directly affecting the disordered mechanism itself. For example, the primary lesion in Parkinson's disease is a decrease in dopamine, but it is alleviated by anticholinergic drugs. This can be further illustrated by reference to a simple model (Figure 50–5). Take the hypothetical situation of four presynaptic neurons

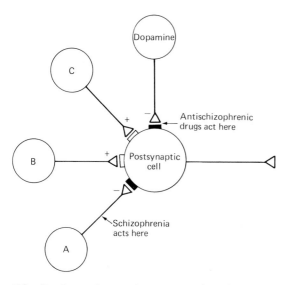

50–5 Scheme showing how an antischizophrenic drug could ameliorate a neural imbalance due to excessive inhibitory action on a particular set of neurons, such as might be caused by schizophrenia, without directly acting on the neurons that are disordered by the disease. Assume that schizophrenia is due to a synaptic imbalance at a particular neural structure as a result of inhibition exceeding excitation due to overactivity of inhibitory neuron. *A.* Blocking the effectiveness of a parallel dopaminergic inhibitory neuron could ameliorate the disease by reducing the net inhibition converging on the postsynaptic cell. (Adapted from R. Zigmond, personal communication.)

converging on a postsynaptic neuron with each presynaptic neuron releasing a different transmitter (transmitter A, transmitter B, transmitter C, and dopamine). Transmitter A and dopamine inhibit the postsynaptic cell, whereas transmitters B and C excite it. If schizophrenia resulted from a defect in neuron A or its transmitter, so that an excess of this inhibitory transmitter could act on the postsynaptic cell, one might improve the symptoms by simply blocking the action of dopamine, the other inhibitory transmitter, because this would reduce net inhibition onto the postsynaptic cell. This model could easily break down—for example the dopamine neuron and neuron A might in turn have very different inputs converging on them. If so, inhibition of dopaminergic transmission might not be an effective treatment. Nonetheless, even this simple example illustrates that despite a correlation between excess dopamine and schizophrenia, information on the molecular basis of the disease is still in-

complete. Fortunately, the momentum behind the search for molecular defects has increased dramatically within the past decade.

From a clinical standpoint the time course action of antipsychotic drugs needs to be explained. These drugs block dopamine receptors rapidly, whereas the core schizophrenic psychosis remits gradually over several weeks. This suggests that blocking dopaminergic transmission may have secondary consequences on other neuronal systems, consequences that are produced over a period of several weeks. Furthermore, antipsychotic drugs are effective only in treating or preventing psychotic episodes; they are completely ineffective for the nonpsychotic residual syndrome—low motivation, shallow affect, and social incompetence—which is such a serious aspect of schizophrenia. The drugs do not worsen the residual syndrome but do not alleviate it; indeed, there is no treatment for it of proved effectiveness. Furthermore, signs of social incompetence precede the first psychotic episode in most schizophrenics. Finally, investigations using computerized tomography, a three-dimensional X-ray technique (described in Appendix IIC) have revealed that many chronic schizophrenics have enlarged ventricles compared to normal people of the same age. This suggests that many schizophrenic patients may suffer from brain atrophy, and raises the possibility that in some forms of schizophrenia the psychotic episodes are secondary to a primary lesion of the brain that has not yet been recognized. Thus, the dopamine hypothesis, even if correct for the psychotic phase, is inadequate to account for the entire illness, and the search continues for the primary brain disturbance and a therapy for it.

Selected Readings and References

Klein, D. F., Gittelman, R., Quitkin, F., and Rifkin, A. 1980. Diagnosis and Drug Treatment of Psychiatric Disorders: Adults and Children. 2nd ed. Baltimore: Williams & Wilkins.

Snyder, S. H. 1976. The dopamine hypothesis of schizophrenia: Focus on the dopamine receptor. Am. J. Psychiatry 133:197–202.

Stevens, J. R. 1973. An anatomy of schizophrenia? Arch. Gen. Psychiatry 29:177–189.

Wynne, L. C., Cromwell, R. L., and Matthysse, S. (eds.). 1978. The Nature of Schizophrenia: New Approaches to Research and Treatment. New York: Wiley.

Other References

Bleuler, E. 1911. Dementia Praecox or the Group of Schizophrenias. Trans. by J. Zinkin. New York: International Universities Press, 1950.

Carlsson, A. 1974. Antipsychotic drugs and catecholamine synapses. J. Psychiatr. Res. 11:57–64.

Cooper, J. R., Bloom, F. E., and Roth, R. H. 1978. The Biochemical Basis of Neuropharmacology. 3rd ed. New York: Oxford University Press.

Davis, J. M., and Garver, D. L. 1978. Neuroleptics: Clinical use in psychiatry. In L. L. Iversen, S. D. Iversen, and S. H. Snyder (eds.), Handbook of Psychopharmacology, Vol. 10: Neuroleptics and Schizophrenia. New York: Plenum, pp. 129–164.

Iversen, L. L. 1975. Dopamine receptors in the brain. Science (Wash., D.C.) 188:1084–1089.

Kallmann, F. J. 1938. The Genetics of Schizophrenia. New York: Augustin.

Kety, S. S. 1978. The biological roots of mental illness: Their ramifications through cerebral metabolism, synaptic activity, genetics, and the environment. Harvey Lect. 71:1–22.

Kety, S. S., Rosenthal, D., Wender, P. H., Schulsinger, F., and Jacobsen, B. 1975. Mental illness in the biological and adoptive families of adopted individuals who have become schizophrenic: A preliminary report based on psychiatric interviews. In R. R. Fieve, D. Rosenthal, and H. Brill (eds.), Genetic Research in Psychiatry. Baltimore: Johns Hopkins University Press, pp. 147–165.

Klein, D. F., and Davis, J. M. 1969. Diagnosis and Drug Treatment of Psychiatric Disorders. Baltimore: Williams & Wilkins.

Kraepelin, E. 1909. Dementia Praecox and Paraphrenia. Trans. by R. M. Barclay from the 8th German edition of Kraepelin's Text-Book of Psychiatry. Edinburgh: Livingstone, 1919.

Matthysse, S. W., and Kety, S. S. (eds.). 1975. Catecholamines and Schizophrenia. Oxford: Pergamon.

Nauta, W. J. H., Smith, G. P., Faull, R. L. M., and Domesick, V. B. 1978. Efferent connections and nigral afferents of the nucleus accumbens septi in the rat. Neuroscience 3:385–401.

Roberts, P. J., Woodruff, G. N., and Iversen, L. L. (eds.). 1978. Dopamine. New York: Raven Press.

Edward J. Sachar

Psychobiology of Affective Disorders

51

O! that this too too solid flesh would melt,
Thaw, and resolve itself into a dew;
Or that the Everlasting had not fix'd
His canon 'gainst self-slaughter! O God! O God!
How weary, stale, flat, and unprofitable
Seem to me all the uses of this world.

Hamlet, Act I, scene ii

Mental illnesses involving depression and mania are called *affective disorders* because a prominent aspect of these disorders is a disturbance of affect—of mood or feeling tone. One type of affective disorder, major depression, was described superbly by Hippocrates. He proposed that moods depend upon the balance of four humors—blood, phlegm, yellow bile, and black bile—and attributed depression to an excess of black bile ("melancholia"). Efforts to update Hippocrates' original psychobiological formulation were hindered until recently by lack of precision in the differential diagnosis of depressive states. As Freud pointed out in 1917 in a paper entitled *Mourning and Melancholia,* "even in descriptive psychiatry the definition of melancholia is uncertain; it takes on various clinical forms—some of them suggesting somatic rather than psychogenic affections—that do not seem definitely to warrant reduction to a unity."

In the past two decades, better systems for classifying affective disorders clinically have been developed, following the strategies outlined in the previous chapter for validation and refinement of diagnostic categories. From the welter of human conditions involving unhappiness, misery, grief, disappointment, and despair have emerged certain depressive syndromes that are readily distinguishable, and which indeed appear to be somatic affections. In this chapter, we shall focus on two of these syndromes: the major depressive disorders of the unipolar (recurrent depressions) and bipolar (manic depressive) types.

The Clinical Features of Major Depressive Disorders Suggest a Hypothalamic Defect

Major Unipolar Depressions

The clinical features of unipolar major depression can be briefly summarized. Untreated, the usual episode of depression lasts 4–12 months and is characterized by a pervasive dysphoric (unpleasant) mood and a generalized loss of interests and the ability to experience pleasure. In Hamlet's words: "How weary, stale, flat, and unprofitable seem to me all the uses of this world!" The diagnosis also requires several additional symptoms: disturbed sleep (usually insomnia, with early morning awakening), diminished appetite, loss of energy, decreased sex drive, psychomotor agitation (restlessness) or retardation (slowing down of thoughts and actions), difficulty in concentration, and guilty, pessimistic, and suicidal thoughts. These thoughts may reach delusional proportions. While not required for diagnosis, other common symptoms are constipation, decreased salivation, and a diurnal variation in severity of symptoms—they are usually worse in the morning. Added to the inclusion criteria are other exclusion criteria; for example, there should be no signs of schizophrenia or organic brain disease. When the syndrome is defined in this manner, it is found that at any given time, about 4% of the general population is suffering from it (8,000,000 people in the United States alone!).

Study of patients with depression has revealed several features that suggest that an intrinsic regulatory defect underlies this disorder. Many of the characteristic symptoms point to a disturbance of functions regulated, at least in part, by the hypothalamus: pervasive disorders of mood, appetite, sexual drive, sleep, and autonomic and motor activity. (When these features

are prominent, the syndrome is termed *endogenous depression* or *melancholia*.) The depressive's insomnia, in fact, has been shown to be associated with very characteristic abnormalities in the sleep electroencephalogram not seen in ordinary patients suffering from insomnia.

The average onset is at 40 years of age and women are affected about two to three times more often than men. In at least 60% of episodes in both men and women, no significant psychosocial precipitating factors are evident. Even in those in which a psychological precipitant is found, the condition, once established, typically appears to be autonomous; it is relatively unresponsive to conventional psychotherapy or environmental changes. In contrast, treatments with medication or electroconvulsive therapy are quite effective (see below). Finally, the disturbance is recurrent; during the 20 years after the first episode, there are usually about four more episodes.

Bipolar (Manic Depressive) Disorders

Patients with bipolar disorders suffer both depressive and manic episodes. The illness affects men and women about equally, and the age of onset is about a decade younger than that of unipolar depression. The depressions are clinically similar to those seen in unipolar illness. The mania is characterized by an elevated, expansive, or irritable mood lasting at least 1 week, associated with several of the following symptoms: overactivity, overtalkativeness, increased energy and libido, pressure of ideas, grandiosity, distractibility, decreased need for sleep, and reckless involvements. In severe cases the patients are delusional.

As in unipolar depression, the syndrome of mania also suggests the involvement of hypothalamic functions, with disturbances in mood, energy, appetite, sleep, and sexual function. In the majority of episodes there is no detectable psychosocial precipitant. It, too, is a recurrent illness, with subsequent affective episodes of both types occurring about twice as often over a 20-year period as in unipolar disease.

There Is a Strong Genetic Predisposition for the Major Depressions

As is the case with schizophrenia, genetic factors are also important in both of the major depressive disorders. There is a much higher morbidity rate of depression in first-degree relatives (parents,

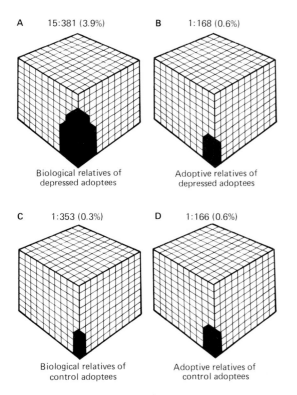

A   15:381 (3.9%)

Biological relatives of
depressed adoptees

B   1:168 (0.6%)

Adoptive relatives of
depressed adoptees

C   1:353 (0.3%)

Biological relatives of
control adoptees

D   1:166 (0.6%)

Adoptive relatives of
control adoptees

51–1 Incidence of suicides among biological and
adoptive relatives of depressed patients. There
is a higher incidence of suicide among biological
relatives of adoptees who suffered from bipolar
depression (**A**) than among their adoptive relatives (**B**)
and among the biological (**C**) and adoptive (**D**) relatives
of mentally healthy adoptees. Each ratio shows the
number of relatives who committed suicide with the
respect to the total number of relatives. (Adapted
from Kety, 1979.)

siblings, and children) of patients with depressive
illness when compared with the general population. The overall concordance rate for identical
(monozygotic) twin pairs is 69%; the rate for fraternal (dizygotic) twins is 13% (the same as for
siblings).

Recently, Seymour Kety, Paul H. Wender, and
David Rosenthal have extended their studies of
schizophrenia in adopted people and studied the
adoptive and biological families of adoptees with
manic depressive disorders. They again investigated the genetic predisposition by evaluating the
biological relatives, and the contribution of the
environment by evaluating the adoptive relatives. They found a higher rate of affective illness
in the biological parents of adoptees who grew up
to develop manic depressive illness than in their
adoptive parents, or in the biological and adoptive

parents of mentally healthy adoptees. As might
be expected, the incidence of suicide among biological relatives of adoptees who suffered from
depression was 6–10 times higher than among
the relatives of normal adoptees (Figure 51–1).

Furthermore, monozygotic twins reared apart
have a concordance rate of 40–60% (similar to
the concordance of those reared together). As is
the case with schizophrenia, the presence of
many discordant monozygotic twin pairs indicates, however, that nongenetic contributing factors influence the liability to affective disorder.
The precise mode of transmission is still unclear.
It is not a classic Mendelian pattern and may be
polygenic.

Recent genetic studies indicate that unipolar
and bipolar depressions are not completely distinct, but are part of a spectrum of depressive illness, in which unipolar depression may represent
the mild form of the spectrum and bipolar depression the severe form of the same disorder.

There Are Effective Somatic Treatments for Major Depression

There are two treatments of proved effectiveness
in major unipolar and bipolar depression: (1) electroconvulsive therapy (ECT), and (2) antidepressant drugs. Of the two modes of treatment electroconvulsive therapy has been used for a longer
period of time, over 4 decades. It is completely
painless and quite safe, and produces full remission or marked improvement in about 90% of
patients with well-defined major depressions.

The critical therapeutic factor in electroconvulsive therapy is the induction of a generalized
central nervous system seizure. A motor seizure
is not necessary or desirable for therapeutic results, and modern ECT is always given under
anesthesia and with complete muscle relaxation.
Approximately 4 to 12 treatments (on the average
6), given at 2-day intervals over a 2–4-week period, usually suffice to produce a complete remission of symptoms. As might be predicted from
our knowledge of seizure activity (Chapter 39),
electroconvulsive therapy produces a broad range
of temporary changes in brain functions, but the
mechanism of its therapeutic action is still not
understood. The only significant side effect is a
transient retrograde disturbance in memory that
clears within 2–3 weeks.

The most widely used antidepressent drugs
fall into two major classes: the *monoamine oxidase (MAO) inhibitors,* such as phenelzine (Fig-

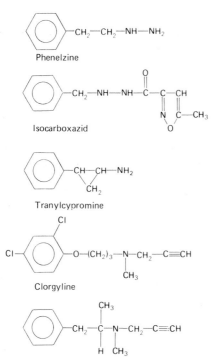

51–2 Structures of monoamine oxidase inhibitor antidepressant drugs. A circle drawn within the hexagonal ring indicates an aromatic (benzene-type) moiety.

ure 51–2); and the *tricyclic compounds*, such as imipramine, so named for their three ring molecular structure (Figure 51–3). (Recently, a number of effective antidepressants with still different chemical structures have been introduced.)

Both monoamine oxidase inhibitors and tricyclic antidepressant drugs produce a remission or marked improvement in about 70% of depressed patients. With high doses and monitoring of blood drug levels so as to reach necessary concentrations, the success rate of tricyclics may reach 80–85%; approaching the effectiveness of ECT. Bipolar depressives occasionally become manic during treatment with either class of antidepressant. Although a few patients begin to improve immediately, there is usually a lag of 1–3 weeks before the symptoms of depression begin to improve, and 4–6 weeks are generally required for full response.

Lithium salts are quite effective in terminating manic episodes, with the improvement beginning as soon as therapeutic blood concentrations are achieved. Maintenance lithium therapy has significant prophylactic effect in preventing or attenuating recurrent manic and depressive episodes, especially the former. Antipsychotic drugs are also quite effective in terminating manic episodes but do not appear to have lithium's prophylactic properties.

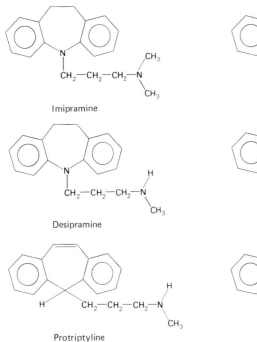

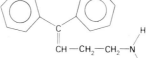

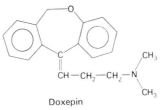

51–3 Structures of tricyclic antidepressant drugs. A circle drawn within the hexagonal ring indicates an aromatic (benzene-type) moiety.

A Biogenic Amine Hypothesis of Depression Has Been Proposed

Currently, the most prevalent idea about the nature of depression is that it involves a functional deficiency in monoamines. This idea has been derived mostly from studies of the effects of antidepressant drugs on the serotonergic and noradrenergic systems of the brain. According to this hypothesis (first proposed by G. M. Everett and J. E. P. Toman and later elaborated by Joseph Schildkraut), depression is caused by a functional deficiency of serotonin or norepinephrine or both, and the antidepressants work by increasing the availability of either or both amines (Figure 51–4). Mania was initially believed to result from the overactivity of noradrenergic systems, but the hypothesis in this simple form is no longer held. As discussed in Chapters 10 and 11, norepinephrine and serotonin are synthesized in appropriate neurons from amino acid precursors (tyrosine and tryptophan, respectively). They are then packaged in storage granules, and on stimulation they are released from the terminals into the synaptic cleft by means of exocytosis. The transmitters then interact with postsynaptic receptors. Both

norepinephrine and serotonin are then actively taken up into the presynaptic terminals and catabolized by the mitochondrial enzyme, monomine oxidase.

The first support for the biogenic amine hypothesis came from the observation, in 1950, that reserpine—then used extensively in the treatment of hypertension—seemed to precipitate depressive syndromes in about 15% of treated patients. This finding had a parallel in animal studies, which showed that reserpine produced a syndrome-like depression in animals, consisting of motor retardation and sedation. Soon thereafter Bernard Brodie and his colleagues at the National Institutes of Health showed that reserpine depletes the brain of serotonin and norepinephrine by releasing these neurotransmitters from their intracellular storage granules. As a result, the transmitters become accessible to degradation by monoamine oxidase (Figure 51–5). The first class of effective antidepressant to be discovered was iproniazid, an inhibitor of monoamine oxidase. Iproniazid was initially synthesized to be used against tuberculosis. In the course of clinical trials it was noted that some depressed tuberculosis patients treated with this drug experienced

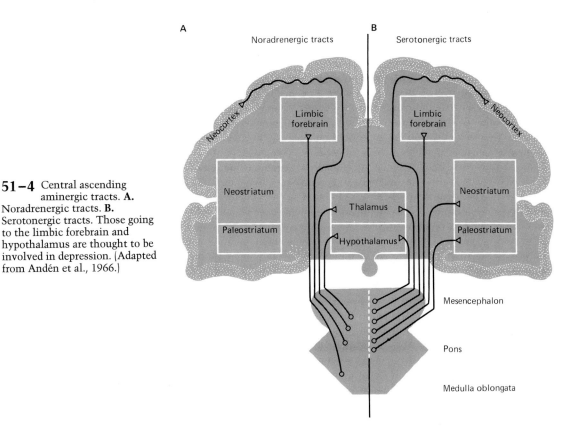

51–4 Central ascending aminergic tracts. **A.** Noradrenergic tracts. **B.** Serotonergic tracts. Those going to the limbic forebrain and hypothalamus are thought to be involved in depression. (Adapted from Andén et al., 1966.)

mood elevations. It was next tried in depressed patients and was found to be effective. Treatment with monoamine oxidase inhibitors increases the content of serotonin and norepinephrine in the brain by decreasing degradation of monoamine oxidase (Figure 51–5). Monoamine oxidase inhibitors were next found to prevent the biochemical and behavioral sedative effects of reserpine in animals.

Further support for the view that monoamine oxidase inhibitors exercise their therapeutic effect by increasing the functional availability of biogenic amines was provided by the discovery of a second class of effective antidepressants—the tricyclic compounds. These agents were soon found to block the active reuptake of released serotonin and norepinephrine by serotonergic and noradrenergic neurons, thereby prolonging the period over which the transmitters persist and act in the synaptic cleft.

Additional evidence came with the use of precursors of serotonin and norepinephrine in depressed patients. L-Tryptophan was found to potentiate the therapeutic effect of monoamine oxidase inhibitors, and, recently, 5-hydroxytryptophan has also been found to act as an antidepressant. While L-DOPA is not particularly effective as an antidepressant, it can precipitate manic or hypomanic episodes in patients with bipolar depression. Amphetamine, which releases catecholamines from nerve endings and, to a lesser extent, blocks their reuptake, transiently elevates mood in normal people and in some depressed patients. Similarly, agents that inhibit serotonin synthesis, such as paracholorophenylalanine (PCPA), can precipitate abrupt relapses in depressed patients who have recovered after therapy with the tricyclic antidepressant. Triiodothyronine (T₃), a hormone that is thought to sensitize catecholamine receptors in the brain, poten-

---

51–5 Schematic model of central noradrenergic and serotonergic neurons indicating possible sites of drug action. (Adapted from Cooper, Bloom, and Roth, 1978.)

A. Noradrenergic synapse.
Step 1. Enzymatic synthesis:
 a. Tyrosine hydroxylase reaction blocked by the competitive inhibitor, α-methyltyrosine.

 b. Dopamine-β-hydroxylase reaction blocked by a dithiocarbamate derivative, Fla-63 bis-(I-methyl-4-homopiperazinyl-thiocarbonyl)-disulfide.
Step 2. Storage: Reserpine and tetrabenazine interfere with the uptake–storage mechanism of the amine granules. The depletion of norepinephrine produced by reserpine is long-lasting and the storage granules are irreversibly damaged. Tetrabenazine also interferes with the uptake–storage mechanism

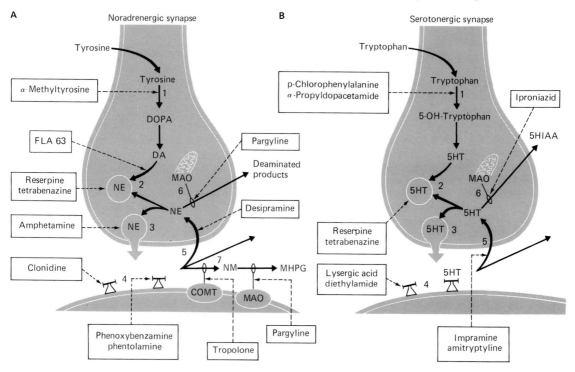

tiates the antidepressant effect of moderate doses of tricyclics.

It has been argued that biogenic amines are transmitters in those neural systems involved in motivation and pleasure. As described in Chapter 37, there are areas or pathways in the brain thought to be concerned with positive motivation (or the perception of pleasure) because electrical stimulation in these areas creates a state in which the animals actively seek further electrical stimulation. These so-called reward or pleasure pathways are thought to be made up primarily of catecholaminergic neurons. The pervasive loss of the feeling of pleasure in depressed patients might be related to disturbances in these systems.

Because norepinephrine and serotonin do not cross the blood–brain barrier, investigators have focused on the metabolites of these transmitters in body fluids of depressed patients and controls.

Urinary excretion of 3-methoxy-4-hydroxyphenyleneglycol (MHPG) is derived in substantial part from the catabolism of brain norepinephrine; in depressed patients of the bipolar type, there is a reduction in its urinary excretion. The major metabolite of serotonin, 5-hydroxyindole acetic acid (5HIAA) has been measured in the spinal fluid of depressed patients; and a reduction in its concentration in spinal fluid, particularly in suicidal patients, has been reported. These biochemical observations are consistent with the notion of decreased norepinephrine or serotonin or both in some depressed patients.

These changes in concentration of transmitter metabolites in peripheral body fluids are difficult to relate directly to specific brain mechanisms. A decrease in a neurotransmitter metabolite could be produced by decreased synthesis of the parent compound, decreased release, or decreased catabolism—and there could be several

---

of the granules, except the effects of this drug do not appear to be irreversible.

Step 3. Release: Amphetamine appears to cause an increase in the net release of norepinephrine. Probably the primary mechanism by which amphetamine causes release is by its ability to block effectively the reuptake mechanism.

Step 4. Receptor interaction: Clonidine appears to be a very potent receptor stimulating drug. Phenoxybenzamine and phentolamine are effective alpha-receptor blocking agents. Recent experiments have indicated that these drugs may also have a presynaptic site of action.

Step 5. Re-uptake: Norepinephrine has its action terminated by being taken up into the presynaptic terminal. The tricyclic drug desipramine is a potent inhibitor of this uptake mechanism.

Step 6. Monoamine oxidase (MAO): Norepinephrine or dopamine present in a free state within the presynaptic terminal can be degraded by the enzyme MAO, which appears to be located in the outer membrane of mitochondria. Pargyline is an effective inhibitor of MAO.

Step 7. Catechol-O-methyl transferase (COMT): Norepinephrine can be inactivated by the enzyme COMT, which is believed to be localized outside the presynaptic neuron. Tropolone is an inhibitor of COMT. The normetanephrine (NM) formed by the action of COMT on NE can be further metabolized by MAO and aldehyde reductase to 3-methoxy-4-hydroxyphenylglycol (MHPG). The MHPG formed can be further metabolized to MHPG-sulfate by the action of a sulfotransferase found in brain.

B. Serotonergic synapse.

Step 1. Enzymatic synthesis: Tryptophan is taken up

into the serotonin-containing neuron and converted to 5-OH-tryptophan by the enzyme tryptophan hydroxylase. This enzyme can be effectively inhibited by p-chlorophenylalanine and α-propyldopacetamide. The next synthetic step involves the decarboxylation of 5-OH-tryptophan to form serotonin (5-HT).

Step 2. Storage: Reserpine and tetrabenazine interfere with the uptake-storage mechanism of the amine granules causing a marked depletion of serotonin.

Step 3. Release: At present there is no drug available which selectively blocks the release of serotonin. However, lysergic acid diethylamide, because of its ability to block or inhibit the firing of serotonin neurons, causes a reduction in the release of serotonin from the nerve terminals.

Step 4. Receptor interaction: Lysergic acid diethylamide acts as a partial agonist at serotonergic synapses in the CNS. A number of compounds have also been suggested to act as receptor blocking agents at serotonergic synapses, but direct proof of these claims at the present time is lacking.

Step 5. Re-uptake: Considerable evidence now exists to suggest that serotonin may have its action terminated by being taken up into the presynaptic terminal. The tricyclic drugs with a tertiary nitrogen such as imipramine and amitryptyline appear to be potent inhibitors of this uptake mechanism.

Step 6. Monoamine oxidase (MAO): Serotonin present in free state within the presynaptic terminal can be degraded by the enzyme MAO, which appears to be located in the outer membrane of mitochondria. Iproniazid and clorgyline are effective inhibitors of MAO.

causes of each. Furthermore, if the neurochemical disturbance in depression involves only a relatively small brain region (as is likely), it would be extraordinarily difficult to detect in measurements of the total pool of metabolites coming from all areas.

The Original Biogenic Amine Hypothesis Is Undergoing Major Revisions

All of these psychopharmacological and biochemical observations provide circumstantial support for the biogenic amine hypothesis. However, the hypothesis fails to account for certain clinical phenomena. For example, whereas the slow time course for inhibition of monoamine oxidase by its inhibitors is consistent with the slow onset of the clinical response, blockade by tricyclics of the high-affinity reuptake systems for serotonin and norepinephrine occurs rapidly, but the clinical response to these drugs takes 2–3 weeks. The tricyclics also vary widely in their relative abilities to block serotonin or norepinephrine reuptake, yet their clinical efficacies in depressed patients are about the same, particularly if doses are adjusted to achieve the proper blood concentrations. Furthermore, certain recently discovered antidepressant drugs, such as mianserin, are effective clinically but have no effect on the reuptake of serotonin or norepinephrine.

A resolution of the paradox between the clinical time course of antidepressant drug action and their action on uptake came with the realization that these drugs act on processes other than uptake. The search for chronic effects of antidepressant drugs on nerve cells has revealed striking changes in the long-term sensitivity of various monoamine receptors; in some sensitivity is increased and in others it is decreased. For example, electroconvulsive therapy, as well as antidepressants of every class, reduces the sensitivity of beta-adrenergic receptors. Some antidepressants (including lithium) also increase the sensitivity of serotonin receptors and alpha-adrenergic receptors. The time required for these changes in receptor sensitivity corresponds to that required for the therapeutic effect of the drugs (2–3 weeks), suggesting that certain of the receptor changes may mediate the clinical effects or, alternatively, that the action on receptors and on uptake may be synergistic.

Thus, the earlier, simple servomechanistic version of the monoamine hypothesis—too little or too much of a particular neurotransmitter—is no longer tenable, but no satisfactory revised theory has yet emerged. Nonetheless, brain serotonergic and noradrenergic pathways are strongly implicated in the chemical pathology of affective disorders and in the clinical response to therapeutic agents.

There Are Disordered Neuroendocrine Functions in Depression

The many clinical signs of hypothalamic disturbance in depression suggest that hypothalamic modulation of neuroendocrine activity might also be affected. Indeed, the neurotransmitter systems most implicated in depression—serotonin and norepinephrine—also play important roles in neuroendocrine regulation. One of the best established neuroendocrine disturbances is a hypersecretion of cortisol in severe depression, secondary to excessive adrenocorticotropin secretion. Normally, there is a pronounced circadian rhythm in the secretion of cortisol, with secretion peaking at 8:00 A.M. and virtually ceasing in the evening and early morning hours. In contrast, about 50% of depressed patients secrete excessive amounts of cortisol, primarily during the afternoon and evening hours (Figure 51–6). The hypersecretion in the afternoon and evening is frequently resistant to feedback suppression after the administration of the potent synthetic corticosteroid, dexamethasone. This cortisol secretory disturbance in depression is independent of stress responses, and it is rarely found in other psychiatric disorders. It returns to normal with clinical recovery.

Because norepinephrine inhibits the action of corticotropin-releasing factor and of adrenocorticotropin, and since depletion of norepinephrine leads to the hypersecretion of adrenocorticotropin and cortisol, cortisol hypersecretion in depression may be secondary to a functional depletion of hypothalamic norepinephrine. In support of this idea, small intravenous doses of amphetamine (a norepinephrine releaser) have been shown to lower cortisol levels rapidly to normal in depressed patients.

Another characteristic endocrine abnormality in depressives is a blunted growth hormone response to hypoglycemia induced by a standard dose of insulin. The growth hormone response can also be blunted by brain norepinephrine and serotonin blockers and depletors, once again suggesting that this neuroendocrine abnormality in

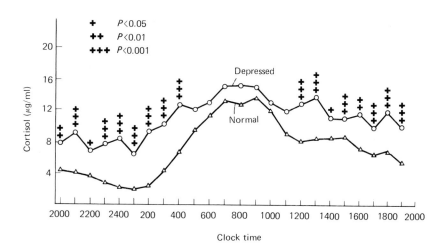

depressive illness may be related to central monoaminergic dysfunction.

An Overall View

Although our understanding of the biochemical mechanisms of depression is only at a very elementary level, the clinical features, genetic data, pharmacological studies, hormonal abnormalities, and biochemical observations all serve to define major depressive illness as an inherited neurochemical disorder primarily affecting the hypothalamus, and probably involving somehow the monoamine pathways. While the precise mechanisms causing the defect and their mode of hereditary transmission remain obscure, the rapid development of this field in less than 2 decades encourages optimism that major depressive illness will be among the first major psychiatric disorders to have its chemical pathology elucidated.

Selected Readings and References

Kety, S. S. 1979. Disorders of the human brain. Sci. Am. 241(3):202–214.

Sachar, E. J., Asnis, G., Halbreich, U., Nathan, R. S., and Halpern, F. 1980. Recent studies in the neuroendocrinology of major depressive disorders. Psychiatr. Clin. North Am. 3:313–326.

See the following articles in M. A. Lipton, A. DiMascio, and K. F. Killam (eds.). 1978. Psychopharmacology: A Generation of Progress. New York: Raven Press.

51–6 Circadian variation in cortisol secretion. Mean hourly plasma cortisol concentration over a 24-hr period for seven unipolar depressed patients compared with the mean for 54 normal subjects. Each **point** represents the mean cortisol concentration during the preceding hours. **Plus signs** indicate the significance of differences between depressed and normal values for each hour.

Murphy, D. L., Campbell, I., and Costa, J. L. Current status of the indoleamine hypothesis of the affective disorders, pp. 1235–1247.

Schildkraut, J. J. Current status of the catecholamine hypothesis of affective disorders, pp. 1223–1234.

Winokur, G. Mania and depression: Family studies and genetics in relation to treatment, pp. 1213–1221.

Other References

Andén, N.–E., Dahlström, A., Fuxe, K., Larsson, K., Olson, L., and Ungerstedt, U. 1966. Ascending monoamine neurons to the telencephalon and diencephalon. Acta. Physiol. Scand. 67:313–326.

Cooper, J. R., Bloom, F. E., and Roth, R. H. 1978. The Biochemical Basis of Neuropharmacology. 3rd ed. New York: Oxford University Press.

Everett, G. M., and Toman, J. E. P. 1959. Mode of action of Rauwolfia alkaloids and motor activity. In J. H. Masserman (ed.), Biological Psychiatry. New York: Grune & Stratton, pp. 75–81.

Pletscher, A., Shore, P. A., and Brodie, B. B. 1956. Serotonin as a mediator of reserpine action in brain. J. Pharmacol. Exp. Ther. 116:84–89.

Eric R. Kandel

Environmental Determinants of Brain Architecture and of Behavior: Early Experience and Learning

52

In earlier chapters we have emphasized that behavior is determined by the functioning of the brain and that mental illness reflects its malfunction. All functions of the brain in turn represent an interaction between inborn and environmental factors such as learning. We have already seen that the structure of the brain is to an important degree specified by genetic and developmental processes. In this final chapter, we shall illustrate that that structure of the brain, specifically the pattern of interconnections between neurons, also depends upon experience.

Although it is an obvious simplification, it is useful to think of the brain as an information processing system, a biological computer. The brain, like a computer, is a precisely wired device that performs a series of logical operations on the input it receives from a variety of sensory receptors. This information is processed by the brain into coherent images that we call thoughts and feelings. On the basis of these images (our perception of the external and internal world), the brain is capable of initiating action. However, the brain as a biological computer differs from electronic computers in at least two ways. First, it is remarkably plastic: it is capable of changing its performance and even its strategies as a result of experience. Second, at certain stages in its development, the integrative action of the brain and, at a cellular level, its very structure, are dependent upon its interaction with its environment.

The action of the environment on the brain and therefore on behavior varies with age. Abnormal patterns of stimulation have more profound effects at early stages of development than at later ones. In this chapter we shall first examine how early experience influences the development of the immature brain. We shall then consider how later experience (such as learning) influences the adult brain.

There Is a Critical Period in the Development of Normal Social and Perceptual Competence

As we have seen, there are critical periods in the development of the brain. These irreversible choice points commit nerve cells to differentiate along one path or another. There are similar critical periods in the development of instinctive behavior, for example, in the acquisition of sexual identity. Recent experiments, ranging from very complex ones in human infants to relatively simple ones in experimental animals, demonstrate that there are critical periods or stages in the development of social and perceptual competence. During these periods the infant must interact with a normal social (or inanimate) environment if further development is to proceed normally.

The best way to show that certain social or perceptual stimuli are important for development is to deprive an infant of these stimuli and to examine the consequences on later performance. Fortunately, deprivation experiments with infants have not been deliberately carried out by ethical scientists; however, sometimes deprivation has been imposed by parents or by public institutions. There are a few reliable histories of wild children who survived abandonment in the forest or jungle and who later were returned to civilization. Anecdotal evidence also abounds on newborn infants who were left unattended during the major part of each day, being fed but not otherwise cared for. As might be expected, the social behavior of these abandoned children is abnormal, and they often are mute and incapable of learning language.

The classic studies of the New York psychoanalyst Rene Spitz, carried out in the 1940s, provided the first coherent evidence that social interaction with other humans is essential in infant development. Spitz compared the develop-

ment of infants raised in a foundling home for abandoned children with the development of infants raised in a nursing home attached to a woman's prison. Both institutions were clean and provided adequate food and medical care. The babies in the nursing home were all cared for by their mothers who, because they were in prison and away from their families, tended to shower affection on their infants in the limited time allotted to them each day. In contrast, in the foundling home the infants were cared for by nurses, each of whom was responsible for seven infants. As a result, children in the foundling home had much less contact with other human beings than those in the prison's nursing home. The two institutions also differed in another respect. In the nursing home the cribs were open, and the infants could readily watch the activity in the ward; they could see other babies play and observe their mothers and the staff go about their business. In the foundling home the bars of the cribs were covered by sheets that prevented the infants from seeing outside. This dramatically reduced the infants' environment. In short, the babies in the foundling home lived under conditions of relative sensory and social deprivation.

Spitz followed a group of newborn infants at each of the two institutions throughout their early years. At the end of the first 4 months, the infants in the foundling home scored better than those in the nursing home on several developmental indices. This suggested to Spitz that genetic factors did not favor the infants in the nursing home. However, 8 months later, at the end of the first year, the performance of the children in the foundling home had fallen far below that of those in the nursing home, and many had developed a syndrome that Spitz called *hospitalism* (now often called *anaclitic depression*). These children were withdrawn, showed little curiosity or gaiety, and were prone to infection. During their second and third years, children in the nursing home were similar to children raised in normal families at home: they walked well and talked actively. In contrast, the development of the children in the foundling home was delayed. Only 2 of 26 children in the foundling home were able to walk, only these 2 spoke at all, and even they could say only a few words. Normal children at this age are agile, have a vocabulary of hundreds of words, and speak in sentences.

Although Spitz's pioneering studies were not well controlled (and have often been criticized for their methodology), several aspects of his work have been confirmed in subsequent, more carefully controlled studies, and most students of infant development now agree that Spitz's conclusions are basically correct. Severe social and sensory deprivation in early childhood can have catastrophic consequences for later development. In contrast, isolation later in life (although often unpleasant) is much better tolerated. The studies of Spitz thus stand as a landmark; they define a paradigm that has since been repeated often and profitably.

Isolated Young Monkeys Do Not Develop Normal Social Behavior

Spitz's work was carried one important step further in the 1960s when Harry and Margaret Harlow at the University of Wisconsin developed an experimental model of human social deprivation by rearing monkeys in isolation. The Harlows found that when newborn monkeys were isolated for 6 months to 1 year they were physically healthy but behaviorally devastated. These monkeys crouched in a corner of their cages and rocked back and forth in the manner that is reminiscent of severely disturbed (autistic) children. They showed no social behavior when interacting with other monkeys, no aggressive behavior, and no sexual behavior. Whereas a 6-month period of social isolation during the first 1.5 years of life produces a persistent and serious behavioral alteration, a comparable period of isolation later in life is innocuous. Thus, in monkeys, as in humans, there is a critical period for social development.

The Harlows next sought to determine the factors that need to be introduced into the isolation experience to prevent the development of the isolation syndrome. They found that the syndrome could be partially reversed by giving an isolated monkey a surrogate mother—a cloth-covered wooden dummy. This elicited clinging behavior in the isolated monkey but was insufficient for the emergence of fully normal social behavior. Social development would occur normally only if, in addition to a surrogate mother, the isolated animal had contact for a few hours each day with a normal infant monkey who spent the rest of its day in the monkey colony. Recently, Stephen Suomi and H. F. Harlow have found that the complete isolation syndrome can sometimes be reversed fully by contact with certain monkeys (monkey psychotherapists) with special personality traits, such as persistence and unflagging gregariousness, who repeatedly engage the isolate in social and aggressive behavior until the isolate begins to respond.

Early Sensory Deprivation Alters Perceptual Development

Early deprivation does not have to be as all-encompassing as social isolation to have behavioral consequences. There is also a critical period in the development of normal perception. Even restricted sensory deprivation has dire consequences. In 1932 Marius von Senden in Germany reviewed the world literature on cataracts in the newborn. He discovered several children who were born with cataracts that were removed much later in life (at age 10–20). Because of the cataracts these children were deprived of patterned vision. When their cataracts were later removed, these patients had no difficulty recognizing colors, but they had difficulty in recognizing shapes and patterns.

The idea that normal sensory experience is required for normal perceptual development was supported by the American psychologist Austin Riesen, who raised newborn monkeys in the dark for the first 3–6 months. When these monkeys were later introduced to a normal visual world, Riesen found that they could not discriminate even simple shapes. It took weeks or even months of training for these monkeys to learn to distinguish a circle from a square. Thus the development of normal perception—the capacity to distinguish between objects in the visual world—requires exposure to patterned visual stimulation early in development.

How is this perceptual development accomplished? Can we begin to understand how the interaction between the perceptual environment and the brain during the critical period influences the functioning of individual nerve cells?

There Are Cellular Correlates to Sensory Deprivation in Animals

An important beginning toward providing answers to the question raised above has been made by David Hubel and Torsten Wiesel of the Harvard Medical School in an imaginative series of studies in newborn kittens and monkeys. Hubel and Wiesel examined the effects of cellular responses in the primary visual (striate) cortex after visual deprivation. They found that a normal adult monkey (or cat) has good binocular interaction (Figure 52–1). Most cells in the cortex respond to an appropriate stimulus presented to either the left eye or the right eye; only a small proportion of cells respond only to the left eye or the right eye (Figure 52–2). However, if a monkey is raised from birth up to 3 months of age with one eyelid sutured closed, the animal is then permanently blind in that eye when later examined after removal of the occluding sutures. Electrical recordings made from single nerve cells in the visual cortex of these animals show that the affected eye has lost its ability to control cortical

neurons. Only very few cells can be driven from the deprived eye (Figure 52–2C,2). Consistent with other effects requiring a critical period, similar visual deprivation in an adult has no effect on vision.

Hubel and Wiesel next found that visual deprivation in newborn monkeys profoundly alters the architecture of ocular dominance columns in the cerebral cortex (see Chapter 21, Figure 21–7). Normally, the fibers from the lateral geniculate nucleus for each eye end in separate and alternating areas in layer IVc of the visual cortex, giving rise to cortical columns of equal size for each eye (Figure 52–3A). These columns are called the ocular dominance columns. After deprivation, the columns that receive input from the normal eye are greatly widened at the expense of those that receive input from the deprived eye (Figure 52–3B).

Here then is direct evidence that sensory deprivation early in life can alter the structure of the cerebral cortex! It is interesting that in 1965 when Hubel and Wiesel first discovered the existence of a critical period for binocular interaction they had only a physiological indication of the effect of sensory deprivation. Using the techniques *then* available, they failed to find any morphological change in the visual cortex. Only in 1972, with the development of new autoradiographic labeling techniques involving axonal transport for mapping connections between neurons (see Chapter 11), could Hubel and Wiesel demonstrate structural features of the disturbance. Thus, in a larger sense, the studies of Hubel and Wiesel make us realize that we are just beginning to develop the techniques to explore the structural organization of the brain and its possible alterations by experience and by disease. No wonder, then, that the understanding of the biological basis of most forms of mental illness—such as schizophrenia and depression—has so far been beyond our reach. It will be interesting, in the future, to see whether social deprivation of the sort studied by Harlow leads to a deterioration or distortion of connections in other areas of the brain.

Adults Also Exhibit Behavioral and Neuronal Plasticity

The consequences of environmental stimuli and of social experience are not restricted to infancy; these factors also influence adults. The simplest examples of the influence of social and psychological factors on cellular functioning in the adult

52–1 In the retinal geniculocortical pathway of higher mammals, the input from the two eyes is segregated until integration is achieved by neurons in the visual cortex. The axons of cells in the lateral geniculate nucleus form synaptic connections with neurons in the primary visual (striate) cortex. These cortical neurons are organized into separate columns and receive input from only one eye, but their axons go to adjacent columns as well as along their own column. This effect creates a mixing of inputs and allows most cells in the upper and lower layers of the cortex to receive input from both eyes.

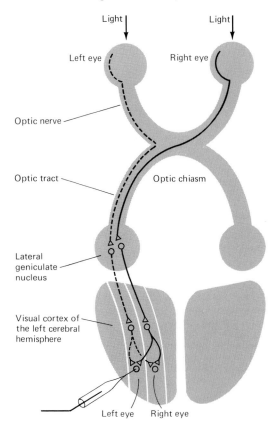

624

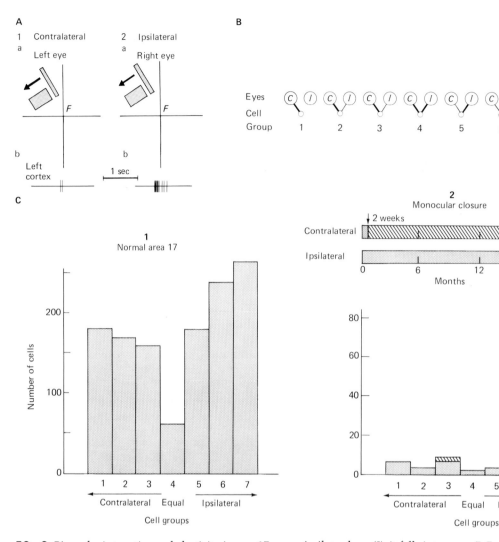

52–2 Binocular interaction and plasticity in area 17 of the monkey's visual (striate) cortex. **A.** The response of a typical neuron in the visual cortex of the left hemisphere to a diagonal bar of light moving to the left. The visual fields as seen by the left eye *(1a)* and the right eye *(2a)* are drawn separately for clarity, although the two are superimposed. The fields in the two eyes are similar in orientation, position, shape, and size and respond to the same form of stimulus (in this case a moving bar). The action potential recordings show that the cortical cell responds more effectively when the stimulus is presented to the ipsilateral eye *(2b)* than to the contralateral eye *(1b)*. *F:* the location of the foveal region in the visual field. **B.** On the basis of the responses of the sort illustrated in part A, Hubel and Wiesel divided the response properties of cortical neurons into seven ocular dominance groups. If a cell **(small circles)** in the visual cortex is influenced only by the contralateral eye *(C)*, it falls into group 1. If it receives input only from the

ipsilateral eye *(I)*, it falls into group 7. For the intermediate groups, one eye may influence the cell much more than the other (groups 2 and 6), or the differences may be slight (groups 3 and 5). According to these criteria, the cell in part A would fall into group 6. **C.** Ocular dominance histograms in normal and monocular monkeys. *1:* This histogram is based on 1256 cells recorded from area 17 in the left hemisphere of normal adult and juvenile monkeys. The cells in layer IV that receive only monocular input were excluded. *2.* This histogram was obtained from the left hemisphere of a monkey in which the right (contralateral) eye was closed from age 2 weeks to 18 months. Subsequently the eye was opened and recordings were made from the left hemisphere. Most of the cells responded only to stimulation of the ipsilateral eye. **Hatched area in histogram:** cells with abnormal responses. (Adapted from Hubel and Wiesel, 1977.)

A   Normal

Occular dominance columns

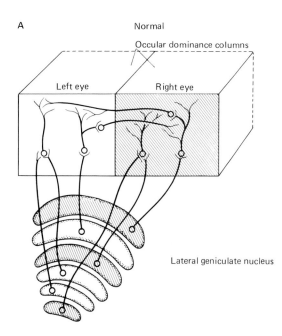

Left eye   Right eye

Lateral geniculate nucleus

B   Right eye closed

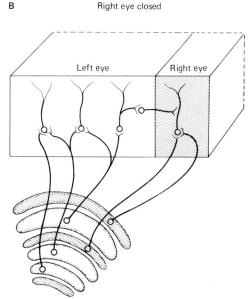

Left eye   Right eye

brain have come from studies of learning and memory. Surprisingly good progress in this area has recently been made by examining simple forms of nonassociative learning (habituation and sensitization; see Chapter 47) in simple vertebrate preparations such as the isolated spinal cord or in the even simpler nervous systems of invertebrates.

Habituation Involves a Depression of Synaptic Transmission

Habituation is a decrease in the strength of a behavioral response that occurs when an initially novel eliciting stimulus is repeatedly presented. When an animal encounters a new stimulus it will at first respond with a series of orienting and defensive reflexes. With repeated presentation of the stimulus, the animal rapidly learns to recognize it. If the stimulus is not rewarding or noxious, the animal will reduce and ultimately suppress its responses. Habituation is thought to be the most ubiquitous of all forms of learning. Through habituation, animals and humans learn to ignore stimuli that have lost novelty or meaning, thereby freeing them to attend to stimuli that are rewarding or significant for survival. Habituation is thought to be the first learning process to emerge in human infants and is used to study the development of intellectual processes such as attention, perception, and memory in the

52–3 Dimensions of the ocular dominance columns in the visual cortex change after closure of one eye. **A.** Ocular dominance columns are normally equal in size for each eye. **B.** After the right eye has been closed, the columns devoted to the right eye are narrow compared to those of the left eye. One hypothesis to account for these changes is indicated in the drawing. According to this scheme, the closing of one eye changes the balance between the opened and the closed eye so that the geniculate cells that receive input from the closed eye regress and lose some of their connections with cortical cells, whereas the geniculate cells that receive input from the opened eye sprout and connect to cortical cells previously occupied by geniculate neurons from the other eye.

newborn. The psychologist Michael Lewis, working at Columbia University, has found that the ability of 1-year-old infants to habituate to the repeated presentation of a visual stimulus correlates well with various measures of intelligence obtained later, at 4 years of age.

The first approach to an animal model of habituation was made by Charles Sherrington in 1906. In the course of studying the behavior underlying posture and locomotion, he observed that habituation of certain reflex forms of behavior, such as the flexion withdrawal of a limb to stimulation of the skin, occurred with repeated stimulation, and that recovery occurred only after many seconds of rest. With characteristic prescience, Sherrington suggested that the habituation of the withdrawal reflex was due to a functional decrease in the effectiveness of the set of synapses through which the motor neurons for the behavior were repeatedly activated. This problem was subsequently reinvestigated by Alden Spencer and Richard Thompson at the University of Oregon, who found close parallels between habituation of the spinal reflexes in the cat and habituation of more complex behavioral responses in man.

The cellular studies by Spencer and Thompson in the isolated spinal cord provided the first evidence that habituation involves changes in synaptic effectiveness. By recording intracellularly from motor neurons, they found that habituation results in a decrease in the synaptic impingement onto the motor neurons of the reflex. However, as we have seen in Chapters 16 and 26, the interneuronal organization of the spinal cord is quite complex and it has been difficult to examine in detail the cellular mechanisms of habituation of the flexion reflex. As a result, the further investigation of habituation has required still simpler systems in which the behavioral response can be reduced to a series of monosynaptic connections.

The most complete analysis of habituation has been carried out on an invertebrate, the marine snail *Aplysia californica*. This animal has a simple nervous system containing only 10^5 cells.

Aplysia has a reflex for withdrawing its respiratory organ, the gill, which is similar to the leg flexion reflex mediated by the spinal cord studied by Spencer and Thompson. The gill-withdrawal response habituates and can be sensitized.

Whereas the neural circuit or wiring diagram of the flexion reflex in the cat is complex, that for gill withdrawal is simple. It is essentially a monosynaptic reflex consisting of a group of motor neurons that mediate the behavior and a group of sensory neurons that synapse on the motor neurons (Figure 52–4). (There are also several interneurons that are converged upon by the sensory neurons and that in turn synapse on the motor neurons). In response to a novel stimulus, the sensory neurons produce large excitatory postsynaptic potentials in the motor cells that summate both temporally and spatially and cause the motor cells to discharge strongly, producing a brisk withdrawal. If the stimulus is repeated 10 times, the synaptic potentials produced by the sensory neurons in the motor cells become progressively smaller, fewer spikes are therefore generated, and the behavior is reduced. Finally, the synaptic potential produced by the sensory neurons becomes very small, at which point no behavior is produced. The memory for habituation is stored as a persistent reduction in the effectiveness of the synaptic connections between the sensory and motor neurons. This leads to a reduced behavior that persists for several hours. Vincent Castellucci, Marc Klein, and Eric Kandel, working at Columbia University, have found that the reason these synapses become less effective is that the sensory neurons release progressively less transmitter. As we have seen (Chapter 8), transmitter release depends upon the influx of Ca^{++} into the terminals with each action potential. The analysis of the mechanisms underlying habituation indicates that the depression of syn-

52–4 Neural circuit for the gill-withdrawal reflex in the marine snail *Aplysia*. There are about 24 mechanoreceptor sensory neurons that innervate the siphon skin, only one of which is illustrated here for the purpose of simplification. These sensory cells project onto a cluster of 6 motor neurons that innervate the gill. In addition, the sensory neurons also excite a group of interneurons, which in turn synapse on the motor neuron. The site of plasticity in this reflex that underlies habituation is at the terminals of the sensory neurons on the central target cells—the interneurons and the motor neurons.

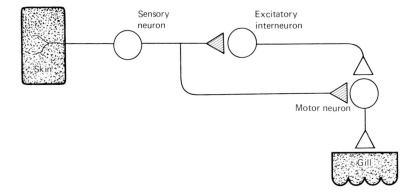

aptic transmission results from a prolonged shutting off (inactivation) of the Ca^{++} channel, leading to a decrease in Ca^{++} influx and a diminished output of chemical transmitter. Thus, in this simple case, short-term memory for a learning task is not due to reverberating activity in a closed chain of neurons (Chapter 47), but a functional (plastic) change in the strength of a previously existing set of connections.

What are the limits of this plasticity? How much can the effectiveness of a given synapse change and how long can the change last? Can changes in synaptic effectiveness also give rise to long-term memory? Whereas a single training session of 10 stimuli produces short-term habituation that lasts for hours, 4 or more repeated training sessions produce long-term habituation that lasts up to 3 weeks. Castellucci, Thomas Carew, and Kandel have compared the connections between the sensory neurons and the motor neuron in control animals with those in animals examined at various times after the acquisition of long-term habituation. In the control animals, 90% of the sensory neurons had detectable connections to the motor neuron (Figure 52–5). In contrast, 1 day and 1 week after long-term habituation, the percentage of detectable connections with the motor cell was reduced to 30%. The remainder of the connections had been inactivated to such a degree that they could not be detected electrophysiologically. Here, then, are fully functioning synaptic connections that are repressed for more than 1 week as a result of a simple learning experience—several brief sessions of habituation training of 10 trials each.

Whereas short-term habituation involves a transient decrease in synaptic effectiveness, long-term habituation leads to a prolonged decrease in synaptic effectiveness and profound functional inactivation of a previously existing synaptic connection. Thus, short- and long-term changes in synaptic efficacy can underlie certain instances of short- and long-term memory. Moreover, at a crucial synapse such as this, which has evolved to mediate the consequences of experience and learning, relatively few stimuli produce long-term changes in synaptic strength.

Sensitization Involves an Enhancement of Synaptic Transmission

Sensitization is a slightly more complex form of learning than habituation: it is the enhancement of an animal's reflex response by a strong or nox-

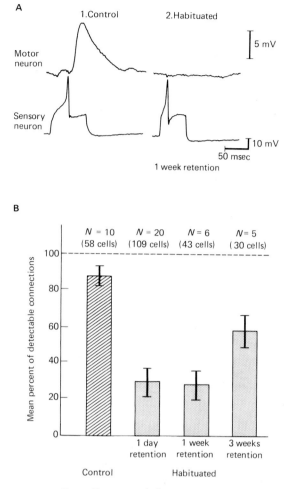

52–5 Effect of long-term habituation on connections between sensory neurons and motor neurons. **A.** Comparison of a synaptic connection between a sensory neuron and the motor neuron L7 in a control (untrained) *Aplysia* (1) and in an *Aplysia* that had been subjected to long-term habituation training (2). To test for connections the sensory neuron was depolarized intracellularly to trigger a single action potential and evoke a monosynaptic excitatory postsynaptic potential. Control animals show an effective synaptic potential whereas the synaptic connection in habituated animals is undetectable even 1 week after training. **B.** Histogram indicating mean percentage of detectable connections in control and habituated animals tested 1 day, approximately 1 week, and approximately 1 month after long-term habituation training. **Error bars:** standard error of the mean; the number of different animals in each group and the number of cells examined are indicated over each bar. (Adapted from Castellucci, Carew, and Kandel, 1978.)

ious stimulus. Whereas habituation requires that the animal learn to recognize and ignore a particular stimulus because its consequences are innocuous or trivial, sensitization requires that the animal attend to that stimulus because it is potentially accompanied by painful or dangerous consequences. As with habituation, sensitization can last from minutes to days and weeks, depending upon the pattern of stimulation. We shall focus on only the short-term form.

At the cellular level sensitization also involves an alteration of synaptic transmission at the synapses made by the sensory neurons on the motor neurons (and other central target cells). Thus, the same synaptic locus can be regulated in opposite ways by opposing forms of learning: it can be depressed by habituation and enhanced by sensitization. Sensitization involves a *presynaptic facilitation* that is mediated by an axoaxonic synapse, a synapse on a synapse (see Figure 8–9). The facilitating neurons that mediate sensitization synapse on the terminals of the sensory neurons and regulate the gain of their synaptic terminals by controlling transmitter release (Figure 52–6).

Sensitization is a remarkably effective form of learning, even when pitted against habituation. Sensitization so enhances behavioral response that it can reverse the synaptic and behavioral depression produced not only by short-term but

even by long-term habituation. It restores the completely inactivated synaptic connections produced by long-term habituation and reverses the depressed behavior (Figure 52–7). Here then, are synaptic pathways, determined by innate genetic and developmental processes, that can be functionally interrupted and then functionally restored by simple learning experiences! These experiences are relatively modest, comparable to the social experience of one person speaking to another. The two people not only make eye contact and voice contact, but also the neurons in the brain of one person have a direct and long-lasting effect on the brain of the other.

The speed with which synaptic connections between sensory and motor neurons can be functionally inactivated and reactivated suggests that these changes do not involve extensive morphological rearrangements such as disconnection of the synapse by retraction of the terminal or its reconnection by terminal sprouting or regrowth; rather, the physiological phenomena are consistent with a subtle change in the size or configuration of the active synaptic site, or perhaps only a biochemical change without any obvious morphological alteration.

Several points emerge from a consideration of these simple examples of learning and memory. One is that both short- and long-term memory can be localized to particular sites. Second, learn-

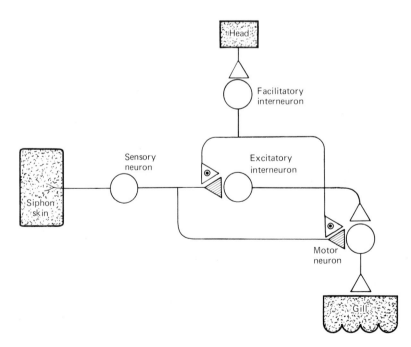

52–6 Neural circuit for presynaptic facilitation of the gill-withdrawal reflex in *Aplysia*. Stimuli to the head activate neurons that excite facilitatory interneurons. The facilitating cells (which are thought to utilize serotonin as their transmitter as indicated by the dense core vesicles) in turn end on the synaptic terminals of the sensory neurons, where they enhance transmitter release by means of presynaptic facilitation.

52–7 Restoration of synaptic transmission and of behavior by a sensitizing stimulus in long-term habituated animals. **A.** A typical inactivated connection from a habituated *Aplysia (1)* and a typical excitatory postsynaptic potential from a sensitized animal that had previously been habituated *(2)*. **B.** *1:* Behavioral scores of control animals **(gray bars)** and experimental animals **(hatched bars)** on day 1 and day 5 of habituation training, and following a single sensitizing stimulus to the experimental animals **(Test).** Both groups of animals exhibited significant habituation on day 5 compared to day 1. The experimental animals showed significant sensitization after a single sensitizing stimulus; the long-term habituation of the control animals remained unchanged. Data are expressed as median ± interquartile ranges. *2:* Summary of 20 experiments in which the number of detectable synaptic connections was determined in control (long-term habituated) animals and in long-term habituated animals that were sensitized. **Error bars:** standard error of the mean. (Adapted from Carew et al., 1979.)

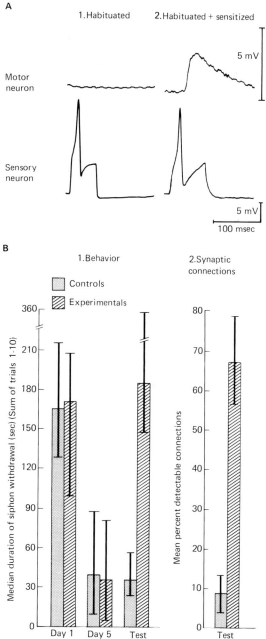

ing need not involve gross anatomical rearrangement in the nervous system. No nerve cell or even synapses are created or destroyed; rather, learning of habituation and sensitization results from changes in the functional effectiveness of previously existing chemical synaptic connections. In these instances, learning modulates the Ca^{++} current of the synaptic terminals of appropriate cells.

Short-Term Learning Occurs Through Modulation of the Ca^{++} Current

Physiological studies indicate that the facilitating neurons that mediate sensitization of the gill-withdrawal reflex in *Aplysia* are serotonergic. These facilitating neurons end on the terminals of the sensory neurons and enhance transmitter release by increasing the amount of cyclic adenosine 3′, 5′-monophosphate (cAMP) in the presynaptic terminals of the sensory neurons. In turn, cAMP acts through a cAMP-dependent protein kinase, a class of enzymes that phosphorylates proteins. Phosphorylation changes the charge and thereby the shape of proteins, activating some and inactivating others. Through a series of intermediate steps thought to involve phosphorylation of the K^+ channel, the protein kinase inactivates the voltage-sensitive K^+ current that normally repolarizes the action potential and leads to an increase in the duration of the action potential of the sensory neuron. As a result of being prolonged, each action potential leads to

a greater influx of Ca^{++} and consequently more transmitter is released (Figure 52–8).

In this sense the mechanism of sensitization resembles that of the action of the accelerator nerve in the vertebrate heart. In both the heart and the synapses facilitated by behavioral sensitization, a biogenic amine (norepinephrine in the heart, serotonin in sensitization) leads to an in-

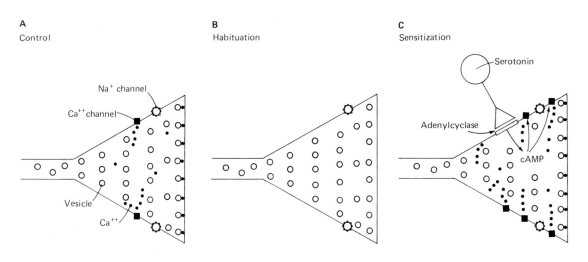

Control

B

Habituation

C

Sensitization

52–8 Model of short-term habituation and
sensitization. **A.** In the control state an action
potential in the terminal membranes of the sensory
neurons opens up a number of Ca^{++} channels (**black
squares**) in parallel with the Na^{+} channels of the
membrane (**hexagons**). As a result, some Ca^{++} flows
into the terminals and allows a certain number of
synaptic vesicles to bind to release sites and be
released. **B.** Repeated action potentials in the
terminals accompanying habituation decrease the
number of open Ca^{++} channels in the sensory
terminal and, in the limit, may shut them down
altogether. The resulting depression in Ca^{++} influx
functionally inactivates the synapse by preventing
synaptic vesicles from binding. **C.** Sensitization
is produced by cells thought to be serotonergic.
Serotonin acts on an adenyl cyclase in the terminals,
which stimulates the synthesis of cAMP. cAMP in
turn acts on a cAMP-dependent protein kinase to
phosphorylate a membrane protein thought to be the
K^{+} channel, which leads to a decrease in the
repolarizing K^{+} current and a broadening of the action
potential. The increase in the duration of the action
potential increases the time during which Ca^{++}
channels can open, leading to a greater influx of Ca^{++}
and greater binding of vesicles to release sites, and
therefore to an increased release. (Adapted from Klein
and Kandel, 1978.)

crease in cAMP that in turn enhances Ca^{++} influx
and thereby strengthens subsequent responses
(stimulus–contraction coupling in the heart;
stimulus–secretion coupling in the presynaptic
terminals). Thus the brain can use common regulatory mechanisms in novel ways to achieve the
read-out for certain types of memory processes.

Subcellular and biochemical analyses have
thus far been carried out only in short-term habituation and sensitization, forms of memory
that persist for an hour or less. The critical question to be answered by the analysis of the long-

term process of memory that lasts days and
weeks (and in humans, years) is: Do long-term
processes involve changes only in the synaptic effectiveness of pre-existing connections—changes
involving the synaptic terminals and postsynaptic receptors—or do they involve more profound
changes? Do synaptic contacts change in size?
Are new active zones created, resulting in greater
strength in the synaptic connection? Because
sprouting of new axonal branches is known to occur as a consequence of injury (see Chapter 13), it
is possible that some forms of memory depend on
the formation of new synapses, or on the
strengthening of existing ones by means of morphological rearrangements such as increasing the
size of the active zone.

Neuronal Changes with Sensory
Deprivation and Learning Have Clinical
Implications for the Classification and
Understanding of Psychiatric Disorders

The experiments showing alteration in the effectiveness of connections with sensory deprivation
and with learning have led us to a new way of
viewing the relationship between social and biological processes in the generation of behavior.
There is a tendency in medicine and psychiatry
to think that biological determinants of behavior
act on a different level of the mind than do social
and functional determinants. For example, it is
still customary to classify psychiatric illnesses
into two major categories: organic and functional.
Organic mental illnesses include the dementias
and the toxic psychoses; the *functional* mental
illnesses include the various depressive syndromes, the schizophrenias, and the neuroses.
This distinction dates to the 19th century, when

neuropathologists examined the brains of patients coming to autopsy and found demonstrable disturbance in the architecture of the brain in some diseases and an absence of disturbance in others. Diseases that produce anatomical evidence of brain lesions were called organic; those lacking these features were called functional.

The experiments reviewed in this chapter show that this distinction is artificial. Sensory deprivation and learning have profound biological consequences, causing an effective disruption of synaptic connections under some circumstances, and a reactivation of connections under others. It therefore seems incorrect to imply that certain diseases—organic diseases—affect mentation by producing biological alterations in the brain, whereas other diseases—functional diseases—do not. All mental processes are biological and any alteration in those processes is organic.

Rather than making the distinction along biological and nonbiological lines, it is more appropriate to ask in each type of mental illness: To what degree is this biological process determined by genetic and developmental factors, to what degree is it determined by a toxic or infectious agent, and to what degree is it environmentally or socially determined? Is it due to exposure to a toxin, or due to exposure to noxious social or sensory experiences? Even in the most socially determined mental disturbances, the end result is biological. Insofar as social intervention, such as psychotherapy or counselling, works, it must work by acting on the brain, and quite likely on the connections between nerve cells. The work of Hubel and Wiesel illustrates nicely that the demonstration of the biological nature of mental functioning will require more subtle anatomical methodology than the light microscopic histology of 19th-century pathologists. In order to clarify these issues it will be necessary to develop a neuropathology of mental illness that is based on function as well as on structure. Various new radiological techniques, such as positron emission tomography (Appendix II-C), may allow the noninvasive exploration of the human brain on a cell-biological level—the level of resolution that is required to understand the mechanisms of mentation and of mental disorders.

An Overall View

Cellular studies thus lead one to think of three ontogenetic stages of synaptic modification. The first stage, that of synapse formation, occurs primarily in the developing animal under genetic and developmental control. The second stage, that of maintenance of newly developed synapses, occurs during critical early periods of development and requires an appropriate pattern of environmental stimulation. The third stage, the regulation of the transient and long-term effectiveness of synapses, occurs throughout later life and is determined by day-to-day behavioral experience. One of the implications of this view is that the potentialities for all behaviors of which humans are capable are built into the brain under genetic and developmental control. Environmental factors and learning bring out these latent capabilities by altering the effectiveness of preexisting pathways, thereby leading to the expression of new patterns of behavior.

It follows from this argument that everything that occurs in the brain—from the most private to the most social thoughts—represents organic (biological) processes. We do not yet have the tools to demonstrate complex ideas and feelings on the cellular level, but the pace of neurobiological research is quickening; in the not too distant future we may begin to have a cellular neuropsychology of human mentation, and, with it, a new and therapeutically more efficacious approach to mental illness.

Selected Readings and References

Harlow, H. F. 1958. The nature of love. Am. Psychol. 13:673–685.

Hubel, D. H., and Wiesel, T. N. 1977. Ferrier Lecture: Functional architecture of macaque monkey visual cortex. Proc. R. Soc. Lond. B Biol. Sci. 198:1–59.

Kandel, E. R. 1976. Cellular Basis of Behavior. San Francisco: Freeman, chap. 12 and 13.

Kandel, E. R. 1979. Cellular insights into behavior and learning. Harvey Lect. 73:19–92.

Kuffler, S. W., and Nicholls, J. G. 1976. From Neuron to Brain. Sunderland, Mass.: Sinauer Associates, chap. 19.

Spitz, R. A. 1945. Hospitalism: An inquiry into the genesis of psychiatric conditions in early childhood. Psychoanal. Study Child 1:53–74.

Spitz, R. A. 1946. Hospitalism: A follow-up report on investigation described in Volume 1, 1945. Psychoanal. Study Child 2:113–117.

Spitz, R. A., and Wolf, K. M. 1946. Anaclitic depression: An inquiry into the genesis of psychiatric conditions in early childhood, II. Psychoanal. Study Child 2:313–342.

Suomi, S. J., and Harlow, H. F. 1975. The role and reason of peer relationships in rhesus monkeys. In M. Lewis and L. A. Rosenblum (eds.), Friendship and Peer Relations. New York: Wiley, pp. 153–185.

Other References

Carew, T., Castellucci, V. F., and Kandel, E. R. 1979. Sensitization in *Aplysia:* Restoration of transmission in synapses inactivated by long-term habituation. Science (Wash., D.C.) 205:417–419.

Castellucci, V. F., Carew, T. J., and Kandel, E. R. 1978. Cellular analysis of long-term habituation of the gill-withdrawal reflex of *Aplysia californica.* Science (Wash., D.C.) 202:1306–1308.

Castellucci, V., and Kandel, E. R. 1976. Presynaptic facilitation as a mechanism for behavioral sensitization in *Aplysia.* Science (Wash., D.C.) 194:1176–1178.

Castellucci, V. F., and Kandel, E. R. 1974. A quantal analysis of the synaptic depression underlying habituation of the gill-withdrawal reflex in *Aplysia.* Proc. Natl. Acad. Sci. U.S.A. 71:5004–5008.

Castellucci, V. F., Kandel, E. R., Schwartz, J. H., Wilson, F. D., Nairn, A. C., and Greengard, P. 1980. Intracellular injection of the catalytic subunit of cyclic AMP-dependent protein kinase simulates facilitation of transmitter release underlying behavioral sensitization in *Aplysia.* Proc. Natl. Acad. Sci. U.S.A. 77:7492–7496.

Harlow, H. F., Dodsworth, R. O., and Harlow, M. K. 1965. Total social isolation in monkeys. Proc. Natl. Acad. Sci. U.S.A. 54:90–97.

Klein, M., and Kandel, E. R. 1978. Presynaptic modulation of voltage-dependent Ca^{2+} current: Mechanism for behavioral sensitization in *Aplysia californica.* Proc. Natl. Acad. Sci. U.S.A. 75:3512–3516.

Klein, M., Shapiro, E., and Kandel, E. R. 1980. Synaptic plasticity and the modulation of the Ca^{2+} current. J. Exp. Biol. 89:117–157.

Lewis, M. 1971. Individual differences in the measurement of early cognitive growth. In J. Hellmuth (ed.), Exceptional Infant, Vol. 2: Studies in Abnormalities. New York: Brunner/Mazel, pp. 172–210.

Riesen, A. H. 1958. Plasticity of behavior: Psychological aspects. In H. F. Harlow and C. N. Woolsey (eds.), Biological and Biochemical Bases of Behavior. Madison: University of Wisconsin Press, pp. 425–450.

Sherrington, C. 1947. The Integrative Action of the Nervous System. 2nd ed. New Haven: Yale University Press.

Spencer, W. A., Thompson, R. F., and Neilson, D. R., Jr. 1966. Response decrement of the flexion reflex in the acute spinal cat and transient restoration by strong stimuli. J. Neurophysiol. 29:221–239.

von Senden, M. 1960. Space and Sight. Trans. by P. Heath. Glencoe, Ill.: Free Press.

Wiesel, T. N., and Hubel, D. H. 1963. Single-cell responses in striate cortex of kittens deprived of vision in one eye. J. Neurophysiol. 26:1003–1017.

Appendix I
Current Flow in Neurons

John Koester

A. Review of Electrical Circuits

Definition of Electrical Parameters

Potential Difference (V or E)
Current (I)
Resistance (R)
Capacitance (C)

Rules for Circuit Analysis

Resistance
Current
Capacitance
Potential Difference

Current Flow in Circuits with Capacitance

Capacitive Circuit
Circuit with Resistor and Capacitor in Series
Circuit with Resistor and Capacitor in Parallel

This section is a review of the basic principles of electrical circuit theory. Familiarity with this material is important for understanding the equivalent circuit model of the neuron that we considered in Chapters 4–8. The appendix is divided into three parts:

1. The definition of basic electrical parameters.
2. A set of rules for elementary circuit analysis.
3. A description of current flow in circuits with capacitance.

Definition of Electrical Parameters
Potential Difference (V or E)

Electrical charges exert an electrostatic force on other charges: like charges repel, opposite charges attract. As the distance between two charges increases, the force that is exerted decreases. Work is done when two charges that initially are separated are brought together: negative work if their polarities are opposite, and positive work if they are the same. The greater the values of the charges and the greater their initial separation, the greater the work that is done (work = $\int_{r'}^{0} F(r)\,dr$, where F is electrostatic force and r' is the initial distance between the two charges). *Potential difference* is a measure of this work. The potential difference between two points is the work that must be done to move a unit of positive charge (1 coulomb), from one point to the other point, i.e., it is the potential energy of the charge. One *volt* (V) is the energy required to move 1 coulomb a distance of 1 meter against a force of 1 newton.

Current (I)

A potential difference exists within a system whenever positive and negative charges are separated. Such regions of charge separation may be generated by a chemical reaction (as in a battery) or by diffusion between two electrolyte solutions with different ionic concentrations across a permeability-selective barrier, such as a cell membrane. If a region of charge separation exists within a conducting medium, then charges will move between the areas of potential difference: positive charges will be attracted to the region with a more negative potential, and negative charges will go to the regions of positive potential. The resulting movement of charges is *current* flow, which is defined as the net movement of positive charge per unit time. In metallic conductors current is carried by electrons, which move in the opposite direction of current flow. In nerve and muscle cells current is carried by positive and negative ions in solution. One *ampere* (A) of current represents the movement of 1 coulomb (of charge) per second.

Resistance (R)

Unless an object is a perfect conductor, it exerts frictional forces on the movement of charges, and is said to possess electrical *resistance*. The unit of electrical resistance is the ohm (Ω). According to Ohm's law, the current that flows through a resistor is directly proportional to the potential difference imposed across it:[1]

$$I = \frac{V}{R}$$

$$\text{Current (A)} = \frac{\text{Potential difference (V)}}{\text{Resistance } (\Omega)}.$$

---

[1]Note the analogy of this formula for current flow to the other formulas for describing flow, e.g., bulk flow of a liquid due to a hydrostatic pressure gradient; flow of a solute in response to a concentration gradient; flow of heat in response to a temperature gradient, etc. In each case flow is proportional to a driving force and inversely proportional to a resistance factor.

As charge carriers move through a resistor, some of their potential energy is lost; it is converted into thermal energy due to the frictional interactions of the charge carriers with the resistive material.

Each type of material has an intrinsic property called *resistivity* (ρ), which is determined by its molecular structure. Metallic conductors have very low resistivities, which means that they conduct electricity extremely well; aqueous solutions with high ionized salt concentrations have somewhat higher values of ρ; and oils and fats (lipids) have very high resistivities—they are poor conductors of electricity and are therefore good insulators. The resistance of an object is proportional to ρ times its length, divided by its cross-sectional area:

$$R = (\rho) \times \frac{\text{Length}}{\text{Area}}.$$

The length dimension is defined as the direction along which one measures resistance (between *a* and *b*).

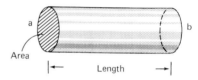

For example, the resistance measured across a piece of cell membrane will be greater if its length (i.e., thickness) is increased, e.g., by myelination. The resistance of a large area of membrane will be less than that of a small area of membrane. *Conductance (g)* is the reciprocal of resistance and measures the ease with which current flows in an object. Conductance is measured in mhos (Ω^{-1}) or in siemens (S): 1 mho = 1 siemen = (1 ohm)$^{-1}$.

Capacitance (C)

A capacitor consists of two conducting plates separated by an insulating layer. The fundamental property of a capacitor is its ability to store or separate charges of opposite sign: positive charge on one plate, negative on the other.

Figure I–1A,*1* shows a capacitor made up of two parallel plates with its two conducting surfaces separated by an insulator (an air gap). There is a net excess of positive charges on plate x, and an equal number of negative charges on plate y, resulting in a potential difference between the

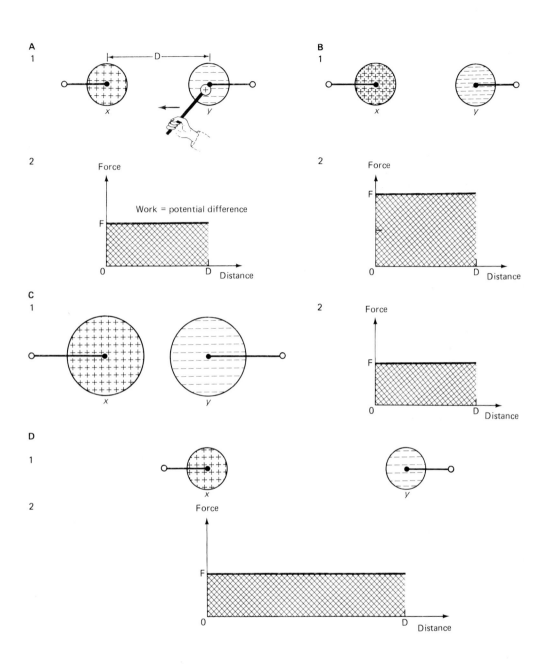

two plates. One can measure this potential difference by determining how much work is required to move a positive "test" charge from the surface of y to that of x. Initially, when the test charge is at y, it is attracted by the negative charges on y, and repelled less strongly by the more distant positive charges on x. The result of these electrostatic interactions is a force F that opposes the movement of the test charge from y to x. As one moves the test charge to the left, across the gap, the attraction by the negative

I–1 The factors that affect the potential difference between two plates of a capacitor. **A.** As a test charge is moved between two charged plates (**A1**), it must overcome a force (**A2**). The work done against this force is the potential difference between the two plates. **B.** Increasing the charge density (c.f., A1, B1) increases the potential difference. **C.** Increasing the area of the plates increases the number of charges required to produce a given potential difference (c.f., A, C). **D.** Increasing the distance between the two plates increases the potential difference between them (c.f., A, D).

charges on y diminishes, but the repulsion by the positive charges on x increases, with the result that the net electrostatic force exerted on the test charge is constant everywhere between x and y (Figure I–1A, 2). Work (W) is force times the distance (D) over which the force is exerted:

$$W = F \times D.$$

Therefore, it is simple to calculate the work done in moving the test charge from one side of the capacitor to the other. It is the area under the curve in Figure I–1A, 2. This work is equal to the difference in electrical potential energy, or potential difference, between x and y.

The greater the density of charges on the capacitor plates, the greater the force acting on the test charge, and the greater is the resulting potential difference across the capacitor (Figure I–1B). Thus, for a given capacitor, there is a linear relationship between the amount of charge (Q) stored on its plates and the potential difference across it:

$$Q \text{ (coulombs)} = C \text{ (farads)} \times V \text{ (volts)} \quad (I–1)$$

where the capacitance, C, is a constant.

The capacitance of a parallel-plate capacitor is determined by two features of its geometry: the area (A) of the two plates, and the distance (D) between them. Increasing the area of the plates increases capacitance, because a greater amount of charge must be deposited on each side to produce the same charge density, which is what determines the force F acting on the test charge (Figures I–1A and C). Increasing the distance D between the plates does not change the force acting on the test charge, but it does increase the work that must be done to move it from one side of the capacitor to the other (Figures I–1A and D). Therefore, for a given charge separation between the two plates, the potential difference between them is proportional to the distance. Put another way, the greater the distance is, the smaller is the amount of charge that must be deposited on the plates to produce a given potential difference, and therefore the smaller is the capacitance (Equation I–1). These geometrical determinants of capacitance can be summarized by the equation

$$C \propto \frac{A}{D}.$$

As shown in Equation I–1, the separation of positive and negative charges on the two plates of a capacitor results in a potential difference between them. The converse of this statement is also true: the potential difference across a capacitor is determined by the excess of positive and negative charges on its plates. In order for the potential across a capacitor to change, the amount of electrical charges stored on the two conducting plates must change first.

Rules for Circuit Analysis

A few basic relationships that are used for circuit analysis are listed below. Familiarity with these rules and conventions will help in understanding the electric circuit examples that follow, and in doing the problems in Appendix IB.

Resistance

This is the symbol for a resistor:

A variable resistor is represented this way:

Resistors in series add:

$$R_{AB} = 15 \ \Omega$$

Resistors in parallel add reciprocally:

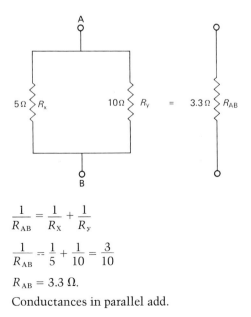

$$\frac{1}{R_{AB}} = \frac{1}{R_X} + \frac{1}{R_y}$$

$$\frac{1}{R_{AB}} = \frac{1}{5} + \frac{1}{10} = \frac{3}{10}$$

$$R_{AB} = 3.3 \ \Omega.$$

Conductances in parallel add.

Current

An *arrow* denotes the direction of current flow (net movement of positive charge).

Ohm's law is

$$I = \frac{V}{R} = Vg.$$

When current flows through a resistor, the end that the current enters is positive with respect to the end that it leaves:

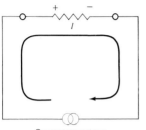

Current generator

The algebraic sum of all currents entering or leaving a junction is zero (we arbitrarily define a current approaching a junction as positive, and current leaving a junction as negative):

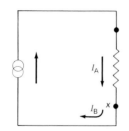

For junction x,

$$I_A = +5 \text{ A}$$
$$I_B = -5 \text{ A}$$
$$I_A + I_B = 0.$$

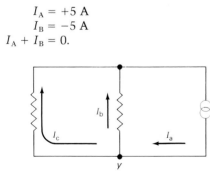

For junction y,

$$I_a = +3 \text{ A}$$
$$I_b = -2 \text{ A}$$
$$I_c = -1 \text{ A}$$
$$I_a + I_b + I_c = 0.$$

Current follows the path of least resistance. For resistive pathways in parallel, the current through each path is proportional to its conductance value divided by the total conductance of the parallel combination:

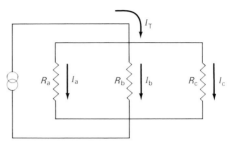

$$I_T = 10 \text{ A}$$
$$R_a = \ \ 3 \ \Omega$$
$$R_b = \ \ 2 \ \Omega$$
$$R_c = \ \ 5 \ \Omega$$

$$I_a = I_T \frac{1/R_a}{1/R_a + 1/R_b + 1/R_c}$$

$$I_a = I_T \frac{g_a}{g_a + g_b + g_c} = 3.2 \text{ A}$$

$$I_b = I_T \frac{g_b}{g_a + g_b + g_c} = 4.8 \text{ A}$$

$$I_c = I_T \frac{g_c}{g_a + g_b + g_c} = 1.9 \text{ A}.$$

Capacitance

This is the symbol for a capacitor:

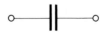

The potential difference across a capacitor is proportional to the charge stored on its plates:

$$V_C = \frac{Q}{C}$$

Potential Difference

This is the symbol for a battery, or electromotive force (EMF):

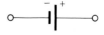

The positive pole is always represented by the longer bar.

Batteries in series add algebraically, but attention must be paid to their polarities. If their polarities are the same, they add; if opposite, they subtract:

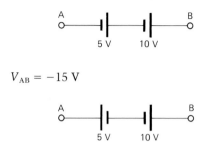

$$V_{AB} = -15 \text{ V}$$

$$V_{AB} = -5 \text{ V}$$

[The convention used here for potential difference is that $V_{AB} = (V_A - V_B)$.]

A battery drives a current around the circuit from its positive to its negative terminal:

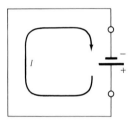

For purposes of calculating the total resistance of a circuit, one may assume that the internal resistance of a battery is zero.

The potential differences across parallel branches of a circuit are equal:

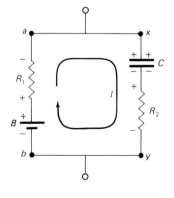

$$V_{ab} = V_{xy}.$$

As one goes around a closed loop in a circuit, the algebraic sum of all the potential differences is zero:

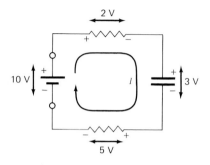

Current Flow in Circuits with Capacitance

Circuits that have capacitive elements are much more complex than those that have only batteries and resistors. This complexity arises because in capacitive circuits current flow varies with time. The time dependence of the changes in current and voltage in capacitive circuits is illustrated qualitatively in the following three examples.

Capacitive Circuit

Capacitive current does not actually flow across the insulating gap in a capacitor; rather, it results in a build-up of positive and negative charges on the capacitor plates. However, one can measure a current flowing into and out of the terminals of a capacitor. Consider the circuit shown in Figure I–2. When switch S is closed (Figure I–2B), a net positive charge will be moved by the battery V_B onto plate a, and an equal amount of net positive charge will be withdrawn from plate b. The result will be current flowing counterclockwise in the circuit. Since the charges that carry this current flow into or out of the terminals of a capacitor, building up an excess of plus and minus charges on its plates, it is called a *capacitive current*. Because there is no resistance in this circuit, the battery V_B can generate a very large amplitude of current, which will charge the capacitance to a value $Q = V_B C$ in an infinitessimally short period of time (Figure I–2D).

Circuit with Resistor and Capacitor in Series

Now consider what happens if one adds a resistor in series with the capacitor in the circuit shown in Figure I–2. The maximum current that can be generated when switch S is closed (Figure I–3B)

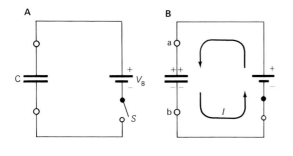

is now limited according to Ohm's law ($I = V/R$). Therefore, the capacitor will charge more slowly. When the potential across the capacitor has finally reached the value $V_c = Q/C = V_B$ (Figure I–3C), there will no longer be a difference in potential as one goes around the loop; i.e., the battery voltage (V_B) will be equal and opposite to the voltage across the capacitor, V_c. The two will thus cancel out, and there will be no source of potential difference left to drive a current around the loop. Immediately after S is closed

I–2 Time course of charging a capacitor. **A.** Circuit before switch S is closed. **B.** Immediately after closing switch S. **C.** After C has become fully charged. **D.** Time course changes in I_c and V_c in response to closing switch S.

I–3 Time course of charging a capacitor in series with a resistor, from a constant voltage source. **A.** Circuit conditions before closing switch S. **B.** Shortly after closing S. **C.** After C has settled at its new level of V. **D.** Time courses of current flow, of the increase in charge deposited on C, and of the increased potential differences across R and C.

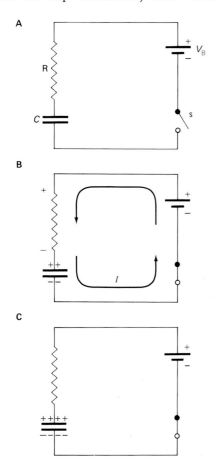

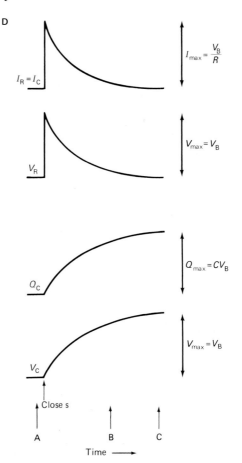

the potential difference will be greatest, so current flow will be at a maximum. As the capacitor begins to charge, however, the net potential difference $(V_c + V_B)$ available to drive a current will become smaller, so current flow will be reduced. The result is that an exponential change in volt-

age and in current flow will occur across the resistor and the capacitor. Note that in this circuit resistive current must equal capacitive current at all times (see Rules for Circuit Analysis, above).

Circuit with Resistor and Capacitor in Parallel

Consider now what happens if we place a parallel resistor and capacitor combination in series with a constant current generator that generates a current I_T (Figure I–4). When switch S is closed (Figure I–4B), current will start to flow around

I–4 Time course of charging a capacitor in parallel with a resistor, from a constant current source. **A.** Circuit conditions before closing switch S. **B.** Shortly after closing switch S. **C.** Later, when the charge deposited on C has reached its final value. **D.** Time course of changes in I_c, V_c, I_R, and V_R in response to closing switch S.

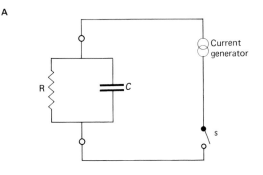

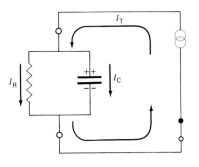

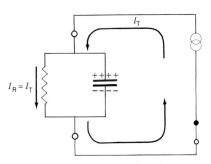

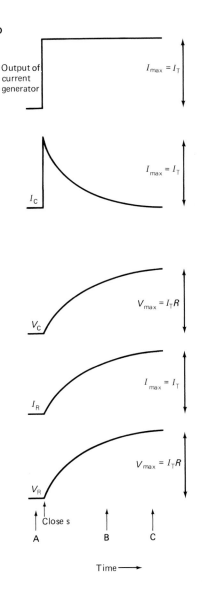

the loop. Initally, in the first instant of time after the current flow begins, all of the current will flow into the capacitor, i.e., $I_T = I_c$. However, as charge builds up on the plates of the capacitor, a potential difference V_c will be generated across it. Since the resistor and capacitor are in parallel, the potential across them must be equal; thus part of the total current begins to flow through the resistor, such that $I_R R = V_R = V_c$. As less and less current flows into the capacitor, its rate of charging will become slower; this accounts for the exponential shape of the curve of voltage versus time. Eventually, a plateau will be reached at which the voltage will no longer change. When this occurs, all of the current will flow through the resistor, and $V_c = V_R = I_T R$.

B. Problem Set for Chapters 3–6

1. The diagram below shows the simplified equivalent circuit for a neuron:

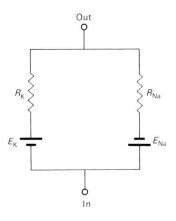

$$E_K = -75 \text{ mV}$$
$$E_{Na} = +55 \text{ mV}$$

$$R_K = 0.2 \times 10^6 \ \Omega$$
$$R_{Na} = 5 \times 10^6 \ \Omega$$

a. What is the net electromotive force that drives current around the loop? Draw in an arrow showing the direction of current flow.
b. What is the total resistance around the loop?
c. What is the value of current flowing around the loop?

d. What is the potential difference across R_K? Across R_{Na}? Show on the diagram the polarities of these potential differences.
e. Calculate the potential across the left-hand (K^+) branch. Do the same for the Na^+ branch. What is the membrane potential of the cell?

2. Assume that for the cell depicted above,

$$R_K = 20 \times 10^6 \ \Omega$$
$$R_{Na} = 500 \times 10^6 \ \Omega$$

Calculate V_m.

3. For the cell shown above, assume that

$$R_K = 5 \times 10^6 \ \Omega$$
$$R_{Na} = 0.2 \times 10^6 \ \Omega$$

(just the opposite of the initial conditions). Calculate V_m.

4. What are the ratios of R_K/R_{Na} for Problems 1, 2, and 3? What does this, along with the values of V_m you just calculated, tell you about the role of the resistances of different channels in determining V_m?

5. Assume that the neuron depicted in Problem 1 has a Na–K pump that works as shown in this diagram:

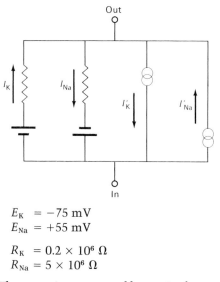

E_K = -75 mV
E_{Na} = $+55$ mV

R_K = 0.2×10^6 Ω
R_{Na} = 5×10^6 Ω

The pump is represented by a pair of constant current generators that generate outward I'_{Na} and inward I'_K. These active currents are opposite to the passive I_{Na} and I_K through the conductance channels. For purposes of calculation, these pumps may be assumed to offer infinite resistance to currents generated elsewhere in the circuit. Assume that the pump is nonelectrogenic, and that the cell is in a steady state, i.e., V_m and $(Na^+)_i$ and $(K^+)_i$ are constant. What are the values of I_{Na} and I_K (see Problem 1c)? What are the values of I'_{Na} and I'_K?

6. For the cell depicted in Problem 5, assume that the pump is electrogenic, such that three Na^+ ions are pumped out for each two K^+ ions pumped in. Assume also that the cell is in a steady state [V_m and $(K^+)_i$ and $(Na^+)_i$ are constant].
   a. Given that I'_{Na} = $+25.32 \times 10^{-9}$ A, calculate I_{Na}.
   b. Using this value of I_{Na}, calculate V_m. Compare this with the value calculated in Problem 1e.
   c. Calculate I_K.

7. A neuron has a total membrane capacitance of 10^{-10} F.
   a. How many coulombs of charge are separated across the membrane when the cell has a resting potential of -50 mV?
   b. What is the charge separation across the membrane at the peak of an action potential when V_m = $+50$ mV?

c. What is the *net* influx of positive charge into the cell during the rising phase of the action potential?
d. Assume that the cell has a volume of 9.2×10^{-11} liter and the total intracellular concentration of ionic charges is 200 mM. What is the percentage change of the total number of intracellular charges when V_m goes from -50 mV to $+50$ mV at the peak of the spike? (There are 1.04×10^{-5} moles of univalent charge per coulomb.)

8. You are investigating the properties of inputs to the cell shown below:

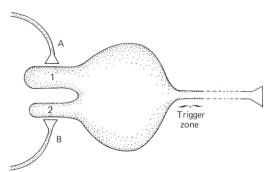

Synapses A and B produce the same depolarization in their respective postsynaptic membranes and are equidistant from the trigger zone. If dendrite 1 has a greater diameter than dendrite 2, which synaptic input will be larger when recorded at the trigger zone?

9. a. What would be the effect on the length constant of an axon of stripping off its myelin sheath?
   b. Why?

10. You are examining the neural circuit shown below:

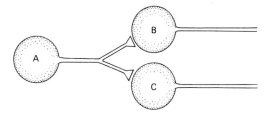

Neuron A excites follower cells B and C. The time constant of cell B is 50 msec and that of cell C is 200 msec.
   a. Neuron A fires in the pattern shown below:

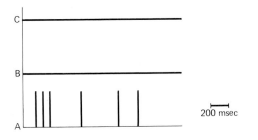

200 msec

Sketch the approximate waveforms of the synaptic responses in cells B and C (assume that they do not fire action potentials).

b. How do the passive properties of neurons B and C affect their ability to integrate signals from presynaptic neurons?

11. An increase in the diameter of an axon will result in an increased conduction velocity because:
   a. membrane capacitance per unit length of axon is increased.
   b. the total number of Na^+ channels is increased.
   c. axoplasmic resistance per unit length of axon is decreased.
   d. membrane resistance per unit length of axon is increased.

12. Neurons A and B have identical geometries, but the membrane resistance of A is 10 times greater than that of B:
   a. A will have a longer time constant than B.
   b. B will have a shorter length constant than A.
   c. A 10-mV synaptic potential generated at the tip of a dendrite will spread toward the trigger zone more effectively in A than in B.
   d. all of the above.

13. Increasing the membrane capacitance (capacitance per unit area of membrane) of a neuron will result in:
   a. an increase in the length constant.
   b. an increase in conduction velocity.
   c. an increase in the duration of the synaptic potentials generated in the cell.
   d. all of the above.

14. Two excitatory postsynaptic potentials generated 3 msec apart at the tip of a dendrite sum together to produce a subthreshold depolarization of 10 mV at the trigger zone. The chance of these postsynaptic potentials triggering a spike would be greater if:

   a. they were generated closer to the cell body.
   b. the membrane capacitance (capacitance per unit area) were lower.

15. Consider a dendrite of a neuron with a certain axoplasmic resistance between the dendrite and the neuron's trigger zone. Assume there are synaptic channels open in the dendrite:

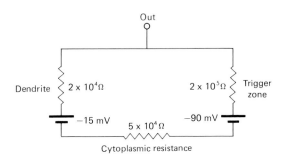

   a. What is the current flowing through the cytoplasmic resistance?
   b. What is the membrane potential at the trigger zone?
   c. What is the membrane potential of the dendrite?
   d. Why is the depolarization across the trigger zone less than the depolarization across the synaptic membrane?

16. A nerve cell is represented by the equivalent circuit diagram below. This diagram is simplified in that the Cl^- channels are not represented and the cable properties of the cell are ignored. The active and passive K^+ channels are lumped together in one branch, and the active and passive Na^+ channels are lumped together in a second branch.

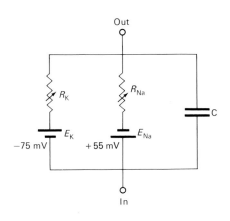

a. Given,

$$R_K = 0.2 \times 10^6 \, \Omega$$
$$R_{Na} = 5 \times 10^6 \, \Omega$$
$$V_m = -70 \text{ mV}$$

for the cell at rest, what is the equation for the potential difference across the Na$^+$ branch of the circuit (the resting potential)?
Use this equation to calculate I_{Na}.
Using the analogous equation for K$^+$, calculate I_K.
What is the value of I_c (the capacitive current)?

b. During the rising phase of an action potential in this cell (at P$_1$), the membrane parameters reach these values:

$$V_m = +20 \text{ mV}$$
$$R_K = 0.195 \times 10^6 \, \Omega$$
$$R_{Na} = 0.005 \times 10^6 \, \Omega.$$

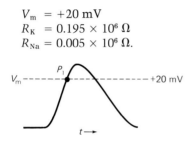

What are the values of I_K, I_{Na}, and I_c?

c. At the peak of the action potential, the membrane parameters are

$$V_m = +50 \text{ mV}$$
$$R_K = 0.19 \times 10^6 \, \Omega$$
$$R_{Na} = 0.0076 \times 10^6 \, \Omega.$$

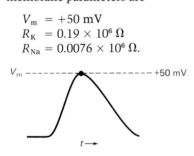

What are the values of I_K, I_{Na}, and I_c?

d. During the falling phase of the spike (P$_2$), the membrane parameters are

$$V_m = +20 \text{ mV}$$
$$R_{Na} = 0.03 \times 10^6 \, \Omega$$
$$R_K = 0.03 \times 10^6 \, \Omega.$$

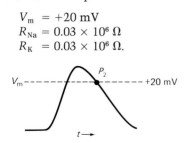

What are the values of I_K, I_{Na}, and I_c?

17. The circuit diagram below shows the synaptic (R_s, E_s) and nonsynaptic, or leakage (R_m, E_m) channels of a neuron. A spike in a presynaptic neuron releases transmitter that causes a brief opening of the synaptic conductance channels (equivalent to closing switch S). The figure on the bottom shows the time course of the change in V_m and of $g_s(1/R_s)$.

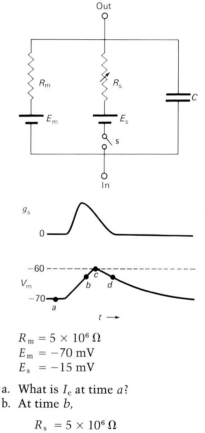

$$R_m = 5 \times 10^6 \, \Omega$$
$$E_m = -70 \text{ mV}$$
$$E_s = -15 \text{ mV}$$

a. What is I_c at time a?
b. At time b,

$$R_s = 5 \times 10^6 \, \Omega$$
$$V_m = -63 \text{ mV}.$$

What are the values of I_{R_s}, I_{R_m}, and I_c?

c. At the peak of the excitatory postsynaptic potential (time c),

$$R_s = 22.5 \times 10^6 \, \Omega$$
$$V_m = -60 \text{ mV}.$$

What are the values of I_{R_s}, I_{R_m}, and I_c?

d. At time d, during the falling phase, all of the synaptic channels have closed (switch S is open):

$$R_s = \infty \, \Omega$$
$$V_m = -63 \text{ mV}.$$

What are the values of I_{R_m}, I_{R_s}, and I_c?

18. The circuit diagram below represents a neuron connected to a current generator by an intracellular and an extracellular electrode. Only the passive elements of the membrane (leakage channels and membrane capacitance) are represented.

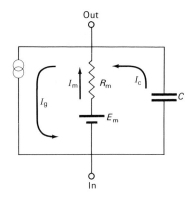

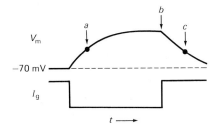

$$E_m = -70 \text{ mV}$$
$$R_m = 5 \times 10^6 \, \Omega$$

a. At time a,

$$I_g = -2.8 \times 10^{-9} \text{ A}$$
$$V_m = -63 \text{ mV}.$$

What are the values of I_m and I_c?

b. At time b,

$$I_g = -2.8 \times 10^{-9} \text{ A}$$
$$I_c = 0.$$

What are the values of I_m and V_m?

c. At time c,

$$I_g = 0$$
$$V_m = -66 \text{ mV}.$$

What are the values of I_m and I_c?

19. The K^+ conductance that is turned on in neurons in response to a long depolarizing pulse:
a. is maintained for the duration of the pulse.
b. precedes the Na^+ conductance.
c. provides positive feedback that produces additional depolarization.
d. none of the above.

20. The refractory period is caused by:
a. a residual increase in K^+ conductance.
b. inactivation of Na^+ conductance channels.
c. Na^+ pump reversal.
d. both (a) and (b).

21. Threshold is the value of membrane potential at which:
a. Na^+ conductance first turns on.
b. net ionic current becomes inward.
c. the action potential becomes an all-or-none, regenerative process.
d. both (b) and (c).

22. When a voltage-clamped axon is stepped in a depolarizing direction from resting potential (-60 mV) to $+10$ mV for 1 sec:
a. an increase in g_{Na} will precede an increase in g_K.
b. the increase in g_{Na} will wane before the end of the pulse.
c. the net electrochemical driving force for inward I_{Na} will be reduced.
d. all of the above.

23. Why does one need a voltage clamp to study active membrane conductances?

24. Given that g_{Na} is graded as a function of depolarization, why does an action potential have a sharp threshold?

25. a. Define the reversal potential of a postsynaptic potential.
b. Must the reversal potential of a postsynaptic potential equal the equilibrium potential of one of the ionic constituents of a neuron?
c. The reversal potential of an increased conductance excitatory postsynaptic potential is always at a more depolarized level than the threshold for initiating an action potential. True or false?
d. The reversal potential of a decreased conductance excitatory postsynaptic potential is always at a more depolarized level than the threshold for initiating an action potential. True or false?

26. What are two ways to increase the synaptic current generated by a postsynaptic potential?

27. What single ions could produce each of the following synaptic responses:

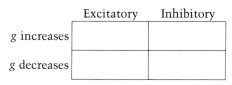

	Excitatory	Inhibitory
g increases		
g decreases		

28. What would be the effect of a large increase in intracellular Na^+ concentrations on:
    a. the amplitude of the action potential?
    b. the amplitude of an excitatory postsynaptic potential due to increased g to both Na^+ and K^+?
    c. the amplitude of an inhibitory postsynaptic potential due to decreased g_{Na}?

29. Do the Na^+ currents of the action potential and the excitatory postsynaptic potential use the same channels through the nerve membranes?

Answers to Problem Set

1. a. 130 mV, or 130×10^{-3} V. The current flows clockwise.
   b. $R_{Na} + R_K = 5.2 \times 10^6 \, \Omega$.
   c. $\dfrac{130 \times 10^{-3} \, V}{5.2 \times 10^6 \, \Omega} = 25 \times 10^{-9}$ A, or 25 nA.
   d. $V_{R_K} = (25 \times 10^{-9} \, A) \, (0.2 \times 10^6 \, \Omega)$
      $= +5$ mV (inside positive).
      $V_{R_{Na}} = (25 \times 10^{-9} \, A) \, (5 \times 10^6 \, \Omega)$
      $= -125$ mV (inside negative).
   e. $V_{K \, branch} = V_{Na \, branch} = V_m = -70$ mV.

2. $V_m = -70$ mV.

3. $V_m = +50$ mV.

4. For Problems 1 and 2, $R_K/R_{Na} = 25/1$ and $V_m = -70$ mV.
   For Problem 3, $R_K/R_{Na} = 1/25$ and $V_m = +50$ mV.
   Thus it is not the *absolute value* of resistance for the Na^+ or the K^+ channels that is important in determining V_m, but rather their values *relative* to each other. For a circuit that has only two branches, V_m will always be closer to the battery of the ion channel type with the lower net resistance.

5. From Problem 1c,

   $I_{Na} = -25$ nA
   $I_K = +25$ nA.

   Since the cell is in a steady state, I_{Na} and I_K are exactly balanced by I'_{Na} and I'_K; thus,

   $I'_{Na} = +25$ nA
   $I'_K = -25$ nA.

6. a. Since the cell is in a steady state,

   $I_{Na} = -I'_{Na}.$

   Therefore,

   $I_{Na} = -25.32$ nA.

   b. $V_m = E_{Na} + R_{Na} I_{Na} = -71.6$ mV.
   c. Because of the pump's electrogenicity,

   $I'_K = -\tfrac{2}{3} \, I'_{Na}.$

   Therefore,

   $I'_K = -16.88$ nA.

   Since the cell is in a steady state,

   $I_K = -I'_K = 16.88$ nA.

   Note that

   $$\frac{I_{Na}}{I_K} = \frac{I'_{Na}}{I'_K} = \frac{3}{2}.$$

7. a. $Q = VC = (10^{-10} \, F) \, (50 \times 10^{-3} \, V) = 5 \times 10^{-12}$ Coul.
   b. $Q = VC = 5 \times 10^{-12}$ Coul.
   c. 5×10^{-12} Coul. are required to bring V_m from -50 to 0 mV, and another 5×10^{-12} are needed to bring it from 0 up to $+50$ mV. Therefore,

   $Q = 5 \times 10^{-12} + 5 \times 10^{-12} = 10^{-11}$ Coul.

   d. The total number of moles of charge that enters is

   $(10^{-11} \, Coul.) \, (1.04 \times 10^{-5} \, mole/Coul.) = 1.04 \times 10^{-16}$ mole.

   The original amount of charge in the cell was

   $(200 \times 10^{-3} \, mole/liter) \, (9.2 \times 10^{-11} \, liter) = 1.84 \times 10^{-11}$ mole.

   Therefore, the percent change in total intracellular charge during the rising phase of the action potential is

   $$\frac{1.04 \times 10^{-16}}{1.84 \times 10^{-11}} \times 100 = 0.0006 \, \%.$$

8. Input A. Dendrite 1 has a longer length constant than dendrite 2 because of its larger diameter. r_m decreases in direct proportion to an increase in dendrite diameter, but r_a decreases in proportion to the diameter squared. Therefore, $\lambda = \sqrt{r_m/r_a}$ is proportional to the square root of the diameter.

9. a. λ would decrease.
   b. Because its effective r_m will decrease, and $\lambda = \sqrt{r_m/r_a}$.

10. a.

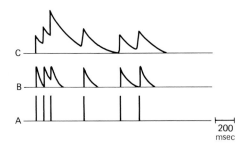

   b. Cell C will be more effective than cell B in summing up repetitive input.

11. c.

12. d.

13. c.

14. a.

15. a. Find the direction of the current flow:

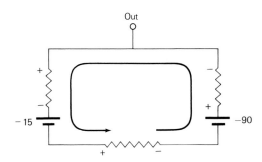

   The two batteries oppose each other and the larger (-90) dominates.
   Current flow in the loop:

   $$I = \frac{V}{R} = \frac{(90 \times 10^{-3}\text{ V}) - (15 \times 10^{-3}\text{ V})}{(2 \times 10^4 + 5 \times 10^4 + 2 \times 10^5\ \Omega)}$$

   $$= \frac{75 \times 10^{-3}\text{ V}}{27 \times 10^4\ \Omega}$$

   $$I = 2.78 \times 10^{-7}\text{ A}.$$

   b. The membrane potential across the trigger zone is given by

   $$\begin{aligned} V_{\text{in}-\text{out}} &= E_{\text{trig}} + (R_{\text{trig}} \times I) \\ &= -90\text{ mV} + (2 \times 10^5\ \Omega) \\ &\quad \times (2.78 \times 10^{-7}\text{ A}) \\ &= -90\text{ mV} + 55.6\text{ mV} \\ &= -34.4\text{ mV}. \end{aligned}$$

   c. The membrane potential across the dendrite is given by

   $$\begin{aligned} V_{\text{in}-\text{out}} &= E_{\text{den}} + (R_{\text{den}} \times I) \\ &= -15\text{ mV} \\ &\quad + (2 \times 10^4\ \Omega)(-2.78 \times 10^{-7}\text{ A}) \\ &= -15\text{ mV} - 5.6\text{ mV} \\ &= -20.6\text{ mV}. \end{aligned}$$

   d. The trigger zone is less depolarized than the dendrite because of the voltage drop across the axoplasmic resistor:

   $$\begin{aligned} V_{\text{axo}} &= R_{\text{axo}} \times I \\ &= (5 \times 10^4\ \Omega)(2.78 \times 10^{-7}\text{ A}) \\ &= 13.9 \times 10^{-3}\text{ V} = 13.9\text{ mV}. \end{aligned}$$

   This drop is the difference between the two values of V_m (dendrite and trigger zone):

   $$\begin{aligned} V_{\text{den}} &= V_{\text{axo}} + V_{\text{trig}} \\ -20.6\text{ mV} &= +13.9\text{ mV} - 34.5\text{ mV}. \end{aligned}$$

16. a. $V_m = E_{Na} + I_{Na}R_{Na}$

   $$I_{Na} = \frac{V_m - E_{Na}}{R_{Na}} = -25 \times 10^{-9}\text{ A}$$

   $$V_m = E_K + I_K R_K$$

   $$I_K = \frac{V_m - E_K}{R_K} = +25 \times 10^{-9}\text{ A}.$$

   The current flowing into junction a must equal the current flowing out.

   $$I_K + I_{Na} + I_c = 0.$$

   Therefore,

   $$I_c = 0.$$

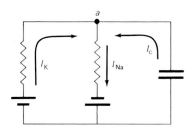

   b. $I_K = \dfrac{V_m - E_K}{R_K}$

   $I_K = 487 \times 10^{-9}\text{ A}$

   $I_{Na} = \dfrac{V_m - E_{Na}}{R_{Na}}$

   $I_{Na} = -7{,}000 \times 10^{-9}\text{ A}$

$I_{Na} + I_K + I_c = 0$

$I_c = 6{,}513 \times 10^{-9}$ A.

  c. $I_K = 658 \times 10^{-9}$ A

    $I_{Na} = -658 \times 10^{-9}$ A

    $I_c = 0$.

  d. $I_{Na} = -1{,}167 \times 10^{-9}$ A

    $I_K = 3{,}167 \times 10^{-9}$ A

    $I_c = -2{,}000 \times 10^{-9}$ A.

Note that when V_m is not increasing or decreasing, $I_c = 0$. When V_m is changing in a depolarizing direction, I_c is outward. When V_m is repolarizing (or hyperpolarizing), I_c is inward. The faster V_m is changing, the greater is the absolute value of I_c.

17. a. Since V_m is not changing at a, no capacitive current can be flowing.
  b. $I_{R_m} = +1.4 \times 10^{-9}$ A
    $I_{R_s} = +9.6 \times 10^{-9}$ A
    $I_c = +8.2 \times 10^{-9}$ A.
  c. $I_{R_s} = -2 \times 10^{-9}$ A
    $I_{R_m} = +2 \times 10^{-9}$ A
    $I_c = 0$.
  d. $I_{R_s} = 0$
    $I_{R_m} = +1.4 \times 10^{-9}$ A
    $I_c = -1.4 \times 10^{-9}$ A.

18. a. $I_m = +1.4 \times 10^{-9}$ A
    $I_c = +1.4 \times 10^{-9}$ A.
  b. $I_m = +2.8 \times 10^{-9}$ A
    $V_m = -56$ mV.
  c. $I_m = +0.8 \times 10^{-9}$ A.
    $I_c = -0.8 \times 10^{-9}$ A.

Note the resemblance between Problems 16b, 17b, and 18a. In all cases, depolarization is occurring because there is a net excess of positive charge flowing into the cell. This net inward ionic current is balanced by an outward capacitive current, which deposits positive charges on the inside of the membrane capacitance. The sources of inward ionic current vary in each of these three cases: it may come through voltage-sensitive ion channels, through synaptic channels, or through an intracellular electrode.

19. a.

20. d.

21. d.

22. d.

23. 1. To separate capacitive and ionic components of membrane current.
   2. To break the regenerative coupling between membrane potential and current.

24. For subthreshold depolarizations, the increase in inward current carried by Na^+ is more than balanced by an increase in outward current carried by leakage ions (K^+ and Cl^-). For depolarization above threshold, the increase in Na^+ current is greater than the increase in K^+ and Cl^- current leading to a net inward current and regenerative response.

25. a. The membrane potential at which the change in membrane current induced by the change in membrane conductance is zero; that is,

$$I_{PSP} = g_{PSP}(V_m - E_{Rev})$$

For $V_m = E_{Rev}$,

$$I_{PSP} = 0.$$

  b. No.
  c. True.
  d. False.

26. 1. Increase the driving force of the postsynaptic potential by altering the membrane potential (V_m) or by altering the reversal potential (E_{Rev}).
   2. Increase the conductance change produced by the neurotransmitter (g_{PSP}) because $I_{PSP} = g_{PSP}(V_m - E_{Rev})$.

27.

	Excitatory	Inhibitory
g increases	Na^+	K^+ or Cl^-
g decreases	K^+ or Cl^-	Na^+

28. a. Decrease amplitude
  b. Decrease amplitude
  c. Decrease amplitude.
  In all these cases E_{Na} will be reduced.

29. No.

Appendix II
Brain Fluids and Neuroradiology

Lewis P. Rowland

A. Blood–Brain Barrier, Cerebrospinal Fluid, Brain Edema, and Hydrocephalus

It is always surprising to realize that the brain—that remarkable organ that makes us what we are—is 80% water, 20% of which is extracellular. In addition to the brain (1400 g), the cranial cavity contains blood (75 ml) and cerebrospinal fluid (75 ml). Consideration of brain fluids and the cerebrospinal fluid (CSF) is essential for understanding both the normal functions of the brain and the clinically important alterations in brain functions that arise from derangements in these fluid systems.

Cerebrospinal Fluid Is Secreted by the Choroid Plexus

Most of the CSF is found within the four ventricles, where it is secreted mainly by the choroid plexuses, capillary networks surrounded by cuboidal or columnar epithelium (Figure II–1). The extrachoroidal CSF is secreted by brain capillaries. CSF flows from the lateral ventricles through the foramina of Monro into the third ventricle. From here it flows into the fourth ventricle through the aqueduct of Sylvius and then through the foramina of Magendie and Luschka into the subarachnoid space (Figure II–1). Within the subarachnoid space, fluid flows down the spinal canal and also upward over the convexity of the brain (Figure II–1). The CSF flowing over the brain extends into the depths of the cerebral cortex in extensions

652

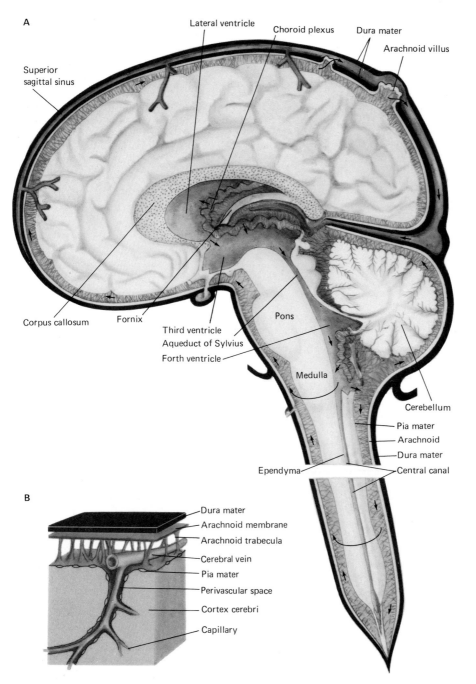

A

Lateral ventricle

Choroid plexus

Dura mater

Arachnoid villus

Superior
sagittal sinus

Corpus callosum

Fornix

Third ventricle

Aqueduct of Sylvius

Forth ventricle

Pons

Medulla

Cerebellum

Pia mater

Arachnoid

Dura mater

Ependyma

Central canal

B

Dura mater

Arachnoid membrane

Arachnoid trabecula

Cerebral vein

Pia mater

Perivascular space

Cortex cerebri

Capillary

II–1 Distribution of CSF. **A.** The CSF pathways: sites of formation, circulation, and absorption of CSF. There are choroidal and extrachoroidal sources of the fluid within the ventricular system. The CSF circulates to the subarachnoid space and is absorbed into the venous system via the arachnoid villi. The presence of arachnoid villi adjacent to the spinal roots supplements the absorption into the intracranial venous sinuses. All spaces containing CSF communicate with each other. **B.** The subarachnoid space is bounded internally by the pia mater and extends along the blood vessels that penetrate the surface of the brain. (Adapted from Kuffler and Nicholls, 1976; and Fishman, 1980.)

of the subarachnoid space along blood vessels called the *Virchow-Robin spaces*. There is free diffusion of small solutes between the extracellular fluid and the CSF in these perivascular spaces and across the ependymal lining of the ventricular system, facilitating the movement of metabolites from deep within the hemispheres to cortical subarachnoid spaces and the ventricular system.

The CSF is absorbed through the *pacchionian granulations,* or *arachnoid villi.* These structures are typically found in clusters and appear as grossly visible herniations of the arachnoid membrane through the dura and into the lumen of the superior sagittal sinus and other venous structures (Figure II–1A). The villi themselves are visible only microscopically and the actual structure is still not fully agreed upon. It is not clear whether the essential structure is a membrane that separates CSF and venous blood (a closed system) or a series of tubules within the villus that communicate directly with venous blood (open system), or whether vacuoles form within cells of the villus membrane to transport fluid from one side of the cell to the other, a form of "vesicular transport" that combines the

characteristics of both a closed and an open system (Figure II–2). In any case, the granulations appear to function as valves that allow one-way flow of CSF from the subarachnoid spaces into venous blood; this one-way flow of CSF is sometimes called *bulk flow* because all constituents of CSF leave with the fluid. Some solutes are also absorbed by the choroid plexus and brain capillaries, clearing metabolites from the brain. The rate of formation of CSF is about 0.35 ml/min or about 500 ml/day.

There Are Specific Permeability Barriers Between Blood and Cerebrospinal Fluid and Between Blood and Brain

The composition of CSF resembles an ultrafiltrate of blood plasma, but the small differences are significant because they affect brain excitability. The concentrations of potassium,

II–2 Giant vacuolar transport in the arachnoid villus: bulk flow reabsorption of CSF from the subarachnoid space to the venous system. The arachnoid cells have tight intercellular junctions. Some vesicles are large enough to encompass red blood cells. (Adapted from Fishman, 1980.)

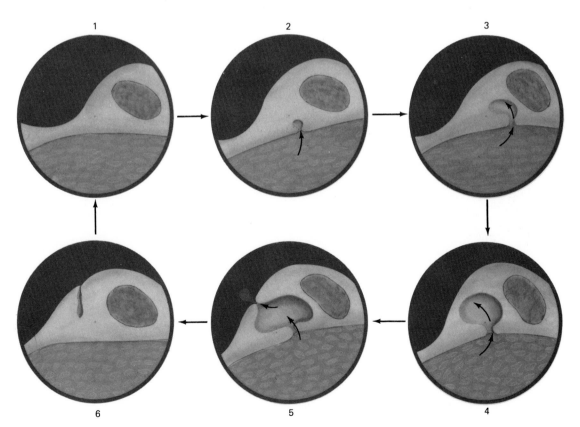

bicarbonate, calcium, and glucose are lower in CSF than in blood plasma, but there is more magnesium and chloride, and the pH is lower in CSF. These differences are due to regulation of the constituents of CSF by active transport. The formation of CSF in the choroid plexus seems to involve both capillary filtration and active epithelial secretion. Normally, blood plasma and CSF are in osmotic equilibrium.

CSF and extracellular fluids of the brain are in equilibrium, and the ultimate composition of these fluids is a function of the *blood–CSF barrier* or the *blood–brain barrier* (these are considered equivalent terms because the extracellular space of the brain is in equilibrium with CSF). The concept of a blood–brain barrier was developed by the great German cell biologist Paul Ehrlich, who found that intravenous injection

of dyes (such as trypan blue) was followed by staining of tissues in most organs, but not in the brain. The brain and CSF are selectively excluded by this barrier function and are normally protected against surging fluctuations in blood content of many constituents.

It is important to recognize that there is not a single, comprehensive barrier (Figures II–3 and II–4); rather, there are many different systems for excluding substances from the brain and conversely for the transport of substances from blood to CSF or brain, and also in the reverse direction. For any solute, the efficacy of the exclusion or the transport is determined by *morphological and functional characteristics of brain capillaries* and also by the *biochemical and biophysical characteristics of the solute*.

It is not certain why the behavior of brain capillaries differs so much from that of vessels in other organs but there are at least three obvious distinctions (Figure II–5). First, there are *tight junctions* between capillary endothelial cells in the brain, unlike systemic capillaries. Second, brain capillaries are surrounded by, and encased in, the glial foot processes of astrocytes. Third, mitochondria are more numerous in endothelial cells of brain capillaries. These and other factors

II–3 Structural and functional relationship among blood, CSF, and brain structures. Tissue elements that may participate in the formation of the barriers are indicated in parentheses. Substances entering the neurons and glial cells (i.e., intracellular compartment) must pass through the cell membrane, which is shown schematically as a protein–lipid structure. **Arrows:** direction of fluid flow under normal conditions. (Adapted from Carpenter, 1978.)

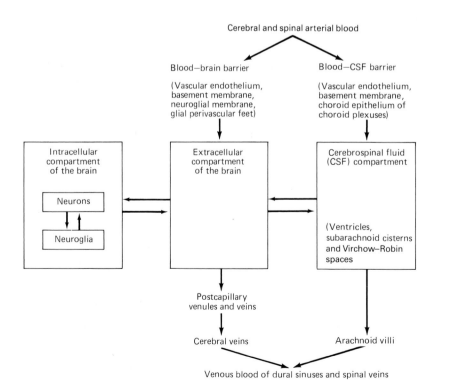

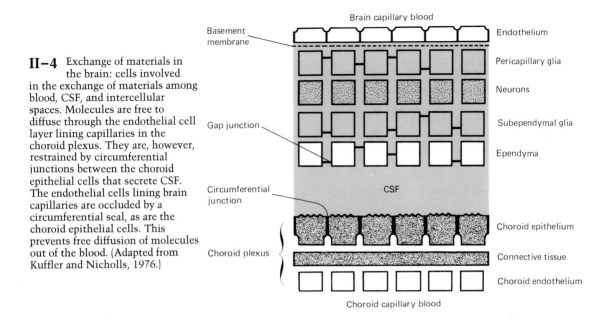

II–4 Exchange of materials in the brain: cells involved in the exchange of materials among blood, CSF, and intercellular spaces. Molecules are free to diffuse through the endothelial cell layer lining capillaries in the choroid plexus. They are, however, restrained by circumferential junctions between the choroid epithelial cells that secrete CSF. The endothelial cells lining brain capillaries are occluded by a circumferential seal, as are the choroid epithelial cells. This prevents free diffusion of molecules out of the blood. (Adapted from Kuffler and Nicholls, 1976.)

give the brain capillary endothelium a special quality that excludes the permeation of many types of molecules and makes it rely on various specialized transport mechanisms. Thus the brain capillary endothelium is functionally more like a secretory membrane than like the capillary endothelium in other organs.

The characteristics of the solute also affect permeability. The size of the molecule is crucial. The rate of entry into the brain of small molecules in the blood, such as sucrose (molecular weight 360), is much more rapid than that of large molecules, such as inulin (molecular weight 5,000), and both enter more rapidly than any protein. This probably accounts for the fact that the normal CSF content of albumin is only 0.5% of that in plasma. Many larger proteins do not enter at all, and, under normal conditions, substances

that are bound to serum proteins (including bilirubin and many drugs) do not enter CSF or extracellular fluids of the brain.

Lipid solubility also enhances the transport of substances. For example, lipid-soluble substances, such as carbon dioxide, oxygen, and many drugs, enter the brain rapidly. Ionized polar compounds, such as bicarbonate, enter the brain slowly unless there is a specific transport system for the solute in question.

The third essential component of the blood–brain barrier comprises the carrier-mediated transport systems for sugars, other metabolites, and some amino acids. The specificity of these transport systems has many practical consequences. For instance, dopamine does not enter brain from blood plasma, but its precursor, dihydroxyphenylalanine (DOPA), does enter and has

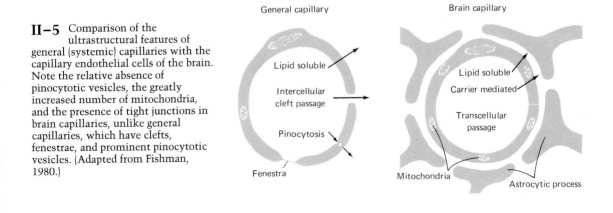

II–5 Comparison of the ultrastructural features of general (systemic) capillaries with the capillary endothelial cells of the brain. Note the relative absence of pinocytotic vesicles, the greatly increased number of mitochondria, and the presence of tight junctions in brain capillaries, unlike general capillaries, which have clefts, fenestrae, and prominent pinocytotic vesicles. (Adapted from Fishman, 1980.)

been used effectively to treat parkinsonism (see Chapter 31). Many of these transport systems are bidirectional, mediating the transport of some substances out of the brain and CSF into the blood plasma, as well as controlling entry.

The potential influence of these barrier systems can be illustrated by considering the actions of penicillin, an important antibiotic used to treat some forms of meningitis. In normal individuals, penicillin is virtually excluded from CSF for at least three reasons: (1) It is an organic acid and of low solubility in lipids. (2) In plasma, penicillin is bound to albumin. (3) In the choroid plexus, there is a transport system that moves penicillin out of CSF and into blood. Each of these characteristics limits the amount of penicillin that enters CSF under normal circumstances. In meningitis, however, the barrier is less effective and the antibiotic does enter in amounts sufficient to be therapeutic.

There are barriers in the capillaries at all levels of the brain and spinal cord, and also in the choroid plexuses. As Robert Fishman has pointed out, the permeability barriers provide a *system to preserve homeostasis in the nervous system, facilitating the entry of necessary metabolites, but blocking entry or facilitating removal of unnecessary metabolites or toxic substances.* It is important to recognize the distinction between *net change* in the content of any constituent of CSF and *exchange* between plasma and CSF, which also occurs at all levels. For instance, if radioactive Na^+ or K^+ is present in the plasma, the isotope may appear in CSF or brain without a change in total concentration of the ion in either plasma or CSF; radioactive and stable ions would have been exchanged without a net change. Water molecules are also exchanged. Furthermore, both water and solutes of CSF are removed by bulk flow through the pacchionian granulations.

The Blood–Brain Barrier Breaks Down in Some Diseases

In many diseases the blood–brain barrier does not function effectively and substances that are normally excluded may enter the brain—as already illustrated by the example of penicillin. Failure of the barrier has practical implications. For instance, albumin labeled with radioactive iodine has been used to detect brain tumors and other focal brain lesions. Because of a breakdown of the barrier within the lesion, albumin enters the lesion but does not label normal parts of the brain; the accumulating radioactivity in the restricted

area of the lesion can therefore be localized by external detectors. Radioactive tracers have now been largely supplanted by computerized tomography, but breakdown of the blood–brain barrier allows the passage of iodinated compounds from blood into the lesion, and can therefore be used to "enhance" the computerized image.

Stanley Rapoport at the National Institutes of Health has found that brief periods of hyperosmolarity can temporarily increase the permeability of the blood–brain barrier, apparently by opening (unzipping) the tight junctions of the capillary endothelial cells. Some investigators are therefore treating brain tumors or infections by administering intracarotid injections of hypertonic solutions of urea, followed by injection of the appropriate antibiotics, chemotherapeutic agents, or specific antibodies. By this means it is sometimes possible to achieve beneficial effects with agents that would ordinarily be excluded from the brain. On the other hand, as we shall see below in relation to cerebral edema, pathological alteration of the barrier may have adverse consequences.

Cerebrospinal Fluid Has Multiple Functions

The composition of CSF is in equilibrium with brain extracellular fluid and is therefore important in maintaining a constant external environment for neurons and glia. CSF also provides a mechanical cushion to protect the brain from impact with the bony calvarium when the position of the head is changed. By its buoyant action, the CSF allows the brain to float, thereby reducing its weight from 1400 g in air to less than 50 g in situ. CSF may also serve as a lymphatic system for the brain and as a conduit for some polypeptide hormones and other substances. The pH of CSF affects both pulmonary ventilation and cerebral blood flow—another example of the homeostatic role of CSF.

The Composition of Cerebrospinal Fluid May Be Altered in Disease

Normally the CSF does not contain red or white blood cells. White blood cell counts greater than $5/mm^3$ are pathological. In acute bacterial meningitis, the count may reach $5000/mm^3$. Cells may be increased moderately in viral infections or in response to cerebral infarction, brain tumor, or other cerebral tissue damage. Tumor cells in CSF can sometimes be collected on filters and identified by their characteristic morphology.

Protein content may be increased by almost any pathological process of brain or spinal cord, presumably due to alterations of vascular permeability to protein. Protein content greater than 500 mg/dl is usually a manifestation of a block in the spinal subarachnoid space by a tumor or other compressive lesion. The gamma-globulin content is disproportionately increased to more than 13% of total protein in multiple sclerosis and a few other diseases; because this may occur without a corresponding increase in blood gamma-globulin content, the increase in CSF is attributed to production of the immunoglobulins within brain. In multiple sclerosis, the abnormal immunoglobulins can also be identified as "oligoclonal bands" by electrophoresis.

The concentration of glucose is decresed in acute bacterial infections and only exceptionally in viral infections. In chronic diseases, CSF glucose content less than 40 mg/dl implies tumor in the meninges, fungal or tuberculous infection, or sarcoidosis. The basis for the reduced CSF glucose content is not clear; it may be due to impaired transport into CSF or excessive utilization by organisms, blood cells, tumor cells, or the brain itself, or combinations of these mechanisms.

Cultures of CSF are used to identify the causal organism in infections. Determinations of other constituents, such as homovanillic acid or cyclic adenosine 3′, 5′-monophosphate (cAMP), are being evaluated but abnormalities have not as yet been shown to be diagnostic of specific disorders.

The gross appearance of CSF is clinically important. The fluid is normally clear and colorless. It may appear cloudy when there are many leukocytes, grossly bloody, or different shades of yellow (xanthochromia) when blood pigments are left behind after a hemorrhage or when CSF protein content is greater than 150 mg(dl, indicating that bilirubin (bound to albumin) has been brought from the plasma to the CSF.

Increased Intracranial Pressure May Harm the Brain

CSF pressure is ordinarily measured by *lumbar puncture*, a procedure in which a needle is inserted through the skin into the lumbar subarachnoid space with the patient lying on his or her side (lateral decubitus position). When the CSF flows freely through the needle, the hub of the needle is attached to a manometer and the fluid is allowed to rise. The normal pressure is 65–195 mm CSF (or water), or 5–15 mm Hg.

In measuring the lumbar CSF pressure as a guide to intracranial pressure, it is assumed that pressures are equal throughout the neuraxis. Normally, this is a reasonable assumption. In many pathological states (such as brain tumor or obstruction of CSF pathways), however, this assumption may not be true. For this reason, and also because the lumbar needle cannot be left in place for prolonged periods, catheters are sometimes inserted into the lateral ventricles to measure pressure there. In addition, attempts have been made to develop pressure-sensitive transducers that can be inserted under the skull for continuous monitoring of intracranial pressure.

In considering the factors that regulate intracranial pressure, the cranium and spinal canal may be regarded as a closed system. According to the *Monro-Kellie doctrine,* an increase in the volume of any one of the contents of the calvarium —brain tissue, blood, and CSF or brain fluids— must be accompanied by a decrease of another component or there will be a marked increase in intracranial pressure because the bony calvarium rigidly fixes the total cranial volume. If there is a sudden increase in intracranial blood volume —for example, during a voluntary Valsalva maneuver or a sneeze—CSF may surge into the cervical subarachnoid space momentarily, because the dura there has elastic qualities. Increased CSF volume may partially compress cerebral blood vessels. Chronic changes may be compensated for by increased absorption or decreased formation of CSF. When these compensatory mechanisms fail, CSF and intracranial pressures rise. Several types of abnormalities lead to this condition and the consequences vary.

Brain Edema Is a State of Increased Brain Volume Due to Increased Water Content

Brain edema may be local (surrounding contusion, infarct, or tumor) or generalized. Local brain edema may cause herniation of brain tissue (cingulate gyrus beneath falx, temporal lobe uncus across tentorium, cerebellar tonsils through foramen magnum, or cerebral cortex outward through calvarial defects after surgery or injury).

Vasogenic Edema Is a State of Increased Extracellular Fluid Volume

Vasogenic edema is the most common form of brain edema; it is attributed to increased permeability of brain capillary endothelial cells, increasing the extracellular fluid volume. White matter is affected more than gray matter. Vasogenic edema is reflected in positive isotope brain scans associated with brain tumor, abscess, infarct, or hemorrhage. This distortion of the blood–brain barrier is also responsible for the enhancement or increased density of lesions seen by computerized tomography after intravenous injection of media that contain iodine. Generalized forms of vasogenic edema occur in head injury, lead encephalopathy, and meningitis. Functional manifestations include focal neurological abnormalities, EEG slowing, intracranial hypertension, and impaired consciousness.

Glucorcorticoids are effective in treating vasogenic edema due to brain tumor or abscess but are of doubtful value in cerebral infarct or pseudotumor (see below). Hypertonic solutions of urea, mannitol, or glycerol are also used to treat vasogenic edema, but they may affect normal brain rather than the focal lesion and, after an initial fall in CSF pressure, there may be a rebound to even higher levels because the solute is not excluded by the defective barrier in the edematous tissue. However, hypertonic solutions are often used in acute situations, as in preparing patients for definitive surgery, or in the diffuse brain edema of head injury or infection. In these conditions, alternative treatments include external drainage of CSF from the ventricles or the administration of barbiturates in doses large enough to depress cerebral metabolism and cerebral blood flow, thereby reducing intracranial volume; both of these treatments are attended by risks and are reserved for extreme conditions.

Cytotoxic Edema Is the Swelling of Cellular Elements

Cytotoxid edema implies intracellular swelling of neurons, glia, and endothelial cells, with concomitant reduction of brain extracellular space. Cytotoxic edema occurs in hypoxia after cardiac arrest or asphyxia because failure of the ATP-dependent $Na-K$ pump allows Na^+, and therefore water, to accumulate within cells. Another cause of cytotoxic edema is water intoxication, which follows the acute systemic hypo-osmolarity associated with acute dilutional hyponatremia, Na^+ depletion, or inappropriate secretion of antidiuretic hormone. Under these circumstances water moves from extracellular to intracellular sites. Cytotoxic edema may also accompany other forms of edema in meningitis, encephalitis and Reye syndrome.

Interstitial Edema Is Attributed to Increased Water and Na in Periventricular White Matter

In interstitial edema, best exemplified by obstructive hydrocephalus, water and Na^+ content increase in periventricular white matter. Pseudotumor cerebri or benign intracranial hypertension is thought by some to be a form of interstitial edema, but this has not been proved. In this condition, CSF pressure is increased and is usually attended by headaches and papilledema, but there is no depression of mental function (as there often is in generalized cerebral edema) or hydrocephalus (as would be expected if absorption of CSF were impaired), and the cause of the increased intracranial pressure is therfore uncertain. The condition may persist for months or years, but often seems to be self-limited.

The most effective treatment of interstitial edema is surgical shunting of CSF to relieve the obstruction. Acetazolamide may reduce CSF formation but does not do so completely; it is of limited value in interstitial edema and of no value in vasogenic or cytotoxic edemas.

Hydrocephalus Is an Increase in the Volume of the Cerebral Ventricles

Hydrocephalus results from one of three possible causes: oversecretion of CSF, impaired absorption of CSF, or obstruction of CSF pathways.

Oversecretion of CSF is rare but is thought to occur in some functioning tumors of the choroid plexus (papillomas) because removal of the tumor may relieve the hydrocephalus. However, subarachnoid hemorrhage and high CSF protein content also characterize these tumors and could impair the absorption of CSF.

Impaired absorption of CSF could conceivably result from any condition that raises the venous pressure, such as thrombosis and occlusion of cerebral venous sinuses, severe congestive heart failure, or removal of the jugular vein during radical neck dissections for tumors. However, well documented cases of this type are rare. Impaired absorption is suspected as the cause of the more common *communicating hydrocephalus*, in which there is no obstruction of CSF flow from the lateral ventricles through the foramina of Luschka and Magendie and all four ventricles are enlarged. In this condition, CSF pressure may be high or normal. In infants, CSF pressure may not rise because the cranial sutures have not yet fused and the cranium can expand. In adults, communicating hydrocephalus may occur in some patients who survive subarachnoid hemorrhage or meningitis; the hydrocephalus is attributed to impaired absorption of CSF because of mechanical obstruction or otherwise impaired function of the arachnoid granulations caused by protein and detritus. A similar mechanism is thought to explain the high CSF pressure in some patients with CSF protein content greater than 500 mg/dl due to acute peripheral neuropathy (Guillain-Barré syndrome) or spinal cord tumor.

Impaired absorption is also held responsible for the syndrome of *normal-pressure hydrocephalus.* This syndrome is of major interest because it causes dementia. Dementia is a major, almost epidemic public health problem; the dementia of this disorder is unusual in that it can be relieved by shunting of CSF. However, it is difficult to identify patients who will respond. In addition to dementia, the clinical syndrome comprises unsteady gait and urinary incontinence. In CT-scan or pneumoencephalogram, the ventricles are uniformly enlarged and there is no evidence of cortical atrophy or enlargement of the subarachnoid spaces over the convexity of the brain. In normal individuals, if ^{125}I-labeled albumin is injected into the lumbar subarachnoid space the isotope can be traced by a gamma camera up to the arachnoid granulations, but it does not enter the ventricles. In patients with normal-pressure hydrocephalus the label does not follow the normal course to the convexities, may reflux into the ventricles, and takes longer to appear in blood. In another test, there is an excessive rise of CSF pressure when sterile saline is infused into the lumbar subarachnoid space at a rate of 0.3 ml/min. Unfortunately, no one of these criteria alone reliably predicts a successful response to shunting, and even all of them together may fail to predict the outcome. Why CSF pressure does not rise in this syndrome is also uncertain.

Obstruction of CSF pathways may result from tumors, congential malformations, or scarring. A particularly vulnerable site for all three mechanisms is the narrow aqueduct of Sylvius. *Aqueductal stenosis* may result from congenital malformations, or scarring due to intrauterine infection or hemorrhage. Later in life, the aqueduct may be occluded by tumor. In another condition, obstruction of the outlets of the fourth ventricle by congenital atresia of the foramina of Magendie and Luschka may lead to enlargement of all four ventricles *(Dandy-Walker syndrome).* In early life, the cranial vault enlarges with the ventricles, but after fusion of the sutures, cranial volume is fixed.

Ideally, the treatment of hydrocephalus should consist of the removal of the causative factor. However, this can be done for only very few of the cases due to tumor. In other cases, CSF can be diverted past the block or to a new site for absorption. Numerous ingenious variations have been attempted, but the most popular are ventriculo-atrial, ventriculo-peritoneal and lumbar-peritoneal shunts. Complications include infection (meningitis or septicemia) or obstruction of either end of the shunt. Drug therapy directed toward decreasing CSF production or enhancing CSF absorption has not been successful in treating hydrocephalus and ethical questions are raised in the treatment of infants with hydrocephalus and severe cortical atrophy.

Selected Readings and References

Bradbury, M. 1979. The Concept of a Blood–Brain Barrier. New York: Wiley.

Cervós–Navarro, J., and Ferszt, R. (eds.). 1980. Brain Edema. Pathology, Diagnosis, and Therapy. New York: Raven Press.

Fishman, R. A. 1975. Brain edema. N. Engl. J. Med. 293:706–711.

Fishman, R. A. 1980. Cerebrospinal Fluid in Diseases of the Nervous System. Philadelphia: Saunders.

Katzman, R., and Pappius H. M. 1973. Brain Electrolytes and Fluid Metabolism. Baltimore: Williams & Wilkins.

Milhorat, T. H. 1972. Hydrocephalus and the Cerebrospinal Fluid. Baltimore: Williams & Wilkins.

Miller, J. D. 1979. Barbiturates and raised intracranial pressure. Ann. Neurol. 6:189–193.

Rapoport, S. I. 1976. Blood–Brain Barrier in Physiology and Medicine. New York: Raven Press.

Stein, S. C., and Langfitt, T. W. 1974. Normal-pressure hydrocephalus: Predicting the results of cerebrospinal fluid shunting, J. Neurosurg. 41:463–470.

Other References

Carpenter, M. B. 1978. Core Text of Neuroanatomy. 2nd ed. Baltimore: Williams & Wilkins.

Kuffler, S. W., and Nicholls, J. G. 1976. From Neuron to Brain. Sunderland, Mass.: Sinauer Associates.

Shu Chien

B. Cerebral Circulation and Metabolism

Proper functioning of the central nervous system depends on an adequate cerebral blood flow that delivers oxygen, glucose, and other nutrient materials and removes carbon dioxide and other metabolic products. Cerebral circulation is supplied by the internal carotid arteries and the vertebral arteries. The venous outflow is drained by the internal jugular veins and the vertebral veins. The arterial supply can be studied by angiography, which involves the intraarterial injection of a radiopaque contrast medium and radiographic examinations.

In this discussion of cerebral blood flow we shall consider how it is measured, how it is regulated, and how it varies in health and disease.

The human brain constitutes only 2% of the total weight of the body, but it receives 15% of the cardiac output and its oxygen consumption is 20% of that for the total body (Table II–1). These values indicate the high metabolic rate and oxygen requirement of the brain. These needs are met by a correspondingly high rate of blood flow per unit brain weight. The values given in Table II–1 are mean values for the whole brain. As will be discussed later, the rates of blood flow and metabolism are greater for gray matter, where the cell bodies of the neurons are located, than for white matter. Since brain tissues contain no more than their fair share of blood volume by weight, the high blood flow reflects a rapid transit time.

Table II–1. Normal Values for Mean Cerebral Blood Flow and Oxygen Consumption

Parameter	Total body	Brain Per 100 g	Total brain	Percent total body
Weight (kg)	70		1.5	2 %
Blood flow (ml/min)	5000	50	750	15 %
Oxygen consumption (cc/min)	250	3.3	50	20 %
Blood volume (ml)	5000	5	75	1.5%

Mean Cerebral Blood Flow and Regional Cerebral Blood Flow Are Measured by Different Techniques

Several methods have been devised to measure cerebral blood flow with relatively noninvasive techniques. These methods have made possible our understanding of the mechanism of regulation of cerebral blood flow in human beings.

Mean Cerebral Blood Flow is Measured by Equilibration with Freely Diffusible Inert Gas

The measurement of cerebral blood flow in human subjects was first done by S. S. Kety and C. F. Schmidt, who applied the Fick principle with the use of an inert gas, N_2O. In this method the subject is asked to breathe a gas mixture containing 15% N_2O, and blood samples are taken at frequent intervals from a systemic artery and from the internal jugular vein. N_2O diffuses readily across pulmonary alveolar and capillary membranes and enters the systemic circulation. During the early phase of N_2O inhalation, the arterial N_2O concentration (C_a) is higher than the venous N_2O concentration (C_v) emerging from the brain because N_2O readily crosses the capillary and cell membranes and is dispersed in the tissue (Figure II–6, insets t_1 and t_2). After approximately 10 min of inhalation (Figure II–6, inset t_{eq}), equilibration of N_2O is achieved between the arterial blood and venous blood, and the blood N_2O concentration $(C_{eq} = C_a = C_v$ at this time, in cubic centimeters N_2O per milliliter blood) is also in equilibrium with that in tissue $(C_t,$ in cubic centimeters N_2O per gram tissue), with the two being related by the tissue–blood partition coefficient $(\lambda,$ in milliliters per gram):

$$C_t = \lambda C_{eq}. \tag{II–1}$$

The λ for N_2O partition between brain and blood is approximately 1 milliliter per gram and hence C_t and C_{eq} have the same numerical value.

The quantity of N_2O dispersed in the brain at

equilibrium $(Q_{eq},$ in cubic centimeters $N_2O)$ is equal to the product of the N_2O concentration in the brain (C_t) and the brain weight $(M,$ in grams):

$$Q_{eq} = C_t M. \tag{II–2}$$

This net quantity is dispersed in the brain during the period of equilibration (from t_0 to t_{eq}), when the rate of N_2O entry $(\dot{V}C_a,$ in cubic centimeters N_2O per minute) via the arterial inflow is greater than its rate of exit $(\dot{V}C_v,$ in cubic centimeters N_2O per minute) via the venous outflow. $\dot{V}$ is the

II–6 Measurement of mean cerebral blood flow by equilibration with N_2O.

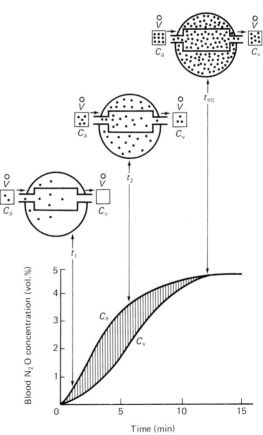

rate of blood flow (in milliliters per minute) and is assumed to be constant during the period of study. Hence, if we sum the cumulative difference between $\dot{V}C_a$ and $\dot{V}C_v$ over the time period t_0 to t_{eq}, we are able to obtain Q_{eq}:

$$Q_{eq} = \dot{V} \sum (C_a - C_v). \qquad (\text{II}-3)$$

The combination of equations II–1, II–2, and II–3 yields

$$\dot{V} \sum (C_a - C_v) = \lambda C_{eq} M$$

or

$$\frac{\dot{V}}{M} = \frac{C_{eq}}{\underset{t_0 \to t_{eq}}{\sum} (C_a - C_v)}. \qquad (\text{II}-4)$$

Therefore, the cerebral blood flow per unit brain weight $(\dot{V}/M)$ can be determined by sequential sampling of arterial and internal jugular venous blood and analysis of their N_2O concentrations throughout the equilibration process during N_2O inhalation. In place of N_2O, other inert gases that are freely diffusible across capillary and cell membranes can also be used for the same determination.

The Kety-Schmidt method provided most of the initial information on the regulation of cerebral blood flow and metabolism. However, it has the following disadvantages: (1) it gives only the mean cerebral blood flow per unit brain weight, without distinguishing between different types of brain tissues (gray matter or white matter) or different regions of the brain; (2) the procedure requires relatively long periods of time and the analysis of many samples. It has now been replaced by techniques that allow the determination of regional cerebral blood flow.

Regional Cerebral Blood Flow Is Measured by the Indicator Dilution Technique

This type of technique usually involves a single injection of a radioactive indicator into the internal carotid artery and the monitoring of intracranial radioactivity by using one or more extracranial detectors. Nondiffusible indicators (e.g., ^{131}I-labeled albumin) have been used, but, most commonly, diffusible indicators (e.g., ^{133}Xe gas) are used.

Figure II–7 is a semilogarithmic plot of the ^{133}Xe radioactivity in the head with time after a single intracarotid injection. The rate of washout (k) of the diffusible indicator from a tissue de-

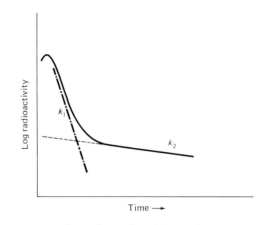

II–7 Semilogarithmic plot of ^{133}Xe radioactivity in the head after intracarotid injection. See text for curve analysis to obtain the rates of washout k_1 and k_2.

pends on the rate of blood flow per unit tissue mass (V/M) and the relative affinities of the tissue and blood for the indicator (λ):

$$k = (\dot{V}/M)/\lambda. \qquad (\text{II}-5)$$

The semilogarithmic curve plotting radioactivity against time shows a two-exponential decay. The later, slower rate of decay (k_2) is attributable to the washout from white matter (w). By extrapolating this slow component back to zero time and subtracting the extrapolated values from the results recorded in the early phase, we obtain the more rapid rate of washout (k_1) from gray matter (g). Hence,

$$(\dot{V}/M)_g = k_1 \lambda_g \qquad (\text{II}-6)$$
$$(\dot{V}/M)_w = k_2 \lambda_w \qquad (\text{II}-7)$$

where λ_g (≈ 0.8 ml/g) and λ_w (≈ 1.5 ml/g) are the tissue–blood partition coefficients for gray matter and white matter, respectively. Flow per unit mass of gray matter, $(\dot{V}/M)_g$, is approximately four times that of white matter, $(\dot{V}/M)_w$.

By using a detector consisting of multiple monitoring probes, one can obtain the washout curves in different regions of the brain (Figure II–8), and regional cerebral blood flows (rCBF) can be determined with the aid of data storage and computation devices. The determination of regional cerebral blood flow is valuable because many of the physiological changes and clinical abnormalities are confined to a certain region and may not be manifested in the average flow measurements made on the whole brain.

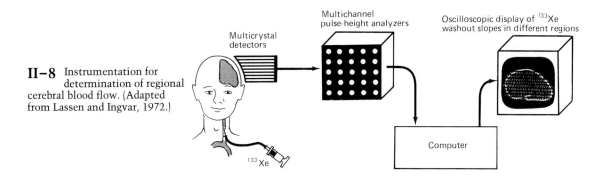

II–8 Instrumentation for determination of regional cerebral blood flow. (Adapted from Lassen and Ingvar, 1972.)

Cerebral Blood Flow Is Regulated by Changes in Arterial Pressure and Cerebral Flow Resistance

The brain is an organ with no significant capacity for anaerobic metabolism; its proper functioning depends on an adequate circulatory transport. The regulation of cerebral blood flow ($\dot{V}_b$) is geared to maintain cerebral metabolism and local homeostasis. $\dot{V}_b$ is a function of the pressure gradient and the cerebral vascular resistance (R_b):

$$\dot{V}_b = (P_a - P_{ijv})/R_b \qquad (II–8)$$

where P_a is the arterial pressure and P_{ijv} is the internal jugular venous pressure. The pressure gradient is determined primarily by the arterial pressure, which is regulated within narrow limits under normal conditions by circulatory reflexes and other control mechanisms. Resistance in cerebral flow is a function of the blood viscosity and the size of cerebral vessels. The factors regulating arterial pressure and cerebral flow resistance are briefly described below.

Arterial Pressure Is Regulated by Circulatory Reflexes

Baroreceptor Reflex. Arterial pressure is regulated by many circulatory reflexes, the most important of which are the baroreceptor reflexes. Baroreceptors are located in the aortic arch and carotid sinuses, and their impulse frequency varies directly with the arterial pressure as well as with the rate of rise of the arterial pressure. An increase in baroreceptor impulses causes reflex inhibition of sympathetic adrenergic efferents to the cardiovascular system and a reflex stimulation of the cardiac vagus nerve, leading to a decrease in arterial pressure. The baroreceptors are tonically active when arterial pressure is normal.

Therefore, a decrease in arterial pressure causes a reduction of baroreceptor impulses and a rise in arterial pressure. It is important to realize that the carotid sinus baroreceptors are located just at the point of inflow to the cerebral circulation. They therefore monitor the perfusion pressure to the brain.

Cerebral Ischemic Response. The baroreceptors cease to discharge when the arterial pressure falls below 50–60 mm Hg. Under these severely hypotensive conditions, vasomotor neurons in the brain are stimulated by the resulting ischemia and cause sympathetic excitation of the cardiovascular system as a last resort to maintain the arterial pressure.

Cerebral Flow Resistance Is Subject to Autoregulation

Blood Viscosity. A major factor in controlling blood viscosity is the concentration of red blood cells. Anemia causes a decrease in blood viscosity and an increase in cerebral blood flow.

Neural Regulation. There is evidence that the sympathetic adrenergic system can cause cerebral vasoconstriction, but this action is weak compared to that seen in many other parts of the circulation.

Autoregulation (Independent of Vasomotor Neurons). Local metabolic factors, such as an increase in p_{CO_2}, a decrease in pH, or a decrease in p_{O_2}, cause vasodilation ($\downarrow R_b$) and an increase in cerebral blood flow (Figure II–9). Changes in these metabolic factors in the opposite direction lead to vasoconstriction and a decrease in cerebral blood flow. The autoregulatory influence of p_{CO_2} on cerebral vascular resistance is probably the

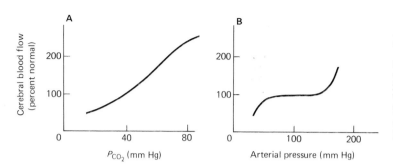

II–9 Changes in cerebral blood flow in response to autoregulation. **A.** Increased p_{CO_2} causes vasodilation and thus an increase in cerebral blood flow. **B.** Variations of arterial pressure between 60 and 140 mm Hg do not cause significant change of cerebral flow because of autoregulation.

most important factor controlling cerebral blood flow.

In addition, smooth muscle in small cerebral arteries and arterioles can change its active tension in response to changes in transmural pressure. Thus, an increase in arterial pressure causes vasoconstriction ($\uparrow R_b$) and a decrease in arterial pressure causes vasodilation ($\downarrow R_b$). Hence, the cerebral blood flow ($\dot{V}_b \simeq P_a/R_b$) remains essentially constant for a range of mean arterial pressures from approximately 60 to 140 mm Hg.

The brain tissue is enclosed in the rigid cranium together with blood vessels and the cerebrospinal fluid. Therefore, variations in either the cerebral blood volume or cerebrospinal fluid volume will exert pressure effects on the other components (for discussion of the Monro-Kellie doctrine, see Appendix IIA). An increase in cerebrospinal fluid pressure compresses cerebral vessels and increases R_b. The autoregulatory response of arteriolar smooth muscle to this transmural pressure change is to undergo active vasodilation, thus reducing the increase in R_b somewhat.

Cerebral Blood Flow and Metabolism Change Under Various Conditions

Mean Cerebral Blood Flow and Metabolism Are Affected by Some Pathological Conditions

Mean cerebral blood flow and metabolism are not significantly affected by daily activities, such as changes in posture, muscular exercise, mental activity, or sleep. Most general anesthetics cause a reduction in cerebral metabolic rate and a concomitant decrease in cerebral blood flow. Large doses of epinephrine stimulate cerebral metabolism and increase cerebral blood flow. Old age or hypertension per se does not change cerebral circulation or metabolism unless there are arterio-

sclerotic changes. Anemia (by decreasing the blood viscosity) and hypoventilation (by causing vasodilation) increase cerebral blood flow, but they have no significant effect on cerebral metabolism. Cerebral metabolism and blood flow both increase in convulsion and are suppressed in coma and barbiturate poisoning. Normal and pathological changes are summarized in Table II–2.

Regional Cerebral Blood Flow and Metabolism Vary with Physiological Activities and Disease

As pointed out above, the mean cerebral blood flow and metabolism of the whole brain often do not reflect regional changes. Thus, in various types of physical and mental activities, regional cerebral blood flow increases in appropriate areas of the brain specifically concerned with the activity. For example, blood flow in the occipital lobe increases during visual stimulation and blood flow in the corresponding motor areas increases during limb movements. Figure II–10 shows the areas of brain tissues with increases in regional cerebral blood flow during a speech test.

Determinations of regional cerebral blood flow provide information on the local derangement of blood flow in disease states and elucidate the intracerebral redistribution of blood flow in various conditions. An example of this is shown in Figure II–11, which depicts the regional cerebral blood flow determined in six areas of the brain of a patient 2 days after a cerebral stroke that caused hemiparesis. All the values are lower than normal. When an attempt was made to increase cerebral blood flow by inhalation of CO_2, there were significant increases (+30% to +50%) in five of the six regions studied. The region with the lowest resting flow (26 milliliters per minute per 100 g), however, suffered a further decrease in

Table II–2. Changes in Mean Cerebral Blood Flow and Metabolism Under Various Physiological and Pathological Conditions

Condition	Blood flow	Metabolism
Daily activity		
Posture (effect of standing)	slight ↓	—
Muscular exercise	—	—
Mental activity	—	—
Sleep	—	—
Drugs		
General anesthetics	↓	↓
Epinephrine (large dose)	↑	↑
Old age	—	—
Diseases		
Sclerosis of cerebral vessels	↓	↓
Hypertension (non cerebral change)	—	—
Anemia	↑	—
Hypoventilation	↑	—
Convulsion	↑	↑
Coma	↓	↓
Barbiturates	↓	↓

Symbols: ↓, decrease; ↑, increase; —, no change.

flow (−26%) upon inhalation of CO_2. Therefore, there was a loss of the vasodilation response to CO_2 in the most severely affected region. When vasodilation was induced by CO_2 in other regions, the blood flow through the undilated region decreased because blood flow was shunted away from the undilated region to the dilated areas.

Recent advances in technology involving computerized tomography and nuclear medicine have made it possible to determine regional metabolism of the human brain by *positron emission tomography*. Substances containing short-lived positron-emitting radionuclides, e.g., ^{15}O, ^{13}N, ^{11}C and ^{18}F, are used for this purpose.

Positrons (positively charged electrons) interact with electrons to yield annihilation radiation and two photons traveling in opposite directions. With the use of radiation coincidence detectors of the two photons and with the aid of computerized processing, the brain image of the distribution of the nuclide can be obtained as a function of time.

Regional cerebral metabolism can also be quantified by using either radiolabeled metabolic substrates (e.g., ^{11}C-glucose) or radiolabeled, metabolically inert analogues of these substrates (e.g., ^{18}F-labeled 2-deoxy-2-fluoro-D-glucose, which is used as a tracer for the exchange of glucose between plasma and brain and glucose

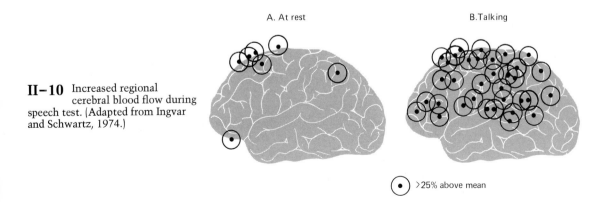

II–10 Increased regional cerebral blood flow during speech test. (Adapted from Ingvar and Schwartz, 1974.)

A. At rest

B. Talking

● >25% above mean

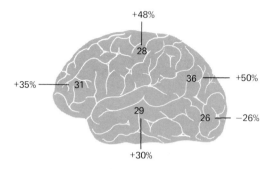

II−11 Regional cerebral blood flow in the brain of a patient 2 days after cerebral stroke resulting in hemiparesis. The numbers over the brain are regional blood flow values in milliliters per minute per 100 g. The effect of carbon dioxide inhalation is shown as + or − percent. (Adapted from Fazio et al., 1971.)

phosphorylation by hexokinase in the tissue). With mathematical modeling, regional cerebral consumption of glucose has been determined in normal human subjects. The values in the gray matter of the cerebral cortex range from approximately 7 mg/min/100 g in the parietal cortex to 10 mg/min/100 g in the visual cortex, and the subcortical white matter has a consumption rate of approximately 4 mg/100 g/min.

Since glucose is the energy source for neurons, cells take up more glucose when they are active than when they are at rest. ^{18}F-labeled 2-deoxy-2-fluoro-D-glucose is taken up by active cells as if it were glucose, but it cannot be metabolized and therefore accumulates. The extent of radioactivity is therefore a marker for the extent of neuronal activity. Thus a subject with eyes open will show much more radioactivity in the occipital lobe than will a subject with eyes closed. By using radioautography in experimental animals or positron emission tomography in humans, this method allows one to localize anatomically a functionally active system in the brain of living humans in a completely safe, noninvasive way.

Selected Readings and References

Kuschinsky, W., and Wahl, M. 1978. Local chemical and neurogenic regulation of cerebral vascular resistance. Physiol. Rev. 58:656–689.

Lassen, N. A. 1974. Control of cerebral circulation in health and disease. Circ. Res. 34:749–760.

Reivich, M., Kuhl, D., Wolf, A., Greenberg, J., Phelps, M., Ido, T., Casella, V., Fowler, J., Hoffman, E., Alavi, A., Som, P., and Sokoloff, L. 1979. The [18F] fluorodeoxyglucose method for the measurement of local cerebral glucose utilization in man. Circ. Res. 44:127–137.

Other References

Fazio, C., Fieschi, C., and Agnoli, A. 1971. The "intracerebral steal": A phenomenon in the pathogenesis of focal brain ischemia. In K. J. Zülch (ed.), Cerebral Circulation and Stroke. New York: Springer, pp. 143–147.

Ingvar, D. H., and Schwartz, M. S. 1974. Blood flow patterns induced in the dominant hemisphere by speech and reading. Brain 97:273–288.

Kety, S. S., and Schmidt, C. F. 1948. The nitrous oxide method for the quantitative determination of cerebral blood flow in man; theory, procedure, and normal values. J. Clin. Invest. 27:476–483.

Lassen, N. A., and Ingvar, D. H. 1972. Radioisotopic assessment of regional cerebral blood flow. Prog. Nucl. Med. 1:376–409.

John C. M. Brust

C. Stroke:
Diagnostic, Anatomical, and Physiological Considerations

The brain requires an uninterrupted supply of glucose and oxygen and can function only for a few minutes if they are reduced below a certain critical level. The brain also requires maintenance of temperature and removal of carbon dioxide and acid (metabolic breakdown products). The total blood flow to the brain is about 750–1000 ml/min; of this amount about 350 ml flows through each internal carotid and about 100–200 ml flows through the vertebral basilar system. Although the brain comprises only about 2 percent of body weight, it receives about 17 percent of the normal cardiac output and about 20 percent of the entire body's oxygen consumption.

Blood flow to the brain is highly protected, yet the brain remains highly susceptible to disturbances of the blood supply, and this is reflected in the high incidence of symptomatic cerebral vascular disease in the population at large. Diseases of the blood vessels are among the most frequent serious neurological disorders, ranking third as a cause of death in the adult American population and probably first as a cause of chronic functional incapacity. Approximately 2,000,000 Americans living today are impaired by the neurological consequences of cerebrovascular disease. Many of them are between 25 and 64 years of age.

The term *stroke*, or *cerebrovascular accident* (CVA), refers to neurological symptoms and signs, usually focal and acute, that result from diseases involving blood vessels. Strokes are either *occlusive* (due to closure of a blood vessel) or *hemorrhagic* (due to bleeding from a vessel). Insufficiency of blood supply is termed *ischemia*; if it is temporary, symptoms and signs may clear with little or no pathological evidence of tissue damage. *Ischemia* is not synonymous with *anoxia*, for a reduced blood supply deprives tissue not only of oxygen, but of glucose as well, and, moreover, prevents the removal of potentially toxic metabolites such as lactic acid. When ischemia is sufficiently severe and prolonged, death of neurons and other cellular elements occurs, and this is called *infarction*.

Hemorrhage may occur at the brain surface (extraparenchymal), for example, from rupture of congenital aneurysms at the circle of Willis, causing *subarachnoid hemorrhage* (SAH). Alternatively, hemorrhage may be intraparenchymal—for example, from vessels damaged by long-standing hypertension—and may cause a blood clot or hematoma within the cerebral hemispheres, in the brain stem, or in the cerebellum. Hemorrhage may be accompanied by ischemia or infarction. The mass effect of an intracerebral hematoma may compromise the blood supply of adjacent brain tissue, or subarachnoid hemorrhage may, by unclear mechanisms, cause reactive vasospasm of cerebral surface vessels, leading to further ischemic brain damage. Conversely, infarcted tissue may become secondarily hemorrhagic.

Although most occlusive strokes are due to atherosclerosis and thrombosis and most hemorrhagic strokes are associated with hypertension or aneurysms, strokes of either type may occur at any age from a legion of causes that include cardiac disease, trauma, infection, neoplasm, blood dyscrasia, vascular malformation, immunological disorder, and exogenous toxins. Diagnostic strategies and treatment will obviously vary accordingly. We shall examine, however, the anatomical and physiological principles relevant to any occlusive or hemorrhagic stroke, and it will be helpful to begin by considering the principles underlying two modern diagnostic techniques, computerized tomography (CT scan) and position emission tomography (PET scan), which have revolutionized neurology by providing high-contrast visualization of various regions of the brain, allowing unprecedented safety and accuracy in neurological diagnosis.

Noninvasive Tomographic Techniques Are Used to Diagnose Stroke

Computerized X-Ray Tomography (CT Scan) Allows Visualization of Soft Tissue and Fluids

A conventional radiograph represents a single, static, pictorial display in which lucency (degree of blackness) is inversely proportional to the absorption of X-ray photons as they pass through tissues toward an X-ray film. Bone, for example, absorbs a good deal of radiation and therefore appears light on radiograms, whereas air absorbs very little and appears dark. In CT scanning, X-ray photons are also used, but the technique is quite different; scintillation crystal (e.g., sodium iodide) detectors replace X-ray film. Both the X-ray tube (giving off a highly collimated beam of radiation) and the detectors rotate 180° about the head. At each degree of rotation, tube and detector, now moving linearly, make a series of transmission readings (up to several hundred, depending on the model). The result, for each transaxial "slice" of brain, is a matrix of thousands of intersecting radiation intensity measurements, which are translated by computer into numbers (*attenuation coefficients*) and are visually displayed as relatively dark or light areas. Several transverse (or coronal) slices are usually obtained at each study, which often includes a repeat series of slices following the intravenous injection of radiopaque iodinated contrast material, allowing "enchancement" of lesions because of either increased vasculature or impaired blood–brain barrier functions (e.g., neoplasm or recent infarction).

The advantages of CT are numerous. Most important, it allows good visualization of the soft tissue (parenchyma) of the brain and of the ventricular system (Figure II–12). This visualization is possible because CT is far more sensitive than conventional radiography in detecting differences in tissue density: cerebrospinal fluid, for example, is shown as less dense than brain but more dense than air, and it is possible to differentiate gray and white matter. Fresh blood has high radiographic density, in contrast to infarction and edema. The cross-sectional display of brain slices and the subtle differentiations of density make possible extraordinary precision in detecting, localizing, and pathologically defining a wide variety of lesions. For example, various clinically important brain regions (such as the basal ganglia) can be clearly delineated. CT is, moreover, non-

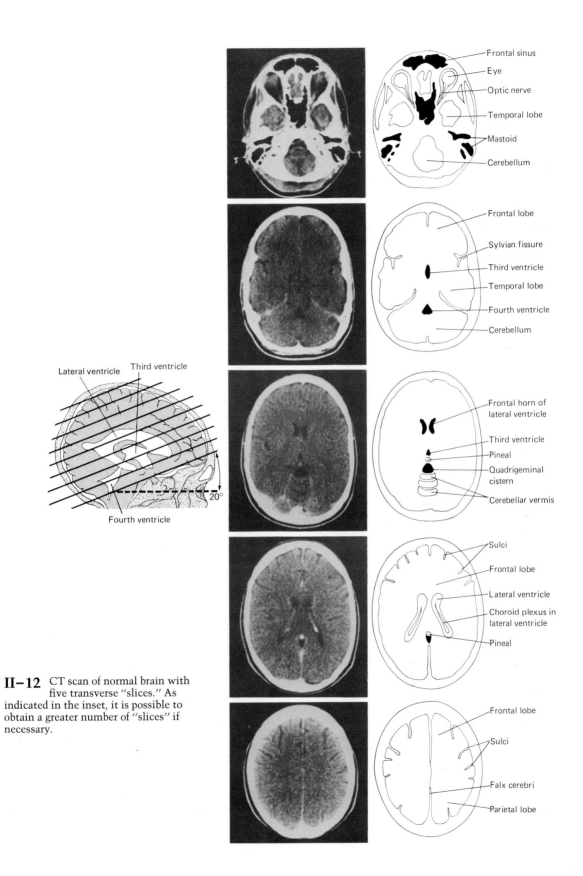

II–12 CT scan of normal brain with five transverse "slices." As indicated in the inset, it is possible to obtain a greater number of "slices" if necessary.

invasive and is therefore considerably safer than such invasive procedures as cerebral angiography or pneumoencephalography.

Positron Emission Tomography (PET Scan) Provides a Dynamic Picture of Brain Function

X-ray CT, as described above, is *transmission tomography:* i.e., the image formation depends upon the relative attenuation of X-rays passing through tissues. *Emission tomography* utilizes similar mathematical principles and hardware to reconstruct, from views taken at different angles around the head or body, images of transaxial sections ("slices"). In emission tomography, however, the image formation depends upon the metabolic distribution in the tissue of an injected or inhaled radionuclide. In other words, CT provides a valuable but static picture of anatomy. Emission tomography, in contrast, provides a dynamic picture of the cellular functions of the brain.

Conventionally used gamma emitters such as ^{99m}Tc or ^{123}I have physical properties, such as a long half-life, that make them generally unsuitable for emission tomography. More promising are a number of compounds that decay after short half-lives, but with the emission of positrons (positively charged electrons), which then undergo antimatter–matter collision with electrons and annihilation. The mass of the two particles is converted into two photons moving at 180° from one another and ultimately reaching two radiation detectors connected to a coincidence circuit, which records an event only when two detections are made simultaneously. Radionuclides such as ^{11}C, ^{13}N, ^{15}O, and ^{18}F can be used to label biological substrates or analogues such as glucose or water, making it possible, with PET, to measure in vivo such metabolic variables as regional cerebral glucose metabolic rate (CMRGlu) and cerebral blood volume. With the ability to label specific neurotransmitters, as well as metabolic substrates, PET may allow us to apply a cell biological approach to the human brain and to revise our present concept, of functional neuroanatomy and physiology. The major disadvantage of PET is that, because isotopes with short half-lives are involved, an on-site cyclotron is required for generating them, making the procedure extremely costly. In contrast to transmission CT, PET is currently more useful for research than for diagnosis.

The Blood Supply of the Brain Can Be Divided into Arterial Territories

Figure II–13 is a schematic illustration of the brain's blood vessels. Each cerebral hemisphere is supplied by an internal carotid artery, which arises from a common carotid artery beneath the angle of the jaw, enters the cranium through the carotid foramen, traverses the cavernous sinus (giving off the ophthalmic artery), penetrates the dura, and divides into the anterior and middle cerebral arteries. The anterior cerebral artery supplies, by large surface branches, the cortex and white matter of the inferior frontal lobe, the medial surface of the frontal and parietal lobes, and the anterior corpus callosum. Smaller penetrating branches supply the deeper cerebrum and diencephalon, including limbic structures, the head of the caudate, and the anterior limb of the internal capsule. The middle cerebral artery supplies, through large surface branches, most of the cortex and white matter of the hemisphere's convexity, including the frontal, parietal, temporal, and occipital lobes, and the insula. Smaller penetrating branches supply the corona radiata and diencephalic structures such as the posterior limb of the internal capsule, the putamen, the outer pallidum, and the body of the caudate. The internal carotid artery also gives off, after its emergence from the cavernous sinus, the anterior choroidal artery, which supplies the anterior hippocampus and, at a caudal level, the posterior limb of the internal capsule.

Each vertebral artery arises from a subclavian artery, enters the cranium through the foramen magnum, and gives off an anterior spinal artery and a posterior inferior cerebellar artery. The vertebral arteries join at the junction of the pons and the medulla to form the basilar artery, which at the level of the pons gives off the anterior inferior cerebellar artery and the internal auditory artery and at the midbrain the superior cerebellar artery. The basilar artery then divides into the two posterior cerebral arteries, which supply, via large surface branches, the inferior temporal and medial occipital lobes and the posterior corpus callosum, and, via smaller pentrating branches, diencephalic structures, including the thalamus and the subthalamic nuclei, as well as parts of the midbrain.

These arterial territories are shown schematically in Figure II–14. Figures II–15, II–16, and

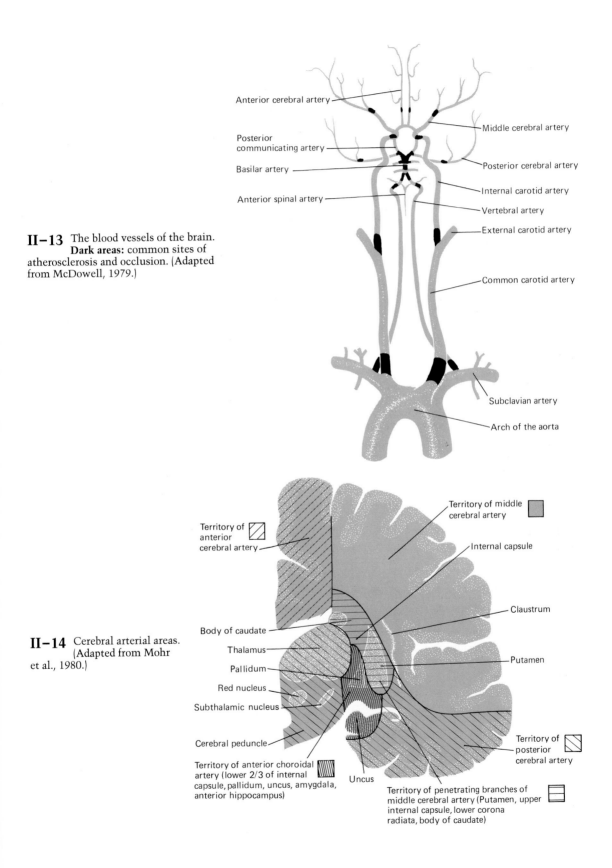

II–13 The blood vessels of the brain. **Dark areas:** common sites of atherosclerosis and occlusion. (Adapted from McDowell, 1979.)

Anterior cerebral artery

Middle cerebral artery

Posterior communicating artery

Basilar artery

Anterior spinal artery

Posterior cerebral artery

Internal carotid artery

Vertebral artery

External carotid artery

Common carotid artery

Subclavian artery

Arch of the aorta

II–14 Cerebral arterial areas. (Adapted from Mohr et al., 1980.)

Territory of middle cerebral artery

Territory of anterior cerebral artery

Internal capsule

Body of caudate

Claustrum

Thalamus

Pallidum

Putamen

Red nucleus

Subthalamic nucleus

Cerebral peduncle

Territory of posterior cerebral artery

Territory of anterior choroidal artery (lower 2/3 of internal capsule, pallidum, uncus, amygdala, anterior hippocampus)

Uncus

Territory of penetrating branches of middle cerebral artery (Putamen, upper internal capsule, lower corona radiata, body of caudate)

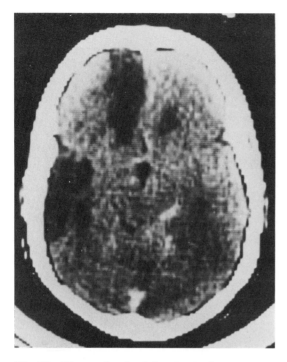

II–15 CT scan showing infarction in the territory of the anterior cerebral artery. (There is also an infarction, on the same side, in the territory of a major branch of the middle cerebral artery.) (Courtesy of Dr. S. R. Ganti and Dr. S. K. Hilal.)

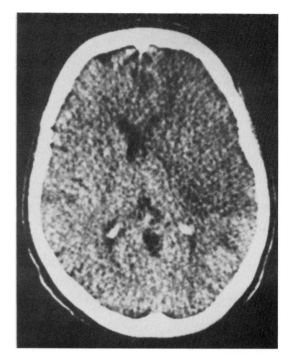

II–16 CT scan showing infarction in the territory of the middle cerebral artery. (Courtesy of Dr. S. R. Ganti and Dr. S. K. Hilal.)

II–17 CT scan showing infarction in the territory of the posterior cerebral artery. (Courtesy of Dr. S. R. Ganti and Dr. S. K. Hilal.)

II–17 are CT scans demonstrating infarction in the territories of the anterior, middle, and posterior cerebral arteries, respectively. (The infarcted tissue is darker than the normal brain.)

Interconnections between blood vessels (anastomoses) protect the brain when part of its vascular supply is compromised. At the circle of Willis the two anterior cerebral arteries are connected by the anterior communicating artery, and the posterior cerebral arteries are connected to the internal carotid arteries by the posterior communicating arteries. The protective importance of the circle of Willis is illustrated by the fact that a congenitally incomplete circle, common in the general population, is significantly more common among patients who have had strokes. Other important anastomoses include connections between the ophthalmic artery and branches of the external carotid artery through the orbit, and connections at the brain surface between branches of the middle, anterior, and posterior cerebral arteries. Figure II–18 is an angiogram showing occlusion of the middle cerebral artery with retrograde filling via anastomoses.

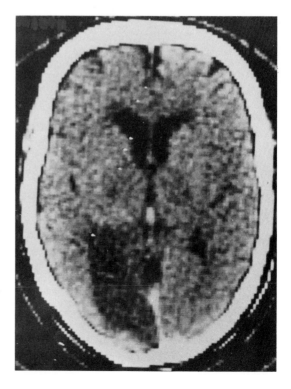

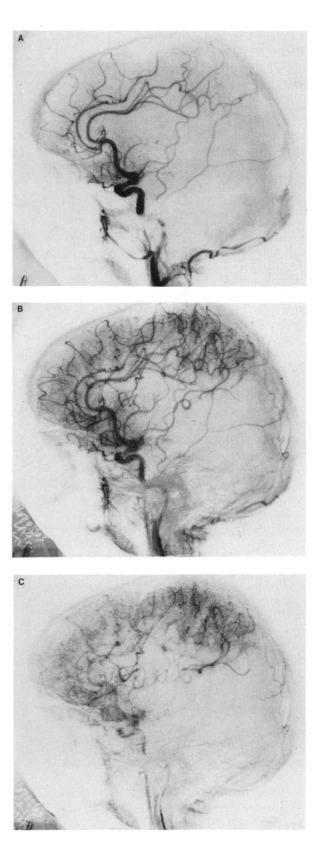

II–18 **A.** Occlusion of middle cerebral artery. No filling is seen in the middle cerebral distribution. **B.** Retrograde filling of middle cerebral artery has begun via distal anastomotic branches of the anterior cerebral artery. **C.** Retrograde filling of middle cerebral artery continues at a time when little contrast material is seen in the anterior cerebral artery. (Courtesy of Dr. Margaret Whelan and Dr. Sadek Hilal.)

Clinical Vascular Syndromes May Follow Vessel Occlusion, Hypoperfusion, or Hemorrhage

Infarction Can Occur in the Middle Cerebral Artery Territory

Infarction in the territory of the middle cerebral artery (cortex and white matter) causes the most frequently encountered stroke syndrome, with contralateral weakness, sensory loss, and visual field cut, and, depending on the hemisphere involved, either language disturbance or impaired spatial perception. Weakness and sensory loss affect the face and arm more than the leg because of the somatotopy of the motor and sensory strips (pre- and post-Rolandic gyri): the face and arm lie on the convexity, whereas the leg resides on the medial surface of the hemisphere. Motor and sensory loss are greatest in the hand, for the more proximal limbs and the trunk tend to have greater representation in both hemispheres. Paraspinal muscles, for example, are hardly ever weak in unilateral cerebral lesions. Similarly, the facial muscles of the forehead and the muscles of the pharynx and jaw are represented bihemispherically and therefore are usually spared. Tongue weakness is variable. If weakness is severe (plegia), muscle tone is usually decreased initially and gradually increases over days or weeks to spasticity with hyperactive tendon reflexes. A Babinski sign, reflecting upper motor neuron disturbance, is usually present from the outset. If weakness is mild, or during recovery, there may be clumsiness or slowness of movement out of proportion to loss of strength; such motor disability may resemble parkinsonian bradykinesia or even cerebellar ataxia.

Acutely, there is often paresis of contralateral conjugate gaze as a result of damage to the convexity of the cortex anterior to the motor strip (the frontal gaze center). The reason this gaze palsy persists for only 1 or 2 days, even when other signs remain severe, is not clear.

Sensory loss tends to involve discriminative and proprioceptive modalities more than affective modalities. Pain and temperature sensation may be impaired or seem altered but are usually not lost. Joint position sense, however, may be severely disturbed, causing limb ataxia, and there may be loss of two-point discrimination, astereognosis (inability to recognize, tactually, a held object), or failure to appreciate a touch stimulus if another is simultaneously delivered to the normal side of the body (extinction).

Visual field impairment (homonymous hemianopsia) is the result of damage to the optic radiations, the deep fiber tracts connecting the thalamic lateral geniculate body to the visual (calcarine) cortex. If the parietal radiation is primarily involved, the field cut may be an inferior quadrantanopsia, whereas in temporal lobe lesions quadrantanopsia may be superior (see Figure 20–8).

As we have seen in Chapter 48, in more than 95% of right-handed persons and in the majority of left-handed individuals, the left hemisphere is dominant for language function. Destruction of left opercular (peri-Sylvian) cortex in such patients causes aphasia, which may, as we have also seen, take a variety of forms depending on the degree and distribution of the damage. Frontal opercular lesions tend to produce particular difficulty with speech output and writing, with relative preservation of language comprehension (Broca aphasia), whereas infarction of the posterior superior temporal gyrus tends to cause severe difficulty in comprehending spoken speech and reading (Wernicke aphasia). When opercular damage is widespread, there is severe language disturbance of mixed type (global aphasia).

Left hemispheric convexity damage, especially parietal, may also cause motor apraxia, a disturbance of learned motor acts not explained by weakness or incoordination, with the ability to perform the act when the setting is altered. For example, a patient unable to imitate lighting a match might be able to perform the act normally if given the appropriate objects.

Right hemispheric convexity infarction, especially parietal, tends to cause disturbances of spacial perception. There may be difficulty in copying simple pictures or diagrams (constructional apraxia), in interpreting maps or finding one's way about (topographagnosia), or in putting on one's clothes properly (dressing apraxia). Awareness of space and the patient's own body contralateral to the lesion may be particularly affected (hemi-inattention or hemi-neglect). The patient may fail to recognize his hemiplegia (anosognosia), his arm (asomatognosia), or any external object to the left of his own midline. Such phenomena may occur independently of visual field defects and in patients otherwise mentally quite intact.

Particular types of language or spatial dysfunction tend to follow occlusion, not of the proximal stem of the middle cerebral artery, but of one of its several main pial branches. In such circumstances other signs (e.g., weakness or visual field cut) may not be present. Similarly, occlusion of the Rolandic branch of the middle cerebral artery may cause motor and sensory loss affecting the face and arm without disturbance of vision, language, or spatial perception.

Infarction Can Occur in the Anterior Cerebral Artery Territory

Infarction in the territory of the anterior cerebral artery causes weakness and sensory loss qualitatively similar to that of convexity lesions but affects mainly the distal contralateral leg. There may be urinary incontinence, but it is uncertain whether this is due to a lesion of the paramedian lobule (medial hemispheric motor and sensory strips) or of a more anterior region concerned with the inhibition of bladder emptying. Damage to the supplementary motor cortex may cause speech disturbance, considered aphasic by some and a type of motor inertia by others. Involvement of the anterior corpus callosum may cause apraxia of the left arm (sympathetic apraxia), which is attributed to disconnection of the left (language-dominant) hemisphere from the right motor cortex.

Bilateral anterior cerebral artery territory infarction (occurring, for example, when both arteries arise anomalously from a single trunk) may cause a severe behavioral disturbance, with profound apathy, motor inertia, and muteness, attributed variably to destruction of the inferior frontal lobes (orbitofrontal cortex), deeper limbic structures, supplementary motor cortices, or cingulate gyri.

Infarction Can Occur in the Posterior Cerebral Artery Territory

Infarction in the territory of the posterior cerebral artery causes contralateral homonymous hemianopia by destroying the calcarine cortex. Macular (central) vision tends to be spared because the occipital pole, where macular vision is represented, receives blood supply from the middle cerebral artery. If the lesion is on the left and the posterior corpus callosum is affected, there may be alexia (without aphasia or agraphia), attributed to disconnection of the seeing right occipital cortex from the language-dominant left hemisphere. If infarction is bilateral (e.g., following thrombosis at the point where both posterior cerebral arteries arise from the basilar artery), there may be cortical blindness with failure of the patient to recognize that he cannot see (Anton syndrome), or, as a result of bilateral damage to the inferomedial temporal lobes, memory disturbance.

If posterior cerebral artery occlusion is proximal, the lesion may include, or especially affect, the following structures: the thalamus, causing contralateral hemisensory loss and sometimes spontaneous pain and dysesthesia (thalamic pain syndrome); the subthalamic nucleus, causing contralateral severe proximal chorea (hemiballism); or even the midbrain, with ipsilateral oculomotor palsy and contralateral hemiparesis or ataxia from involvement of the corticospinal tract or the crossed superior cerebellar peduncle (dentatothalamic tract).

The Anterior Choroidal and Penetrating Arteries Can Become Occluded

Anterior choroidal artery occlusion should, in theory, cause infarction of the posterior limb of the internal capsule, with contralateral hemiparesis, hypesthesia, and hemianopia; however, such a lesion, often suspected clinically, remains to be demonstrated pathologically.

As mentioned above, the deeper cerebral white matter and diencephalon are supplied by small penetrating arteries—variably called the *lenticulostriates*, the *thalamogeniculates*, or the *thalamoperforates*—which arise from the circle of Willis or the proximal portions of the middle, anterior, and posterior cerebral arteries. These end-arteries lack anastomotic interconnections, and occlusion of individual vessels, usually in association with hypertensive damage to the vessel wall, causes small (less than 1 cm in diameter) infarcts ("lacunes"), which, if critically located, are followed by characteristic syndromes. For example, lacunes in the pyramidal tract area of the internal capsule cause "pure hemiparesis," with arm and leg weakness of equal severity, but little or no sensory loss, visual field disturbance, aphasia, or spatial disruption. Lacunes in the ventral posterior nucleus of the thalamus produce "pure hemisensory loss," with discriminative and affective modalities both involved and little motor, visual, language, or spatial disturbance. Most lacunes occur in redundant areas, e.g., nonpyramidal corona radiata, and so are asymptomatic. If bilateral and numerous, however, they may cause a characteristic syndrome (état lacunaire) of progressive dementia, shuffling gait, and pseudobulbar palsy (spastic dysarthria and dysphagia, with lingual and pharyngeal paralysis and hyperactive palate and gag reflexes, plus lability of emotional response, with abrupt crying or laughing out of proportion to mood).

The Carotid and Basilar Arteries Can Become Occluded

Atherothrombotic vessel occlusion often occurs in the internal carotid artery rather than the intracranial vessels. Particularly in a patient with an incomplete circle of Willis, infarction may then include the territories of both the middle and anterior cerebral arteries, with arm and leg weakness and sensory loss equally severe. Another cause of leg weakness and sensory loss in association with a convexity syndrome is occlusion of the middle cerebral artery at its proximal stem; capsular (and other diencephalic) structures supplied by the middle cerebral artery's lenticulostriate branches will then be affected in addition to the cortex of the cerebral convexity.

The medial and lateral syndromes of brain stem infarction, which tend to bear annoying eponyms, have been discussed in Chapter 36. To recapitulate briefly, lateral syndromes—for example, following lateral medullary infarction, with vertigo, nystagmus, ipsilateral limb ataxia, loss of pain and temperature sensation on the ipsilateral face and contralateral arm and leg, and ipsilateral ptosis, miosis, and facial anhidrosis (Horner syndrome)—result from the occlusion of large branches of the vertebral or basilar arteries supplying the lateral brain stem and cerebellum. Medial syndromes—for example, following medial pontine infarction, with ipsilateral abducens, gaze, or facial palsy and contralateral hemiparesis—result from occlusion of small paramedian penetrating vertebral or basilar artery branches. In fact, most brain stem infarcts follow occlusion of the vertebral or basilar arteries, and the resulting symptoms and signs are less stereotyped than classical descriptions imply. Involvement of the posterior fossa structures in an infarct is suggested by (1) bilateral long tract (motor or sensory) signs, (2) crossed (e.g., left face and right limb) motor or sensory signs, (3) cerebellar signs, (4) stupor or coma (from involvement of the ascending reticular activating system), (5) disconjugate eye movements or nystagmus, including the syndrome of internuclear ophthalmoplegia (medial longitudinal fasciculus syndrome), and (6) involvement of cranial nerves not usually affected by single hemispheric infarcts (e.g., unilateral deafness or pharyngeal weakness).

Diffuse Hypoperfusion Can Cause Ischemia or Infarction

Brain ischemia or infarction may accompany diffuse hypoperfusion (shock), and in such circumstances the most vulnerable regions are often the border zones (watershed areas) between large arterial territories and the end zones of deep penetrating vessels. Following recovery from, for example, carbon monoxide poisoning or cardiac arrest, a patient may have paralysis and sensory loss in both arms (from bilateral infarction of the cortex at the junction of the middle and anterior arterial supply, affecting the arm area of the motor and sensory strips), or disturbed vision or memory (from infarction of occipital or temporal lobes at the junction of middle and posterior cerebral arterial supply). There may also be ataxia (from cerebellar border zone infarction) or abnormal movements such as chorea or myoclonus (presumably from involvement of basal ganglia). Such signs may exist alone or in combination and may be accompanied by a variety of aphasic or other cognitive disturbances.

The Rupture of Microaneurysms Is the Most Common Cause of Hemorrhagic Stroke

The two commonest causes of hemorrhagic stroke—hypertensive intraaxial hemorrhage and rupture of berry aneurysms—tend to occur at particular sites and to cause recognizable syndromes. Hypertensive hemorrhage is the result of damage to the same small penetrating vessels which, when occluded, cause lacunes; in this instance, however, the damaged vessels develop weakened walls (Charcot-Bouchard microaneurysms) that eventually rupture. The commonest sites are the putamen, thalamus, pons, internal capsule and corona radiata, and cerebellum. Large diencephalic hemorrhages tend to cause stupor and hemiplegia and have a high mortality rate. With putaminal lesions, the eyes are usually deviated ipsilaterally (due to disruption of capsular pathways descending from the frontal gaze center), whereas with thalamic hemorrhage the eyes tend to be deviated downward and the pupils may not react to light (due to involvement of midbrain pretectal structures essential for upward gaze and pupillary light reactivity—Parinaud syndrome). Small hemorrhages may not impair alertness; with thalamic hemorrhage, sensory loss may then be found to exceed weakness. Moreover, CT has shown that small thalamic

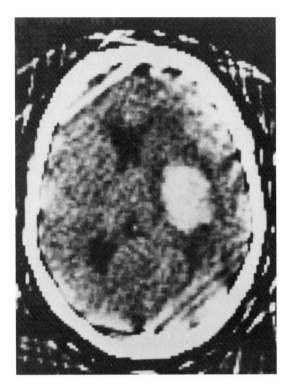

II–19 CT scan showing putaminal hemorrhage. (Courtesy of Dr. S. R. Ganti and Dr. S. K. Hilal.)

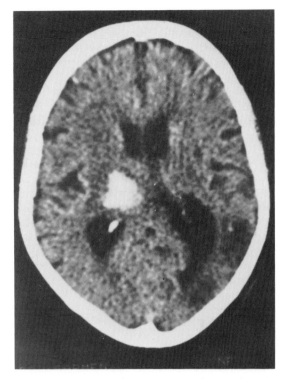

II–20 CT scan showing thalamic hemorrhage. (There is also infarction of the parieto-occipital area of the opposite hemisphere.) (Courtesy of Dr. S. R. Ganti and Dr. S. K. Hilal.)

hemorrhages may cause aphasia when on the left and hemi-inattention when on the right. Figures II–19 and II–20 are CT scans showing a large putaminal and a small thalamic hemorrhage, respectively. (The hematoma is much denser radiographically than surrounding brain.) Pontine hemorrhage, unless quite small, usually causes coma (by disrupting the reticular activating system) and quadriparesis (by transecting the corticospinal tract). Eye movements, spontaneous or reflex (e.g., to ice water in either external auditory canal), are absent, and pupils are pinpoint in size, perhaps in part from transection of descending sympathetic pathways and in part from destruction of reticular inhibitory mechanisms on the Edinger-Westphall nucleus of the midbrain. Pupillary light reactivity, however, is usually preserved, for the pathway subserving this reflex, from retina to midbrain, is intact. Respirations may be irregular, presumably from reticular formation involvement. Such a clinical state is nearly always fatal.

Cerebellar hemorrhage, which tends to occur in the region of the dentate nucleus, typically causes a sudden inability to stand or walk (astasia–abasia), with ipsilateral limb ataxia. There may be ipsilateral abducens or gaze palsy, or facial weakness, presumably from pontine compression. Long tract motor and sensory signs, however, are usually absent. As swelling increases, further brain stem damage may cause coma, ophthalmoplegia, miosis, and irregular respiration, with fatal outcome.

The Rupture of Berry Aneurysms Causes Subarachnoid Hemorrhage

Berry aneurysms (not to be confused with hypertensive Charcot-Bouchard aneurysms) are most often found at the junction of the anterior communicating artery with an anterior cerebral artery, at the junction of a posterior communicating artery with an internal carotid artery, and at the first bifurcation of a middle cerebral artery in the Sylvian fissure. Each, upon rupture, tends to cause not only sudden severe headache, but a characteristic syndrome. By producing a hematoma directly over the oculomotor nerve as it traverses the base of the brain, a ruptured posterior communicating artery aneurysm often causes ipsilateral pupillary dilation with loss of light reactivity. A middle cerebral artery aneurysm may, by either hematoma or secondary infarction, cause a clinical picture resembling that of middle cerebral artery occlusion. After rupture of an anterior communicating artery aneurysm, there may be no focal signs, but simply a decreased level of alertness or a behavioral change. Posterior fossa aneurysms most often occur at the rostral bifurcation of the basilar artery or at the origin of the posterior inferior cerebellar artery. They cause a wide variety of cranial nerve and brain stem signs. Rupture of an aneurysm at any site may cause abrupt coma; the reason is uncertain but may be related to sudden increased intracranial pressure and functional disruption of vital pontomedullary structures.

Stroke Alters the Vascular Physiology of the Brain

As noted In Appendix IIB, brain vessels respond in a unique fashion to changes in arterial pressure or blood gases. Brain arterioles constrict when the blood pressure is raised and dilate when it is lowered (autoregulation). Both of these adjustments tend to maintain optimal cerebral blood flow. The result is that normal individuals maintain a constant cerebral blood flow between mean arterial pressures of approximately 60 to 160 mm Hg. Above or below these levels cerebral blood flow rises or falls linearly.

When arterial p_{CO_2} is raised, brain arterioles dilate, and cerebral blood flow increases; with hypocarbia there is vasoconstriction, and cerebral blood flow decreases. The response is exquisitely sensitive: inhalation of 5% CO_2 increases cerebral blood flow by 50%, and 7% CO_2 doubles it. Changing arterial p_{O_2} causes an opposite and less pronounced response: breathing 100% O_2 lowers cerebral blood flow by about 13%; 10% O_2 raises it by 35%.

The mechanism of these responses is uncertain and controversial, but they serve protective functions, preserving blood flow in the presence of hypotension and increasing the delivery of oxygen and the removal of acid metabolites in the presence of hypoxia, ischemia, or tissue damage. After a stroke, however, cerebral blood flow and the responses to blood pressure or arterial gases are altered.

The term *luxury perfusion* refers to the frequent appearance, after brain infarction, of hyperemia relative to demand. Red venous blood may be seen draining infarcts, and regional cerebral blood flow may or may not be absolutely increased. In addition, there may be vasomotor paralysis, with loss of autoregulation and then blunted responses to changes in p_{O_2} or p_{CO_2}. Such physiological abnormalities occur both within and around ischemic lesions. In such patients, carbon dioxide (or other cerebral vasodilators) may produce a paradoxical response, increasing cerebral blood flow in brain regions distant from the infarct without affecting the vessels around the lesion. Blood may therefore be shunted from ischemic to normal brain (intracerebral steal). Conversely, cerebral vasoconstrictors, by decreasing cerebral blood flow in normal brain without affecting the vessels of ischemic brain, may shunt blood into the area of ischemia or infarction (inverse intracerebral steal or Robin Hood syndrome).

There is controversy about the frequency of these phenomena. Hyperperfusion is not invariable in infarcted brain, and it may coexist with adjacent hypoperfusion. Similarly, intracerebral steal, while probably commonest with very large infarcts, is, particularly in duration, quite unpredictable in any single patient. Nor is it clear whether increasing cerebral blood flow to infarcted or ischemic areas improves matters by increasing oxygen delivery and the removal of tissue-damaging metabolites or makes matters worse by increasing edema, mass effect, and anastomotic compromise. Until the vagaries of cerebral blood flow and metabolism in individual stroke patients can be better defined (e.g., with the future use of PET, which can noninvasively measure regional cerebral blood flow and metabolic rates for oxygen and glucose), it seems reasonable to withhold both vasoconstrictors and vasodilators in the treatment of occlusive stroke. The probable loss of autoregulation makes it reasonable to withhold antihypertensive treatment for 1 or 2 weeks (unless blood pressure is dangerously high or CT scan shows that the stroke is hemorrhagic) and to keep patients at bed rest unless other considerations outweigh the fear of postural hypotension and further brain ischemia.

Cerebral edema, as noted in Appendix IIA, may be either cytotoxic (intracellular, with normal vascular permeability) or vasogenic (extracellular, with leaky blood vessels). The nature of edema in stroke, and its treatment, are controversial, but most workers agree that at its earliest stages it is predominantly cytotoxic, resulting from the vulnerability of membrane Na^+-K^+-ATPase to anoxia, with failure of the Na^+ pump and increased intracellular water. Later, vessel permeability increases and extracellular fluid accumulates. The implication of this sequence of events is that in the first few days after a stroke, agents that decrease vasogenic edema, such as corticosteroids, are unlikely to be of benefit; a number of clinical studies support this hypothesis. On the other hand, the pathophysiology of edema in stroke, like that of cerebral blood flow and metabolism, is undoubtedly more complicated than the simple dichotomy of cytotoxic and vasogenic types would suggest. If tissue swelling in stroke, particularly when hemorrhagic, seems life threatening (by causing transtentorial brain herniation), corticosteroids should probably be used, but the outlook is likely to be gloomy in any case.

Selected Readings and References

Ascherl, G. F., Ganti, S. R., and Hilal, S. K. 1980. Neuroradiology for the clinician. In R. N. Rosenberg (ed.), Neurology, Vol. 5 of The Science and Practice of Clinical Medicine. New York: Grune & Stratton, pp. 634–718.

McDowell, F. H. 1979. Cerebrovascular diseases. In P. B. Beeson and W. McDermott (eds.), Textbook of Medicine. 15th ed. Philadelphia: Saunders, pp. 777–801.

Mohr, J. P., Fisher, C. M., and Adams, R. D. 1980. Cerebrovascular diseases. In K. J. Isselbacher, R. D. Adams, E. Braunwald, R. G. Petersdorf, and J. D. Wilson (eds.), Harrison's Principles of Internal Medicine. 9th ed. New York: McGraw-Hill, pp. 1911–1942.

Raichle, M. E. 1979. Tracer strategy in emission tomography. In T. R. Price and E. Nelson (eds.), Cerebrovascular Diseases. New York: Raven, pp. 91–98.

Appendix III
Neuroophthalmology

Peter Gouras

A. Physiological Optics, Accommodation, and Stereopsis

The eye resembles a camera with automatic brightness and focal control. It is equipped with rapid, automatic development and renewable film of two different varieties: one, the rod system, is a highly sensitive but coarse-grained achromatic film; the other, the cone system, is a less sensitive but more finely grained color film. The information in this film is analyzed by the visual system—a sophisticated image-processing computer located mainly, but not entirely, in the cerebral cortex.

The Lens Focuses an Inverted Image on the Photoreceptors

The basic principles of image formation in the eye depend upon the rules of geometrical optics, first described by Johannes Kepler in the 16th century (Figure III–1). As light passes through the eyes, an inverted image of the external luminous environment is focused on the retinal photoreceptors that line the back of the eye like photographic film. Unlike most cameras, however, this light-sensitive film is arranged along a spherical rather than a flat surface. The focusing of this image depends upon the transparency of all the intervening structures—cornea, aqueous humor, crystalline lens, vitreous humor and the neural retina—through which light must pass to reach the photoreceptors.

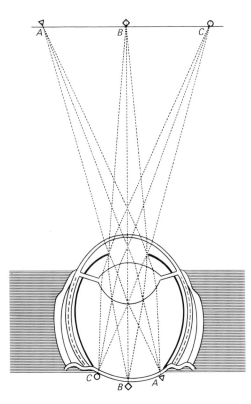

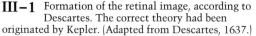

III—1 Formation of the retinal image, according to
        Descartes. The correct theory had been
originated by Kepler. (Adapted from Descartes, 1637.)

The optical effects of the neural retina are
greatly minimized in its central region—the
part of the retina that is used when we look directly at an object. Within this area is a small
depression, the central fovea, and along the floor
of the fovea (the foveola) the diameter of the retina is reduced to its thinnest dimension. Light
that is not absorbed by the receptor's outer segment travels on to the pigment epithelium and
choroid layer. If this light were scattered back
onto the retina, image degradation could occur.
This is prevented to a large degree by the presence
of light-absorbing pigment granules (melanin)
that are present both in the processes of pigment
epithelial cells that interleaf between the light-
sensitive structures of the photoreceptors and in
melanocytes found in the choroid.

Light Is Refracted in the Eye
Snell's Law Predicts the Refraction of Light

A guiding principle in image formation by optical
systems is the law enunciated by Snell van Rojen
of Leiden in the beginning of the 17th century

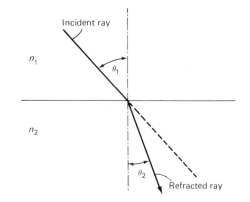

III—2 Snell's law and the index of refraction: the
        behavior of a light ray as it passes from a
medium of lower refractive index (N_1) into one of
higher refractive index (N_2). The refractive index of
each medium is determined by the ratio n = velocity
of light in vacuum/velocity of light in medium. Upon
entering the denser medium, the light ray is bent
(refracted) toward the perpendicular. The angle that
the light ray forms to a line perpendicular to the
surface is θ. For a given wavelength of light and pair
of media the ratio of the sine of the angle of incidence
(θ_1) to the sine of the angle of refraction (θ_2) is a
constant. This relationship, $n_1 \sin \theta_1 = n_2 \sin \theta_2$, is
Snell's law. (Adapted from Ogle, 1961.)

(Snell's law). The essential features of this law are
illustrated in Figure III—2. A light ray entering a
denser medium (i.e., one of higher refractive index[1]) will be bent toward a line normal to that
surface, such as occurs when light goes from air
into glass. If there is no difference in refractive
index between two surfaces or if the ray itself is
normal to the surface, no refraction or bending of
the light path will occur. This property of light
provides a means of focusing and magnifying visual objects. Any curved object that is transparent
to light and of a different refractive index than air
will bend incident light rays. Such objects are
called *lenses,* and the cornea and lens of the eye
are relevant examples.

In general there are two classes of lenses (Figure III—3): converging (convex) and diverging
(concave). Convex lenses bring light rays together
and concave lenses spread light rays farther apart.
That point at which all of the parallel light rays
meet after interacting with the lens is called the
principal focus or *focal point.* The distance from
the center of the lens to the principal focus is

---

[1]The *refractive index* is the ratio of the velocity of light in a
vacuum to its velocity in the medium considered.

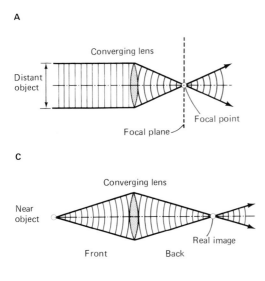

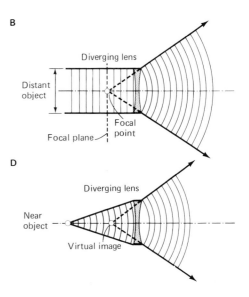

called the *focal length* of the lens. The bending or refractive power of a lens is expressed by diopter units. A *diopter* is the reciprocal (in meters) of the focal length of the lens. A 1-diopter lens focuses parallel light at 1 m; a 2-diopter lens does this at 0.5 m, etc. Converging lenses focus parallel rays on the opposite side of the lens, arbitrarily called positive; diverging lenses produce a virtual focus (a point from which divergent light rays appear to come but in fact do not) of parallel rays on the same side on which they arrive. Similarly, diverging lenses form virtual images while convex lenses form real images. Distant light rays traveling through a convex lens pass through those points occupied by the image and can be viewed if a screen is placed along this plane. These images are referred to as real images and are inverted. The diverging light rays that leave a concave lens, however, do not pass through the points occupied by the image. This virtual image is upright and cannot be formed on a screen but can be viewed by looking through the lens.

Thin Lens Formulas Are Derived from Snell's Law

A simplified explanation of image formation by lenses can be obtained by assuming that all lenses are infinitely thin without significant curvature. By applying Snell's law to thin lenses simple formulas can be derived that provide good approximations to what occurs in real (thick) lenses. Figure III–4A shows how three rays (from an infinite number) emanating from a light source are re-

III–3 Focusing of light by converging and diverging lenses. The refraction of parallel light rays emanating from a distant object is shown for a converging (**A**) and diverging (**B**) lens; and the refraction of divergent rays arising from a nearby object is shown for a converging (**C**) and diverging (**D**) lens. The focusing of light by converging lenses (A and C) produces a real image at a focal point in back of the lens. Light rays interacting with diverging lenses (B and D), however, spread apart and never form a real focus. By projecting the paths of these divergent rays, one finds they meet at a point in front of the lens known as the **virtual focus,** which is taken as the focal point of the lens. A virtual image is formed along this plane. (Adapted from Ogle, 1961.)

fracted by a thin convex lens. Ray 1 is parallel to the optical axis of the lens and is refracted through the focal point (F_1) of the lens. Ray 2 is undeviated and travels in a straight line to intersect ray 1 at the image (S') of the light source (S). Ray 3 passes through the other focal point (F_2) of the lens and exits parallel to the optical axis to intersect rays 1 and 2 in the image (S'). According to Snell's law, all the rays from source S within the solid angle that projects through this lens will meet in the image S'. Two of these rays (Figure III-4B) can be used to derive several useful relationships of thin lens optics between the object and image distance and the focal length, where

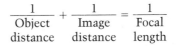

$$\frac{1}{\text{Object distance}} + \frac{1}{\text{Image distance}} = \frac{1}{\text{Focal length}}$$

This formula allows one to determine the distance of images of lenses of any focal length.

A

Light source   Lens   Image

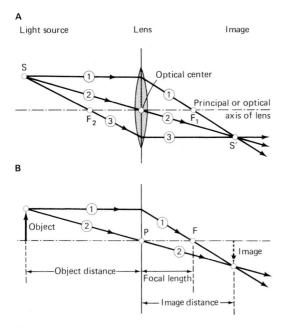

B

III–4 Refraction of light by a thin convex lens.
A. By assuming that this convex lens is
infinitely thin and applying Snell's law to light rays
1 and *2*, a useful relationship between image and
object distance and focal length can be determined,
B. A thin convex lens is shown forming a real
inverted image of a real object. Given the object
distance and focal length, the image distance can be
determined. F_1 and F_2, focal points of lens; *S*, light
source; *S'*, image. (Adapted from Ogle, 1961.)

III–5 Application of thin lens formulas to a
multiple-lens system. Numerous refracting
surfaces of a complex optical system can be reduced
to two principal planes, one associated with the
object side of the system *(H)*, and the other
associated with the image side *(H')*. *F*, focal point of
the system. (Adapted from Ogle, 1961.)

The linear magnification of such lenses can also
be obtained:

$$\frac{\text{Image size}}{\text{Object size}} = \frac{\text{Distance of image from the lens}}{\text{Distance of object from the lens}}$$

The following conventions of sign apply to these
thin lens equations:

1. Real object and image distances are positive;
   virtual object and image distances are negative.
2. The focal length of a converging lens is positive; that of a diverging lens is negative.

Most optical systems, such as the eye, are
composed of numerous refracting surfaces with
different indices of refraction. Any such complex
optical system can be reduced to, at the most, two
principal planes: one that pertains to the object
side and the other to the image side. Figure III–5
illustrates this for a converging lens system (two
lenses).

In order to use the thin lens equations, one
measures the object distance to the first principal
plane (H) and the image distance to the second
principal plane (H'). The two principal planes are
two of the six cardinal points that define any
complex optical system (see below).

Real lenses have significant thickness and
curvature that also affect their refractive properties (i.e., their ability to bend light). If one restricts the problem to rays that are not too far
from the optical axis of a lens, a simplified expression for the image position across such an optical surface is

$$\frac{n_2}{\substack{\text{Image} \\ \text{distance}}} + \frac{n_1}{\substack{\text{Object} \\ \text{distance}}} = \frac{n_2 - n_1}{\substack{\text{Radius of curvature} \\ \text{of the lens}}}$$

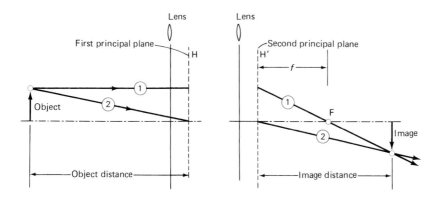

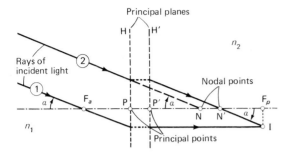

III−6 Cardinal points of optical reference. The path
of light in a complex optical system—i.e.,
one containing multiple elements with different
refracting surfaces—can be accurately traced by
simplifying the system to six cardinal reference points
and applying the thin lens equations. The six points
are the anterior (F_a) and posterior (F_p) focal points,
the two principal planes (H, H') or points (P, P'), and
the two nodal points (N, N'); n_1, n_2, lower and higher
refractive indices, respectively. (Adapted from Ogle,
1961.)

where n_1 and n_2 are the refractive indices of the
media. This expression provides a means of tracing the image position and size across such a refracting surface having significant curvature (R),
such as the cornea. One can then redo the calculation for the second surface of the lens and continue the process for multiple optical elements
such as those in the eye. The factor $(n_2 - n_1)/R$
is called the *dioptric power of the surface*. If the
radius of curvature is a small number (i.e., high
curvature) and/or the refractive change is large,
the dioptric power of the surface is great.

Another consideration that applies to the eye,
but not to most optical systems, is the fact that
the image is formed within a medium different
from that in which the object is usually seen (air).
In this case the focal length on the image side of
the lens system is different from the focal length
on the object side. This arrangement requires the
use of another factor, the *nodal points of the optical system*; at the nodal points the angle subtended by the object equals the angle subtended
by the image (Figure III−6). The two focal points
(anterior and posterior), the two principal points
(or planes), and the two nodal points are collectively referred to as the *cardinal points of reference* of any optical system. The dimensions of the
critical reference points for the average human
eye are shown in Figure III−7; they can be used to
analyze the path of light through the eye and to
determine quantitative aspects of image formation on the retina. A useful application of the
nodal points is in the determination of the size of
an object on the retina:

$$\frac{\text{Image size}}{\text{Object size}} = \frac{\text{Distance of image to N' (17 mm)}}{\text{Distance of object to N}}$$
$$\text{(distance from cornea + 7.1 mm)}$$

III−7 Dimensions of the six cardinal reference
points of the average human eye. Dimensions
are given in milliliters. These data can be used to
define the properties of light as it travels through the
eye and allow the determination of such features as
retinal image size. Symbols as in Figure III−6.
(Adapted from Ogle, 1961.)

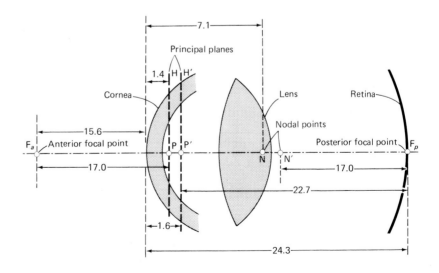

Table III–1. Optical Constants of Normal Eye

	Radius of curvature mm	Refractive index		Power diopters
		Anterior	Posterior	
Cornea				
anterior	7.8	1	1.376	+48.8
posterior	6.8	1.376	1.376	−5.9
Lens margin				
anterior	10.0	1.336	1.386	+7.4
posterior	−6.0	1.386	1.386	+12.3
Eye + Lens		=		+58.9

Source: Adapted from Westheimer, G., 1974. The eye. In V. Mountcastle (ed.), Medical Physiology, 13th ed., St. Louis: Mosby, vol. 1, pp. 440–457.

If, for example, one wanted to estimate the size of the image on the retina formed by a building 50 m high at a distance of 3 km, then

$$\frac{\text{Retinal image}}{5 \times 10^4 \text{ mm}} = \frac{17 \text{ mm}}{3 \times 10^6 \text{ mm} + 7.1 \text{ mm}}.$$

From this calculation the retinal image of the building at this distance is 0.28 mm, a dimension that is slightly less than the diameter of the fovea.

Image Formation in Monocular Vision Has Physical Limitations

Table III–1 shows important optical constants of the cornea and lens. The total dioptric power of the eye is not the simple sum of the individual values but also depends upon the distance between each refracting surface. The major change in refractive index occurs at the anterior surface of the cornea, which, combined with the radius of curvature of the cornea, is responsible for most of the dioptric power of the eye. The refractive power of the lens depends mainly on the radius of curvature of both of its surfaces. The refractive index of the lens, increasing from 1.37 at its margin to 1.42 at its core, makes any simple treatment of this element difficult but has the advantage of minimizing spherical and chromatic aberration.

The radius of curvature of the anterior surface of the lens is 10 mm, but, by contraction of the ciliary muscles, it can be reduced to 6 mm, thus providing the lens with the ability to change its dioptric power. The ability to vary the shape of the lens ensures that the focal length remains constant and is called *accommodation. Accommodation provides the major means of modifying the refractive power of the eye, which allows focusing on near objects.* The curvature of the back surface of the lens changes relatively little (6–5.5 mm) during accommodation.

Alterations in Refractive Power Affect Image Formation

Normally, with minimum lens curvature, the eye is sharply focused on objects at the horizon (the far point) and remains in sharp focus if these objects approach to about 9 m (*emmetropia*; Figure III–8A). Changes in the axial position of images of objects, which move to this 9-m point from the horizon, are relatively insignificant along the plane of the outer segments of photoreceptors because of the considerable minification of the retinal image. When objects move closer than the far point, however, they are focused beyond the plane of the outer segments, somewhere in the retinal pigment epithelial layer or beyond, and some modification of lens curvature is required in order to bring them back into focus on the outer segments. Infants can modify their lens curvature to bring objects just beyond their nose into focus, but with age we progressively lose this ability. At about 45 years of age it is no longer possible to focus on objects closer than about an arm's length away without artificial lenses, a condition known as *presbyopia*.

The far points of some eyes are closer than the horizon (*myopia or nearsightedness*; parallel rays are focused in front of the retina. Such eyes tend to have longer axial lengths than normal (Figure III–8B) and need diverging lenses in order for the subject to see distant objects sharply. The far points of other eyes are farther than infinity (*hyperopia or farsightedness*; Figure III–8C). Subjects with hyperopic eyes may be able to see

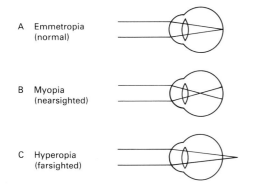

III–8 Refractive errors. **A.** In the normal eye, with the ciliary muscles relaxed, an image of a distant object is focused on the retina. As the object distance is reduced, the ciliary muscles make the lens more convex, thereby keeping the image on the retina. Refractive errors can occur in the eye, resulting in abnormal refraction and image focusing in front or behind the retina. **B.** In the myopic eye, light rays from a distant object are focused in front of the retina because the axial length of the eyeball is too great for its lens. As the ciliary muscles cannot reduce the radius of curvature of the relaxed lens, a diverging lens must be used to reduce this refraction and correct nearsightedness. **C.** When the length of the eye is shorter than normal images of distant objects are focused at a point beyond the retina (hyperopia). This condition can be corrected by normal accommodation changes, making the lens more convex or by wearing converging lenses.

distant objects by changing the curvature of the lens (accommodating). Such eyes tend to have shorter axial lengths than normal and need converging lenses in order for the subjects to see distant objects without accommodating.

Some eyes do not have the same corneal curvature along different axes (astigmatism) and require an axial correction. Contact lenses can vary corneal refraction by altering the air–epithelial interface of the cornea directly, whereas spectacle lenses can only counteract and not eliminate corneal errors.

The Image Can Be Degraded by Spherical and Chromatic Aberrations

Refracting systems such as the eye have inherent physical limitations that can produce degradation or blurring of the image. The two major causes of blur in the normal eye are spherical and chromatic aberration.

Spherical aberration occurs when light rays are refracted more strongly by the periphery than by the center of a lens (Figure III–9). Nature has made attempts to reduce this problem. The cornea is flatter at its margin than at its center, and the lens has a higher refractive index at its center than at its margins. Both of these factors tend to reduce spherical aberration. The directional selectivity of cones, called the *Stiles-Crawford effect,* makes the cones (but not the rods) more sensitive to central or axial rays than to rays passing through the margin of the lens (Figure III–10). This also minimizes the effects of lens aberrations on cones. Cones are more sensitive to blur since they play a much greater role than rods in fine visual discrimination.

Chromatic aberration results because short wavelengths are refracted more strongly than long ones (Figure III–11). This produces differences in both the size and axial position of chromatically different retinal images formed in white light. Camera lenses are routinely corrected for this form of aberration by combining lens elements of different types of glass (crown and flint glass). The eye has resorted to a different approach to this important optical problem.

The eye greatly restricts the spectral window within which it resolves fine visual detail. Insects

III–9 Spherical aberration. Light rays entering near the periphery of a spherical lens are refracted more strongly than those passing through its center. This results in the focusing of peripheral rays at a point (**P′**) closer to the lens than central rays. (**P″**).

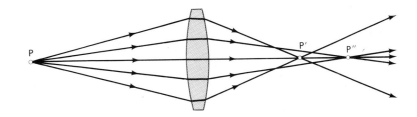

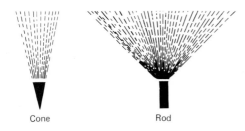

III-10 Directional selectivity of cones. **Dotted lines:** angles light rays can have and still strongly affect the photoreceptors. The receptive angle of rods is much larger than that of cones; this makes cones less sensitive to rays traversing the periphery of the lens.

use ultraviolet light, snakes and perhaps mosquitoes have infrared detectors, and Superman has X-ray vision, but the human fovea uses only a small portion of the electromagnetic spectrum (approximately 500 to 700 nm), centered near spectral yellow, for resolving fine detail. This, as we have seen in Chapter 22, has been done by synthesizing three light-sensitive proteins in cones that are most sensitive to these wavelengths (red- and green-sensitive cones of trichromatic color vision). Blue-sensitive cones, as well as rods, which are most sensitive to shorter wavelengths, are kept out of the central fovea and consequently have little to do with fine visual resolution. In addition, an inert pigment, macular yellow, which strongly absorbs blue and violet light (and hence looks yellow), is deposited in the fo-

III-11 Chromatic aberration. Light of short wavelength (violet in this diagram) is refracted more strongly than light of longer wavelength (red). The light rays of shorter wavelength are brought to focus at a point closer to the lens than the rays of longer wavelength. The violet image (**P'**, **Q'**) is therefore smaller than the image formed by red light (**P''**, **Q''**), an effect known as *chromatic change of magnification.*

vea, and this pigment considerably blocks short wavelengths from affecting foveal cones. It is mainly at the short-wavelength region of the spectrum that chromatic aberration is most destructive to image formation and it is this spectral region that the fovea most avoids.

Color vision, which identifies objects by wavelength, in contrast to mere energy differences across contours (luminance), becomes more significant as objects become larger. In color vision all three cone mechanisms act together, with the blue cones assuming a much greater role than they have in discriminating fine detail.

Blurs Can Be Caused By Diffraction

Peripheral rays, which produce spherical and chromatic aberration blur, can be blocked by pupillary constriction, which consequently increases depth of field, just as in a photographic camera. Excessive pupillary constriction has diminishing returns, however, because of another cause of blur, diffraction (Figure III-12). Diffraction occurs due to the wave nature of light and the interference these waves exert on one another.

This factor ultimately determines the limit of resolution or minimum resolvable detail of the finest optical system. The larger the entrance aperture of an optical system, the greater will be its resolving power, because of the reduction in diffraction blur. This relationship is reflected in the *numerical aperture* (NA), which is equal to the product of the sine of the half-angle of the cone of rays admitted by the system and the refractive index of the media. The larger the pupillary aperture, however, the greater will be the blur caused by spherical and chromatic aberrations. This is the Scylla and Charybdis of the eye. For best resolving power a pupillary aperture of 2 mm is desirable because it optimally trades off the blur of lens aberration with that of diffraction. At this pupil size and at the near point (25 cm) the numerical aperture of the eye is 0.004 and the lin-

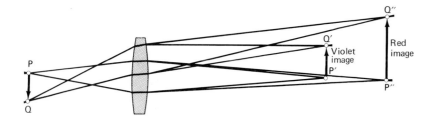

Aperture   Light distribution
on screen

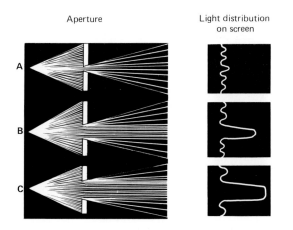

III–12 Diffraction. **A.** The aperture is so small that light rays interfere with each other and destroy any image of the source on a screen. **B** and **C.** When the aperture is increased, the effects of diffraction are reduced.

ear separation of two just resolvable point objects is about 0.1 mm. The distance between the centers of the diffraction discs on the retina for two such resolvable points will be about 0.01 mm (10 μm), which is just about the distance between foveal cones. We can actually resolve even closer objects than this if the objects are broken lines (vernier acuity). This is true in part because of the relatively random distribution of cones in the fovea and the convergence of this information onto orientation detectors within the cerebral cortex (Chapter 21).

Ocular Reflexes Adapt the Eye to Changing Conditions

The Pupillary Light Reflex Is an Automatic Brightness Control Mechanism

The pupillary light reflex is a control mechanism similar to those in many cameras. The range of brightness control is limited; it can change retinal illumination by a factor of about 16 (pupillary diameters range from 8 to 2 mm), which is relatively small compared to the enormous operating range of human vision. Going from dim moonlight to bright sunlight alters retinal illumination by a factor of approximately 10^{15}. The importance of the pupillary reflex stems from its rapidity as compared to the slower but much more profound mechanisms of retinal adaptation. Retinal cells and the photoreceptors, in particu-

lar, are capable of altering their sensitivity if light levels are too high; this sensitivity loss is traded off for a considerable increase in their speed of response. The neural pathways that mediate the pupillary light reflex are described in Chapter 20.

Accommodation Allows the Eye to Focus Up Close

Accommodation is another ocular reflex that employs the pupillary system, in addition to the lens and ocular muscles, in order to allow the eye to focus on objects closer than the far point. When objects move closer than the far point, they not only go out of focus but also shift position relative to the fovea of each eye. To restore focus and retain stereoscopic vision, three separate processes occur: the curvature of the lens is increased, the pupil constricts toward 2 mm, and the eyes converge. Lens curvature is altered in a two-stage process—one active, the other passive. In the active process, contraction of the ciliary muscle relaxes tension on the zonule fibers of the lens; in the passive process, the release of tension on the zonule fibers allows the elastic properties of the lens to increase its curvature. The elastic properties of the lens decrease with age; this process starts shortly after birth and progresses throughout life. Its effects are only noticed, however, when it no longer becomes possible to focus on objects held at arm's length. The signal that induces the accommodation reflex appears to arise mainly from blur in the retinal image. The detection of blur in contrast to light itself, as in the pupillary light reflex, requires a much more sophisticated decision. It is for this reason that accommodation involves the visual cortex in its reflex arc. The afferent loop of the accommodation reflex involves optic fibers whose receptive fields are in the fovea. These fibers synapse in the lateral geniculate nucleus, which in turn relays to the striate cortex. From this point it is not clear how the afferent signals reach the oculomotor nucleus after the decision (mostly unconscious) about blur has been made by the visual cortex. The efferent loop of this reflex originates in neurons of the oculomotor complex and the message is carried by fibers of the third nerve to the ciliary process, the iris, and the medial recti muscles. Both the light and the accommodative reflexes can be elicited in both eyes by monocular stimulation, i.e., they are consensual reflexes (Figure III–13). These reflexes are important for diagnos-

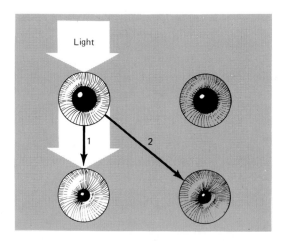

III–13 Consensual light response. Monocular illumination results in constriction of the pupil both of the illuminated eye (*1, direct light response*) and the contralateral eye (*2, consensual light response.*)

tic purposes. The differences in the pathways of the pupillary light and the accommodative reflexes are occasionally highlighted by disease. One of the most notorious of these is the Argyll Robertson pupil of the syphilitic patient, in which the pupillary light but not the accommodative reflex is destroyed. In contrast, age destroys the accommodative but not the light reflex.

III–14 The Vieth–Müller horopter circle. **A.** The images of points **P** and **Q** fall on geometrically corresponding points in the two retinas. **B.** The relative positions of the Vieth–Müller circle and the empirical horopter, the overlapping areas for stereopsis and for binocular single vision, and the regions where diplopia begins. (Adapted from Bishop, 1973.)

Binocular Vision Is Important for Depth Perception

All of the preceding discussion pertained to monocular vision. Binocular vision not only broadens one's horizon but also creates a totally new visual dimension—depth. *Stereopsis* allows us to perceive objects in spatial depth, an aspect of perception that would be impossible with monocular vision. Stereopsis occurs when the same object stimulates appropriate retinal regions in each eye.

For a given fixation point, there is a locus of points, called the *horopter,* along which images fall on corresponding points of the two retinas. *The Vieth-Müller circle* is an attempt to define this horopter geometrically as a circle that passes through the fixation point and the optical center of each eye (Figure III–14A). At a viewing distance of about 1 m, the horopter actually follows a fixation plane concave to the observer and lying between the Vieth-Müller circle and the *fronto-parallel plane,* which passes through the horopter (Figure III–14B). In fact, the actual locus of positions that induce stereopsis for a given fixation depth in space involves a three-dimensional zone around the horopter, named after its proposer, *Panum's (1858) fusional area.* It is called a fusional area because objects in this region, lying off the horopter, are seen as single structures in depth. Objects lying outside the fusional area are seen doubly. To see this effect, fix your eyes on the tip of a pencil about 8 inches in front of you. Place your index finger behind the pencil and slowly move the finger away from you. Initially your finger will appear as a single structure, lying further in depth than the pencil. When your arm is fully extended, you should see your finger doubly. It is now outside Panum's fusional area.

There are at least two separate aspects to stereopsis: one pertains to the information avail-

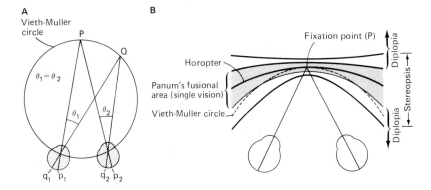

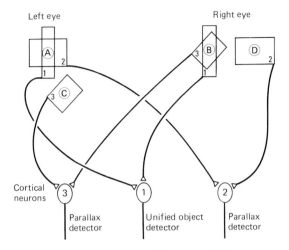

Left eye   Right eye

Cortical
neurons

Parallax   Unified object   Parallax
detector   detector   detector

III–15 The phenomenon of receptive field
disparity may be used to explain how two
retinal elements, one in each eye, can, at the same
time and for a given fixation point, be disparate, to
take account of binocular parallax, and yet
correspond, in the interest of single vision. Cortical
neuron 1 receives information from the same region
in each eye. This central neuron can therefore code
for a completely unified image of one object. Cortical
neurons 2 and 3, however, receive disparate
information (same area as neuron 1 in one eye and a
different area in the other eye), allowing the
visualization of the object in spatial depth. (Adapted
from Bishop, 1973.)

able from binocular parallax, and the other involves fusion of these double images into one.
Figure III–15 shows how cortical neurons can receive input from both retinal areas that are exactly in register or from those containing disparate
or parallax information about the same object.
Note that neuron 1 receives information that is
completely in register from corresponding areas
in each eye (area A in one eye and B in the
other); this unit codes for a unified single image
of the object (i.e., no double vision). Neurons 2
and 3 receive information from the same area in
one eye and from a noncorresponding retinal area
in the other eye, i.e., disparate information. This
contributes to seeing the object in depth.

For points along the horopter, the area of temporal retina stimulated by light in one eye will
correspond to a nasal area in the other eye. This
arrangement led Isaac Newton to suggest that
there might be a partial decussation of optic nerve
fibers from each eye in order anatomically to associate corresponding areas of visual space in the
brain. Two centuries later this idea was confirmed by the neuroanatomical demonstration of

such a decussation in the human optic chiasm.
The neurophysiological work of David Hubel and
Torsten Wiesel has now shown that these corresponding retinal areas are registered by single
cells in the visual cortex (Chapter 52).

The decussation of optic nerve fibers along the
vertical meridian through the fovea creates an
unusual problem for the recombination of corresponding retinal areas around the area of fixation,
precisely where stereopsis is best. The unfilled
regions are areas of visual space where the corresponding areas of each retina end up in opposite
cerebral hemispheres (Figure III–16A). The hypothesis to explain this curious problem in stereopsis is that either there is some overlap in the
cells subserving the vertical meridian of each eye
or the critical information is relayed from one
hemisphere to another via the corpus callosum
(Figure III–16B).

When fixation shifts to a different depth in
space, all the corresponding retinal points must
be rearranged to reflect a different horopter. Similarly, within the brain there is an associated shift
to a totally different population of neurons
matched to this different set of corresponding retinal points. *Although the same population of retinal ganglion cells is used to detect all objects
in space, entirely different populations of cortical cells are used to detect the same object at different depths in space.* Consider that when an object moves away from you, your eyes must begin
to diverge in order to maintain binocular fixation
on this object. This shift in the position of the
two eyes generates a new horopter in external visual space and a new set of homonymous visual
areas in each retina become geometrically linked
on the locus of this new horopter (in Figure III–
15 the As will be linked with a new set of Bs and
the Cs and Ds will change accordingly). The same
retinal ganglion cells will be used but their outputs will be rearranged in a different set of cortical detectors. For each subjective shift in depth a
new population of cortical neurons will be used
to create stereopsis. The use of large populations
of neurons to extract different aspects of the retinal image reflects a general principle in the central nervous system and reveals an extravagance
only permissible in a structure as richly endowed
with neurons as the cerebral cortex.

An interesting question about the processing
of visual information by the cerebral cortex for
stereopsis is whether we neurally process the
shape of an object before we put it in proper perspective in depth. Ingenious experiments by Bela

A

B

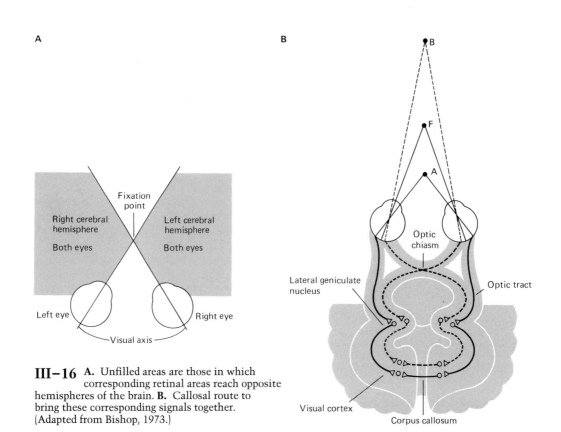

III-16 **A.** Unfilled areas are those in which corresponding retinal areas reach opposite hemispheres of the brain. **B.** Callosal route to bring these corresponding signals together. (Adapted from Bishop, 1973.)

Julesz at the Bell Laboratories with computer generated random dot stereograms, which contain depth clues due to parallax but are devoid of monocular information about the shape of these three-dimensional objects, indicate that the process of stereopsis precedes the stage at which shape is recognized. Thus, stereopsis, like color vision, facilitates object detection in addition to adding a new and aesthetic dimension to visual perception.

Selected Readings and References

Bishop, P. O. 1973. Neurophysiology of binocular single vision and stereopsis. In R. Jung (ed.), Handbook of Sensory Physiology, Vol. 7, Part 3A: Central Processing of Visual Information. New York: Springer, pp. 255–305.

Gouras, P. 1972. Light and dark adaptation. In M. G. F. Fuortes (ed.), Handbook of Sensory Physiology, Vol. 7, Part 2: Physiology of Photoreceptor Organs. New York: Springer, pp. 609–634.

Julesz, B. 1971. Foundations of Cyclopean Perception. Chicago: University of Chicago Press.

Moses, R. A. 1975. Accommodation. In R. A. Moses (ed.), Adler's Physiology of the Eye. 6th ed. St. Louis: Mosby, pp. 298–319.

Moses, R. A. 1975. The iris and the pupil. In R. A. Moses (ed.), Adler's Physiology of the Eye. 6th ed. St. Louis: Mosby, pp. 320–352.

Ogle, K. N. 1961. Optics: An Introduction for Ophthalmologists. Springfield, Ill,: Thomas.

Westheimer, G. 1972. Visual acuity and spatial modulation thresholds. In D. Jameson and L. M. Hurvich (eds.), Handbook of Sensory Physiology, Vol. 7, Part 4: Visual Psychophysics. New York: Springer-Verlag, 170–187.

Other References

Descartes, R. 1637. La Dioptrique. Leyden.

Westheimer, G. 1980. The eye. In V. B. Mountcastle (ed.), Medical Physiology. Vol. 1. 14th ed. St. Louis: Mosby, pp. 481–503.

Bibliography

A

Adams, R. D., and Victor, M. 1977. Principles of Neurology. New York: McGraw-Hill.

Adrian, E. D. 1932. The Mechanism of Nervous Action: Electrical Studies of the Neurone. Philadelphia: University of Pennsylvania Press.

Adrian, E. D., and Zotterman, Y. 1926. The impulses produced by sensory nerve endings. Part II. The response of a single end organ. J. Physiol. (Lond.) 61:151–171.

Ahrens, R. 1954. Beitrag zur Entwicklung des Physiognomie-und Mimikerkennens. Z. Exp. Angew. Psychol. 2:412–454; 599–633.

Allen, G. I., and Tsukahara, N. 1974. Cerebrocerebellar communication systems. Physiol. Rev. 54:957–1006.

Almers, W. 1978. Gating currents and charge movements in excitable membranes. Rev. Physiol. Biochem. Pharmacol. 82:96–190.

Albuquerque, E. X., Rash, J. E., Mayer, R. F., and Satterfield, J. R. 1976. An electrophysiological and morphological study of the neuromuscular junction in patients with myasthenia gravis. Exp. Neurol. 51:536–563.

Anand, B. K., and Brobeck, J. R. 1951. Localization of a "feeding center" in the hypothalamus of the rat. Proc. Soc. Exp. Biol. Med. 77:323–324.

Andén, N.-E., Dahlström, A., Fuxe, K., Larsson, K., Olson, L., and Ungerstedt, U. 1966. Ascending monoamine neurons to the telencephalon and diencephalon. Acta. Physiol. Scand. 67:313–326.

Andersson, B. 1978. Regulation of water intake. Physiol. Rev. 58:582–603.

Arkin, A. M., Antrobus, J. S., and Ellman, S. J. (eds.). 1978. The Mind in Sleep: Psychology and Psychophysiology. Hillsdale, N.J.: Lawrence Erlbaum Associates.

Arshavskii, Yu. I., Berkinblit, M. B., Gel'fand, I. M., Orlovskii, G. N., and Fukson, O. I. 1972. Activity of the neurones of the ventral spinocerebellar tract during locomotion. Biophysics 17:926–935.

Arshavsky, Yu. I., Berkinblit, M. B. Fukson, O. I., Gelfand, I. M., and Orlovsky, G. N. 1972 Recordings of neurones of the dorsal spinocerebellar tract during evoked locomotion. Brain Res. 43:272–275.

Asanuma, H. 1973. Cerebral cortical control of movement. Physiologist 16:143–166.

Ascherl, G. F., Ganti, S. R., and Hilal, S. K. 1980. Neuroradiology for the clinician. In R. N. Rosenberg (ed.), Neurology, Vol. 5 of The Science and Practice of Clinical Medicine. New York: Grune & Stratton, pp. 634–718.

Aschoff, J. 1969. Desynchronization and resynchronization of human circadian rhythms. Aerosp. Med. 40:844–849

Ash, P. R., and Keltner, J. L. 1979. Neuro-ophthalmic signs in pontine lesions. Medicine (Baltimore) 58:304–320.

Attardi, D. G., and Sperry, R. W. 1963. Preferential selection of central pathways by regenerating optic fibers. Exp. Neurol. 7:46–64.

Axelsson, J., and Thesleff, S. 1959. A study of supersensitivity in denervated mammalian skeletal muscle. J. Physiol. (Lond.) 147:178–193.

Ayala, G. F., Dichter, M., Gumnit, R. J., Matsumoto, H., and Spencer, W. A. 1973. Genesis of epileptic interictal spikes. New knowledge of cortical feedback systems suggests a neurophysiological explanation of brief paroxysms. Brain Res. 52:1–17.

B

Babinski, J. 1896. Sur le réflexe cutané plantaire dans certaines affections organiques du système nerveux central. C. R. Soc. Biol. (Paris) 48:207–208.

Baker, P. F., Hodgkin, A. L., and Ridgway, E. B. 1971. Depolarization and calcium entry in squid giant axons. J. Physiol. (Lond.) 218:709–755.

Bard, P. 1928. A diencephalic mechanism for the expression of rage with special reference to the sympathetic nervous system. Am. J. Physiol. 84:490–515.

Bard, P. 1938. Studies on the cortical representation of somatic sensibility. Harvey Lect. 33:143–169.

Bard, P., and Mountcastle, V. B. 1948. Some forebrain mechanisms involved in expression of rage with special reference to suppression of angry behavior. Res. Publ. Assoc. Res. Nerv. Ment. Dis. 27:362–404.

Barraclough, C. A., and Gorski, R. A. 1962. Studies on mating behaviour in the androgen-sterilized female rat in relation to the hypothalamic regulation of sexual behaviour. J. Endocrinol. 25:175–182.

Barrett, J. N. 1975. Motoneuron dentrites: Role in synaptic integration. Fed. Proc. 34:1398–1407.

Batini, C., Moruzzi, G., Palestini, M., Rossi, G. F., and Zanchetti, A. 1958. Persistent patterns of wakefulness in the pretrigeminal midpontine preparation. Science (Wash., D.C.) 128:30–32.

Bauer, G., Gerstenbrand, F., and Rumpl, E. 1979. Varieties of the locked-in syndrome. J. Neurol. 221: 77–91.

Baylor, D. A., and O'Bryan, P. M. 1971. Electrical signaling in vertebrate photoreceptors. Fed. Proc. 30: 79–83.

Beach, F. A., Noble, R. G., and Orndoff, R. K. 1969. Effects of perinatal androgen treatment on responses of male rats to gonadal hormones in adulthood. J. Comp. Physiol. Psychol. 68:490–497.

Bear, D. M. 1979. The temporal lobes: An approach to the study of organic behavioral changes. In M. S. Gazzaniga (ed.), Handbook of Behavioral Neurobiology, Vol. 2. New York: Plenum, pp. 75–95.

Bellisle, F. 1979. Human feeding behavior. Neurosci. Biobehav. Rev. 3:163–169.

Bennett, M. V. L. 1977. Electrical transmission: A functional analysis and comparison to chemical transmission. In E. R. Kandel (ed.), Handbook of Physiology; The Nervous System, Vol. 1, Part I. Bethesda, Md.: American Physiological Society, pp. 357–416.

Bennett, M. V. L., and Goodenough, D. A. 1978. Gap junctions, electrotonic coupling, and intercellular communication. Neurosci. Res. Program Bull. 16: 371–486.

Bennett, M. V. L., Sandri, C., and Akert, K. 1978. Neuronal gap junctions and morphologically mixed synapses in the spinal cord of a teleost, Sternarchus albifrons (gymnotoidei). Brain Res. 143:43–60.

Benson, D. F. 1978. Neurological correlates of aphasia and apraxia. In W. B. Matthews and G. H. Glaser (eds.), Recent Advances in Clinical Neurology, Number 2. Edinburgh: Churchill Livingstone, pp. 163–175.

Benson, D. F. 1979. Aphasia, Alexia, and Agraphia. New York: Churchill Livingstone.

Benson, D. F., and Geschwind, N. 1976. The aphasias and related disturbances. In A. B. Baker and L. H. Baker (eds.), Clinical Neurology, Vol. 1. New York: Harper & Row, chap. 8.

Benson, D. F., Sheremata, W. A., Bouchard, R., Segarra, J. M., Price, D., and Geschwind, N. 1973. Conduction aphasia. Arch. Neurol. 28:339–346.

Berger, T. W., and Thompson, R. F. 1978. Identification of pyramidal cells as the critical elements in hippocampal neuronal plasticity during learning. Proc. Natl. Acad. Sci. U.S.A. 75:1572–1576.

Bergland, R. M., and Page, R. B. 1979. Pituitary–brain vascular relations: A new paradigm. Science (Wash., D.C.) 204:18–24.

Bermant, G., and Davidson, J. M. 1974. Biological Bases of Sexual Behavior. New York: Harper & Row.

Bernard, C. 1878. Leçons sur les phénomènes de la vie communs aux animaux et aux végétaux. Paris: Baillière.

Bernstein, J. 1902. Investigations on the thermodynamics of bioelectric currents. Translated from Pflügers Arch. 92:521–562. In G. R. Kepner (ed.), Cell Membrane Permeability and Transport. Stroudsburg, Pa.: Dowden, Hutchinson & Ross, 1979.

Bertler, Å., and Rosengren, E. 1959. Occurrence and distribution of dopamine in brain and other tissues. Experientia 15:10–11.

Betz, V. 1874. Anatomischer Nachweis zweier Gehirncentra. Centralbl. Med. Wiss. 12:578–580; 595–599.

Birkmayer, W., and Hornykiewicz, O. (eds.). 1976. Advances in Parkinsonism, Fifth International Symposium on Parkinson's Disease, Vienna. Basle: Roche.

Bishop, P. O. 1973. Neurophysiology of binocular single vision and stereopsis. In R. Jung (ed.), Handbook of Sensory Physiology, Vol. 7, Part 3A: Central Processing of Visual Information. New York: Springer, pp. 255–305.

Black, P. McL. 1978. Brain death (first of two parts). N. Engl. J. Med. 299:338–344.

Black, P. McL. 1978. Brain death (second of two parts). N. Engl. J. Med. 299:393–401.

Blalock, A., Mason, M. F., Morgan, H. J., and Riven, S. S., 1939. Myasthenia gravis and tumors of the thymic region. Report of a case in which the tumor was removed. Ann. Surg. 110:544–561.

Bleuler, E. 1911. Dementia Praecox or the Group of Schizophrenias. Trans. by J. Zinkin. New York: International Universities Press, 1950.

Bligh, J. 1973. Temperature Regulation in Mammals and Other Vertebrates. Amsterdam: North-Holland.

Bodemer, C. W. 1968. Modern Embryology. New York: Holt, Rinehart and Winston.

Bodnar, R. J., Kelly, D. D., Brutus, M., and Glusman, M. 1980. Stress-induced analgesia: Neural and hormonal determinants. Neurosci. Biobehav. Rev. 4:87–100.

Boivie, J. 1979. An anatomical reinvestigation of the termination of the spinothalamic tract in the monkey. J. Comp. Neurol. 186:343–369.

Booth, D. A., Toates, F. M., and Platt, S. V. 1976. Control system for hunger and its implications in animals and man. In D. Novin, W. Wyrwicka, and G. A. Bray (eds.), Hunger: Basic Mechanisms and Clinical Implications. New York: Raven Press, pp. 127–143.

Boring, E. G. 1942. Sensation and Preception in the History of Experimental Psychology. New York: Appleton-Century.

Bowsher, D. 1976. Role of the reticular formation in responses to noxious stimulation. Pain 2:361–378.

Boycott, B. B., and Wässle, H. 1974. The morphological types of ganglion cells of the domestic cat's retina. J. Physiol. (Lond.) 240:397–419.

Boyd, I. A., and Martin, A. R. 1956. The end-plate potential in mammalian muscle. J. Physiol. (Lond.) 132:74–91.

Boyd, W. D., Graham-White, J., Blackwood, G., Glen, I., and McQueen, J. 1977. Clinical effects of choline in Alzheimer senile dementia. Lancet Vol. II, No. 8040, p. 711.

Boynton, R. M. 1979. Human Color Vision. New York: Holt, Rinehart and Winston.

Bradbury, M. 1979. The Concept of a Blood–Brain Barrier. New York: Wiley.

The Brain. 1979. Sci. Am. 241(3).

Branch, C., Milner, B., and Rasmussen, T. 1964. Intracarotid sodium amytal for the lateralization of cerebral speech dominance. J. Neurosurg. 21:399–405.

Brecha, N., Karten, H. J., and Davis, B. 1980. Localization of neuropeptides, including vasoactive intestinal polypeptide and glucogen, within the adult and developing retina. Soc. Neurosci. 6:346.

Brecha, N., Karten, H. J., and Laverack, C. 1979. Enkephalin-containing amacrine cells in the avian retina: Immunohistochemical localization. Proc. Natl. Acad. Sci. U.S.A. 76:3010–3014.

Bremer, F. 1936. Nouvelles recherches sur le mécanisme du sommeil. C. R. Séances Soc. Biol. Fil. 122:460–464.

Brenner, S. 1974. The genetics of Caenorhabditis elegans. Genetics 77:71–94.

Britt, R. H., Herrick, M. K., and Hamilton, R. D. 1977. Traumatic locked-in syndrome. Ann. Neurol. 1:590–592.

Broca, P. 1865. Sur le siége de la faculté du langage articulé. Bull. Soc. Anthropologie 6:377–393.

Brodal, A. 1981. Neurological Anatomy. 3rd ed. New York: Oxford University Press.

Brodmann, K. 1909. Vergleichende Lokalisationslehre der Grosshirnrinde. Leipzig: J. A. Barth.

Brooke, M. H. 1977. A Clinician's View of Neuromuscular Diseases. Baltimore: Williams & Wilkins.

Brooks, C. McC., Ishikawa, T., Koizumi, K., and Lu, H-H. 1966. Activity of neurones in the paraventricular nucleus of the hypothalamus and its control. J. Physiol. (Lond.) 182:217–231.

Brooks, V. B. 1979. Control of intended movements by the lateral and intermediate cerebellum. In H. Asanuma and V. J. Wilson (eds.), Integration in the Nervous System. Tokyo: Igaku-Shoin, pp. 321–357.

Broughton, R. J. 1968. Sleep disorders: Disorders of arousal? Science (Wash., D.C.) 159:1070–1078.

Brown, K. T. 1980. Physiology of the retina. In V. B. Mountcastle (ed.), Medical Physiology, 14th ed., Vol. 1. St. Louis: Mosby, pp. 504–543.

Brown, T. G. 1911. The intrinsic factors in the act of progression in the mammal. Proc. R. Soc. Lond. B Biol. Sci. 84:308–319.

Brownstein, M. J., Russell, J. T., and Gainer, H. 1980. Synthesis, transport, and release of posterior pituitary hormones. Science (Wash., D.C.) 207:373–378.

Buller, A. J., Eccles, J. C., and Eccles, R. M. 1960. Interactions between motoneurones and muscles in respect of the characteristic speeds of their responses. J. Physiol. (Lond.) 150:417–439.

Bunge, R. P. 1968. Glial cells and the central myelin sheath. Physiol. Rev. 48:197–121.

Burgess, P. R., and Perl, E. R. 1973. Cutaneous mechanoreceptors and nociceptors. In A. Iggo (ed.), Handbook of Sensory Physiology, Vol. 2, The Somatosensory System. New York: Springer, pp. 29–78.

Burke, D., Knowles, L., Andrews, C., and Ashby, P. 1972. Spasticity, decerebrate rigidity and the clasp-knife phenomenon: An experimental study in the cat. Brain 95:31–48.

Burke, R. E., Rudomin, P., and Zajac, III, F. E. 1976. The effect of activation history on tension production by individual muscle units. Brain Res. 109:515–529.

Burnstock, G. Hökfelt, T., Gershon, M. D., Iversen, L. L., Kosterlitz, H. W., and Szurszewski, J. H. 1979. Non-adrenergic, non-cholinergic autonomic neurotransmission mechanisms. Neurosci. Res. Program Bull. 17:377–519.

C

Cajal, S. R. 1892. A new concept of the histology of the central nervous system. D. A. Rottenberg (trans.). See also historical essay by S. L. Palay, preceding Cajal's paper. In D. A. Rottenberg and F. H. Hochberg (eds.), Neurological Classics in Modern Translation. New York: Hafner, 1977, pp. 7–29.

Cajal, S. R. 1894. La fine structure des centres nerveux. Proc. R. Soc. Lond. 55:444–468.

Cajal, S. R. 1906. The structure and connexions of neurons. In Nobel Lectures: Physiology or Medicine, 1901–1921. Amsterdam: Elsevier, 1967, pp. 220–253.

Cajal, S. R. 1908. Neuron Theory or Reticular Theory? Objective Evidence of the Anatomical Unity of Nerve Cells. M. U. Purkiss and C. A. Fox (trans.). Madrid: Consejo Superior de Investigaciones Cientificas Instituto Ramon y Cajal, 1954.

Cajal, S. R. 1911. Histologie du Système Nerveux de l'Homme & des Vertébrés. L. Azoulay (trans.). Vol. 2. Paris: Maloine. Republished in 1955. Madrid: Instituto Ramon y Cajal.

Cajal, S. R. 1929. Etude sur la neurogenèse de quelques vertébrés. Trans. by L. Guth as Studies on Vertebrate Neurogenesis. Springfield, Ill.: Thomas, 1960.

Cajal, S. R. 1933. Histology. 10th ed. Baltimore: William Wood.

Cajal, S. R. 1937. Recollections of My Life. E. Horne Craigie (trans.). Edited in 2 vols. as Memoirs of the American Philosophical Society, Philadelphia.

Cannon, J. T., Liebeskind, J. C., and Frenk, H. 1978. Neural and neurochemical mechanisms of pain inhibition. In R. A. Sternbach (ed.), The Psychology of Pain. New York: Raven Press, pp. 27–47.

Cannon, W. B., and Britton, S. W. 1925. Studies on the conditions of activity in endocrine glands. XV. Am. J. Physiol. 72:283–294.

Caplan, L. R. 1980. "Top of the basilar" syndrome. Neurology 30:72–79.

Carew, T., Castellucci, V. F., and Kandel, E. R. 1979. Sensitization in Aplysia: Restoration of transmission in synapses inactivated by long-term habituation. Science (Wash., D.C.) 205:417–419.

Carlsson, A. 1959. The occurrence, distribution and physiological role of catecholamines in the nervous system. Pharmacol. Rev. 11:490–493.

Carlsson, A. 1974. Antipsychotic drugs and catecholamine synapses. J. Psychiatr. Res. 11:57–64.

Carpenter, M. B. 1976. Human Neuroanatomy. 7th ed. Baltimore: Williams & Wilkins.

Carpenter, M. B. 1978. Core Text of Neuroanatomy. 2nd ed. Baltimore: Williams & Wilkins.

Cartwright, R. D. 1978. A Primer on Sleep and Dreaming. Reading, Mass.: Addison-Wesley.

Case, J. 1966. Sensory Mechanisms. New York: Macmillan.

Castellucci, V., and Kandel, E. R. 1976. Presynaptic facilitation as a mechanism for behavioral sensitization in *Aplysia*. Science (Wash., D.C.) 194:1176–1178.

Castellucci, V. F., Carew, T. J., and Kandel, E. R. 1978. Cellular analysis of long-term habituation of the gill-withdrawal reflex of *Aplysia californica*. Science (Wash., D.C.) 202:1306–1308.

Castellucci, V. F., and Kandel, E. R. 1974. A quantal analysis of the synaptic depression underlying habituation of the gill-withdrawal reflex in *Aplysia*. Proc. Natl. Acad. Sci. U.S.A. 71:5004–5008.

Castellucci, V. F., Kandel, E. R., Schwartz, J. H., Wilson, F. D., Nairn, A. C., and Greengard, P. 1980. Intracellular injection of the catalytic subunit of cyclic AMP-dependent protein kinase simulates facilitation of transmitter release underlying behavioral sensitization in *Aplysia*. Proc. Natl. Acad. Sci. U.S.A. 77:7492–7496.

Ceccarelli, B., Hurlbut, W. P., and Mauro, A. 1973. Turnover of transmitter and synaptic vesicles at the frog neuro-muscular junction. J. Cell Biol. 57:599–524.

Cervós–Navarro, J., and Ferszt, R. (eds.). 1980. Brain Edema. Pathology, Diagnosis, and Therapy. New York: Raven Press.

Chambers, M. R. Andres, K. H., von Duering, M., and Iggo, A. 1972. The structure and function of the slowly adapting type II mechanoreceptor in hairy skin. Q. J. Exp. Physiol. 57:417–445.

Chambers, W. W., Liu, C. N., and McCouch, G. P. 1973. Anatomical and physiological correlates of plasticity in the central nervous system. Brain, Behav. Evol. 8:5–26.

Changeux, J.-P., Kasai, M., and Lee, C.-Y. 1970. Use of a snake venom toxin to characterize the cholinergic receptor protein. Proc. Natl. Acad. Sci. U.S.A. 67:1241–1247.

Chomsky, N. 1957. Syntactic Structures. The Hague: Mouton.

Christensen, B. N., and Perl, E. R. 1970. Spinal neurons specifically excited by noxious or thermal stimuli: Marginal zone of the dorsal horn. J. Neurophysiol. 33:293–307.

Clark, R. G. 1975. Manter and Gatz's Essentials of Clinical Neuroanatomy and Neurophysiology. 5th ed. Philadelphia: Davis.

Cogan, D. G. 1956. Neurology of the Ocular Muscles. 2nd ed. Springfield, Ill.: Thomas.

Cole, K. S., and Curtis, H. J. 1939. Electric impedance of the squid giant axon during activity. J. Gen Physiol. 22:649–670.

A Collaborative Study. 1977. An appraisal of the criteria of cerebral death. A summary statement. J.A.M.A. 237:982–986.

Collier, B. 1977. Biochemistry and physiology of cholinergic transmission. In E. R. Kandel (ed.), Handbook of Physiology; The Nervous System, Vol. 1, Part I. Bethesda, Md., American Physiological Society, pp. 463–492.

Coombs, J. S., Eccles, J. C., and Fatt, P. 1955. The specific ionic conductances and the ionic movements across the motoneural membrane that produce the inhibitory post-synaptic potential. J. Physiol (Lond.) 130:326–373.

Cooper, J. R., Bloom, F. E., and Roth, R. H. 1978. The Biochemical Basis of Neuropharmacology. 3rd ed. New York: Oxford University Press.

Corbit, J. D. 1973. Voluntary control of hypothalamic temperature. J. Comp. Physiol. Psychol. 83:394–411.

Corey, D. P., and Hudspeth, A. J. 1979. Ionic basis of the receptor potential in a vertebrate hair cell. Nature (Lond.) 281:675–677.

Costanzo, R. M., and Gardner, E. P. 1980. A quantitative analysis of responses of direction-sensitive neurons in somatosensory cortex of awake monkeys. J. Neurophysiol. 43:1319–1341.

Côté, L. J., and Kremzner, L. T. 1975. Age-dependent changes in the activities of enzymes related to the formation and degradation of neurotransmitters in human brain; correlation with the levels of polyamines. In VIIth International Congress of Neuropathology, Budapest, Hungary. Amsterdam: Excerpta Medica, pp. 433–441.

Cotzias, G. C., Van Woert, M. H., and Schiffer, L. M. 1967. Aromatic amino acids and modification of Parkinsonism. N. Engl. J. Med. 276:374–379.

Couteaux, R. 1974. Remarks on the organization of axon terminals in relation to secretory processes at synapses. Adv. Cytopharmacol. 2:369–379.

Couteaux, R., Akert, K., Heuser, J. E., Reese, T. S. 1977. Ultrastructural evidence for vesicle exocytosis. Neurosci. Res. Program Bull. 15:603–607.

Couteaux, R., and Pécot-Dechavassine, M. 1970. Vésicules synaptiques et poches au niveau des "zones actives" de la jonction neuromusculaire. C. R. Hebd. Séances Acad. Sci. Sér. D. Sci. Nat. 271:2346–2349.

Cowan, W. M. 1979. The development of the brain. Sci. Am. 241(3):112–133.

Cross, B. A., and Green, J. D. 1959. Activity of single neurones in the hypothalamus: Effect of osmotic and other stimuli. J. Physiol. (Lond.) 148:554–569.

Crowe, A., and Matthews, P. B. C. 1964. The effects of stimulation of static and dynamic fusimotor fibres on the response to stretching of the primary endings of muscle spindles. J. Physiol. (Lond.) 174:109–131.

Curtis, B. A., Jacobson, S., and Marcus, E. M. 1972. An Introduction to the Neurosciences. Philadelphia: Saunders.

Curzon, G. 1977. The biochemistry of the basal ganglia and Parkinson's disease. Postgrad. Med. J. 53:719–725.

D

Dahlström, A., and Fuxe, K. 1964. Evidence for the existence of monoamine-containing neurons in the central nervous system. Acta Physiol. Scand. 62:Suppl. 232:1–55.

Dale, H. 1935. Pharmacology and nerve-endings. Proc. R. Soc. Med. 28:319–332.

Dale, H. H., Feldberg, W., and Vogt, M. 1936. Release of acetylcholine at voluntary motor nerve endings. J. Physiol. (Lond.) 86:353–380.

Darwin, C. 1860. On the Origin of Species by Means of Natural Selection. New York: Appleton.

Darwin, C. 1872. The Expression of the Emotions in Man and Animals. London: Murray.

Dastur, D. K., Lane, M. H., Hansen, D. B., Kety, S. S., Butler, R. N., Perlin, S., and Sokoloff, L. 1963. Effects of aging on cerebral circulation and metabolism in man. In J. E. Birren et al. (eds.), Human Aging: A Biological and Behavioral Study. Public Health Service Publ. No. 986. Washington, D.C.: U.S. Government Printing Office, pp. 57–76.

Dau, P. C. (ed.). 1979. Plasmapheresis and the Immunobiology of Myasthenia Gravis. Boston: Houghton Miffflin.

Davies, P., and Maloney, A. J. F. 1976. Selective loss of central cholinergic neurons in Alzheimer's disease. Lancet Vol. II, No. 8000, p. 1403.

Davis, J. M., and Garver, D. L. 1978. Neuroleptics: Clinical use in psychiatry. In L. L. Iversen, S. D. Iversen, and S. H. Snyder (eds.), Handbook of Psychopharmacology, Vol. 10: Neuroleptics and Schizophrenia. New York: Plenum, pp. 129–164.

De Armond, S. J., Fusco, M. M., and Dewey, M. M. 1976. Structure of the Human Brain. 2nd ed. New York: Oxford University Press.

Deecke, L. Scheid, P., and Kornhuber, H. H. 1969. Distribution of readiness potential, pre-motion positivity, and motor potential of the human cerebral cortex preceding voluntary finger movements. Exp. Brain Res. 7:158–168.

DeJong, R. N. 1979. The Neurologic Examination. 4th ed. New York: Harper & Row.

Del Castillo, J., and Katz, B. 1954. The effect of magnesium on the activity of motor nerve endings. J. Physiol. (Lond.) 124:553–559.

Del Castillo, J., and Katz, B. 1957. La base "quantale" de la transmission neuro-musculaire. In Microphysiologie comparée des éléments excitables. Colloq. Int. Cent. Natl. Rech. Sci. 67:245–258.

DeLong, M. R. 1974. Motor functions of the basal ganglia: Single-unit activity during movement. In F. O. Schmitt, and F. G. Worden (eds.), The Neurosciences: Third Study Program. Cambridge, Mass.: MIT Press, pp. 319–325.

Dement, W. C. 1965. An essay on dreams: The role of physiology in understanding their nature. In New Directions in Psychology, Vol. 2. New York: Holt, Rinehart and Winston, pp. 135–257.

Dement W., Guilleminault, C., and Zarcone, V. 1975. The pathologies of sleep: A case series approach. In D. B. Tower (ed.), The Nervous System, Vol. 2: The Clinical Neurosciences. New York: Raven Press, pp. 501–518.

De Robertis. E. 1960. Some observations on the ultrastructure and morphogenesis of photoreceptors. J. Gen. Physiol. 43 Suppl. 2:1–13.

Deutsch, J. A., and Howarth, C. I. 1963. Some tests of a theory of intracranial self-stimulation. Psychol. Rev. 70:444–460.

DeWied, D., and Gispen, W. H. 1977. Behavioral effects of peptides. In H. Gainer (ed.), Peptides in Neurobiology. New York: Plenum, pp. 397–448.

DiGirolamo, M., and Rudman, D. 1968. Variations in glucose metabolism and sensitivity to insulin of the rat's adipose tissue, in relation to age and body weight. Endocrinology 82:1133–1141.

Divac, I., LaVail, J. H., Rakic, P., and Winston, K. R. 1977. Heterogeneous afferents to the inferior parietal lobule of the rhesus monkey revealed by the retrograde transport method. Brain Res. 123:197–207.

Doty, R. W., and Bosma, J. F. 1956. An electromyographic analysis of reflex deglutition. J. Neurophysiol. 19:44–60.

Dowling, J. E. 1970. Organization of vertebrate retinas. Invest. Ophthalmol. 9:655–680.

Dowling, J. E. 1974. Synaptic arrangements in the vertebrate retina: The photoreceptor synapse. In M. V. L. Bennett (ed.), Synaptic Transmission and Neuronal Interaction. New York: Raven Press, pp. 87–103.

Dowling, J. E. 1979. Information processing by local circuits: The vertebrate retina as a model system. In F. O. Schmitt and F. G. Worden (eds.), The Neurosciences: Fourth Study Program. Cambridge, Mass.: MIT Press, pp. 163–181.

Drachman, D. B. 1978. Myasthenia gravis. N. Engl. J. Med. 298:136–142; 186–193.

DuBois-Reymond, E. 1848–1849. Untersuchungen über Thierische Elektricität. Vols. I–II. Berlin: Reimer.

Duffy, P. (ed.). 1974. Neuropathology: An Illustrated Course. Philadelphia. Davis.

DuVigneaud, V. 1956. Hormones of the posterior pituitary gland: Oxytocin and vasopressin. Harvey Lect. 50:1–26.

Dyck, P. J. 1979. Diseases of the peripheral nervous system. In P. B. Beeson, W. McDermott, and J. B. Wyngaarden (eds.), Cecil Textbook of Medicine, 15th ed. Philadelphia: Saunders, pp. 899–913.

E

Eaton, L. M., and Lambert, E. H. 1957. Electromyography and electric stimulation of nerves in diseases of motor unit. Observations on myasthenic syndrome associated with malignant tumors. J.A.M.A. 163:1117–1124.

Eccles, J. 1976. From electrical to chemical transmission in the central nervous system. The closing address of the Sir Henry Dale Centennial Symposium. Notes Rec. R. Soc. Lond. 30:219–230.

Eccles, J. C. 1936. Synaptic and neuro-muscular transmission. Ergeb. Physiol. Biol. Chem. Exp. Pharmakol. 38:339–444.

Eccles, J. C. 1957. The Physiology of Nerve Cells. Baltimore: Johns Hopkins Press.

Eccles, J. C. 1964. The Physiology of Synapses. Berlin: Springer.

Eccles, J. C., Fatt, P., and Koketsu, K. 1954. Cholinergic and inhibitory synapses in a pathway from motor-axon collaterals to motoneurones. J. Physiol. (Lond.) 126:524–562.

Eccles, J. C., Ito, M., and Szentágothai, J. 1967. The Cerebellum as a Neuronal Machine. New York: Springer.

Eccles, R. M., and Lundberg, A. 1959. Synaptic actions in motoneurones by afferents which may evoke the flexion reflex. Arch. Ital. Biol. 97:199–221.

Edds, M. V., Jr. 1967. Neuronal specificity in neurogenesis. In G. C. Quarton, T. Melnechuk, and F. O. Schmitt (eds.), The Neurosciences: A Study Program. New York: Rockefeller University Press, pp. 230–240.

Ehrlich, P. 1913. Chemotheraputics: Scientific principles, methods, and results. Lancet 2:445–451.

Eibl-Eibesfeldt, I. 1970. Ethology, The Biology of Behavior. New York: Holt, Rinehart and Winston.

Elmqvist, D., Hofmann, W. W., Kugelberg, J., and Quastel, D. M. J. 1964. An electrophysiological investigation of neuromuscular transmission in myasthenia gravis. J. Physiol. (Lond.) 174:417–434.

Enroth-Cugell, C., and Robson, J. G. 1966. The contrast sensitivity of retinal ganglion cells of the cat. J. Physiol. (Lond.) 187:517–552.

Etienne, P., Gauthier, S., Johnson, G., et al. 1978. Clinical effects of choline in Alzheimer's disease. Lancet Vol. I, No. 8062, pp. 508–509.

Evarts, E. V. 1967. Representation of movements and muscles by pyramidal tract neurons of the precentral motor cortex. In M. D. Yahr and D. P. Purpura (eds.), Neurophysiological Basis of Normal and Abnormal Motor Activities. Hewlett, New York: Raven Press, pp. 215–253.

Evarts, E. V. 1968. Relation of pyramidal tract activity to force exerted during voluntary movement. J. Neurophysiol. 31:14–27.

Evarts, E. V. 1976. Neurophysiological mechanisms in Parkinson's disease. In W. Birkmayer, and O. Hornykiewicz (eds.), Advances in Parkinsonism, Fifth International Symposium on Parkinson's Disease, Vienna. Basle: Roche, pp. 37–54.

Evarts, E. V., Bizzi, E., Burke, R. E., DeLong, M., and Thach, Jr., W. T. 1971. Central control of movement. Neurosci. Res. Program Bull. 9:1–170.

Evarts, E. V., and Tanji, J. 1976. Reflex and intended responses in motor cortex pyramidal tract neurons of monkey. J. Neurophysiol. 39:1069–1080.

Everett, G. M., and Toman, J. E. P. 1959. Mode of action of Rauwolfia alkaloids and motor activity. In J. H. Masserman (ed.), Biological Psychiatry. New York: Grune & Stratton, pp. 75–81.

F

Falck, B. 1962. Observations on the possibilities of the cellular localization of monoamines by a fluorescence method. Acta Physiol. Scand. Suppl. 197.

Falck, B., Hillarp, N.-Å., Thieme, G., and Torp, A. 1962. Fluorescence of catechol amines and related compounds condensed with formaldehyde. J. Histochem. Cytochem. 10:348–354.

Fambrough, D. M., Drachman, D. B., and Satyamurti, S. 1973. Neuromuscular junction in myasthenia gravis: Decreased acetylcholine receptors. Science (Wash., D.C.) 182:293–295.

Fatt, P., and Katz, B. 1951. An analysis of the end-plate potential recorded with an intra-cellular electrode. J. Physiol. (Lond.) 115:320–370.

Fatt, P., and Katz, B. 1952. Spontaneous subthreshold activity at motor nerve endings. J. Physiol. (Lond.) 117:109–128.

Fazio, C., Fieschi, C., and Agnoli, A. 1971. The "intracerebral steal": A phenomenon in the pathogenesis of focal brain ischemia. In K. J. Zülch (ed.), Cerebral Circulation and Stroke. New York: Springer, pp. 143–147.

Feinberg, I. 1969. Effects of age on human sleep patterns. In A. Kales (ed.), Sleep Physiology & Pathology. Philadelphia: Lippincott, pp. 39–52.

Ferrier, D. 1875. Experiments on the brain of monkeys. —No. I. Proc. R. Soc. Lond. 23:409–430.

Ferrier, D. 1890. The Croonian Lectures on Cerebral Localisation. London: Smith, Elder.

Fertuck, H. C., and Salpeter, M. M. 1974. Localization of acetylcholine receptor by ^{125}I-labeled α-bungarotoxin binding at mouse motor endplates. Proc. Natl. Acad. Sci. U.S.A. 71:1376–1378.

Fields, H. L., and Basbaum, A. I. 1978. Brainstem control of spinal pain-transmission neurons. Annu. Rev. Physiol. 40:217–248.

Fieve, R. R., Rosenthal, D., and Brill, H. (eds.). 1975. Genetic Research in Psychiatry. Baltimore: Johns Hopkins University Press.

Finkelstein, A., and Mauro, A. 1977. Physical principles and formalisms of electrical excitability. In E. R. Kandel (ed.), Handbook of Physiology; The Nervous System, Vol. 1, Part I. Bethesda, Md.: American Physiological Society, pp. 161–213.

Fishman, R. A. 1975. Brain edema. N. Engl. J. Med. 293:706–711.

Fishman, R. A. 1980. Cerebrospinal Fluid in Diseases of the Nervous System. Philadelphia: Saunders.

Flock, Å. 1964. Structure of the macula utriculi with special reference to directional interplay of sensory responses as revealed by morphological polarization. J. Cell Biol. 22:413–431.

Flock, Å. 1965. Transducing mechanisms in the lateral line canal organ receptors. Cold Spring Harbor Symp. Quant. Biol. 30:133–145.

Flourens, P. 1824. Recherches expérimentales sur les propriétés et les fonctions du système nerveux, dans les animaux vertébrés. Paris: Chez Crevot.

Forssberg, H., Grillner, S., and Rossignol. S. 1975. Phase dependent reflex reversal during walking in chronic spinal cats. Brain Res. 85:103–107.

Foulkes, D. 1966. The Psychology of Sleep. New York: Scribner's.

Foulkes, W. D. 1962. Dream reports from different stages of sleep. J. Abnorm. Soc. Psychol. 65:14–25.

Freud, S. 1940. An Outline of Psychoanalysis. Trans. by J. Strachey. New York: Norton, 1949.

Freud, S. 1953. The Interpretation of Dreams. Translated by J. Strachey. Vols. IV and V. London: Hogarth Press and The Institute of Psycho-Analysis.

Friedman, M. I., and Stricker, E. M. 1976. The physiological psychology of hunger: A physiological perspective. Psychol. Rev. 83:409–431.

Fritsch, G., and Hitzig, E. 1870. Ueber die elektrische Erregbarkeit des Grosshirns. Arch. Anat. Physiol. Wiss. Med., pp. 300–332. G. von Bonin (trans.). In Some Papers on the Cerebral Cortex. Springfield, Ill.: Thomas, 1960, pp. 73–96.

Fuchs, A. F. 1967. Saccadic and smooth pursuit eye movements in the monkey. J. Physiol. (Lond.) 191:609–631.

Fuchs, A. F. 1971. The saccadic system. In P. Bach-y-Rita, and C. C. Collins (eds.), The Control of Eye Movements. New York: Academic, pp. 343–362.

Fuchs, A. F., and Luschei, E. S. 1970. Firing patterns of abducens neurons of alert monkeys in relationship to horizontal eye movement. J. Neurophysiol. 33:382–392.

Fulton, J. F. 1951. Frontal Lobotomy and Affective Behavior: A Neurophysiological Analysis. New York: Norton.

Fulton, J. F., and Keller, A. D. 1932. The Sign of Babinski. A Study of the Evolution of Cortical Dominance in Primates. Springfield, Ill.: Thomas.

Furshpan, E. J., and Potter, D. D. 1957. Mechanism of nerve-impulse transmission at a crayfish synapse. Nature (Lond.) 180:342–343.

Furshpan, E. J., and Potter, D. D. 1959. Transmission at the giant motor synapses of the crayfish. J. Physiol. (Lond.) 145:289–325.

G

Gajdusek, D. C. 1978. Slow infections with unconventional viruses. Harvey Lect. 72:283–353.

Galvani, L. 1791. Commentary on the Effect of Electricity on Muscular Motion. R. M. Green (trans.). Cambridge, Mass.: Licht, 1953.

Gastaut, H., and Broughton, R. 1965. A clinical and polygraphic study of episodic phenomena during sleep. In J. Wortis (ed.), Recent Advances in Biological Psychiatry, vol. 7. New York: Plenum, pp. 197–221.

Gatz, A. J. 1966. Manter's Essentials of Clinical Neuroanatomy and Neurophysiology. 3rd ed. Philadelphia: Davis.

Gay, V. L. 1972. The hypothalamus: Physiology and clinical use of releasing factors. Fertil. Steril. 23:50–63.

Gaze, R. M., Keating, M. J., and Chung, S. H. 1974. The evolution of the retinotectal map during development in Xenopus. Proc. R. Soc. Lond. B Biol. Sci. 185:301–330.

Gazzaniga, M. S., and LeDoux, J. E. 1978. The integrated Mind. New York: Plenum.

Geffen, L. B., and Jarrott, B. 1977. Cellular aspects of catecholaminergic neurons. In E. R. Kandel (ed.), Handbook of Physiology; The Nervous System, Vol. 1, Part I. Bethesda, Md.: American Physiological Society, pp. 521–571.

Geffen, L. B., and Livett, B. G. 1971. Synaptic vesicles in sympathetic neurons. Physiol. Rev. 51:98–157.

Gellhorn, E. (ed.). 1968. Biological Foundations of Emotion: Research and Commentary. Glenview, Ill.: Scott, Foresman.

Gershon, M. D. 1977. Biochemistry and physiology of serotonergic transmission. In E. R. Kandel (ed.), Handbook of Physiology; The Nervous System, Vol. 1, Part I. Bethesda, Md.: American Physiological Society, pp. 573–623.

Geschwind, N. 1967. The varieties of naming errors. Cortex 3:97–112.

Geschwind, N. 1971. Current concepts: Aphasia. N. Engl. J. Med. 284:654–656.

Geschwind, N. 1974. Selected Papers on Language and the Brain. Dordrecht, Holland: Reidel.

Geschwind, N. 1975. The apraxias. Neural mechanisms of disorders of learned movement. Am. Sci. 63: 188–195.

Geschwind, N. 1979. Specializations of the human brain. Sci. Am. 241(3):180–199.

Geschwind, N., and Fusillo, M. 1966. Color-naming defects in association with alexia. Arch. Neurol. 15:137–146.

Geschwind, N., and Levitsky, W. 1968. Human brain: Left–right asymmetries in temporal speech region. Science (Wash., D.C.) 161:186–187.

Geschwind, N., Quadfasel, F. A., and Segarra, J. M.

1968. Isolation of the speech area. Neuropsychologia 6:327–340.

Ghez, C., and Vicario, D. 1978a. Discharge of red nucleus neurons during voluntary muscle contraction: Activity patterns and correlations with isometric force. J. Physiol. (Paris) 74:283–285.

Ghez, C., and Vicario, D. 1978b. The control of rapid limb movement in the cat. II. Scaling of isometric force adjustments. Exp. Brain Res. 33:191–202.

Gibbs, C. J., Jr., Gajdusek, D. C., Asher, D. M., Alpers, M. P., Beck, E., Daniel, P. M., and Matthews, W. B. 1968. Creutzfeldt-Jakob disease (spongiform encephalopathy): Transmission to the chimpanzee. Science (Wash., D.C.) 161:388–389.

Giesler, Jr., G. J., and Liebeskind, J. C. 1976. Inhibition of visceral pain by electrical stimulation of the periaqueductal gray matter. Pain 2:43–48.

Gilman, S. 1973. Significance of muscle receptor control systems in the pathophysiology of experimental postural abnormalities. In J. E. Desmedt (ed.), New Developments in Electromyography and Clinical Neurophysiology, Vol. 3. Basel: Karger, pp. 175–193.

Gintzler, A. R., Levy, A., and Spector, S. 1976. Antibodies as a means of isolating and characterizing biologically active substances: Presence of a nonpeptide, morphine-like compound in the central nervous system. Proc. Natl. Acad. Sci. U.S.A. 73: 2132–2136.

Glaser, G. H. 1979. Convulsive disorders (epilepsy). In H. H. Merritt, A Textbook of Neurology. 6th ed. Philadelphia: Lea & Febiger, pp. 843–883.

Glaser, J. R. 1978. Neuro-Ophthalmology. Hagerstown, Md.: Harper & Row.

Gobel, S., and Binck, J. M. 1977. Degenerative changes in primary trigeminal axons and in neurons in nucleus caudalis following tooth pulp extirpations in the cat. Brain Res. 132:347–354.

Goldman, D. E. 1943. Potential, impedance, and rectification in membranes. J. Gen. Physiol. 27:37–60.

Goldman, P. S., Crawford, H. T., Stokes, L. P., Galkin, T. W., and Rosvold, H. E. 1974. Sex-dependent behavioral effects of cerebral cortical lesions in the developing rhesus monkey. Science (Wash., D.C.) 186:540–542.

Goldstein, A., Tachibana, S., Lowney, L. I., Hunkapiller, M., and Hood, L. 1979. Dynorphin-(1–13), an extraordinarily potent opioid peptide. Proc. Natl. Acad. Sci. U.S.A. 76:6666–6670.

Goldstein, K. 1948. Language and Language Disturbances. New York: Grune & Stratton.

Goldstein, Jr., M. H. 1980. The auditory periphery. In V. B. Mountcastle (ed.), Medical Physiology, 14th ed., Vol. 1. St. Louis: Mosby, pp. 428–456.

Golgi, C. 1906. The neuron doctrine—theory and facts. In Nobel Lectures: Physiology or Medicine, 1901–1921. Amsterdam: Elsevier, 1967, pp. 189–217.

Gonshor, A., and Melvill Jones, G. 1976. Short-term adaptive changes in the human vestibulo-ocular reflex arc. J. Physiol. (Lond.) 256:361–379.

Goodwin, G. M., McCloskey, D. I., and Matthews, P. B. C. 1972. The contribution of muscle afferents to kinaesthesia shown by vibration induced illusions of movement and by the effects of paralysing joint afferents. Brain 95:705–748.

Gorski, R. A., Gordon, J. H., Shryne, J. E., and Southam,

A. M. 1978. Evidence for a morphological sex difference within the medial preoptic area of the rat brain. Brain Res. 148:333–346.

Gouras, P. 1972. Light and dark adaptation. In M. G. F. Fuortes (ed.), Handbook of Sensory Physiology, Vol. 7, Part 2: Physiology of Photoreceptor Organs. New York: Springer, pp. 609–634.

Gouras, P., and Krüger, J. 1979. Responses of cells in foveal visual cortex of the monkey to pure color contrast. J. Neurophysiol. 42:850–860.

Goy, R. W., and Goldfoot, D. A. 1973. Hormonal influences on sexually dimorphic behavior. In R. O. Greep and E. B. Astwood (eds.), Handbook of Physiology; Section 7: Endocrinology, Vol. 2. Washington, D.C.: American Physiological Society, pp. 169–186.

Goy, R. W., and Goldfoot, D. A. 1975. Neuroendocrinology: Animal models and problems of human sexuality. Arch. Sex. Behav. 4:405–420.

Grafstein, B., and Forman, D. S. 1980. Intracellular transport in neurons. Physiol. Rev. 60:1167–1283.

Granit, R. 1955. Receptors and Sensory Perception. New Haven: Yale University Press.

Graubard, K., and Calvin, W. H. 1979. Presynaptic dendrites: Implications of spikeless synaptic transmission and dendritic geometry. In F. O. Schmitt and F. G. Worden (eds.), The Neurosciences: Fourth Study Program. Cambridge, Mass.: MIT Press, pp. 317–331.

Gray, E. G. 1959. Axo-somatic and axo-dendritic synapses of the cerebral cortex: An electron microscope study. J. Anat. 93:420–433.

Gray, E. G. 1963. Electron microscopy of presynaptic organelles of the spinal cord. J. Anat. 97:101–106.

Grillner, S. 1973. Locomotion in the spinal cat. In R. B. Stein, K. G. Pearson, R. S. Smith, and J. B. Redford (eds.), Control of Posture and Locomotion. New York: Plenum, pp. 515–535.

Grillner, S. 1975. Locomotion in vertebrates: Central mechanisms and reflex interaction. Physiol. Rev. 55:247–304.

Grillner, S., and Shik, M. L. 1973. On the descending control of the lumbosacral spinal cord from the "mesencephalic locomotor region." Acta Physiol. Scand. 87:320–333.

Grillner, S., and Zangger, P. 1975. How detailed is the central pattern generation for locomotion? Brain Res. 88:367–371.

Grob, D. (ed.). 1976. Myasthenia Gravis. Ann. N.Y. Acad. Sci. 274:1–682.

Grundfest, H. 1957. Excitation at synapses. J. Neurophysiol. 20:316–327.

Guillemin, R. 1978. Control of adenohypophysial functions by peptides of the central nervous system. Harvey Lect. 71:71–131.

Gurfinkel', V. S., Surguladze, T. D., Mirskii, M. L., and Tarko, A. M. 1970. Work of human motor units during rhythmic movements. Biophysics 15:1131–1137.

H

Hagins, W. A. 1972. The visual process: Excitatory mechanisms in the primary receptor cells. Annu. Rev. Biophys. Bioeng. 1:131–158.

Hamburger, V. 1934. The effects of wing bud extirpation on the development of the central nervous system in chick embryos. J. Exp. Zool. 68:449–494.

Hamburger, V. 1977. The developmental history of the motor neuron. The F. O. Schmitt Lecture in Neuroscience. Neurosci. Res. Program Bull. 15 Suppl.: 1–37.

Hamlyn, L. H. 1963. An electron microscope study of pyramidal neurons in the Ammon's Horn of the rabbit. J. Anat. 97:189–201.

Hardy, M. 1934. Observations on the innervation of the macula sacculi in man. Anat. Rec. 59:403–418.

Hardyck, C., and Petrinovich, L. F. 1977. Left-handedness. Psychol. Bull. 84:385–404.

Harlow, H. F. 1958. Behavioral contributions to interdisciplinary research. In H. F. Harlow and C. N. Woolsey (eds.), Biological and Biochemical Bases of Behavior. Madison: University of Wisconsin Press, pp. 3–23.

Harlow, H. F. 1958. The nature of love. Am. Psychol. 13:673–685.

Harlow, H. F., Dodsworth, R. O., and Harlow, M. K. 1965. Total social isolation in monkeys. Proc. Natl. Acad. Sci. U.S.A. 54:90–97.

Harris, D. A., and Henneman, E. 1980. Feedback signals from muscle and their efferent control. In V. B. Mountcastle (ed.), Medical Physiology, 14th ed., Vol. 1. St. Louis: Mosby, pp. 703–717.

Harris, G. M. 1955. Neural Control of the Pituitary Gland. Monograph of The Physiology Society. London: E. Arnold.

Harrison, R. G. 1907. Observations on the living developing nerve fiber. Anat. Rec. 1:116–118.

Harrison, R. G. 1935. On the origin and development of the nervous system studied by the methods of experimental embryology. Proc. R. Soc. Lond. B Biol. Sci. 118:155–196.

Hartmann, E. L. 1973. The Functions of Sleep. New Haven: Yale University Press.

Harvey, A. M., and Masland, R. L. 1941. The electromyogram in myasthenia gravis. Bull. Johns Hopkins Hosp. 69:1–13.

Hatton, G. I. 1976. Nucleus circularis: Is it an osmoreceptor in the brain? Brain Res. Bull. 1:123–131.

Hayflick, L. 1975. Current theories of biological aging. Fed. Proc. 34:9–13.

Hayflick, L. 1980. The cell biology of human aging. Sci. Am. 242(1):58–65.

Head, H. 1921. Release of function in the nervous system. Proc. R. Soc. Lond. B. Biol. Sci. 92:184–209.

Head, H. 1926. Aphasia and Kindred Disorders of Speech. 2v. Cambridge: Cambridge University Press. Reprinted in 1963. New York: Hafner, 1963.

Heilman, K. M., and Scholes, R. J. 1976. The nature of comprehension errors in Broca's, conduction and Wernicke's aphasics. Cortex 12:258–265.

Heilman, K. M., Scholes, R., and Watson, R. T. 1975. Auditory affective agnosia. Disturbed comprehension of affective speech. J. Neurol. Neurosurg. Psych. 38:69–72.

Helmholtz, H. von. 1850. Monatsber. Preuss. Akad. Wiss. Berl, pp. 14–15. Trans. in W. Dennis (comp. and ed.), Readings in the History of Psychology. New York: Appleton-Century-Crofts, 1948, pp. 197–198.

Helmholtz, H. L. F. 1877. On the Sensations of Tone. 2nd Eng. ed. New York: Dover, 1954.

Hendry, I. A., Stöckel, K., Thoenen, H., and Iversen, L. L. 1974. The retrograde axonal transport of nerve growth factor. Brain Res. 68:103–121.

Henneman, E. 1980. Motor functions of the brain stem and basal ganglia. In V. B. Mountcastle (ed.), Medical Physiology, 14th ed., Vol. 1. St. Louis: Mosby, pp. 787–812.

Henneman, E. 1980. Organization of the spinal cord and its reflexes. In V. B. Mountcastle (ed.), Medical Physiology, 14th ed., Vol. 1. St. Louis: Mosby, pp. 762–786.

Henneman, E. 1980. Skeletal muscle. The servant of the nervous system. In V. B. Mountcastle (ed.), Medical Physiology, 14th ed., Vol. 1. St. Louis: Mosby, pp. 674–702.

Hentall, I. D., and Fields, H. L. 1979. Segmental and descending influences on intraspinal thresholds of single C-fibers. J. Neurophysiol. 42:1527–1537.

Hess, W. R. 1954. Diencephalon: Autonomic and Extrapyramidal Functions. New York: Grune & Stratton.

Hetherington, A. W., and Ranson, S. W. 1942. The spontaneous activity and food intake of rats with hypothalamic lesions. Am. J. Physiol. 136:609–617.

Heuser, J. E., and Reese, T. S. 1977. Structure of the synapse. In E. R. Kandel (ed.), Handbook of Physiology; The Nervous System, Vol. 1, Part I. Bethesda, Md.: American Physiological Society, pp. 261–294.

Heuser, J. E., Reese, T. S., Dennis, M. J., Jan, Y., Jan, L., and Evans, L. 1979. Synaptic vesicle exocytosis captured by quick freezing and correlated with quantal transmitter release. J. Cell Biol. 81:275–300.

Hilgard, E. R., and Bower, G. H. 1975. Theories of Learning. 4th ed. Englewood Cliffs N.J.: Prentice-Hall.

Hille, B. 1977. Ionic basis of resting and action potentials. In E. R. Kandel (ed.), Handbook of Physiology; The Nervous System, Vol. 1, Part I. Bethesda, Md. American Physiological Society, pp. 99–136.

Hille, B. 1978. Ionic channels in excitable membranes. Biophys. J. 22:283–294.

Hirsch, J. (ed.). 1967. Behavior–Genetic Analysis. New York: McGraw-Hill.

Hobson, J. A. 1974. The cellular basis of sleep cycle control. Adv. Sleep Res. 1:217–250.

Hobson, J. A., McCarley, R. W., and Wyzinski, P. W. 1975. Sleep cycle oscillation: Reciprocal discharge by two brainstem neuronal groups. Science (Wash., D.C.) 189:55–58.

Hodgkin, A. L. 1964. The Conduction of the Nervous Impulse. Springfield, Ill.: Thomas.

Hodgkin, A. L. 1976. Chance and design in electrophysiology: An informal account of certain experiments on nerve carried out between 1934 and 1952. J. Physiol. (Lond.) 263:1–21.

Hodgkin, A. L., and Huxley, A. F. 1952. A quantitative description of membrane current and its application to conduction and excitation in nerve. J. Physiol. (Lond.) 117:500–544.

Hodgkin, A. L., and Katz, B. 1949. The effect of sodium ions on the electrical activity of the giant axon of the squid. J. Physiol. (Lond.) 108:37–77.

Hökfelt, T., Johansson, O., Ljungdahl, Å., Lundberg, J. M., and Schultzberg, M. 1980. Peptidergic neurones. Nature (Lond.) 284:515–521.

Hökfelt, T., Kellerth, J. O., Nilsson, G., and Pernow, B. 1975. Substance P: Localization in the central nervous system and in some primary sensory neurons. Science (Wash., D.C.) 190:889–890.

Holmes, G. 1922. Clinical symptoms of cerebellar disease and their interpretation. Lancet 1:1177–1182; 1:1231–1237; 2:59–65; 2:111–115.

Holtzman, E. 1977. The origin and fate of secretory packages, especially synaptic vesicles. Neuroscience 2:327–355.

Homma, S. (ed.). 1976. Understanding the stretch reflex. Prog. Brain Res. 44:1–507.

Hornykiewicz, O. 1966. Metabolism of brain dopamine in human Parkinsonism: Neurochemical and clinical aspects. In E. Costa, L. J. Côté, and M. D. Yahr (eds.), Biochemistry and Pharmacology of the Basal Ganglia. Hewlett, New York: Raven Press, pp. 171–185.

Horton, J. C., Greenwood, M. M., and Hubel, D. H. 1979. Non-retinotopic arrangement of fibres in cat optic nerve. Nature (Lond.) 282:720–722.

Hotta, Y., and Benzer, S. 1976. Courtship in *Drosophila* mosaics: Sex-specific foci for sequential action patterns. Proc. Natl. Acad. Sci. U.S.A. 73:4154–4158.

Houk, J., and Henneman, E. 1967. Responses of Golgi tendon organs to active contractions of the soleus muscle of the cat. J. Neurophysiol. 30:466–481.

Houk, J. C. 1979. Motor control processes: New data concerning motoservo mechanisms and a tentative model for stimulus-response processing. In R. E. Talbott and D. R. Humphrey (eds.), Posture and Movement. New York: Raven Press, pp. 231–241.

Hubbard, J. I., Llinás, R., and Quastel, D. M. J. 1969. Electrophysiological Analysis of Synaptic Transmission. Baltimore: Williams & Wilkins.

Hubbell, W. L., and Bownds, M. D. 1979. Visual transduction in vertebrate photoreceptors. Annu. Rev. Neurosci. 2:17–34.

Hubel, D. H., and Wiesel, T. N. 1959. Receptive fields of single neurones in the cat's striate cortex. J. Physiol. (Lond.) 148:574–591.

Hubel, D. H., and Wiesel, T. N. 1962. Receptive fields, binocular interaction and functional architecture in the cat's visual cortex. J. Physiol. (Lond.) 160:106–154.

Hubel, D. H., and Wiesel, T. N. 1965. Binocular interaction in striate cortex of kittens reared with artificial squint. J. Neurophysiol. 28:1041–1059.

Hubel, D. H., and Wiesel, T. N. 1972. Laminar and columnar distribution of geniculo-cortical fibers in the macaque monkey. J. Comp. Neurol. 146:421–450.

Hubel, D. H., and Wiesel, T. N. 1977. Ferrier Lecture: Functional architecture of macaque monkey visual cortex. Proc. R. Soc. Lond. B Biol. Sci. 198:1–59.

Hubel, D. H., and Wiesel, T. N. 1979. Brain mechanisms of vision. Sci. Am. 241(3):150–162.

Hudspeth, A. J., and Corey, D. P. 1977. Sensitivity, polarity, and conductance change in the response of vertebrate hair cells to controlled mechanical stimuli. Proc. Natl. Acad. Sci. U.S.A. 74:2407–2411.

Hughes, J. Smith, T. W., Kosterlitz, H. W., Fothergill, L. A., Morgan, B. A., and Morris, H. R. 1975. Identification of two related pentapeptides from the brain with potent opiate agonist activity. Nature (Lond.) 258:577–579.

Hunt, C. C. 1954. Relation of function to diameter in afferent fibers of muscle nerves. J. Gen. Physiol. 38:117–131.

Hunt, C. C., and Kuffler, S. W. 1951. Stretch receptor discharges during muscle contraction. J. Physiol. (Lond.) 113:298–315.

Hunt, C. C., and Perl, E. R. 1960. Spinal reflex mechanisms concerned with skeletal muscle. Physiol. Rev. 40:538–579.

Hursh, J. B. 1939. Conduction velocity and diameter of nerve fibers. Am. J. Physiol. 127:131–139.

Hurvich, L. M. 1972. Color vision deficiencies. In D. Jameson and L. M. Hurvich (eds.), Handbook of Sensory Physiology, Vol. 7, Part 4. New York: Springer, pp. 582–624.

Hyvärinen, J., and Poranen, A. 1978. Movement-sensitive and direction and orientation-selective cutaneous receptive fields in the hand area of the postcentral gyrus in monkeys. J. Physiol. (Lond.) 283: 523–537.

I

Iggo, A. 1974. Cutaneous receptors. In J. I. Hubbard (ed.), The Peripheral Nervous System. New York: Plenum, pp. 347–404.

Iggo, A., and Muir, A. R. 1969. The structure and function of a slowly adapting touch corpuscle in hairy skin. J. Physiol. (Lond.) 200:763–796.

Ingvar, D. H., and Schwartz, M. S. 1974. Blood flow patterns induced in the dominant hemisphere by speech and reading. Brain 97:273–288.

Iurato, S. 1967. Submicroscopic Structure of the Inner Ear. Oxford: Pergamon.

Iversen, L. L. 1975. Dopamine receptors in the brain. Science (Wash., D.C.) 188:1084–1089.

Iversen, L. L. 1978. Neurobiology of peptides. Neurosci. Res. Program Bull. 16:209–370.

J

Jack, J. 1979. An introduction to linear cable theory. In F. O. Schmitt and F. G. Worden (eds.), The Neurosciences: Fourth Study Program. Cambridge, Mass.: MIT Press, pp. 423–437.

Jack, J. J. B., Noble, D., and Tsien, R. W. 1975. Electric Current Flow in Excitable Cells. Oxford: Clarendon Press, chaps. 1–5, 7; pp. 276–277.

Jackson, J. H. 1884. The Croonian Lectures on evolution and dissolution of the nervous system. Br. Med. J. 1:591–593; 660–663; 703–707.

Jackson, J. H. 1931–1932. Selected Writings of John Hughlings Jackson. J. Taylor (ed.). 2 vol. London: Hodder and Stoughton.

Jacobsen, C. F. 1935. Functions of frontal association area in primates. Arch. Neurol. Psychiatry 33:558–569.

Jacobson, A., Kales, A., Lehmann, D., and Zweizig, J. R. 1965. Somnambulism: All-night electroencephalographic studies. Science (Wash., D.C.) 148:975–977.

Jacobson, M. 1968. Development of neuronal specificity in retinal ganglion cells of Xenopus. Dev. Biol. 17:202–218.

Jacobson, M. 1978. Developmental Neurobiology. 2nd ed. New York: Plenum.

Jan, Y. N., Jan, L. Y., and Kuffler, S. W. 1979. A peptide as a possible transmitter in sympathetic ganglia of the frog. Proc. Natl. Acad. Sci. U.S.A. 76:1501–1505.

Jessell, T. M., and Iversen, L. L. 1977. Opiate analgesics inhibit substance P release from rat trigeminal nucleus. Nature (Lond.) 268:549–551.

Jessell, T. M., Siegel, R. E., and Fischbach, G. D. 1979. Induction of acetylcholine receptors on cultured skeletal muscle by a factor extracted from brain and spinal cord. Proc. Natl. Acad. Sci. U.S.A. 76:5397–5401.

Jewett, D. L., and Williston, J. S. 1971. Auditory-evoked far fields averaged from the scalp of humans. Brain 94:681–696.

Jones, E. G., and Powell, T. P. S. 1973. Anatomical organization of the somatosensory cortex. In A. Iggo (ed.), Handbook of Sensory Physiology, Vol. 2, The Somatosensory System. New York: Springer, pp. 579–620.

Jones, E. G., and Wise, S. P. 1977. Size, laminar and columnar distribution of efferent cells in the sensory–motor cortex of monkeys. J. Comp. Neurol. 175:391–437.

Jouvet, M. 1974. The role of monoaminergic neurons in the regulation and function of sleep. In O. Petre-Quadens and J. D. Schlag (eds.), Basic Sleep Mechanisms. New York: Academic, pp. 207–236.

Julesz, B. 1971. Foundations of Cyclopean Perception. Chicago: University of Chicago Press.

K

Kaas, J. H., Nelson, R. J., Sur, M., Lin, C.-S., and Merzenich, M. M. 1979. Multiple representations of the body within the primary somatosensory cortex of primates. Science (Wash., D.C.) 204:521–523.

Kales, A. (ed.). 1969. Sleep Physiology & Pathology. Philadelphia: Lippincott.

Kales, A., and Kales, J. 1973. Recent advances in the diagnosis and treatment of sleep disorders. In G. Usdin (ed.), Sleep Research and Clinical Practice. New York: Brunner/Mazel, pp. 59–94.

Kallmann, F. J. 1938. The Genetics of Schizophrenia. New York: Augustin.

Kandel, E. R. 1964. Electrical properties of hypothalamic neuroendocrine cells. J. Gen. Physiol. 47:691–717.

Kandel, E. R. 1976. Cellular Basis of Behavior: An Introduction to Behavioral Neurobiology. San Francisco: Freeman.

Kandel, E. R. 1979. Cellular insights into behavior and learning. Harvey Lect. 73:19–92.

Kaneko, A. 1979. Physiology of the retina. Annu. Rev. Neurosci. 2:169–191.

Kanfer, F. H., and Phillips, J. S. 1970. Learning Foundations of Behavior Therapy. New York: Wiley.

Karlin, A. 1980. Molecular properties of nicotinic acetylcholine receptors. Cell Surface Rev.

Katz, B. 1966. Nerve, Muscle, and Synapse. New York: McGraw-Hill.

Katz, B. 1969. The Release of Neural Transmitter Substances. Springfield, Ill.: Thomas.

Katz, B., and Miledi, R. 1967a. A study of synaptic transmission in the absence of nerve impulses. J Physiol. (Lond.) 192:407–436.

Katz, B., and Miledi, R. 1967b. The timing of calcium

action during neuromuscular transmission. J. Physiol. (Lond.) 189:535–544.

Katz, B., and Miledi, R. 1970. Membrane noise produced by acetylcholine. Nature (Lond.) 226:962–963.

Katzman, R., and Pappius H. M. 1973. Brain Electrolytes and Fluid Metabolism. Baltimore: Williams & Wilkins.

Keesey, R. E., Boyle, P. C., Kemnitz, J. W., and Mitchel, J. S. 1976. The role of the lateral hypothalamus in determining the body weight set point. In D. Novin, W. Wyrwicka, and G. A. Bray (eds.), Hunger: Basic Mechanisms and Clinical Implications. New York: Raven Press, pp. 243–255.

Kelly, J. P., and Cowan, W. M. 1972. Studies on the development of the chick optic tectum. III. Effects of early eye removal. Brain Res. 42:263–288.

Kelly, J. P., and Van Essen, D. C. 1974. Cell structure and function in the visual cortex of the cat. J. Physiol. (Lond.) 238:515–547.

Kelly, R. B., Deutsch, J. W., Carlson, S. S., and Wagner, J. A. 1979. Biochemistry of neurotransmitter release. Annu. Rev. Neurosci. 2:399–446.

Kerr, F. W. L., and Wilson, P. R. 1978. Pain. Annu. Rev. Neurosci. 1:83–102.

Kety, S. S. 1960. Sleep and the energy metabolism of the brain. In G. E. W. Wolstenholme and M. O'Connor (eds.), The Nature of Sleep. Boston: Little, Brown, pp. 375–381.

Kety, S. S. 1978. The biological roots of mental illness: Their ramifications through cerebral metabolism, synaptic activity, genetics, and the environment. Harvey Lect. 71:1–22.

Kety, S. S. 1979. Disorders of the human brain. Sci. Am. 241(3):202–214.

Kety, S. S., Rosenthal, D., Wender, P. H., and Schulsinger, F. 1968. The types and prevalence of mental illness in the biological and adoptive families of adopted schizophrenics. In D. Rosenthal and S. S. Kety (eds.), The Transmission of Schizophrenia. Oxford: Pergamon, pp. 345–362.

Kety, S. S., Rosenthal, D., Wender, P. H., Schulsinger, F., and Jacobsen, B. 1975. Mental illness in the biological and adoptive families of adopted individuals who have become schizophrenic: A preliminary report based on psychiatric interviews. In R. R. Fieve, D. Rosenthal, and H. Brill (eds.), Genetic Research in Psychiatry. Baltimore: Johns Hopkins University Press, pp. 147–165.

Kety, S. S., and Schmidt, C. F. 1948. The nitrous oxide method for the quantitative determination of cerebral blood flow in man; theory, procedure, and normal values. J. Clin. Invest. 27:476–483.

Keynes, R. D. 1979. Ion channels in the nerve-cell membrane. Sci. Am. 240(3):126–135.

Khodorov, B. I. 1974. The Problem of Excitability. New York: Plenum.

Kiang, N. Y.-S. 1965. Discharge Patterns of Single Fibers in the Cat's Auditory Nerve. Cambridge, Mass.: MIT Press.

Kievit, J., and Kuypers, H. G. J. M. 1975. Basal forebrain and hypothalamic connections to frontal and parietal cortex in the rhesus monkey. Science (Wash., D.C.) 187:660–662.

Klein, D. F., and Davis, J. M. 1969. Diagnosis and Drug Treatment of Psychiatric Disorders. Baltimore: Williams & Wilkins.

Klein, D. F., Gittelman, R., Quitkin, F., and Rifkin, A. 1980. Diagnosis and Drug Treatment of Psychiatric Disorders: Adults and Children. 2nd ed. Baltimore: Williams & Wilkins.

Klein, M., and Kandel, E. R. 1978. Presynaptic modulation of voltage-dependent Ca^{2+} current: Mechanism for behavioral sensitization in Aplysia californica. Proc. Natl. Acad. Sci. U.S.A. 75:3512–3516.

Klein, M., Shapiro, E., and Kandel, E. R. 1980. Synaptic plasticity and the modulation of the Ca^{2+} current. J. Exp. Biol. 89:117–157.

Klüver, H. 1937. "Psychic blindness" and other symptoms following bilateral temporal lobectomy in rhesus monkeys. Am. J. Physiol. 119:352–353.

Klüver, H., and Bucy, P. C. 1939. Preliminary analysis of functions of the temporal lobes in monkeys. Arch. Neurol. Psychiatry 42:979–1000.

Knibestöl, M., and Vallbo, Å. B. 1976. Stimulus-response-functions of primary afferents and psychophysical intensity estimation on mechanical skin stimulation in the human hand. In Y. Zotterman (ed.), Sensory Functions of the Skin in Primates with Special Reference to Man. Oxford: Pergamon, pp. 201–213.

Konishi, M. 1965. The role of auditory feedback in the control of vocalization in the white-crowned sparrow. Z. Tierpsychol. 22:770–783.

Korein, J. (ed.). 1978. Brain death: Interrelated medical and social issues. Ann. N. Y. Acad. Sci. 315:1–454.

Kraepelin, E. 1909. Dementia Praecox and Paraphrenia. Trans. by R. M. Barclay from the 8th German edition of Kraepelin's Text-Book of Psychiatry. Edinburgh: Livingstone, 1919.

Kravitz, E. A. 1967. Acetylcholine, γ-aminobutyric acid, and glutamic acid: Physiological and chemical studies related to their roles as neurotransmitter agents. In G. C. Quarton, T. Melnechuk, and F. O. Schmitt (eds.), The Neurosciences: A Study Program. New York: Rockefeller University Press, pp. 433–444.

Krieger, D. T., and Hughes, J. C. 1980. Neuroendocrinology. Sunderland, Mass.: Sinauer Associates.

Kuffler, S. W. 1952. Neurons in the retina: Organization, inhibition and excitation problems. Cold Spring Harbor Symp. Quant. Biol. 17:281–292.

Kuffler, S. W. 1953. Discharge patterns and functional organization of mammalian retina. J. Neurophysiol. 16:37–68.

Kuffler, S. W. 1967. Neuroglial cells: Physiological properties and a potassium mediated effect of neuronal activity on the glial membrane potential. Proc. R. Soc. Lond. B Biol. Sci. 168:1–21.

Kuffler, S. W., and Nicholls, J. G. 1976. From Neuron to Brain: A Cellular Approach to the Function of the Nervous System. Sunderland, Mass.: Sinauer Associates.

Kuhar, M. J., and Murrin, L. C. 1978. Sodium-dependent, high affinity choline uptake. J. Neurochem. 30:15–21.

Kupfermann, I., and Weiss, K. R. 1978. The command neuron concept. Behav. Brain Sci. 1:3–39.

Kuschinsky, W., and Wahl, M. 1978. Local chemical and neurogenic regulation of cerebral vascular resistance. Physiol. Rev. 58:656–689.

Kuypers, H. G. J. M. 1973. The anatomical organization of the descending pathways and their contributions to motor control especially in primates. In J. E. Desmedt (ed.), New Developments in Electromyography and Clinical Neurophysiology, Vol. 3. Basel: Karger, pp. 38–68.

L

LaMotte, R. H., and Campbell, J. N. 1978. Comparison of responses of warm and nociceptive C-fiber afferents in monkey with human judgments of thermal pain. J. Neurophysiol. 41:509–528.

Land, E. H. 1977. The retinex theory of color vision. Sci. Am. 237(6):108–128.

Landau, W. M., and Clare, M. H. 1959. The plantar reflex in man, with special reference to some conditions where the extensor response is unexpectedly absent. Brain 82:321–355.

Langley, J. N. 1906. On nerve endings and on special excitable substances in cells. Proc. R. Soc. Lond. B. Biol. Sci. 78:170–194.

Laporte, Y., and Lloyd, D. P. C. 1952. Nature and significance of the reflex connections established by large afferent fibers of muscular origin. Am. J. Physiol. 169:609–621.

Lashley, K. S. 1929. Brain Mechanisms and Intelligence: A Quantitative Study of Injuries to the Brain. Chicago: University of Chicago Press.

Lashley, K. S. 1950. In search of the engram. Symp. Soc. Exp. Biol. 4:454–482.

Lassen, N. A. 1974. Control of cerebral circulation in health and disease. Circ. Res. 34:749–760.

Lassen, N. A., and Ingvar, D. H. 1972. Radioisotopic assessment of regional cerebral blood flow. Prog. Nucl. Med. 1:376–409.

LeDouarin, N. M., Renaud D., Teillet, M. A., and LeDouarin, G. H. 1975. Cholinergic differentiation of presumptive adrenergic neuroblasts in interspecific chimeras after heterotopic transplantations. Proc. Natl. Acad. Sci. U.S.A. 72:728–732.

Lee, C. Y. 1972. Chemistry and pharmacology of polypeptide toxins in snake venoms. Annu. Rev. Pharmacol. 12:265–286.

Lee, T., Seeman, P., Rajput, A., Farley, I. J., and Hornykiewicz, O. 1978. Receptor basis for dopaminergic supersensitivity in Parkinson's disease. Nature (Lond.) 273:59–61.

Le Gros Clark, W. E., and Penman, G. G. 1934. The projection of the retina in the lateral geniculate body. Proc. R. Soc. Lond. B Biol. Sci. 114:291–313.

Levi-Montalcini, R. 1952. Effects of mouse tumor transplantation on the nervous system. Ann. N.Y. Acad. Sci. 55:330–343.

Levi-Montalcini, R. 1975. NGF: An uncharted route. In F. G. Worden, J. P. Swazey, and G. Adelman (eds.), The Neurosciences: Paths of Discovery. Cambridge, Mass.: MIT Press, pp. 245–265.

Levin, B. E., and Margolis, G. 1977. Acute failure of automatic respirations secondary to a unilateral brainstem infarct. Ann. Neurol. 1:583–586.

Levy, J., Trevarthen, C., and Sperry, R. W. 1972. Perception of bilateral chimeric figures following hemispheric deconnexion. Brain 95:61–78.

Lewis, M. 1971. Individual differences in the measurement of early cognitive growth. In J. Hellmuth (ed.), Exceptional Infant, Vol. 2: Studies in Abnormalities. New York: Brunner/Mazel, pp. 172–210.

Leyton, A. S. F., and Sherrington, C. S. 1917. Observations on the excitable cortex of the chimpanzee, orang-utan, and gorilla. Q. J. Exp. Physiol. 11:135–222.

Liddell, E. G. T., and Sherrington, C. 1924. Reflexes in response to stretch (myotatic reflexes). Proc. R. Soc. Lond. B Biol. Sci. 96:212–242.

Liddell, E. G. T., and Sherrington, C. 1925. Further observations on myotatic reflexes. Proc. R. Soc. Lond. B Biol. Sci. 97:267–283.

Lieberman, A. R. 1971. The axon reaction. Int. Rev. Neurobiol. 14:49–124.

Liepmann, H. 1914. Bemerkungen zu v. Monakows Kapitel "Die Lokalisation der Apraxie." Monatsschr. Psychiatr. Neurol. 35:490–516.

Liley, A. W. 1956. The quantal components of the mammalian end-plate potential. J. Physiol. (Lond.) 133:571–587.

Lincoln, D. W., and Wakerley, J. B. 1974. Electrophysiological evidence for the activation of supraoptic neurones during the release of oxytocin. J. Physiol. (Lond.) 242:533–554.

Lindsley, D. B., Schreiner, L. H., and Magoun, H. W. 1949. An electromyographic study of spasticity. J. Neurophysiol. 12:197–205.

Lindstrom, J. 1979. Autoimmune response to acetylcholine receptors in myasthenia gravis and its animal model. Adv. Immunol. 27:1–50.

Lindstrom, J. M., and Lambert, E. H. 1978. Content of acetylcholine receptor and antibodies bound to receptor in myasthenia gravis, experimental autoimmune myasthenia gravis, and Eaton-Lambert syndrome. Neurology 28:130–138.

Llinás, R. 1980. Applicability of channel analyses in molluscs to vertebrate central neurons. In J. Koester and J. H. Byrne (eds.), Molluscan Nerve Cells: From Biophysics to Behavior. Cold Spring Harbor, New York: Cold Spring Harbor Laboratories (in press).

Llinás, R., and Nicholson, C. 1971. Electrophysiological properties of dendrites and somata in alligator Purkinje cells. J. Neurophysiol. 34:532–551.

Llinás, R., and Sugimori, M. 1980. Electrophysiological properties of in vitro Purkinje cell somata in mammalian cerebellar slices. J. Physiol. (Lond.) 305: 171–195.

Llinás, R., and Sugimori, M. 1980. Electrophysiological properties of in vitro Purkinje cell dendrites in mammalian cerebellar slices. J. Physiol. (Lond.) 305: 197–213.

Llinás, R. R. 1977. Calcium and transmitter release in squid synapse. In W. M. Cowan and J. A. Ferrendelli (eds.), Approaches to the Cell Biology of Neurons. Soc. Neurosci. Symp., vol. II, pp. 139–160.

Llinás, R. R., and Heuser, J. E. 1977. Depolarization-release coupling systems in neurons. Neurosci. Res. Program Bull. 15:555–687.

Lloyd, D. P. C. 1941. The spinal mechanism of the pyramidal system in cats. J. Neurophysiol. 4:525–546.

Lloyd, D. P. C. 1943. Conduction and synaptic transmission of the reflex response to stretch in spinal cats. J. Neurophysiol. 6:317–326.

Lloyd, D. P. C. 1960. Spinal mechanisms involved in somatic activities. In H. W. Magoun (ed.), Handbook of Physiology, Section 1: Neurophysiology, Vol. 2. Washington, D.C.: American Physiological Society, pp. 929–949.

Lloyd, D. P. C., and Chang, H.-T. 1948. Afferent fibers in muscle nerves. J. Neurophysiol. 11:199–208.

Loewenstein, W. R., and Mendelson, M. 1965. Components of receptor adaptation in a Pacinian corpuscle. J. Physiol. (Lond.) 177:377–397.

Loewi, O. 1960. An autobiographic sketch. Perspect. Biol. Med. 4:3–25.

Lømo, T., and Rosenthal, J. 1972. Control of ACh sensitivity by muscle activity in the rat. J. Physiol. (Lond.) 221:493–513.

Lømo, T., and Westgaard, R. H. 1976. Control of ACh sensitivity in rat muscle fibers. Cold Spring Harbor Symp. Quant. Biol. 50:263–274.

Lømo, T., Westgaard, R. H., and Dahl, H. A. 1974. Contractile properties of muscle: Control by pattern of muscle activity in the rat. Proc. R. Soc. Lond. B Biol. Sci. 187:99–103.

Lopresti, V., Macagno, E. R., and Levinthal, C. 1973. Structure and development of neuronal connections in isogenic organisms: Cellular interactions in the development of the optic lamina of Daphnia. Proc. Natl. Acad. Sci. U.S.A. 70:433–437.

Lorenz, K. Z. 1950. The comparative method in studying innate behaviour patterns. Symp. Soc. Exp. Biol. 4:221–268.

Lund, R. D. 1978. Development and Plasticity of the Brain. New York: Oxford University Press.

Lundberg, A. 1975. Control of spinal mechanisms from the brain. In D. B. Tower (ed.), The Nervous System, Vol. 1, The Basic Neurosciences. New York: Raven Press, pp. 253–265.

Lundberg, A. 1979. Integration in a propriospinal motor centre controlling the forelimbs in the cat. In H. Asanuma and V. J. Wilson (eds.), Integration in the Nervous System. Tokyo: Igaku-Shoin, pp. 47–64.

M

Magni, F., Moruzzi, G., Rossi, G. F., and Zanchetti, A. 1959. EEG arousal following inactivation of the lower brain stem by selective injection of barbiturate into the vertebral circulation. Arch. Ital. Biol. 97:33–46.

Magoun, H. W. 1963. Reticulo-spinal influences and postural regulation. In H. W. Magoun, The Waking Brain. 2nd ed. Springfield, Ill.: Thomas, pp. 23–28.

Magoun, H. W., and Rhines, R. 1946. An inhibitory mechanism in the bulbar reticular formation. J. Neurophysiol. 9:165–171.

Makowski, L., Caspar, D. L. D., Phillips, W. C., and Goodenough, D. A. 1977. Gap junction structures. II. Analysis of the X-ray diffraction data. J. Cell Biol. 74:629–645.

Manning, A. 1972. An Introduction to Animal Behavior. 2nd ed. Reading, Mass.: Addison-Wesley.

Mark, V. H., Ervin, F. R., and Yakovlev, P. I. 1963. Stereotactic thalamotomy. III. The verification of anatomical lesion sites in the human thalamus. Arch. Neurol. 8:528–538.

Marks, J. 1977. Physiology of abnormal movements. Postgrad. Med. J. 53:713–718.

Marks, W. B., Dobelle, W. H., and MacNichol, Jr., E. F. 1964. Visual pigments of single primate cones. Science (Wash., D.C.) 143:1181–1183.

Marler, P., and Hamilton, W. J. III. 1966. Mechanisms of Animal Behavior. New York: Wiley.

Marsden, C. D., and Harrison, M. J. G. 1972. Outcome of investigation of patients with presenile dementia. Br. Med. J. 2:249–252.

Marshall, W. H., and Talbot, S. A. 1942. Recent evidence for neural mechanisms in vision leading to a general theory of sensory acuity. In H. Klüver (ed.), Visual Mechanisms. Lancaster, Pennsylvania: Cattell, pp. 117–164.

Marshall, W. H., Woolsey, C. N., and Bard, P. 1941. Observations on cortical somatic sensory mechanisms of cat and monkey. J. Neurophysiol. 4:1–24.

Martin, A. R. 1977. Junctional transmission. II: Presynaptic mechanisms. In E. R. Kandel (ed.), Handbook of Physiology; The Nervous System, Vol. 1, Part I. Bethesda, Md.: American Physiological Society, pp. 329–355.

Matthews, B. H. C. 1933. Nerve endings in mammalian muscle. J. Physiol. (Lond.) 78:1–53.

Matthews, P. B. C. 1964. Muscle spindles and their motor control. Physiol. Rev. 44:219–288.

Matthews, P. B. C. 1972. Mammalian Muscle Receptors and Their Central Actions. Baltimore: Williams & Wilkins.

Matthysse, S. W., and Kety, S. S. (eds.). 1975. Catecholamines and Schizophrenia. Oxford: Pergamon.

Mauk, M. D., Olson, G. A., Kastin, A. J., and Olson, R. D. 1980. Behavioral effects of LH-RH. Neurosci. Biobehav. Rev. 4:1–8.

Mayer, D. J., and Price, D. D. 1976. Central nervous system mechanisms of analgesia. Pain 2:379–404.

McDougall, W. 1908. An Introduction to Social Psychology. London: Morrison & Gibb. Reprinted London: Methuen, 1960, and New York: Barnes & Noble, 1960.

McDowell, F. H. 1979. Cerebrovascular diseases. In P. B. Beeson and W. McDermott (eds.), Textbook of Medicine. 15th ed. Philadelphia: Saunders, pp. 777–801.

McEwen. B. S. 1976. Interactions between hormones and nerve tissue. Sci. Am. 235(1):48–58.

McGaugh, J. L., and Herz, M. J. 1972. Memory Consolidation. San Francisco: Albion.

McGeer, E., and McGeer, P. L. 1976. Neurotransmitter metabolism in the aging brain. In R. D. Terry and S. Gershon (eds.), Aging, Vol. 3: Neurobiology of Aging. New York: Raven Press, pp. 389–403.

McGeer, P. L., Eccles, J. C., and McGeer, E. G. 1978. Molecular Neurobiology of the Mammalian Brain. New York: Plenum.

Medvedev, Zh. A. 1972. Repetition of molecular–genetic information as a possible factor in evolutionary changes of life span. Exp. Gerontol. 7:227–238.

Melzack, R., and Wall, P. D. 1965. Pain mechanisms: A new theory. Science (Wash., D.C.) 150:971–979.

Mendell, L. M., and Henneman, E. 1971. Terminals of single Ia fibers: Location, density, and distribution within a pool of 300 homonymous motoneurons. J. Neurophysiol. 34:171–187.

Mendell, L. M., Munson, J. B., and Scott, J. G. 1976. Alterations of synapses on axotomized motoneurones. J. Physiol. (Lond.) 255:67–79.

Merton, P. A. 1953. Speculations on the servo-control of movement. In G. E. W. Wolstenholme (ed.), The Spinal Cord. London: Churchill Livingstone, pp. 247–255.

Merton, P. A. 1972. How we control the contraction of our muscles. Sci. Am. 226(5):30–37.

Meyer-Lohmann, J., Hore, J., and Brooks, V. B. 1977. Cerebellar participation in generation of prompt arm movements. J. Neurophysiol. 40:1038–1050.

Meyerson, B. J. 1979. Hypothalamic hormones and behaviour. Med. Biol. 57:69–83.

Meynert, T. 1885. Psychiatry. A Clinical Treatise on Diseases of the Forebrain Based upon a Study of Its Structure, Functions, and Nutrition. Part I. B. Sachs (trans.). New York: Hafner, 1968.

Michael, C. R. 1978a. Color vision mechanisms in monkey striate cortex: Dual-opponent cells with concentric receptive fields. J. Neurophysiol. 41:572–588.

Michael, C. R. 1978b. Color vision mechanisms in monkey striate cortex: Simple cells with dual opponent-color receptive fields. J. Neurophysiol. 41:1233–1249.

Miledi, R., Molinoff, P., and Potter, L. T. 1971. Isolation of the cholinergic receptor protein of *Torpedo* electric tissue. Nature (Lond.) 229:554–557.

Milhorat, T. H. 1972. Hydrocephalus and the Cerebrospinal Fluid. Baltimore: Williams & Wilkins.

Miller, J. D. 1979. Barbiturates and raised intracranial pressure. Ann. Neurol. 6:189–193.

Miller, J. M., and Towe, A. L. 1979. Audition: Structural and acoustical properties. In T. Ruch and H. D. Patton (eds.), Physiology and Biophysics. 20th ed. Philadelphia: Saunders, pp. 339–375.

Miller, N. E. 1969. Learning of visceral and glandular responses. Science (Wash., D.C.) 163:434–445.

Miller, R. J., and Pickel, V. M. 1980. The distribution and functions of the enkephalins. J. Histochem. Cytochem. 28:903–917.

Milner, B. 1966. Amnesia following operation on the temporal lobes. In C. W. M. Whitty and O. L. Zangwill (eds.), Amnesia. London: Butterworths, pp. 109–133.

Milner, B. 1968. Visual recognition and recall after right temporal-lobe excision in man. Neuropsychologia 6:191–209.

Milner, B. 1974. Hemispheric specialization: Scope and limits. In F. O. Schmitt and F. G. Worden (eds.), The Neurosciences: Third Study Program. Cambridge, Mass.: MIT Press, pp. 75–89.

Mitchell, P. 1979. Keilin's respiratory chain concept and its chemiosmotic consequences. Science (Wash., D.C.) 206:1148–1159.

Mohr, J. P., Fisher, C. M., and Adams, R. D. 1980. Cerebrovascular diseases. In K. J. Isselbacher, R. D. Adams, E. Braunwald, R. G. Petersdorf, and J. D. Wilson (eds.), Harrison's Principles of Internal Medicine. 9th ed. New York: McGraw-Hill, pp. 1911–1942.

Money, J., and Ehrhardt, A. A. 1972. Man and Woman, Boy and Girl. Baltimore: Johns Hopkins University Press

Moniz, E. 1936. Tentatives Opératoires dans le Traitement de Certaines Psychoses. Paris: Masson.

Monnier, M., Koller, Th., and Graber, S. 1963. Humoral influences of induced sleep and arousal upon electrical brain activity of animals with crossed circulation. Exp. Neurol. 8:264–277.

Moore, R. Y., and Lenn, N. J. 1972. A retinohypothalamic projection in the rat. J. Comp. Neurol. 146:1–14.

Moruzzi, G., and Magoun, H. W. 1949. Brain stem reticular formation and activation of the EEG. Electroencephalogr. Clin. Neurophysiol. 1:455–473.

Moses, R. A. 1975. Accommodation. In R. A. Moses (ed.), Adler's Physiology of the Eye. 6th ed. St. Louis: Mosby, pp. 298–319.

Moses, R. A. 1975. The iris and the pupil. In R. A. Moses (ed.), Adler's Physiology of the Eye. 6th ed. St. Louis: Mosby, pp. 320–352.

Moss, R. L., and McCann, S. M. 1973. Induction of mating behavior in rats by luteinizing hormone-releasing factor. Science (Wash., D.C.) 181:177–179.

Mosso, J. A., and Kruger, L. 1973. Receptor categories represented in spinal trigeminal nucleus caudalis. J. Neurophysiol. 36:472–488.

Mott, F. W., and Sherrington, C. S. 1895. Experiments upon the influence of sensory nerves upon movement and nutrition of the limbs. Preliminary communication. Proc. R. Soc. Lond. 57:481–488.

Mountcastle, V. B. 1957. Modality and topographic properties of single neurons of cat's somatic sensory cortex. J. Neurophysiol. 20:408–434.

Mountcastle, V. B. 1975. The view from within: Pathways to the study of perception. Johns Hopkins Med. J. 136:109–131.

Mountcastle, V. B. 1976. The world around us: Neural command functions for selective attention. Neurosci. Res. Program Bull. 14:Suppl.

Mountcastle, V. B. 1978. An organizing principle for cerebral function: The unit module and the distributed system. In G. M. Edelman and V. B. Mountcastle, The Mindful Brain. Cambridge, Mass.: MIT Press, pp. 7–50.

Mountcastle, V. B. 1980. Neural mechanisms in somesthesis. In V. B. Mountcastle (ed.), Medical Physiology, 14th ed., Vol. 1. St. Louis: Mosby, pp. 348–390.

Mountcastle, V. B. 1980. Pain and temperature sensibilities. In V. B. Mountcastle (ed.), Medical Physiology, 14th ed., Vol. 1. St. Louis: Mosby, pp. 391–427.

Mountcastle, V. B. 1980. Sensory receptors and neural encoding: Introduction to sensory processes. In V. B. Mountcastle (ed.), Medical Physiology, 14th ed., Vol. 1. St. Louis: Mosby, pp. 327–347.

Mountcastle, V. B., and Darian-Smith, I. 1968. Neural mechanisms in somesthesia. In V. B. Mountcastle (ed.), Medical Physiology, 12th ed., Vol. II. St. Louis: Mosby, pp. 1372–1423.

Mountcastle, V. B., and Henneman, E. 1952. The representation of tactile sensibility in the thalamus of the monkey. J. Comp. Neurol. 97:409–439.

Mountcastle, V. B., Lynch, J. C., Georgopoulos, A., Sakata, H., and Acuna, C. 1975. Posterior parietal association cortex of the monkey: Command functions for operations within extrapersonal space. J. Neurophysiol. 38:871–908.

Murphy, D. L., Campbell, I., and Costa, J. L. 1978. Current status of the indoleamine hypothesis of the affective disorders. In M. A. Lipton, A. DiMascio and K. F. Killam (eds.), Psychopharmacology: A Generation of Progress. New York: Raven Press, pp. 1235–1247.

Myers, R. E. 1955. Interocular transfer of pattern discrimination in cats following section of crossed optic fibers. J. Comp. Physiol. Psychol. 48:470–473.

N

Nachmansohn, D. 1959. Chemical and Molecular Basis of Nerve Activity. New York: Academic.

Nagasaki, H., Kitahama, K., Valatx, J.-L., and Jouvet, M. 1980. Sleep-promoting effect of the sleep-promoting substance (SPS) and delta sleep–inducing peptide (DSIP) in the mouse. Brain Res. 192:276–280.

Nashner, L. M. 1976. Adapting reflexes controlling the human posture. Exp. Brain Res. 26:59–72.

Nauta, W. J. H. 1975. Anatomical organization of pain pathways in the central nervous system. In S. H. Snyder and S. Matthysse (eds.), Opiate Receptor Mechanisms. Neurosci. Res. Program Bull. 13: 84–87.

Nauta, W. J. H., Smith, G. P., Faull, R. L. M., and Domesick, V. B. 1978. Efferent connections and nigral afferents of the nucleus accumbens septi in the rat. Neuroscience 3:385–401.

Neher, E., and Sakmann, B. 1976. Single-channel currents recorded from membrane of denervated frog muscle fibres. Nature (Lond.) 260:799–802.

Nelson, R., Famiglietti, Jr., E. V., and Kolb, H. 1978. Intracellular staining reveals different levels of stratification for on- and off-center ganglion cells in cat retina. J. Neurophysiol. 41:472–483.

Nernst, W. 1888. On the kinetics of substances in solution. Translated from Z. physik. Chemie 2:613–622; 634–637. In G. R. Kepner, (ed.), Cell Membrane Permeability and Transport. Stroudsburg, Pa.: Dowden, Hutchinson & Ross, 1979.

Nichols, T. R., and Houk, J. C. 1973. Reflex compensation for variations in the mechanical properties of a muscle. Science (Wash., D.C.) 181:182–184.

Noble, D. 1966. Applications of Hodgkin-Huxley equations to excitable tissues. Physiol. Rev. 46:1–50.

Norrsell, U. 1980. Behavioral studies of the somatosensory system. Physiol. Rev. 60:327–354.

Nottebohm, F. 1979. Origins and mechanisms in the establishment of cerebral dominance. In M. S. Gazzaniga (ed.), Handbook of Behavioral Neurobiology, Vol. 2. New York: Plenum, pp. 295–344.

O

Obata, K. 1977. Biochemistry and physiology of amino acid transmitters. In E. R. Kandel (ed.), Handbook of Physiology; The Nervous System, Vol. 1, Part I. Bethesda, Md.: American Physiological Society, pp. 625–650.

Ochs, S. 1972. Fast transport of materials in mammalian nerve fibers. Science (Wash., D.C.) 176:252–260.

Ogle, K. N. 1961. Optics: An Introduction for Ophthalmologists. Springfield, Ill.: Thomas.

Olds, J., and Milner, P. 1954. Positive reinforcement produced by electrical stimulation of septal area and other regions of rat brain. J. Comp. Physiol. Psychol. 47:419–427.

Orkand, R. K. 1977. Glial cells. In E. R. Kandel (ed.), Handbook of Physiology; Cellular Biology of Neurons, Vol. 1, Part II. Bethesda, Md.: American Physiological Society, pp. 855–875.

Otsuka, M., Kravitz, E. A., and Potter, D. D. 1967. Physiological and chemical architecture of a lobster ganglion with particular reference to gamma-aminobutyrate and glutamate. J. Neurophysiol. 30:725–752.

P

Palay, S. L. 1958. The morphology of synapses in the central nervous system. Exp. Cell. Res. Suppl. 5:275–293.

Palay, S. L., and Chan-Palay, V. 1977. General morphology of neurons and neuroglia. In E. R. Kandel (ed.), Handbook of Physiology; The Nervous System, Vol. 1, Part I. Bethesda, Md.: American Physiological Society, pp. 5–37.

Papez, J. W. 1937. A proposed mechanism of emotion. Arch. Neurol. Psychiatry 38:725–743.

Pappas, G. D., and Waxman, S. G. 1972. Synaptic fine structure-morphological correlates of chemical and electrotonic transmission. In G. D. Pappas and D. P. Purpura (eds.), Structure and Function of Synapses. New York: Raven Press, pp. 1–43.

Pappenheimer, J. R. Miller, T. B., and Goodrich, C. A. 1967. Sleep-promoting effects of cerebrospinal fluid from sleep-deprived goats. Proc. Natl. Acad. Sci. U.S.A. 58:513–517.

Patrick, J., and Lindstrom, J. 1973. Autoimmune response to acetylcholine receptor. Science (Wash., D.C.) 180:871–872.

Patten, J. 1977. Neurological Differential Diagnosis. London: Starke; New York: Springer.

Patterson, P. H. 1978. Environmental determination of autonomic neurotransmitter functions. Annu. Rev. Neurosci. 1:1–17.

Patton, H. D. 1965. Reflex regulation of movement and posture. In T. C. Ruch and H. D. Patton (eds.), Physiology and Biophysics. 19th ed. Philadelphia: Saunders, pp. 181–206.

Pavlov, I. P. 1927. Conditioned Reflexes: An Investigation of the Physiological Activity of the Cerebral Cortex. London: Oxford University Press.

Pearson, K. 1976. The control of walking. Sci. Am. 235(6):72–86.

Penfield, W. (ed.) 1932. Cytology & Cellular Pathology of the Nervous System, Vol. 2. New York: Paul B. Hoeber.

Penfield, W. 1954. Mechanisms of voluntary movement. Brain 77:1–17.

Penfield, W. 1958. Functional localization in temporal and deep Sylvian areas. Res. Publ. Assoc. Res. Nerv. Ment. Dis. 36:210–226.

Penfield, W., and Rasmussen, T. 1950. The Cerebral Cortex of Man. A Clinical Study of Localization of Function. New York: Macmillan.

Penfield, W., and Roberts, L. 1959. Speech and Brain-Mechanisms. Princeton: Princeton University Press.

Perl, E. R. 1968. Myelinated afferent fibres innervating the primate skin and their response to noxious stimuli. J. Physiol. (Lond.) 197:593–615.

Peters, A., Palay, S. L., and Webster, H. De F. 1976. The Fine Structure of the Nervous System: The Neurons and Supporting Cells. Philadelphia: Saunders.

Pfaff, D. W. 1973. Luteinizing hormone-releasing factor potentiates lordosis behavior in hypophysectomized ovariectomized female rats. Science (Wash., D.C.) 182:1148–1149.

Pfenninger, K., Sandri, C., Akert, K., and Eugster, C. H. 1969. Contribution to the problem of structural organization of the presynaptic area. Brain Res. 12:10–18.

Phillips, C. G., and Porter, R. 1977. Corticospinal Neurones: Their Role in Movement. London: Academic.

Phoenix, C. H., Goy, R. W., Gerall, A. A., and Young, W. C. 1959. Organizing action of prenatally administered testosterone propionate on the tissues mediating mating behavior in the female guinea pig. Endocrinology 65:369–382.

Piaget, J., and Inhelder, B. 1969. The Psychology of the Child. New York: Basic Books.

Picton, T. W., Hillyard, S. A., Krausz, H. I., and Galambos, R. 1974. Human auditory evoked potentials. I: Evaluation of components. Electroencephalogr. Clin. Neurophysiol. 36:179–190.

Piéron, H. 1913. Le Problème Physiologique du Sommeil. Paris: Masson.

Pletscher, A., Shore, P. A., and Brodie, B. B. 1956. Serotonin as a mediator of reserpine action in brain. J. Pharmacol. Exp. Ther. 116:84–89.

Plum, F., and Posner, J. B. 1972. The Diagnosis of Stupor and Coma. 2nd ed. Philadelphia: Davis.

Poggio, G. F., and Mountcastle, V. B. 1960. A study of the functional contributions of the lemniscal and spinothalamic systems to somatic sensibility. Bull. Johns Hopkins Hosp. 106:266–316.

Poggio, G. F., and Mountcastle, V. B. 1963. The functional properties of ventrobasal thalamic neurons studied in unanesthetized monkeys. J. Neurophysiol. 26:775–806.

Pollock, L. J., and Davis, L. 1930. The reflex activities of a decerebrate animal. J. Comp. Neurol. 50:377–411.

Pollock, L. J., and Davis, L. 1931. Studies in decerebration. VI. The effect of deafferentation upon decerebrate rigidity. Am. J. Physiol. 98:47–49.

Pompeiano, O. 1967. Functional organization of the cerebellar projections to the spinal cord. Prog. Brain Res. 25:282–321.

Prince, D. A. 1978. Neurophysiology of epilepsy. Annu. Rev. Neurosci. 1:395–415.

Purves, D., and Lichtman, J. W. 1978. Formation and maintenance of synaptic connections in autonomic ganglia. Physiol. Rev. 58:821–862.

Q

Quinn, W. G., and Gould, J. L. 1979. Nerves and genes. Nature (Lond.) 278:19–23.

R

Raichle, M. E. 1979. Tracer strategy in emission tomography. In T. R. Price and E. Nelson (eds.), Cerebrovascular Diseases. New York: Raven, pp. 91–98.

Raisman, G. 1974. Evidence for a sex difference in the neuropil of the rat preoptic area and its importance for the study of sexually dimorphic functions. Res. Publ. Assoc. Res. Nerv. Ment. Dis. 52:42–49.

Raisman, G., and Field, P. M. 1971. Sexual dimorphism in the preoptic area of the rat. Science (Wash., D.C.) 173:731–733.

Rakic, P. 1971. Neuron–glia relationship during granule cell migration in developing cerebellar cortex. A Golgi and electronmicroscopie study in Macacus rhesus. J. Comp. Neurol. 141:283–312.

Rakic, P. 1973. Kinetics of proliferation and latency between final cell division and onset of differentiation of cerebellar stellate and basket neurons. J. Comp. Neurol. 147:523–546.

Rakic, P. 1975. Local circuit neurons. Neurosci. Res. Program Bull. 13:289–446.

Rakic, P., and Sidman, R. L. 1973. Weaver mutant mouse cerebellum: Defective neuronal migration secondary to abnormality of Bergmann glia. Proc. Natl. Acad. Sci. U.S.A. 70:240–244.

Rall, W. 1977. Core conductor theory and cable properties of neurons. In E. R. Kandel (ed.), Handbook of Physiology; The Nervous System, Vol. 1, Part I. Bethesda, Md.: American Physiological Society, pp. 39–97.

Ranson, S. W. 1934. The hypothalamus: Its significance for visceral innervation and emotional expression. Trans. College Physicians Phila. Ser. 4. 2:222–242.

Ranson, S. W., and Clark, S. L. 1953. The Anatomy of the Nervous System. 9th ed. Philadelphia: Saunders.

Raphan, T., and Cohen, B. 1978. Brainstem mechanisms for rapid and slow eye movements. Annu. Rev. Physiol. 40:527–552.

Rapoport, S. I. 1976. Blood–Brain Barrier in Physiology and Medicine. New York: Raven Press.

Reichlin, S. 1978. Introduction. In S. Reichlin, R. J. Baldessarini, and J. B. Martin (eds.), The hypothalamus. Res. Publ. Assoc. Res. Nerv. Ment. Dis. 56:1–14.

Reivich, M., Kuhl, D., Wolf, A., Greenberg, J., Phelps, M., Ido, T., Casella, V., Fowler, J., Hoffman, E., Alavi, A., Som, P., and Sokoloff, L. 1979. The [^{18}F] fluorodeoxyglucose method for the measurement of local cerebral glucose utilization in man. Circ. Res. 44:127–137.

Rexed, B. 1952. The cytoarchitectonic organization of the spinal cord in the cat. J. Comp. Neurol. 96:415–495.

Riesen, A. H. 1958. Plasticity of behavior: Psychological aspects. In H. F. Harlow and C. N. Woolsey (eds.), Biological and Biochemical Bases of Behavior. Madison: University of Wisconsin Press, pp. 425–450.

Ritchie, J. M., and Rogart, R. B., 1977. The binding of saxitoxin and tetrodotoxin to excitable tissue. Rev. Physiol. Biochem. Pharmacol. 79:1–50.

Roberts, P. J., Woodruff, G. N., and Iversen, L. L. (eds.). 1978. Dopamine. New York: Raven Press.

Robinson, D. A. 1968. Eye movement control in primates. Science (Wash., D.C.) 161:1219–1224.

Robinson, D. A. 1976. Adaptive gain control of vestibulo-ocular reflex by the cerebellum. J. Neurophysiol. 39:954–969.

Robinson, D. A. 1981. The use of control systems analysis in the neurophysiology of eye movements. Annu. Rev. Neurosci (in press).

Robinson, D. L., Goldberg, M. E., and Stanton, G. B. 1978. Parietal association cortex in the primate: Sensory mechanisms and behavioral modulations. J. Neurophysiol. 41:910–932.

Rodieck, R. W. 1973. The Vertebrate Retina—Principles of Structure and Function. San Francisco: Freeman.

Roffwarg, H. P., Muzio, J. N., and Dement, W. C. 1966. Ontogenetic development of the human sleep–dream cycle. Science (Wash., D.C.) 152:604–619.

Rose, J. E., and Mountcastle, V. B. 1952. The thalamic tactile region in rabbit and cat. J. Comp. Neurol. 97:441–489.

Rosenkilde, C. E. 1979. Functional heterogeneity of the prefrontal cortex in the monkey: A review. Behav. Neural Biol. 25:301–345.

Ross, E. D. 1981. The aprosodias: Functional-anatomical organization of the affective components of language in the right hemisphere. Arch. Neurol. 37 (in press).

Roth, M. 1978. Diagnosis of senile and related forms of dementia. In R. Katzman, R. D. Terry, and K. L. Bick (eds.), Aging, Vol. 7: Alzheimer's Disease: Senile Dementia and Related Disorders. New York: Raven Press, pp. 71–85.

Rowland, L. P. 1977. Myasthenia gravis. In E. S. Goldensohn and S. H. Appel (eds.), Scientific Approaches to Clinical Neurology, Vol. 2, Philadelphia: Lea & Febiger, pp. 1518–1554.

Rowland, L. P. 1978. Myasthenia gravis. In W. B. Matthews and G. H. Glaser (eds.), Recent Advances in Clinical Neurology, Number 2. Edinburgh: Churchill Livingstone, pp. 25–46.

Rowland, L. P. 1979. Diseases of muscle and neuromuscular junction. In P. B. Beeson, W. McDermott, and J. B. Wyngaarden (eds.), Cecil Textbook of Medicine. 15th ed. Philadelphia: Saunders, pp. 914–930.

Rowland, L. P., and Layzer, R. B. 1977. Muscular dystrophies, atrophies, and related diseases. In A. B. Baker (ed.), Clinical Neurology, Vol. 3. New York: Harper & Row, pp. 1–109.

Rubin, M. L., and Walls, G. L. 1969. Fundamentals of Visual Science. Springfield, Ill.: Thomas.

Ruda, M. A. 1976. Autoradiographic Study of the Efferent Projections of the Midbrain Central Gray in the Cat. Ph.D. Dissertation, University of Pennsylvania, Philadelphia.

Rusak, B., and Zucker, I. 1979. Neural regulation of circadian rhythms. Physiol. Rev. 59:449–526.

S

Sachar, E. J., Asnis, G., Halbreich, U., Nathan, R. S., and Halpern, F. 1980. Recent studies in the neuroendocrinology of major depressive disorders. Psychiatr. Clin. North Am. 3:313–326.

Sackett, G. P. 1966. Monkeys reared in isolation with pictures as visual input: Evidence for an innate releasing mechanism. Science (Wash., D.C.) 154: 1468–1473.

Samorajski, T., and Ordy, J. M. 1972. Neurochemistry of aging. In C. M. Gaitz (ed.), Advances in Behavioral Biology, Vol. 3: Aging and the Brain. New York: Plenum, pp. 41–61.

Sastre, J.-P., and Jouvet, M. 1979. Le comportement onirique du chat. Physiol. Behav. 22:979–989.

Satinoff, E. 1964. Behavioral thermoregulation in response to local cooling of the rat brain. Am. J. Physiol. 206:1389–1394.

Saunders, J. W., Jr. 1970. Patterns and Principles of Animal Development. New York: Macmillan.

Schachter, S. 1971. Some extraordinary facts about obese humans and rats. Am. Psychol. 26:129–144.

Schally, A. V. 1978. Aspects of hypothalamic regulation of the pituitary gland. Its implications for the control of reproductive processes. Science (Wash., D.C.) 202:18–28.

Scharrer, E., and Scharrer, B. 1954. Hormones produced by neurosecretory cells. Recent Prog. Horm. Res. 10:182–232.

Scheibel, M. E., and Scheibel, A. B. 1958. Structural substrates for integrative patterns in the brain stem reticular core. In H. H. Jasper, L. D. Proctor, et al. (eds.), Reticular Formation of the Brain (Henry Ford Hosp. International Symposium). Boston: Little, Brown, pp. 31–55.

Scheibel, M. E., and Scheibel, A. B. 1975. Structural changes in the aging brain. In H. Brody, D. Harman, and J. M. Ordy (eds.), Aging, Vol. 1: Clinical, Morphologic, and Neurochemical Aspects in the Aging Central Nervous System. New York: Raven Press, pp. 11–37.

Schildkraut, J. J. 1978. Current status of the catecholamine hypothesis of affective disorders. In M. A. Lipton, A. DiMascio, and K. F. Killam (eds.), Psychopharmacology: A Generation of Progress. New York: Raven Press, pp. 1223–1234.

Schmidt, R. F. 1978. Somatovisceral sensibility. In R. F. Schmidt (ed.), Fundamentals of Sensory Physiology. New York: Springer, pp. 81–125.

Schnedorf, J. G., and Ivy, A. C. 1939. An examination of the hypnotoxin theory of sleep. Am. J. Physiol. 125:491–505.

Schoenenberger, G. A., and Monnier, M. 1977. Characterization of a delta-electroencephalogram (-sleep) –inducing peptide. Proc. Natl. Acad. Sci. U.S.A. 74: 1282–1286.

Schoener, T. W. 1971. Theory of feeding strategies. Annu. Rev. Ecol. Syst. 2:369–404.

Schultze, M. 1866. Zur Anatomie und Physiologie der Retina. Arch. Mikrosk. Anat. 2:175–286.

Schwartz, J. H. 1979. Axonal transport: Components, mechanisms, and specificity. Annu. Rev. Neurosci. 2:467–504.

Schwartz, J. H. 1980. The transport of substances in nerve cells. Sci. Am. 242(4):152–171.

Schwartzkroin, P. A., and Wyler, A. R. 1980. Mechanisms underlying epileptiform burst discharge. Ann. Neurol. 7:95–107.

Sclafani, A. 1976. Appetite and hunger in experimental obesity syndromes. In D. Novin, W. Wyrwicka, and G. A. Bray (eds.), Hunger: Basic Mechanisms and Clinical Implications. New York: Raven Press, pp. 281–295.

Sears, E. S., and Franklin, G. M. 1980. Diseases of the cranial nerves. In R. N. Rosenberg (ed.), Neurology, Vol. 5 of the Science and Practice of Clinical Medicine. New York: Grune & Stratton, pp. 471–494.

Shepherd, G. M. 1974. The Synaptic Organization of the Brain. An Introduction. New York: Oxford University Press.

Shepherd, G. M. 1978. Microcircuits in the nervous system. Sci. Am. 238(2):92–103.

Sherrington, C. S. 1897. The Central Nervous System. Part III of M. Foster, A Text Book of Physiology. 7th ed. London: Macmillan.

Sherrington, C. S. 1898. Decerebrate rigidity, and reflex coordination of movements. J. Physiol. (Lond.) 22:319–332.

Sherrington, C. S. 1900. The muscular sense. In E. A. Schäfer, Text-book of Physiology, Vol. 2. Edinburgh & London: Pentland, pp. 1002–1025.

Sherrington, C. S. 1947. The Integrative Action of the Nervous System. 2nd ed. New Haven: Yale University Press.

Shik, M. L., Severin, F. V., and Orlovskii, G. N. 1966. Control of walking and running by means of electrical stimulation of the mid-brain. Biophysics 11: 756–765.

Shurrager, P. S., and Culler, E. 1940. Conditioning in the spinal dog. J. Exp. Psychol. 26:133–159.

Signoret, J. L., Whiteley, A., and Lhermitte, F. 1978. Influence of choline on amnesia in early Alzheimer's disease. Lancet Vol. II No. 8094, p. 837.

Simon, E. J., Hiller, J. M., and Edelman, I. 1973. Stereospecific binding of the potent narcotic analgesia [³H] etorphine to rat-brain homogenate. Proc. Natl. Acad. Sci. U.S.A. 70:1947–1949.

Simpson, J. A. 1960. Myasthenia gravis: A new hypothesis. Scott. Med. J. 5:419–436.

Simpson, J. F., and Magee, K. R. 1973. Clinical Evaluation of the Nervous System. 2nd ed. Boston: Little, Brown.

Sjöqvist, O. 1938. Studies on pain conduction in the trigeminal nerve. Acta Psychiatr. Neurol. Suppl. 17: 1–139.

Smith, A. M., Hepp-Reymond, M.-C., and Wyss, U. R. 1975. Relation of activity in precentral cortical neurons to force and rate of force change during isometric contractions of finger muscles. Exp. Brain Res. 23:315–332.

Smith, V. C., and Pokorny, J. 1972. Spectral sensitivity of color-blind observers and the cone photopigments. Vision Res. 12:2059–2071.

Snyder, S. H. 1976. The dopamine hypothesis of schizophrenia: Focus on the dopamine receptor. Am. J. Psychiatry 133:197–202.

Snyder, S. H. 1977. Opiate receptors and internal opiates. Sci. Am. 236(3):44–56.

Snyder, S. H. 1980. Brain peptides as neurotransmitters. Science (Wash., D.C.) 209:976–983.

Snyder, S. H., and Childers, S. R. 1979. Opiate receptors and opioid peptides. Annu. Rev. Neurosci. 2:35–64.

Solomon, F., White, C. C., Parron D. L., and Mendelson, W. B. 1979. Sleeping pills, insomnia, and medical practice (summary of report of the Institute of Medicine, National Academy of Sciences). N. Engl. J. Med. 300:803–808.

Spemann, H. 1938. Embryonic Development and Induction. New Haven: Yale University Press.

Spencer, W. A. 1977. The physiology of supraspinal neurons in mammals. In E. R. Kandel (ed.), Handbook of Physiology; Cellular Biology of Neurons, Vol. 1, Part II. Bethesda, Md.,: American Physiological Society, pp. 969–1021.

Spencer, W. A., and Kandel, E. R. 1961. Electrophysiology of hippocampal neurons. IV. Fast prepotentials. J. Neurophysiol. 24:272–285.

Spencer, W. A., and Kandel, E. R. 1968. Cellular and integrative properties of the hippocampal pyramidal cell and the comparative electrophysiology of cortical neurons. Internat. J. Neurol. 6:266–296.

Spencer, W. A., Thompson, R. F., and Neilson, D. R., Jr. 1966. Response decrement of the flexion reflex in the acute spinal cat and transient restoration by strong stimuli. J. Neurophysiol. 29:221–239.

Sperry, R. W. 1951. Mechanisms of neural maturation. In S. S. Stevens (ed.), Handbook of Experimental Psychology. New York: Wiley, pp. 236–280.

Sperry, R. W. 1964. The great cerebral commissure. Sci. Am. 210(1):42–52.

Sperry, R. W. 1968. Mental unity following surgical dis-

connection of the cerebral hemispheres. Harvey Lect. 62:293–323.

Spiedel, C. C. 1933. Studies of living nerves. II. Activities of ameboid growth cones, sheath cells, and myelin segments, as revealed by prolonged observation of individual nerve fibers in frog tadpoles. Am. J. Anat. 52:1–79.

Spitz, R. A. 1945. Hospitalism: An inquiry into the genesis of psychiatric conditions in early childhood. Psychoanal. Study Child 1:53–74.

Spitz, R. A. 1946. Hospitalism: A follow-up report on investigation described in Volume 1, 1945. Psychoanal. Study Child 2:113–117.

Spitz, R. A., and Wolf, K. M. 1946. Anaclitic depression: An inquiry into the genesis of psychiatric conditions in early childhood, II. Psychoanal. Study Child 2:313–342.

Spoendlin, H. 1966. Ultrastructure of the vestibular sense organ. In R. J. Wolfson (ed.), The Vestibular System and Its Diseases. Philadelphia: University of Pennsylvania Press, pp. 39–68.

Springer, A. D., Heacock, A. M., Schmidt, J. T., and Agranoff, B. W. 1977. Bilateral tectal innervation by regenerating optic nerve fibers in goldfish: A radioautographic, electrophysiological and behavioral study. Brain Res. 128:417–427.

Spurzheim, J. G. 1825. Phrenology, or the Doctrine of the Mind. 3rd ed. London: Knight.

Squire, L. R., Slater, P. C., and Chace, P. M. 1975. Retrograde amnesia: Temporal gradient in very long term memory following electroconvulsive therapy. Science (Wash., D.C.) 187:77–79.

Starr, A. 1978. Sensory evoked potentials in clinical disorders of the nervous system. Annu. Rev. Neurosci. 1:103–127.

Stein, R. B. 1974. Peripheral control of movement. Physiol. Rev. 54:215–243.

Stein, S. C., and Langfitt, T. W. 1974. Normal-pressure hydrocephalus: Predicting the results of cerebrospinal fluid shunting, J. Neurosurg. 41:463–470.

Stent, G. S. (ed.). 1977. Function and Formation of Neural Systems. Berlin: Dahlem Konferenzen.

Sternberger, L. A. 1974. Immunocytochemistry. Englewood Cliffs, N.J.: Prentice-Hall.

Stevens, C. F. 1979. The neuron. Sci. Am. 241(3): 54–65.

Stevens, J. R. 1973. An anatomy of schizophrenia? Arch. Gen. Psychiatry 29:177–189.

Stevens, S. S. 1953. On the brightness of lights and the loudness of sounds. Science (Wash., D.C.) 118:576.

Stevens, S. S. 1961. The psychophysics of sensory function. In W. A. Rosenblith (ed.), Sensory Communication. Cambridge, Mass.: MIT Press, pp. 1–33.

Stiles, W. S. 1978. Mechanisms of Colour Vision. New York: Academic.

Stockard, J. J., and Rossiter, V. S. 1977. Clinical and pathologic correlates of brain stem auditory response abnormalities. Neurology 27:316–325.

Stone, J., Dreher, B., and Leventhal, A. 1979. Hierarchical and parallel mechanisms in the organization of visual cortex. Brain Res. Rev. 1:345–394.

Strauss, A. J. L., Seegal, B. C., Hsu, K. C., Burkholder, P. M., Nastuk, W. L., and Osserman, K. E. 1960. Immunofluorescence demonstration of a muscle binding, complement-fixing serum globulin fraction in myasthenia gravis. Proc. Soc. Exp. Biol. Med. 105: 184–191.

Strehler, B., Hirsch, G., Gusseck, D., Johnson, R., and Bick, M. 1971. Codon-restriction theory of aging and development. J. Theor. Biol. 33:429–474.

Strehler, B. L. 1975. Implications of aging research for society. Fed. Proc. 34:5–8.

Sundsten, J. W., and Sawyer, C. H. 1961. Osmotic activation of neurohypophysial hormone release in rabbits with hypothalamic islands. Exp. Neurol. 4:548–561.

Suomi, S. J., and Harlow, H. F. 1975. The role and reason of peer relationships in rhesus monkeys. In M. Lewis and L. A. Rosenblum (eds.), Friendship and Peer Relations. New York: Wiley, pp. 153–185.

Szentágothai, J. 1969. Architecture of the cerebral cortex. In H. H. Jasper, A. A. Ward, Jr., and A. Pope (eds.), Basic Mechanisms of the Epilepsies. Boston: Little, Brown, pp. 13–28.

T

Takeuchi, A. 1977. Junctional transmission. I. Postsynaptic mechanisms. In E. R. Kandel (ed.), Handbook of Physiology; The Nervous System, Vol. 1, Part I. Bethesda, Md.: American Physiological Society, pp. 295–327.

Talbot, S. A., and Marshall, W. H. 1941. Physiological studies on neural mechanisms of visual localization and discrimination. Am. J. Ophthalmol. 24:1255–1264.

Tanji, J., and Evarts, E. V. 1976. Anticipatory activity of motor cortex neurons in relation to direction of an intended movement. J. Neurophysiol. 39:1062–1068.

Tanner, Jr., W. P., and Swets, J. A. 1954. A decision-making theory of visual detection. Psychol. Rev. 61:401–409.

Terenius, L. 1973. Characteristics of the "receptor" for narcotic analgesics in synaptic plasma membrane fraction from rat brain. Acta Pharmacol. Toxicol. 33:377–384.

Teuber, H.-L., Corkin, S. H., and Twitchell, T. E. 1977. Study of cingulotomy in man: A summary. In W. H. Sweet, S. Obrador, and J. G. Martín-Rodríguez (eds.), Neurosurgical Treatment in Psychiatry, Pain, and Epilepsy. Baltimore: University Park Press, pp. 355–362.

Thach, W. T. 1978. Correlation of neural discharge with pattern and force of muscular activity, joint position, and direction of intended next movement in motor cortex and cerebellum. J. Neurophysiol. 41:654–676.

Thach, W. T., Jr. 1980. The cerebellum. In V. B. Mountcastle (ed.), Medical Physiology, 14th ed., Vol. 1. St. Louis: Mosby, pp. 837–858.

Thoenen, H., Otten, U., and Schwab, M. 1979. Orthograde and retrograde signals for the regulation of neuronal gene expression: The peripheral sympathetic nervous system as a model. In F. O. Schmitt and F. G. Worden (eds.), The Neurosciences: Fourth Study Program. Cambridge, Mass.: MIT Press, pp. 911–928.

Thompson, R. F. 1975. Introduction to Physiological Psychology. New York: Harper & Row.

Thorndike, E. L. 1911. Animal Intelligence. New York: Macmillan.

Thorpe, W. H. 1956. Learning and Instinct in Animals. Cambridge, Mass.: Harvard University Press.

Tinbergen, N. 1951. The Study of Instinct. Oxford: Clarendon Press.

Toivonen, S., and Saxen, L. 1968. Morphogenetic interaction of presumptive neural and mesodermal cells mixed in different ratios. Science (Wash., D.C.) 159:539–540.

Tomlinson, B. E., and Henderson, G. 1976. Some quantitative cerebral findings in normal and demented old people. In R. D. Terry and S. Gershon (eds.), Aging, Vol. 3: Neurobiology of Aging. New York: Raven Press, pp. 183–204.

Toran-Allerand, C. D. 1976. Sex steroids and the development of the newborn mouse hypothalamus and preoptic area in vitro: Implications for sexual differentiation. Brain Res. 106:407–412.

Toran-Allerand, C. D. 1978. Gonadal hormones and brain development: Cellular aspects of sexual differentiation. Am. Zool. 18:553–565.

Tower, S. S. 1940. Pyramidal lesion in the monkey. Brain 63:36–90.

Toyka, K. V., Drachman, D. B., Pestronk, A., and Kao, I. 1975. Myasthenia gravis: Passive transfer from man to mouse. Science (Wash., D.C.) 190:397–399.

Tuček, S. 1978. Acetylcholine Synthesis in Neurons. London: Chapman and Hall.

Tucker, D. M., Watson, R. T., and Heilman, K. M. 1977. Discrimination and evocation of affectively intoned speech in patients with right parietal disease. Neurology 27:947–950.

U

Ungerstedt, U., Ljungberg, T., Hoffer, B., and Siggins, G. 1975. Dopaminergic supersensitivity in the striatum. In D. Calne, T. N. Chase, and A. Barbeau (eds.), Advances in Neurology, Vol. 9: Dopaminergic Mechanisms. New York: Raven Press, 57–65.

Usdin, E., Weiner, N., and Youdim, M. B. H. (eds.). 1977. Structure and Function of Monoamine Enzymes. New York: Marcel Dekker.

Uttal, W. R. 1975. Cellular Neurophysiology and Integration. An Interpretive Introduction. Hillsdale, N.J.: Lawrence Erlbaum Associates.

Uttal, W. R. 1978. The Psychobiology of Mind. Hillsdale, N.J.: Lawrence Erlbaum Associates.

V

Vallbo, Å. B. 1970. Discharge patterns in human muscle spindle afferents during isometric voluntary contractions. Acta Physiol. Scand. 80:552–566.

Vallbo, Å. B. 1971. Muscle spindle response at the onset of isometric voluntary contractions in man. Time difference between fusimotor and skeletomotor effects. J. Physiol. (Lond.) 218:405–431.

Vallbo, Å. B., Hagbarth, K.-E., Torebjörk, H. E., and Wallin, B. G. 1979. Somatosensory, proprioceptive, and sympathetic activity in human peripheral nerves. Physiol. Rev. 59:919–957.

Van Essen, D. C. 1979. Visual areas of the mammalian cerebral cortex. Annu. Rev. Neurosci. 2:227–263.

Verney, E. B. 1947. The antidiuretic hormone and the factors which determine its release. Proc. R. Soc. Lond. B. Biol. Sci. 135:25–106.

vom Saal, F. S., and Bronson, F. H. 1980. Sexual characteristics of adult female mice are correlated with their blood testosterone levels during prenatal development. Science (Wash., D.C.) 208:597–599.

von Békésy, G. 1960. Experiments in Hearing. New York: McGraw-Hill.

von Senden, M. 1960. Space and Sight. Trans. by P. Heath. Glencoe, Ill.: Free Press.

Vrensen, G., Nunes Cardozo, J. Müller, L., and Van Der Want, J. 1980. The presynaptic grid: A new approach. Brain Res. 184:23–40.

W

Wald, G. 1959. The photoreceptor process in vision. In H. W. Magoun (ed.), Handbook of Physiology, Vol. 1, Neurophysiology. Washington D.C.: American Physiological Society, pp. 671–692.

Wald, G. 1964. The receptors of human color vision. Science (Wash., D.C.) 145:1007–1016.

Wald, G. 1968. Molecular basis of visual excitation. Science (Wash., D.C.) 162:230–239.

Walford R. L. 1974. Immunologic theory of aging: Current status. Fed. Proc. 33:2020–2027.

Walker, M. B. 1934. Treatment of myasthenia gravis with physostigmine. Lancet 1:1200–1201.

Walker, M. B. 1935. Case showing the effect of prostigmin on myasthenia gravis. Proc. R. Soc. Med. 28:759–761.

Wall, P. D., and Taub, A. 1962. Four aspects of trigeminal nucleus and a paradox. J. Neurophysiol. 25:110–126.

Warren, J. M., and Akert, K. (eds.). 1964. The Frontal Granular Cortex and Behavior. New York: McGraw-Hill.

Warrington, E. K., and Weiskrantz, L. 1970. Amnesic syndrome: Consolidation or retrieval? Nature (Lond.) 228:628–630.

Watson, J. B. 1930. Behaviorism. Rev. ed. New York: Norton.

Weeds, A. G., Trentham, D. R., Kean, C. J. C., and Buller, A. J. 1974. Myosin from cross-reinnervated cat muscles. Nature (Lond.) 247:135–139.

Weiss, P., and Hiscoe, H. B. 1948. Experiments on the mechanism of nerve growth. J. Exp. Zool. 107:315–395.

Werner, G. 1974. Introduction to feature extraction by neurons and behavior. In F. O. Schmidt and F. G. Worden (eds.), The Neurosciences: Third Study Program. Cambridge: MIT Press, pp. 93–94.

Werner, G., and Whitsel, B. L. 1973. Functional organization of the somatosensory cortex. In A. Iggo (ed.), Handbook of Sensory Physiology, Vol. 2, The Somatosensory System. New York: Springer, pp. 621–700.

Wernicke. K. 1908. The symptom-complex of aphasia. In A. Church (ed.), Diseases of the Nervous System. New York: Appleton, pp. 265–324.

Wersäll, J., and Flock, Å. 1965. Functional anatomy of the vestibular and lateral line organs. In W. Neff (ed.), Contributions to Sensory Physiology. New York: Academic, pp. 39–61.

Wersäll, J., Flock, Å., and Lundquist, P.-G. 1965. Structural basis for directional sensitivity in cochlear and vestibular sensory receptors. Cold Spring Harbor Symp. Quant. Biol. 30:115–132.

Westheimer, G. 1954. Mechanism of saccadic eye movements. A.M.A. Arch. Ophthalmol. 52:710–724.

Westheimer, G. 1972. Visual acuity and spatial modulation thresholds. In D. Jameson and L. M. Hurvich (eds.), Handbook of Sensory Physiology, Vol. 7, Part 4: Visual Psychophysics. New York: Springer, 170–187.

Westheimer, G. 1980. The eye. In V. B. Mountcastle (ed.), Medical Physiology, 14th ed., Vol. 1. St. Louis: Mosby, pp. 448–503.

Westrum, L. E., Canfield, R. C., and Black, R. G. 1976. Transganglionic degeneration in the spinal trigeminal nucleus following removal of tooth pulps in adult cats. Brain Res. 101:137–140.

Whalen, R. E., and Edwards, D. A. 1967. Hormonal determinants of the development of masculine and feminine behavior in male and female rats. Anat. Rec. 157:173–180.

Whalen, R. E., and Massicci, J. 1975. Subcellular analysis of the accumulation of estrogen by the brain of male and female rats. Brain Res. 89:255–264.

White, P., Goodhardt, M. J., Keet, J. P., Hiley, C. R., Carrasco, L. H., Williams, I. E. I., and Bowen, D. M. 1977. Neocortical cholinergic neurons in elderly people. Lancet Vol. I, No. 8013, pp. 668–671.

Whitehorn, D., and Burgess, P. R. 1973. Changes in polarization of central branches of myelinated mechanoreceptor and nociceptor fibers during noxious and innocuous stimulation of the skin. J. Neurophysiol. 36:226–237.

Whitsel, B. L., Rustioni, A., Dreyer, D. A., Loe, P. R., Allen, E. E., and Metz, C. B. 1978. Thalamic projections to S-I in macaque monkey. J. Comp. Neurol. 178:385–409.

Whittaker, V. P., Michaelson, I. A., and Kirkland, R. J. A. 1964. The separation of synaptic vesicles from nerve-ending particles ("synaptosomes"). Biochem. J. 90:293–303.

Wiersma, C. A. G. 1938. Function of the giant fibers of the central nervous system of the crayfish. Proc. Soc. Exp. Biol. Med. 38:661–662.

Wiesel, T. N., and Hubel, D. H. 1963. Single-cell responses in striate cortex of kittens deprived of vision in one eye. J. Neurophysiol. 26:1003–1017.

Williams, R. L., and Karacan, I. 1973. Clinical disorders of sleep. In G. Usdin (ed.), Sleep Research and Clinical Practice. New York: Brunner/ Mazel, pp. 23–57.

Wilson, V. J., and Melvill Jones, G. 1979. Mammalian Vestibular Physiology. New York: Plenum.

Winokur, G. 1978. Mania and depression: Family studies and genetics in relation to treatment. In M. A. Lipton, A. DiMascio, and K. F. Killam (eds.), Psychopharmacology: A Generation of Progress. New York: Raven Press, pp. 1213–1221.

Wiśniewski, H. M., and Terry, R. D. 1973. Morphology of the aging brain, human and animal. Prog. Brain Res. 40:167–186.

Witelson, S. F. 1976. Sex and the single hemisphere: Specialization of the right hemisphere for spatial processing. Science (Wash., D.C.) 193:425–427.

Wolpe, J. 1958. Psychotherapy by Reciprocal Inhibition. Stanford: Stanford University Press.

Woolsey, C. N. 1958. Organization of somatic sensory and motor areas of the cerebral cortex. In H. F. Harlow and C. N. Woolsey (eds.), Biological and Biochemical Bases of Behavior. Madison: University of Wisconsin Press, pp. 63–81.

Woolsey, T. A., and Van der Loos, H. 1970. The structural organization of layer IV in the somatosensory region (S I) of mouse cerebral cortex. The description of a cortical field composed of discrete cytoarchitectonic units. Brain Res. 17:205–242.

Wynne, L. C., Cromwell, R. L., and Matthysse, S. (eds.). 1978. The Nature of Schizophrenia: New Approaches to Research and Treatment. New York: Wiley.

Y

Yaksh, T. L., Farb, D. H., Leeman, S. E., and Jessell, T. M. 1979. Intrathecal capsaicin depletes substance P in the rat spinal cord and produces prolonged thermal analgesia. Science (Wash., D.C.) 206: 481–483.

Yates, A. J. 1970. Behavior Therapy. New York: Wiley.

Yoon, M. C. 1976. Topographic polarity of the optic tectum studied by reimplantation of the tectal tissue in adult goldfish. Cold Spring Harbor Symp. Quant. Biol. 50:503–519.

Yoss, R. E., and Daly, D. D. 1960. Narcolepsy. Arch. Intern. Med. 106:168–171.

Young, J. Z. 1950. The Life of Vertebrates. Oxford: Clarendon Press, chap. 5.

Young, R. W. 1970. Visual cells Sci Am. 223(4):80–91.

Z

Zeki, S. 1980. The representation of colours in the cerebral cortex. Nature (Lond.) 284:412–418.

Zeki, S. M. 1976. The functional organization of projections from striate to prestriate visual cortex in the rhesus monkey. Cold Spring Harbor Symp. Quant. Biol. 40:591–600.

Zimmerman, E. A., Carmel, P. W., Husain, M. K., Ferin, M., Tannenbaum, M., Frantz, A. G., and Robinson, A. G. 1973. Vasopressin and neurophysin: High concentrations in monkey hypophyseal portal blood. Science (Wash., D.C.) 182:925–927.

Zimmermann, M. 1978. Neurophysiology of sensory systems. In R. F. Schmidt (ed.), Fundamentals of Sensory Physiology. New York: Springer, pp. 31–80.

Index

Illustration and Table Credits

We wish to thank all the authors who have kindly supplied us with published and unpublished materials, photographs, and information, and have given us permission to reproduce, incorporate, or quote these in the text. In addition, the following have given us permission to reproduce published textual, pictorial, or tabular materials in the book.

Academic Press: Figure 43–5 adapted from Attardi and Sperry, Exp. Neurol. 7:46–64 (1963); Figure 48–3 adapted from Rosenkilde, Behav. Biol. 25:301–345 (1979); Figures 48–5 and 48–6 adapted from Sperry, The Harvey Lecture Series 62:293–323 (1968); Table 34–2 adapted from Fuchs, Bach-y-Rita et al. (eds.), The Control of Eye Movements (1971); Table 50–1 adapted from Kety, The Harvey Lecture Series 71: 1–22 (1978).

Acta Physiologica Scandinavica: Figure 51–4 adapted from Anden et al., Vol. 67, pp. 313–326 (1966).

Aerospace Medicine: Figure 40–1 adapted from Aschoff, Vol. 40, pp. 844–849 (1969), with the permission of Aerospace Medicine.

American Medical Association: Table 41–2 adapted from A collaborative study: An appraisal of the criteria of cerebral death, J.A.M.A. 237:982–986 (1977). Copyright 1977, American Medical Association.

American Physiological Association: Figure 13–4 adapted from Bunge, Physiol. Rev. 48:197–251 (1968); Figure 17–5 and 17–6 adapted from Marshall et al., J. Neurophysiol. 4:1–24 (1941); Figure 17–11 adapted from Mountcastle, J. Neurophysiol. 20:408–434 (1957); Figure 17–12 adapted from Costanzo and Gardner, J. Neurophysiol. 43:1319–1341 (1980); Figure 21–8 adapted from Hubel and Wiesel, J. Neurophysiol. 28:1041–1059 (1965); Figures 22–4 and 22–5 adapted from Michael, J. Neurophysiol. 41:572–588 (1978); Figure 22–6 adapted from Michael, J. Neurophysiol. 41:1233–1249 (1978); Figure 25–4 adapted from Matthews, Physiol. Rev. 44:219 –288 (1964); Figure 29–2 adapted from Asanuma, Physiologist 166:143–266 (1973); Figure 29–4 adapted from Avarts, J. Neurophysiol. 31:14–27 (1968); Figure 30–6 adapted from Allen and Tsukahara, Physiol. Rev. 54:957–1006 (1974); Figure 34–10 adapted from Fuchs and Luschei, J. Neurophysiol. 33:382–392 (1970); Figure 38–3 adapted from Satinoff, Am. J. Physiol. 206:1389–1394 (1964); Figure 38–8 adapted from Corbit, J. Comp. Physiol. Psychol. 83:394–411 (1973); Figure 39–2 adapted from Llinas and Nicholson, J. Neurophysiol. 34:532–551 (1971); Figure 39–2 adapted from Orkand in Handbook of Physiology: Cellular Biology of Neurons, E. R. Kandel (ed.), Vol. I, Part II, pp. 855–875 (1977); Figure 44–5 adapted from Beach et al., J. Comp. Physiol. Psychol. 68:490–496 (1969); Figure 46–3 adapted from Doty and Bosma, J. Neurophysiol. 19:44–60 (1956).

American Zoologist: Figure 44–6 adapted from Toran-Allerand, Vol. 18, pp. 553–565 (1978).

Annual Reviews Inc.: Figure 34–12 reprinted, with permission, from the Annual Review of Neuroscience, Volume 4. © 1981 by Annual Reviews Inc.

Archivio di Scienze Biologiche: Figure 41–5 adapted from Magni et al., Vol. 97, pp. 33–46 (1959).

Basic Books, Inc.: Figure 47–4 adapted from Piaget and Inhelder, The Psychology of the Child (1969).

Brain: Figure 48–7 adapted from Levy et al., Vol. 95, pp. 61–78 (1972); Figure II–10 adapted from Ingvar and Schwartz, Vol. 97, pp. 273–288 (1974).

Brain Research: Figure 7–1B adapted from Bennett, Vol. 143, pp. 43–60 (1978); Figure 11–2 adapted from Divac et al., Vol. 123, pp. 197–207 (1977); Figure 33–8 adapted from Woolsey and VanderLoos, Vol. 17, pp. 205–242 (1970); Figure 39–9 adapted from Ayala et al., Vol. 52, pp. 1–17 (1973).

Brunner/Mazel: Figures 41–1 and 41–2 reprinted with permission from Gene Usdin, Sleep Research and Clinical Practice, New York, 1973, pp. 74 and 76.

Dr. James Case: Figures 19–4 and 19–5 adapted from Sensory Mechanisms (1966). Copyright James Case.

Cold Spring Harbor Laboratory: Figure 21–3 adapted from Kuffler, Quant. Biol. 17:281–293 (1952); Figure 23–3 adapted from Wersall et al., Quant. Biol. 30:115–132 (1965); Figure 35–6 adapted from Quant. Biol. 30:133–145 (1965).

F.A. Davis: Figures 32–1, 32–2, and 32–3 adapted from Clark in Manter and Gatz (eds.), Essentials of Clinical Neuroanatomy and Neurophysiology, 5th ed. (1975); Figure 36–7 adapted from Gatz in Manter and Gatz, Essentials of Clinical Neuroanatomy and Neurophysiology, 3rd ed. (1966); Figures 45–2, 45–3, 45–4, and 45–5 adapted from Duffy (ed.), Neuropathology: An Illustrated Course (1974); Table 41–1 adapted from Plum and Possner, The Diagnosis of Stupor and Coma, 2nd ed. (1972).

Lawrence Earlbaum Associates: Figure 1–7 adapted from Uttal, Psychobiology of the Mind (1978); Figure 19–4 adapted from Uttal, Cellular Neurophys-

iology and Integration: An Interpretive Introduction (1975).

Electroencephalography and Clinical Neurophysiology: Figure 39–8 adapted from Picton et al., Vol. 36, pp. 179–190 (1974).

Elsevier North Holland, Inc.: Table 10–3 adapted from Miller and Pickel, J. Histochem. Cytochem. 28:903–917 (1980).

Endocrinology: Figure 38–1 adapted from DiGirolamo and Rudman, Vol. 82, pp. 1133–1141 (1968).

Federation Proceedings: Figure 45–1 reprinted from Fed. Proc. 34:5–8 (1975).

Fertility and Sterility: Figure 37–6 adapted from Gay, Vol. 23, pp. 50–63 (1972).

Grune & Stratton: Figure 36–3 adapted from Sears and Franklin, in Neurology, Vol. 5 of The Science and Practice of Clinical Medicine (R. N. Rosenberg, ed.), p. 478 (1980).

Harper & Row: Figure 48–1 adapted from Thompson, Foundations of Physiological Psychology (1967).

Holt, Rinehart & Winston: Figures 40–2, 40–4, and 40–5 adapted from Dement in New Directions in Psychology, Vol. 2, pp. 135–257 (1965).

Hospital Practice: Figures 37–3 and 37–4 adapted from Krieger and Hughes (eds.), Neuroendocrinology.

International Journal of Neurology: Figure 39–3 adapted from Spencer and Kandel, Vol. 6, pp. 266–296 (1968).

Investigative Ophthalomology: Figure 19–6 adapted from Dowling, Vol. 9, pp. 655–680 (1970).

Journal of Comparative and Physiological Psychology: Figure 38–3 adapted from Corbit, Vol. 83, pp. 394–411 (1973); Figure 44–5 adapted from Beach et al., Vol. 68, pp. 490–497 (1969).

Journal of General Physiology: Figure 25–5 adapted from Hunt, Vol. 38, pp. 117–131 (1954).

Journal of Physiology (London): Figures 8–1 and 8–2 adapted from Katz and Miledi, Vol. 192, pp. 407–436 (1967); Figure 8–4 adapted from Katz and Miledi, Vol. 189, pp. 535–544 (1967); Figure 8–5A adapted from Liley, Vol. 133, pp. 571–587 (1956); Figure 8–5B adapted from Boyd and Martin, Vol. 132, pp. 74–91 (1956); Figure 15–5 adapted from Perl, Vol. 197, pp. 593–615 (1968); Figures 21–4, 21–5B, 21–6, and 21–9 adapted from Hubel and Wiesel, Vol. 160, pp. 106–154 (1962); Figure 21–5A adapted from Hubel and Wiesel, Vol. 148, pp. 574–591 (1959); Figure 25–7 adapted from Crow and Matthews, Vol. 174, pp. 109–131 (1964); Figure 25–8 adapted from Hunt and Kuffler, Vol. 113, pp. 298–315 (1951); Figures 34–6 and 34–7 adapted from Fuchs, Vol. 191, p. 609 (1967); Figure 37–8 adapted from Lincoln and

Wakerley, Vol. 242, pp. 533–554 (1974); Figure 39–5 adapted from Kelly and VanEssen, Vol. 238, pp. 515–547 (1974); Figure 43–2 adapted from Axelsson and Thesleff, Vol. 147, pp. 178–193 (1959); Table 34–2 adapted from Fuchs, Vol. 191, pp. 609–631 (1967).

Journal of Neurosurgery: Table 48–1 adapted from Branch, Milner, and Rasmussen, Vol. 21, pp. 399–405 (1964).

S. Karger, AG: Figures 24–4 and 24–5 adapted from Kuypers in J. E. Desmedt (ed.), New Developments in Electromyography and Clinical Neurophysiology (1973), Vol. 3, pp. 33–68; Figure 29–3 adapted from Gilman in J. E. Desmedt (ed.), New Developments in Electromyography and Clinical Neurophysiology (1973), Vol. 3, pp. 175–193; Figure II–8 adapted from Lassen and Ingvar, Progress in Nuclear Medicine, Volume 1, pp. 376–409 (1972).

Lippencott/Harper & Row: Figure 40–3 adapted from Feinberg in A. Kales (ed.), Sleep Physiology and Pathology (1969), pp. 39–52.

Little, Brown and Company: Figures 32–18 and 40–6 adapted from Scheibel and Scheibel in Jasper, Procter, et al. (eds.), Reticular Formation of the Brain (Henry Ford Hospital International Symposium) (1958); Figure 39–1 adapted from Szentagothai in Jasper, Ward, and Pope (eds.), Basic Mechanisms of the Epilepsies (1969), pp. 13–28.

Macmillan Publishing Co., Inc.: Figures 1–6, 17–7, and 29–1 adapted from Penfield and Rasmussen, The Cerebral Cortex of Man (1950), pp. 44 and 57. Copyright 1950 by Macmillan Publishing Co., Inc., renewed 1978 by Theodore Rasmussen; Figures 42–3, 42–4, and 42–7 adapted from Saunders, Patterns and Principles of Animal Development, Copyright © 1970, John W. Saunders, Jr.

Masson: Figure 29–5 adapted from Ghez and Vicario, J. Physiol. (Paris) 74:283–285 (1978), Masson S. A., Paris.

McGraw-Hill Book Company: Figure 23–7 adapted from Experiments in Hearing by von Bekesy. Copyright © 1960 by the McGraw-Hill Book Company and used with permission; Figure 36–6 adapted from Principles of Neurology by Adams and Victor. Copyright © 1977 by the McGraw-Hill Book Company and used with permission; Figure 48–2 adapted from The Frontal Granular Cortex and Behavior by Warren and Akert. Copyright © 1964 by the McGraw-Hill Book Company and used with permission; Figure II–14 adapted from Isselbacher et al. in Harrison's Principles of Internal Medicine. Copyright © by the McGraw-Hill Book Company and used with permission.

The MIT Press: Figure 9–2 reprinted from Neuroscience Research Program Bulletin 15:4, Llinas and Heuser, "Depolarization-release coupling systems in neurons"; Figure 9–7 reprinted from Neuroscience Research Program Bulletin 15:4, Couteaux,

Akert, Heuser, and Reese, "Ultrastructural evidence for vesicle exocytosis"; Figure 9–15B reprinted from Neuroscience Research Program Bulletin 13, Rakic, "Local Circuit Neurons"; Figures 19–7, 19–8, and 19–9 reprinted from The Neurosciences: Fourth Study Program (Schmitt and Worden, eds.), Dowling, "Information processing by local circuits: The vertebrate retina as a model system" (1979), pp. 163–181; Figure 23–10 reprinted from Kiang, Discharge Patterns of Single Fibers in Cat's Auditory Nerve (1965); Figures 31–2 and 31–3 reprinted from The Neurosciences (Schmitt and Worden, eds.), DeLong, "Motor functions of the basal ganglia: Single unit activity during movements" (1974), pp. 319–325. All by permission of The MIT Press, Cambridge, Massachusetts.

C. V. Mosby Company: Figure 17–10 modified from Mountcastle, Vernon B., and Darian-Smith, Ian: Neural mechanisms in somesthesis. In Mountcastle, Vernon B., editor: Medical Physiology, ed. 12, St. Louis, 1968, The C. V. Mosby Co.; Figure 19–6 adapted from Dowling, Investigative Ophthalmology 9:655–680 (1970); Appendix Table 1 adapted from Westheimer, Gerald: The eye, including central nervous system control of eye movements. In Mountcastle, Vernon B., editor: Medical Physiology, ed. 14, St. Louis, 1980, The C. V. Mosby Co.

Nature (London): Figure 7–10A adapted from Neher and Sakmann, Vol. 260, pp. 799–802. Reprinted by permission from Nature. Copyright © 1976 by Macmillan Journals Limited.

Oxford University Press (New York): Figure 9–15A adapted from Shepherd, The Synaptic Organization of the Brain, An Introduction (1974); Figure 32–17 adapted from DeArmond, Fusco, and Dewey, Structure of the Human Brain, 2nd ed. (1976); Figures 32–19, 32–21, 50–2, and 51–5 adapted from Cooper, Bloom, and Roth, The Biochemical Basis of Neuropharmacology, 3rd ed. (1978), chap. 7; Figure 43–6 adapted from Lund, Development and Plasticity of the Brain (1978).

Oxford Clarendon Press (London): Figure 32–4 adapted from Young, The Life of Vertebrates (1950); Figure 46–1 adapted from Tinbergen, The Study of Instinct in Animals (1951).

Pergamon Press (Oxford): Figure 22–2 adapted from Smith and Pokorny, Vision Res. 284:2059–2071 (1972); Figures 35–1 and 35–9 adapted from Iurato, Submicroscopic Structure of the Inner Ear (1967); Figure 44–1 adapted from Bermant and Davidson, Biological Bases of Sexual Behavior (1974).

Plenum: Figures 42–8, 42–11, 42–12, and 42–13 adapted from Jacobson, Developmental Neurobiology, 2nd ed. (1978).

Princeton University Press: Figure 1–5 adapted from Penfield and Roberts, Speech and Brain Mechanisms (1959).

Proceedings of the National Academy of Sciences

(USA): Figure 7–13 adapted from Jan, Jan, and Kuffler, Vol. 76, pp. 1501–1505 (1979); Figure 10–2 adapted from Fertuck and Salpeter, Vol. 71, pp. 1376–1378 (1974); Figure 35–4 adapted from Hudspeth and Corey, Vol. 74, pp. 2407–2411 (1977); Figures 42–9 and 42–10 adapted from LeDouarin, Renaud, Teillet, and LeDouarin, Vol. 72, pp. 728–732 (1975); Figure 52–8 adapted from Klein and Kandel, Vol. 75, pp. 3512–3516 (1978).

Proceedings of the Royal Society of London B Biological Sciences: Figure 13–5 adapted from Le Gros Clark and Penman, Vol. 114, pp. 291–313 (1934); Figure 52–2 adapted from Hubel and Wiesel, Vol. 198, pp. 1–59 (1977).

Raven Press: Figure 26–7 adapted from Houk in R. E. Talbott and D. R. Humphrey (eds.), Posture and Movement (1979), pp. 231–241; Figure 37–5 adapted from Reichlin in Reichlin, Baldessarini and Martin (eds.), The Hypothalamus. Association for Research in Nervous and Mental Disease. Res. Publ. 56 (1978); Figures 38–4 and 38–6 adapted from Keesey et al. in Noven, Wyrmicha, and Bray (eds.), Hunger: Basic Mechanisms and Clinical Implications (1976); Figure 41–4 adapted from Dement, Guilleminault, and Zarcone in Tower (ed.), The Nervous System, Vol. 2, The Clinical Neurosciences (1975), pp. 501–518; Figure 45–6, 45–7, and 45–8 adapted from Scheibel and Scheibel in H. Brody, D. Harman, and J. M. Ordy (eds.), Aging, Vol. I (1975), pp. 11–37.

Research Publications Association for Research in Nervous and Mental Disease: Table 44–1 adapted from G. Raisman, Vol. 52, pp. 42–49 (1974).

The Rockefeller University Press: Figure 7–1A adapted from J. Cell. Biol. 74:629–645 (1977); Figure 35–3 adapted from Flock, J. Cell Biol. 22:413–431 (1964).

W. B. Saunders (Philadelphia): Figure 9–3 adapted from Peters, A., Palay, A. L., and Webster, H. de F.: The Fine Structure of the Nervous System: The Neurons and Supporting Cells (1976); Figures 13–2, 16–10, 20–9, 23–13, 31–1, and 32–7 adapted from Brodal, Neurological Anatomy, 2nd ed. (1969); Figures 16–6, 23–11, 32–8, 32–9, 32–10, 32–11, 32–12, 32–13, 32–14, 33–4, and 33–6 adapted from Ranson, S. W., and Clark, S. L.: The Anatomy of the Nervous System. Ninth edition (1953); Figure 25–6 adapted from Patton, H. D.: Reflex regulation of movement and posture. In Ruch, T. C., and Patton, H. D.: Physiology and Biophysics. 19th edition (1965); Figure 33–1 adapted from Haymaker and Woodhall, Peripheral Nerve Injuries (1965); Figure 36–1 adapted from Curtis, B. A., Jacobson, S., and Marcus, E. M.: An Introduction to the Neurosciences (1972); Figures II–2 and II–5 adapted from Fishman, R. A.: Cerebrospinal Fluid in Diseases of the Nervous System (1980); Figure II–13 adapted from McDowell, F. H. in Beeson, P. B., McDermott, W., and Wyngaarden, J. B.: Textbook of Medicine. 15th edition (1979).

Science: Table 10–2 adapted from Snyder, Vol. 209, pp. 976–983, copyright 1980 by the American Associa-

tion for the Advancement of Science; Figure 11–3 adapted from Ochs, Vol. 176, pp. 252–260, copyright 1972 by the American Association for the Advancement of Science; Figure 12–1 adapted from Fambrough et al., Vol. 182, pp. 293–295, copyright 1973 by the American Association for the Advancement of Science; Figures 19–4 and 19–5 adapted from Wald, Vol. 162, pp. 230–239, copyright 1968 by the American Association for the Advancement of Science; Figure 22–1 adapted from Marks, Dobelle, and MacNichol, Jr., Vol. 143, pp. 1181–1183, copyright 1964 by the American Association for the Advancement of Science; Figure 34–13 adapted from Robinson, Vol. 161, pp. 1219–1334, copyright 1968 by the American Association for the Advancement of Science; Figure 41–3 adapted from Jacobson et al., Vol. 148, pp. 975–977, copyright 1965 by the American Association for the Advancement of Science; Figure 42–6 adapted from Toivonen and Saxen, Vol. 159, pp. 539–540, copyright 1968 by the American Association for the Advancement of Science; Figure 47–2 adapted from Squire et al., Vol. 187, pp. 77–79, copyright 1975 by the American Association for the Advancement of Science; Figure 48–8 adapted from Geschwind and Levistky, Vol. 161, pp. 186–187, copyright 1968 by the American Association for the Advancement of Science; Figure 52–5 adapted from Castellucci et al., Vol. 202, pp. 1306–1308, copyright 1978 by the American Association for the Advancement of Science; Figure 52–7 adapted from Carew et al., Vol. 205, pp. 417–419, copyright 1979 by the American Association for the Advancement of Science.

Scientific American (published by W. H. Freeman and Company, 660 Market Street, San Francisco, CA 94104): Figure 1–4 adapted from Geschwind, Vol. 241(3), pp. 180–201 (1970); Figures 2–2, 7–10, and 10–3 adapted from Stevens, Vol. 241(3), pp. 54–65 (1979); Figure 11–3 adapted from Schwartz, Vol. 242 (4), pp. 152–171 (1980); Figure 26–3 adapted from Merton, Vol. 226(5), pp. 30–37 (1972); Figure 28–3 adapted from Pearson, Vol. 235(6), pp. 72–86 (1976); Figures 42–1 and 42–2 adapted from Cowan, Vol. 241(3), pp. 112–133 (1979); Figures 44–3 and 44–4 adapted from McEwen, Vol. 235(1), pp. 48–58 (1976); Figure 51–1 adapted from Kety, Vol. 241(3), pp. 202–214 (1979).

Charles Scribner's Sons: Table 40–1 adapted from Foulkes, The Psychology of Sleep (1966).

Sinauer Associates: Figures 2–3, 21–5A, 21–9, II–1, II–4 adapted from Kuffler and Nicholls, From Neuron to Brain (1976).

Society for Neuroscience Symposia: Figure 8–3 adopted from Llinas, Vol. 2, pp. 139–160, 1977.

Springer-Verlag: Figure 15–3 adapted from Zimmermann in R. F. Schmidt (ed.), Neurophysiology of Sensory Systems (1975), pp. 191–232; Figure 16–2 adapted from Zimmermann in R. F. Schmidt (ed.), Neurophysiology of Sensory Systems (1978), pp. 31–80; Figure 28–2 adapted from Nashner, Exp. Brain Res. 26:59–72 (1976); Figure 29–6 adapted from

Ghez and Vicario, Exp. Brain Res. 33:191–202 (1978); Figure 29–7 adapted from Deecke, Kornhuber, Exp. Brain Res. 7:158–169 (1969); Figure 30–4 adapted from Eccles, Ito, and Sirpingothai, The Cerebellum as a Neuronal Machine (1967); Figures 36–2, 36–4, and 36–5 adapted from Patten, Neurological Differential Diagnosis (1977); Figure II–11 adapted from Fazio, Fieschi, and Agnoli in K. J. Zulch (ed.), Cerebral Circulation and Stroke (1971), pp. 143–147; Figures III–14, III–15, and III–16 adapted from Bishop in R. Jung (ed.), Handbook of Sensory Physiology, Vol. 7, Part 3A (1973), pp. 255–305.

Charles C. Thomas: Figure 6–7 adapted from Hodgkin, The Conduction of the Nervous Impulse (1964); Figures III–3, III–4, III–5, III–6, and III–7 adapted from Ogle, Optics: An Introduction for Ophthalmologists (1961). All courtesy of Charles C. Thomas, Publisher, Springfield, Illinois.

University of Pennsylvania Press: Figures 35–3 and 35–11 adapted from Spoendlin, in Wolfson (ed.), The Vestibular System and Its Diseases (1966).

University of Wisconsin Press (Madison): Figure 48–4 adapted from Harlow in Harlow and Woolsey, Biological and Biochemical Bases of Behavior (1958), pp. 3–23.

William Wood & Co.: Figure 2–1 adapted from Cajal, Histology, 10th ed. (1933).

Williams & Wilkins: Figures 16–11, 16–8, 16–9, and 20–7 adapted from Carpenter, Human Neuroanatomy, 7th ed. (1976); Figures 34–4 and II–3 adapted from Carpenter, Core Text of Neuroanatomy, 2nd ed. (1978); Table 50–2 adapted from Klein and Davis, Diagnosis and Drug Treatment of Psychiatric Disorders (1969).

The Wistar Institute Press: Figure 33–7 adapted from V. B. Mountcastle and E. Henneman, J. Comp. Neurol. 97:409–439. Copyright 1952 by the Wistar Institute Press, Philadelphia. Reprinted with permission; Figure 34–9 adapted from Brodel in M. Hardy, Anatomical Record 59:402–418. Copyright 1934 by the Wistar Institute Press, Philadelphia. Reprinted with permission; Figure 42–14 adapted from P. Rakic, J. Comp. Neurol. 141:283–312. Copyright 1971 by the Wistar Institute Press, Philadelphia. Reprinted with permission; Figure 42–15 adapted from P. Rakic, J. Comp. Neurol. 147:523–546. Copyright 1973 by the Wistar Institute Press, Philadelphia. Reprinted with permission.

Zeitschrift für experimentelle angewandte Psychologie: Figure 46–5 adapted from Vol. 2, pp. 412–454, 499–533 (1970).

Columns II (left) and IV (right) of the Edwin Smith Surgical Papyrus

This papryus, written in the Seventeenth Century B.C., contains the earliest reference to the brain anywhere in human records. According to James Breasted, who translated and published the document in 1930, the word brain ('yś) occurs only 8 times in ancient Egyptian, 6 of them on these pages of the Smith Papyrus describing the symptoms, diagnosis and prognosis of two patients, wounded in the head, who had compound fractures of the skull. The entire treatise is now in the Rare Book Room of the New York Academy of Medicine.

Reference: Breasted, James Henry. The Edwin Smith Surgical Papyrus, 2 volumes. The University of Chicago Press, Chicago. 1930.

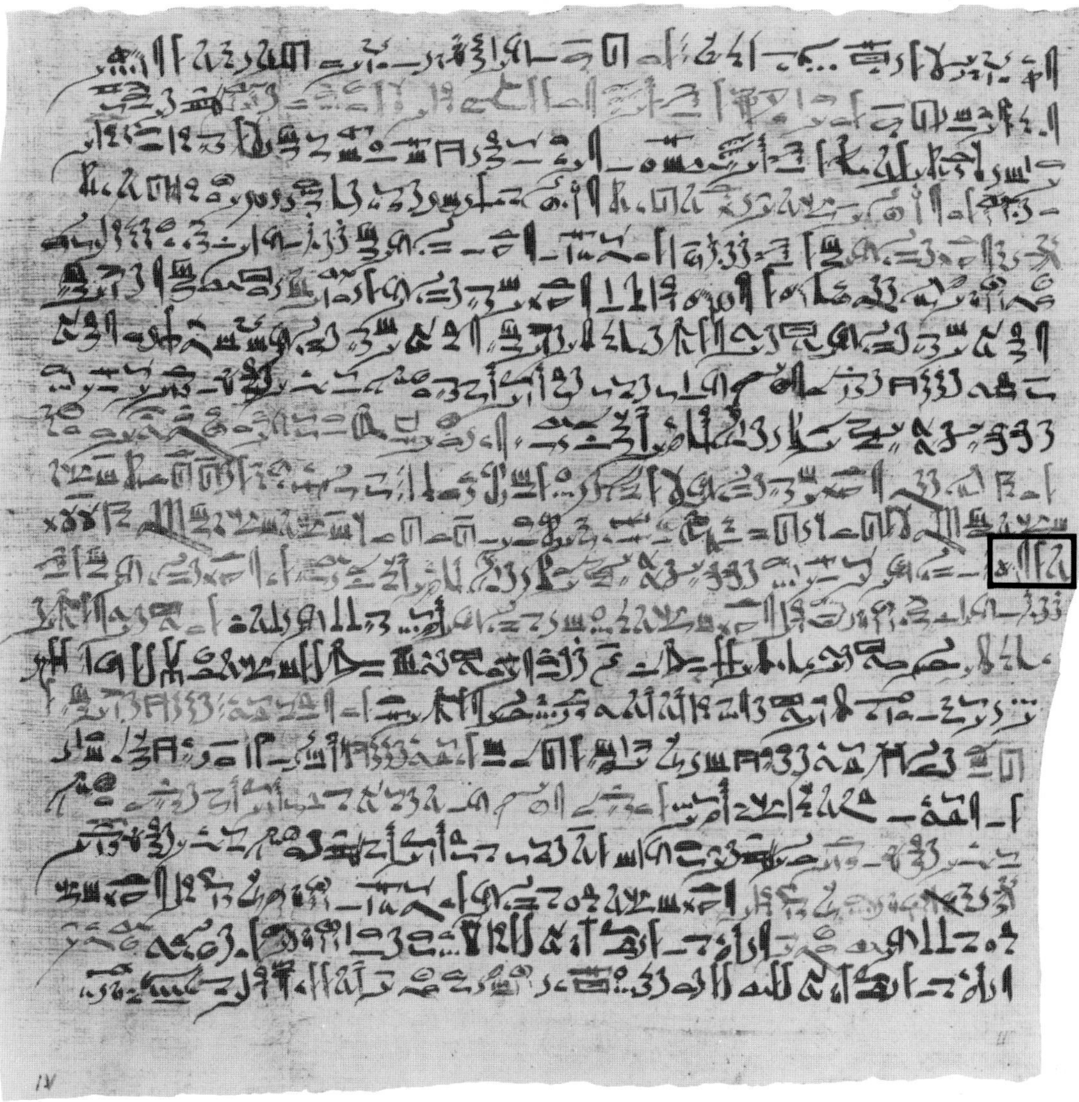